O9-ABH-987

CATHEDRAL
OF THE IMMACULATE CONCEPTION

THIRD EDITION

WORSHIP

A Hymnal and Service Book for Roman Catholics

GIA PUBLICATIONS, INC.
CHICAGO

Design by Michael Tapia. Cover design by John Buscemi. Engraved and typeset by the Hornseth Company, Hyattsville, Maryland.

Published with ecclesiastical approval, Archdiocese of Chicago.

ISBN 0-941050-02-5

3 4 5 6 7 8 9 10 11 12 13 14 15 16 17 18 19 20

PREFACE

This third edition of *Worship* makes its appearance in the wake of the nearly quarter-century development of the Roman Rite since the Second Vatican Council. The two previous editions, 1971 and 1975, supplied American parishes with service music and hymns which were needed to cultivate vocal prayer, both spoken and sung. These hymnals attempted to move American Catholics more toward the mainstream of Christian hymnody. The present edition reflects our perception of that growth which has taken place during this period of rapid development, as well as our vision of what is needed by way of a hymnal and service book to accompany the Church into the 21st century.

The structure of this edition represents a different direction from that taken with its predecessor. The ordering of the second edition tended to be functional, e.g, hymns in alphabetical order, while the new edition has been organized to mirror who we are and how we pray as Roman Catholics within the larger Christian community.

We begin with the *Liturgy of the Hours,* the Church's daily prayer, edited in such a way so as to enable parishes to celebrate the official rite on all Sundays, solemnities and feasts of the Lord throughout the year, plus the Office for the Dead. The Psalter, which follows, includes all of the psalms and canticles required for Morning Prayer, Evening Prayer and Night Prayer on those days, arranged for singing according to the Gelineau psalmody, as well as a wide range of alternate tones. A separate volume, *Worship - Liturgy of the Hours - Leaders' Edition,* is published for presider, cantor, lector and organist.

In our presentation of the rites for this edition, we have taken into account the fact that the average worshipper experiences these rites infrequently, and unlike his or her experience of the eucharist, is generally unfamiliar with all but certain key elements of the structure. We also remained constantly aware of the uniqueness of the assembly which gathers for weddings, funerals and infant baptism. Therefore, it was our concern that the presentation of the rites offers good practical catechesis, and when combined with competent leadership, makes possible the full and active participation of the gathered assembly.

A number of subtle, but distinctly different directions have been taken in our presentation of music for the eucharist. Complete settings of the mass ordinary texts are presented in course, and eucharistic prayer acclamations from the same source are grouped together. The most significant difference, however, is that the Order of Mass (no. 229) is presented with music rather than as text alone. We have compiled what we judge to be a basic music repertoire for the mass — music which is reprinted in both the marriage and funeral rites — and music which we would hope every parish will learn, in an effort to create a common repertoire that can be sung on those occasions when the eucharist is celebrated by an assembly gathered from different communities.

At the heart of this book is the corpus of just over 400 hymns: texts, with accompanying tunes. Texts which are based almost entirely on scripture. Texts which, we hope, will place on the lips of our assemblies words which enable them to express their faith in praise and petition; to pray in song. We have attempted to collect a body of texts which are theologically sound, embrace the fullness of liturgical practice, and are poetically substantive.

As we began the job of compiling this collection of hymns, our work took us first to the *Lectionary for Mass.* We analyzed the scriptures for each Sunday in all three cycles and for all the principal feasts and solemnities, and attempted to provide at least one "hymn for the day" either based on, or supportive of, each day's readings. In our search for hymns to include in this collection we capitalized on the great hymn writing explosion of the last twenty years and combed the rich heritage of the past. The result of this work is found in the index of Hymns for the Church Year (no. 1205) as well as the liturgical and topical indexes which follow. To support further the lectionary basis of our worshiplife as a Christian people, the entire hymn section is arranged according to the *Lectionary for Mass,* with "Ordinary Time" represented by the large selection of general hymns.

Once again, we offer two people's editions of *Worship,* one with and one without the Sunday scriptures. While we share a deep concern for the Word as aural tradition, the concern is tempered by a realization of common communication disabilities as well as acoustical limitations. There are clearly two sides to the question, and to us the verdict is still not clear. Therefore, we felt the need to continue the dialogue by making both options available.

The language of the hymn texts reflects a contemporary concern that language be just, as well as poetic. We have altered texts that use exclusive terms to refer to both men and women, and we have modernized some pronouns, verb forms and other archaisms whenever we felt the result yielded a better text for contemporary use. In rare cases, e.g., "Faith of Our Fathers," alteration seemed inadvisable, or in a few other cases, was not permitted by the copyright holder. Similarly, at our request the Grail prepared an inclusive language version of their psalm translation, but it failed to gain the approval of the National Conference of Catholic Bishops for use with the lectionary and hours.

A good deal of research was done in order to find the original harmonizations for many of the hymn tunes. In some instances this unearthed a setting which introduces a fresh "new" sound to the repertoire. The normative range of the tunes extends to a fourth-line treble clef "D". For use at an early hour, or when a tune is still unfamiliar, a low key accompaniment book with music only is available. However, under most circumstances we strongly urge that the hymns be played in the keys in which they are printed in the regular accompaniment and people's editions. In most hymns of duple meter, the half note represents the unit of pulse, while hymns having triple meter may be considered to have one beat per measure.

We are grateful to Gabe Huck who wrote the introductions and commentaries on the rites and the lectionary, and to John A. Gurrieri and Ronald F. Krisman, directors of the secretariat of the Bishops' Committee on the Liturgy, for their guidance and assistance. We also acknowledge Gabe Huck for compiling the section of devotional prayers. These are intended both for the individual and for family use in the home, and have been selected to offer a suitable range of texts for daily use.

Special acknowledgement is extended to the following for their immeasurable contributions to this project: to Catherine Salika, our bibliographer, researcher, and author of the *Worship Companion;* to Michael A. Cymbala, permissions editor; to Neil Borgstrom, editorial assistant; and to Ronald F. Krisman, W. Thomas Smith and Paul A. Westermeyer for their detailed evaluations of the hymn section.

The composers or sources of refrains, psalm tones, and certain other brief musical elements are identified throughout by their initials. They are: RJB, Robert J. Batastini; LB, Laurence Bevenot, OSB; IB, Ingrid Brustle; JRC, J. Robert Carroll; JJC, James J. Chepponis; MC, Michael Connolly; PC, Patricia Craig; RC,

Randolph Currie; EE, Eugene Englert; JG, Joseph Gelineau, SJ; DRH, David R. Haas; PH, Peter Hallock; MH, Marty Haugen; CWH, Clifford W. Howell, SJ; HH, Howard Hughes, SM; DH, David Hurd; RMH, Robert M. Hutmacher, OFM; DCI, David Clark Isele; MJ, Michael Joncas; CK, Columba Kelly, OSB; RKK, Robert Knox Kennedy; MK, Marie Kremer; REK, Robert E. Kreutz; RK, Ronald F. Krisman; RL, Robert LeBlanc; *LBW, Lutheran Book of Worship; LW, Lutheran Worship;* DLSM, DeLaSalle McKeon, CSJ; JAM, John Allyn Melloh, SM; DM, Douglas Mews; AGM, A. Gregory Murray, OSB; PP, Peter Peacock, OFM Cap; CAP, C. Alexander Peloquin; RP, Richard Proulx; DJR, Donald J. Reagan; JR, Joseph Roff; TFS, Thomas F. Savoy; JS, John Schiavone; FS, Frank Schoen; JBS, Joseph B. Smith; RJT, Robert J. Thompson; ST, Suzanne Toolan, SM; RCV, Ralph C. Verdi, CPPS; CW, Chrysogonus Waddell, OCSO; GW, Guy Weitz; and MEY, Michael E. Young. We are grateful to those who have composed settings especially for this edition.

Finally, we the editors once again pay tribute to our publisher, Edward J. Harris, for his confidence in our ability, his support of our decisions, and his personal integrity.

We have attempted to create a service book and hymnal for a church which moves into the third millenium of its existence. It is a movement of great confidence; confident that this Church will continue its role in the history of salvation brought about by the life, the death, the resurrection and the promise to come again of the Lord Jesus Christ.

Robert J. Batastini, General Editor and Project Director
Fred Moleck, Text Editor
Robert H. Oldershaw, Liturgical and Index Editor
Richard Proulx, Music Editor

Contents

The Liturgy of the Hours

1 Invitatory
3 Morning Prayer/Lauds
10 Evening Prayer/Vespers
19 Night Prayer/Compline
24 Psalter

Rites of the Church

100 Christian Initiation of Adults
104 The Baptism of Children
114 Confirmation
119 Holy Communion Outside Mass
125 Reconciliation of Several Penitents
134 Marriage
155 Anointing of the Sick
160 Funeral Mass
179 Psalm Responses/Rites

Mass

229 The Order of Mass
251 Setting One - A Community Mass
257 Setting Two - Mass of the Bells
264 Setting Three - New Plainsong
270 Service Music
340 Cantus Missae

Hymns

355 Advent
374 Christmas
414 Lent
441 Easter
472 Pentecost
502 General
691 Feasts
720 Rites

Lectionary

765 Advent/Christmas
786 Lent/Easter
858 Ordinary Time
967 Weekdays/Seasons
1022 Weekdays/Saints
1069 Seasonal Psalms
1076 Seasonal Refrains

Prayers of the Individual and Household

1152 Introduction
1153 Morning Prayers
1163 Daytime Prayers
1168 Evening Prayers
1173 Night Prayers
1179 Meal Prayers
1181 Sunday Prayers
1185 Prayer for Fridays
1186 Times of Need
1194 Penance and Reconciliation
1200 Various Prayers

Indexes

1203 Acknowledgements
1204 Scripture Passages Related to Hymns
1205 Hymns for the Church Year
1206 Liturgical Index
1207 Topical Index
1208 Index of Hymns Which May Be Sung in Canon
1209 Index of Composers, Authors and Sources
1210 Metrical Index
1211 Tune Index
1212 Index of Psalm Refrains Set to Music
1213 Index of First Lines and Common Titles

The Liturgy of the Hours

When darkness gives way before the sun's light and a new day begins, 1
people of all religions have had their rites of morning: words and songs and gestures with which to pray. It has been the same at the end of the day's light, and again in the last moments before sleep.

Christians from the beginning learned ways of morning and evening and night prayer. These moments are the hinges of daily life. As they came round each day they have been occasions to repeat what every child has learned by heart: words to praise God for a new morning, to thank the Father for Christ who is our light as evening comes, to invoke God's strong protection through the hours of night.

The daily prayers of Christians were fashioned at first from very simple things: the sign of the cross, the Lord's Prayer, a few verses and songs and short psalms, intercessions. And for most Christians morning and night remain times for such simple prayers always said by heart. The portion of this book called "Prayers of the Individual and Household" (nos. 1152-1202) contains many of the texts which continue to be part of morning, evening and night prayer.

The pages of this present section offer a form of daily prayer that grew from this same tradition. When Christians have gathered in the early morning, at day's end, just before retiring, the simple prayers for the individual have grown more elaborate. The daily assemblies of men and women religious gave shape to what became known as the divine office or "liturgy of the hours." In recent times, these prayers have been restored to some of their original simplicity and are again being prayed in parish churches and Christian households.

In using and in adapting the forms of morning, evening and night prayer given below, two things are especially important. First, these are not to be prayers which could be prayed any time. Rather, they are prayers (in word, song, gesture, silence) which are prompted by the morning itself, by the evening, by the night. Their content and pace should reflect what is unique to each of these moments. Second, these prayers are not meant to be followed in and read from books. The assembly's parts are to be gradually learned by heart. Simplicity, repetition, care for times of silence, the use of refrains: all make it possible for these prayers to belong fully to those who assemble.

*The proper antiphons, readings, intercessions and prayers for each day are found in the **Worship - Liturgy of the Hours - Leaders' Edition** or **Christian Prayer**.*

INVITATORY

All make the sign of the cross on their lips.

Presider:
Assembly:
O Lord, + o - pen my lips.
And my mouth will pro-claim your praise.

2 PSALM 95–TO GOD WITH GLADNESS SING

The cantor sings the proper antiphon for Psalm 95.

Psalm 95
Para. by James Quinn, SJ, 1919

CAMANO, 6 6 6 6 4 44 4
Richard Proulx, b.1937

1. To God with glad - ness sing, Your
2. He cra - dles in his hand The
3. Your heav'n - ly Fa - ther praise, Ac-

Rock and Sav - ior bless; With - in his tem - ple
heights and depths of earth; He made the sea and
claim his on - ly Son, Your voice in hom - age

bring Your songs of thank - ful - ness!
land, He brought the world to birth!
raise To him who makes all one!

O God of might, To you we sing, En-
O God most high, We are your sheep, On
O Dove of peace, On us de - scend That

throned as King On heav - en's height!
us you keep Your Shep - herd's eye!
strife may end And joy in - crease!

Alternate setting found at no. 51.

MORNING PRAYER/LAUDS

The church's sense for how to pray in the morning comes from our Jewish 3
heritage. Whatever the day, whatever the difficulties, the tradition has been to begin the day with praise for the creator. Thus the whole of morning prayer is in the verse: "O Lord, open my lips. And my mouth will proclaim your praise." The sign of the cross, first traced on the Christian at baptism, is again made to begin the new day and its prayer. In the hymn and the psalms, in the scripture and intercessions, each one who prays and the community together finds what it is to stand at the beginning of a new day as a Christian. The morning's prayer gives the day its meaning when, through the years, these prayers become one's own.

This verse and response are omitted when the hour begins with the invitatory.

All make the sign of the cross.

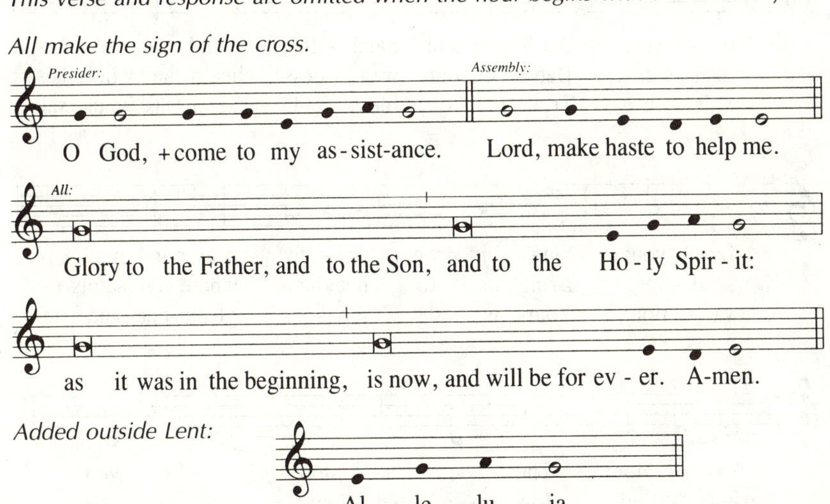
Presider:
O God, + come to my as-sist-ance.
Assembly:
Lord, make haste to help me.
All:
Glory to the Father, and to the Son, and to the Ho-ly Spir-it:
as it was in the beginning, is now, and will be for ev-er. A-men.
Added outside Lent:
Al-le-lu-ia.

4 HYMN

Nocte Surgentes
Attr. to St. Gregory the Great, 540-604
Tr. by Percy Dearmer, 1867-1936, att.

CHRISTE SANCTORIUM, 11 11 11 5
Paris Antiphoner, 1681

1. Fa - ther, we praise you, now the night is
2. Mak - er of all things, fit us for your
3. All - ho - ly Fa - ther, Son and e - qual
o - ver, Ac - tive and watch - ful, stand we all be-
man - sions; Ban - ish our weak - ness, health and whole-ness
Spir - it, Trin - i - ty bless - ed, send us your sal-
fore you; Sing - ing we of - fer pray'r and med - i-
send - ing; Bring us to heav - en, where your saints u-
va - tion; Yours is the glo - ry, gleam-ing and re-
ta - tion: Thus we a - dore you.
nit - ed Joy with - out end - ing.
sound - ing Through all cre - a - tion.

PSALMODY

The psalms, canticle and their antiphons are taken from the proper of the day.

READING

5 RESPONSE TO THE WORD OF GOD

Cantor, then all:

Robert LeBlanc, 1984

A. Advent	Christ,	Son	of	the
B. Christmas	The		Lord	has
C. Lent	Christ,	Son	of	the
D. Easter	Christ,	Son of the living God, have	mer	-
E. General	Christ,	Son	of	the

liv - ing God, have mer - cy on us.
made known, alleluia, al - le - lu - ia.
liv - ing God, have mer - cy on us.
cy on us, alleluia, al - le - lu - ia.
liv - ing God, have mer - cy on us.
Cantor:
A. You are the one who is to come,
B. His saving power,
C. You were wounded for our of - fenses,
D. You have risen from the dead,
E. You are seated at the right hand of the Father,
All:
have mer - cy on us.
alleluia, al - le - lu - ia.
have mer - cy on us.
alleluia, al - le - lu - ia.
have mer - cy on us.
Cantor:
Glo - ry to the Fa - ther, and to the Son,
and to the Ho - ly Spir - it:
All:
A. Christ, Son of the
B. The Lord has
C. Christ, Son of the
D. Christ, Son of the living God, have mer -
E. Christ, Son of the
liv - ing God, have mer - cy on us.
made known, alleluia, al - le - lu - ia.
liv - ing God, have mer - cy on us.
cy on us, alleluia, al - le - lu - ia.
liv - ing God, have mer - cy on us.

6 GOSPEL CANTICLE

The cantor sings the proper antiphon.
All make the sign of the cross.

FOREST GREEN, CMD
English
Harm. by Ralph Vaughn Williams, 1872-1958

James Quinn, SJ, b.1919

1. Blessed + be the God of Is - ra - el, The
2. Through ho - ly proph - ets did he speak His
3. Of old he gave his sol - emn oath To
4. O ti - ny child, your name shall be The
5. The ris - ing Sun shall shine on us To

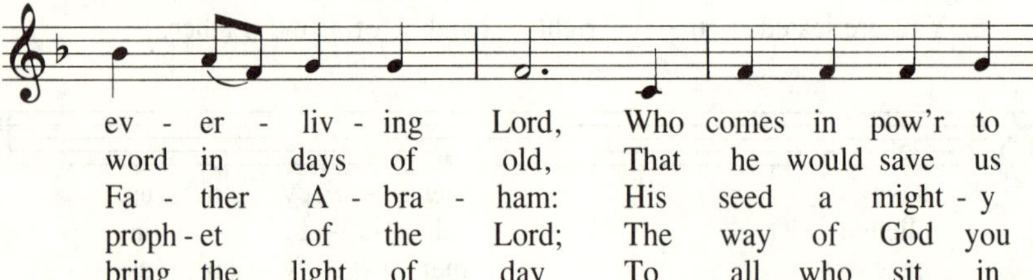
ev - er - liv - ing Lord, Who comes in pow'r to
word in days of old, That he would save us
Fa - ther A - bra - ham: His seed a might - y
proph - et of the Lord; The way of God you
bring the light of day To all who sit in

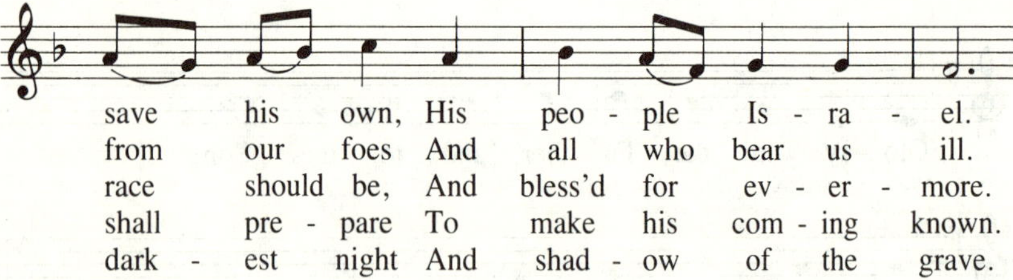
save his own, His peo - ple Is - ra - el.
from our foes And all who bear us ill.
race should be, And bless'd for ev - er - more.
shall pre - pare To make his com - ing known.
dark - est night And shad - ow of the grave.

For Is - ra - el he rais - es up Sal-
To our an - ces - tors did he give His
He vowed to set his peo - ple free From
You shall pro - claim to Is - ra - el Sal-
Our foot - steps God shall safe - ly guide To

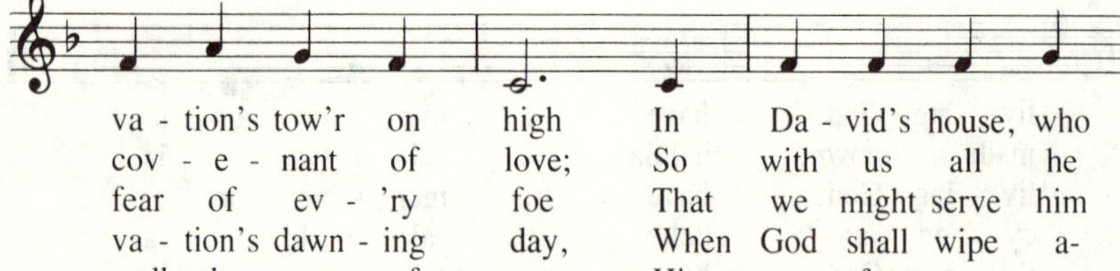
va - tion's tow'r on high In Da - vid's house, who
cov - e - nant of love; So with us all he
fear of ev - 'ry foe That we might serve him
va - tion's dawn - ing day, When God shall wipe a-
walk the ways of peace. His name for ev - er-

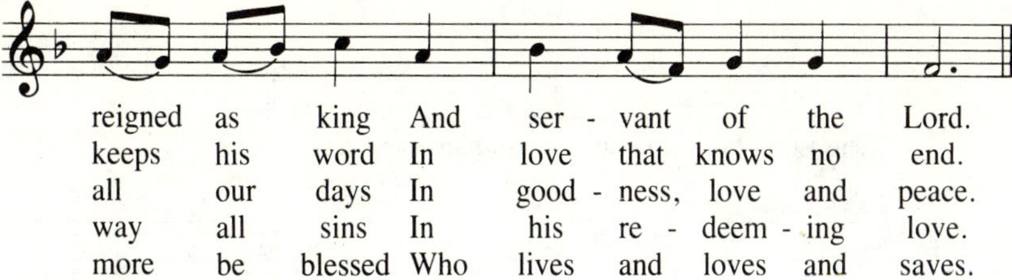
reigned as king And ser - vant of the Lord.
keeps his word In love that knows no end.
all our days In good - ness, love and peace.
way all sins In his re - deem - ing love.
more be blessed Who lives and loves and saves.

Alternate setting found at no. 89.

INTERCESSIONS 7

The response will be indicated by the leader.

LORD'S PRAYER

Adapt. by Robert Snow, 1964

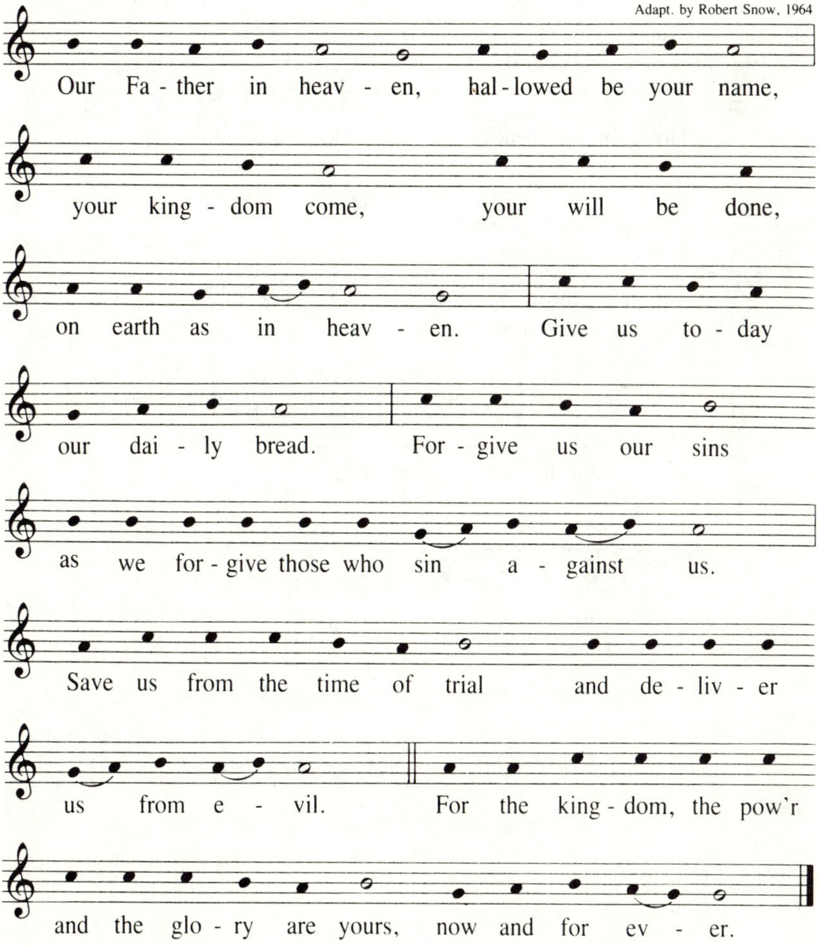

Our Fa - ther in heav - en, hal - lowed be your name,
your king - dom come, your will be done,
on earth as in heav - en. Give us to - day
our dai - ly bread. For - give us our sins
as we for - give those who sin a - gainst us.
Save us from the time of trial and de - liv - er
us from e - vil. For the king - dom, the pow'r
and the glo - ry are yours, now and for ev - er.

The concluding prayer follows:

8 DISMISSAL

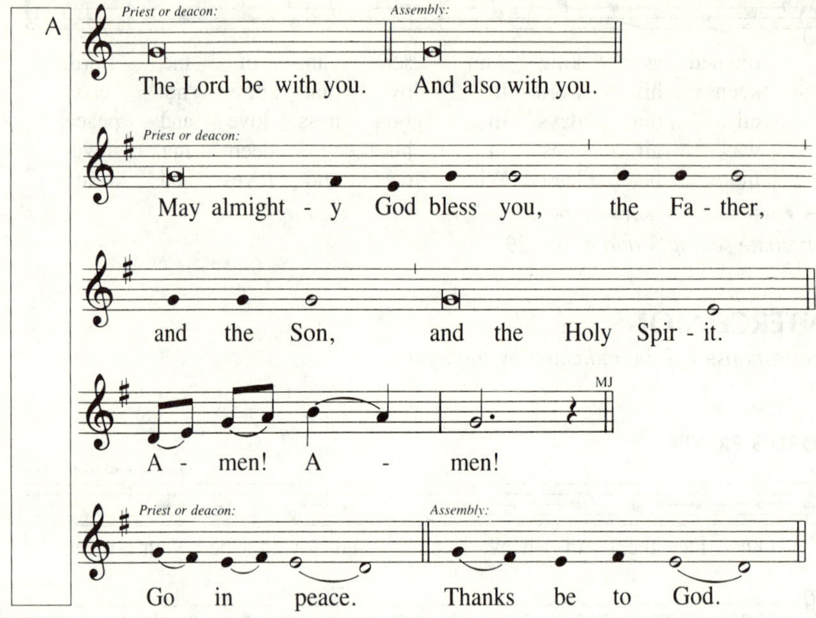
A
Priest or deacon:
Assembly:
The Lord be with you. And also with you.
Priest or deacon:
May almight - y God bless you, the Fa - ther,
and the Son, and the Holy Spir - it.
A - men! A - men!
MJ
Priest or deacon:
Assembly:
Go in peace. Thanks be to God.

9 *Dismissal, if the leader is not a priest or deacon:*

B
Presider:
May the Lord bless us, protect us from all evil
and bring us to everlasting life.
All:
A - men! A - men!
MJ

All may conclude the celebration by exchanging a sign of peace.

EVENING PRAYER/VESPERS 10

The church gathers in the evening to give thanks for the day that is ending. In the earliest tradition, this began with the lighting of the lamps as darkness fell and the hymn of praise of Christ who is "radiant Light...of God the Father's deathless face." The evening psalms and the Magnificat bring the day just past to focus for the Christian: "God has cast down the mighty from their thrones, and has lifted up the lowly"; "God has remembered the promise of mercy, the promise made to our ancestors." Prayers of intercession are almost always part of the church's liturgy, but those which conclude evening prayer are especially important. As day ends, the church again and again lifts up to God the needs and sorrows and failures of all the world. Such intercession is the daily task and joy of the baptized.

*The proper antiphons, readings, intercessions and prayers for each day are found in the **Worship - Liturgy of the Hours - Leaders' Edition** or **Christian Prayer.***

All make the sign of the cross.

A

Presider:
O God, + come to my as - sist - ance.
Assembly:
Lord, make haste to help me.
All:
Glory to the Father, and to the Son, and to the Ho - ly Spir - it:
as it was in the beginning, is now, and will be for ev-er. A-men.
Al - le - lu - ia.

Added outside Lent:

B

If Evening Prayer begins with a service of light (lucernarium), the following greeting may be used: 11

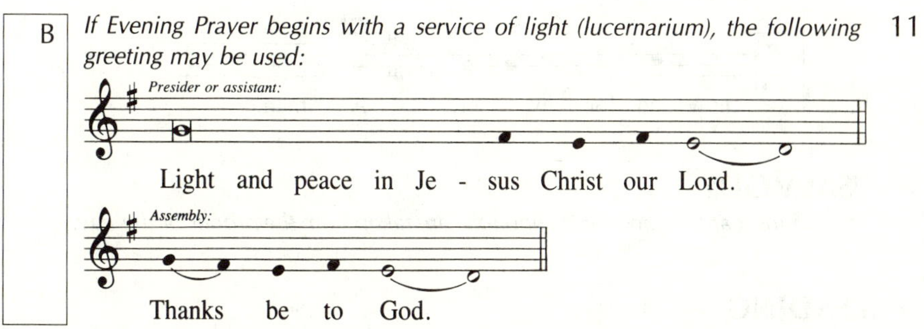
Presider or assistant:
Light and peace in Je - sus Christ our Lord.
Assembly:
Thanks be to God.

12 **HYMN**

Phos Hilaron
Greek, c.200
Tr. by William G. Storey, b. 1923

JESU DULCIS MEMORIA, LM
Acc. by Richard Proulx, b.1937

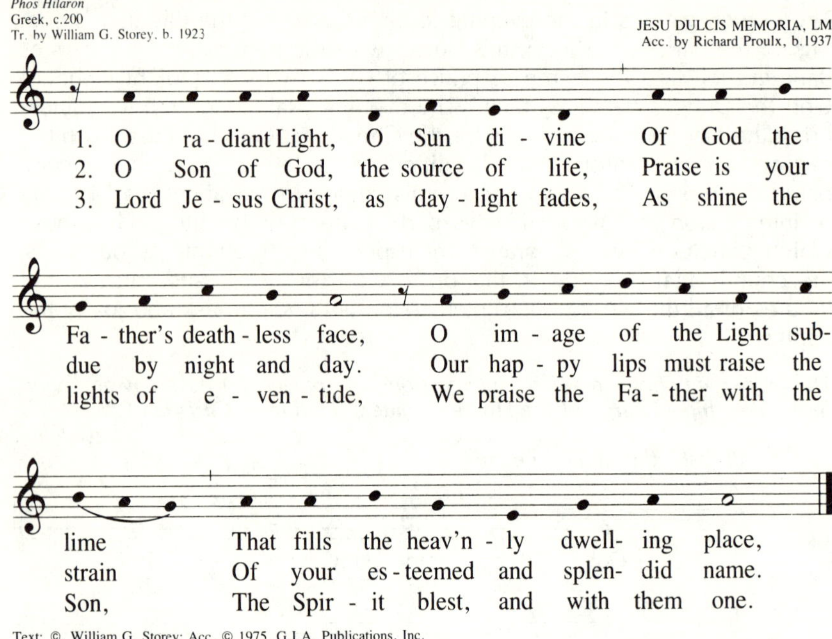
1. O ra - diant Light, O Sun di - vine Of God the
2. O Son of God, the source of life, Praise is your
3. Lord Je - sus Christ, as day - light fades, As shine the
Fa - ther's death - less face, O im - age of the Light subdue by night and day. Our hap - py lips must raise the
lights of e - ven - tide, We praise the Fa - ther with the
lime That fills the heav'n - ly dwell- ing place,
strain Of your es - teemed and splen- did name.
Son, The Spir - it blest, and with them one.

13 Optional *If the lucernarium is celebrated, the evening thanksgiving may be sung.*

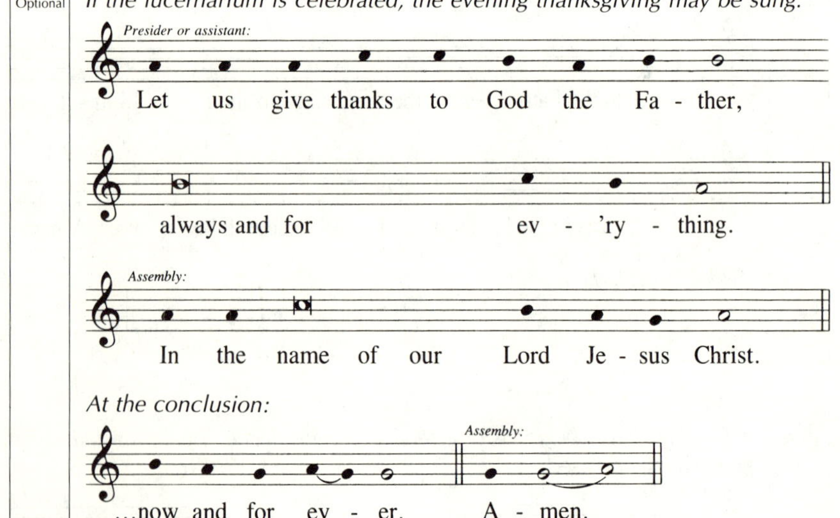
Presider or assistant:
Let us give thanks to God the Fa - ther,
always and for ev - 'ry - thing.
Assembly:
In the name of our Lord Je - sus Christ.

At the conclusion:

Assembly:
...now and for ev - er. A - men.

PSALMODY

The psalms, canticle and their antiphons are taken from the proper of the day.

READING

RESPONSE TO THE WORD OF GOD 14

Robert LeBlanc, 1984
Cantor, then all:
A. Advent Lord, show us
B. Christmas The Word was made man,
C. Lent Listen to us, O Lord, and have mercy,
D. Easter The Lord is ris - en,
E. General The whole crea - tion pro - claims
your mer - cy and love.
allelu - ia, al - le - lu - ia.
for we have sinned a - gainst you.
allelu - ia, al - le - lu - ia.
the great - ness of your glo - ry.
Cantor:
A. And grant us your sal - va - tion,
B. He lived a - mong us,
C. Christ Jesus, hear our hum - ble pe - ti - tions
D. He has ap - peared to Si - mon,
E. E - ter - nal a - ges praise
All:
your mer - cy and love.
allelu - ia, al - le - lu - ia.
for we have sinned a - gainst you.
allelu - ia, al - le - lu - ia.
the great - ness of your glo - ry.
Cantor:
Glo - ry to the Fa - ther, and to the Son,
and to the Ho - ly Spir - it:
All:
A. Lord, show us
B. The Word was made man,
C. Listen to us, O Lord, and have mercy,
D. The Lord is ris - en,
E. The whole crea tion pro - claims

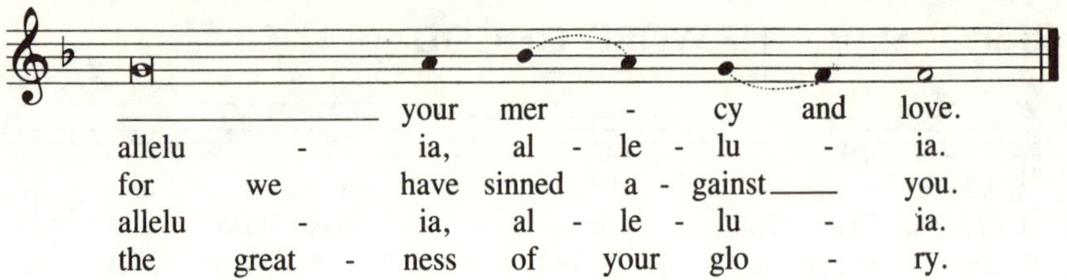
your mer - cy and love.
allelu - ia, al - le - lu - ia.
for we have sinned a - gainst you.
allelu - ia, al - le - lu - ia.
the great - ness of your glo - ry.

15 GOSPEL CANTICLE

The cantor sings the proper antiphon.
All make the sign of the cross.

Magnificat anima mea
Tr. by John T. Mueller, 1940

MAGNIFICAT, LMD
Michael Joncas, b.1951
Harm. by Mark V. Smith, b.1956

1. My soul + gives glo - ry to the Lord, In
2. His mer - cy goes to all who fear, From
3. He raised his ser - vant Is - ra - el, Re-

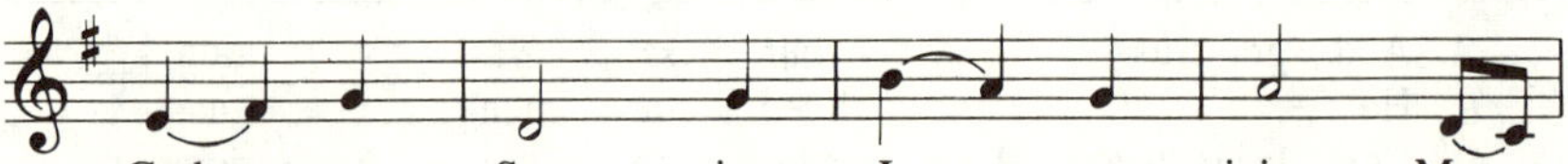

God my Sav - ior I re - joice. My
age to age and to all parts. His
mem - b'ring his e - ter - nal grace, As

low - li - ness he did re - gard, Ex-
arm of strength to all is near; He
from of old he did fore - tell To

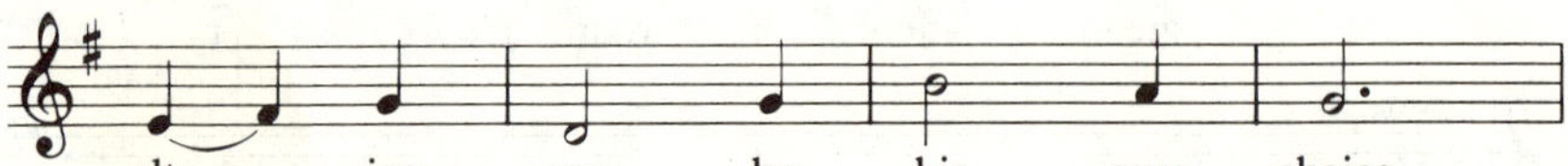

alt - ing me by his own choice.
scat - ters those who have proud hearts.
A - bra - ham and all his race.

From this day all shall call me blest, For
He casts the might - y from their throne And
O Fa - ther, Son and Spir - it blest, In

he has done great things for me, Of
rais - es those of low de - gree; He
three - fold Name are you a - dored, To

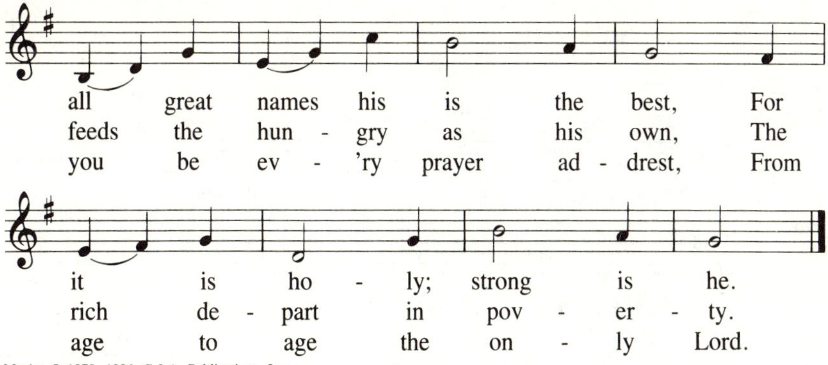
all great names his is the best, For
feeds the hun - gry as his own, The
you be ev - 'ry prayer ad - drest, From
it is ho - ly; strong is he.
rich de - part in pov - er - ty.
age to age the on - ly Lord.

Alternate settings found at nos. 87 and 88.

INTERCESSIONS 16

The response will be indicated by the leader.

LORD'S PRAYER

Adapt. by Robert Snow, 1964

Our Fa - ther in heav - en, hal - lowed be your name,
your king - dom come, your will be done,
on earth as in heav - en. Give us to - day
our dai - ly bread. For - give us our sins
as we for - give those who sin a - gainst us.
Save us from the time of trial and de - liv - er
us from e - vil. For the king - dom, the pow'r
and the glo - ry are yours, now and for ev - er.

The concluding prayer follows.

17 **DISMISSAL**

A

Priest or deacon:
The Lord be with you.
Assembly:
And also with you.
Priest or deacon:
May almight - y God bless you, the Fa - ther,
and the Son, and the Holy Spir - it.
All:
A - men! A - men!
MJ
Priest or deacon:
Go in peace.
Assembly:
Thanks be to God.

18 B *Dismissal, if the leader is not a priest or deacon:*

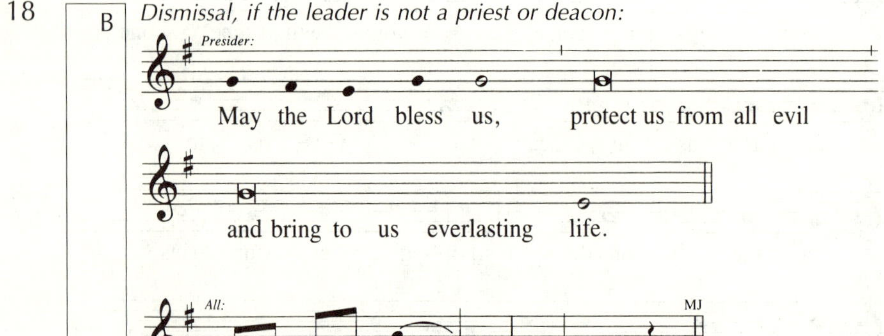
Presider:
May the Lord bless us, protect us from all evil
and bring to us everlasting life.
All:
A - men! A - men!
MJ

All may conclude the celebration by exchanging a sign of peace.

NIGHT PRAYER/COMPLINE

19

The church's prayers at night are direct and simple. The Christian remembers with sorrow the day's evil and failure, and places this before the mercy of God. Before surrendering to sleep, there is prayer for God's protection through the night and an expression of acceptance: "Now, Lord, you may dismiss your servant." The night prayer concludes by binding together the sleep of this night with the final falling asleep in the Lord: "May the all-powerful Lord grant us a restful night and a peaceful death." Night's last words are often a gentle invocation of our mother, "When this exile is ended, show us your womb's blessed fruit, Jesus."

The proper antiphons, readings, intercessions and prayers for each day are found in the ***Worship–Liturgy of the Hours–Leaders' Edition*** *or* ***Christian Prayer.***

All make the sign of the cross.

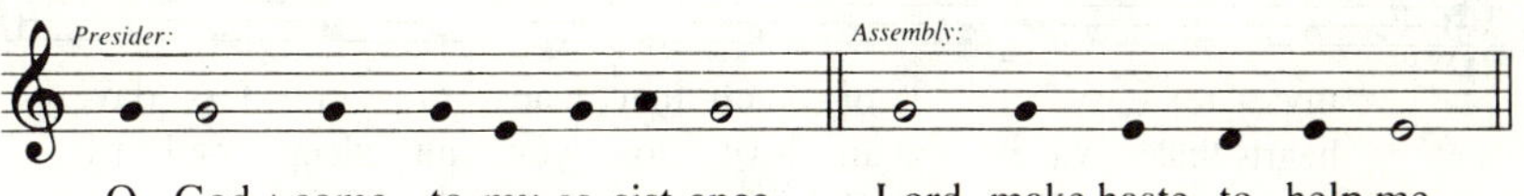
Presider:
Assembly:
O God,+come to my as-sist-ance.
Lord, make haste to help me.

All:
Glory to the Father, and to the Son, and to the Ho-ly Spir-it:

as it was in the beginning, is now and will be for ev - er. A-men.

Added outside Lent:

Al - le - lu - ia.

Optional

A brief examination of conscience may be made. At its conclusion, the following may be said:

I confess to almighty God,
and to you, my brothers and sisters,
that I have sinned through my own fault
in my thoughts and in my words,
in what I have done,
and in what I have failed to do;
and I ask blessed Mary, ever virgin,
all the angels and saints,
and you, my brothers and sisters,
to pray for me to the Lord our God.

20 **HYMN**

Benedictine Nuns of St. Mary's Abbey
West Malling, Kent, 1967

TE LUCIS ANTE TERMINUM, LM
Adapt. by Howard Hughes, SM, b.1930

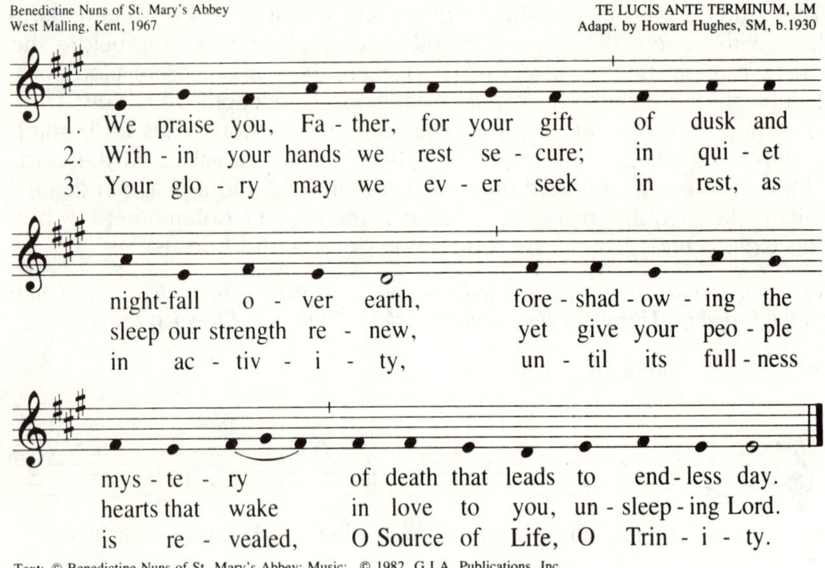
1. We praise you, Fa - ther, for your gift of dusk and
2. With - in your hands we rest se - cure; in qui - et
3. Your glo - ry may we ev - er seek in rest, as
night-fall o - ver earth, fore - shad - ow - ing the
sleep our strength re - new, yet give your peo - ple
in ac - tiv - i - ty, un - til its full - ness
mys - te - ry of death that leads to end - less day.
hearts that wake in love to you, un - sleep - ing Lord.
is re - vealed, O Source of Life, O Trin - i - ty.

PSALMODY

The psalm, antiphon and psalm prayer are taken from the proper of the day of the week.

21 **READING**

RESPONSORY

In Manus Tuas
Sarum Tone
Adapt. by Richard Proulx, 1984

Cantor:
In - to your hands, O Lord, I com - mend my spir - it.
All:
In - to your hands, O Lord, I com - mend my spir - it.
Cantor:
You have re - deemed us, Lord God of truth.
All:
I com - mend my spir - it.
Cantor:
Glo-ry to the Fa - ther, and
to the Son, and to the Ho - ly Spir - it.

All:
In - to your hands, O Lord, I com - mend my spir - it.

GOSPEL CANTICLE 22

Nunc Dimittis
Sarum Tone
Adapt. by Richard Proulx, 1984

Antiphon

Pro - tect us, Lord, as we stay a - wake; watch

o - ver us as we sleep, that a - wake we may keep

watch with Christ, and a - sleep rest in his peace.

Verses

1. Lord, now you let your ser-vant go in peace: your word has

been ful - filled. 2. My own eyes have seen the sal - va - tion

which you have prepared in the sight of ev - 'ry peo - ple.

3. A light to re - veal you to the na - tions and the glory

of your peo-ple Is - ra - el. 4. Glory to the

Fa - ther, and to the Son and to the

Ho - ly Spir - it: as it was in the be - gin - ning,

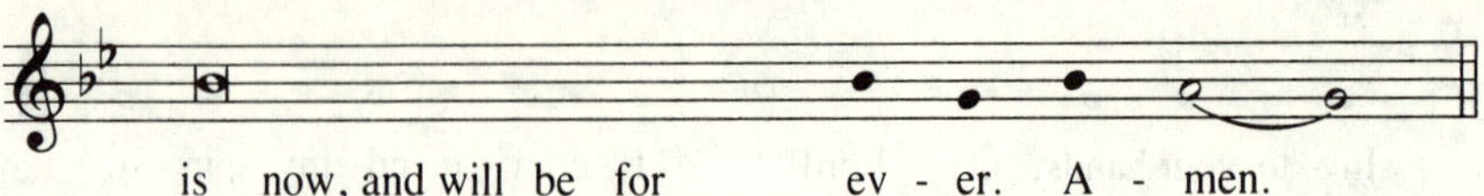
is now, and will be for ev - er. A - men.

Alternate setting found at no. 90. For a metrical setting of the "Nunc Dimittis" use hymn no. 691, stanzas 1,2,& 5.

23 **PRAYER**

CONCLUSION

Presider:
May the all-powerful Lord grant us a restful night and a peaceful death.

All:
MJ
A - men! A - men!

The Marian antiphon, "Salve Regina," no. 703, or during Easter season, "Regina Caeli," no. 443, may follow.

Psalm 1 24

Antiphon

PP
Bless-ed are they who de - light in the law of the Lord.

Psalm Tone

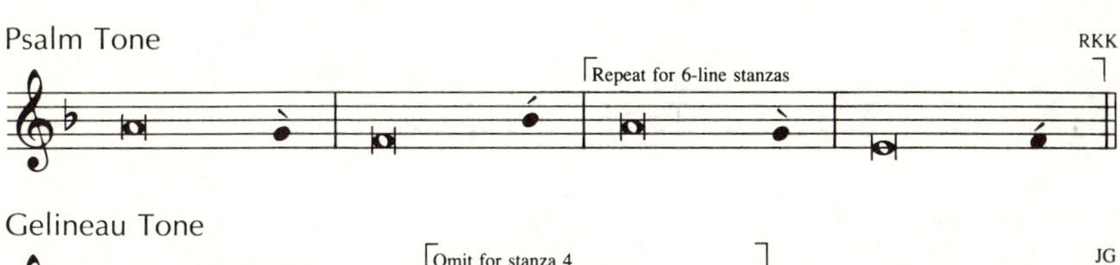
RKK
Repeat for 6-line stanzas

Gelineau Tone

Omit for stanza 4

JG

Beatus vir qui non abiit

[1] **Happy** in**deed** is the **màn**
who **fol**lows not the **coun**sel of the **wíck**ed,
nor **lin**gers in the **way** of **sìn**ners
nor **sits** in the **com**pany of **scór**ners,
[2] but whose de**light** is the **law** of the **Lòrd**
and who **pon**ders his **law** day and **níght**.

[3] **He** is like a **tree** that is **plànt**ed
be**side** the **flow**ing **wá**ters,
that **yields** its **fruit** in due **sè**ason
and whose **leaves** shall **never** **fáde**;
and **all** that he **does** shall **pròs**per.
[4] Not **so** are the **wick**ed, not **só**!

For **they** like **win**nowed **chàff**
shall be **dri**ven a**way** by the **wínd**.
[5] When the **wick**ed are **judged** they shall not **stànd**,
nor find **room** among **those** who are **jú****st**;
[6] for the **Lord** guards the **way** of the **jùst**
but the **way** of the **wick**ed leads to **doóm**.

Give **praise** to the **Fa**ther Al**mìghty**,
to his **Son**, Jesus **Christ**, the **Lórd**,
to the **Spir**it who **dwells** in our **heàrts**,
both **now** and for **ev**er. A**mén**.

25 Psalm 4

Antiphon

EE

Have mer - cy, Lord, and hear my prayer.

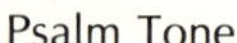
Psalm Tone

AGM

Gelineau Tone

Cum invocarem

2 When I **call**, **an**swer me, O **Gòd** of **jus**tice;
from **an**guish you re**leased** me, have **mer**cý and **hear** me!

3 O **men**, how **long** will your **heàrts** be **closed**,
will you **love** what is **fu**tile and **seek** whát is **false**?

4 It is the **Lord** who grants **fa**vors to **those** whòm he **loves**;
the **Lord hears** me whene**vér** I **call** him.

5 Fear him; do not **sin**: **pon**der on your **bed** ànd be **still**.
6 Make **jus**tice your **sa**crifice and **trust** ín the **Lord**.

7 "What can **bring** us **hap**piness?" **mà**ny **say**.
Lift up the **light** of your **face** on ús, O **Lord**.

8 You have **put** into my **heart** a **greà**ter **joy**
than **they** have from a**bun**dance of **corn** ánd new **wine**.

9 I will **lie** down in **peace** and **sleep** còmes at **once**
for **you** alone, **Lord**, make me **dwéll** in **safe**ty.

Give **praise** to the **Fa**ther, the **Son** and Hòly **Spir**it,
both **now** and for **a**ges un**end**íng. **A**men.

Psalm 6 26

Antiphon

RP
Re - turn, O Lord, and res - cue my soul.

Psalm Tone

Gelineau Tone

LW
Omit for 5-line sts.
Omit for 4-line stanza

Domine, ne in furore

2 **Lord**, do not re**prove** me ìn your **an**ger;
punish me **not**, ín your **rage**.
3 Have **mer**cy on me, **Lord**, I hàve no **strength**;
Lord, **heal** me, my **bod**y is **racked**,
4 my **soul** is **rácked** with **pain**.

But **you**, O **Lòrd**…how **long**?
5 Re**turn**, Lord, **res**cúe my **soul**.
Save me in your **mer**cìful **love**;
6 for in **death no** one remem**bers** you;
from the **grave**, **who** can gíve you **praise**?

7 **I** am ex**haust**ed wìth my **groan**ing;
every **night** I drench my **pil**low with **tears**;
I be**dew** my **béd** with **weep**ing.
8 My **eye** wastes a**wày** with **grief**;
I have grown **old** sur**round**ed bý my **foes**.

9 **Leave** me, all **you** whò do **e**vil,
for the **Lord** has **héard** my **weep**ing.
10 The **Lord** has **hèard** my **plea**,
the **Lord** will ac**cépt** my **prayer**.
11 All my **foes** will re**tire** ìn con**fu**sion,
foiled and **sud**denlý con**found**ed.

9 Give **praise** to the **Fa**thèr Al**migh**ty,
to his **Son**, Jesus **Chríst**, the **Lord**,
to the **Spir**it who **dwells** ìn our **hearts**,
both **now** and for **e**vér. **A**men.

27 Psalm 8

Antiphon I

AGM
How great is your name, O Lord our God, through all the earth!

Antiphon II

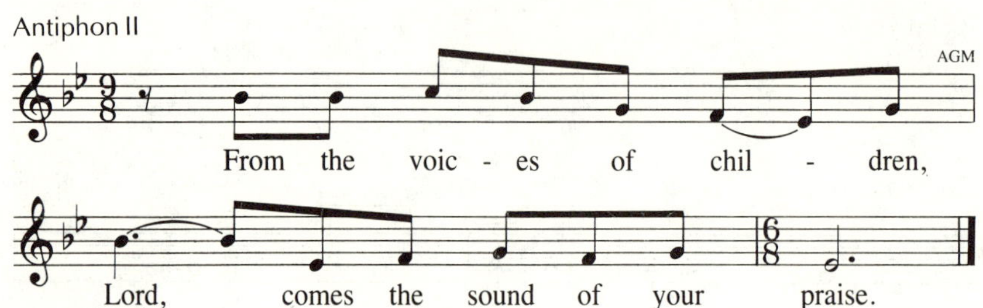
AGM
From the voic - es of chil - dren,
Lord, comes the sound of your praise.

Psalm Tone

Gelineau Tone

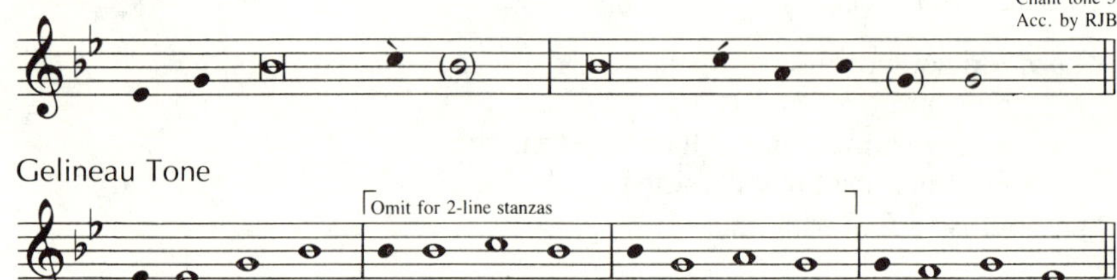
Chant tone 5
Acc. by RJB
Omit for 2-line stanzas

Domine, Dominus noster

*2 How **great** is your **name**, O Lòrd our **God**
thróugh all the **earth**!

Your **maj**esty is **praised** above the **hè**avens;
3 on the **lips** of **chíl**dren and of **babes**
you have found **praise** to **foil** your **è**nemy,
to **si**lence the **fóe** and the **reb**el.

4 When I see the **heav**ens, the **work** of yòur **hands**,
the **moon** and the **stárs** which you ar**ranged**,
5 what is **man** that you should **keep** him in **mìnd**,
mortal **man** thát you **care** for **him**?

6 Yet you have **made** him little **less** than a **gòd**;
with **glo**ry and **hó**nor you **crowned** him,
7 gave him **pow**er over the **works** of yòur **hand**,
put **all** things **ún**der his **feet**.

**Omitted when Antiphon I is used.*

8 **All** of them, **sheep** and **cà****t**tle,
yes, **e**ven thé **sa**vage **beasts**,
9 **birds** of the **air**, and **fìsh**
that **make** their **way** throúgh the **wa**ters.

*10 How **great** is your **name**, O Lòrd our **God**
throúgh all the **earth**!

Give **glo**ry to the **Fa**ther Al**mìghty**,
to his **Son**, Jésus **Christ**, the **Lord**,
to the **Spir**it who **dwells** in òur **hearts**,
both **now** and for **é**ver. A**men**.

28 Psalm (12)13

Antiphon

RP
I trust in your mer - ci - ful love.

Psalm Tone

Omit for 2-line stanza
Repeat for 5-line stanza
LB

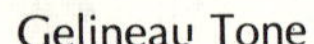
Gelineau Tone

St. 1

St. 2-4
Omit for 2-line stanza

Usquequo, Domine?

1 How **long**, O **Lord**, will yòu for**get** me?
How **long** will you **híde** your **face**?
2 How **long** must I bear **grief** ìn my **soul**,
this **sor**row in my **heart** dáy and **night**?
How **long** shall my **en**emý pre**vail**?

3 **Look** at me, **an**swer me, **Lòrd** my **God**!
Give **light** to my **eyes** lest I **fall** asléep in **death**,
4 lest my **en**emy **say**: **"I** have òver**come** him";
lest my **foes** re**joice** to **sée** my **fall**.

5 As for **me**, I **trust** in your **mer**cìful **love**.
Let my **heart** re**joice** in your **sá**ving **help**.
6 Let me **sing** to the **Lord** for his **good**nèss to **me**,
singing **psalms** to the **name** of the **Lórd**, the Most **High**.

Give **praise** to the **Fa**ther, the **Son** and Hòly **Spir**it,
both **now** and for **a**ges un**end**íng. **A**men.

Psalm (14)15 29

Antiphon

RP
He who does jus - tice will live
in the pres - ence of the Lord.

Psalm Tone

Omit for stanza 1
CW

Gelineau Tone

Omit for stanza 1

Domine, quis habitabit?

1 Lord, **who** shall be ad**mit**ted tò your **tent**
and **dwell** on your **holý** **moun**tain?

2 **He** who **walks** wìthout **fault**,
he who **acts** wíth **jus**tice
and **speaks** the **truth** from hìs **heart**,
3 **he** who does not **slan**der with hís **tongue**,

he who **does** no **wrong** tò his **bro**ther,
who **casts** no **slur** on hís **neigh**bor,
4 who **holds** the **god**less in dìs**dain**,
but **hon**ors those who **fear** thé **Lord**;

he who **keeps** his **pledge**, còme what **may**,
5 who **takes** no **in**terest on á **loan**
and ac**cepts** no **bribes** against thè **in**nocent.
Such a man will **stand** firm fór **ever**.

Give **praise** to the **Fa**thèr, Al**migh**ty,
to his **Son**, Jesus **Christ**, thé **Lord**,
to the **Spir**it who **dwells** in oùr **hearts**,
both **now** and for **ev**er. Á**men**.

30 Psalm (15)16

Antiphon
EE
In you, my God, my bod - y will rest in hope.
Psalm Tone
LB
Omit for 3-line stanza
Repeat for 5-line stanza
Gelineau Tone
St. 1-5
Omit for 4-line stanzas
Omit for 3-line stanza
St. 6-7
Omit for 3-line stanza

Conserva me, Domine

1 **Preserve** me, **God**, I take **ref**úge in **you**.
2 I **say** to the **Lord**: "**You** áre my **God**.
My **hap**piness **lies** in yóu **alone**."

3 He has **put** into my **heart** a **mar**vèlous **love**
for the **faith**ful **ones** who **dwell** ín his **land**.
4 Those who **choose** other **gods** incrèase their **sor**rows.
Never will I **of**fer their **of**feríngs of **blood**.
Never will I **take** their **name** upón my **lips**.

5 O **Lord**, it is **you** who are my **por**tiòn and **cup**,
it is **you** your**self** who áre my **prize**.
6 The **lot** marked **out** for me is mỳ de**light**,
welcome in**deed** the **her**itage that fálls to **me**!

7 I will **bless** the **Lord** who gìves me **coun**sel,
who **e**ven at **night** dirécts my **heart**.
8 I **keep** the **Lord** ever ìn my **sight**;
since **he** is at my **right** hand, **I** shál stand **firm**.

9 And so my **heart** rejoices, my sòul is **glad**;
even my **bod**y shall **ré**st in **safe**ty.
10 For **you** will not **leave** my **soul** amòng the **dead**,
nor **let** your be**loved** **knów** de**cay**.

11 You will **show** me the **pàth** of **life**,
the **full**ness of **joy** ín your **pres**ence,
at your **right** hand **hap**pinéss for **e**ver.

Give **praise** to the **Fa**thèr Al**might**y,
to his **Son**, Jesus **Chríst**, the **Lord**,
to the **Spir**it who **dwells** ìn our **hearts**,
both **now** and forevér. **A**men.

31 Psalm (21)22

Antiphon

FS
My God, my God, why have you a - ban-doned me?
Psalm Tone
A
B
C
D
LB

Gelineau Tone

Omit for 4-line stanza
Omit for 2-line stanza
St. 1, 12-15

Omit for 5 lines
Omit for 4-line stanzas
St.2-11

Deus, Deus meus

[2]My **God**, my **God**, **why** have yòu for**sak**en me?
You are **far** from my **plea** and the **cry** of mý dis**tress**.
[3]O my **God**, I call by **day** and you **give** nò re**ply**;
I **call** by **night** and I **fínd** no **peace**.

[4]Yet **you**, O **Gòd**, are **ho**ly,
en**throned** on the **praisés** of **Is**rael.
[5]In **you** our **fa**thers pùt their **trust**;
they **trust**ed and you **sét** them **free**. *[Repeat C+D]*
[6]When they **cried** to **you**, thèy es**caped**.
In you they **trust**ed and **nevér** in **vain**.

[7]But **I** am a **worm** ànd no **man**, *[Omit B+C]*
the butt of **men**, laughing-**stock** óf the **peo**ple.
[8]**All** who **see** mè de**ride** me.
They curl their **lips**, they **tóss** their **heads**.
[9]"He **trust**ed in the **Lord**, lèt him **save** him;
let him re**lease** him if **this** ís his **friend**."

10 Yes, it was **you** who **took** me from the **womb**,
entrusted me to my mother's **breast**.
11 To **you** I was committed from my **birth**,
from my **mother's** womb **you** have been my **God**. *[Repeat C+D]*
12 Do not **leave** me alone in my distress;
come **close**, there is **none** else to **help**.

13 **Many bulls** have surrounded me,
fierce **bulls** of **Bashan** close me **in**.
14 **Against** me they open wide their **jaws**,
like lions, **rending**, and **roaring**.

15 Like **water I** am poured **out**,
disjointed are **all** my **bones**.
My **heart** has become like **wax**,
it is **melted** within my **breast**. *[Repeat C+D]*
16 **Parched** as burnt **clay** is my **throat**,
my **tongue cleaves** to my **jaws**.

17 **Many dogs** have surrounded me,
a **band** of the **wicked** beset me.
They tear **holes** in my **hands** and my **feet**,
16 and **lay** me in the **dust** of **death**.

18 I can **count** every **one** of my **bones**.
These **people stare** at me and **gloat**;
19 they divide my **clothing** among them.
They **cast lots** for my **robe**.

20 O **Lord**, do not **leave** me **alone**, *[Omit B+C]*
my **strength**, make **haste** to **help** me!
21 **Rescue** my **soul** from the **sword**,
my **life** from the **grip** of these **dogs**.
22 Save my **life** from the **jaws** of these **lions**,
my poor **soul** from the **horns** of these **oxen**.

23 I will **tell** of your **name** to my **brethren**,
and **praise** you where **they** are **assembled**.
24 "You who **fear** the **Lord**, give him **praise**;
all **sons** of **Jacob**, give him **glory**.
Revere him, **Israel's sons**.

25 For **he** has **never despised**
nor **scorned** the **poverty** of the **poor**.
From **him** he has not **hidden** his **face**,
but he **heard** the **poor** man when he **cried**."

26 **You** are my **praise** in the **grèat** assem**bly**.
My **vows** I will **pay** before **thóse** who **fear** him,
27 The **poor** shall **eat** and shall **hàve** their **fill**.
They shall **praise** the **Lord**, **thóse** who **seek** him. *[Repeat D]*
May their **hearts live** for **evér** and **ever**!

28 All the **earth** shall re**mem**ber and re**turn** tò the **Lord**,
all **fam**ilies of the **na**tions **worshíp** be**fore** him;
29 for the **king**dom is the **Lord's**, he is **rul**er òf the **na**tions.
30 They shall **wor**ship him, **all** the **migh**ty óf the **earth**; *[Repeat D]*
be**fore** him shall **bow** all who go **down** tó the **dust**.

31 And my **soul** shall live for **him**, my **chìl**dren **serve** him.
They shall **tell** of the **Lord** to gene**ra**tions yét to **come**,
32 de**clare** his **faith**fulness to **peo**ples yèt un**born**:
"**These things** the **Lórd** has **done**."

Give **praise** to the **Fa**ther, the **Son** and Hòly **Spir**it, *[Omit B+C]*
both **now** and for **a**ges un**endíng**. **A**men.

32 Psalm (22)23

Antiphon I

JG
My shep-herd is the Lord, noth-ing in-deed shall I want.

Antiphon II

AGM
His good - ness shall fol - low me
al - ways to the end of my days.

Antiphon III
AGM
The Lord is my shep-herd, noth-ing shall I want: he
leads me by safe paths, noth-ing shall I fear.
Psalm Tone
Omit for 4-line stanzas
RP

Gelineau Tone

Omit for 4-line stanzas

Dominus regit me

1 The **Lord** is my **shep**herd;
there is **noth**ing I shall **want**.
2 **Fresh** and **green** are the **pas**tures
where he **gives** me re**pose**.
Near **rest**ful **wa**ters he **leads** me,
3 to re**vive** my drooping **spirit**.

He **guides** me a**long** the right **path**;
he is **true** to his **name**.
4 If I should **walk** in the **val**ley of **dark**ness
no **e**vil would I **fear**.
You are **there** with your **crook** and your **staff**;
with **these** you give me **comfort**.

5 You have pre**pared** a **ban**quet for **me**
in the **sight** of my **foes**.
My **head** you have a**noint**ed with **oil**,
my **cup** is over**flowing**.

6 Surely **good**ness and **kind**ness shall **fol**low me
all the **days** of my **life**.
In the **Lord's** own **house** shall I **dwell**
for **ev**er and **ever**.

To the **Fa**ther and **Son** give **glo**ry,
give **glo**ry to the **Spir**it.
To God who **is**, who **was**, and who **will** be
for **ev**er and **ever**.

33 Psalm (24)25

Antiphon
AGM
To you I lift up my soul, O Lord my God.
CW
Psalm Tone
Repeat for stanza 1
Repeat for 6-line stanzas
Gelineau Tone
Omit for stanza 1
Omit for 4-line stanzas

Ad te, Domine, levavi

1 To you, O **Lord**, I **lift** ùp my **soul**.
2 I **trust** you, let me **not** be disáp**point**ed;
do not **let** my **en**emiès **tri**umph.
3 Those who **hope** in you shall **not** be disáp**point**ed,
but only **those** who **wan**tonly bréak **faith**.

4 **Lord,** make me **knòw** your **ways**.
Lord, teach me yóur **paths**.
5 Make me **walk** in your **truth,** ánd **teach** me,
for **you** are **God** mỳ **savior**.

In **you** I **hope** àll day **long**
7c **because** of your **good**ness, Ó **Lord**.
6 Re**mem**ber your **mer**cỳ, **Lord**,
and the **love** you have **shown** from óf **old**.
7 Do not re**mem**ber the **sins** of mỳ **youth**.
In your **love** re**mem**bér **me**.

8 The **Lord** is **gòod** and **up**right.
He shows the **path** to **those** whó **stray**,
9 he guides the **hum**ble in the **rìght path**,
he **teach**es his **way** to thé **poor**.

10 His **ways** are **faith**fulnèss and **love**
for those who **keep** his **co**venant ánd **will**.
11 **Lord**, for the **sake** of yòur **name**
for**give** my **guilt**, for it ís **great**.

12 If **an**yone **fèars** the **Lord**
he will **show** him the **path** he shóuld **choose**.
13 His **soul** shall **live** ìn **hap**piness
and his **chil**dren shall pos**sess** thé **land**.
14 The Lord's **friend**ship is for **those** who rè**vere** him;
to **them** he re**veals** hís **co**venant.

15 My **eyes** are **al**ways òn the **Lord**,
for he **res**cues my **feet** from thé **snare**.
16 **Turn** to **me** and hàve **mer**cy
for **I** am **lone**ly ánd **poor**.

17 Re**lieve** the **an**guish òf my **heart**
and set me **free** from **my** dístress.
18 **See** my af**flic**tion and mỳ **toil**
and **take** all my **sins** áway.

19 **See** how **man**y àre my **foes**,
how **vi**olent their **ha**tred fór **me**.
20 Pre**serve** my **life** and **res**cùe me.
Do not disap**point** me, **you** are mý **re**fuge.
21 May **in**nocence and **up**rightness prò**tect** me,
for my **hope** is in **you**, Ó **Lord**.

22 Re**deem** Is**ra**èl, O **God**,
from **all its** dís**tress**.
To the **Fa**ther, the **Son** and Holỳ **Spir**it,
give **praise** for **ev**er. Á**men**.

34 Psalm (26)27

Antiphon
IB
I will sing and make mu - sic for the Lord.

Psalm Tone
Repeat for 6-line stanzas
LB
Gelineau Tone
Repeat for 6-line stanzas

St.6

Dominus illuminatio

1 The **Lord** is my **light** ànd my **help**;
whom shál l I **fear**?
The **Lord** is the **strong**hold òf my **life**;
before **whom** shál l I **shrink**?

2 When **evil**doèrs draw **near**
to de**voúr** my **flesh**,
it is **they**, my **ene**mìes and **foes**,
who **stum**blé and **fall**.

3 Though an **ar**my en**càmp** **against** me
my **heart** wóuld not **fear**.
Though **war** break **òut** **against** me
even **then** wóuld I **trust**.

4 There is **one** thing I **ask** òf the **Lord**,
for **thís** I **long**,
to **live** in the **house** òf the **Lord**,
all the **days** óf my **life**,
to **sa**vor the **sweet**ness òf the **Lord**,
to be**hóld** his **tem**ple.

5 For **there** he keeps me **safe** ìn his **tent**,
in the **dáy** of evil.
He **hides** me in the **shel**ter òf his **tent**,
on a **rock** he séts me **safe**.

6 And **now** my **head** shall be **raised**
above my **foes** who sur**round** me,
and I shall **of**fer with**in** his **tent**
a **sacri**fice of **joy**.
I will **sing** and make **mu**sic for the **Lord**.

7 O **Lord**, hear my **voice** when I **call**;
have **mer**cy and **an**swer.
8 Of **you** my **heart** has **spo**ken:
"**Seek** his **face**."

It is your **face**, O **Lord**, that I **seek**;
9 **hide** not your **face**.
Dis**miss** not you **ser**vant in **an**ger;
you have been my **help**.

Do not a**ban**don or for**sake** me,
O **God** my **help**!
10 Though **fa**ther and **moth**er for**sake** me,
the **Lord** will re**ceive** me.

11 **Instruct** me, **Lord**, in your **way**;
on an **e**ven path **lead** me.
When they **lie** in **am**bush 12 pro**tect** me
from my **en**emy's **greed**.
False **wit**nesses **rise against** me,
breathing out **fu**ry.

13 I am **sure** I shall **see** the Lord's **good**ness
in the **land** of the **liv**ing.
14 Hope in **him**, hold **firm** and take **heart**.
Hope in the **Lord**!

Praise the **Fa**ther, the **Son** and Holy **Spir**it,
both **now** and for **ev**er,
the God who **is**, who **was**, and is to **come**,
at the **end** of the **a**ges.

35 Psalm (30)31

Antiphon
RC
Lord, God, be my ref - uge and my strength.
Psalm Tone
Omit for 3-line stanza
AGM
Gelineau Tone
St. 1-5
St. 6-20
Omit for 3-line stanza

In te, Domine, speravi

[2] In **you**, O **Lord**, Ì take **ref**uge.
Let me **nev**er be **pút** to **shame**.
In your **jus**tice, **sèt** me **free**,
[3] **hear** me and **speed**ily **rés**cue me.

Be a **rock** of **refù**ge for **me**,
a **might**y **strong**hóld to **save** me,
[4] for **you** are my **ròck**, my **strong**hold.
For your **name's** sake, **lead** mé and **guide** me.

[5] **Re**lease me from the **snares** thèy have **hid**den
for **you** are my **ré**fuge, **Lord**.
[6] Into your **hands** I com**mènd** my **spir**it.
It is **you** who will re**deém** me, **Lord**.

O **God** of **truth**, [7] yòu de**test**
those who **wor**ship **false** and émpty **gods**.
[8] As for **me**, I **trust** ìn the **Lord**;
let me be **glad** and re**joice** ín your **love**.

You, who have **seen** mỳ af**flic**tion
and taken **heed** of my **sóul's** dis**tress**,
[9] have not **hand**ed me **o**ver tò the **en**emy,
but **set** my **feét** at **large**.

[10]Have **mer**cy on **mè**, O **Lord**,
for **I** am ín dis**tress**.
Tears have **wast**èd my **eyes**,
my **throat**, ánd my **heart**.

[11]For my **life** is **spènt** with **sor**row
and my **yéars** with **sighs**.
Af**flic**tion has **bro**ken dòwn my **strength**
and my **bones** wáste **away**.

[12]In the **face** of **àll** my **foes**
I am à re**proach**,
an **ob**ject of **scorn** tò my **neigh**bors
and of **fear** tó my **friends**.

Those who **see** me ìn the **street**
run **far** awáy from **me**.
[13]**I** am like a **dead** màn for**got**ten,
like a **thing** thrówn **away**.

[14]I have **heard** the **slan**der òf the **crowd**,
fear is áll a**round** me,
as they **plot** to**geth**èr **a**gainst me,
as they **plan** to táke my **life**.

[15]But as for **me**, I **trùst** in **you**, Lord;
I say: "**You** áre my **God**.
[16]My **life** is in your **hands**, de**lì**ver me
from the **hands** of thóse who **hate** me.

[17]Let your **face shine** òn your **ser**vant.
Save me ín your **love**.
[18]Let me **not** be put to **shame** fòr I **call** you,
let the **wick**éd be **shamed**!

Let them be **si**lenced ìn the **grave**,
[19]let **ly**ing líps be **mute**,
that speak **haugh**tily **a**gàinst the **just**
with **pride** ánd con**tempt**."

[20]How **great** is the **gòod**ness, **Lord**,
that you **keep** for thóse who **fear** you,
that you **show** to **thòse** who **trust** you
in the **síght** of **men**.

[21]You **hide** them in the **shel**ter òf your **pres**ence
from the **plot**tíng of **men**;
you **keep** them **safe** withìn your **tent**
from dis**pú**ting **tongues**.

[22]**Bless**ed be the **Lord** whò has **shown** me
the **won**ders óf his **love**
in a **fort**ífied **city**.

[23]"**I** am far re**moved** fròm your **sight**,"
I **said** in mý a**larm**.
Yet you **heard** the **voice** òf my **plea**
when I **críed** for **help**.

[24]**Love** the **Lord**, àll you **saints**.
He **guárds** his **faith**ful
but the **Lord** will **repay** tò the **full**
those who áct with **pride**.

[25]Be **strong**, let your **heàrt** take **cour**age,
all who **hope** ín the **Lord**.
Praise the **Fa**ther, the **Son**, and Hòly **Spir**it,
for **evér** and **ev**er.

36 Psalm (33)34

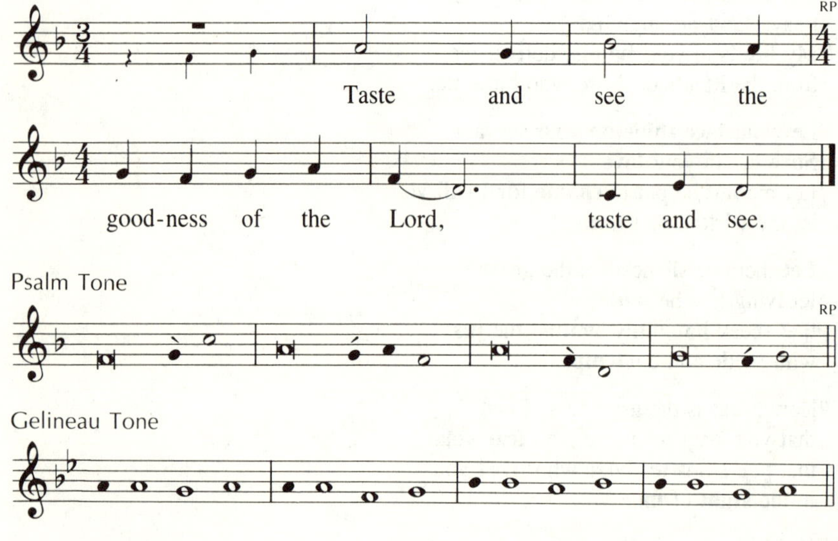
Antiphon
RP
Taste and see the
good-ness of the Lord, taste and see.
Psalm Tone
RP
Gelineau Tone

Benedicam Dominum

[2]I will **bless** the **Lord** at àll **times**,
his **praise al**ways ón my **lips**;
[3]in the **Lord** my **soul** shall make ìts **boast**.
The **hum**ble shall **hear** and bé **glad**.

4 **Glo**rify the **Lord** with **me**.
Together let us **praise** his **name**.
5 I **sought** the **Lord** and he **an**swered me;
from all my **ter**rors he **set** me **free**.

6 **Look** towards **him** and be **ra**diant,
let your **fa**ces **not** be a**bashed**.
7 This **poor** man **called**; the Lord **heard** him
and **res**cued him from **all** his dis**tress**.

8 The **an**gel of the **Lord** is en**camped**
around **those** who re**vere** him, to **res**cue them.
9 Taste and **see** that the **Lord** is **good**.
He is **hap**py who seeks **ref**uge in **him**.

10 Re**vere** the **Lord**, you his **saints**.
They lack **noth**ing, **those** who re**vere** him.
11 Strong **li**ons suffer **want** and go **hun**gry
but **those** who seek the **Lord** lack no **bless**ing.

12 **Come**, children and **hear** me
that I may **teach** you the **fear** of the **Lord**.
13 Who is **he** who **longs** for **life**
and many **days**, to en**joy** his pros**per**ity?

14 Then **keep** your **tongue** from **e**vil
and your **lips** from **speak**ing de**ceit**.
15 Turn a**side** from **e**vil and do **good**;
seek and **strive** after **peace**.

16 The **Lord** turns his **face** against the **wick**ed
to de**stroy** their re**mem**brance from the **earth**.
17 The **Lord** turns his **eyes** to the **just**
and his **ears** to **their** ap**peal**.

18 They **call** and the **Lord hears**
and **res**cues them in **all** their dis**tress**.
19 The Lord is **close** to the **bro**ken**heart**ed;
those whose **spir**it is **crushed** he will **save**.

20 **Man**y are the **tri**als of the **just** man
but from them **all** the **Lord** will **res**cue him.
21 He will keep **guard** over **all** his **bones**,
not **one** of his **bones** shall be **bro**ken.

22 Evil brings **death** to the **wick**ed;
those who **hate** the **good** are **doomed**.
23 The Lord **ran**soms the **souls** of his **ser**vants.
Those who **hide** in him shall **not** be con**demned**.

Give **praise** to the **Fa**ther Al**mighty**,
to his **Son**, Jesus **Christ** the **Lord**,
to the **Spir**it who **dwells** in our **hearts**,
both **now** and for **ev**er. A**men**.

37 Psalm (41)42

Antiphon
JG
My soul is thirst - ing for the Lord:
when shall I see him face to face?
Psalm Tone
DM
Repeat for 6-line stanza

Gelineau Tone

Repeat for 6-line stanza

Quemadmodum

[2] **Like** the **dèer** that **yearns**
for **rúnning streams**,
so my **sòul** is **yearn**ing
for **yóu**, my **God**.

[3] My **soul** is **thirst**ìng for **God**,
the **God** óf my **life**;
when can I **en**tèr and **see**
the **fáce** of **God**?

[4] My **tears** have be**còme** my **bread**,
by **níght**, by **day**,
as I **hear** it **said** all thè day **long**:
"**Where** ís your **God**?"

[5] **These** things will **Ì** re**mem**ber
as I **pour** óut my **soul**,
how I would **lead** the re**jòi**cing **crowd**
into the **hóuse** of **God**,
amid **cries** of **glad**ness ànd thanks**giv**ing,
the **throng** wíld with **joy**.

[6] **Why** are you cast **dòwn**, my **soul**,
why **gróan** with**in** me?
Hope in **God**;/I will **pràise** him **still**,
my **sav**ior ánd my **God**.

7 My **soul** is cast **dòwn** with**in** me
so I **thínk** of **you**,
from the **coun**try of **Jor**dan ànd Mount **Her**mon,
from the **Híll** of **Mi**zar.

8 **Deep** is **call**ìng on **deep**,
in the **róar** of **wa**ters;
your **tor**rents and **àll** your **waves**
swept óver **me**.

9 By **day** the **Lòrd** will **send**
his **ló**ving **kind**ness;
by **night** I will **sìng** to **him**,
praise the **God** óf my **life**.

10 I will **say** to **Gòd**, my **rock**:
"**Why** hàve yóu for**got**ten me?
why do **Ì** go **mourn**ing,
op**pressed** bý the **foe**?"

11 With **cries** that **pierce** me tò the **heart**,
my **en**emíes re**vile** me,
saying to me **àll** day **long**:
"**Where** ís your **God**?"

12 **Why** are you cast **dòwn**, my **soul**,
why **gróan** with**in** me?
Hope in **God**; I will **prà**ise him **still**,
my **sa**vior ánd my **God**.

Praise the **Fa**ther, the **Son** and Hòly **Spir**it,
both **now** ánd for **ev**er,
the God who **is**, who **was** ànd who **will** be,
world wíthout **end**.

38 Psalm (42)43

Antiphon I
JG
I will go to the al - tar of
God: praise the God of my joy.

Antiphon II
AGM
Send forth your light and your truth: let these be my guide.

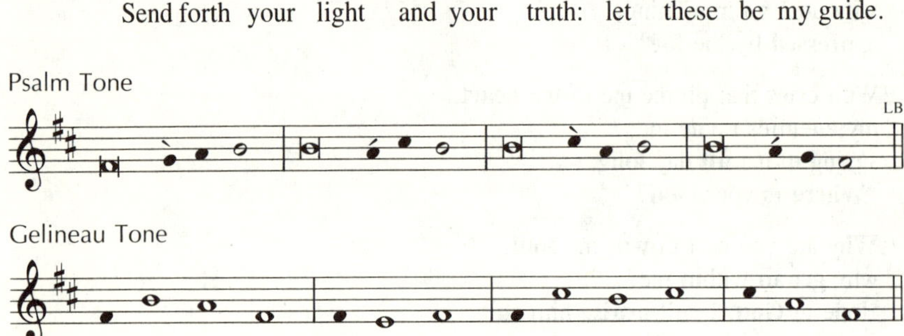
Psalm Tone
LB
Gelineau Tone

Judica me, Deus

1 De**fend** me, O **God**, and plèad my **cause**
against a **gód**less **na**tion.
From de**ceit**ful and **cù**nning **men**
rescue mé, O **God**.

2 Since **you**, O **God**, àre my **strong**hold,
why have yóu re**ject**ed me?
Why do **I** go **mourn**ing,
op**pressed** bý the **foe**?

3 O **send** forth your **light** ànd your **truth**;
let **these** bé my **guide**.
Let them **bring** me to your **hò**ly **moun**tain
to the **place** whére you **dwell**.

4 And I will **come** to the **al**tàr of **God**,
the **God** óf my **joy**.
My re**deem**er, I will **thank** you òn the **harp**,
O **Gód**, my **God**!

5 **Why** are you cast **dòwn**, my **soul**,
why **gróan** with**in** me?
Hope in **God**; I will **pràise** him **still**,
my **sa**vior ánd my **God**.

Praise the **Fa**ther, the **Son** and Hòly **Spir**it,
both **now** ánd for **ev**er,
the God who **is**, who **was** ànd who **will** be,
world wíthout **end**.

39 Psalm (45)46

Antiphon (Obligatory after stanzas 1,2, and 3)
AGM
The Lord of hosts is with us; the
God of Ja - cob is our strong - hold.

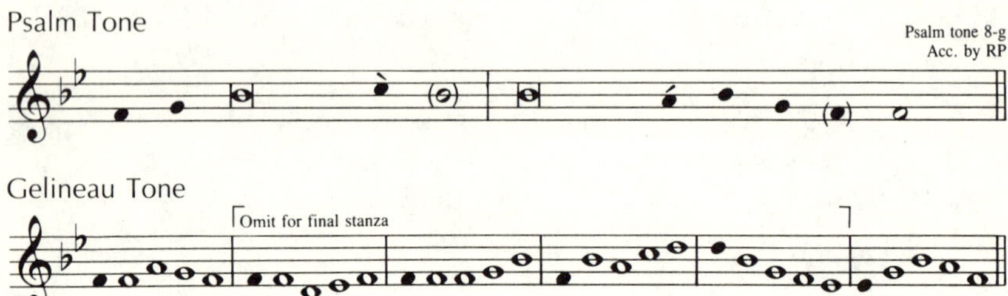
Psalm Tone
Psalm tone 8-g
Acc. by RP
Gelineau Tone
Omit for final stanza

Deus noster refugium

[2] **God** is for **us** a **ref**uge and **strèngth**,
a **help**er close at **hand**, in **tíme** of dis**tress**,
[3] so **we** shall not **fear** though the **earth** should **ròck**,
though the **moun**tains **fall** into the **dépths** of the **sea**;
[4] even **though** its **wa**ters **rage** and **fòam**,
even **though** the **moun**tains be **shá**ken by its **waves**.

[5] The **wa**ters of a **ri**ver give **joy** to God's **cì**ty,
the **ho**ly **place** whére the **Most** High **dwells**.
[6] **God** is with**in**, it **can**not be **shà**ken;
God will **help** it at the **dáwn**ing of the **day**.
Nations are in **tu**mult, **king**doms are **shà**ken;
he **lifts** his **voice**, the **eárth** shrinks a**way**.

[9] **Come**, consi**d**er the **works** of the **Lòrd**,
the re**doubt**able **deeds** he has **dóne** on the **earth**.
[10] He puts an **end** to **wars** over **all** the **eàrth**;
the **bow** he **bréaks**, the **spear** he **snaps**.
[11] "Be **still** and **know** that **I** am **Gòd**,
su**preme** among the **na**tions, su**préme** on the **earth**!"

Give **praise** to the **Fa**ther, the **Son** and Holy **Spì**rit
both **now** and for **a**ges un**énd**ing. **A**men.

Psalm (46)47 40

Antiphon

AGM
Sing praise to our king, sing praise:
for God is king of all the earth.

Psalm Tone

DH

Gelineau Tone

Omnes gentes, plaudite

2 All **peo**ples, **clàp** your **hands**,
cry to **Gód** with **shouts** of **joy**!
3 For the **Lord**, the Most **High**, wè
must **fear**,
great **king** óver **all** the **earth**.

4 He sub**dues** **pè**oples **un**der us
and **na**tions **ún**der <u>our</u> **feet**.
5 Our in**her**itance, our **glo**ry, ís from
him,
given to **Já**cob out of **love**.

6 God goes **up** with **shòuts** of **joy**;
the Lord goes **úp** with **trum**pet
blast.
7 Sing **praise** for **Gòd**, sing **praise**,
sing **praise** tó our **king**, sing **praise**.

8 God is **king** of **àll** the **earth**.
Sing **práise** with **all** your **skill**.
9 God is **king** **o**vèr the **na**tions;
God **reigns** ón his **ho**ly **throne**.

10 The **prin**ces of the **peo**ples àre
as**sem**bled
with the **peo**ple of **Á**bra<u>ham's</u> **God**.
The **ru**lers of the **earth** belòng to **God**,
to **God** whó **reigns** over **all**.

Give **praise** to the **Fa**thèr Al**migh**ty,
to his **Son**, Jésus **Christ** the **Lord**,
to the **Spir**it who **dwells** ìn our
hearts,
both **now** and for éver. <u>A</u>**men**.

41 Psalm (50)51

Antiphon I

JG
Have mer - cy, Lord cleanse me from all my sins.

Antiphon II

AGM
Lord, if you will, you can make me clean.

Psalm Tone

Gelineau Tone

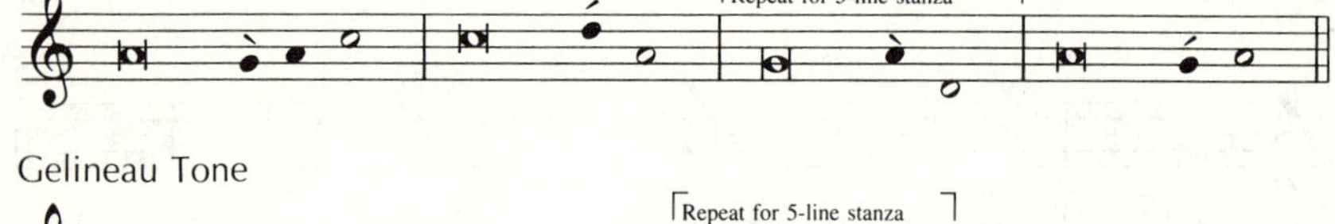
Repeat for 5-line stanza
CW

Miserere mei, Deus

3 Have **mer**cy on me, **God**, ìn your **kind**ness.
In your com**pass**ion blot **out** my óf**fence**.
4 O **wash** me more and **more** from mỳ **guilt**
and **cleanse** me **from** mý **sin**.

5 My of**fen**ces **tru**lỳ I **know** them;
my **sin** is **al**ways bé**fore** me.
6 Against **you**, you a**lone**, have Ì **sinned**;
what is **e**vil in your **sight** I háve **done**.

That you may be **jus**tified **when** yòu give **sen**tence
and be with**out** re**proach** when yóu **judge**,
7 O **see**, in **guilt** I wàs **born**,
a **sin**ner was **I** cón**ceived**.

8 **Indeed** you love **truth** ìn the **heart**;
then in the **se**cret of my **heart** teach mé **wis**dom.
9 O **pu**rify me, **then** I shall bè **clean**;
O **wash** me, I shall be **whit**er thán **snow**.

10 Make me **hear** re**joic**ìng and **glad**ness,
that the **bones** you have **crushed** máy **thrill**.
11 From my **sins** turn a**way** yòur **face**
and **blot** out **all** mý **guilt**.

12 A **pure** heart cre**ate** for me, O **God**,
put a **stead**fast **spir**it with**in** me.
13 Do not **cast** me a**way** from your **pres**ence,
nor de**prive** me of your **ho**ly **spir**it.

14 Give me a**gain** the **joy** of your **help**;
with a **spir**it of **fer**vor sus**tain** me,
15 that I may **teach** trans**gres**sors your **ways**,
and **sin**ners may re**turn** to **you**.

16 O **res**cue me, **God**, my **help**er,
and my **tongue** shall **ring** out your **good**ness.
17 O **Lord**, open my **lips**,
and my **mouth** shall de**clare** your **praise**.

18 For in **sac**rifice you **take** no de**light**,
burnt **of**fering from **me** you would re**fuse**;
19 my **sac**rifice, a **con**trite **spir**it,
a **hum**bled, contrite **heart** you will not **spurn**.

20 In your **good**ness, show **fa**vor to **Zi**on;
re**build** the **walls** of Je**ru**salem.
21 **Then** you will be **pleased** with lawful **sac**rifice,
burnt **of**ferings **whol**ly con**sumed**,
then you will be **of**fered young **bulls** on your **al**tar.

Give **glo**ry to the **Fa**ther Al**might**y,
to his **Son**, Jesus **Christ**, the **Lord**,
to the **Spir**it who **dwells** in our **hearts**,
both **now** and for **ev**er. A**men**.

42 Psalm (62)63:2-9

Antiphon I

RP
My soul is thirst - ing for you, O
Lord, thirst - ing for you my God.

Antiphon II

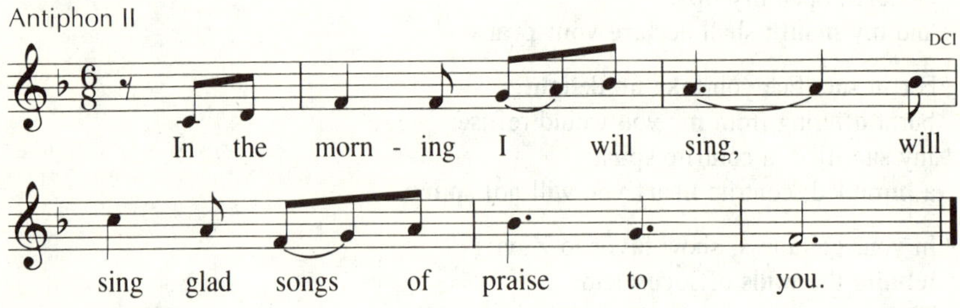
DCI
In the morn - ing I will sing, will
sing glad songs of praise to you.

Psalm Tone

Gelineau Tone

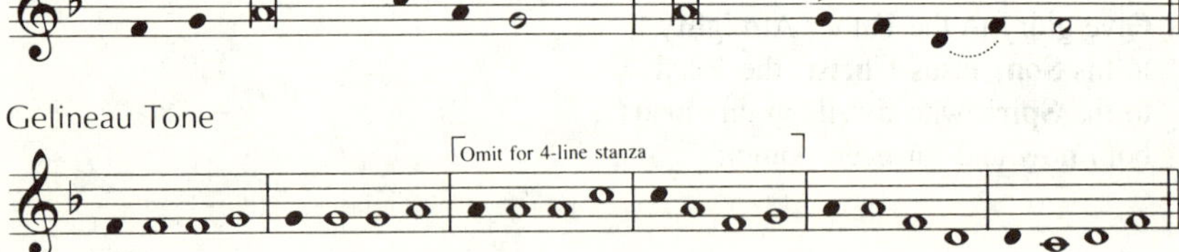
RP
Omit for 4-line stanza

Deus, Deus meus

[2]O **God**, you are my **God**, for yòu I
long;
for yóu my **soul** is **thirst**ing.
My **bod**y **pìnes** for **you**
like a **dry**, weary **lánd** without **wa**ter.
[3]So I **gaze** on **you** in the **sànc**tuary
to **see** your **stréngth** and your **glo**ry.

[4]For your **love** is **bèt**ter than **life**,
my **líps** will **speak** your **praise**.
[5]So I will **bless** you **àll** my **life**,
in your **name** I will **líft** up my
hands.
[6]My **soul** shall be **filled** as wìth a
banquet,
my **mouth** shall **práise** you with **joy**.

[7]On my **bed** I re**mèm**ber **you**.
On **you** I **múse** through the **night**
[8]for **you** have **bèen** my **help**;
in the **shad**ow of your **wíngs** I
rejoice.
[9]My **soul clìngs** to **you**;
your **ríght** hand **holds** me **fast**.

Give **praise** to the **Fà**ther Al**migh**ty,
to his **Son**, Jésus **Christ** the **Lord**,
to the **Spir**it who **dwèlls** in our
hearts,
both **now** and for **é**ver. **A**men.

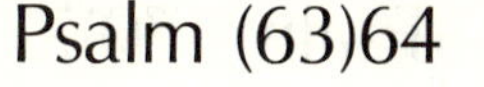
Psalm (63)64 43

Antiphon

ST
The just will re - joice in the Lord;
their hearts will be filled with glo - ry.

Psalm Tone

LB
Repeat for 6-line stanzas

Gelineau Tone

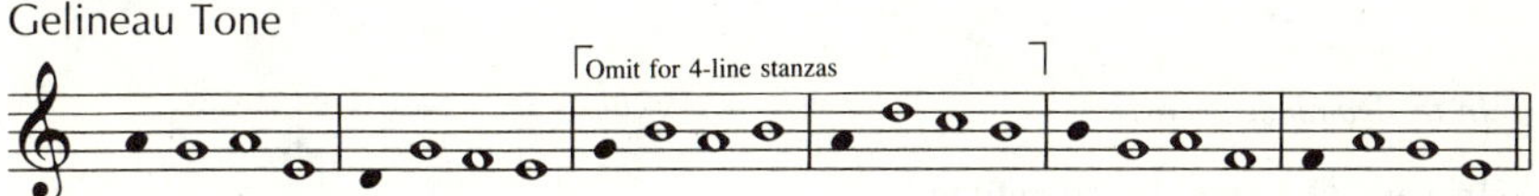
Omit for 4-line stanzas

Exaudi, Deus

2 Hear my **voice**, O **God**, as Ì com**plain**,
guard my **life** from **dread** óf the **foe**.
3 **Hide** me from the **band** òf the **wick**ed,
from the **throng** of **those** whó do **e**vil.

4 They **sharp**en their **tòngues** like **swords**;
they **aim** bitter **wórds** like **ar**rows
5 to **shoot** at the **in**nocènt from **am**bush,
shooting **sud**denlý and **reck**lessly.

6 They **scheme** their èvil **course**;
they con**spire** to **lay** sécret **snares**.
They **say**: "**Whò** will **see** us?
7 **Who** can **search** óut our **crimes**?"

He will **search** who **search**ès the **mind**
and **knows** the **depths** òf the **heart**.
8 **God** has **shot** them wìth his **ar**row
and **dealt** them **súd**den **wounds**.

9 Their own **tongue** has **brought** thèm to **ru**in
and **all** who **sée** them **mock**.

10 **Then** will **àll** men **fear**;
they will **tell** what **Gód** has **done**.
They will **under**st**à**nd God's **deeds**.
11 The **just** will re**joice** ín the **Lord**
and **fly** to **hìm** for **ref**uge.
All the **up**right **héarts** will **glor**y.

Give **praise** to the **Fa**thèr Al**might**y,
to his **Son**, Jesus **Chríst**, the **Lord**,
to the **Spir**it who **dwells** ìn our **hearts**,
both **now** and for **evér**. **A**men.

44 Psalm (70)71

Antiphon

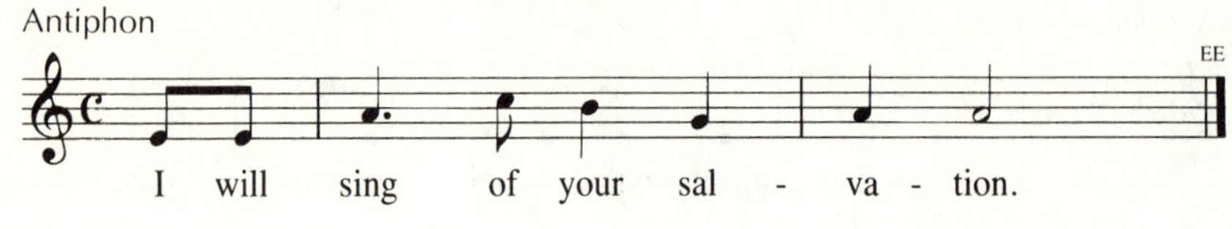
EE
I will sing of your sal - va - tion.

Psalm Tone

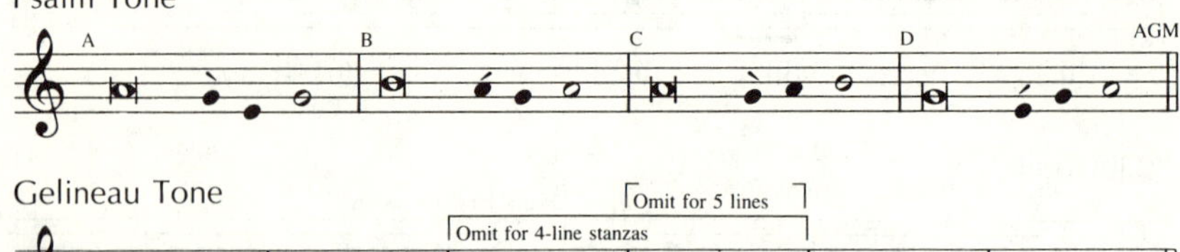
A
B
C
D
AGM

Gelineau Tone

Omit for 5 lines
Omit for 4-line stanzas

In te, Domine, speravi

1 In **you,** O **Lord**, Ì take **ref**uge;
Let me **nev**er be **pút** to **shame**.
2 In your **jus**tice **res**cùe me, **free** me;
pay **heed** to **mé** and **save** me.

3 Be a **rock** where **I** càn take **ref**uge,
a **might**y **strong**hóld to **save** me; *[Repeat B]*
for **you** are my **róck**, my **strong**hold.
4 **Free** me from the **hand** òf the **wick**ed,
from the **grip** of the un**just**, of thé op**pres**sor.

5 It is **you**, O **Lord**, who àre my **hope**,
my **trust**, O **Lord**, sínce my **youth**. *[Repeat B]*
6 On **you** I have **leaned** fróm my **birth**,
from my mother's **womb** you have **bèen** my **help**.
My **hope** has **al**ways béen in **you**.

7 My **fate** has filled **man**ỳ with **awe**
but **you** are **mý** strong **ref**uge.
8 My **lips** are **filled** wìth your **praise**,
with your **glo**ry **all** thé day **long**. *[Repeat C+D]*
9 Do not re**ject** me **now** that Ì am **old**;
when my **strength** fails **do** nót for**sake** me.

10 For my **en**emies are **speak**ìng a**bout** me;
those who **watch** me take **coun**sél to**geth**er
11 saying: "**God** has for**sak**èn him; **fol**low him,
seize him; there is **no** oné to **save** him." *[Repeat C+D]*
12 O **God**, do not **stày** far **off**:
my **God**, make **háste** to **help** me!

13 Let them be **put** to **shame** ànd des**troyed**,
all **those** who **séek** my **life**.
Let them be **co**vered with **shame** ànd con**fu**sion,
all **those** who **séek** to **harm** me.

14 But as for **me**, I will **àl**ways **hope**
and **praise** you **móre** and **more**.
15 My **lips** will **tell** òf your **jus**tice
and **day** by **day** óf your **help** *[Repeat D]*
(though I can **ne**ver **téll** it **all**).

16 I will de**clare** the **Lord's** mìghty **deeds**
pro**claim**ing your **jus**tice, yóurs a**lone**.
17 O **God**, you have **taught** me fròm my **youth**
and I pro**claim** your **wón**ders **still**.

18 **Now** that I am **old** ànd grey-**head**ed, *[Omit B+C]*
do not for**sáke** me, **God**.
Let me **tell** of your **pow**er tò all **a**ges,
19 praise your **strength** and **jus**tice tó the **skies**,
tell of **you** who have **wòrked** such **won**ders.
O **God**, **who** ís like **you**?

20 You have **bur**dened me with **bìt**ter **trou**bles
but **you** will give me **báck** my **life**.
You will **raise** me from the **depths** òf the **earth**;
21 you will ex**alt** me and con**sole** mé a**gain**.

22 So I will **give** you **thanks** òn the **lyre**
for your **faith**ful **lóve**, my **God**.
To **you** will I **sing** wìth the **harp**,
to **you**, the **Ho**ly Óne of **Is**rael. *[Repeat C+D]*
23 When I **sing** to you my **lips** shàll re**joice**
and my **soul**, which **you** háve re**deemed**.

24 And **all** the day **lòng** my **tongue**
shall **tell** the **tale** óf your **jus**tice:
for **they** are put to **shame** ànd dis**graced**,
all **those** who **séek** to **harm** me.

Give **praise** to the **Fa**thèr Al**migh**ty,
to his **Son**, Jesus **Chríst**, the **Lord**,
to the **Spir**it who **dwells** ìn our **hearts**,
both **now** and for **evér**. Amen.

45 Psalm (83)84

Antiphon

AGM
How love - ly is your dwell - ing place, O Lord of hosts.

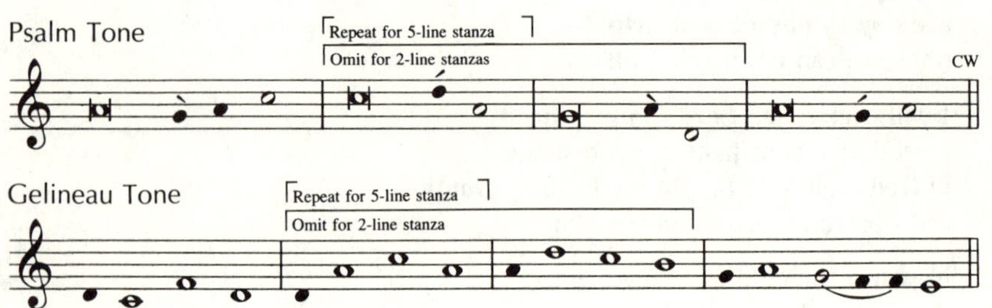
Psalm Tone
Repeat for 5-line stanza
Omit for 2-line stanzas
CW
Gelineau Tone
Repeat for 5-line stanza
Omit for 2-line stanza

Quam dilecta

2 How **lovely is** your **dwèll**ing place,
Lord, **God** óf **hosts**.

3 My **soul** is **long**ìng and **yearn**ing,
is **yearn**ing for the **courts** of thé **Lord**.
My **heart** and my **soul** ring our thèir **joy**
to **God**, the **liv**íng **God**.

4 The **spar**row her**self** fìnds a **home**
and the **swal**low a **nest** for hér **brood**;
she **lays** her **young** by yòur **al**tars,
Lord of **hosts**, my **king** and mý **God**.

5 They are **hap**py, who **dwell** ìn your **house**,
for **ever sing**ing yóur **praise**.
6 They are **hap**py, whose **strength** is ìn **you**,
in whose **hearts** are the **roads** tó **Zi**on.

7 As they **go** through the **Bì**tter **Val**ley
they **make** it a **place** óf **springs**,
[the **au**tumn rain **co**vers it wíth **bless**ings].
8 They **walk** with **ev**er growìng **strength**,
they will **see** the God of **gods** ín **Zi**on.

9 O **Lord** God of **hosts**, hèar my **prayer**,
give **ear**, O **God** óf **Ja**cob.
10 Turn your **eyes**, O **God**, oùr **shield**,
look on the **face** of your á**noint**ed.

11 **One** day within your **courts**
is **bet**ter than a **thous**and **else**where.
The **thresh**old of the **house** of **God**
I pre**fer** to the **dwell**ings of the **wick**ed.

12 For the Lord **God** is a **ram**part, a **shield**;
he will **give** us his **fa**vor and **glor**y.
The **Lord** will not re**fuse** any **good**
to **those** who **walk** without **blame**.

13 **Lord**, **God** of **hosts**,
happy the **man** who **trusts** in **you**.

Give **praise** to the **Fa**ther Al**might**y,
to his **Son,** Jesus **Christ** the **Lord**,
to the **Spir**it who **dwells** in our **hearts**,
both **now** and for **ev**er. A**men**.

46 Psalm (85)86

Antiphon

JS
O Lord, our God, un - wea-ried is your love for us.

Psalm Tone

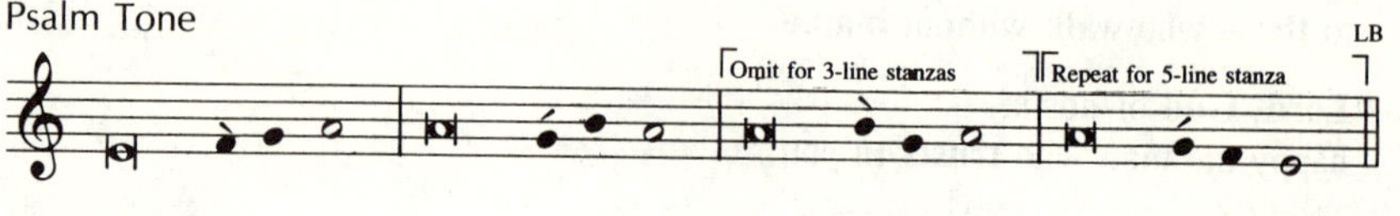
LB
Omit for 3-line stanzas
Repeat for 5-line stanza

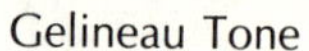
Gelineau Tone

Omit for 3-line stanzas
Repeat for 5-line stanza

Inclina, Domine

1 Turn your **ear**, O **Lord**, ànd give **an**swer
for **I** am **póor** and **nèed**y.
2 **Pre**serve my **life**, for Ì am **faith**ful;
save the **ser**vant who **trústs** in **you**.

3 You are my **God**, have **mer**cy òn me, **Lord**,
for I **cry** to you **all** thé day **long**.
4 Give **joy** to your **ser**vànt, O **Lord**,
for to **you** I **lift** úp my **soul**.

5 O **Lord**, you are **good** ànd for**giv**ing,
full of **love** to **áll** who **call**.
6 Give **heed**, O **Lord**, tò my **prayer**
and at**tend** to the **sound** óf my **voice**.

7 In the **day** of dis**tress** Ì will **call**
and **sure**ly **you** wíll re**ply**.
8 Among the **gods** there is **none** like yòu, O **Lord**,
nor **work** to com**páre** with **yours**.

9 All the **na**tions shall **come** tò a**dore** you
and **glo**rify your **nàme**, O **Lord**,
10 for you are **great** and do **marvè**lous **deeds**,
you who a**lóne** are **God**.

11 **Show** me, **Lòrd**, your **way**
so that **I** may **walk** ín your **truth**.
Guide my **heart** to **féar** your **name**.

12 I will **praise** you, Lord my **God**, with àll my **heart**
and **glo**rify your **náme** for **ev**er;
13 for your **love** to **me** hàs been **great**,
you have **saved** me from the **depths** óf the **grave**.

14 The **proud** have **ris**èn **against** me;
ruthless **men** séek my **life**;
to **you** they **páy** no **heed**.

15 But **you**, God of **mer**cy ànd com**pas**sion,
slow to **an**gér, O **Lord**,
abounding in **lòve** and **truth**,
16 **turn** and take **pit**ý on **me**.

O **give** your **strength** tò your **ser**vant
and **save** your **hánd**maid's **son**.
17 **Show** me a **sign** òf your **fa**vor
that my **foes** may **see** tó their **shame**
that you con**sole** me and **give** mé your **help**.

Give **praise** to the **Fa**thèr Al**migh**ty,
to his **Son,** Jesus **Chríst**, the **Lord**,
to the **Spir**it who **dwells** ìn our **hearts**,
both **now** and for **ev**ér. **A**men.

47 Psalm (87)88

Antiphon

ST
Day and night I cry to you, my God.

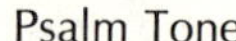
Psalm Tone

CW

Gelineau Tone

Domine, Deus

2 Lord my **God**, I call for **hèlp** by **day**;
I **cry** at **night** be**fóre** you.
3 Let my **prayer** come **in**to yòur **pres**ence.
O **turn** your **ear** to mý **cry**.

4 For my **soul** is **fìlled** with **e**vils;
my **life** is on the **brink** of thé **grave**.
5 I am **reck**oned as **one** in thè **tomb**;
I have **reached** the **end** of mý **strength**,

6 like one **alone** a**mòng** the **dead**,
like the **slain ly**ing in théir **graves**,
like **those** you re**mem**ber nò **more**,
cut **off**, as they **are**, from yóur **hand**.

7 You have **laid** me in the **depths** òf the **tomb**,
in **pla**ces that are **dark**, in thé **depths**.
8 Your **an**ger **weighs** down ùp**on** me;
I am **drowned** be**neath** yóur **waves**.

9 You have **tak**en a**wày** my **friends**
and **made** me **hate**ful in théir **sight**.
Im**pris**oned, I **can**not è**scape**;
10 my **eyes** are **sunk**en wíth **grief**.

I **call** to you, **Lord**, all thè day **long**;
to **you** I **stretch** out mý **hands**.
11 Will you **work** your **won**ders for thè **dead**?
Will the **shades stand** ánd **praise** you?

12 Will your **love** be **told** ìn the **grave**
or your **faith**fulness a**mong** thé **dead**?
13 Will your **won**ders be **known** in thè **dark**
or your **jus**tice in the **land** of óblivion?

14 As for **me**, Lord, I **call** to yòu for **help**;
in the **morn**ing my **prayer** comes bé**fore** you.
15 **Lord**, **why** do you rè**ject** me?
Why do you **hide** yóur **face**?

16 **Wretch**ed, close to **death** fròm my **youth**,
I have **borne** your **tri**als; I ám **numb**.
17 Your **fu**ry has **swept** down ù**pon** me;
your **ter**rors have **ut**terly dé**stroyed** me.

18 They sur**round** me all the **day** lìke a **flood**,
they as**sail** me **all** tó**geth**er.
19 Friend and **neigh**bor you have **tak**en à**way**;
my **one** com**pan**ion ís **dark**ness.

Give **praise** to the **Fa**thèr Al**mighty**,
to his **Son**, Jesus **Christ**, thé **Lord**,
to the **Spir**it who **dwells** in òur **hearts**
both **now** and for **ev**er. À**men**.

48 Psalm (89)90

Antiphon

EE
In ev-'ry age, O Lord, you have been our ref - uge.

Psalm Tone

Repeat for 5-line stanzas
AGM
Omit for 4-line stanzas

Gelineau Tone

Domine, refugium

1 O **Lord**, **you** have bèen our **ref**uge
from **one** gener**a**tion tó the **next**.
2 Be**fore** the **moun**tàins were **born**
or the **earth** or the **wòrld** brought **forth**,
you are **God**, without be**ginn**íng or **end**.

3 You **turn** men **back** ìnto **dust**
and **say**: "Go **back**, sóns of **men**."
4 To your **eyes** a **thòu**sand **years**
are like **yes**terday, **còme** and **gone**,
no **more** than a **watch** ín the **night**.

5 You **sweep** men a**way** lìke a **dream**,
like **grass** which springs **up** ín the **morn**ing.
6 In the **morn**ing it **springs** ùp and **flow**ers;
by **eve**ning it **with**érs and **fades**.

7 So **we** are de**stroyed** ìn your **an**ger,
struck with **ter**ror ín your **fur**y.
8 Our **guilt** lies **op**èn be**fore** you,
our **se**crets in the **light** óf your **face**.

9 All our **days** pass a**way** ìn your **an**ger.
Our **life** is **o**ver líke a **sigh**.
10 Our **span** is **sev**ènty **years**
or **eigh**ty for **those** whó are **strong**.

And **most** of these are **emp**tinèss and **pain**.
They pass **swift**ly and **wé** are **gone**.
11 Who **un**derstands the **pow**er òf your **an**ger
and **fears** the **strength** óf your **fu**ry?

12 Make us **know** the **short**ness òf our **life**
that **we** may gain **wis**dóm of **heart**.
13 Lord, re**lent**! Is your **an**gèr for **e**ver?
Show **pi**ty **tó** your **ser**vants.

14 In the **morn**ing, **fill** us wìth your **love**;
we shall ex**ult** and re**joice** áll our **days**.
15 Give us **joy** to **bal**ance òur af**flic**tion
for the **years** when we **knéw** mis**for**tune.

16 Show **forth** your **work** tò your **ser**vants;
let your **glo**ry **shine** ón their **chil**dren.
17 Let the **fa**vor of the **Lord** bè up**on** us:
give suc**cess** to the **work** òf our **hands**,
(give suc**cess** to the **work** óf our **hands**).

Give **praise** to the **Fa**thèr Al**might**y,
to his **Son**, Jesus **Chríst**, the **Lord**,
to the **Spir**it who **dwells** ìn our **hearts**,
both **now** and for **evér**. A**men**.

49 Psalm (90)91

Antiphon I
AGM
My ref-uge, my strong-hold, my God in whom I trust!
Antiphon II
JG
Call up - on the Lord and he will hear you.
Antiphon III
PH
Acc. by MC
Night holds no ter-rors for me sleep - ing un-der God's wings.

Psalm Tone

RP

Gelineau Tone

Qui habitat

1 He who **dwells** in the **shel**ter of thè Most **High**
and a**bides** in the **shade** of the Ál**migh**ty
2 **says** to the **Lord**: "Mỳ **ref**uge,
my **strong**hold, my **God** in whom Í **trust**!"

3 It is **he** who will **free** you fròm the **snare**
of the **fowl**er who **seeks** to déstroy you;
4 **he** will con**ceal** you with hìs **pin**ions
and **un**der his **wings** you will fínd **ref**uge.

5 You will not **fear** the **ter**ror òf the **night**,
nor the **ar**row that **flies** bý **day**
nor the **plague** that **prowls** in thè **dark**ness
nor the **scourge** that lays **waste** át **noon**.

7 A **thous**and may **fall** át your **side**,
ten thousand **fall** at yóur **right**,
you, it will **nev**er àp**proach**;
4c his **faith**fulness is **buck**ler ánd **shield**.

8 Your **eyes** have **on**lý to **look**,
to **see** how the **wick**ed are ré**paid**,
9 **you** who have said: "**Lord**, mỳ **ref**uge!"
and have **made** the Most **High** yóur **dwell**ing.

10 Upon **you** no **e**vìl shall **fall**,
no **plague** ap**proach** where yoú **dwell**.
11 For **you** has he com**mand**ed hìs **an**gels,
to **keep** you in **all** yóur **ways**.

12 They shall **bear** you upòn their **hands**
lest you **strike** your **foot** against á **stone**.
13 On the **li**on and the **vi**per you wìll **tread**
and **tram**ple the young **li**on and thé **drag**on.

14 Since he **clings** to me in **love**, Ì will **free** him,
pro**tect** him for he **knows** mý **name**.
15 When he **calls** I shall **an**swer: "I àm **with** you."
I will **save** him in dis**tress** and give hím **glo**ry.

16 With **length** of **life** I wìll con**tent** him;
I shall **let** him see my **sav**íng **pow**er.
To the **Fa**ther, the **Son** and Holỳ **Spir**it
give **praise** for **ev**er. Á**men**.

50 Psalm (92)93

Antiphon I

AGM
The Lord is King for ev - er - more.

Antiphon II

AGM
Al - le - lu - ia, al - le - lu - ia, al - le - lu - ia.

Psalm Tone

Psalm tone 8-g
Acc. by RP

Gelineau Tone

Dominus regnavit

1 The Lord is **king**, with **maj**esty en**rōbed**;
the **Lord** has **robed** himself with **mìght**,
he has **gird**ed him**sélf** with **pow**er.

The **world** you made **firm**, not to be **mōved**;
2 your **throne** has stood **firm** from of **òld**.
From all **e**ternitý, O **Lord**, you **are**.

3 The **wa**ters have **lift**ed up, O **Lōrd**,
the **wa**ters have **lift**ed up their **vòice**,
the **wa**ters have **lift**ed úp their **thun**der.

4 **Great**er than the **roar** of mighty **wa**tērs,
more **glo**rious than the **sur**gings of the **sèa**,
the **Lord** is **gló**rious on **high**.

5 **Tru**ly, your de**crees** are to be **trust**ēd.
Holiness is **fit**ting to your **hòuse**,
O **Lord**, untíl the **end** of **time**.

Give **glo**ry to the **Fa**ther Al**mighty**̄,
to his **Son**, Jesus **Christ**, the **Lòrd**,
to the **Spir**it who **dwélls** in our **hearts**.

Psalm (94)95 51

Antiphon I

JG
O come, let us wor - ship the Lord.

Antiphon II

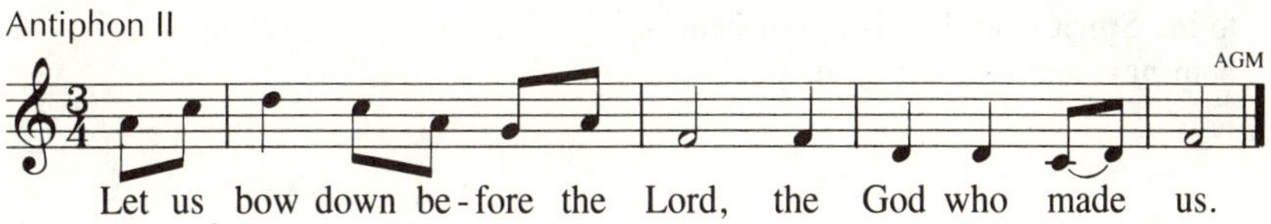
AGM
Let us bow down be-fore the Lord, the God who made us.

Psalm Tone

Gelineau Tone

Chant tone 1-f
Acc. by RP
Omit for 5-line sts.
Omit for 4-line stanzas

Venite, exultemus

[1]Come, **ring** out our **jòy** to the **Lord**;
hail the **róck** who **saves** us.
[2]Let us **come** **befòre** him, giving **thanks**,
with **songs** lét us **hail** the **Lord**.

[3]A **mighty** **God** is the **Lōrd**,
a **great** kìng a**bove** all **gods**.
[4]In his **hand** are the **dépths** of the **earth**;
the **heights** of the **moun**tains are **hīs**.
[5]To **him** belongs the **sèa**, for he **made** it,
and the **dry** land **sháped** by his **hands**.

[6]Come **in**; let us **bòw** and bend **low**;
let us **kneel** befóre the **God** who **made** us
[7]for **he** is our **God** and **wē**
the **peo**ple who be**lòng** to his **pas**ture,
the **flock** that is **léd** by his **hand**.

O that to**day** you would **lis**ten to his **vōice**!
[8]"**Hard**en not your **hèarts** as at **Mer**ibah,
as on that **day** at **Mássah** in the **des**ert
[9]when your **fa**thers **pùt** me to the **test**;
when they **tried** me, **thóugh** they saw my **work**.

10 For forty **years** I was **wear**ied of these **peo**plē
and I **said**: 'Their **hèarts** are a**stray**,
these **peo**ple dó not **know** my **ways**'.
11 **Then** I took an **òath** in my **an**ger:
'**Ne**ver shall they **én**ter my **rest**.'"

Give **glo**ry to the **Fà**ther Al**might**y,
to his **Son**, Jésus **Christ**, the **Lord**,
to the **Spir**it who **dwèlls** in our **hearts**,
both **now** and for **é**ver. A-**men**.

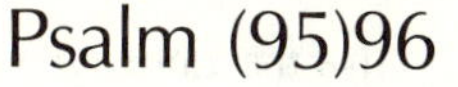

Psalm (95)96 52

Antiphon I

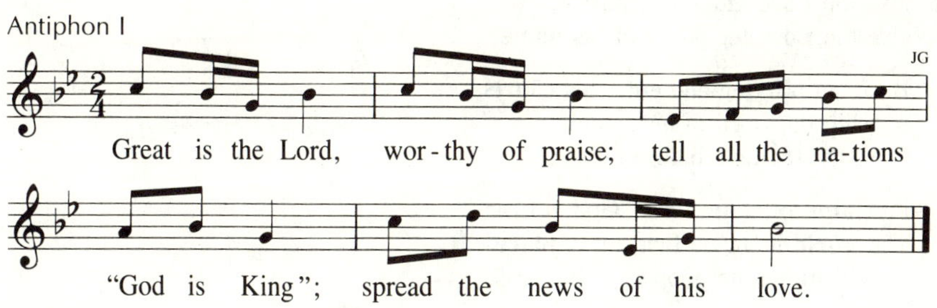
JG
Great is the Lord, wor-thy of praise; tell all the na-tions
"God is King"; spread the news of his love.

Antiphon II

CWH
Bring an of-fer-ing and en-ter his courts:
in his tem - ple wor-ship the Lord.

Psalm Tone

Chant tone 5
Acc. by RJB

Gelineau Tone

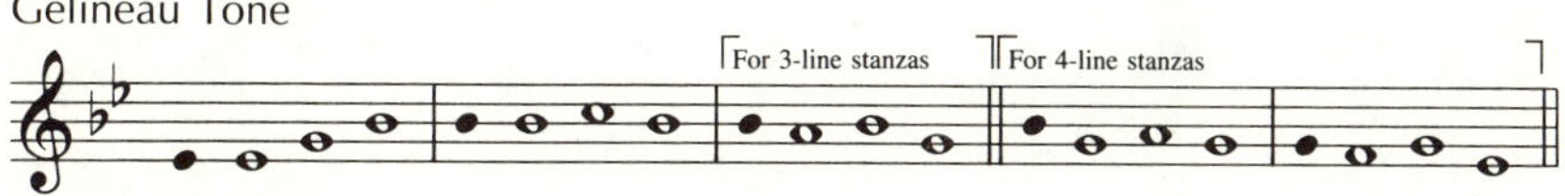
For 3-line stanzas
For 4-line stanzas

Cantate Domino

1 O **sing** a new **song** to the **Lōrd**,
sing to the **Lord** all the **eàrth**.
2 O **sing** to the **Lórd**, bless his **name**.

Pro**claim** his **help** day by **dāy**,
3 **tell** among the **na**tions his **glò**ry
and his **won**ders a**móng** all the **peo**ples.

4 The Lord is **great** and **wor**thy of **prāise**,
to be **feared** a**bove** all **gòds**;
5 the **gods** of the **héath**ens are **naught**.

It was the **Lord** who **made** the **heav**ēns,
6 his are **ma**jesty and **state** and **pò**wer
and **splen**dor in hís **ho**ly **place**.

7 Give the **Lord**, you **fam**ilies of **peo**plēs,
give the **Lord glor**y and **pò**wer;
8 give the **Lord** the **gló**ry of his **name**.

Bring an **of**fering and **en**ter his **cōurts**,
9 **wor**ship the **Lord** in his **tèm**ple,
O **earth**, **trém**ble be**fore** him.

10 Pro**claim** to the **na**tions: "God is **kīng**."
The **world** he made **firm** in its **plàce**;
he will **judge** the **pé**oples in **fair**ness.

11 Let the **hea**vens re**joice** and earth be **glàd**,
let the **sea** and all with**ín** it thunder **praise**,
12 let the **land** and all it **bears** re**joìce**,
all the **trees** of the **wóod** shout for **joy**

13 at the **pre**sence of the **Lord** for he **còmes**,
he **cómes** to **rule** the **earth**.
With **jus**tice he will **rule** the **wòrld**,
he will **judge** the **pé**oples with his **truth**.

Give **praise** to the **Fa**ther Al**mìghty**,
to his **Son**, Jésus **Christ** the **Lord**,
to the **Spir**it who **dwells** in òur **hearts**,
both **now** and for éver. **A**men.

Psalm (99)100 53

Antiphon I
JG
A - rise, come to your God,
sing him your songs of re - joic - ing.

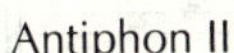
Antiphon II

AGM
Al - le - lu - ia, al - le - lu - ia, al - le - lu - ia.

Psalm Tone

Chant tone 8-g
Acc. by RP

Gelineau Tone

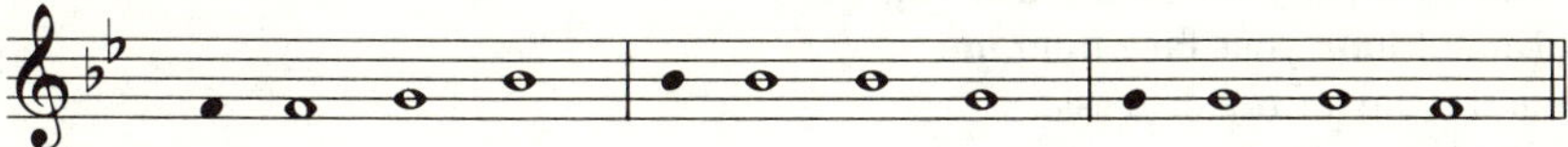

Jubilate Deo

1 Cry out with **joy** to the **Lord**, all the **ēarth**.
2 **Serve** the **Lord** with **glàd**ness.
Come be**fore** him, **sínging** for **joy**.

3 Know that **he**, the **Lord**, is **Gōd**.
He **made** us, we be**lòng** to **him**,
we are his **peo**ple, the **shéep** of his **flock**.

4 **Go** within his **gates**, giving **thānks**.
Enter his **courts** with **sòngs** of **praise**.
Give **thanks** to hím and **bless** his **name**.

5 **Indeed**, how **good** is the **Lōrd**,
eternal his **mer**ciful **lòve**.
He is **faith**ful fróm **age** to **age**.

Give **glo**ry to the **Fa**ther Al**mightȳ**,
to his **Son**, Jesus **Chrìst**, the **Lord**,
to the **Spir**it who **dwélls** in our **hearts**.

54 Psalm (101)102

Antiphon

RP
O Lord, hear my prayer; let my cry come to you.

Psalm Tone

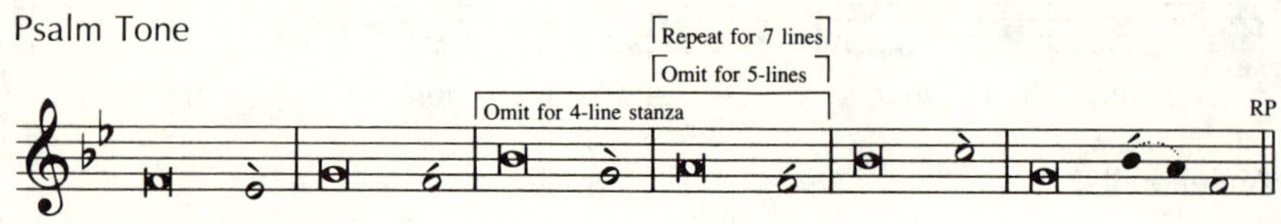
Repeat for 7 lines
Omit for 5-lines
Omit for 4-line stanza
RP

Gelineau Tone

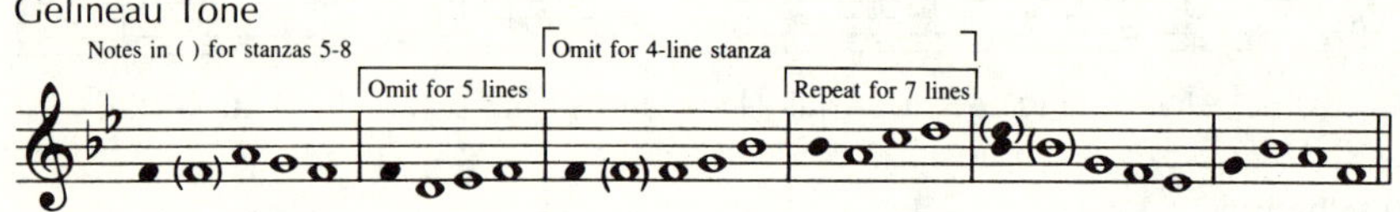
Notes in ( ) for stanzas 5-8
Omit for 5 lines
Omit for 4-line stanza
Repeat for 7 lines

Domine, exaudi

2 O **Lord, lis**ten to my **pràyer**
and let my **cry** for **help reach** yóu.
3 Do not **hide** your **face** from **mè**
in the **day** of **my** dis**tréss**.
Turn your **ear to**wards mè
and **an**swer me **quick**ly whén I **call**.

4 For my **days** are **van**ishing like **smòke**,
my **bones** burn a**way** like a **fíre**.
5 My **heart** is **with**ered like the **gràss**.
I for**get** to **eat** my **bréad**.
6 I **cry** with **all** my **strèngth**
and my **skin clings** tó my **bones**.

7 I have be**come** like a **pel**ican in the **wil**dèrness,
like an **owl** in **des**olate **placés**.
8 I **lie** a**wake** and I **mòan**
like some **lone**ly **bird** on a **róof**.
9 All day **long** my **foes** re**vìle** me;
those who **hate** me use my **name** ás a **curse**.

10 The **bread** I **eat** is **ash**ès;
my **drink** is **min**gled with **téars**.
11 In your **an**ger, **Lord**, and your **fu**rỳ
you have **lift**ed me **up** and thrown me **dówn**.
12 My **days** are like a **pass**ing **shàd**ow
and I **with**er a**way** líke the **grass**.

13 But **you**, O **Lord**, will en**dure** for **e**vèr
and your **name** from **age** to **áge**.
14 **You** will a**rise** and have **mer**cy on **Zi**òn:
for **this** is the **time** to have **mer**cý,
(yes, the **time** appoin**ted** has **cóme**)
15 for your **ser**vants **love** her **ve**ry **stònes**,
are moved with **pi**ty **e**ven fór her **dust**.

16 The **na**tions shall **fear** the **name** of the **Lòrd**
and **all** the earth's **kings** your **glo**rý,
17 when the **Lord** shall **build** up **Zi**on **agàin**
and ap**pear** in **all** his **gló**ry.
18 **Then** he will **turn** to the **prayers** of the **hèlp**less;
he will **not** des**píse** their **prayers**.

19 Let **this** be **writ**ten for **a**ges to **còme**
that a **peo**ple yet un**born** may praise the **Lórd**;
20 for the **Lord** leaned **down** from his **sanc**tuary on **hìgh**.
He looked **down** from **hea**ven to the **eárth**
21 that **he** might **hear** the **groans** of the **prìs**oners
and **free** those con**démned** to **die**.

29 The **sons** of your **ser**vants shall **dwell** un**trou**blèd
and their **race** shall en**dure** be**fore** yóu
22 that the **name** of the **Lord** may be pro**claimed** in **Zì**on
and his **praise** in the **heart** of Jeru**sá**lem,
23 when **peo**ples and **king**doms are **ga**thered to**gèth**er
to **pay** their **hom**age tó the **Lord**.

24 He has **bro**ken my **strength** in mid-**còurse**;
he has **short**ened the **days** of my **lífe**.
25 I say to **God**: "Do not **take** me a**wày**
be**fore** my **days** are com**plète**,
you, whose **days** last from **áge** to **age**.

26 Long a**go** you **found**ed the **eàrth**
and the **hea**vens are the **work** of your **hánds**.
27 They will **per**ish but **you** will re**màin**.
They will **all** wear **out** like a **gár**ment.
You will **change** them like **clothes** that are **chànged**.
28 But **you** neither **change**, nor **háve** an **end**."

Give **praise** to the **Fa**ther Al**mighty̆**,
to his **Son**, Jesus **Christ**, the **Lórd**,
to the **Spir**it who **dwells** in our **heàrts**,
both **now** and for **ev**er. **Ámen**.

55 Psalm (102)103

Antiphon
RP
My soul, give thanks to the
Lord, and bless his Ho - ly Name.
Psalm Tone
RP
Gelineau Tone
Omit for 5 lines
Omit for 4-line stanzas

Benedic, anima mea

1 My **soul**, give **thanks** tò the **Lord**,
all my **being**, **bléss** his holy **name**.
2 My **soul**, give **thanks** tò the **Lord**
and **never** for**get** áll his **bless**ings.

3 It is **he** who for**gives** àll your **guilt**,
who **heals** every **óne** of your **ills**,
4 who re**deems** your **life** fròm the **grave**,
who **crowns** you with **love** ánd com**pass**ion,
5 who **fills** your **life** wìth good **things**,
re**new**ing your **youth** líke an **ea**gle's.

6 The **Lord** does **deeds** of jùstice,
gives **judge**ment for **áll** who are op**pressed**.
7 He made **known** his **ways** to Mòses
and his **deeds** to Ísrael's **sons**.

8 The **Lord** is com**pass**ion ànd **love**,
slow to **an**ger and **rích** in **mer**cy.
9 His **wrath** will **come** to àn **end**;
he will **not** be ángry for **ev**er.
10 He does not **treat** us ac**cord**ing tò our **sins**
nor re**pay** us ac**cór**ding to our **faults**.

11 For as the **heav**ens are **high** abòve the **earth**
so **strong** is his **love** for thóse who **fear** him.
12 As **far** as the **éast** is fròm the **west**
so **far** does hé **remove** our **sins**.

13 As a **fa**ther has com**pas**sion òn his **sons**,
the Lord has **pi**ty on **thóse** who **fear** him;
14 for he **knows** of **what** wè are **made**,
he re**mem**bers thát **we** are **dust**.

15 As for **man**, his **days** are like **gràss**;
he **flow**ers like the **fló**wer of the **field**;
16 the wind **blows** and **hè** is **gone**
and his **place** never **sées** him a**gain**.

17 But the **love** of the **Lord** is ever**làst**ing
upon **those** who **hóld** him in **fear**;
his **jus**tice reaches **out** to children's **chil**dren
18 when they **keep** his **co**venant ìn **truth**,
when they **keep** his **wíll** in their **mind**.

19 The **Lord** has set his **sway** in **hèa**ven
and his **king**dom is **rú**ling over **all**.
20 Give **thanks** to the **Lord**, all his **an**gels,
mighty in **pow**er, ful**fill**ing hìs **word**,
who **heed** the **vóice** of his **word**.

21 Give **thanks** to the **Lord**, àll his **hosts**,
his **ser**vants whó **do** his **will**.
22 Give **thanks** to the **Lord**, all his **works**,
in **ev**ery **place** whère he **rules**.
My **soul**, give **thánks** to the **Lord**!

Give **praise** to the **Fa**ther Al**mìght**y,
to his **Son**, Jésus **Christ** the **Lord**,
to the **Spir**it who **dwells** in òur **hearts**,
both **now** and for éver. A**men**.

56 Psalm (103)104

Antiphon
AGM
The earth is full of your rich - es, O
Lord, in wis - dom you made them all.
Psalm Tone
LB
Omit for 3-line stanza
Repeat for 5-line stanzas
Repeat for 6-line stanzas
Gelineau Tone
Stanzas of 3 and 4 lines
Omit for 3-line stanza
Stanzas of 5, 6 and 7 lines
Omit for 5 lines
Repeat for 7 lines

Benedic, anima mea

1 **Bless** the **Lòrd**, my **soul**!
Lord **God**, how **gréat** you **are**,
clothed in **majestỳ** and **glory**,
2 **wrapped** in **light** as ín a **robe**!

You **stretch** out the **heav**ens lìke a **tent**.
3 Above the **rains** you **buíld** your **dwell**ing.
You **make** the **clòuds** your **char**iot,
you **walk** on the **wings** óf the **wind**;
4 you **make** the **wìnds** your **mes**sengers
and **flash**ing **fíre** your **ser**vants.

5 You **found**ed the **earth** òn its **base**,
to stand **firm** from **áge** to **age**.
6 You **wrapped** it with the **o**cean lìke a **cloak**:
the **wa**ters stood **high**er thán the **moun**tains.

7 At your **threat** they **tòok** to **flight**;
at the **voice** of your **thundér** they **fled**.
8 They **rose** over the **moun**tains ànd flowed **down**
to the **place** which **you** hád ap**point**ed.
9 You set **lim**its they **mìght** not **pass**
lest they re**turn** to **co**vér the **earth**.

10 You make **springs** gush **forth** ìn the **val**leys;
they **flow** in be**twéen** the **hills**.
11 They give **drink** to all the **beasts** òf the **field**;
the wild **asses** **quénch** their **thirst**.
12 On their **banks** dwell the **bìrds** of **hea**ven;
from the **bran**ches they **síng** their **song**.

13 From your **dwel**ling you **wa**tèr the **hills**;
earth drinks its **fill** óf your **gift**.
14 You **make** the grass **grow** fòr the **cat**tle
and the **plants** to **sérve** man's **needs**,

that he may **bring** forth **bread** fròm the **earth**
15 and **wine** to **chéer** man's **heart**;
oil to **make** hìs face **shine**
and **bread** to **strengthén** man's **heart**.

16 The **trees** of the **Lord** drìnk their **fill**,
the **ce**dars he **plant**éd on **Leb**anon;
17 there the **birds** **buìld** their **nests**;
on the **tree**top the **stork** hás her **home**.
18 The **goats** find a **home** òn the **moun**tains
and **rab**bits **hide** ín the **rocks**.

19 You made the **moon** to **màrk** the **months**;
the **sun** knows the **time** fór its **set**ting.
20 When you **spread** the **dark**ness ìt is **night**
and all the **beasts** of the **forést** creep **forth**.
21 The young **li**ons **roar** fòr their **prey**
and **ask** their **fóod** from **God**.

22 At the **ris**ing of the **sun** they stèal a**way**
and **go** to **rest** ín their **dens**.
23 **Man** goes **forth** tò his **work**,
to **la**bor till **evé**ning **falls**.

24 How **ma**ny are your **wòrks**, O **Lord**!
In **wis**dom you have **máde** them **all**.
The **earth** is **full** óf your **ri**ches.

25 **There** is the **sea**, vàst and **wide**,
with its **moving swárms** past **count**ing,
living **things**, **grèat** and **small**.
26 The **ships** are **mó**ving **there**
and the **mon**sters you **máde** to **play** with.

27 **All** of **these** lòok to **you**
to **give** them their **food** ín due **sea**son.
28 You **give** it, they **gathèr** it **up**;
you **o**pen your **hand**, they háve their **fill**.

29 You **hide** your **face**, they àre dis**mayed**;
you take **back** your **spir**ít, they **die**,
re**turn**ing to the **dust** from whìch they **came**.
30 You **send** forth your **spir**it, they áre cre**a**ted;
and you re**new** the **face** óf the **earth**.

31 May the **glo**ry of the **Lord** làst for **e**ver!
May the **Lord** re**joice** ín his **works**!
32 He **looks** on the **earth** ànd it **trem**bles;
the **moun**tains send forth **smoke** át his **touch**.

33 I will **sing** to the **Lord** àll my **life**,
make **mu**sic to my **God** whíle I **live**.
24 May my **thoughts** be **pleas**ìng to **him**.
I **find** my **joy** ín the **Lord**.
35 Let **sin**ners **van**ish from the **earth**
and the **wick**ed exìst no **more**.
Bless the **Lórd**, my **soul**.

Give **praise** to the **Fa**thèr Al**migh**ty,
to his **Son**, Jesus **Chríst**, the **Lord**,
to the **Spir**it who **dwells** ìn our **hearts**,
both **now** and for **evér**. **A**men.

Psalm (109)110:1-5, 7 57

Antiphon

RP
The Lord said to my Lord:
"Sit at my right hand."
Psalm
Dixit Dominus
1. The Lord's reve - lation to my Master:
2. The Lord will wield from Zion
3. A prince from the day of your birth
4. The Lord has sworn an oath he will not change
5. The Mas - ter standing at your right hand
6. He shall drink from the streams by the wayside
7. To the Father, the Son and Holy Spirit
"Sit on my right; your
your scep - ter of pow'r; rule
on the ho - ly mountains; from the
"You are a priest for ever, a
will shat - ter kings in the
and there - fore he shall
give praise for ever, give
foes I will put be - neath your feet."
in the midst of all your foes.
womb be- fore the dawn I be - got you.
priest like Mel - chi - ze - dek of old."
day of his wrath.
lift up his head.
praise for ev - er. A - men.

58 Psalm (110)111

Antiphon

RC
I thank you, Lord, for your faith - ful - ness and love.

Psalm Tone

DH
Omit for 3-line stanzas

Gelineau Tone

Omit for 3-line stanzas

Confitebor tibi

I will **thank** the **Lord** with àll my **heart**
in the **meet**ing of the **jús**t and their assem**bly**.
[2] **Great** are the **works** òf the **Lord**,
to be **pon**déred by **all** who **love** them.

[3] Ma**jes**tic and **glor**ìous his **work**,
his **jus**tíce stands **firm** for **ev**er.
[4] He **makes** us re**mem**bèr his **won**ders.
The **Lord** is com<u>**pás**</u>sion and **love**.

[5] He gives **food** to **thòse** who **fear** him;
keeps his **cov**enant <u>**év**</u>er in **mind**.
[6] He has **shown** his **might** tò his **peo**ple
by **giv**ing them the <u>**lánds**</u> of the **na**tions.

[7] His **works** are **jus**tìce and **truth**,
his **pre**cepts are <u>**áll**</u> of them **sure**,
[8] standing **firm** for **ev**èr and **ev**er;
they are **made** in **ú**prightness and **truth**.

[9] He has **sent** de**liv**erance to his **peo**ple
and es**tab**lished his **cov**enànt for **ev**er.
Holy his <u>**náme**</u>, to be **feared**.

10 To fear the **Lord** is the **first** stàge of **wis**dom;
all who **do** so **prove** themselves **wise**.
His **prá****ise** shall **last** for **ev**er!

Give **praise** to the **Fa**thèr Al**mighty**,
to his **Son**, Jésus **Christ**, the **Lord**,
to the **Spir**it who **dwells** ìn our **hearts**,
both **now** and for **è**v̲er. **Amen**.

59 Psalm (111)112

Antiphon

RP
The just man is a light
in dark - ness to the up - right.

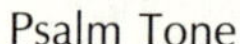
Psalm Tone

RP

Gelineau Tone

Omit for 3-line stanzas

Beatus vir

1 **Hap**py the **man** who fears the **Lord**,
who **takes** de**light** in his com**mands**.
2 His **sons** will be **pow**erful on **earth**;
the **chil**dren of the **up**right are
blessed.

3 **Rich**es and **wealth** are in his **house**;
his **jus**tice stands **firm** for ever.
4 He is a **light** in the **dark**ness for the
upright;
he is **gen**erous, **mer**ciful and **just**.

5 The **good** man takes **pit**y and **lends**,
he con**ducts** his af**fairs** with **hon**or.
6 The **just** man will **nev**er **wa**ver,
he will be re**mem**bered for **ev**er.

7 He **has** no **fear** of evil **news**;
with a **firm** heart he **trusts** in the
Lord.
8 With a **stead**fast **heart** he will not
fear;
he will **see** the **down**fall of his **foes**.

9 Open**hand**ed, he **gives** to the **poor**;
his **jus**tice stands **firm** for **ev**er.
His **head** will be **raised** in **glo**ry.

10 The **wick**ed man **sees** and is **an**gry,
grinds his **teeth** and fades **a**way;
the de**sire** of the **wick**ed leads to
doom.

Give **praise** to the **Fa**ther Al**might**y,
to his **Son**, Jesus **Christ**, the **Lord**,
to the **Spir**it who **dwells** in our
hearts,
both **now** and for ever. **A**men.

Psalm (113A)114 60

Antiphon

RP
God has freed us and re-
deemed us with his might - y arm.

Psalm Tone

LB

Gelineau Tone

In exitu Israel

When **Is**rael came **fòrth** from **E**gypt,
Jacob's **sons** from an **al**íen **peo**ple,
2 **Ju**dah be**came** thè Lord's **tem**ple,
Israel be**cáme** his **king**dom.

3 The **sea fled** àt the **sight**,
the **Jor**dan turned **back** ón its **course**,
4 the **moun**tains **lèapt** like **rams**
and the **hills** like **yéar**ling **sheep**.

5 **Why** was it, **sea**, thàt you **fled**,
that you **turned** back, **Jor**dan, ón your **course**?
6 **Moun**tains, that you **lèapt** like **rams**,
hills, like **yéar**ling **sheep**?

7 **Trem**ble, O **earth**, befòre the **Lord**,
in the **pre**sence of the **Gód** of **Ja**cob,
8 who **turns** the **rock** intò a **pool**
and **flint** into a **spríng** of **wa**ter.

Give **praise** to the **Fa**thèr Al**migh**ty,
to his **Son**, Jesus **Chríst**, the **Lord**,
to the **Spi**rit who **dwells** ìn our **hearts**,
both **now** and for **ev**ér. **A**men.

61 Psalm (113B)115

Antiphon

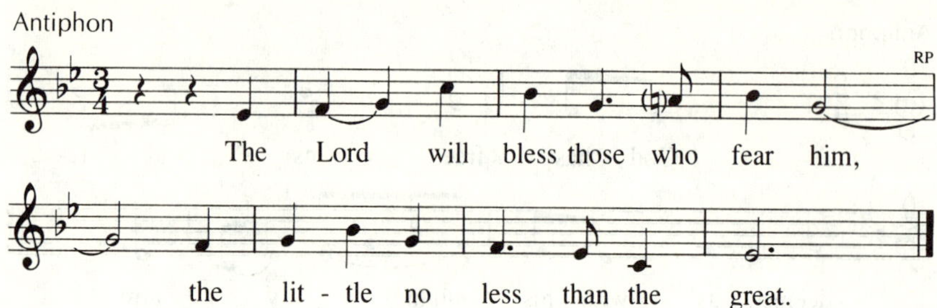
RP
The Lord will bless those who fear him,
the lit - tle no less than the great.

Psalm Tone

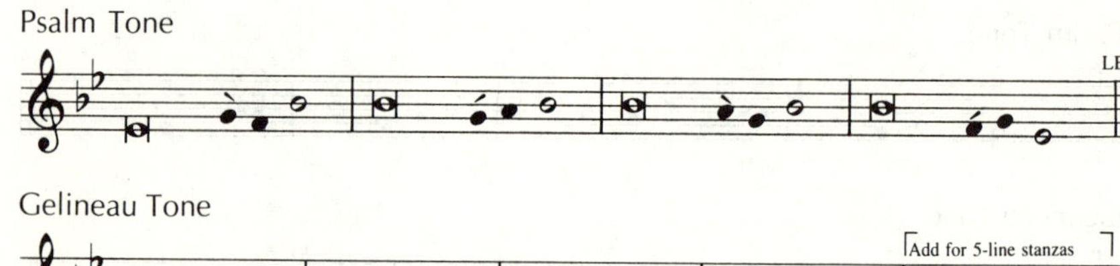
LB

Gelineau Tone

Add for 5-line stanzas

Non nobis, Domine

[1] Not to **us**, Lord, **nòt** to **us**,
but **to** your **name** gíve the **glory**
for the **sake** of your **love** ànd your **truth**,
[2] lest the **hea**then say: "**Where** ís their **God**?"

[3] But our **God**, he is **ìn** the **hea**vens;
he **does** whatevér he **wills**.
[4] Their **i**dols are **sil**vèr and **gold**,
the **work** of **hú**man **hands**.

[5] They have **mouths** but they **cà**nnot **speak**;
they have **eyes** but they **cá**nnot **see**;
[6] they have **ears** but they **cà**nnot **hear**;
they have **nos**trils but they **cá**nnot **smell**.

[7] With their **hands** they **cà**nnot **feel**;
with their **feet** they **cá**nnot **walk**.
No **sound comes** fròm their **throats**.
[8] Their **ma**kers will **come** to be like **them**
and so will **all** who **trúst** in **them**.

[9] Sons of **Is**rael, **trust** ín the **Lord**;
he is their **help** ánd their **shield**.
[10] Sons of **Aa**ron, **trust** ìn the **Lord**;
he is their **help** ánd their **shield**.

11 You who **fear** him, **trust** in the **Lord**;
he is their **help** and their **shield**.
12 He re**mem**bers us, and **he** will **bless** us;
he will **bless** the **sons** of **Is**rael.
He will **bless** the **sons** of **Aar**on.

13 The **Lord** will bless **those** who **fear** him,
the **lit**tle no **less** than the **great**;
14 to **you** may the **Lord** grant **in**crease,
to **you** and **all** your **chil**dren.

15 **May** you be **blessed** by the **Lord**,
the **mak**er of **heav**en and **earth**.
16 The **hea**vens be**long** to the **Lord**
but the **earth** he has **giv**en to **men**.

17 The **dead** shall not **praise** the **Lord**,
nor **those** who go **down** into the **si**lence.
18 But **we** who **live** bless the **Lord**
now and for **ev**er. **A**men.

Give **praise** to the **Fa**ther Al**migh**ty,
to his **Son**, Jesus **Christ**, the **Lord**,
to the **Spir**it who **dwells** in our **hearts**,
both **now** and for **ev**er. **A**men.

62 Psalm (114)116:1-9

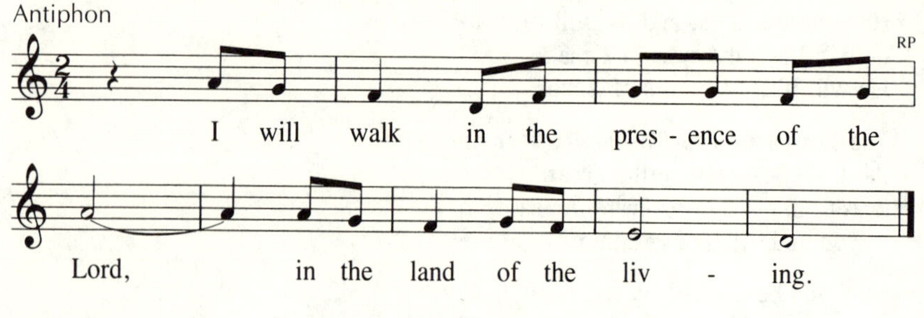
Antiphon
RP
I will walk in the pres - ence of the
Lord, in the land of the liv - ing.

Psalm Tone
RP
Gelineau Tone
Repeat for stanza 4
Repeat for stanza 2

Dilexi, quoniam

I love the **Lord** for **he** has **heard**
the **cry** of my ap**peal**;
2 for he **turned** his **ear** to **me**
in the **day** when I **called him**.

3 They sur**round**ed me, the **snares** of **death**,
with the **an**guish of the **tomb**;
they **caught** me, **sor**row and dis**tress**.
4 I **called** on the **Lord's name**.
O **Lord**, my **God**, de**li**ver me!

5 How **gra**cious is the **Lord**, and **just**;
our **God** has com**passion**.
6 The **Lord** pro**tects** the simple **hearts**;
I was **help**less so he **saved me**.

7 Turn **back**, my **soul**, to your **rest**
for the **Lord** has been **good**;
8 he has **kept** my **soul** from **death**,
(my **eyes** from **tears**)
and my **feet** from **stumbling**.

9 I will **walk** in the **pres**ence of the **Lord**
in the **land** of the **liv**ing.
Praise the **Fa**ther, the **Son** and Holy **Spir**it,
for **ever** and **ever**.

Psalm (115)116:10-19

Antiphons I & II

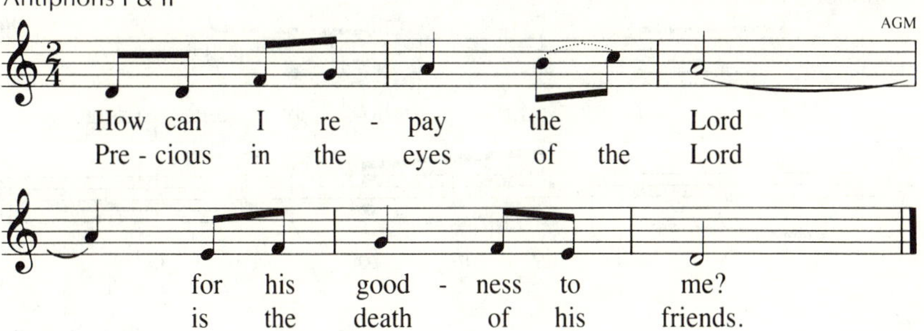
AGM
How can I re - pay the Lord
Pre - cious in the eyes of the Lord
for his good - ness to me?
is the death of his friends.

Psalm Tone

LW

Gelineau Tone

Credidi, propter

[10] I **trust**ed, **e**ven whèn I **said**:
"I am **sore**lý af**flict**ed,"
[11] and **when** I **said** in mỳ a**larm**:
"No **man** cán be **trust**ed."

[12] How **can** I re**pày** the **Lord**
for his **good**néss to **me**?
[13] The **cup** of sal**va**tion Ì will **raise**;
I will **call** ón the **Lord's** name.

[14] My **vows** to the **Lord** I wìll ful**fill**
be**fore** áll his **peo**ple.
[15] O **pre**cious in the **eyes** òf the **Lord**
is the **death** óf his **faith**ful.

[16] Your **ser**vant, Lord, your **serv**ànt am **I**;
you have **loos**enéd my **bonds**.
[17] A **thanks**giving **sac**rifìce I **make**;
I will **call** ón the **Lord's** name.

[18] My **vows** to the **Lord** I wìll ful**fill**
be**fore** áll his **peo**ple,
[19] in the **courts** of the **house** òf the **Lord**,
in your **midst,** Ó Je**ru**salem.

Praise the **Fa**ther, the **Son**, and Hòly **Spir**it,
both **now** ánd for **ev**er,
the God who **is**, who **was** and ìs to **come**
at the **end** óf the **a**ges.

64 Psalm (116)117

Antiphon

HH
Ho - ly is God, ho - ly and strong,
ho - ly and liv - ing for ev - er!
Psalm
Laudate Dominum
Cantor:
HH
1. O praise the Lord, all you na - tions,
ac - claim him all you peo - ples!
Strong is his love for us; he is faith - ful for ev - er.
2. Give glo - ry to the Fa - ther Al - might - y,
to his Son, Je - sus Christ, the Lord,
to the Spir - it who dwells in our hearts,
both now and for ev - er. A - men.

Psalm (117)118 65

Antiphon

CW
Give thanks to the Lord for he is
good, his love is ev - er - last - ing.

Psalm Tone

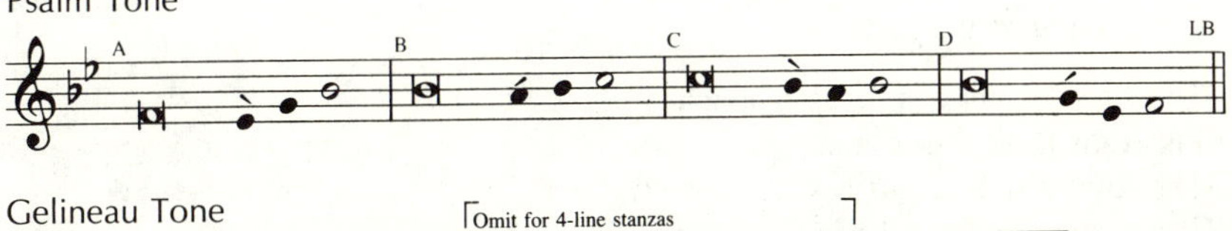
A
B
C
D
LB

Gelineau Tone

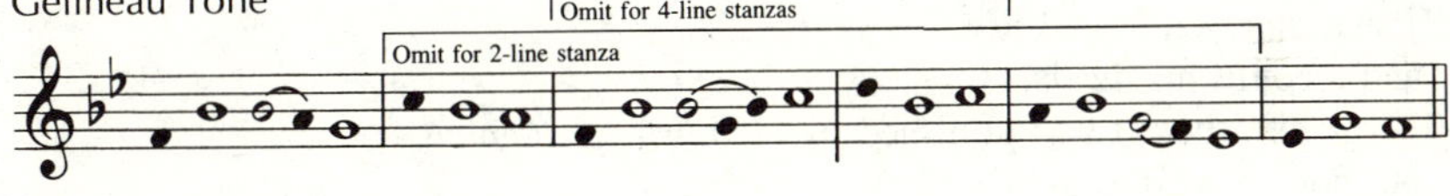
Omit for 4-line stanzas
Omit for 2-line stanza

Confitemini Domino

Give **thanks** to the **Lord** for hè is **good**, *[Omit B+C]*
for his **love** endúres for **ev**er.

2 Let the **sons** of Isràel **say**:
"His **love** endúres for **ev**er."
3 Let the **sons** of **Aà**ron **say**:
"His **love** endúres for **ev**er." *[Repeat C+D]*
4 Let **those** who **fear** thè Lord **say**:
"His **love** endúres for **ev**er."

5 I **called** to the **Lord** in mỳ dis**tress**;
he **ans**wéred and **freed** me.
6 The **Lord** is at my **side**; I dò not **fear**.
What can **man** dó **against** me? *[Repeat C+D]*
7 The **Lord** is at my **side** às my **help**er;
I shall look **down** ón my **foes**.

8 It is **bet**ter to take **ref**uge ìn the **Lord**
than to **trúst** in **men**;
9 it is **bet**ter to take **ref**uge ìn the **Lord**
than to **trúst** in **prin**ces.

10 The **nations** **àll** encom**passed** me;
in the **Lord's** náme I **crushed** them.
11 They **com**passed me, **com**passed mè a**bout**;
in the **Lord's** náme I **crushed** them.
* 12 They **com**passed me a**bòut** like **bees**;
they **blazed** like a **fire** ámong **thorns**. *[Omit C]*
In the **Lord's** náme I **crushed** them.

13 I was thrust **down**, thrust **dòwn** and **fall**ing
but the **Lord** wás my **help**er.
14 The **Lord** is my **strength** ànd my **song**;
he wás my **sav**ior. *[Repeat C+D]*
15 There are **shouts** of **jòy** and **vic**tory
in the **tents** óf the **just**.

The **Lord's** right **hànd** has **tri**umphed;
16 his **ríght** hand **raised** me.
The **Lord's** right **hànd** has **tri**umphed;
* 17 I shall not **die,** I shall **live**
and re**cóunt** his **deeds**.
18 I was **pun**ished, I was **pun**ished bỳ the **Lord,** *[Omit B+C]*
but **not** dóomed to **die**.

19 Open to **me** the **gàtes** of **ho**liness:
I will **en**ter ánd give **thanks**.
20 **This** is the **Lòrd's** own **gate**
where the **júst** may **en**ter.
21 I will **thank** you for **yòu** have **an**swered *[Omit B+C]*
and **you** áre my **sav**ior.

22 The **stone** which the **buildèrs** re**ject**ed
has be**cóme** the **cor**nerstone.
23 **This** is the **work** òf the **Lord**;
a **mar**vel ín our **eyes**. *[Repeat C+D]*
24 This **day** was **made** bỳ the **Lord**;
we re**joice** ánd are **glad**.

25 O **Lord, grant** ùs sal**va**tion
O **Lord**, gránt suc**cess**.
26 **Bless**ed in the **name** òf the **Lord**
is **hé** who **comes**. *[Repeat C+D]*
We **bless** you from the **house** òf the **Lord**;
27 the Lord **God** ís our **light**.

**Repeat musical phrase for additional line of text.*

Go **for**ward in procession with **branch**es
even tó the **al**tar.
28 **You** are my **Gòd**, I **thank** you.
My **Gód**, I **praise** you.
29 Give **thanks** to the **Lord** for hè is **good**; *[Omit B + C]*
for his **love** endúres for **ever**.

Praise the **Fa**ther, the **Son**, and Hòly **Spir**it,
both **now** ánd for **ev**er,
the God who **is**, who **was**, ànd who **will** be,
world wíthout **end**.

66 Psalm (120)121

Antiphon

AGM
The Lord will guide me and guard me for ev - er.

Psalm Tone

LB

Gelineau Tone

Levavi oculos

1 I **lift** up my **eyes** tò the **moun**tains;
from **where** shall cóme my **help**?
2 My **help** shall **come** fròm the **Lord**
who made **heav**én and **earth**.

3 May he **ne**ver al**low** yòu to **stum**ble!
Let him **sleep** nót, your **guard**.
4 **No**, he **sleeps** nòt nor **slum**bers,
Isráel's **guard**.

5 The **Lord** is your **guard** ànd your **shade**;
at your **right** síde he **stands**.
6 By **day** the **sun** shàll not **smite** you
nor the **moon** ín the **night**.

7 The **Lord** will **guard** yòu from **e**vil,
he will **guárd** your **soul**.
8 The Lord will **guard** your **gò**ing and **com**ing
both **now** ánd for **e**ver.

Praise the **Fa**ther, the **Son** and Hòly **Spir**it,
both **now** ánd for **e**ver,
the God who **is**, who **was** ànd who **will** be,
world wíthout **end**.

Psalm (121)122 67

Antiphon

AGM
We shall go up with joy to the house of our God.

Psalm Tone

LB

Gelineau Tone

Laetatus sum

1 I re**joiced** when I **hèard** them **say**:
"Let us **go** tó God's **house**."
2 And **now** our **fèet** are **stand**ing
within your **gates**, Ó **Jeru**sa**lem**.

3 **Jeru**salem is **built** às a **cit**y
stronglý com**pact**.
4 It is **there** that the **trìbes** go **up**,
the **tribes** óf the **Lord**.

For **Is**rael's **làw** it **is**
there to **praise** thé Lord's **name**.
5 **There** were set the **thrònes** of **judg**ment
of the **hóuse** of **Da**vid.

6 For the **peace** of Jeru**sà**lem, **pray**:
"**Peace** be tó your **homes**!
7 May **peace reign** ìn your **walls**,
in your **pal**áces, **peace**!"

8 For **love** of my **breth**rèn and **friends**
I say:"**Peace** úpon **you**!"
9 For **love** of the **house** òf the **Lord**
I will **ask** fór your **good**.

Praise the **Fa**ther, the **Son** and Hòly **Spir**it,
both **now** ánd for **ev**er,
the God who **is**, who **was** and ìs to **come**
at the **end** óf the **a**ges.

68 Psalm (122)123

Antiphon

AGM
We lift our eyes to the Lord till he show us his mer - cy.

Psalm Tone

RP
Repeat for 5-line stanza
Gelineau Tone
Repeat for 5-line stanza

Ad te levavi oculos meos

1 To **you** have I **lift**ed ùp my **eyes**,
you who **dwell** in thé **heav**ens;
2 my **eyes**, like the **eyes** òf **slaves**
on the **hand** of théir **lords**.

Like the **eyes** òf a **ser**vant
on the **hand** of hér **mis**tress,
3 so our **eyes** are on the **Lord** òur **God**
till he **show** us hís **mer**cy.

4 Have **mer**cy on us, **Lòrd**, have **mer**cy.
We are **filled** with cón**tempt**.
5 **In**deed, all too **full** is òur **soul**
with the **scorn** of thé **rich**,
(with the **proud** man's dís**dain**.)

Praise the **Fa**ther, the **Son** and Hòly **Spir**it,
both **now** and fór **ev**er,
the God who **is**, who **was** and whò **will** be,
world withóut **end**.

Psalm (125)126 69

Antiphon
RP
The Lord has done great things for us;
we are filled with joy, we are filled with joy.

Psalm Tone

JBS

Gelineau Tone

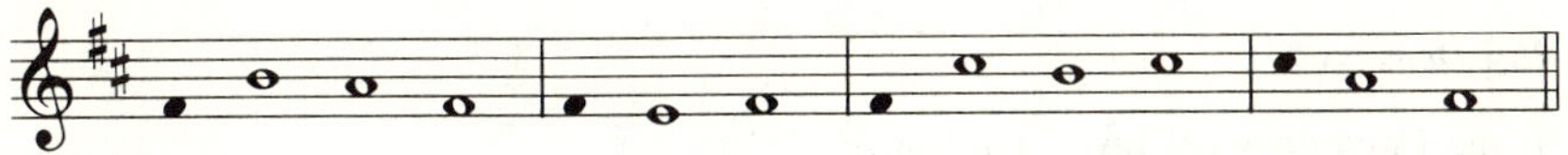

In convertendo

1 When the **Lord** delivered **Zi**òn from **bond**age,
it **seemed** líke a **dream**.
2 **Then** was our **mouth** fìlled with **laugh**ter,
on our **lips** thére were **songs**.

The **heath**ens them**selves** sàid: "What **mar**vels
the **Lord** wórked for **them**!"
3 What **mar**vels the **Lord** wòrked for **us**!
In**deed**, wé were **glad**.

4 De**liv**er us O **Lord**, fròm our **bond**age
as **stréams** in dry **land**.
5 **Those** who **sòw** in **tears**
sing ás they **reap**.

6 They go **out**, they go **out**, fùll of **tears**,
carrying **seed** fór the **sow**ing;
they come **back**, they come **back**, fùll of **song**,
carrýing their **sheaves**.

Praise the **Fa**ther, the **Son** and Hòly **Spir**it,
both **now** ánd for **ev**er,
the God who **is**, who **was** ànd who **will** be,
world wíthout **end**.

70 Psalm (126)127

Antiphon
AGM
May the Lord watch o - ver this house, and keep us in peace.

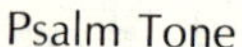
Psalm Tone

LB

Gelineau Tone

Nisi Dominus

1 If the **Lord** does not **bùild** the **house**,
in **vain** do its **búilders** **la**bor;
if the **Lord** does not **watch** ovèr the **ci**ty,
in **vain** does the **watch**mán keep **vi**gil.

2 In **vain** is your **ear**lìer **ris**ing,
your **go**ing **la**tér to **rest**,
you who **toil** for the **brèad** you **eat**,
when he pours **gifts** on his be**lov**ed whíle they **slum**ber.

3 Truly **sons** are a **gift** fròm the **Lord**,
a **bless**ing, the **fruit** óf the **womb**.
4 In**deed**, the **sòns** of **youth**
are like **ar**rows in the **hand** óf a **war**rior.

5 **O** the **hap**piness òf the **man**
who has **filled** his **quiv**er wíth these **ar**rows!
He will have no **càuse** for **shame**
when he dis**putes** with his **foes** ín the **gate**ways.

Give **praise** to the **Fa**thèr Al**might**y,
to his **Son**, Jesus **Chríst**, the **Lord**,
to the **Spir**it who **dwells** ìn our **hearts**,
both **now** and for **agés** un**end**ing.

Psalm (129)130 71

Antiphon I

JG
I place all my trust in you, my God;
all my hope is in your sav - ing word.

Antiphon II

CWH
If you, O Lord, should mark our
sins, Lord, who would sur - vive?

Antiphon III

RC
Out of the depths I cry to you, O Lord.

Psalm Tone

AGM
Repeat for 6-line stanza

Gelineau Tone

Repeat for 6-line stanzas

De profundis

1 Out of the **depths** I **cry** to yòu, O **Lord**,
2 **Lord**, héar my **voice**!
O **let** your **ears** bè atten**tive**
to the **voice** óf my **pleading**.

3 If you, O **Lord**, should **màrk** our **guilt**,
Lord, who wóuld sur**vive**?
4 But with **you** is **foùnd** forgive**ness**:
for **this** wé revere **you**.

5 My **soul** is **wait**ing fòr the **Lord**,
I **count** ón his **word**.
6 My **soul** is **long**ing fòr the **Lord**,
more than **watch**mán for **daybreak**.
(Let the **watch**man **cò****unt** on **day**break
7 and **Is**rael **ón** the **Lord**.)

Be**cause** with the **Lord** thère is **mer**cy
and **full**ness óf re**demp**tion,
8 **Is**rael in**deed** he wìll re**deem**
from **all** íts ini**qui**ty.

To the **Fa**ther Al**might**ỳ give **glo**ry,
give **glo**ry tó his **Son**,
to the **Spir**it most **Ho**lỳ give **praise**,
whose **reign** ís for **ev**er.

Psalm (133)134 72

Antiphon

HH
In the si - lent hours of night, bless the Lord.

Psalm

Ecce nunc

HH

1. O come, bless the Lord, all you who serve the Lord,
who stand in the house of the Lord,
in the courts of the house of our God.

2. Lift up your hands to the ho - ly place
and bless the Lord through the night.

3. May the Lord bless you from Zi - on,
he who made both heav- en and earth.

4. Glory to the Father, and the Son, and to the Ho - ly
Spir - it: as it was in the be - gin - ning,
is now, and will be for ev - er. A - men.

73 Psalm (138)139

Antiphon
AGM
Your hand is ev - er up - on me;
you lead me and hold me fast.
Psalm Tone
Repeat for 5-line stanza
Repeat for 6-line stanza
LB
Gelineau Tone
Omit for 5-line st.
Omit for 4-line stanzas

Domine, probasti

1 O **Lord,** you **search** me ànd you **know** me,
2 you **know** my **rest**ing ánd my **ris**ing,
you dis**cern** my **pur**pose fròm a**far**.
3 You **mark** when I **walk** òr lie **down**,
all my **ways** lie opén to **you**.

4 Before **ev**er a **word** is òn my **tongue**
you **know** it, O **Lord**, thróugh and **through**.
5 Be**hind** and be**fore** yòu be**siege** me,
your **hand** ever **láid** up**on** me.
6 Too **won**derful for **mè**, this **know**ledge,
too **high**, beyónd my **reach**.

7 O **where** can I **go** fròm your **spir**it,
or **where** can I **flee** fróm your **face**?
8 If I **climb** the **heav**ens yòu are **there**.
If I **lie** in the **grave**, yóu are **there**.

9 If I **take** the **wings** òf the **dawn**
and **dwell** at the **sea's** fúrthest **end**,
10 even **there** your **hànd** would **lead** me,
your **right** hand would **hóld** me **fast**.

11 If I **say**: "Let the **dàrk**ness **hide** me
and the **light** a**round** mé be **night**,"
12 even **dark**ness is not **dàrk** for **you**
and the **night** is as **clear** ás the **day**.

13 For it was **you** who cre**at**èd my **be**ing,
knit me to**geth**er in my **mó**ther's **womb**.
14 I **thank** you for the **won**der òf my **be**ing,
for the **won**ders of **all** yóur cre**a**tion.

Al**read**y you **knèw** mý **soul**,
15 my **bod**y held no **se**crét from **you**
when **I** was being **fash**iòned in **se**cret
and **mold**ed in the **depths** óf the **earth**.

16 Your **eyes** saw **àll** my **ac**tions,
they were **all** of them **writ**ten ín your **book**;
every **one** of my **days** wàs de**creed**
before **one** of them **came** ínto **be**ing.

17 To **me**, how mys**te**riòus your **thoughts**,
the **sum** of them **not** tó be **num**bered!
18 If I **count** them, they are **more** thàn the **sand**;
to **fin**ish, I must be e**ter**nál, like **you**.

19 O **God**, that you would **slày** the **wick**ed!
Men of **blood** keep **fár away** from me!
20 With de**ceit** they re**bèl** a**gainst** you
and **set** your de**sígns** at **naught**.

21 Do I not **hate thòse** who **hate** you,
ab**hor** those who **ríse** a**gainst** you?
22 I **hate** them with a **pèr**fect **hate**
and **they** are **fóes** to **me**.

23 O **search** me **God** and knòw my **heart**.
O **test** me and **knów** my **thoughts**.
24 See that I **fol**low nòt the **wrong path**
and **lead** me in the **path** of lífe e**ter**nal.

Give **praise** to the **Fa**thèr Al**might**y,
to his **Son**, Jesus **Chríst**, the **Lord**,
to the **Spir**it who **dwells** ìn our **hearts**,
both **now** and for evèr. **A**men.

74 Psalm (140)141

Antiphon

RJB
My prayers rise like in - cense, my
hands like the eve - ning of - f'ring.

Psalm Tone

Gelineau Tone

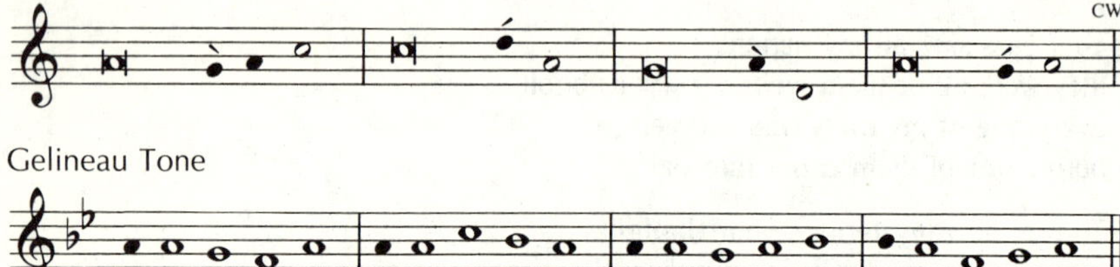
CW

Domine, clamavi

1 I have **called** to you, **Lord**; **has**tèn to **help** me!
Hear my **voice** when I **cry** tó **you**.
2 Let my **prayer** a**rise** be**fore** you lìke **in**cense,
the **rais**ing of my **hands** like and **eve**ning óbla**tion**.

3 **Set**, O **Lord**, a **guard** ovèr my **mouth**;
Keep **watch**, O **Lord**, at the **door** of mý **lips**!
4 Do not **turn** my **heart** to **things** that àre **wrong**,
to **evil** **deeds** with **men** who áre **sin**ners.

Never al**low** me to **share** ìn their **feast**ing.
5 If a **good** man **strikes** or re**proves** me it ís **kind**ness;
but let the **oil** of the **wick**ed not a**noint** mỳ **head**.
Let my **prayer** be **ever** a**gainst** théir **mal**ice.

6 Their **prin**ces were thrown **down** by the **side** òf the **rock**;
then they under**stood** that my **words** wére **kind**.
7 As a **mill**stone is **shat**tered to **pie**ces on thè **ground**,
so their **bones** were **strewn** at the **mouth** of thé **grave**.

8 To **you**, Lord **God**, my **è**yes are **turned**;
in **you** I take **ref**uge; **spare** mý **soul**!
9 From the **trap** they have **laid** for me **keep** mè **safe**;
keep me from the **snares** of **those** who dó **e**vil.

10 Let the **wick**ed fall **in**to the **traps** thèy have **set**
whilst I pur**sue** my **way** únharmed.
Give **praise** to the **Fa**ther, the **Son** ánd Holỳ **Spir**it,
both **now** and for **a**ges un**end**ing. Á**men**.

Psalm (142)143:1-11 7

Antiphon

RC
Do not hide your face from me: In you I put my trust.

Psalm Tone

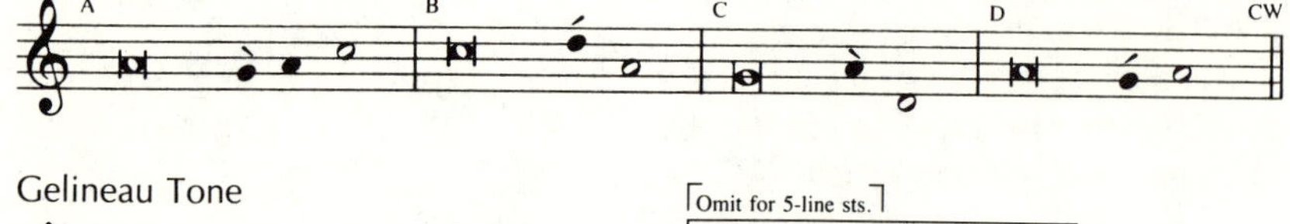
A
B
C
D
CW

Gelineau Tone

Omit for 5-line sts.
Omit for 4-line stanzas

Domine, exaudi

1 **Lord**, **lis**ten tò my **prayer**,
turn your **ear** to my áp**peal**.
You are **faith**ful, you are **just**; gìve **an**swer.
2 Do not **call** your **ser**vant to **judg**ment
for **no** one is **just** in yóur **sight**.

3 The **en**emy pur**suès** my **soul**;
he has **crushed** my **life** to thé **ground**;
he has **made** me **dwell** ìn **dark**ness
like the **dead, long** fór**got**ten. [Repeat C + D]
4 **There**fore my **spi**rìt **fails**;
my **heart** is **numb** wí**thin** me.

5 I re**mem**ber the **days** thàt are **past**,
I **pon**der **all** yóur **works**.
I **muse** on what your **hand** hàs **wrought**
6 and to **you** I **stretch** out mý **hands**. [Repeat D]
Like a **parched** land my **soul** thirsts fór **you**.

7 **Lord**, make **hàste** and **an**swer;
for my **spir**it **fails** wí**thin** me.
Do not **hide** yòur **face**
lest I be**come** like **those** in thé **grave**.

8 In the **morn**ing let me **knòw** your **love**
for I **put** my **trust** ín **you**.
Make me **know** the **way** I shòuld **walk**;
to **you** I **lift** up mý **soul**.

9 **Res**cue me, **Lord**, fròm my **en**emies;
I have **fled** to **you** fór **ref**uge.
10 **Teach** me to **do** yòur **will**
for **you**, O **Lord**, are mý **God**. *[Repeat C + D]*
Let your good **spir**ìt **guide** me
in **ways** that are **lev**el ánd **smooth**.

11 For your **name's** sake, **Lord**, sàve my **life**; *[Omit B + C]*
in your **jus**tice save my **soul** from dístress.
Give **praise** to the **Fa**thèr Al**mighty**,
to his **Son**, Jesus **Christ**, thé **Lord**,
to the **Spir**it who **dwells** in òur **hearts**,
both **now** and for **ev**er. Á**men**.

76 Psalm (144)145

Antiphon
RC
Your king - dom is ev - er - last-
ing; you shall reign for ev - er!
Psalm Tone
Omit for 3-line stanza
Repeat for 6-line stanza
REK
Gelineau Tone
Omit for 3-line stanza
Repeat for 6-line stanza

Exaltabo te, Deus

1 I will give you **glo**ry, O **Gòd** my **King**,
I will **bless** your **náme** for **ev**er.
2 I will **bless** you **day** àfter **day**
and **praise** your **náme** for **ev**er.
3 The Lord is **great**, **high**ly tò be **praised**,
his **great**ness **cann**ót be **meas**ured.

4 Age to **age** shall pro**clàim** your **works**,
shall de**clare** your **míght**y **deeds**,
5 shall **speak** of your **splen**dòr and **glo**ry,
tell the **tale** of your **won**dérful **works**.

6 They will **speak** of your **ter**rìble **deeds**,
re**count** your **great**néss and **might**.
7 They will re**call** your a**bùn**dant **good**ness;
age to **age** shall **ring** óut your **jus**tice.

8 The Lord is **kind** and **full** òf com**pas**sion,
slow to **an**ger, a**bound**íng in **love**.
9 How **good** is the **Lòrd** to **all**,
com**pas**sionate to **áll** his **crea**tures.

10 All your **crea**tures shall **thank** yòu, O **Lord**,
and your **friends** shall re**péat** their **bless**ing.
11 They shall **speak** of the **glo**ry òf your **reign**
and de**clare** your **míght**, O **God**,

12 to make **known** to **men** your mìghty **deeds**
and the **glo**rious **spen**dor óf your **reign**.
13 **Yours** is an **ever**làsting **king**dom;
your **rule** lasts from **áge** to **age**.

The Lord is **faith**ful in **àll** his **words**
and **lov**ing in **áll** his **deeds**.
14 The **Lord** sup**ports** àll who **fall**
and **rais**es **all** who áre bowed **down**.

15 The **eyes** of all **crea**tures lòok to **you**
and you **give** them their **food** ín due **time**.
16 You **o**pen **wìde** your **hand**,
grant the de**sires** of **áll** who **live**.

17 The Lord is **just** in **àll** his **ways**
and **lov**ing in **áll** his **deeds**.
18 He is **close** to **àll** who **call** him,
who **call** on **him** fróm their **hearts**.

19 He **grants** the de**sires** of thòse who **fear** him,
he **hears** their **cry** ánd he **saves** them.
20 The **Lord** pro**tects** àll who **love** him;
but the **wick**ed he will **ut**terlý de**stroy**.

21 Let me **speak** the **praise** òf the **Lord**,
let all man**kind bless** his hòly **name**
for **ev**er, for agés un**end**ing.

Give **praise** to the **Fa**thèr Al**mighty**,
to his **Son**, Jesus **Chríst**, the **Lord**,
to the **Spir**it who **dwells** ìn our **hearts**
both **now** and for evér. **A**men.

77 Psalm (145)146

Antiphon

I will praise my God all the days of my life.
JS

Psalm Tone

Gelineau Tone

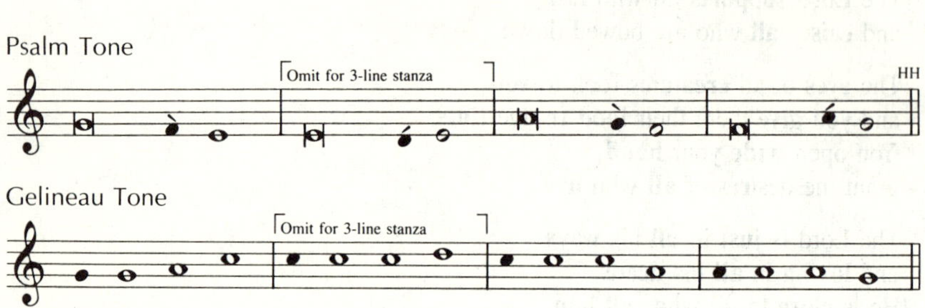
Omit for 3-line stanza
HH
Omit for 3-line stanza

Lauda, anima mea

My **soul**, give **praise** to thè **Lord**;
2 I will **praise** the **Lord** all mỳ **days**,
make **mu**sic to my **God** while Í **live**.

3 **Put** no **trust** ìn **prin**ces,
in mortal **men** in **whom** there is nó **help**.
4 Take their **breath**, they re**turn** tò **clay**
and their **plans** that **day** come tó **noth**ing.

5 He is **hap**py who is **helped** by Jacòb's **God**,
whose **hope** is in the **Lord** hís **God**,
6 who a**lone** made **hea**ven ànd **earth**,
the **seas** and **all** they cón**tain**.

It is **he** who keeps **faith** fòr **ev**er,
7 who is **just** to **those** who are óp**pressed**.
It is **he** who gives **bread** to thè **hun**gry,
the **Lord**, who sets **pri**sonérs **free**,

8 the **Lord** who gives **sight** to thè **blind**,
who **rai**ses up **those** who are bówed **down**,
9 the **Lord**, who pro**tects** thè **stran**ger
and up**holds** the **wid**ow ánd **or**phan.

8c It is the **Lord** who **loves** thè **just**,
9c but **thwarts** the **path** of thé **wick**ed.
10 The **Lord** will **reign** fòr **ever**,
Zion's **God**, from **age** tó **age**.

Give **praise** to the **Fa**ther À**lmighty**,
to his **Son**, Jesus **Christ**, thé **Lord**,
to the **Spir**it who **dwells** in òur **hearts**,
both **now** and for **ev**er. Á**men**.

78 Psalm (147)147b:12-20

Antiphon
TFS
O praise the Lord, Je - ru - sa-lem! Zi-on, praise your God!

Psalm Tone
RP
Gelineau Tone
Omit for stanza 1

Lauda, Jerusalem

12 O **praise** the **Lord**, Jer**ù**salem!
Zión, **praise** your **God**!

13 He has **strength**ened the **bars** of your **gàtes**,
he has **blessed** the **chil**drén with**in** you.
14 He es**tab**lished **peace** on your **bòr**ders,
he **feeds** you wíth **fin**est **wheat**.

15 He **sends** out his **word** to the **eàrth**
and **swift**ly **rúns** his com**mand**.
16 He **show**ers down **snow** whìte as **wool**,
he **scat**ters **hoar**fróst like **ash**es.

17 He **hurls** down **hail**stones like **crùmbs**.
The **wa**ters are **fró**zen at his **touch**;
18 he **sends** forth his **word** and it **mèlts** them;
at the **breath** of his **móuth** the waters **flow**.

19 He **makes** his word **known** to **Jà**cob,
to **Is**rael his **láws** and de**crees**.
20 He has **not** dealt **thus** with other **nà**tions;
he has **not** táught **them** his de**crees**.

Give **praise** to the **Fa**ther Al**mìghty**,
to his **Son**, Jésus **Christ**, the **Lord**,
to the **Spir**it who **dwells** in our **hèarts**,
both **now** and for éver. A**men**.

Psalm 148 79

Antiphon

TFS
Let all cre - a - tion praise the Lord.

Psalm Tone

Omit for 2-line stanza
LB

Gelineau Tone

Omit for 2-line stanza

Laudate Dominum

Praise the **Lord** from the **heavens**,
praise him in the **heights**.
2 **Praise** him, all his **an**gels,
praise him, **all** his **host**.

3 **Praise** him, **sun** and **moon**,
praise him, shining **stars**.
4 **Praise** him, highest **hea**vens
and the **wa**ters a**bove** the **hea**vens.

5 Let them **praise** the **name** of the **Lord**.
He com**mand**ed: they were **made**.
6 He **fixed** them for **ev**er,
gave a **law** which shall **not** pass **away**.

7 **Praise** the **Lord** from the **earth**,
sea creatures **and** all **o**ceans,
8 fire and **hail**, snow and **mist**,
stormy **winds** that o**bey** his **word**;

9 **all moun**tains and **hills**,
all **fruit** trees and **ce**dars,
10 **beasts**, wild and **tame**,
reptiles and **birds** on the **wing**;

11 **all** earth's **kings** and **peo**ples,
earth's **prin**ces and **ru**lers;
12 **young** men and **maid**ens,
old men to**geth**er with **chil**dren.

13 Let them **praise** the **name** of the **Lord**,
for he a**lone** is ex**alt**ed.
The **splen**dor of his **name**
reaches beyond **hea**ven and **earth**.

14 He ex**alts** the **strength** of his **peo**ple.
He is the **praise** of all his **saints**,
of the **sons** of **Is**rael,
of the **peo**ple to **whom** he comes **close**.

To the **Fa**ther, the **Son** and Holy **Spir**it
give **praise** for ever. **A**men.

80 Psalm 149

Antiphon

EE
Sing a new song to the God of sal - va - tion.

Psalm Tone

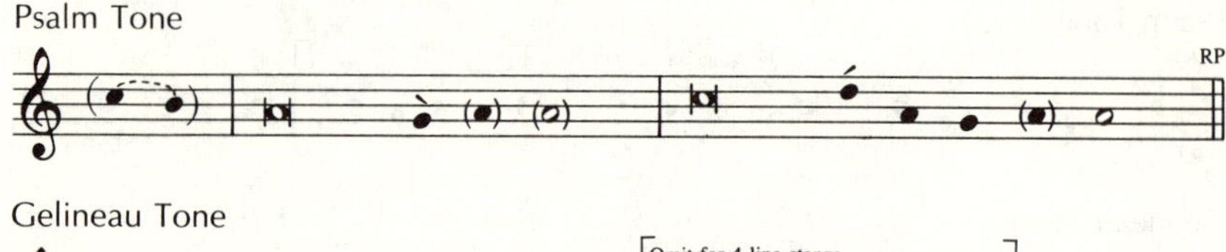
RP

Gelineau Tone

Omit for 4-line stanza

Cantate Domino

Sing a new **song** to thè **Lord**,
his **praise** in the assémbly of the **faith**ful.
2 Let **Is**rael re**joice** in ìts **Ma**ker,
let Zion's **sons** ex**últ** in their **king**.
3 Let them **praise** his **name** wìth **danc**ing
and make **mu**sic with **tím**brel and **harp**.

4 For the **Lord** takes de**light** in hìs **peo**ple.
He **crowns** the **póor** with sal**va**tion.
5 Let the **faith**ful re**joice** in thèir **glo**ry,
shout for **jóy** and **take** their **rest**.
6 Let the **praise** of **God** be on thèir **lips**
and a **two**-edged **swórd** in their **hand**,

7 to **deal** out **venge**ance to thè **na**tions
and **pun**ishment on **áll** the **peo**ples;
8 to **bind** their **kings** ìn **chains**
and their **no**bles in **fét**ters of **i**ron;
9 to **car**ry out the **sen**tence pre-òr**dained**:
this **hon**or is for **áll** his **faith**ful.

Give **praise** to the **Fa**ther À**l**m**igh**ty,
to his **Son**, Jésus **Christ**, the **Lord**,
to the **Spir**it who **dwells** in òur **hearts**,
both **now** and for éver. A**men**.

Psalm 150 81

Antiphon

RC
Let ev-'ry -thing that lives give praise to the Lord.

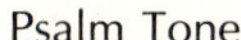
Psalm Tone

LB

Gelineau Tone

Laudate Dominum

Praise **God** in his **hò**ly **place**,
praise him in his **míght**y **hea**vens.
2 **Praise** him for his **pow**èrful **deeds**,
praise his sur**páss**ing **great**ness.

3 O **praise** him with **sòund** of **trum**pet,
praise him with **lúte** and **harp**.
4 **Praise** him with **tim**brèl and **dance**,
praise him with **stríngs** and **pipes**.

5 O **praise** him with res**òund**ing **cym**bals,
praise him with **clash**íng of **cym**bals.
6 Let **ev**erything that **lives** ànd that **breathes**
give **praise** to the **Lórd**. **Amen**.

Give **praise** to the **Fa**thèr Al**might**y,
to his **Son**, Jesus **Chríst** the **Lord**,
to the **Spir**it who **dwells** ìn our **hearts**,
both **now** and for **ev**ér. **A**men.

82 Isaiah 38:10-14, 17-20

Antiphon

MEY
I will sing to the Lord all the days of my life.

Psalm Tone

AGM

Gelineau Tone

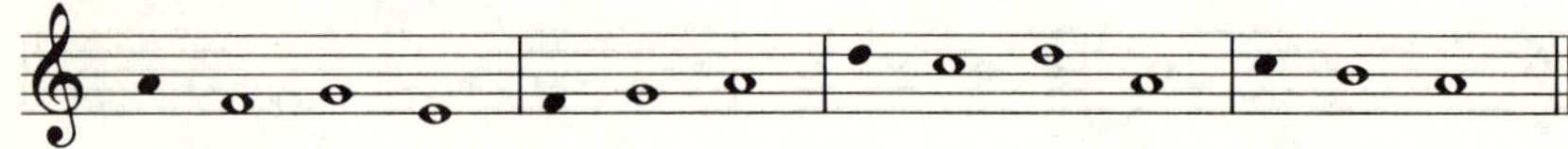

Ego dixi

1. I **said**: "So I must **gò** away,
my **lífe** half **spent**,
as**signed** to the **wòrld** be**low**
for the **rest** óf my **years**."

2. I said: "No **more** shall I **sèe** the **Lord**
in the **land** óf the **liv**ing,
no **more** shall I **look** ùpon **men**
with**ín** this **world**.

3. My **home** is pulled **up** ànd re**moved**
like a **shé**pherd's **tent**.
Like a **weav**er you have **rolled** ùp my **life**,
you **cut** it fróm the **loom**.

4. Between **eve**ning and **morn**ìng you **fin**ish it.
I cry for **help** úntil **dawn**.
I **suf**fer as **thòugh** a **li**on
weré **break**íng my **bones**.

5. I **cry** out in **grief** lìke a **swal**low,
I **moan** líke a **dove**.
My **eyes** look **wear**ilỳ to **heav**en.
Take **care** óf me, **Lord**!"

6. **You** have held **bàck** my **life**
from the **pít** of **doom**.
You have cast **far** fròm your **sight**
every **one** óf my **sins**.

7. For the **world** be**low** cànnot **thank** you,
 nor **death** gíve you **praise**.
 Those who go **down** tò the **grave**
 cannot **hope** fór your **mer**cy.

8. The **liv**ing, the **liv**ìng man **thanks** you,
 as **I** dó this **day**;
 the **fa**ther shall **tèll** his **chil**dren
 of your **faíth**ful **mer**cy.

9. O **Lord**, **come** tò our **res**cue,
 and **we** shál l sing **psalms**,
 sing **psalms** all the **days** òf our **life**
 in the **house** óf the **Lord**.

10. Praise the **Fa**ther, the **Son** and Hòly **Spir**it,
 both **now** ánd for **ev**er,
 the God who **is**, who **was** and ìs to **come**
 at the **end** óf the **a**ges.

83 Jeremiah 14:17-21

Antiphon

RL
Tru - ly we know our of - fens - es, Lord,
for we have sinned a - gainst you.

Psalm Tone

Tonus Peregrinus

Deducant oculi

1. Let my eyes strèam with tears
   day and night, wíthout rest

2. over the destruction which overwhelms the virgin daughtèr
   of my péople,
   over her incúrable wound.

3. If I walk out ìnto a field,
   look! those slain bý the sword:

4. if I ènter the city,
   look! those consúmed by hunger.

5. Even the prophèt and the priest
   forage in a land théy know not.

6. Have you cast Judàh off completely?
   Is Zion lóathsome to you?

7. Why have you strùck us a blow
   that cannót be healed?

8. We wait for peace, tò no avail;
   for a time of healing, but terror cómes instead.

9. We recognize, O Lord, our wickedness, the guilt of our fathers;
that we have sinned against you.

10. For your name's sake spurn us not,
disgrace not the throne of your glory;

11. Remember your covenant with us,
and break it not.

12. Glory to the Father and to the Son and to the Holy Spirit:
as it was in the beginning, is now and will be for ever. Amen.

84 Song of the Three Children/Daniel 3:52-57

Benedictus es, Domine

JG

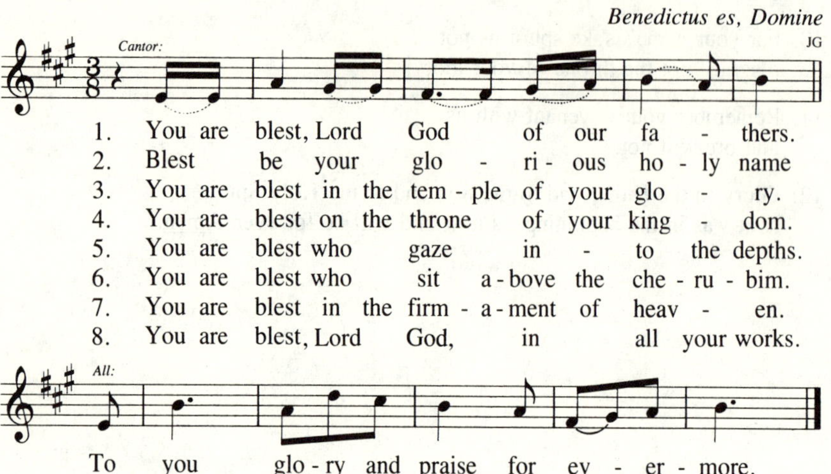
Cantor:
1. You are blest, Lord God of our fa - thers.
2. Blest be your glo - ri - ous ho - ly name
3. You are blest in the tem - ple of your glo - ry.
4. You are blest on the throne of your king - dom.
5. You are blest who gaze in - to the depths.
6. You are blest who sit a - bove the che - ru - bim.
7. You are blest in the firm - a - ment of heav - en.
8. You are blest, Lord God, in all your works.
All:
To you glo - ry and praise for ev - er - more.

Song of the Three Children/Daniel 3:57-88 85

Benedicite, omnia

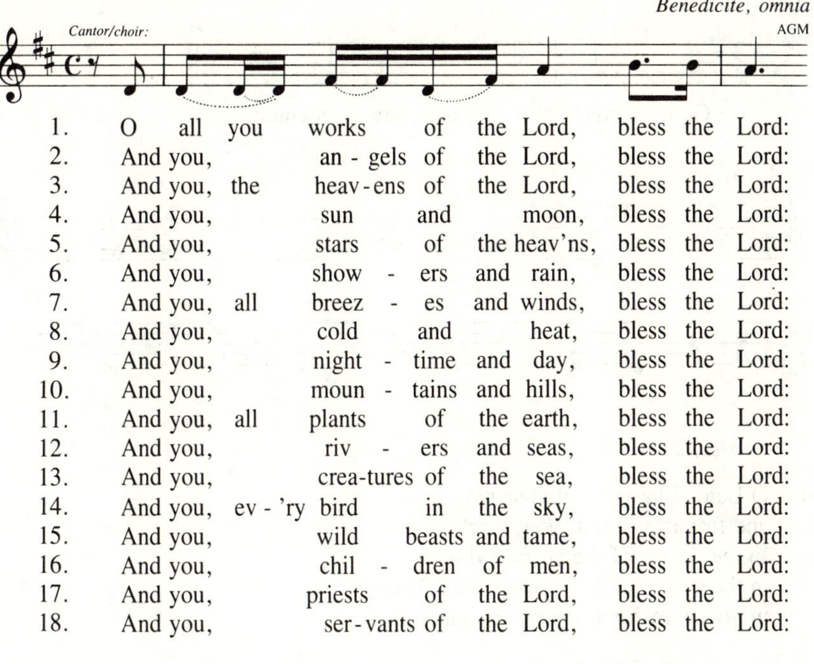
AGM
Cantor/choir:
1. O all you works of the Lord, bless the Lord:
2. And you, an - gels of the Lord, bless the Lord:
3. And you, the heav-ens of the Lord, bless the Lord:
4. And you, sun and moon, bless the Lord:
5. And you, stars of the heav'ns, bless the Lord:
6. And you, show - ers and rain, bless the Lord:
7. And you, all breez - es and winds, bless the Lord:
8. And you, cold and heat, bless the Lord:
9. And you, night - time and day, bless the Lord:
10. And you, moun - tains and hills, bless the Lord:
11. And you, all plants of the earth, bless the Lord:
12. And you, riv - ers and seas, bless the Lord:
13. And you, crea-tures of the sea, bless the Lord:
14. And you, ev - 'ry bird in the sky, bless the Lord:
15. And you, wild beasts and tame, bless the Lord:
16. And you, chil - dren of men, bless the Lord:
17. And you, priests of the Lord, bless the Lord:
18. And you, ser-vants of the Lord, bless the Lord:

All:
To him be high-est glo - ry and praise for ev - er.

86 Habakkuk 3:2-4, 13a, 15-19

Antiphon
RC
God, my Lord, is my strength.

Psalm Tone
Repeat for 5-line stanzas
RC

Domine, audivi

1. O Lord, I have heard your renòwn,
and feared, O Lord, your wòrk.
In the course of the years revíve it,
in the course of the years màke it known;
in your **wrath** re**mem**ber com**pas**sion!

2. God comes from Tèman,
the Holy One from Mount Páran.
Covered are the heavens wìth his glory;
with his **praise** the **earth** is **filled**.

3. His splendor spreads like the lìght;
rays shine forth from besìde him,
where his power is concéaled.
You came forth to sàve your people
to **save** your a**noint**ed **one**.

4. You tread the sea with your stèeds
amid the churning of the deep wáters.
I hear, and my bòdy trembles;
at the **sound**, my **lips** **qui**ver.

5. Decay invades my bònes,
my legs tremble benéath me.
I await the day òf distress
that will **come** to the **peo**ple who **hate** us.

6. For though the fig tree blossom nòt
nor fruit be on the vínes,
though the yield of the òlive fail
and the **fields** pro**duce** no **nour**ishment,

7. though the flocks disappear from the fòld
   and there be no herd in the stálls,
   yet will I rejoice ìn the Lord
   and ex**ult** in my **sav**ing **God**.

8. God, my Lord, is my strèngth;
   he makes my feet swift as those of hínds
   and enables mè to go
   up on**to** the **moun**tain **heights**.

9. Glory to the Father, and to the Sòn,
   and to the Holy Spírit,
   as it was in the beginnìng, is now,
   and will **be** for **e**ver. **A**men.

87 Canticle of Mary/Luke 1:46-55

Antiphon

RJB
My soul re - joic - es, my soul re - joic - es in my God.

Psalm Tone

LW

Gelineau Tone

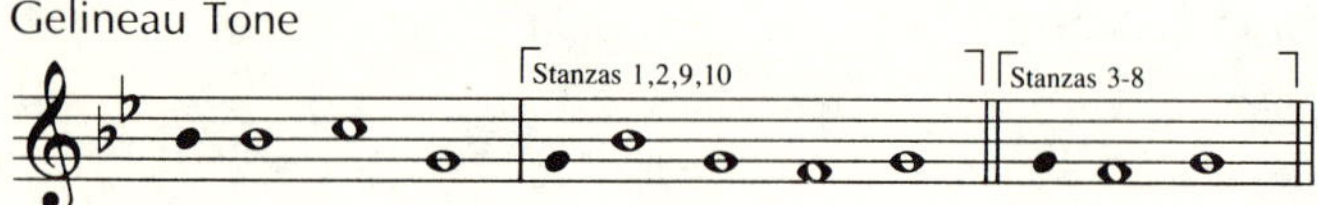
Stanzas 1,2,9,10
Stanzas 3-8

Magnificat anima mea

1. My **soul glo**rifies the **Lord**,
my **spir**it re**joic**es in **Gód**, my **Sav**ior.

2. He **looks** on his **ser**vant in her **noth**ingness;
hence**forth** all **a**ges will **cáll** me **bless**ed.

3. The Al**might**y works **mar**vels for **me**.
Holý his **name**!

4. His **mer**cy is from **age** to **age**,
on **thóse** who **fear** him.

5. He **puts** forth his **arm** in **strength**
and **scat**ters thé proud**heart**ed.

6. He **casts** the **might**y from their **thrones**
and **rais**és the **low**ly.

7. He **fills** the **star**ving with good **things**,
sends the **rich** áway **emp**ty.

8. He pro**tects Is**rael his **ser**vant,
re**mem**bering his **mer**cy,

9. the **mer**cy **prom**ised to our **fa**thers,
for **Abra**ham and his **sóns** for **ev**er.

10. Praise the **Fa**ther, the **Son** and Holy **Spir**it,
both **now** and for **a**ges un**end**ing. **A**men.

Canticle of Mary/Luke 1:46-55 88

Magnificat anima mea

JG
Cantor:
1. My soul glori- fies the Lord, my spirit re- joices in God, my Savior.
2. He looks on his servant in her nothingness; hence- forth all ages will call me blessed.
All:
Al - le - lu - ia.
Cantor:
3. The Al- mighty works mar- vels for me. Ho- ly his name!
4. His mercy is from age to age on those who fear him.
All:
Al - le - lu - ia.

Cantor:

5. He puts forth his arm in strength / and scatters the proud- hearted.
6. He casts the mighty from their thrones / and rais- es the lowly.
7. He fills the starving with good things, / sends the rich a- way empty.
8. He pro- tects Israel, his servant, / re- member- ing his mercy,

All: Al - le - lu - ia.

Cantor:

9. the mercy promised to our fathers, / for Abra- ham and his sons for ever.
10. Praise the Father, the Son and Ho- ly Spirit, / both now and for ever, world without end.

All: Al - le - lu - ia.

89 Canticle of Zachariah/Luke 1:68-79

Antiphon

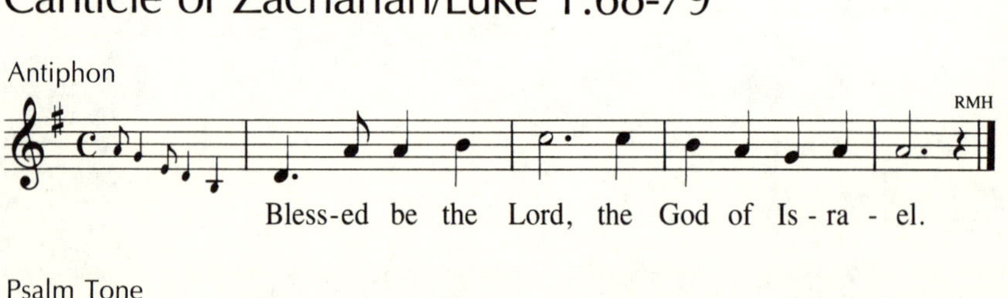
RMH
Bless-ed be the Lord, the God of Is - ra - el.
RP

Psalm Tone

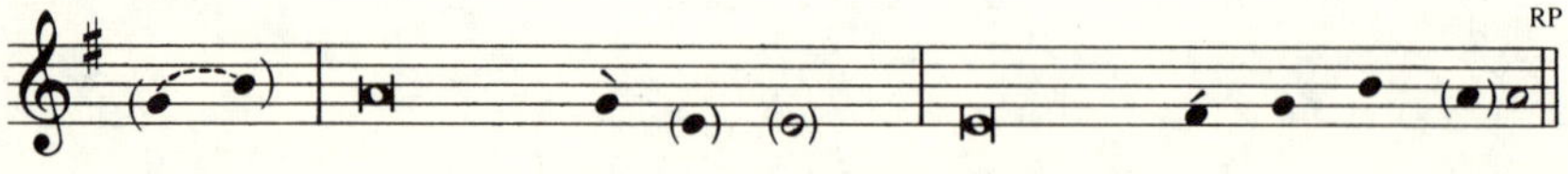

Gelineau Tone

Omit for 3-line stanza
Omit for 5 lines

Benedictus Dominus

1. Blessed be the **Lord**, the **God** of Ìsrael!
He has **vis**ited his **peo**ple ánd re**deemed** them.
He has **raised** up for **us** a mighty **sà**vior
in the **house** of **Dá**vid his **ser**vant
as he **prom**ised by the **lips** of hòly **men**,
those who were his **próph**ets from of **old**.

2. A **sav**ior who would **free** us fròm our **foes**,
from the **hands** of **áll** who **hate** us.
So his **love** for our **fa**thers ìs ful**filled**
and his holy **cov**enánt re**mem**bered.

3. He **swore** to Abraham our **fà**ther
to **grant** ús that, **free** from **fear**,
and **saved** from the **hands** of òur **foes**,
we might **serve** him in **ho**liness and **jus**tice
all the **days** of our **lives** ín his **pres**ence.

4. As for **you**, little **child**, you shàll be **called**
a **proph**et of **Gód** the Most **High**.
You shall go a**head** of the **Lòrd**
to pre**pare** his **wáys** be**fore** him.

5. To make **known** to his **peo**ple their sal**và**tion,
through for**give**néss of **all** their **sins**,
the loving **kind**ness of the **heàrt** of our **God**
who **vis**its us like **dáwn** from on **high**.

6. **He** will give **light** to those in **dark**ness,
those who **dwell** in the **shad**ow òf **death**,
and guide us **intó** the **way** of **peace**.

7. Give **praise** to the **Fa**ther Al**mìghty**,
to his **Son**, Jésus **Christ**, the **Lord**,
to the **Spir**it who **dwells** in our **heàrts**,
both **now** and for éver. **A**men.

90 Canticle of Simeon/Luke 2:29-32

Antiphon

GW/AGM
Guard us, O Lord, while we sleep, and keep us in peace.

Psalm Tone

Gelineau Tone

Chant tone 3-b
Acc. by RP
Omit for 3-line stanza

Nunc dimittis

1. At **last** all-**pow**erful **Mas**ter,
   you give **leave** to your **sè**rvant to **go**
   in **peace**, ac**cord**ing to yóur **prom**ise.

2. For my **eyes** have **sèen** your sal**va**tion
   which **you** have pre**pared** for áll **na**tions,
   the **light** to en**lìght**en the **Gen**tiles
   and give **glo**ry to **Is**rael, yóur **peo**ple.

3. Give **praise** to the **Fà**ther Al**mighty**,
   to his **Son**, Jesus **Chríst**, the **Lord**,
   to the **Spir**it who **dwèlls** in our **hearts**,
   both **now** and for evér. **A**men.

Ephesians 1:3-10 91

Antiphon

EE
Bless - ed be God who chose us in Christ.

Psalm Tone

EE

Benedictus Deus

1. Praised be the God and Father of our Lord Jesus Christ,
who bestowed on ús in Christ
every spiritual blessing ín the heavens.

2. God chose us in him
before the wórld began
to be holy and blameless ín his sight.

3. He predestined us to be his adopted children through Jesus Christ,
such was his will and pleasure, that all might praise the glórious favor
he has bestowed on us in hís beloved.

4. In him and through his blood, we have been redeemed,
and our síns forgiven,
so immeasurably generous is God's favór to us.

5. God has given us the wisdom
to understand fullý the mystery,
the plan he was pleased to decrée in Christ.

6. A plan to be carried out in Christ, in the fullness of time,
to bring all things into óne in him,
in the heavens and ón the earth.

7. Glory to the Father, and to the Son, and to the Holy Spirit:
as it was in thé beginning,
is now, and will be for evér. Amen.

92 Philippians 2:6-11

Qui cum in forma Dei

HH

Cantor:
1. Though he was in the form of God, Jesus did not deem equality with God
some-thing to be grasped at.
(Cantor:)
JE - SUS CHRIST IS LORD!
Assembly:
JE - SUS CHRIST IS LORD!
Cantor:
2. Rather, he emptied him - self
and took the form of a slave, being born in the like - ness of men.
(Cantor:)
JE - SUS CHRIST IS LORD!
Assembly:
JE - SUS CHRIST IS LORD!
3. He was known to be of hu - man es - tate, and it was thus that he hum-
bled him-self, obediently accepting e - ven death, death on a cross!
(Cantor:)
JE - SUS CHRIST IS LORD!
Assembly:
JE - SUS CHRIST IS LORD!
Cantor:
4. Be - cause of this, God high - ly ex - alt - ed him
and bestowed on him the name a - bove ev - 'ry oth - er name,
(Cantor:)
JE - SUS CHRIST IS LORD!
Assembly:
JE - SUS CHRIST IS LORD!

Cantor:
5. so that at Je - sus' name ev - 'ry knee must bend
in the heav'ns, on the earth, and un - der the earth,
and ev-'ry tongue pro-claim to the glo-ry of God the Fa - ther:
(Cantor:)
JE - SUS CHRIST IS LORD!
Assembly:
JE - SUS CHRIST IS LORD!
Cantor:
6. Glo - ry to the Fa - ther, and to the Son,
and to the Ho - ly Spir - it:
as it was in the be - gin - ning, is
now, and will be for ev - er. A - men.
(Cantor:)
JE - SUS CHRIST IS LORD!
Assembly:
allargando
JE - SUS CHRIST IS LORD!

93 Colossians 1:12-20

Antiphon

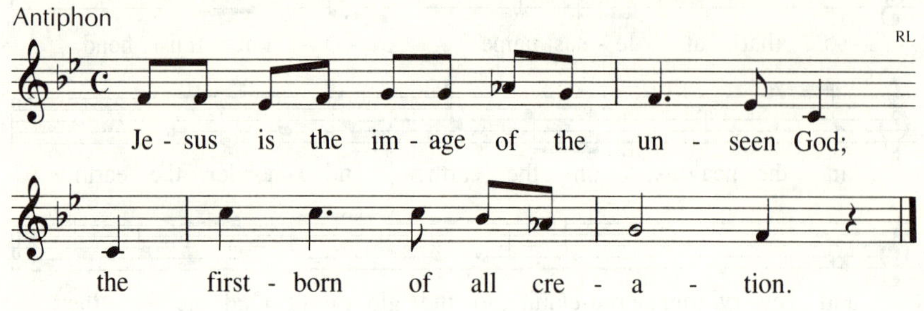
RL
Je - sus is the im - age of the un - seen God;
the first - born of all cre - a - tion.

Psalm Tone

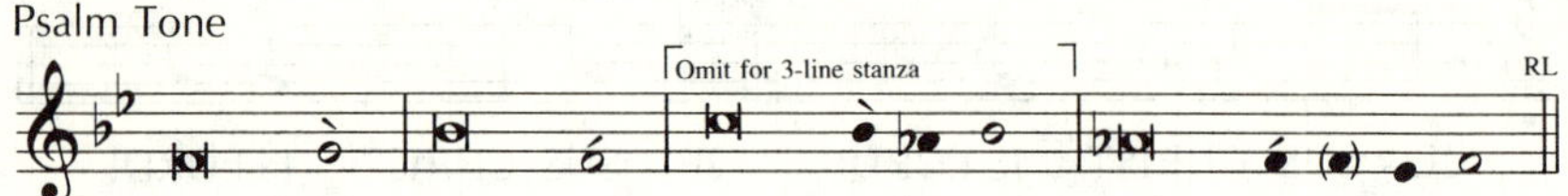
Omit for 3-line stanza
RL

Gratias agentes

1. Let us give thanks to the Fàther
   for having made you wórthy
   to share the lot of the sáints in light.

2. He rescued us from the power of dàrkness
   and brought us into the kingdom of his beloved Són.
   Through him we hàve redemption,
   the forgiveness óf our sins.

3. He is the image of the invisible Gòd,
   the first-born of all créatures.
   In him everything in heaven and on earth wàs created,
   things visible ánd invisible.

4. All were created through hìm;
   all were created for hím.
   He is before all èlse that is.
   In him everything contínues in being.

5. It is he who is head of the body, the chùrch;
   he who is the begínning,
   the first-born òf the dead,
   so that primacy may be hís in everything.

6. It pleased God to make absolute fullness reside in hìm
and, by means of him, to reconcile everything in his pérson,
both on earth and ìn the heavens,
making peace through the blóod of his cross.

7. Glory to the Father, and to the Sòn,
and to the Holy Spírit:
as it was in thè beginning,
is now, and will be for éver. Amen.

94 From 1 Timothy 3:16

Cantor, then all:
RMH
Praise the Lord, all na - tions.
Cantor:
Christ man - i - fest - ed in the flesh.
Christ jus - ti - fied in the Spir - it.
Cantor, then all:
Praise the Lord, all na - tions.
Cantor:
Christ was seen by the an - gels.
Christ pro-claimed by un - be - liev - ers.
Cantor, then all:
Praise the Lord, all na - tions.
Cantor:
Christ, be - lieved through - out the world,
Christ, ex - alt - ed in glo - ry.
Cantor, then all:
Praise the Lord, all na - tions.

1 Peter 2:21-24 95

Antiphon

RP
By your wounds, O Christ, we have been healed.

Psalm Tone

RP

In hoc enim

Melody

RP

1. Christ suf-fered for you, and left you àn ex - am - ple,
to have you fol - low in hís foot-steps. 2. He did no wrong,
no de - ceit was found in hìs mouth. When he was
in - sult - ed, he re-turned nó in - sult. 3. When he was
made to suf - fer, he did not coun - tèr with threats.
In - stead he de - liv - ered him - self up to the
One who judg - és just - ly. 4. In his own bod - y
he brought your sins to the Cross, so that all

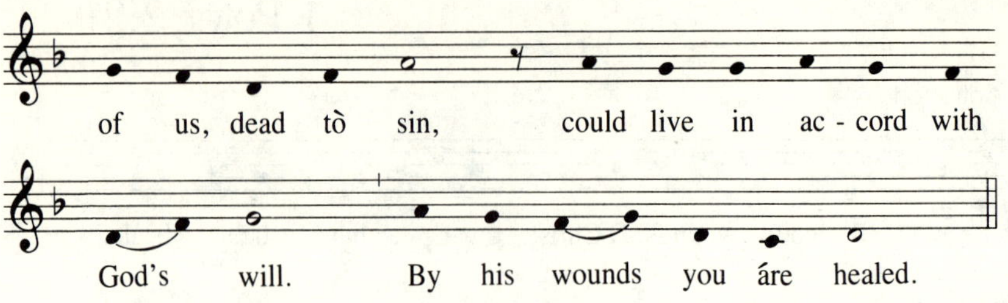
of us, dead tò sin, could live in ac - cord with
God's will. By his wounds you áre healed.

Revelation 4:11; 5:9, 10, 12 96

Antiphon

DCI
Wor - thy, wor - thy is the Lamb that was slain.

Psalm Tone

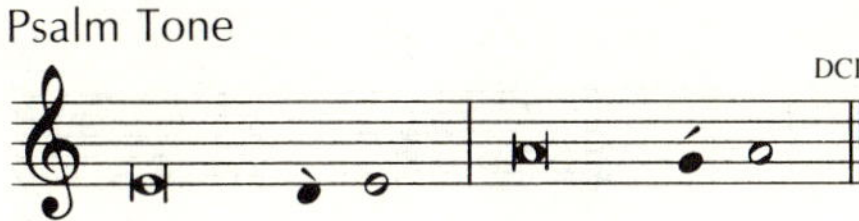
DCI

Dignus es

1. O Lord our God, you àre worthy
to receive glory and honor ánd power.

2. For you have created àll things;
by your will they came to be and wére made.

3. Worthy are you, Ò Lord,
to receive the scroll and break open íts seals.

4. For you wère slain;
with your blood you purchased fór God
men and women of every race ànd tongue,
of every people ánd nation.

5. You made of them a kingdom,
and priests to serve òur God,
and they shall reign on thé earth.

6. Worthy is the Lamb that wàs slain
to receive power ánd riches,
wisdom ànd strength,
honor and glory ánd praise.

7. Glory to the Father, and to thè Son,
and to the Holý Spirit:
as it was in the bèginning,
is now, and will be for ever. Ámen.

97 Revelation 11:17-18; 12:10b-12a

Antiphon

JJC
We praise you, O Lord, who is and who was.

Psalm Tone

JJC

Gratias agimus tibi

1. We praise you, the Lord Gòd Almighty,
who is ánd who was.
You have assumed yòur great power,
you have begún your reign.

2. The nations have ràged in anger,
but then came your day of wrath
and the moment to júdge the dead:
the time to reward your servants the prophets
and the holy ones whò revere you,
the great and smáll alike.

3. Now have salvation and pòwer come,
the reign of our God and the authority of hís Anointed One.
For the accuser of our brothers ìs cast out,
who night and day; accused them béfore God.

4. They defeated him by the blood òf the Lamb
and by the word of their téstimony;
love for life did not deter thèm from death.
So rejoice, you heavens, and you that dwéll therein!

Revelation 15:3-4 98

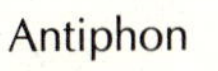
Antiphon

CW
Your works, O Lord, are might - y and won - der - ful.

Psalm Tone

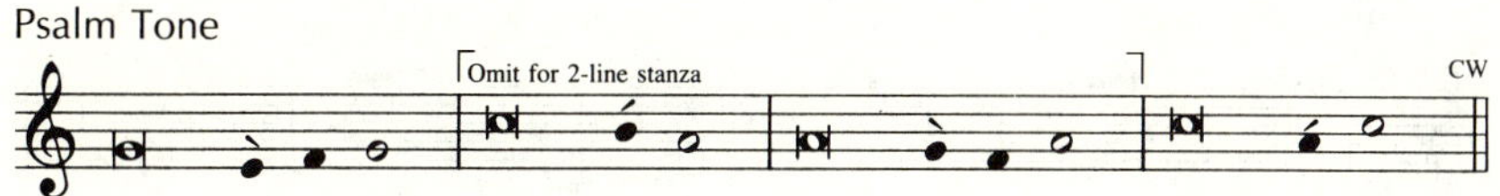
Omit for 2-line stanza
CW

Magna et mirabilia

1. Mighty and wonderful àre your works,
   Lord God álmighty!
   Righteous and true àre your ways,
   O King of thé nations!

2. Who would dare refùse you honor,
   or the glory due your name, Ó Lord?

3. Since you alòne are holy,
   all nations shåll come
   and worship ìn your presence.
   Your mighty deeds are clearlý seen.

4. Glory to the Father, and tò the Son,
   and to the Holý Spirit:
   as it was in thè beginning,
   is now, and will be for ever. Ámen.

99 Revelation 19:1-7

Antiphon
3
HH
All pow'r is yours, Lord God, our might - y King, al - le - lu - ia!

Refrain I
Al - le - lu - ia, al - le - lu - ia!

Verse
Refrain II
Al - le - lu - ia!

Verse
Refrain I
Al - le - lu - ia, al - le - lu - ia!

Salus, et gloria

1. Salvation, glory and pòwer to our Gód: (Alleluia!)
   his judgements are hònest and trúe. (Alleluia, alleluia!)

2. Sing praise to our God, àll you his sérvants, (Alleluia!)
   all who worship him reverently, greàt and smáll. (Alleluia, alleluia!)

3. The Lord our all-powerful Gòd is Kíng; (Alleluia!)
   let us rejoice, sing pràise, and give him glóry. (Alleluia, alleluia!)

4. The wedding feast of the Làmb has begún, (Alleluia!)
   and his bride is prepàred to wélcome him. (Alleluia, alleluia!)

5. Glory to the Father, and to the Sòn, and to the Holy Spírit, (Alleluia!)
   as it was in the beginning, is now, and will be for èver. Amén. (Alleluia, alleluia!)

Christian Initiation of Adults

The passage of an adult into the Christian community takes place over an extended period of time. The members of the local church, the catechists and sponsors, the clergy and the diocesan bishop take part in the journey from inquiry through the catechumenate to baptism, confirmation and eucharist. The candidates are invited by example to pray, reflect on the scriptures, to fast and to join in the community's practice of charity. They are to learn the way of Jesus from the members of the church. 100

This journey of the candidates and community is marked by liturgical rites; thus the community publicly acknowledges, encourages and strengthens the candidates. The first of these is the rite of becoming catechumens. It concludes the sometimes lengthy period during which those who have come to ask about the way of the church and the life of a Christian have heard the gospel proclaimed and seen it practiced. Those who then feel called to walk in this way of Christ's church ask to begin the journey toward baptism. If the church judges the inquirers ready, they are accepted into the order of catechumens (no. 101).

Those who have entered the catechumenate are already part of the household of Christ. During this time the catechumens are to hear and reflect on God's word, to learn the teachings and practices of the church, to become gradually accustomed to the ways of prayer and discipline in the church, to observe and to join in the good works of Christians. Ordinarily the catechumens are present on Sunday for the liturgy of the word but are dismissed after the homily–to continue prayer and study with their catechists–since they cannot join in the eucharist.

Rites of exorcism and blessing may be celebrated during the catechumenate. Through such rites the church prays that the catechumens will be purified, strengthened against all evil and thus eagerly grow in faith and good works. The very presence of the catechumens–at the Sunday liturgy, in these special rites and in everyday life–is itself a source of strength and blessing to the faithful.

Each year as Lent begins, the bishop, with the help of the local pastor and others involved with the catechumens, is to call those catechumens who are judged ready to prepare themselves for baptism at the Easter Vigil. Thus the catechumens become the "elect", the chosen, and for the forty days of Lent they make preparations: praying, fasting, doing good works. All the faithful join them in this. On several Sundays in Lent the rites of scrutiny take place when the assembled church prays over the elect. During Lent also the catechumens may publicly receive the words of the church's creed and of the Lord's Prayer. (The Rite of Election is found with the First Sunday of Lent, no. 787; the scrutiny rites are found with the Third, Fourth and Fifth Sundays of Lent, nos. 793, 796 and 799.)

Good Friday and Holy Saturday are days of prayer, fasting and preparation for the rites of the Easter Vigil. On the night between Saturday and Sunday, the church assembles to keep vigil and listen to many readings from scripture. Then the catechumens are called forward for baptism and confirmation. (These rites are found in the Easter Vigil, no. 818 and following.)

The newly baptized, now called neophytes, take a special place in the Sunday eucharist throughout the fifty days of Eastertime. This is a time for their full incorporation into the local community.

All of these stages of initiation take place in the midst of the community. In various rites, the faithful affirm their support for the catechumens. The daily lives of the faithful show the Christian life to the inquirers and catechumens. In turn, the faithful are strengthened and challenged in their faith by the presence of the catechumens.

Those who seek to belong to the Roman Catholic church and who are already baptized may take some part in the catechumenate but they are not baptized again. Rather, they are received into the full communion of the Roman Catholic Church.

101 ACCEPTANCE INTO THE ORDER OF CATECHUMENS

INTRODUCTORY RITES

The presider greets the assembly: candidates, sponsors, members of the parish. The candidates are asked what it is that they seek and each replies. Before or during this rite an appropriate psalm (for example, Psalm 63, no. 42) may be sung.

CANDIDATES' FIRST ACCEPTANCE OF THE GOSPEL

The presider solemnly asks if the candidates are ready to begin walking this way of the gospel. The sponsors and all present are asked if they stand ready to assist the candidates as they strive to know and follow Christ. All respond: **We are.**

SIGNING OF THE CANDIDATES WITH THE CROSS

The sign of the cross marks the candidates for their new way of life. The presider signs each on the forehead saying:

N., receive the cross on your forehead.
It is Christ himself who now strengthens you
with this sign of his love.
Learn now to know him and follow him.

Sponsors and others also sign the candidates. Ears and eyes and other senses may also be signed. The presider prays that the catechumens may share in the saving power of the cross.

INVITATION TO THE CELEBRATION OF THE WORD OF GOD

The assembly may go into the church for the liturgy of the word singing an appropriate psalm (for example, Psalm 34, no. 36).

LITURGY OF THE WORD 102

There may be one or more readings from scripture, together with a responsorial psalm. After the homily, a book containing the scriptures may be given to the new catechumens for their study and prayer throughout the time of the catechumenate.

INTERCESSIONS

All join in prayer for the new catechumens.

Cantor:
Assembly:
Byzantine Chant
(Intention) Let us pray to the Lord.
Lord, hear our prayer.

If the eucharist is to be celebrated, the catechumens are first dismissed.

RITES OF THE CATECHUMENATE 103

DISMISSAL OF THE CATECHUMENS

When the catechumens are present at Mass, they are usually dismissed after the homily. Only when they have been baptized are they able to join the faithful for the liturgy of the eucharist. After their dismissal, the catechumens remain together and are joined by their catechists or others to pray and reflect on the scripture.

CELEBRATIONS OF THE WORD OF GOD

On Sundays, after the catechetical sessions, before the liturgical seasons and at other times the catechumèns and others may join for liturgy: song, reading of scripture, psalmody, prayer and silence are normally part of such a service.

MINOR EXORCISMS

At appropriate times during the catechumenate, the catechists or other ministers may lead the community in prayers of exorcism over the catechumens. These prayers acknowledge the struggle against evil and ask that God strengthen the catechumens.

BLESSINGS OF THE CATECHUMENS

Prayers of blessing and the laying on of hands may take place whenever the catechumens gather for instruction or other purposes. Catechists or other ministers ask these blessings over the catechumens.

ANOINTINGS AND PRESENTATIONS

During the catechumenate or during Lent, the candidates may be anointed with the oil of catechumens as a sign of strength given for their struggle to live the gospel. At some point in this time they are publicly presented with the church's treasury of prayer and faith, the Our Father and the Creed.

RITE OF ELECTION OR ENROLLMENT OF NAMES

See the First Sunday of Lent, no. 787.

SCRUTINIES

See the Third, Fourth and Fifth Sundays of Lent, nos. 793, 796 and 799.

PREPARATORY RITES

See Holy Saturday, no. 817.

SACRAMENTS OF INITIATION

See the Easter Vigil, no. 818.

PERIOD OF MYSTAGOGIA

"Mystagogia" refers to the fifty-day period of postbaptismal celebration when the newly baptized are gradually drawn by the community into the fullness of Christian life and prayer. The newly baptized retain a special place in the assembly and are mentioned in the prayers of intercession. A special celebration, on Pentecost or just before, may mark the conclusion of the whole period of initiation.

The Baptism of Children

Children are baptized in the faith of the church: of parents, godparents, the local parish, the church throughout the world, the saints. Bringing their children for baptism, the parents profess their commitment to make a home where the gospel is lived. And the godparents and all members of the community promise to support the parents in this. Thus the children enter the waters of baptism and so are joined to this people, all baptized into the death and resurrection of Christ. 104

Baptism is celebrated above all at the Easter Vigil, but also on other Sundays, for Sunday is the Lord's day, the day when the church gathers to proclaim the paschal mystery. Baptism may take place at the Sunday Mass and is always to be celebrated in an assembly of members of the church.

RECEPTION OF THE CHILDREN 105

The parents and godparents are welcomed by all. The presider asks the names of the children and questions the parents about their own expectations and willingness to take on the responsibilities this baptism brings. The godparents are asked if they are ready to assist the parents to become Christian mothers and fathers.

With joy, then, the presider, the parents and godparents make the sign of the cross on the child's forehead: "I claim you for Christ our Savior by the sign of his cross."

All then go in procession to the place where the scriptures will be read. The following antiphon, or a hymn, may be sung during this procession.

Calvin Hampton, 1984
Acc. by Chris De Blasio, 1985

Cantor:
Assembly:
There is one God, one Fa-ther of all. There is
Cantor:
one God, one Fa-ther of all. He is o-ver all, and

Assembly:
through all, he lives in all of us. There is one God, one
Fa-ther of all.
Cantor:
All of us are one, u-nit-ed in Christ
Je-sus.
Assembly:
There is one God, one Fa-ther of all.

106 LITURGY OF THE WORD

FIRST READINGS

One or more passages from scripture are read. At the conclusion of each:

Reader: This is the Word of the Lord.

Assembly: **Thanks be to God.**

RESPONSORIAL PSALM

The following psalm (or another from nos. 179 to 182) may follow the first reading.

Ps. (26)27, 1.4.8-9.13-14 / 759-2

RP
The Lord is my light and my sal-va-tion.

The Lord is my light and my help;
whom shall I fear?
The Lord is the stronghold my life;
before whom shall I shrink? ℟.

There is one thing I ask of the Lord,
for this I long,
to live in the house of the Lord,
all the days of my life,
to savor the sweetness of the Lord,
to behold his temple. ℟.

It is your face, O Lord, that I seek;
hide not your face.
Dismiss not your servant in anger;
you have been my help.
Do not abandon or forsake me,
O God my help! ℟.

I am sure I shall see the Lord's goodness
in the land of the living.
Hope in him, hold firm and take heart.
Hope in the Lord! ℟.

GOSPEL 107

Before the gospel reading, this acclamation is sung:

Cantor, then all:
Chant Mode VI
Al - le - lu - ia, al - le - lu - ia, al - le - lu - ia,

During Lent:

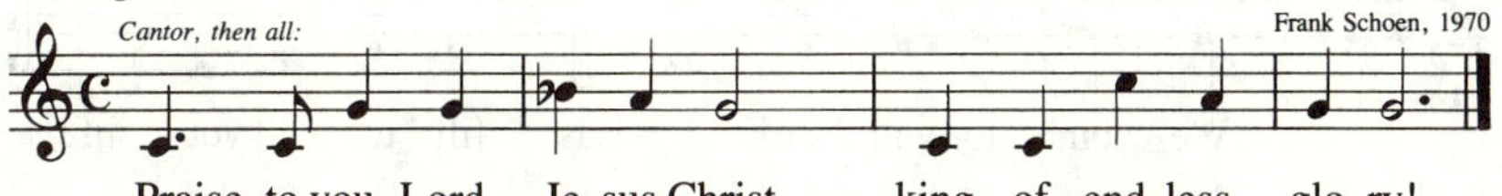
Cantor, then all:
Frank Schoen, 1970
Praise to you, Lord Je-sus Christ, king of end-less glo-ry!

Deacon (or priest): The Lord be with you.

Assembly: **And also with you.**

Deacon: A reading from the holy gospel according to N.

Assembly: **Glory to you, Lord.**

After the reading:

Deacon: This is the gospel of the Lord.

Assembly: **Praise to you, Lord Jesus Christ.**

GENERAL INTERCESSIONS 108

All join in prayer for the church, the needs of the world, the poor, the children to be baptized and their parents.

Cantor:
Assembly:
Byzantine Chant
(Intention) Let us pray to the Lord. Lord, hear our prayer.

This prayer concludes with the litany of the saints which may include the patron saints of the children and of the local church. 109

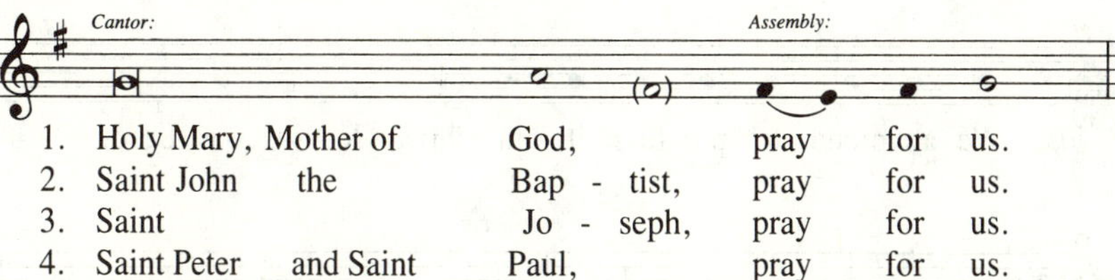
Cantor:
Assembly:
1. Holy Mary, Mother of God, pray for us.
2. Saint John the Bap - tist, pray for us.
3. Saint Jo - seph, pray for us.
4. Saint Peter and Saint Paul, pray for us.

The names of other saints may be added here. The litany concludes:

5. All you saints of God, pray for us.

110 **PRAYER OF EXORCISM AND ANOINTING**

The presider stands before the parents with their infants and prays that God deliver these children from the power of evil. The children may be anointed with the oil of catechumens, an anointing which makes them strong for their struggle against evil in their lives. The presider lays hands on each child to show the love and concern the Church has for them. If there is a procession to the baptistry, the following may be sung.

Cantor, then all:
Ronald Arnatt, 1984
We come to you, Lord Je - sus, fill us with your life.

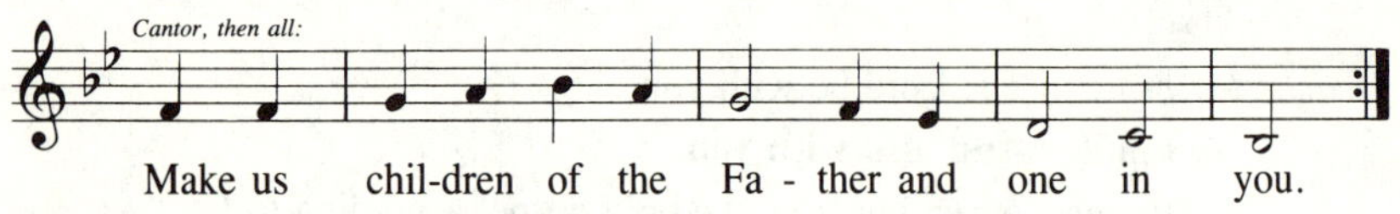
Cantor, then all:
Make us chil-dren of the Fa - ther and one in you.

111 SACRAMENT OF BAPTISM

BLESSING AND INVOCATION OF GOD OVER BAPTISMAL WATER

When all are gathered at the font, the presider leads a blessing of the water, unless the baptismal water has already been blessed.

RENUNCIATION OF SIN AND PROFESSION OF FAITH

The presider then questions the parents and godparents, and they make a renunciation of sin and evil and profess their faith. The assembly listens to their responses. The presider then invites all to give their assent to this profession of faith:

Presider:
This is our faith. This is the faith of the Church.

We are proud to pro-fess it, in Christ Je - sus our Lord.

All:
Danish
A - men, a - men, a - men.

BAPTISM 112

One by one, the infants are brought to the font by their parents. There the parents express their desire to have their child baptized in the faith of the church which they have professed. The infant is then immersed in the water three times (or water is poured over the infant's head three times) as the presider says: "N., I baptize you in the name of the Father, and of the Son, and of the Holy Spirit." All may respond to each baptism with an acclamation.

Howard Hughes, SM, 1977

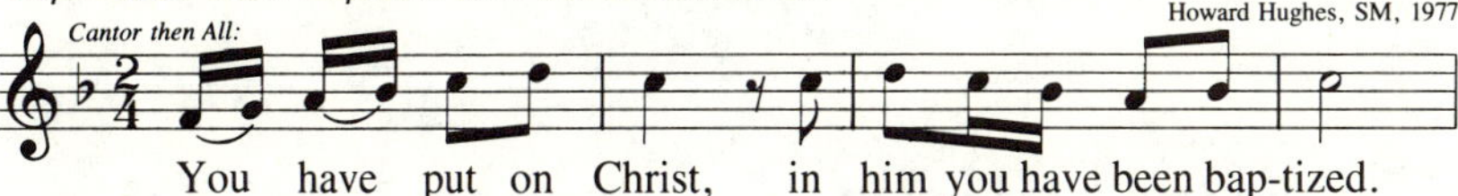
Cantor then All:
You have put on Christ, in him you have been bap-tized.

Al - le - lu - ia, al - le - lu - ia.

ANOINTING WITH CHRISM 113

The presider anoints each child on the crown of the head with holy chrism, a mixture of oil and perfume. The word "Christ" means "anointed." The baptized child has been "Christ-ed" and the sweet smell of the anointing reminds all of this.

CLOTHING WITH THE BAPTISMAL GARMENT AND GIVING OF THE CANDLE

The infants are then clothed in baptismal garments and a candle for each of the newly baptized is lighted from the paschal candle.

Optional *The presider may touch the ears and mouth of each child: "May Jesus soon touch your ears to receive his word, and your mouth to proclaim his faith."*

CONCLUSION AND BLESSING

If baptism is celebrated at Mass, the liturgy continues with the eucharist. Otherwise, all process to the altar, carrying lighted candles. The above acclamation may be sung again during this procession. All then pray the Lord's Prayer, the parents are blessed and the liturgy concludes with a hymn of praise and thanksgiving.

Confirmation

114 Confirmation is a sacrament of initiation. With baptism and eucharist, confirmation climaxes the making of a Christian. It is the seal of baptism, the giving of the Holy Spirit. Adults are confirmed immediately after their baptism at the Easter Vigil. Children who have been baptized as infants are often confirmed some years later. The presider is the bishop or his delegate. The rite is usually celebrated within Mass; the introductory rites are done in the usual way.

115 LITURGY OF THE WORD

FIRST READINGS

One or more passages from scripture are read. At the conclusion of each:

Reader: This is the Word of the Lord.

Assembly: **Thanks be to God.**

RESPONSORIAL PSALM

The following psalm (or another from nos. 183 to 186) may follow the first reading.

Ps. (103)104, 1.24.27-28.30-31.33-34 / 765-4

RP

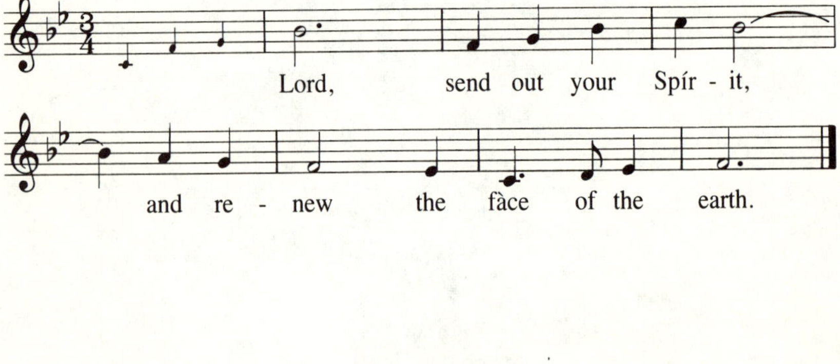

Lord, send out your Spír - it,

and re - new the fàce of the earth.

Bless the Lord, my soul!
Lord God, how great you are.
How many are your works, O Lord!
In wisdom you have made them all.
The earth is full of your riches. ℟.

All of these look to you
to give them their food in due
season.
You give it, they gather it up;
you open your hand, they have their
fill. ℟.

You send forth your spirit, they are
created;
and you renew the face of the earth.
May the glory of the Lord last for
ever!
May the Lord rejoice in his
works! ℟.

I will sing to the Lord all my life,
make music to my God while I live.
May my thoughts be pleasing to him.
I find my joy in the Lord. ℟.

GOSPEL 116

Before the gospel reading, this acclamation is sung:

Cantor, then all:
Chant Mode VI
Al - le - lu - ia, al - le - lu - ia, al - le - lu - ia.

During Lent:

Cantor, then all:
Frank Schoen, 1970
Praise to you, Lord Je-sus Christ, king of end-less glo-ry!

Deacon (or priest): The Lord be with you.
Assembly: **And also with you.**
Deacon: A reading from the holy gospel according to N.
Assembly: **Glory to you, Lord.**

After the reading:

Deacon: This is the gospel of the Lord.
Assembly: **Praise to you, Lord Jesus Christ.**

SACRAMENT OF CONFIRMATION 117

PRESENTATION OF THE CANDIDATES

The pastor or another minister calls the candidates by name to come forward. Sponsors may accompany candidates.

HOMILY

RENEWAL OF BAPTISMAL PROMISES

The bishop leads the candidates in the renunciation of sin and evil and the profession of their faith. When the candidates have responded, the bishop proclaims:

Bishop:
This is our faith. This is the faith of the Church.
We are proud to pro-fess it, in Christ Je-sus our Lord.
All:
A-men, a-men, a-men.
Danish

118 **LAYING ON OF HANDS**

Over and over the church makes this gesture in the sacraments as a blessing, a sign of solidarity and of love. Here the bishop prays for the coming of the Holy Spirit on those confirmed.

ANOINTING WITH CHRISM

Chrism is a mixture of oil and perfume that has been blessed by the bishop at the end of Lent. The meaning of "Christ" is "the anointed," so in this gesture the candidate is anointed, sealed, to follow in the way of Christ. The bishop rubs the chrism into the forehead of each candidate and says: "N., be sealed with the gift of the Holy Spirit," and the newly confirmed person responds: "Amen." The bishop then says, "Peace be with you," and the newly confirmed person responds, "And also with you." The assembly may join in song during the anointing.

After the anointing, the liturgy continues with the intercessions and the liturgy of the eucharist. If confirmation is celebrated apart from Mass, the intercessions are followed by the Lord's Prayer (see nos. 246, 331 and 332), the blessing, and the concluding hymn.

Holy Communion Outside Mass

When for good reason communion cannot be received at Mass, the faithful may share in the paschal mystery through the liturgy of the word and the reception of holy communion. 119

INTRODUCTORY RITES

An appropriate hymn or psalm may be sung.

GREETING 120

If the minister is a priest or deacon, the usual form of greeting is used:

Assembly: **And also with you.**

If the minister is not a priest or deacon, another form of greeting may be used:

Assembly: **Blessed be God forever.**

PENITENTIAL RITE

The minister invites silent reflection and repentance. After some silence:

Assembly: **I confess to almighty God,**
and to you, my brothers and sisters,
that I have sinned through my own fault
in my thoughts and in my words,
in what I have done,
and in what I have failed to do;
and I ask blessed Mary, ever virgin,
all the angels and saints,
and you, my brothers and sisters,
to pray for me to the Lord our God.

The forms found at no. 231 may also be used.

121 CELEBRATION OF THE WORD OF GOD

FIRST READINGS

One or more passages from scripture are read. At the conclusion of each:

Reader: This is the Word of the Lord.

Assembly: **Thanks be to God.**

RESPONSORIAL PSALM

The following psalm (or another appropriate psalm) may follow the first reading.

Psalm (33)34, 2-3.4-5.6-7.8-9

RP
Taste and see the good - ness of the Lord.

I will bless the Lord at all times,
his praise always on my lips;
in the Lord my soul shall make its boast.
The humble shall hear and be glad. ℟.

Glorify the Lord with me,
together let us praise his name.
I sought the Lord and he answered me;
from all my terrors he set me free. ℟.

Look towards him and be radiant;
let your faces not be abashed.
This poor man called; the Lord heard him
and rescued him from all his distress. ℟.

The angel of the Lord is encamped
around those who revere him, to rescue them.
Taste and see that the Lord is good.
He is happy who seeks refuge in him. ℟.

122 GOSPEL

Before the gospel reading, this acclamation is sung:

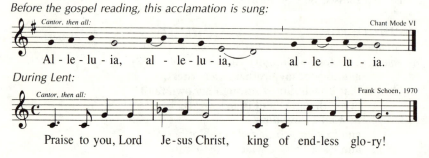

Cantor, then all:
Chant Mode VI
Al - le - lu - ia, al - le - lu - ia, al - le - lu - ia.

During Lent:

Frank Schoen, 1970

Cantor, then all:

Praise to you, Lord Je-sus Christ, king of end-less glo-ry!

Reader: The Lord be with you.

Assembly: **And also with you.**

Reader: A reading from the holy gospel according to N.

Assembly: **Glory to you, Lord.**

After the reading:

Reader: This is the gospel of the Lord.

Assembly: **Praise to you, Lord Jesus Christ.**

GENERAL INTERCESSIONS 123

The assembly joins in prayer for the needs of the world, of the poor and of the church.

Cantor:
Assembly:
Byzantine Chant
(Intention) Let us pray to the Lord. Lord, hear our prayer.

HOLY COMMUNION 124

The minister invites all to join in the Lord's Prayer, then to exchange a sign of peace. The minister then raises the Bread and all respond to the invitation.

Assembly: **Lord, I am not worthy to receive you,**
but only say the word and I shall be healed.

A psalm or hymn may be sung during communion. Afterwards, there may be a period of silence or the singing of a psalm or hymn. The minister then recites a concluding prayer.

CONCLUDING RITE

All are blessed and dismissed.

Minister: Go in the peace of Christ.

Assembly: **Thanks be to God.**

Reconciliation of Several Penitents

125 The sacrament of penance, also called the sacrament of reconciliation, may be celebrated with one penitent or with many. The latter form, the communal penance service, is a gathering of a few or a large number of Christians. Together they listen to the scriptures, sing psalms and hymns, pray, individually confess their sins and receive absolution, then praise God whose mercy and love are greater than our evil. In the rite of penance, the members of the church confront the struggle that was entered at baptism. There has been failure, evil done and good undone, but the penitent church comes again and again to name and renounce its sins and to return to the way of the Lord.

INTRODUCTORY RITES

An appropriate hymn or psalm may be sung.

126 **GREETING**

The presider and people greet each other in these or other words:

Presider: Grace, mercy, and peace be with you from God the Father and Christ Jesus our Savior.

Assembly: **And also with you.**

OPENING PRAYER

After silent prayer, the presider concludes the gathering rite with a solemn prayer.

127 CELEBRATION OF THE WORD OF GOD

FIRST READINGS

One or more passages from scripture are read. At the conclusion of each:

Reader: This is the Word of the Lord.

Assembly: **Thanks be to God.**

RESPONSORIAL PSALM

The following psalm (or another from nos. 206 through 213) may follow the first reading.

Psalm (50)51, 3-4.5-6.12-13.14-15

HH
Give back to me the joy of your sal - va - tion.

Have mercy on me, God, in your
 kindness.
In your compassion blot out my
 offense.
O wash me more and more from my
 guilt
and cleanse me from my sin. ℟.

My offenses truly I know them;
my sin is always before me.
Against you, you alone, have I
 sinned;
what is evil in your sight I have
 done. ℟.

A pure heart create for me, O God,
Put a steadfast spirit within me.
Do not cast me away from your
 presence,
nor deprive me of your holy
 spirit. ℟.

Give me again the joy of your hélp;
with a spirit of fervor sustain me,
that I may teach transgressors your
 ways
and sinners may return to you. ℟.

GOSPEL 128

Before the gospel reading, this acclamation is sung:

Cantor, then all:
Chant Mode VI
Al - le - lu - ia, al - le - lu - ia, al - le - lu - ia.

During Lent:

Cantor, then all:
Frank Schoen, 1970
Praise to you, Lord Je-sus Christ, king of end-less glo-ry!

Deacon (or priest): The Lord be with you.
Assembly: **And also with you.**
Deacon: A reading from the holy gospel according to N.
Assembly: **Glory to you, Lord.**

After the reading:

Deacon: This is the gospel of the Lord.
Assembly: **Praise to you, Lord Jesus Christ.**

HOMILY

EXAMINATION OF CONSCIENCE

In silence or through some other manner all reflect on their lives with sorrow for their sins.

129 SACRAMENT OF PENANCE

GENERAL CONFESSION OF SINS

Kneeling (or with another posture that expresses sorrow,) all join in confession. This form may be used:

I confess to almighty God,
and to you, my brothers and sisters,
that I have sinned through my own fault
in my thoughts and in my words,
in what I have done,
and in what I have failed to do;
and I ask blessed Mary, ever virgin,
all the angels and saints,
and you, my brothers and sisters,
to pray for me to the Lord our God.

130 *Standing, all join in a litany using one of the following responses, or a song asking God's mercy. The Lord's Prayer is then recited or sung (see nos. 246, 331 and 332).*

A **We pray you, hear us.**

B **Lord, be merciful to me, a sinner.**

C **Lord, have mercy.**

131 INDIVIDUAL CONFESSION AND ABSOLUTION

One by one the penitents approach the priest confessors. All confess their sins, accept some fitting act of satisfaction and the counsel of the confessor. Then the priest extends his hands over the penitent's head and speaks the prayer of absolution, concluding: "Through the ministry of the Church may God give you pardon and peace, and I absolve you from your sins in the name of the Father, and of the Son, and of the Holy Spirit." The penitent responds, "Amen." (Note: On those occasions when general absolution is permitted, the rest of the rite remains the same.)

PROCLAMATION OF PRAISE FOR GOD'S MERCY 132

The presider invites all to give thanks and to show by their lives—and in the life of the whole community—the grace of repentance. A psalm, canticle or hymn may be sung to proclaim God's mercy.

Isaiah 12:1-6
RJB

Praise the Lord and call up-on his name.

I thank you, Lord, you were angry with me
but your anger has passed and you give me comfort. ℟.

Truly, God is my salvation,
I trust, I shall not fear.
For the Lord is my strength, my song,
he became my savior.
With joy you will draw water
from the wells of salvation. ℟.

Give thanks to the Lord, give praise to his name!
Make his mighty deeds known to the peoples!
Declare the greatness of his name,
sing a psalm to the Lord!
For he has done glorious deeds,
make them known to all the earth! ℟.

People of Zion, sing and shout for joy
for great in your midst is the Holy One of Israel. ℟.

CONCLUDING PRAYER OF THANKSGIVING 133

This prayer is spoken by the presider.

BLESSING AND DISMISSAL

The presider blesses all present and the deacon or other minister dismisses the assembly. All respond:

Thanks be to God.

Marriage

134 Many rituals of various kinds and origins surround a wedding. These rites of preparation and of celebration are ways for the couple, the families and friends to share in and to strengthen the making of a marriage. The marriage rite itself is the covenant made by bride and groom, the consent each gives to and accepts from each other. The church assembles to witness and bless this union.

INTRODUCTORY RITES

PROCESSION

The ministers, including bride and groom, enter in procession to appropriate music.

135 **GREETING**

Presider: In the name of the Father, and of the Son, and of the Holy Spirit.

Assembly: **Amen.**

A

Presider: The grace of our Lord Jesus Christ and the love of God and the fellowship of the Holy Spirit be with you all.

Assembly: **And also with you.**

B

Presider: The grace and peace of God our Father and the Lord Jesus Christ be with you.

Assembly: **Blessed be God, the Father of our Lord Jesus Christ.**
or: **And also with you.**

C

Presider: The Lord be with you. *(Bishop:* Peace be with you.)

Assembly: **And also with you.**

PENITENTIAL RITE 136

The presider invites the people to recall their sins in silence and repent of them. After the silence, one of the following forms is used.

A *Assembly:* **I confess to almighty God,**
and to you my brothers and sisters,
that I have sinned through my own fault
in my thoughts and in my words,
in what I have done,
and in what I have failed to do;
and I ask blessed Mary, ever virgin,
all the angels and saints,
and you, my brothers and sisters,
to pray for me to the Lord our God.

B *Presider:* Lord, we have sinned against you:
Lord, have mercy.

Assembly: **Lord, have mercy.**

Presider: Lord, show us your mercy and love.

Assembly: **And grant us your salvation.**

C *The presider or another minister makes a series of invocations according to the following pattern.*

Presider (or other minister):
Assembly:
Richard Proulx, 1970
(Invocation) Lord, have mer - cy. Lord, have mer - cy.
Presider:
Assembly:
(Invocation) Christ, have mer - cy. Christ, have mer - cy.
Presider:
Assembly:
(Invocation) Lord, have mer - cy. Lord, have mer - cy.

The penitential rite always concludes:

Presider: May almighty God have mercy on us, forgive us our sins, and bring us to everlasting life.

Assembly: **Amen.**

KYRIE 137

Unless form C of the penitential rite has been used, the Kyrie follows. The people repeat each invocation after the presider or other minister.

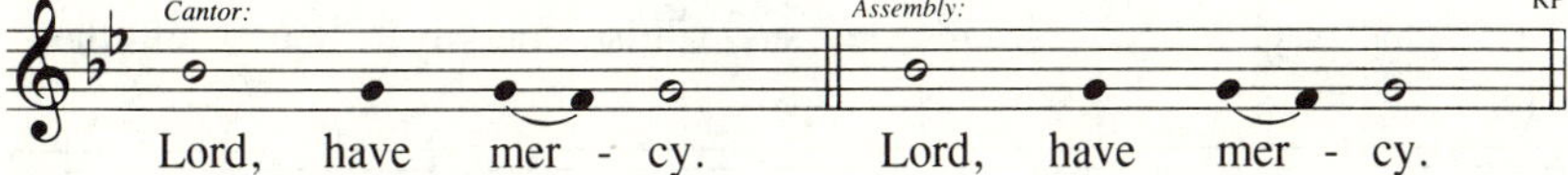
Cantor:
Assembly:
RP
Lord, have mer - cy. Lord, have mer - cy.

Cantor:
Christ, have mer - cy.
Assembly:
Christ, have mer - cy.
Cantor:
Lord, have mer - cy.
Assembly:
Lord, have mer - cy.

Or:

138

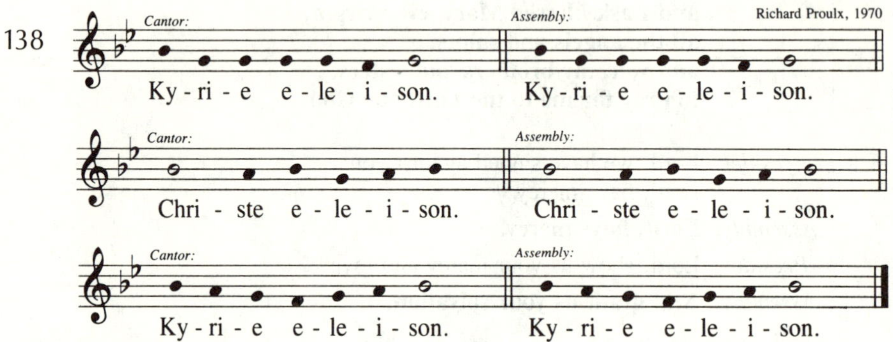
Richard Proulx, 1970
Cantor:
Ky - ri - e e - le - i - son.
Assembly:
Ky - ri - e e - le - i - son.
Cantor:
Chri - ste e - le - i - son.
Assembly:
Chri - ste e - le - i - son.
Cantor:
Ky - ri - e e - le - i - son.
Assembly:
Ky - ri - e e - le - i - son.

139 **GLORIA**

The Gloria is omitted during Advent and Lent.

"A New Mass for Congregations"
Carroll Thomas Andrews, 1970

mf

Glo - ry to God in the high - est, and

peace to his peo - ple on earth. Lord God,

heav - en - ly King, *f* al - might - y God and Fa - ther, we

wor - ship you, we give you thanks, we praise you for your

glo - ry. *mf* Lord Je - sus Christ, on - ly Son of the

Fa - ther, Lord God, Lamb of God, you take a - way the

sin of the world: have mer - cy on us;
you are seat - ed at the right hand of the Fa - ther:
re - ceive our prayer.
Tempo primo
f
For you a-lone are the Ho - ly One, you a - lone are the
Lord, you a - lone are the Most High,
Je - sus Christ, with the Ho - ly Spir - it, in the glo - ry of
ff
God the Fa - ther. A - men.

OPENING PRAYER 140

The gathering rites conclude with a silent prayer and a prayer spoken by the presider.

LITURGY OF THE WORD 141

FIRST READINGS

One or more passages from scriptures are read. At the conclusion of each:

Reader: This is the Word of the Lord.

Assembly: **Thanks be to God.**

RESPONSORIAL PSALM

The following psalm (or another from nos. 187 through 192) may follow the first reading.

Psalm (32)33, 12.18.20.21.22 / 776-1
JRC
Cantor, then all:
The earth is full of the good-ness, the good-ness of the Lord.

They are happy, whose God is the
 Lord,
the people he has chosen as his own.
The Lord looks on those who revere
 him,
on those who hope in his love. ℞.

Our soul is waiting for the Lord.
The Lord is our help and our shield.
In him do our hearts find joy.
We trust in his holy name. ℞.

May your love be upon us, O Lord,
as we place all our hope in you. ℞.

142 **GOSPEL**

Before the gospel reading, this acclamation is sung:

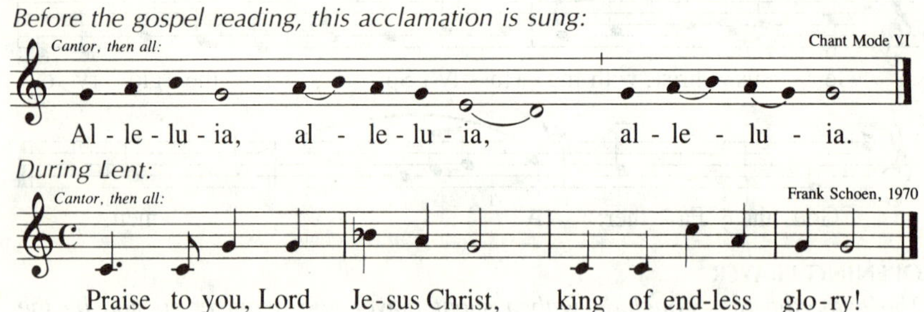
Cantor, then all:
Chant Mode VI
Al-le-lu-ia, al-le-lu-ia, al-le-lu-ia.
During Lent:
Cantor, then all:
Frank Schoen, 1970
Praise to you, Lord Je-sus Christ, king of end-less glo-ry!

Deacon (or priest): The Lord be with you.

Assembly: **And also with you.**

Deacon: A reading from the holy gospel according to N.

Assembly: **Glory to you, Lord.**

After the reading:

Deacon: This is the gospel of the Lord.

Assembly: **Praise to you, Lord Jesus Christ.**

HOMILY

143 SACRAMENT OF MARRIAGE

The presider invites the couple to give their consent to each other freely in the presence of the church. When they have done so, the presider receives their consent in the name of the church. The wedding rings, a sign of love and fidelity, are then blessed and exchanged.

GENERAL INTERCESSIONS 144

The church joins in prayer for the needs of the world, for the poor, for the community and for the couple.

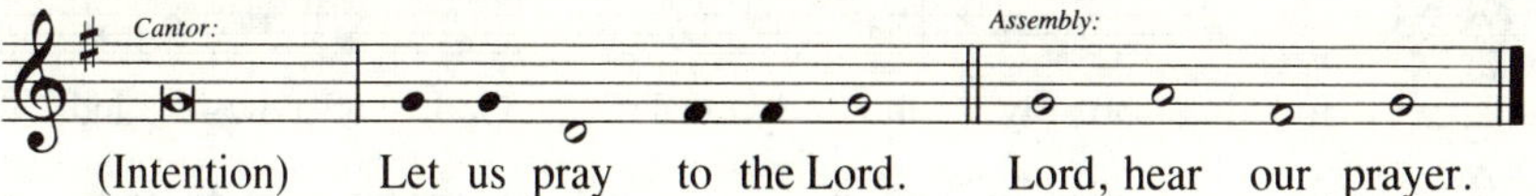
Cantor:
Assembly:
(Intention) Let us pray to the Lord. Lord, hear our prayer.

LITURGY OF THE EUCHARIST 145

PREPARATION OF THE GIFTS

Bread and wine are brought to the table. If there is no music, all may respond to the prayers of preparation:

Assembly: **Blessed be God for ever.**

The preparation concludes with the priest inviting all to pray:

Assembly: **May the Lord accept the sacrifice at your hands**
for the praise and glory of his name,
for our good, and the good of all his church.

EUCHARISTIC PRAYER 146

The presider invites the assembly to join in giving thanks and praise to God for the wonders of creation and the works of salvation.

Presider:
Assembly:
Sacramentary, 1974
The Lord be with you. And al - so with you.
Presider:
Assembly:
Lift up your hearts. We lift them up to the Lord.
Presider:
Let us give thanks to the Lord our God.
Assembly:
It is right to give him thanks and praise.

During the eucharistic prayer, the assembly sings acclamations of praise and thanksgiving. The first is the "Sanctus":

"A Community Mass"
Richard Proulx, 1970

147 *mf*

Ho - ly, ho - ly, ho - ly Lord, God of pow - er and
might, heav'n and earth are full of your
glo - ry. Ho - san na in the high-est, ho - san - na in the
high-est. Blest is he who comes in the
name of the Lord. Ho - san - na in the
high-est, ho - san - na in the high - est.

The second is the response to the invitation, "Let us proclaim the mystery of faith":

"A Community Mass"
Richard Proulx, 1970

148

f
Christ has died, Christ is
ris - en, Christ will come a - gain.

Finally, the assembly ratifies the entire eucharistic prayer.

149 *Presider:* Through him, with him, in him, in the unity of the Holy Spirit, all glory and honor is yours, almighty Father, for ever and ever.

Danish

All:
A - men, a - men, a - men.

150 **COMMUNION RITE**

The presider invites the assembly to join in the Lord's Prayer.

Robert Snow, 1964
Acc. by Gerard Farrell, OSB, 1984

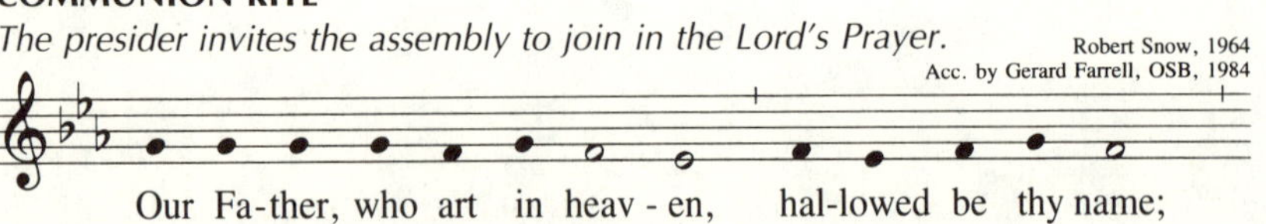
Our Fa-ther, who art in heav - en, hal-lowed be thy name;

thy king-dom come; thy will be done on earth as it
is in heav - en. Give us this day our dai - ly bread;
and for-give us our tres-pass-es as we for-give
those who tres-pass a - gainst us; and lead us not into temp - ta - tion, but de - liv - er us from e - vil.

In the nuptial blessing, the presider prays that God will surround this couple with love, with peace, with the strength to be faithful to one another and to be an example of kindness to all. After the blessing, all are invited to exchange a sign of peace. 151

Presider:
The peace of the Lord be with you al-ways.
Assembly:
And al - so with you.

As the bread is broken to be shared in communion, the assembly joins in singing the "Lamb of God." 152

Agnus Dei XVIII
Acc. by Gerard Farrell, OSB, 1984

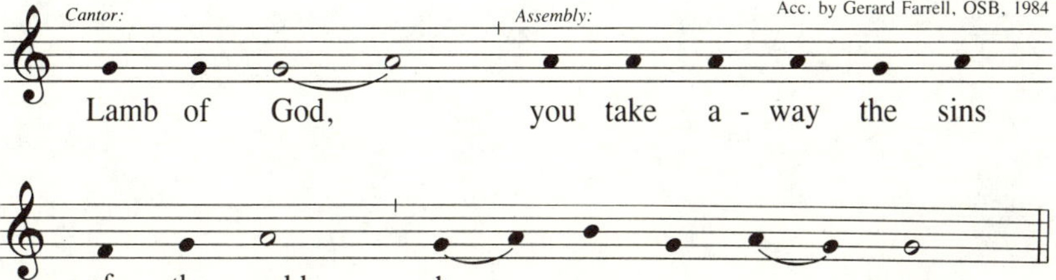
Cantor:
Lamb of God,
Assembly:
you take a - way the sins
of the world: have mer - cy on us.

This is sung two or more times. When the bread has been prepared, the "Lamb of God" concludes:

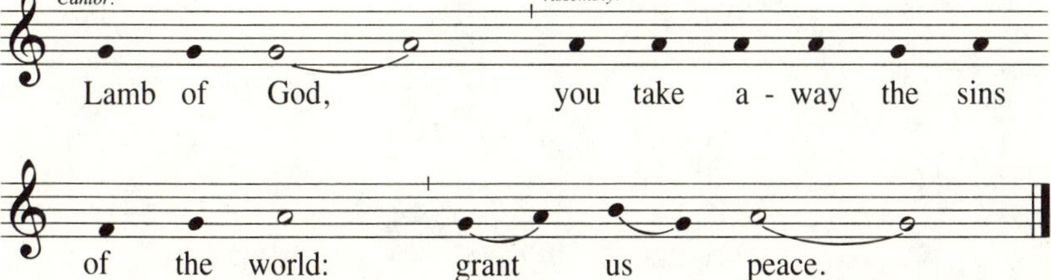
Cantor:
Lamb of God,
Assembly:
you take a - way the sins
of the world: grant us peace.

153 *The presider invites the assembly to share holy communion.*

Assembly: **Lord, I am not worthy to receive you,
but only say the word and I shall be healed.**

After communion there is a time of silence which is concluded with a prayer spoken by the presider.

154 CONCLUDING RITE

Presider: The Lord be with you.

Assembly: **And also with you.**

BLESSING

First the couple, then the whole assembly is blessed.

DISMISSAL

Deacon (or presider):
Assembly:

Go in the peace of Christ.
or: The Mass is end - ed, go in peace. Thanks be to God.
or: Go in peace to love and serve the Lord.

The liturgy may conclude with an appropriate song or instrumental music.

[When the rite of marriage is celebrated apart from Mass, all of the above may be used but the "Liturgy of the Eucharist" is omitted. After the prayers of intercession, the nuptial blessing is given. The rite concludes with the Lord's Prayer (no. 150) and the blessing of the couple and the assembly.]

Anointing of the Sick

The sacrament of anointing is celebrated when a Christian's health is seriously impaired by sickness or old age. If possible, it is celebrated when the sick person is able to take part in the rite. When the sick person is able to receive holy communion, the rite of anointing may be celebrated within the liturgy of the Mass. 155

Through the anointing with the blessed oil of the sick, the church supports those who struggle against illness or injury and continues the healing work of Christ. The anointing is intended to bring hope and comfort to the one anointed and, to the gathered family and friends, a spirit of support and sharing in the sufferings of our brothers and sisters.

The Mass begins in the usual way, but after the greeting the presider welcomes the sick.

LITURGY OF THE WORD 156

FIRST READINGS

One or more passages from scripture are read. At the conclusion of each:

Reader: This is the Word of the Lord.

Assembly: **Thanks be to God.**

RESPONSORIAL PSALM

The following psalm (or another from nos. 214 through 228) may follow the first reading.

Ps.(70)71, 1-2.5-6.8-9.14-15
HH
My God, come quick - ly to help me.

In you, O Lord, I take refuge;
let me never be put to shame.
In your justice rescue me, free me;
pay heed to me and save me. ℟.

It is you, O Lord, who are my hope,
my trust, O Lord, since my youth.
On you I have leaned from my birth,
from my mother's womb you have been my help.
My hope has always been in you. ℟.

My lips are filled with your praise,
with your glory all the day long.
Do not reject me now that I am old;
When my strength fails do not forsake me. ℟.

But as for me, I will always hope
and praise you more and more.
My lips will tell of your justice
and day by day of your help. ℟.

157 GOSPEL

Before the gospel reading, this acclamation is sung:

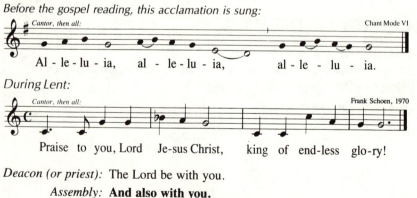

Cantor, then all:
Chant Mode VI
Al - le - lu - ia, al - le - lu - ia, al - le - lu - ia.

During Lent:

Cantor, then all:
Frank Schoen, 1970
Praise to you, Lord Je-sus Christ, king of end-less glo-ry!

Deacon (or priest): The Lord be with you.
Assembly: **And also with you.**
Deacon: A reading from the holy gospel according to N.
Assembly: **Glory to you, Lord.**

After the reading:

Deacon: This is the gospel of the Lord.
Assembly: **Praise to you, Lord Jesus Christ.**

HOMILY

LITURGY OF ANOINTING 158

LITANY

The assembly joins in prayers for the sick and for those who care for them.

Cantor:
Assembly:
Byzantine Chant
(Intention) Let us pray to the Lord. Lord, hear our prayer.

LAYING ON OF HANDS

The presider silently lays hands on the head of each sick person in a gesture of prayer, healing and solidarity.

PRAYER OVER THE OIL

If the oil is already blessed, the presider leads a prayer of thanksgiving over it. After each prayer:

Assembly: **Blessed be God who heals us in Christ.**

If the oil is not blessed, the presider leads the prayer of blessing.

ANOINTING

The presider anoints each sick person on the forehead in a sign of strength and soothing comfort.

Presider: Through this holy anointing may the Lord in his love and mercy help you with the grace of the Holy Spirit.

Assembly: **Amen.**

The presider anoints the hands of each sick person.

Presider: May the Lord who frees you from sin save you and raise you up.

Assembly: **Amen.**

The presider may anoint other parts of the body.

PRAYER AFTER ANOINTING 159

The presider prays for those who have been anointed. Then the liturgy of the eucharist is celebrated with special prayers for the sick.

[If the rite of anointing is celebrated outside of Mass, the liturgy begins with the greeting, rite of sprinkling and penitential rite. After the scriptures and homily, the liturgy of anointing is celebrated as above. Then the Lord's Prayer is recited or sung and the rite may conclude with holy communion.]

Funeral Mass

160 The rites which surround the death of a Christian extend from the Viaticum (last communion) and final prayers before death through the wake service and funeral Mass to the burial of the body or ashes. In all of this the community affirms its faith in the communion of saints and the resurrection of the dead. The family and friends are helped in their time of sorrow with prayer and song. Thus they express present grief even as they hold to the church's lasting hope. Following is the rite of the funeral Mass.

INTRODUCTORY RITES

GREETING

One of the following is spoken.

A

Presider: The grace of our Lord Jesus Christ and the love of God and the fellowship of the Holy Spirit be with you all.

Assembly: **And also with you.**

B

Presider: The grace and peace of God our Father and the Lord Jesus Christ be with you.

Assembly: **And also with you.**

C

Presider: The grace and peace of God our Father, who raised Jesus from the dead, be always with you.

Assembly: **And also with you.**

D

Presider: May the Father of mercies, the God of all consolation, be with you.

Assembly: **And also with you.**

The body is sprinkled with holy water, a reminder of baptism. The family or pall bearers spread the pall over the body, a garment like that which the Christian received at baptism. The funeral procession then moves into the church accompanied by the following song or an appropriate hymn.

Psalm (114) 115
RJB

161

Give him/her e - ter - nal rest, O Lord,
and may your light shine on him/her for ev - er.

I love the Lord for he has heard
the cry of my appeal;
for he turned his ear to me
in the day when I called him. ℞.

They surround me, the snares of death,
with the anguish of the tomb;
they caught me, sorrow and distress.
I called on the Lord's name,
O Lord, our God, deliver us. ℞.

How gracious is the Lord, and just;
our God has compassion.
The Lord protects the simple hearts,
I was helpless so he saved me. ℞.

Turn back, my soul, to your rest
for the Lord has been good,
he has kept my soul from death
and my feet from stumbling. ℞.

I will walk in the presence of
the Lord
in the land of the living.
Praise the Father, the Son and
the Holy Spirit,
for ever and ever. ℞.

OPENING PRAYER 162

The presider invites all to pray and leads an opening prayer. All respond: **Amen.**

LITURGY OF THE WORD 163

FIRST READINGS

One or more passages from scripture are read. At the conclusion of each:

Reader: This is the Word of the Lord.

Assembly: **Thanks be to God.**

RESPONSORIAL PSALM

The following psalm (or another from nos. 193 through 205) may follow the first reading.

Ps.(22) 23, 1-3.3-4.5.6 / 791-1
RP
The Lord is my shep-herd; there is noth-ing I shall want.

The Lord is my shepherd;
there is nothing I shall want.
Fresh and green are the pastures
where he gives me repose.
Near restful waters he leads me,
to revive my drooping spirit. ℟.

He guides me along the right path;
he is true to his name.
If I should walk in the valley of
darkness
no evil would I fear.
You are there with your crook and
your staff;
with these you give me comfort. ℟.

You have prepared a banquet for me
in the sight of my foes.
My head you have anointed with oil;
my cup is overflowing. ℟.

Surely goodness and kindness shall
follow me
all the days of my life.
In the Lord's own house shall I dwell
for ever and ever. ℟.

164 GOSPEL

Before the gospel reading, this acclamation is sung:

Cantor, then all:
Chant Mode VI
Al - le - lu - ia, al - le - lu - ia, al - le - lu - ia.

During Lent:

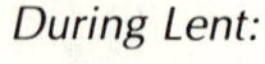
Cantor, then all:

Frank Schoen, 1970
Praise to you, Lord Je - sus Christ, king of end-less glo-ry!

Deacon (or priest): The Lord be with you.

Assembly: **And also with you.**

Deacon: A reading from the holy gospel according to N.

Assembly: **Glory to you, Lord.**

After the reading:

Deacon: This is the gospel of the Lord.

Assembly: **Praise to you, Lord Jesus Christ.**

HOMILY

GENERAL INTERCESSIONS 165

All pray for the church, the local community, those in need, the deceased and those who mourn.

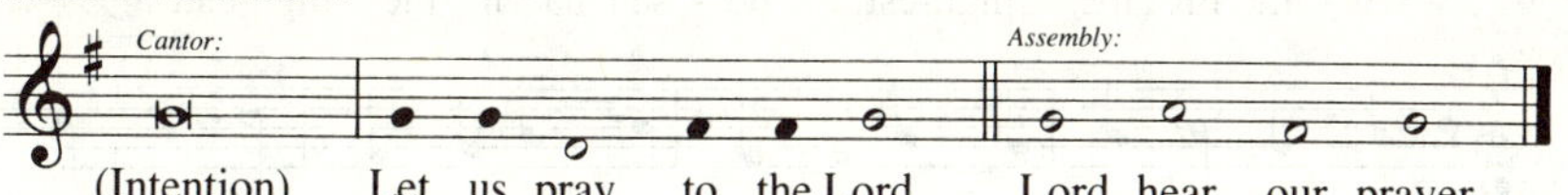
Cantor:
Assembly:
(Intention) Let us pray to the Lord. Lord, hear our prayer.

LITURGY OF THE EUCHARIST 166

PREPARATION OF THE ALTAR AND GIFTS

Bread and wine are brought to the table and the deacon or presider prepares these gifts. If there is no music, the prayers of preparation may be said aloud, and all may respond: **Blessed be God for ever.** *The presider then invites all to pray.*

Assembly: **May the Lord accept the sacrifice at your hands
for the praise and glory of his name,
for our good, and the good of all his church.**

The presider says the prayer over the gifts and all respond: **Amen.**

EUCHARISTIC PRAYER 167

This central prayer of the liturgy begins with this dialogue:

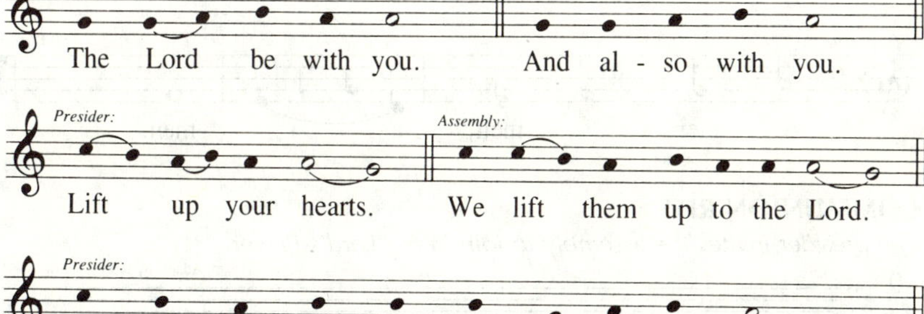
Presider:
Assembly:
Sacramentary, 1974
The Lord be with you. And al - so with you.
Presider:
Assembly:
Lift up your hearts. We lift them up to the Lord.
Presider:
Let us give thanks to the Lord our God.

Assembly:
It is right to give him thanks and praise.

The Sanctus acclamation concludes the first part of the eucharistic prayer.

"A Community Mass"
Richard Proulx, 1970

168

mf
Ho - ly, ho - ly, ho - ly Lord, God of pow-er and might,
heav'n and earth are full of your glo-ry. Ho-

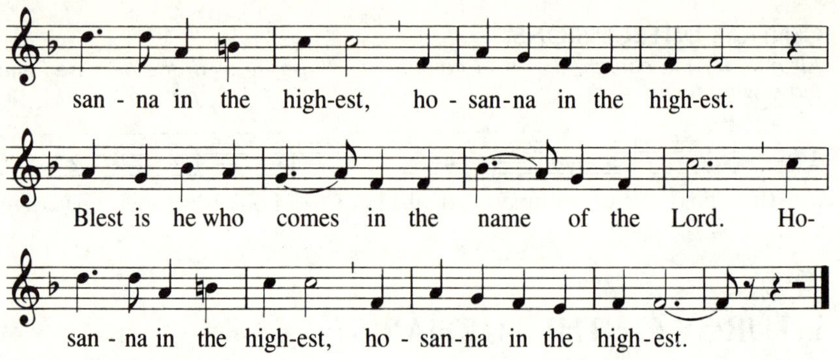
san - na in the high-est, ho - san-na in the high-est.
Blest is he who comes in the name of the Lord. Ho-
san - na in the high-est, ho - san-na in the high-est.

The following acclamation comes in response to the presider's invitation to proclaim the mystery of faith.

169

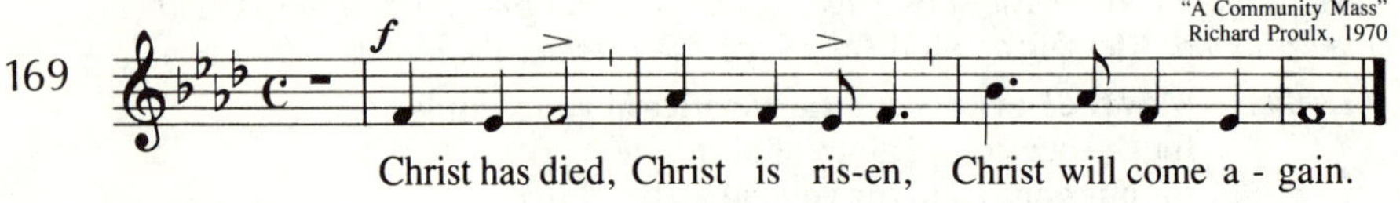
"A Community Mass"
Richard Proulx, 1970
f
Christ has died, Christ is ris-en, Christ will come a - gain.

The eucharistic prayer concludes:

170 *Presider:* Through him, with him, in him, in the unity of the Holy Spirit, all glory and honor is yours, almighty Father, for ever and ever.

All:
Danish
A - men, a - men, a - men.

171 **COMMUNION RITE**

The presider invites the assembly to join in the Lord's Prayer.

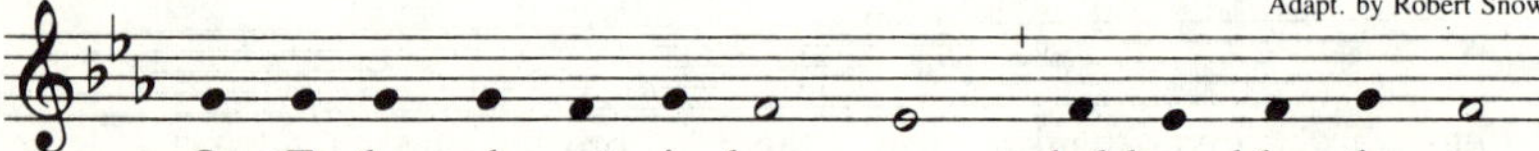
Adapt. by Robert Snow, 1964
Our Fa-ther, who art in heav - en, hal-lowed be thy name;

thy king-dom come; thy will be done on earth as it is in
heav - en. Give us this day our dai - ly bread; and for-give

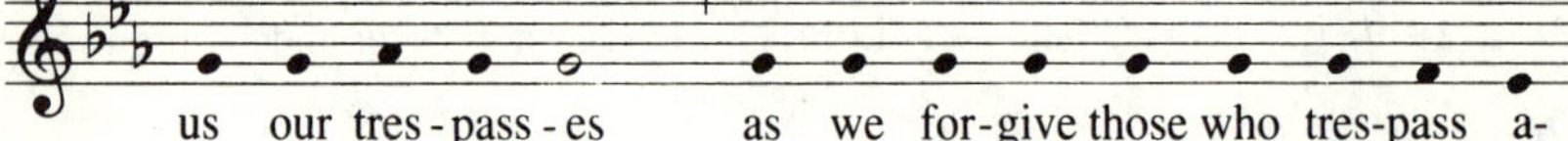
us our tres-pass-es as we for-give those who tres-pass a-

gainst us; and lead us not in - to temp - ta - tion,
but de - liv - er us from e - vil.

Presider: Deliver us, Lord...for the coming of our Savior, Jesus Christ.

For the king - dom, the pow'r, and the
glo - ry are yours, now and for ev - er.

Following the prayer "Lord, Jesus Christ," the presider invites the sign of peace. 172

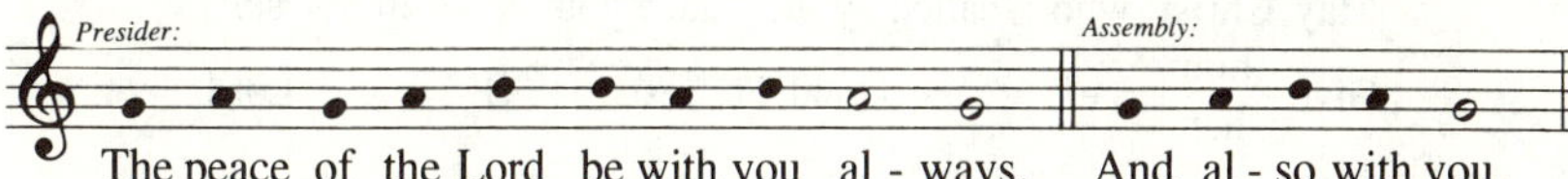
Presider:
Assembly:
The peace of the Lord be with you al - ways. And al - so with you.

All exchange a sign of peace.

As the bread is broken to be shared in communion, the assembly joins in singing the "Lamb of God." 173

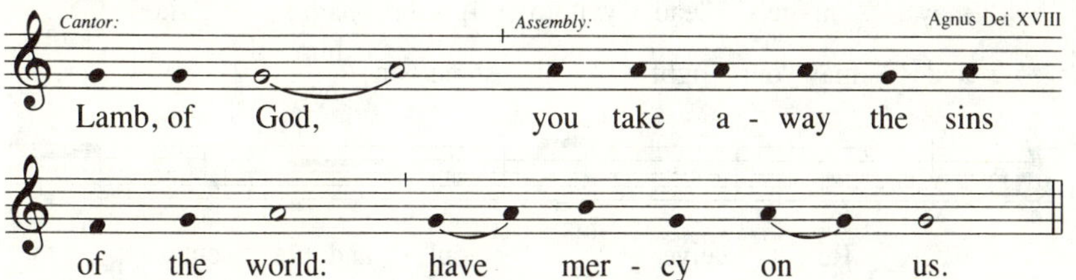
Cantor:
Assembly:
Agnus Dei XVIII
Lamb, of God, you take a - way the sins
of the world: have mer - cy on us.

This is sung two or more times. When the bread has been prepared, the "Lamb of God" concludes:

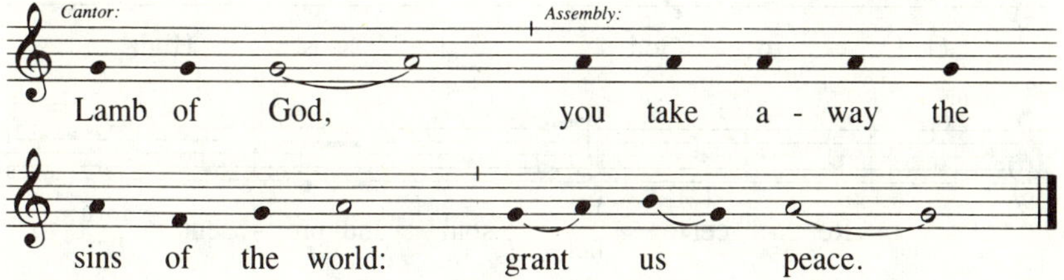
Cantor:
Assembly:
Lamb of God, you take a - way the
sins of the world: grant us peace.

174 *The presider then invites the assembly to share in the holy communion. All respond to the invitation:*

Assembly: **Lord, I am not worthy to receive you,**
but only say the word and I shall be healed.

A song or psalm may be sung during communion. After communion, a time of silence is observed. The rite concludes with the prayer after communion to which all respond: **Amen.**

175 FINAL COMMENDATION AND FAREWELL

The ministers and assembly surround the body. After the invitation, prayer and silence, one of the following may be sung as the body is sprinkled with holy water and honored with incense.

RESPONSORY

Cantor:
Richard Proulx, 1975
Saints of God, come to his/her aid!
May Christ who called you, take you to him - self;
Give him/her e - ter - nal rest, O Lord,
Come to meet him,/her, an - gels of the Lord!
may an-gels lead you to A - bra-ham's side.
and may your light shine on him/her for ev - er.
Re - ceive his/her soul and pre - sent him/her to
God, to God the Most High.
All:
Re - ceive his/her soul and pre - sent him/her to
God, to God the Most High.

ALTERNATE RESPONSORY

Howard Hughes, SM, 1977

Cantor:
I know that my Re-deem-er lives, and on the last day I shall rise a-gain; in my bod-y I shall look on God, my Sav-ior,
rall.
All: a tempo
in my bod-y I shall look on God, my Sav-ior.
Cantor:
I my-self shall see him; my own eyes will gaze on him, my own eyes will gaze on him; in my bod-y I shall look on God, my
rall.
All: a tempo
Sav-ior, in my bod-y I shall look on God, my Sav-ior.
rall.
Cantor:
This is the hope I cher-ish, this is the hope I cher-ish in my heart; in my bod-y I shall look on God, my Sav-ior,
All:
in my bod-y I shall look on God, my Sav-ior.
molto rit.

After the concluding prayer, one of the following songs or an appropriate hymn is sung while the body is being taken away.

In Paradisum
ICEL, 1985
TALLIS' CANON, LM
Thomas Tallis, c.1505-1585
177
1. May saints and an - gels lead you on,
2. Come to the peace of A - bra - ham
Es - cort - ing you where Christ has gone.
And to the sup - per of the Lamb:
Now he has called you, come to him
Come to the glo - ry of the blessed,
Who sits a - bove the ser - a - phim.
And to per - pet - ual light and rest.
In Paradisum
Trans. Hymnal Version, 1986
Mode VII
Acc. by Richard Proulx, 1985
178
In pa - ra - dí - sum de - dú - cant te án-
May choirs of an - gels es - cort you in - to
ge - li: in tu - o ad - vén - tu
par - a - dise: and at your ar - ri - val
su - scí - pi - ant te már - ty - res,
may the mar - tyrs re - ceive and wel - come you;
et per - dú - cant te in ci - vi - tá - tem san - ctam
may they bring you home in - to the ho - ly cit - y,

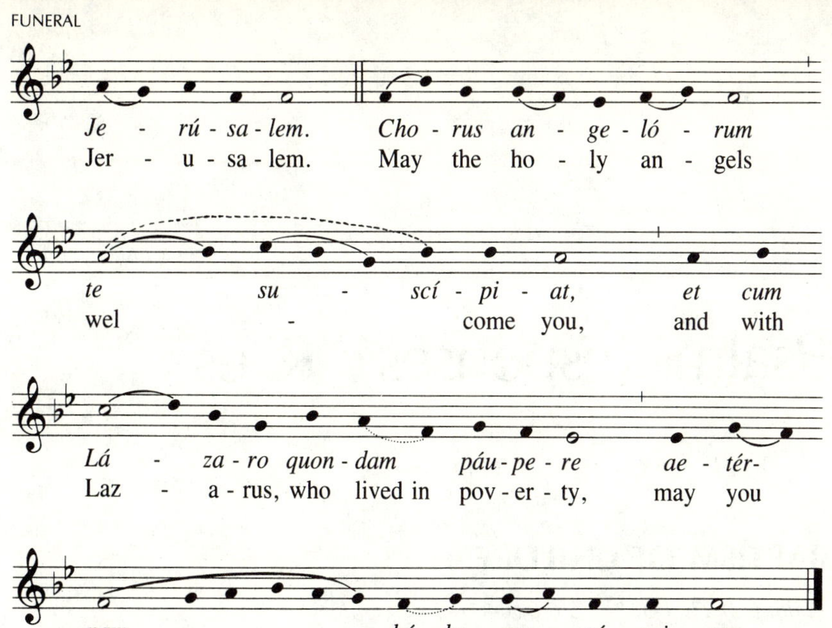
Je - rú - sa - lem. Cho - rus an - ge - ló - rum
Jer - u - sa - lem. May the ho - ly an - gels
te su - scí - pi - at, et cum
wel - come you, and with
Lá - za - ro quon - dam páu - pe - re ae - tér-
Laz - a - rus, who lived in pov - er - ty, may you
nam há - be - as ré - qui - em.
have ev - er - last - ing rest.

Psalm Responses / Rites

BAPTISM OF CHILDREN

179 *Psalm (22) 23, 1-3. 3-4. 5.6 (no. 32)*

RP
The Lord is my shep-herd; there is noth-ing I shall want.

180 *Psalm (26) 27, 1.4. 8-9. 13-14 (no. 34)*

MJ
Wake up and rise from death; Christ will shine up-on you.

181 *Psalm (33) 34, 2-3. 6-7. 8-9. 14-15. 16-17. 18-19 (no. 36)*

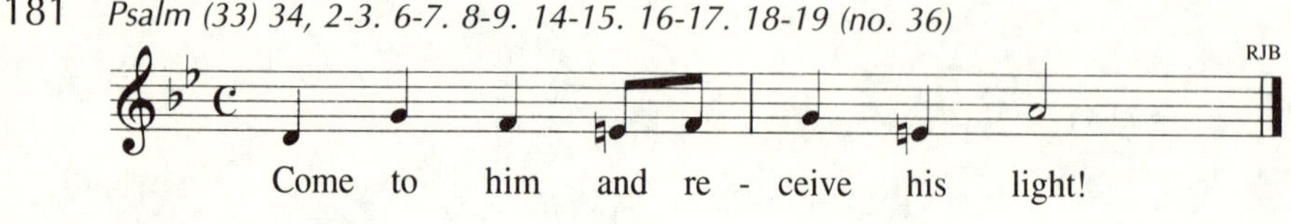
RJB
Come to him and re - ceive his light!

182 *Psalm (33) 34, 2-3. 6-7. 8-9. 14-15. 16-17. 18-19 (no. 36)*

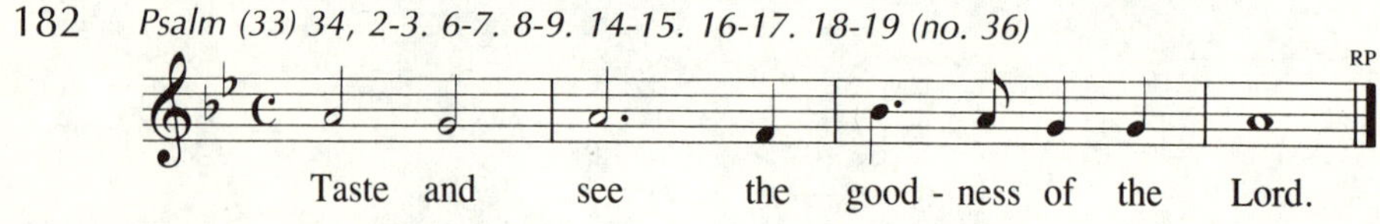
RP
Taste and see the good - ness of the Lord.

CONFIRMATION

183 *Psalm (21) 22, 23-24. 26-27. 28. 31-32 (no. 31)*

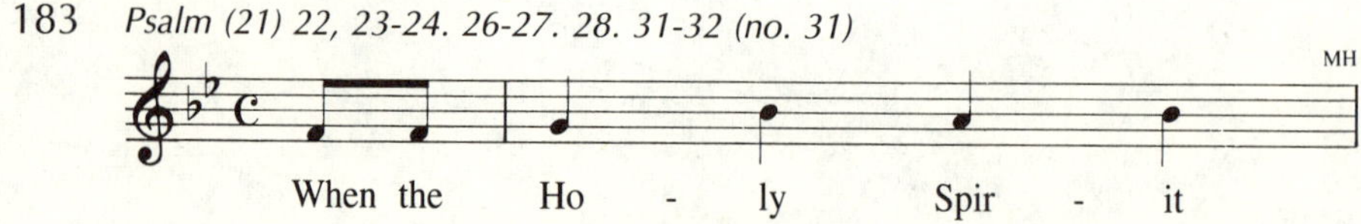
MH
When the Ho - ly Spir - it

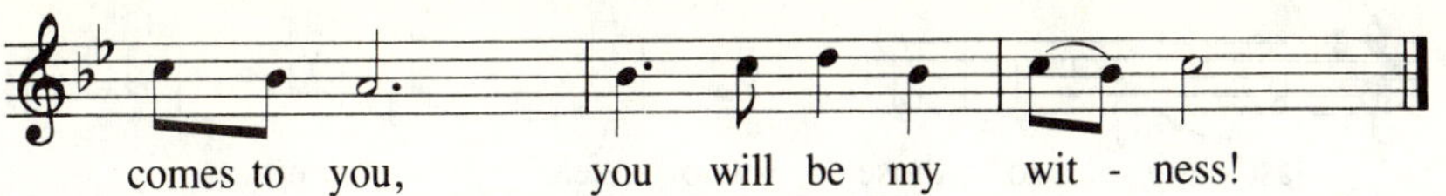
comes to you, you will be my wit - ness!

Psalm (95) 96, 1-2. 2-3. 9-10. 11-12 (no. 52) 184

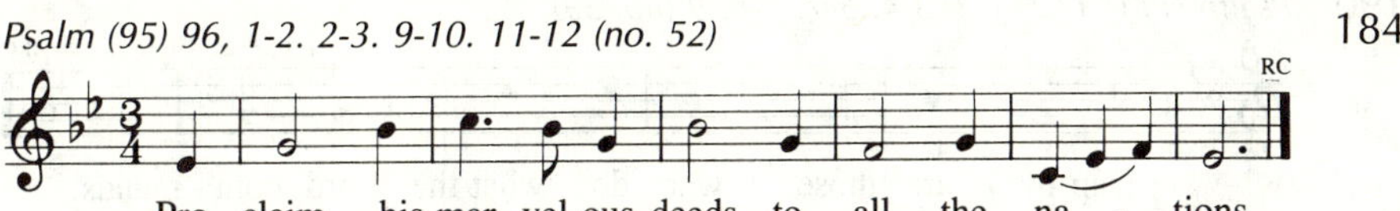
RC
Pro - claim his mar - vel-ous deeds to all the na - tions.

Psalm (116) 117, 1. 2 (no. 64) 185

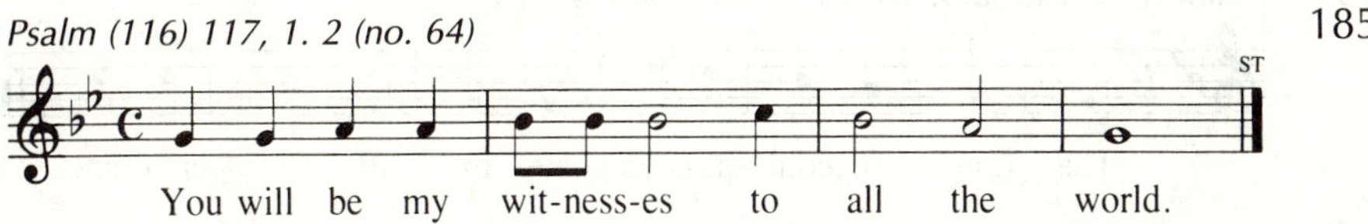
ST
You will be my wit-ness-es to all the world.

Psalm (144) 145, 2-3. 4-5. 8-9. 10-11. 15-16. 21 (no. 76) 186

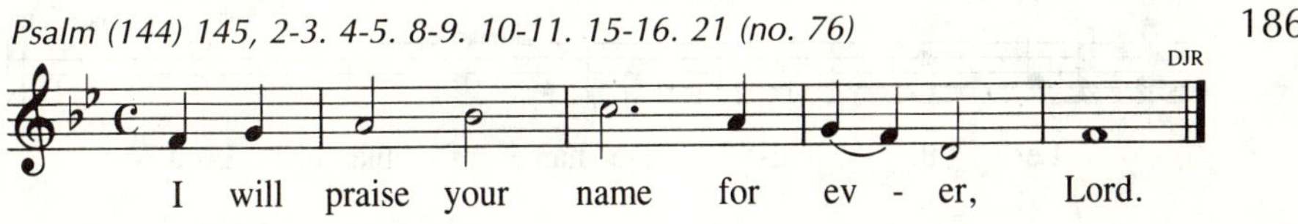
DJR
I will praise your name for ev - er, Lord.

For Confirmation, Psalm (22) 23 with the refrain "The Lord is my shepherd" (no. 179), may also be used.

MARRIAGE

Psalm (33) 34, 2-3. 4-5. 6-7. 8-9 (no. 36) 187

JRC
I will bless the Lord, I will
bless the Lord at all times.

Also, these verses of Psalm (33) 34 with the refrain "Taste and see" (no. 182).

Psalm (102) 103, 1-2. 8. 13. 17-18 (no. 55) 188

DH
The Lord is kind and mer - ci - ful.

Psalm (102) 103, 1-2. 8. 13. 17-18 (no. 55) 189

HH
The Lord's kind - ness is ev - er-

last - ing to those who fear him.
190 Psalm (111) 112, 1-2. 3-4. 5-7. 7-8. 9 (no. 59)
JRC
Hap-py are those who do what the Lord com - mands.
191 Psalm (144) 145, 8-9. 10. 15. 17-18 (no. 76)
MH
The Lord is com - pas - sion - ate to all his crea-tures.
192 Psalm 148, 1-2. 3-4. 9-10. 11-12 (no. 79)
RJB/Acc. RP
Let all praise the name of the Lord.
FUNERAL MASS
193 Psalm (24) 25, 6-7. 17-18. 20-21 (no. 33)
RJT
To you, O Lord, I lift my soul.
194 Psalm (26) 27, 1. 4. 7. 8. 9. 13-14 (no. 34)
RP
The Lord is my light and my sal - va - tion.
195 Psalm (26) 27, 1. 4. 7. 8. 9. 13-14 (no. 34)
CK
I be - lieve that I shall see the good things of the
Lord in the land of the liv - ing.

196 *Psalm (41) 42, 2. 3. 5; (42) 43, 3. 4. 5 (nos. 37 & 38)*

HH

My soul is thirst-ing for the liv-ing God.

Psalm (62) 63, 2. 3-4. 5-6. 8-9 (no. 42) 197

RP

My soul is thirst-ing for you, O Lord, thirst-ing for you my God.

Psalm (102) 103, 8. 10. 13-14. 15-16. 17-18 (no. 55) 198

DH

The Lord is kind and mer - ci - ful.

Psalm (113) 114, 5. 6; (115) 116, 10-11. 15-16 (nos. 60 & 63) 199

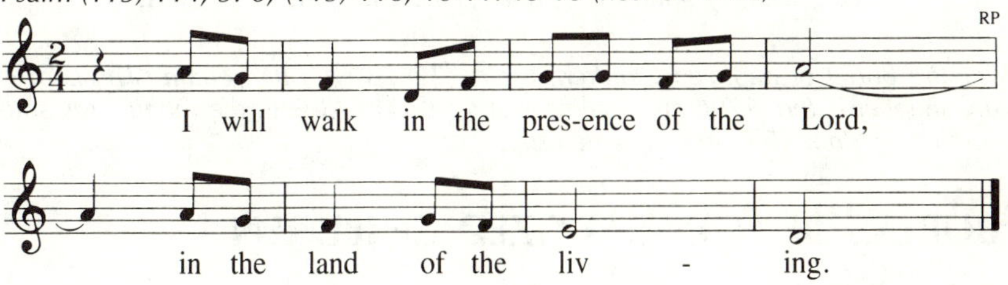

RP

I will walk in the pres-ence of the Lord, in the land of the liv - ing.

Psalm (121) 122, 1-2. 3-4. 4-5. 6-7. 8-9 (no. 67) 200

RJB

I re - joiced when I heard them say: let us go to the house of the Lord.

Psalm (129) 130, 1-2. 3-4. 4-6. 7-8 (no. 71) 201

JRC

I hope in the Lord, I trust in his word.

For funerals, Psalm (129) 130 with Antiphon III (no. 71) may also be used.

Psalm (142) 143, 1-2. 5-6. 7. 8. 10 (no. 75) 202

RP
O Lord, hear my prayer,

hear my prayer, O Lord.

BURIAL OF BAPTIZED CHILDREN

203 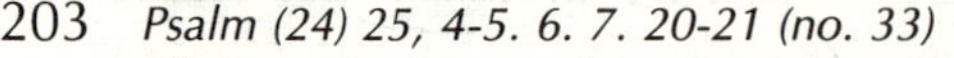
Psalm (24) 25, 4-5. 6. 7. 20-21 (no. 33)

RJT
To you, O Lord, I lift my soul.

204 *Psalm 148, 1-2. 11-12. 12-14. 14 (no. 79)*

RJB / Acc. RP
Let all praise the name of the Lord.

For the Burial of Baptized Children, Psalm (22) 23 with the refrain "The Lord is my shepherd" (no. 179), and Psalms (41) 42 & (42) 43 with the refrain "My soul is thirsting" (no. 196), may also be used.

BURIAL OF NON-BAPTIZED CHILDREN

205 *Psalm (24) 25, 4-5. 6. 7. 17. 20 (no. 33)*

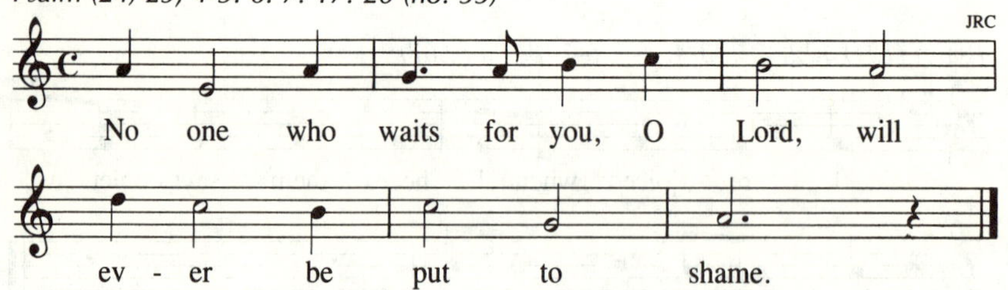
JRC
No one who waits for you, O Lord, will
ev - er be put to shame.

Also, these verses of Psalm (24) 25 with the refrain "To you, O Lord" (no. 193).

PENANCE

206 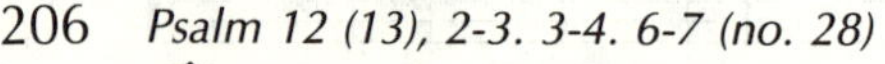
Psalm 12 (13), 2-3. 3-4. 6-7 (no. 28)

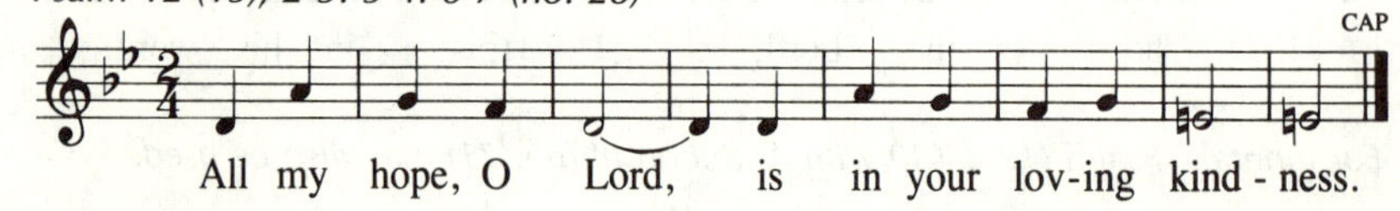
CAP
All my hope, O Lord, is in your lov-ing kind - ness.

207 *Psalm (24) 25, 2-3. 4-5. 10-11. 15-16 (no. 33)*

RC
Turn to me, Lord, and have mer - cy.

Psalm (30) 31, 2-3. 3-4. 5-6 (no. 35)
208
RK
You have re - deemed us, Lord, God of truth.
Psalm (89) 90, 1-2. 12-13. 14-15 (no. 48)
209
RJB
Fill us with your love, O Lord, and we will sing for joy!
Psalm (122) 123, 1-2. 2-3. 4-5 (no. 68)
210
RP
Our eyes are fixed on the Lord.
Psalm (129) 130, 1-2. 3-4. 5-7. 7-8 (no. 71)
211
JRC
With the Lord there is mer - cy,
and full - ness of re - demp - tion.
Psalm (138) 139, 1-2. 3-4. 13-14 (no. 73)
212
RP
You have searched me, and you know me, Lord.
Psalm (142) 143, 1-2. 5-6. 7. 9-10 (no. 75)
213
HH
Teach me to do your will, my God.
ANOINTING OF THE SICK
Isaiah 38, 10. 11. 12. 16. (no. 82)
214
CAP
You saved my life, O Lord; I shall not die.

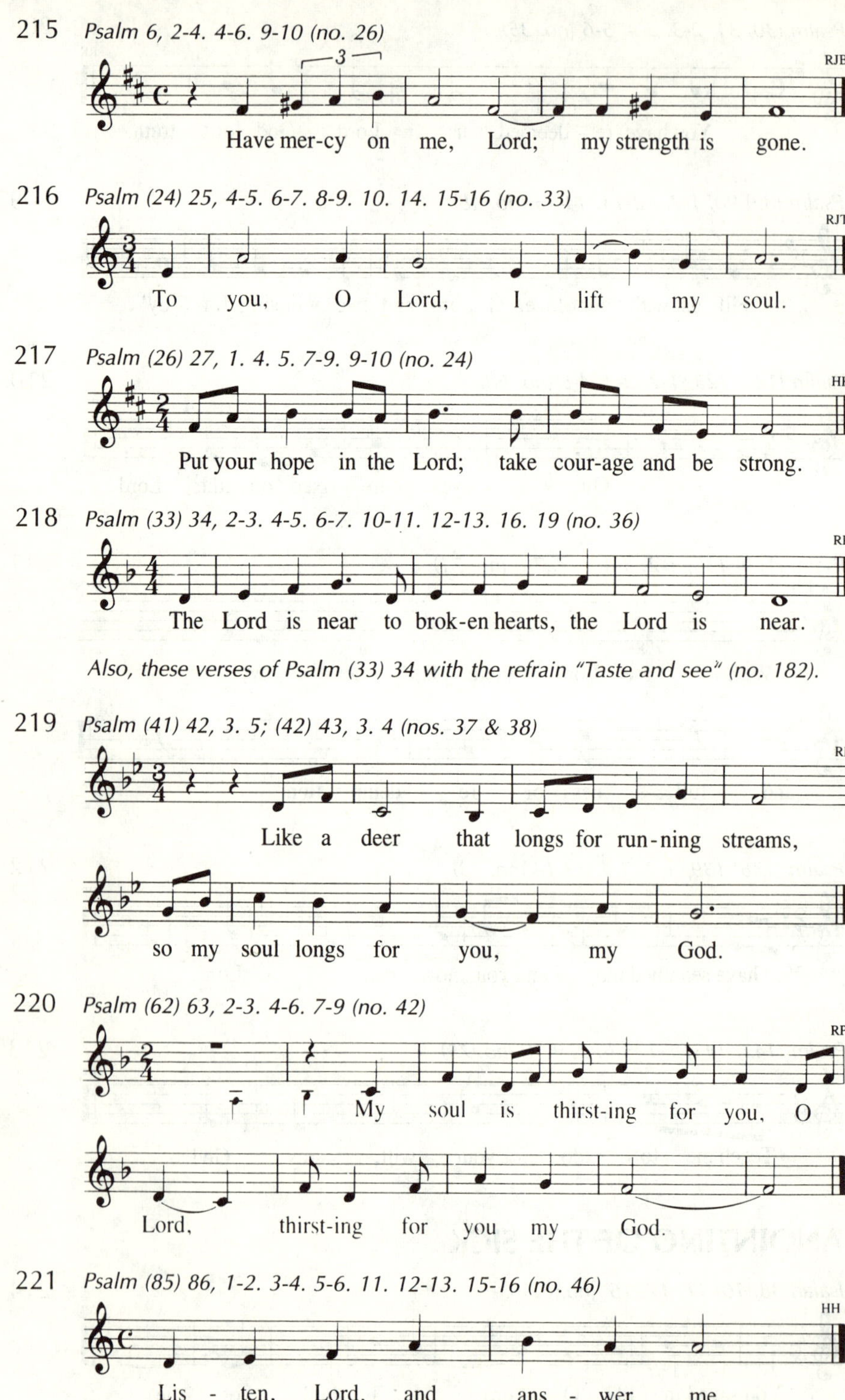
215 Psalm 6, 2-4. 4-6. 9-10 (no. 26)
RJB
Have mer-cy on me, Lord; my strength is gone.
216 Psalm (24) 25, 4-5. 6-7. 8-9. 10. 14. 15-16 (no. 33)
RJT
To you, O Lord, I lift my soul.
217 Psalm (26) 27, 1. 4. 5. 7-9. 9-10 (no. 24)
HH
Put your hope in the Lord; take cour-age and be strong.
218 Psalm (33) 34, 2-3. 4-5. 6-7. 10-11. 12-13. 16. 19 (no. 36)
RP
The Lord is near to brok-en hearts, the Lord is near.
Also, these verses of Psalm (33) 34 with the refrain "Taste and see" (no. 182).
219 Psalm (41) 42, 3. 5; (42) 43, 3. 4 (nos. 37 & 38)
RP
Like a deer that longs for run-ning streams,
so my soul longs for you, my God.
220 Psalm (62) 63, 2-3. 4-6. 7-9 (no. 42)
RP
My soul is thirst-ing for you, O
Lord, thirst-ing for you my God.
221 Psalm (85) 86, 1-2. 3-4. 5-6. 11. 12-13. 15-16 (no. 46)
HH
Lis - ten, Lord, and ans - wer me.

Psalm (85) 86, 1-2. 3-4. 5-6. 11. 12-13. 15-16 (no. 46)
222
RJB
God, you are mer-ci-ful and kind; turn to me and have mer - cy.
Psalm (89) 90, 2. 3-4. 5-6. 10 & 12. 14. 16 (no. 48)
223
CAP
In ev-'ry age, O Lord, you have been our re - fuge.
Psalm (101) 102, 2-3. 24-25. 26-28. 19-21 (no. 54)
224
RL
O Lord, hear my prayer, and let my cry come to you.
Psalm (102) 103, 1-2. 3-4. 11-12. 13-14. 15-16. 17-18 (no. 55)
225
JS
O bless the Lord, O bless the Lord, my soul.
Psalm (102) 103, 1-2. 3-4. 11-12. 13-14. 15-16. 17-18 (no. 55)
226
CAP
The Lord is kind and mer - ci - ful;
slow to an - ger, and rich in com - pas - sion.
Psalm (122) 123, 1-2. 2-3 (no. 68)
227
ST
Our eyes are fixed on the Lord,
plead - ing for his mer - cy.
Psalm (142) 143, 1-2. 5-6. 10 (no. 75)
228
RJB
For the sake of your name, O Lord, save my life.

The Order of Mass

229 Each church gathers on the Lord's Day to listen to the scriptures, to offer prayers, to give thanks and praise to God while recalling God's gifts in creation and saving deeds in Jesus, and to share in holy communion.

In these rites of word and eucharist, the church keeps Sunday as the Lord's Day, the day of creation and resurrection, the "eighth day" when the fullness of God's kingdom is anticipated. The Mass of the Christian community has rites of gathering, of word, of eucharist, of dismissal. All those who gather constitute the assembly. One member of this assembly who has been ordained to the presbyterate, the priesthood, presides by leading the opening and closing prayers and the eucharistic prayer. A member ordained to the diaconate may assist, read the gospel and preach. Other members of the assembly are chosen and trained for various ministries: These are the readers, ushers, musicians, communion ministers. All of these assist the assembly. It is the assembly itself, all those present, that does the liturgy.

The order of Mass which follows is familiar to all who regularly join in this assembly. It is learned through repetition. This order of Mass leaves many things to the local community and to the season of the liturgical year.

INTRODUCTORY RITES

The rites which precede the liturgy of the word assist the assembly to gather as a community. They prepare that community to listen to the scriptures and to celebrate the eucharist together. The procession and entrance song are ways of expressing the unity and spirit of the assembly.

GREETING

After the sign of the cross one of the greetings is given.

Presider: In the name of the Father, and of the Son, and of the Holy Spirit.

Assembly: **Amen.**

A

Presider: The grace of our Lord Jesus Christ and the love of God and the fellowship of the Holy Spirit be with you all.

Assembly: **And also with you.**

B

Presider: The grace and peace of God our Father and the Lord Jesus Christ be with you.

Assembly: **Blessed be God, the Father of our Lord Jesus Christ.**
or: **And also with you.**

C

Presider: The Lord be with you. *(Bishop:* Peace be with you.)

Assembly: **And also with you.**

BLESSING AND SPRINKLING OF HOLY WATER 230

On Sundays, instead of the penitential rite below, the blessing and sprinkling of holy water may be done. The following or another appropriate song is sung.

Cantor, then all:
Joseph Roff, 1984
Cleanse us, O Lord, from all our sins; wash us, and we

1. and last time
2.
Cantor:
shall be clean, clean as new snow. snow. I will

D.C.al 𝄋
pour clean wa - ter o - ver you and wash a-way all your sins.

Cantor:
D.C.
snow. A new heart will I give you, says the Lord.

PENITENTIAL RITE 231

The presider invites all to be mindful of human sinfulness and of the great mercy of God. After a time of silence, one of the following forms is used.

A

Assembly: **I confess to almighty God,**
and to you, my brothers and sisters,
that I have sinned through my own fault
in my thoughts and in my words,
in what I have done,
and in what I have failed to do;
and I ask blessed Mary, ever virgin,
all the angels and saints,
and you, my brothers and sisters,
to pray for me to the Lord our God.

B

Presider: Lord, we have sinned against you:
Lord, have mercy,

Assembly: **Lord, have mercy.**

Presider: Lord, show us your mercy and love.

Assembly: **And grant us your salvation.**

C

The presider or another minister makes a series of invocations according to the following pattern.

Presider:
Assembly:
Richard Proulx, 1970
(Invocation) Lord, have mer - cy. Lord, have mer - cy.
Presider:
Assembly:
(Invocation) Christ, have mer - cy. Christ, have mer - cy.
Presider:
Assembly:
(Invocation) Lord, have mer- cy. Lord, have mer- cy.

The penitential rite always concludes:

Presider: May almighty God have mercy on us, forgive us our sins, and bring us to everlasting life.

Assembly: **Amen.**

232 **KYRIE**

Unless form C of the penitential rite has been used, the Kyrie follows.

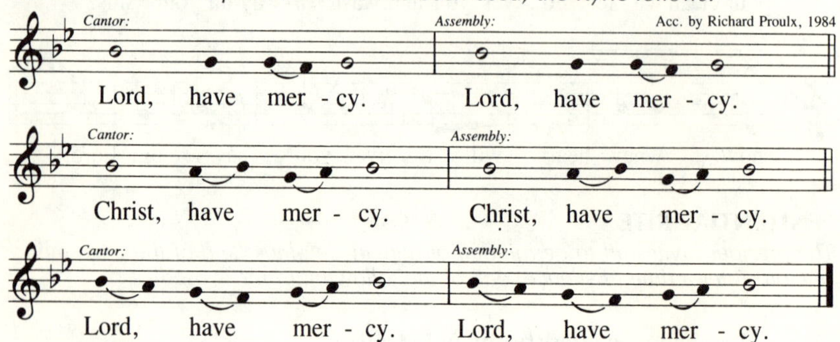
Cantor:
Assembly:
Acc. by Richard Proulx, 1984
Lord, have mer - cy. Lord, have mer - cy.
Cantor:
Assembly:
Christ, have mer - cy. Christ, have mer - cy.
Cantor:
Assembly:
Lord, have mer - cy. Lord, have mer - cy.

Or:

233

Cantor:
Assembly:
Acc. by Richard Proulx, 1984
Ky - ri - e e - le - i - son. Ky - ri - e e - le - i - son.

Cantor:
Chri - ste e - le - i - son.
Assembly:
Chri - ste e - le - i - son.
Cantor:
Ky - ri - e e - le - i - son.
Assembly:
Ky - ri - e e - le - i - son.

GLORIA

234

The Gloria is omitted during Advent and Lent.

"A New Mass for Congregations"
Carroll T. Andrews, 1970

mf

Glo - ry to God in the high - est, and

peace to his peo - ple on earth. Lord God,

f

heav - en - ly King, al - might - y God and

Fa - ther, we wor - ship you, we give you thanks, we

f

praise you for your glo - ry.

Slightly slower

mf *Choir (Congr. ad lib.):*

Lord Je - sus Christ, on - ly Son of the Fa - ther,

Lord God, Lamb of God, you take a - way the

sin of the world: have mer - cy on

us; you are seat - ed at the right hand of the

Fa - ther: re - ceive our prayer.
All: f tempo primo
For you a - lone are the Ho - ly One,
you a - lone are the Lord, you a - lone are the
Most High, Je - sus Christ, with the Ho - ly Spir - it,
ff
rit.
in the glo - ry of God the Fa - ther. A - men.

235 **OPENING PRAYER**

After the invitation from the presider, all pray for a while. The introductory rites conclude with the proper prayer of the day and the Amen of the assembly.

236 LITURGY OF THE WORD

When the church assembles, the book of the scriptures is opened and all listen as lectors and deacon (or presider) read from the places assigned. The first reading is normally from the Hebrew Scriptures, the second from the letters of the New Testament, and the third from the Book of Gospels. Over a three-year cycle, the church reads through the letters and gospels and a portion of the Hebrew Scriptures. During the Sundays of Ordinary Time, the letters and gospels are read in order, each Sunday continuing near the place where the previous Sunday's readings ended. During Advent/Christmas and Lent/Easter, the readings are those which are traditional and appropriate to these seasons.

The church listens to and–through the weeks and years–is shaped by the scriptures. Those who have gathered for Sunday liturgy are to give their full attention to the words of the reader. A time of silence and reflection follows each of the first two readings. After the first reading, this reflection continues in the singing of the psalm. A homily, bringing together the scriptures and the life of the community, follows the gospel. The liturgy of the word concludes with the creed, the dismissal of the catechumens and the prayers of intercession. In the latter, the assembly continues its constant work of recalling and praying for the universal church and all those in need.

This reading and hearing of the word–simple things that they are–are the foundation of the liturgical celebration. The public reading of the scriptures and the rituals which surround this–silence and psalm and acclamation, posture and gesture, preaching and litany of intercession–gather the church generation after generation. They gather and sustain and gradually make of us the image of Christ.

READING I

In conclusion:

Reader: This is the Word of the Lord.

Assembly: **Thanks be to God.**

After a period of silence, the responsorial psalm is sung.

READING II

In conclusion:

Reader: This is the Word of the Lord.

Assembly: **Thanks be to God.**

A time of silence follows the reading.

GOSPEL 237

Before the gospel, an acclamation is sung.

Cantor, then all:
Chant Mode VI
Al - le - lu - ia, al - le - lu - ia, al - le - lu - ia.

During Lent one of the following acclamations replaces the alleluia.

A
Cantor, then all:
Frank Schoen, 1970
Praise to you, Lord Je-sus Christ, king of end-less glo - ry!

Or:

B **Praise and honor to you, Lord Jesus Christ!**

C **Glory and praise to you, Lord Jesus Christ!**

D **Glory to you, Word of God, Lord Jesus Christ!**

Deacon (or priest): The Lord be with you.

Assembly: **And also with you.**

Deacon: A reading from the holy gospel according to N.

Assembly: **Glory to you, Lord.**

After the reading:

Deacon: This is the gospel of the Lord.

Assembly: **Praise to you, Lord Jesus Christ.**

HOMILY

238 PROFESSION OF FAITH

We believe in one God,
the Father, the Almighty,
maker of heaven and earth,
of all that is seen and unseen.

We believe in one Lord, Jesus Christ,
the only Son of God,
eternally begotten of the Father,
God from God, Light from Light,
true God from true God,
begotten, not made, one in Being with the Father.
Through him all things were made.
For us men and for our salvation he came down from heaven:

All bow at the following words up to: and became man.

by the power of the Holy Spirit
he was born of the Virgin Mary, and became man.
For our sake he was crucified under Pontius Pilate;
he suffered, died, and was buried.
On the third day he rose again
in fulfillment of the Scriptures;
he ascended into heaven
and is seated at the right hand of the Father.
He will come again in glory to judge the living and the dead,
and his kingdom will have no end.

We believe in the Holy Spirit, the Lord, the giver of life,
who proceeds from the Father and the Son.
With the Father and the Son he is worshiped and glorifed.
He has spoken through the Prophets.
We believe in one holy catholic and apostolic Church.
We acknowledge one baptism for the forgiveness of sins.
We look for the resurrection of the dead,
and the life of the world to come. Amen.

At Masses with children, the Apostles' Creed may be used: 239

We believe in God, the Father almighty,
creator of heaven and earth.

We believe in Jesus Christ, his only Son, our Lord.
He was conceived by the power of the Holy Spirit
and born of the Virgin Mary.
He suffered under Pontius Pilate,
was crucified, died, and was buried.
He descended to the dead.
On the third day he arose again.
He ascended into heaven,
and is seated at the right hand of the Father.
He will come again to judge the living and the dead.

We believe in the Holy Spirit,
the holy catholic Church,
the communion of saints,
the forgiveness of sins,
the resurrection of the body,
and the life everlasting. Amen.

GENERAL INTERCESSIONS 240

The people respond to each petition as follows, or according to local practice.

Cantor:
Assembly:
Byzantine Chant
(Intention) Let us pray to the Lord.
Lord, hear our prayer.

LITURGY OF THE EUCHARIST 241

To do the eucharist means to give God thanks and praise. When the table has been prepared with the bread and wine, the assembly joins the presider in remembering the gracious gifts of God in creation and God's saving deeds. The center of this is the paschal mystery, the death of our Lord Jesus Christ which destroyed the power of death and his rising which brings us life. That mystery into which we were baptized we proclaim each Sunday at eucharist. It is the very shape of Christian life. We find this in the simple bread and wine which stir our remembering and draw forth our prayer of thanksgiving. "Fruit of the earth and work of human hands," the bread and wine become our holy communion in the body and blood of the Lord. We eat and drink and so proclaim that we belong to one another and to the Lord.

The members of the assembly quietly prepare themselves even as the table is prepared. The presider then invites all to lift up their hearts and join in the eucharistic prayer. All do this by giving their full attention and by singing the acclamations from the "Holy, holy" to the great "Amen." Then the assembly joins in the Lord's Prayer, the sign of peace and the "Lamb of God" litany which accompanies the breaking of bread. Ministers of communion assist the assembly to share the bread and wine. A time of silence and prayer concludes the liturgy of the eucharist.

PREPARATION OF THE ALTAR AND THE GIFTS

Bread and wine are brought to the table and the deacon or presider prepares these gifts. If there is no music, the prayers may be said aloud, and all may respond: **"Blessed be God for ever."** *The presider then invites all to pray.*

Assembly: **May the Lord accept the sacrifice at your hands**
for the praise and glory of his name,
for our good, and the good of all his church.

The presider says the prayer over the gifts and all respond: **Amen.**

242 **EUCHARISTIC PRAYER**

The central prayer of the Mass begins with this greeting and invitation between presider and assembly.

Presider:
The Lord be with you.
Assembly:
And al - so with you.
Sacramentary, 1974
Presider:
Lift up your hearts.
Assembly:
We lift them up to the Lord.
Presider:
Let us give thanks to the Lord our God.
Assembly:
It is right to give him thanks and praise.

The Sanctus acclamation is sung to conclude the introduction to the eucharistic prayer.

243

"A Community Mass"
Richard Proulx, 1970
mf
Ho - ly, ho - ly, ho - ly Lord, God of pow - er and
might, heav'n and earth are
full of your glo - ry. Ho - san - na in the
high - est, ho - san - na in the high - est.
Blest is he who comes in the name of the

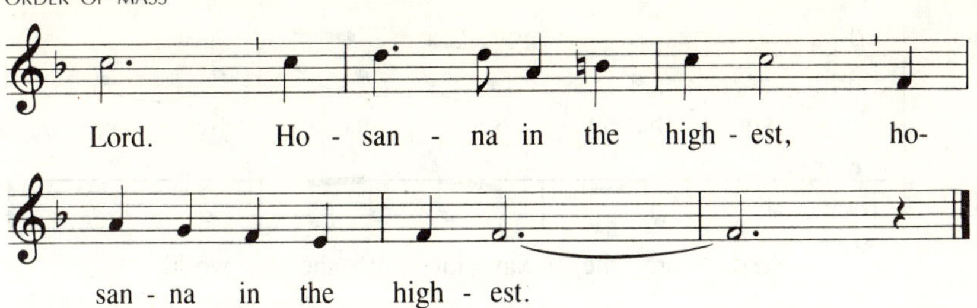
Lord. Ho - san - na in the high - est, ho-
san - na in the high - est.

One of the following acclamations follows the deacon's or presider's invitation: "Let us proclaim the mystery of faith." 244

"A Community Mass"
Richard Proulx, 1970

A

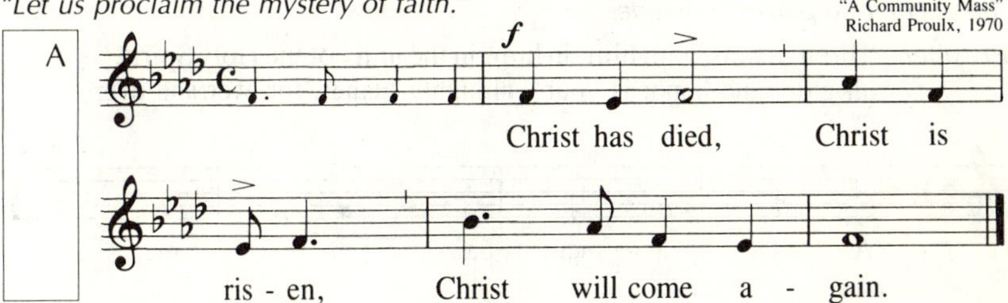
Christ has died, Christ is
ris - en, Christ will come a - gain.

B

John Lee, 1970

Dy - ing you de - stroyed our death,
ris - ing you re - stored our life.
Lord Je - sus, come in glo - ry.

C

John Lee, 1970

When we eat this bread and drink this cup,
we pro - claim your death, Lord Jesus, un - til you come in glo - ry.

D

Adapted from *Genevan Psalter*, 1551
Harm. by Claude LeJeune, 1601

Lord, by your cross and re - sur - rec - tion

you have set us free.
You are the Sav - ior of the world.

The eucharistic prayer concludes:

245 *Presider:* Through him, with him, in him, in the unity of the Holy Spirit, all glory and honor is yours, almighty Father, for ever and ever.

All:
Danish
A - men, a - men, a - men.

246 COMMUNION RITE

The presider invites all to join in the Lord's Prayer.

Robert Snow, 1964
Acc. by Gerard Farrell, OSB, 1984
Our Fa-ther, who art in heav - en, hal-lowed be thy name;
thy king-dom come; thy will be done on earth as it
is in heav - en. Give us this day our dai - ly bread;
and for-give us our tres-pass - es as we for - give those who
tres-pass a - gainst us; and lead us not in - to temp-
ta - tion, but de - liv - er us from e - vil.

Presider: Deliver us, Lord...
for the coming of our Savior, Jesus Christ.

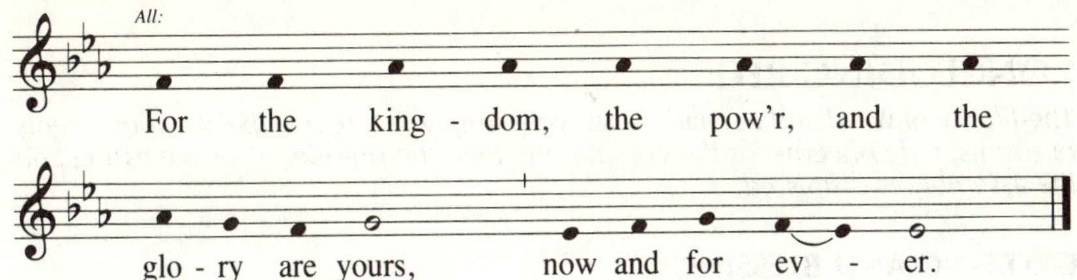
All:
For the king - dom, the pow'r, and the
glo - ry are yours, now and for ev - er.

Following the prayer "Lord, Jesus Christ," the presider invites the sign of peace. 247

Presider:
The peace of the Lord be with you al - ways.
Assembly:
And al - so with you.

All exchange a sign of peace.

Then the bread is solemnly broken and the bread and wine prepared for holy communion. The litany "Lamb of God" is sung through the breaking of the bread: 248

Agnus Dei XVIII
Acc. by Gerard Farrell, OSB, 1984

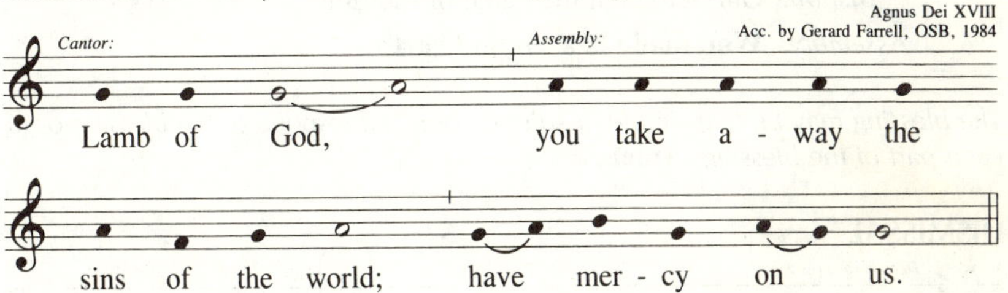
Cantor:
Lamb of God,
Assembly:
you take a - way the
sins of the world; have mer - cy on us.

Other invocations, such as "Bread of life" and "Prince of peace" may be added. When the preparation is completed, the litany concludes:

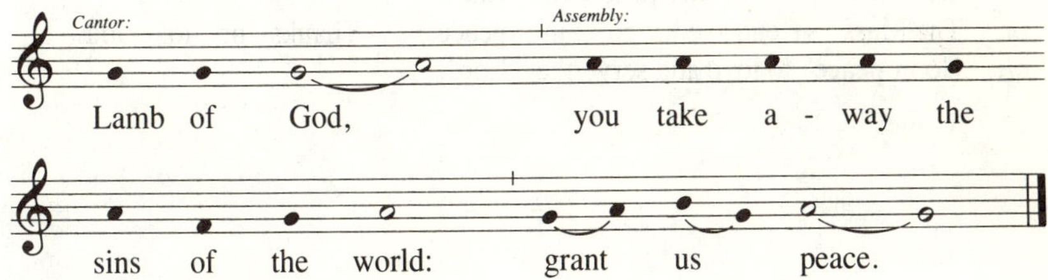
Cantor:
Lamb of God,
Assembly:
you take a - way the
sins of the world: grant us peace.

The presider then invites all to share in the holy communion. 249

Assembly: **Lord, I am not worthy to receive you,**
but only say the word and I shall be healed.

Minister of communion: The body of Christ.

Or:

The blood of Christ.

Communicant: **Amen.**

A song or psalm is ordinarily sung during communion. After communion, a time of silence is observed or a song of thanksgiving is sung. The rite concludes with the prayer after communion to which all respond: **Amen.**

250 CONCLUDING RITE

The liturgy of word and eucharist ends very simply. There may be announcements of events and concerns for the community, then the presider gives a blessing and the assembly is dismissed.

GREETING AND BLESSING

Presider: The Lord be with you.

Assembly: **And also with you.**

Optional

When the bishop blesses the people he adds the following:

Bishop: Blessed be the name of the Lord.

Assembly: **Now and for ever.**

Bishop: Our help is in the name of the Lord.

Assembly: **Who made heaven and earth.**

The blessing may be in a simple or solemn form. All respond to the blessing or to each part of the blessing: **Amen.**

DISMISSAL

Deacon (or presider):
Assembly:

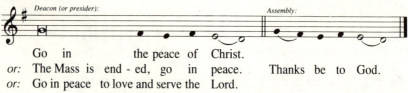

Go in the peace of Christ.

or: The Mass is end - ed, go in peace. Thanks be to God.

or: Go in peace to love and serve the Lord.

Setting One

KYRIE ELEISON 251

"A Community Mass"
Richard Proulx, 1970

p Cantor:
Assembly:
Lord, have mer - cy. Lord, have mer - cy.
mp Cantor:
Assembly:
Christ, have mer - cy. Christ, have mer - cy.
mf Cantor:
Assembly:
Lord, have mer - cy. Lord, have mer - cy.
f
Glo - ry to God in the high - est, and
peace to his peo-ple on earth. Lord God, heav-en - ly
King, al - might - y God and Fa - ther, We

GLORIA 252

"A Community Mass"
Richard Proulx, 1970

wor - ship you, we give you thanks, we praise you for your
glo - ry. Lord Je - sus Christ, on - ly
Son of the Fa - ther, Lord God,
Lamb of God, you take a - way the sin of the
world: have mer - cy on us; You are
seat - ed at the right hand of the Fa - ther:
re - ceive our pray'r, re - ceive, receive our pray'r. For you a - lone are the
Ho - ly One, you a - lone are the Lord, you a-
lone are the Most High, Je - sus Christ with the Ho - ly

Spir - it in the glo - ry of God the Fa - ther.
A - men. A - men.

SANCTUS 253

"A Community Mass"
Richard Proulx, 1970

mf

Ho - ly, ho - ly, ho - ly Lord, God of pow - er and
might, heav'n and earth are
full of your glo - ry. Ho - san - na in the
high - est, ho - san - na in the high - est.
Blest is he who comes in the name of the
Lord. Ho - san - na in the high - est, ho-
san - na in the high - est.

MEMORIAL ACCLAMATION 254

"A Community Mass"
Richard Proulx, 1970

f
Christ has died,
Christ is ris - en, Christ will come a - gain.

255 AMEN

"A Community Mass"
Richard Proulx, 1970

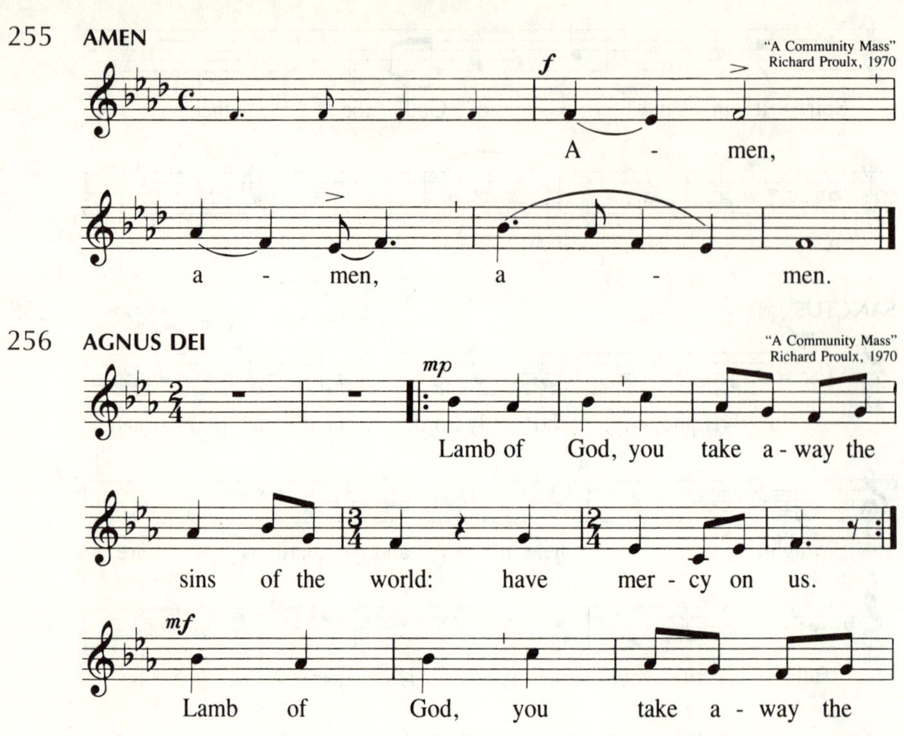
f
A - men,
a - men, a - men.

256 AGNUS DEI

"A Community Mass"
Richard Proulx, 1970

mp
Lamb of God, you take a-way the
sins of the world: have mer - cy on us.
mf
Lamb of God, you take a - way the
sins of the world: grant us peace.

Setting Two

KYRIE ELEISON 257

"Mass of the Bells"
Alexander Peloquin, 1972

mf
Lord, have mer - cy.
Lord, have mer - cy.
mp
Christ, have mer - cy.
Christ, have mer - cy.
mf
Lord, have mer - cy. Lord, have
mer - cy.
4

258 GLORIA

"Mass of the Bells"
Alexander Peloquin, 1972

All:

Glo-ry to God in the high-est, and peace to his peo-ple on earth. Glo-ry to God in the high-est, and peace to his peo-ple on earth.

Cantor or T. B.:

Lord God, heav-en-ly King, al-might-y God and Fa-ther.

All:

Glo-ry to God in the high-est, and peace to his peo-ple on earth.

Cantor or S. A.:

We wor-ship you, we give you thanks, we praise you for your glo-ry.

All:

Glo-ry to God in the high-est, and peace to his peo-ple on earth.

Cantor or T. B.:

Lord Je-sus Christ, on-ly Son of the Fa-ther.

All:
Glo-ry to God in the high-est, and peace to his peo-ple on
earth.
Cantor or S. A.:
Lord God, Lamb of God, you take a-way the
sin of the world;
T. B.:
have mer-cy on us;
S. A.:
you are seat-ed at the right hand of the Fa-ther:
T. B.:
re-ceive our pray-er.
All:
Glo-ry to God in the
high-est, and peace to his peo-ple on earth.
Glo-ry to God in the high-est, and peace to his peo-ple on
earth.
Cantor or T. B.:
For you a-lone are the Ho-ly One,
All or S. A.:
(Glo-ry to God!)
Cantor or T. B.:
you a-lone are the Lord,

All or S. A.:
Cantor or T. B.:
(Glo-ry to God!) you a-lone are the Most High,
All or S. A.
T. B.
All or S. A.
(Glo-ry to God!) Je - sus Christ, (Glo -ry to God!)
Choir:
All:
with the Ho - ly Spir - it, (Glo -ry to God!)
Choir:
in the glo-ry of God, the Fa - ther.
Broader
All:
Glo-ry to God in the high-est, and peace to his peo-ple on
earth. Glo-ry to God in the high-est, and
peace to his peo-ple on earth.
still broader
A - men. A - men. A - men.
A - men.

ALLELUIA

259

"Mass of the Bells"
Alexander Peloquin, 1972

Al - le - lu - ia. Al - le - lu - ia. Al - le - lu - ia.

Al - le - lu - ia.

SANCTUS

260

Resounding and rhythmic

"Mass of the Bells"
Alexander Peloquin, 1972

Ho - ly, ho - ly, ho - ly Lord,

God of pow'r and might, heav'n and

earth are full of your glo - ry. Ho - san-

na in the high - est.

Choir or Cantor: Bless - ed is

he who comes in the name of the Lord.

Cong. and S. A. Ho - san - na in the high - est. Ho - san-

na in the high - est. Ho - san - na in the

high-est. Ho - san - na in the
softer
high-est, high-est.
4

261 MEMORIAL ACCLAMATION

"Mass of the Bells"
Alexander Peloquin, 1972

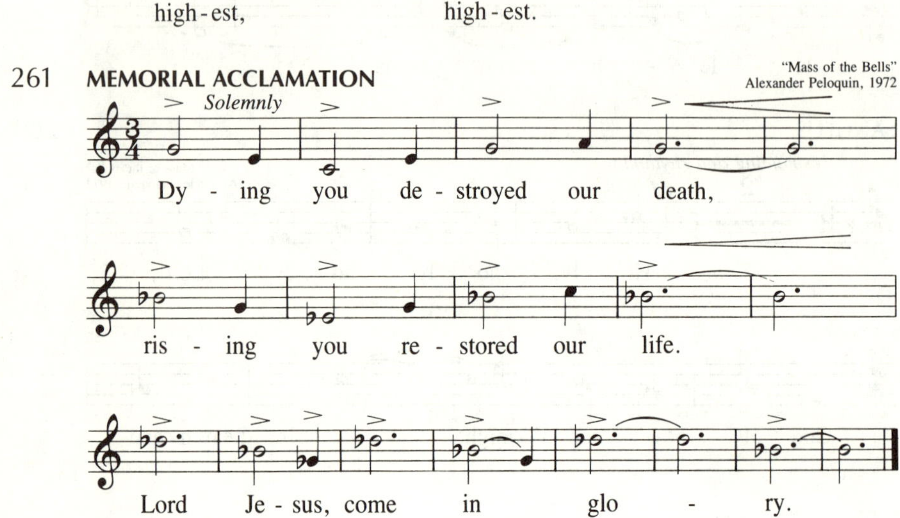
Solemnly
Dy - ing you de - stroyed our death,
ris - ing you re - stored our life.
Lord Je - sus, come in glo - ry.

262 AMEN

"Mass of the Bells"
Alexander Peloquin, 1972

ff Resoundingly
A - men, a - men, a - men.

263 AGNUS DEI

"Mass of the Bells"
Alexander Peloquin, 1972

Peacefully
Cantor:
mp
Lamb of God, you take a - way the
sins of the world:
All:
have mer-cy on us.
Cantor or Choir:
mf
Lamb of God, you take a - way the sins of the

All:
world: have mer-cy on us.
f
Lamb of God, you take a - way the
sins of the world: grant
rit.
mf Slower
us peace.
3

Setting Three

264 **KYRIE ELEISON**

"New Plainsong"
David Hurd, 1985
Cantor:
Assembly:
Ky - ri - e e - le - i - son. Ky - ri - e e - le - i - son.
Cantor:
Assembly:
Chri - ste e - le - i - son. Chri - ste e - le - i - son.
Cantor:
Assembly:
Ky - ri - e e - le - i - son. Ky - ri - e e - le - i - son.
"New Plainsong"
David Hurd, 1980
Glo - ry to God in the high - est, and peace to his
peo-ple on earth. Lord God, heav-en - ly King, Al-might-y,
God and Fa - ther, we wor-ship you, we give you thanks,
we praise you for your glo - ry. Lord Je - sus Christ,

265 **GLORIA**

only Son of the Father, Lord God, Lamb of God,

You take away the sin of the world: have mercy on us;

you are seated at the right hand of the Father:

receive our prayer. For you alone are the Holy One,

you alone are the Lord, you alone are the

Most High, Jesus Christ, with the Holy Spirit.

in the glory of God the Father, Amen.

SANCTUS 266

"New Plainsong"
David Hurd, 1980

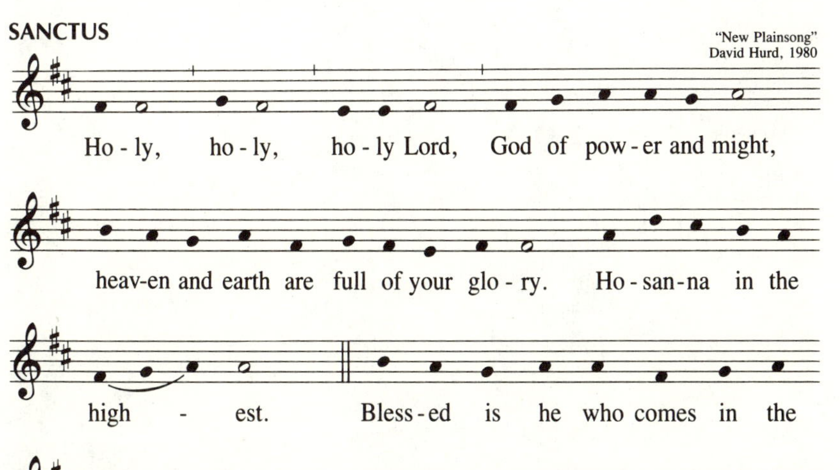
Ho - ly, ho - ly, ho - ly Lord, God of pow - er and might,
heav-en and earth are full of your glo - ry. Ho - san - na in the
high - est. Bless - ed is he who comes in the
name of the Lord. Ho - san - na in the high - est.

267 MEMORIAL ACCLAMATION
"New Plainsong"
David Hurd, 1980
Christ has died, Christ is ris - en, Christ will come a-gain.
268 AMEN
"New Plainsong"
David Hurd, 1980
A - men, a - men, a - men.
269 AGNUS DEI
"New Plainsong"
David Hurd, 1980
Lamb of God, you take a-way the sins of the world: have mer-cy on us.
Lamb of God, you take a-way the sins of the world: have mer-cy on us.
Lamb of God, you take a-way the sins of the world: grant us peace.

Service Music

RITE OF SPRINKLING

270

Chant Mode VII
Adapt. by Richard Proulx, 1975

A - spér - ges me, Dó - mi - ne hys-
Cleanse me from sin, O Lord God, wash
só - po, et mun-dá - bor: la - vá - bis me,
me with hys - sop branch - es: cleanse me from guilt,
et su - per ni - vem de - al - bá - bor.
and I shall be clean as the new snow.
Mis - se - rére me - i, De - us, se - cún-
Have mer - cy on me, O my God, ac - cord-
D.C. (ad lib)
dum magnam miseri - cór - di - am tu - am.
ing to your great com - pas - sion.
Gló - ri - a Patri, et Filio, et Spi - rí - tu - i San - cto:
Glo - ry be to the Father
and to the Son, and to the Ho - ly Spir - it:

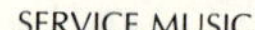

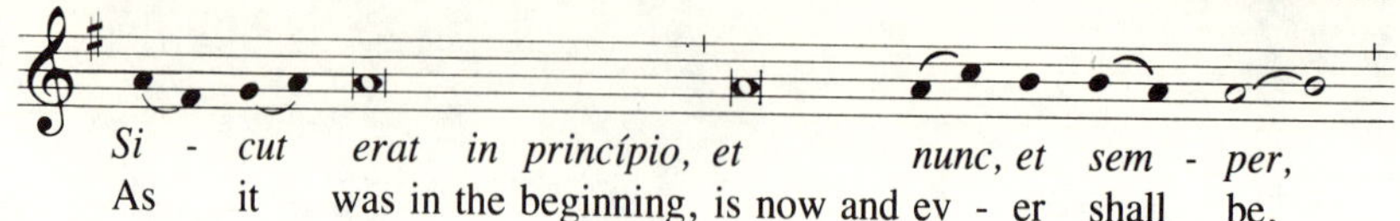
Si - cut erat in princípio, et nunc, et sem - per,
As it was in the beginning, is now and ev - er shall be,

D.C.
et in saécula sae-cu - ló-rum. A - men.
world with - out end. A - men.

271 RITE OF SPRINKLING

Moderately slow
"Festival Liturgy"
Richard Hillert, 1983
Lord Je-sus, from your wound - ed

side flowed streams of cleans-ing wa - ter. Al- le - lu - ia,

al - le - lu - ia, al - le - lu - ia. The world was

wash'd of all its sin, all life made new a - gain. Al-

le - lu - ia, al - le - lu - ia, al - le - lu - ia.

272 RITE OF SPRINKLING

Cantor, then all:
Howard Hughes, SM, 1985
Cleanse us, Lord, from all our sins;
wash us, and we shall be clean as new snow.

Cantor:

I will pour clean wa - ter o - ver you and wash a-way all your sins.

All:

Cleanse us, Lord, from all our sins; wash us, and we shall be clean as new snow.

Cantor:

A new heart, a new heart will I give you, says the Lord.

All:

Cleanse us, Lord, from all our sins; wash us, and we shall be clean as new snow.

Last time

Cleanse us, Lord, from all our sins; wash us, and we shall be clean as new snow.

KYRIE

273

"Deutsche Mass"
Franz Schubert, 1826
Adapt. by Richard Proulx, 1985

Moderately (Massig)
p
Lord, have mer - cy. Lord, have
mer - cy. Christ, have mer - cy.

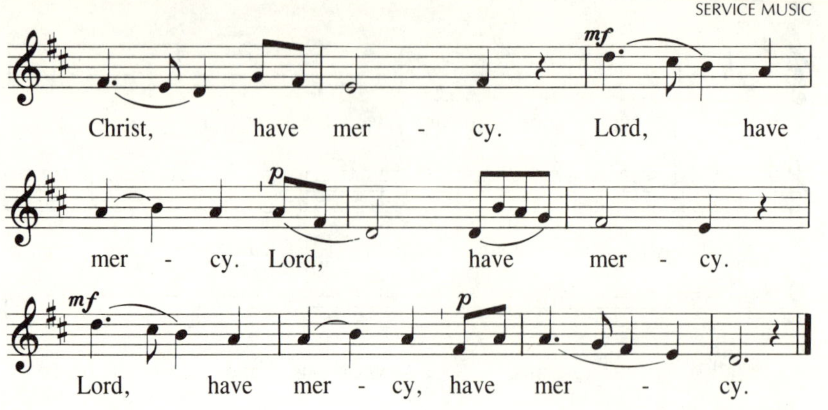
mf
p
Christ, have mer - cy. Lord, have
mer - cy. Lord, have mer - cy.
Lord, have mer - cy, have mer - cy.

274 KYRIE

"Kyrie cum Jubilo"
Acc. by Gerard Farrell, OSB, 1985

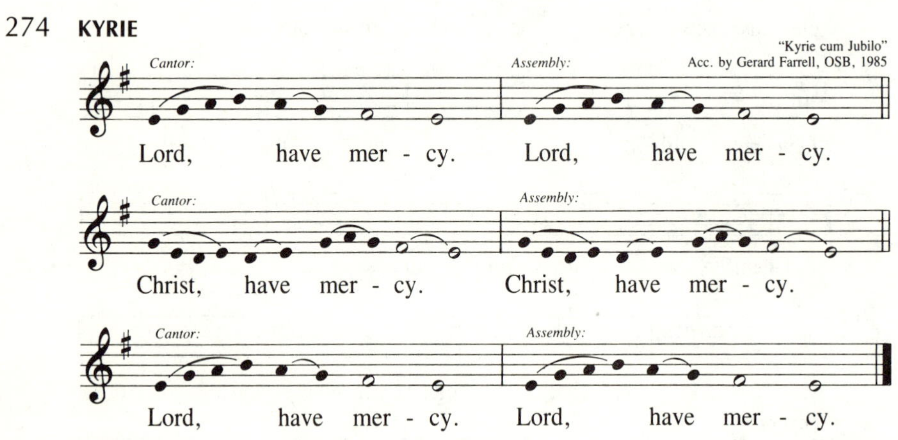
Cantor:
Assembly:
Lord, have mer - cy. Lord, have mer - cy.
Christ, have mer - cy. Christ, have mer - cy.
Lord, have mer - cy. Lord, have mer - cy.

275 KYRIE

"Music for Celebration"
David Hurd, 1979

Choir or cantor, then all:
Ky - ri - e e - le - i - son, Ky - ri - e e - le - i - son,
1.
2.
Ky - ri - e e - le - i - son.
Cantor:
Chri - ste e - le - i - son, Chri -
ste e - le - i - son, Chri - ste e-

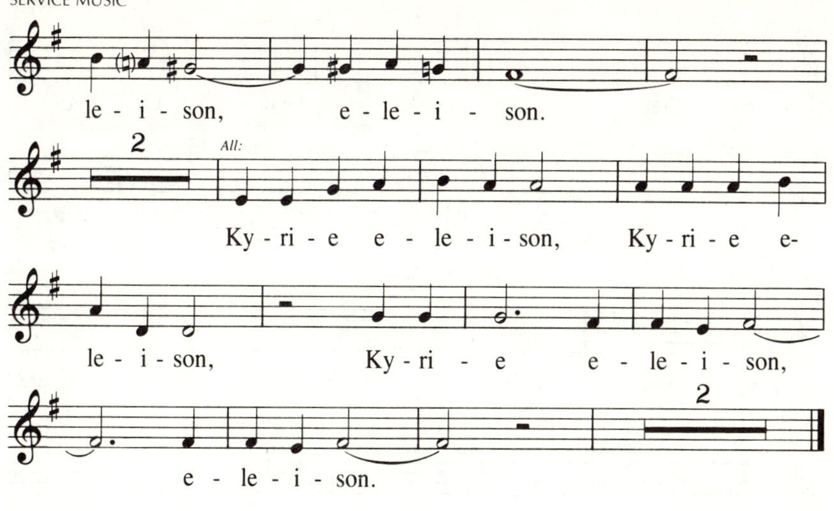
le - i - son, e - le - i - son.
2
All:
Ky - ri - e e - le - i - son, Ky - ri - e e-
le - i - son, Ky - ri - e e - le - i - son,
e - le - i - son.
2

GLORIA 276

John Rutter, 1972

f
Glo - ry to God in the high - est, and
peace to his peo - ple on earth.
mf
Lord God, heav'n - ly King, al-
might - y God and Fa - ther, *f* we
wor - ship you, we give you thanks, we
praise you for your glo - ry.
p
Lord Je - sus Christ, on - ly Son of the

Fa - ther, Lord God, Lamb of

God, you take a - way the sin of the

world: have mer - cy on us; you are

seat - ed at the right hand of the Fa - ther:

re - ceive our prayer. For

you a - lone are the Ho - ly One,

you a - lone are the Lord,

you a - lone are the Most High, Je - sus

Christ, with the Ho - ly Spir - it,

in the glo - ry of God the Fa - ther.

A - men.

GLORIA

"Intercession Mass"
David Hurd, 1979

f
f
Glo - ry to God in the
high-est, and peace to his peo - ple on earth.
2
Lord God, heav - en - ly King, al-
might - y God and Fa - ther,
we wor-ship you, we give you thanks, we
praise you for your glo - ry.
2
3
p
mp
Lord Je - sus Christ, on - ly Son of the Fa - ther,
4
Lord God, Lamb of God, you
take a - way the sin of the world: have
mer - cy on us;
2
you are
seat - ed at the right hand of the Fa - ther, re-

Tempo primo
f
ceive our prayer. For
you a - lone are the Ho - ly One, you a - lone are the
2
Lord, you a - lone are the Most High,
Je - sus Christ, with the Ho - ly Spir - it, in the
glo - ry of God the Fa - ther. A - men.

GLORIA 278

"Congregational Mass"
John Lee, 1970

I (Cantor/Choir)
Glo-ry to God in the high - est, and peace to his peo-ple on earth.
II (Assembly)
Lord God, heav'n-ly King, al-might - y God and Fa - ther.
I
We wor-ship you, we give you thanks, we praise you for your glo - ry.
II
Lord Je - sus Christ, on - ly Son of the Fa - ther,
Lord God, Lamb of God,
I
you take a - way the sin of the world:
have mer-cy on us;
II
you are seat - ed at the right hand of the
Fa - ther: re - ceive our prayer.
I
For you a - lone are the
Ho - ly One, you a - lone are the Lord, you a-
lone are the Most High, Je-sus Christ,
II
with the Ho - ly Spir - it,
Slower
in the glo - ry of God the Fa - ther. A - men.

279 **ALLELUIA**

A.Gregory Murray, OSB, 1958
Al - le - lu - ia, al - le - lu - ia, al - le - lu - ia.

280 **ALLELUIA**

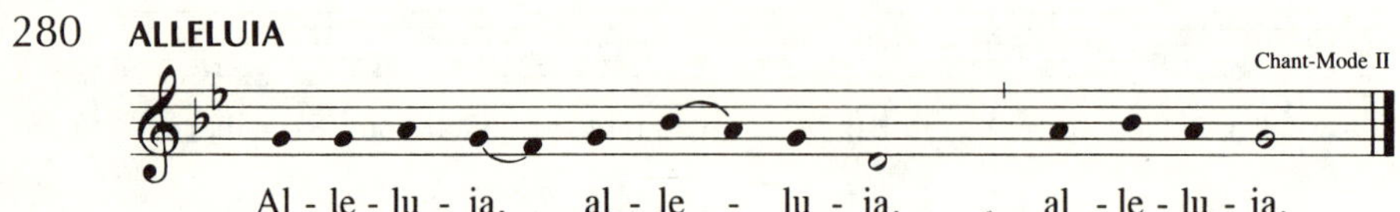
Chant-Mode II
Al - le - lu - ia, al - le - lu - ia, al - le - lu - ia.

281 **ALLELUIA**

Richard Proulx, 1975
4
Al - le - lu - ia,
al - le - lu - ia, al - le - lu - ia, al - le-
lu - ia, al - le - lu - ia.

282 **ALLELUIA**

Howard Hughes, SM, 1973
Cantor:
Al - le - lu - ia, al - le - lu - ia!
Assembly:
Al - le - lu - ia, al - le - lu - ia!
Cantor:
Al - le - lu - ia,
al - le - lu - ia!
Assembly:
Al - le - lu - ia, al - le - lu - ia!
Cantor:
Al - le - lu - ia, al - le - lu - ia!
Assembly:
Al - le - lu - ia,
al - le - lu - ia!
Cantor:
Al - le - lu - ia, al - le - lu - ia!

Assembly:
Al - le - lu - ia, al - le - lu - ia!

ALLELUIA 283

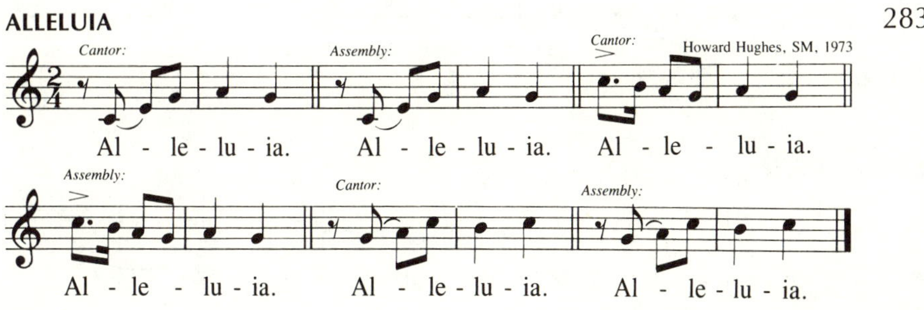
Cantor:
Assembly:
Cantor:
Howard Hughes, SM, 1973
Al - le - lu - ia. Al - le - lu - ia. Al - le - lu - ia.
Assembly:
Cantor:
Assembly:
Al - le - lu - ia. Al - le - lu - ia. Al - le - lu - ia.

ALLELUIA 284

Richard Proulx, 1980
Al - le - lu - ia, al - le-
lu - ia, al - le - lu - ia, al - le - lu - ia,
al - le - lu - ia.

ALLELUIA 285

William H. Monk, 1823-1889
Al - le - lu - ia, al - le - lu - ia, al - le - lu - ia.

ALLELUIA 286

Melchior Vulpius c.1560-1616
Al - le - lu - ia, al - le - lu - ia, al - le - lu - ia.

287 ALLELUIA

Taizé Community
Jacques Berthier, 1984

Al - le - lu - ia, al - le - lu - ia, al - le - lu - ia.
Al - le - lu - ia, al - le - lu - ia, al - le - lu - ia.

288 ALLELUIA

Jerry Sinclair, 1971
Arr. Betty C. Pulkingham, 1971

Al - le - lu - ia, al - le - lu - ia,
al - le - lu - ia, al - le - lu - ia, al - le - lu - ia,
al - le - lu - ia, al - le - lu - ia,
To repeat
Last time
al - le - lu - ia. lu - ia.

289 ALLELUIA

Ralph C. Verdi, CPPS, 1977

Cantor:
Assembly:
Al - le - lu - ia. Al - le-
lu - ia.
Cantor:
Al - le - lu-
ia.
Assembly:
Al - le - lu - ia.
Last time
Cantor:
Assembly:
Al - le - lu - ia. Al - le - lu - ia.

LENTEN ACCLAMATION 290

From "Kyrie Orbis Factor"
Acc. by David Hurd, 1979

Praise and hon - or, to you, O Lord Je-sus Christ.

LENTEN ACCLAMATION 291

From "Kyrie Orbis Factor"
Acc. by David Hurd, 1979

Glo - ry and praise, to you, O Lord Je-sus Christ.

LENTEN ACCLAMATION 292

David M. Young, 1981

Glo - ry and praise to you, Lord Je - sus Christ!

LENTEN ACCLAMATION 293

Richard Proulx, 1975

Glo - ry to you, O
Word of God, Lord Je - sus Christ!

LENTEN ACCLAMATION 294

Howard Hughes, SM, 1980

Glo-ry to you, Word of God, Lord Je - sus Christ!

295 CREDO

Taizé Community
Jacques Berthier, 1984

Refrain
1. Cre - do in u - num De - um,
2. Cre - do in u - num De - um,
cre - do in u - num Dó - mi - num.
cre - do in u - num Spí - ri - tum.

The Apostles' Creed

1. I believe in God, the Father almighty, creator of heaven and earth.

Refrain

2. I believe in Jesus Christ, his only Son, our Lord. He was conceived by the power of the Holy Spirit and born of the Virgin Mary.

Refrain

3. He suffered under Pontius Pilate, was crucified, died, and was buried. He descended to the dead.

Refrain

4. On the Third day he rose again. He ascended into heaven, and is seated at the right hand of the Father. He will come again to judge the living and the dead.

Refrain

5. I believe in the Holy Spirit, the holy catholic Church, the communion of saints, the forgiveness of sins, the resurrection of the body, and the life everlasting.

GENERAL INTERCESSIONS 296

From the Litany of the Saints
Lord, we ask you, hear our prayer.

GENERAL INTERCESSIONS 297

Taizé Community
Jacques Berthier, 1984
Ky - ri - e, Ky - ri - e e - le - i - son; Ky - ri - e,
Ky - ri - e e - le - i - son. (hum)

GENERAL INTERCESSIONS 298

Taizé Community
Jacques Berthier, 1980
Ky - ri - e, Ky - ri - e e - le - i - son. (hum)

GENERAL INTERCESSIONS 299

Ronald F. Krisman, 1977
Gra - cious Lord, hear us, we pray.

GENERAL INTERCESSIONS 300

Robert M. Hutmacher, OFM, 1979
Je - sus, Je - sus, hear our prayer.

301 PREFACE DIALOG

Presider:
Assembly:
Sacramentary, 1966
The Lord be with you. And al - so with you.
Presider:
Assembly:
Lift up your hearts. We lift them up to the Lord.
Presider:
Let us give thanks to the Lord our God.
Assembly:
It is right to give him thanks and praise.

302 SANCTUS

Sacramentary, 1974
Acc. by Robert J. Batastini, 1975
Ho - ly, ho - ly, ho - ly Lord, God of pow'r and might,
heav - en and earth are full of your glo - ry.
Ho - san - na in the high - est. Bless-ed is he who
comes in the name of the Lord. Ho - san - na in the high - est.

303 MEMORIAL ACCLAMATION

Sacramentary, 1974
Adapt. by Robert J. Batastini, 1975
Christ has died, Christ is ris - en, Christ will come a - gain.

SANCTUS

304

"Deutsche Messe"
Franz Schubert, 1826
Adapt. by Richard Proulx, 1984

mp Slowly (Langsam)
Ho - ly, ho - ly, ho - ly Lord, God of
pow'r and might, Ho - ly, ho - ly,
ho - ly Lord, God of pow'r and might,
f
heav - en and earth are full,
mf
full of your glo - ry. Ho - san - na
in the high - est, ho - san - na in the
f
high - est. Bless - ed is he who comes
mp
in the name of the Lord. Ho - san - na in the
dim.
high - est, ho - san - na in the high - est.

SANCTUS

305

Joseph Gelineau, SJ, 1979
Adapt. from Eucharistic Prayer for Children
by Richard Proulx, 1985

Cantor:
Ho - ly, ho - ly, ho - ly Lord, God of pow - er and
might,
Assembly:
Ho - ly, ho - ly, ho - ly Lord,

Cantor:
God of pow-er and might, heav'n and earth are full of your glo - ry.
Ho - san - na in the high - est.
Assembly:
Ho - san - na in the high - est.
Cantor:
Blest is he who comes in the name of the Lord.
Ho - san - na in the high - est.
Assembly:
Ho - san - na in the high - est.
306 SANCTUS
With Majesty
"A Festival Eucharist"
Richard Proulx, 1975
Choir:
Ho - ly, ho - ly, ho - ly Lord, God of pow'r and might,
All:
ho - ly, ho - ly ho - ly Lord, God of pow'r and might,
Choir:
heav - en and earth are full of your glo - ry, God of pow'r and might.
All:
God of pow'r and might.
Choir:
Ho - san - na in the high - est, ho -

san - na in the high - est, ho - san - na in the
high - est. Ho - san - na in the high - est, ho-
san - na in the high - est, ho - san - na in the
high - est. Bless - ed is he who
comes in the name of the Lord. Ho-
san - na in the high - est, ho - san - na in the
high - est, ho - san - na in the high - est, ho-
san - na in the high - est.
ff All:
mf Choir:
MEMORIAL ACCLAMATION
307
"A Festival Eucharist"
Richard Proulx, 1975
f
When we eat this
bread and drink this cup, we pro - claim your death, Lord
Je - sus, un - til you come in glo - ry.

308 AMEN
"A Festival Eucharist"
Richard Proulx, 1975
ff
A - men,
a - men, a -
men, a - men.
309 SANCTUS
"Land of Rest"
Adapt. by Marcia Pruner, 1980
Acc. by Richard Proulx, 1984
Ho - ly, ho - ly, ho - ly Lord,
God of pow - er and might,
heav - en and earth are full of your glo - ry. Ho-
san - na in the high - est. Bless - ed is
he who comes in the name of the
Lord. Ho - san - na in the
high - est, ho - san - na in the high - est.

MEMORIAL ACCLAMATION 310

"Land of Rest"
Adapt. by Richard Proulx, 1984

SANCTUS 311

"Mass of the Divine Word"
Howard Hughes, SM, 1981

Christ has died, Christ is ris - en,
Christ will come a - gain. Christ has died,
Christ is ris - en, Christ will come a - gain.
All:
Ho - san - na! Ho - san - na! Ho - san - na in the high-est!
Choir or cantor:
Ho - ly, ho - ly, ho - ly Lord God of pow'r and might—
All:
Ho - san - na! Ho - san - na! Ho - san - na in the high - est! —
Cantor or choir:
heav-en and earth are full of your glo - ry.
All:
Ho - san - na! Ho - san - na! Ho - san - na in the high - est!
Cantor:
Bless-ed is he, bless-ed is he who comes in the name of the Lord.
All:
Ho - san - na! Ho - san - na! Ho - san - na in the high - est!

312 MEMORIAL ACCLAMATION

"Mass of the Divine Word"
Howard Hughes, SM, 1984
Cantor:
When we eat this bread and drink this cup,
Assembly:
When we eat this bread and drink this cup,
Cantor:
we pro - claim your death, Lord Je - sus,
Assembly:
we pro - claim your death, Lord Je - sus,
Cantor:
un - til you come in glo - ry,
Assembly:
un - til you come in glo - ry.
313 AMEN
"Mass of the Divine Word"
Howard Hughes, SM, 1984
A - men, a - men, a - men!
314 SANCTUS
"Mass of Creation"
Marty Haugen, 1984
f
Ho - ly, ho - ly, ho - ly, Lord,
God of pow - er, God of might,

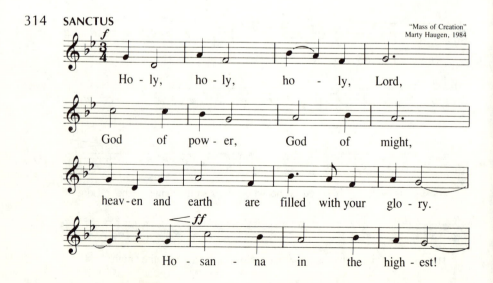

heav - en and earth are filled with your glo - ry.

ff

Ho - san - na in the high - est!

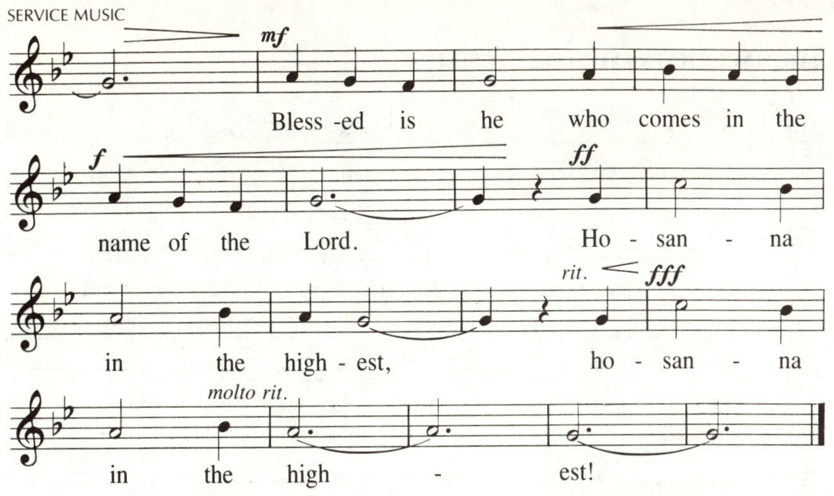
mf
Bless -ed is he who comes in the
f
ff
name of the Lord. Ho - san - na
rit.
fff
in the high - est, ho - san - na
molto rit.
in the high - est!

MEMORIAL ACCLAMATION 315

"Mass of Creation"
Marty Haugen, 1984

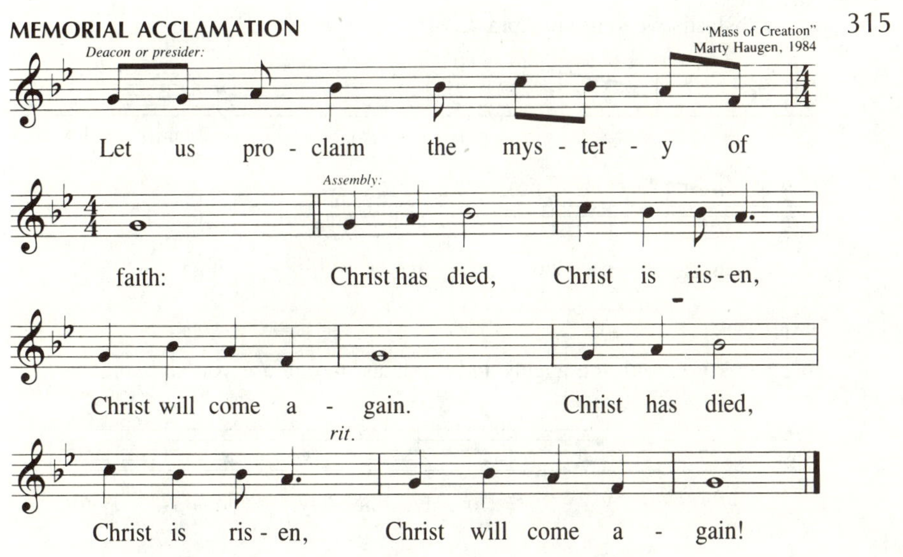
Deacon or presider:
Let us pro - claim the mys - ter - y of
faith:
Assembly:
Christ has died, Christ is ris - en,
Christ will come a - gain. Christ has died,
rit.
Christ is ris - en, Christ will come a - gain!

AMEN 316

"Mass of Creation"
Marty Haugen, 1984

f
A - men, a - men, a-
men!
rit.
molto rit.
A - men, a - men, a - men!

317 EUCHARISTIC PRAYER FOR CHILDREN II

Presider:
Assembly:
Richard Proulx, 1982
The Lord be with you. And al - so with you.
Presider:
Assembly:
Lift up your hearts. We lift them up to the Lord.
Presider:
Let us give thanks to the Lord our God.
Assembly:
It is right to give him thanks and praise.

Three different times during the Preface we sing the following acclamation after the priest says:

...With Jesus we sing your praise:

mf
Ho - san - na, ho-
san - na, ho - san - na in the high - est.

318 SANCTUS

We thank you with the angels and saints as they praise you and sing:

f
Ho - ly, ho - ly, ho - ly Lord,
God of pow-er and might, heav - en and
earth are full of your glo - ry. Ho-
san - na, ho - san - na, ho - san - na in the

ff
high - est. Ho - ly, ho - ly, ho - ly Lord,
God of pow-er and might. Bless - ed is
he who comes in the name of the
Lord. Ho - san - na, ho - san - na, ho-
san - na in the high - est.

…He promised to send the Holy Spirit, to be with us always so that we can live as your children.

f
Bless - ed is he who comes in the
name of the Lord. Ho - san - na, ho-
san - na, ho - san - na in the high - est.

319 MEMORIAL ACCLAMATION

The following is sung as the priest shows the consecrated host to the people, and again when he shows the chalice:

f
Je - sus has giv - en his life for us.

The following is sung after each of these four texts:

...He put himself into our hands to be the sacrifice we offer you.
...all other bishops, and all who serve your people.
...Bring them home to you to be with you for ever.
...friends of Jesus the Lord will sing a song of joy.

f
We praise you, we
bless you, we thank you.

320 AMEN

...almighty Father, for ever and ever.

f
*[𝄐]
A - men, a - men, a - men.
A - men, a - men, a - men, a - men.
*[𝄐]
A - men, a - men, a - men.
ff
A - men, a - men, a - men.
A - men, a - men, a - men, a - men.

**Possible endings*

A - men, a - men, a - men.

MEMORIAL ACCLAMATION 321

"Mass of the Redeemer"
Richard Proulx, 1972

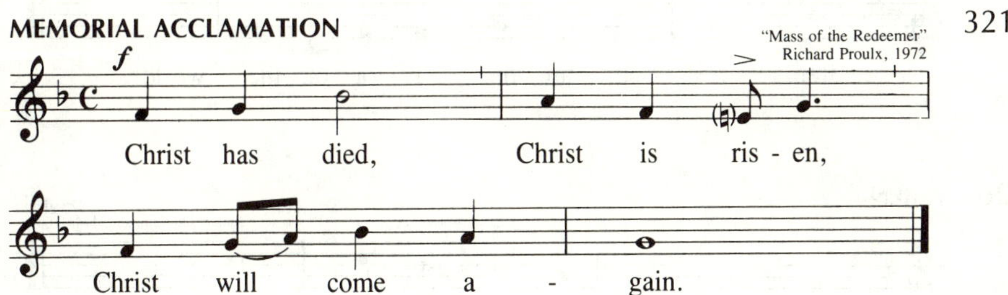
f
Christ has died, Christ is ris - en,
Christ will come a - gain.

MEMORIAL ACCLAMATION 322

Christus Vincit
Adapt. by Richard Proulx, 1985

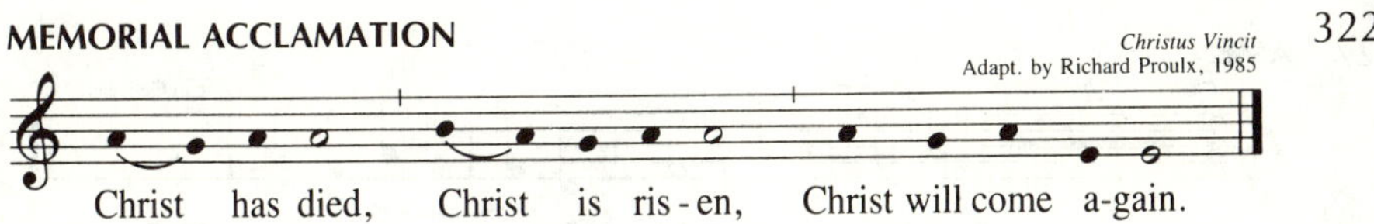
Christ has died, Christ is ris - en, Christ will come a-gain.

MEMORIAL ACCLAMATION 323

John Rutter, 1982

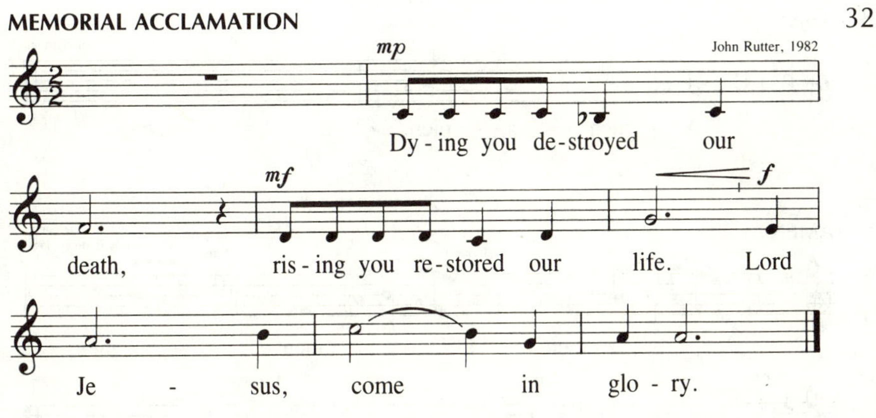
mp
Dy - ing you de - stroyed our
mf
f
death, ris - ing you re - stored our life. Lord
Je - sus, come in glo - ry.

MEMORIAL ACCLAMATION 324

John Lee, 1970

Lord, by your cross and res - ur - rec - tion, you have
set us free. You are the Sav - ior of the world.

325 **MEMORIAL ACCLAMATION**

Howard Hughes, SM 1975
f
Lord, by your cross and res - ur - rec-tion you have set us
free. You are the Sav-ior of the world.

326 **AMEN**

Dresden
Johann G. Naumann, 1741-1801
A - men, a - men.

327 **AMEN**

Choir:
4
All:
Joseph Gelineau, 1953
A - men, A - men,

328 **AMEN**

Anonymous
A - men, a - men, a - men.

329 **AMEN**

Taizé Community
Jacques Berthier, 1980
Cantor:
Assembly:
Cantor:
A - men, a - men. A - men,
Assembly:
Cantor:
Assembly:
a - men. A - men, a - men.

330 **AMEN**

From Sanctus VIII
Acc. by Richard Proulx, 1985
A - men. A - men. A - men.

LORD'S PRAYER

"Lyric Liturgy"
Alexander Peloquin, 1974

Presider:
Let us pray with con - fi - dence to the Fa - ther
in the words our Sav - ior gave us:
Expressively
All:
Our Fa - ther, who art in heav - en,
hal - lowed be thy name; thy
king - dom come; thy will be done on
earth as it is in heav - en.
Give us this day our dai - ly bread; and forgive us our tres - pass - es as we forgive those who tres - pass a - gainst us; and
lead us not in - to temp - ta - tion, but de-
liv - er us from e - vil.

After the prayer "Deliver Us":

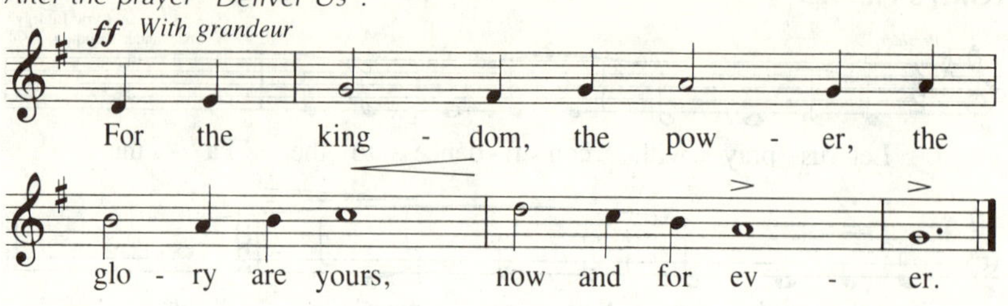
ff With grandeur
For the king - dom, the pow - er, the
glo - ry are yours, now and for ev - er.

332 **LORD'S PRAYER**

"A Festival Eucharist"
Richard Proulx, 1975

mp

Our Fath - er, who art in
heav-en, hal-lowed be thy name; thy
king - dom come; thy will be done on
earth as it is in heav - en.
Give us this day our dai - ly bread; and forgive us our tres - pass - es as
we for-give those who tres - pass a - gainst
us; and lead us not in - to temp-
ta - tion, but de - liv - er us from e - vil.

After the prayer "Deliver Us":

For the king-dom the pow - er, and the
glo - ry are yours, now and for ev - er.
Rall.
AGNUS DEI
333
Richard Proulx, 1975
Lamb of God, you take a - way the
sins of the world: have mer - cy on us.
Lamb of God, you take a - way the sins of the
world: grant us peace, grant us peace.
AGNUS DEI
334
"Lyric Liturgy"
Alexander Peloquin, 1974
Cantor or choir, then all:
Lamb of God, you take a - way the sins of the world:
have mer - cy on us.
Cantor or choir, then all:
Lamb of God, you take a - way the sins of the world:
have mer - cy on us.

Cantor or Choir:
Lamb of God, you take a - way the
sins of the world: have mer - cy on us.
All: ff
Lamb of God, you take a - way the
sins of the world: grant us peace.
335 AGNUS DEI
Cantor:
Howard Hughes, SM, 1981
Lamb of God,
you take a - way the sins of the world: have
mer - cy on us. Assembly: Have mer - cy on us.
Cantor:
Lamb of God, you take a - way the sins of the world: have
mer - cy on us. Assembly: Have mer - cy on us.
Cantor:
Lamb of God, you take a - way the sins of the world:
grant us peace. Assembly: Grant us peace.

AGNUS DEI 336

Ostinato Response

Taizé Community
Jacques Berthier, 1984

p
Do - na no - bis pa - cem.

AGNUS DEI 337

Canon

Taizé Community
Jacques Berthier, 1980

A
Grave
B
A - gnus De - i qui tol - lis pec - ca - ta
C
D
mun - di, mi - se - re - re no - bis.
Last time: do - na no - bis pa - cem.

AGNUS DEI 338

"Festival Liturgy"
Richard Hillert, 1983

Moderately Slow
Choir or cantor:
Lamb of God,
Assembly:
To repeat
you take a - way the sins of the world, have
Last time
mer - cy on us. world, grant
us peace.

AGNUS DEI 339

"Holy Cross Mass"
David Clark Isele, 1979

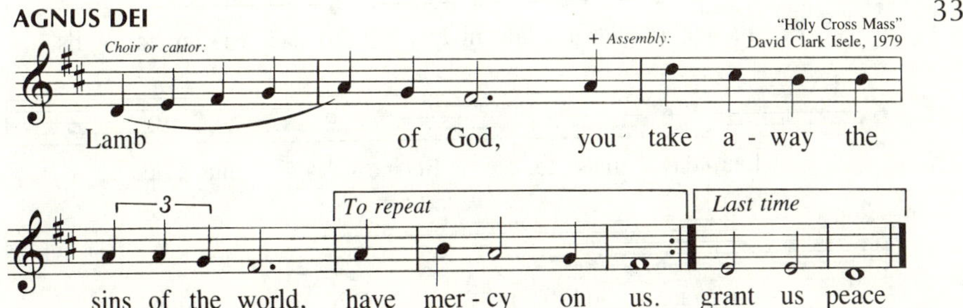
Choir or cantor:
+ Assembly:
Lamb of God, you take a - way the
3
To repeat
Last time
sins of the world, have mer - cy on us. grant us peace

Cantus Missae

INTRODUCTORY RITES

340 **KYRIE**

ed. Vat. XVI
Acc. by Gerard Farrell, OSB, 1985
Ky - ri - e, e - le - i - son. Ky - ri - e, e - le - i - son.
Chri-ste, e - le - i - son. Chri - ste, e - le - i - son. Ky - ri-
e, e - le - i - son. Ky-ri - e, e - le - i - son.
341 GLORIA
ed. Vat. VIII
Gerard Farrell, OSB, 1985
Glo - ri - a in ex - cel - sis De - o.
Et in ter - ra pax ho - mi - ni - bus bo-nae vo-lun - ta - tis.
Lau - da - mus te. Be - ne - di - ci - mus te.
A - do - ra - mus te. Glo - ri - fi - ca-mus te.

Gra-ti-as a-gi-mus ti-bi pro-pter ma-gnam glo-ri-am
tu-am. Do-mi-ne De-us, Rex cae-les-tis,
De-us Pa-ter om-ni-po-tens. Do-mi-ne Fi-li
u-ni-ge-ni-te, Je-su Chri-ste. Do-mi-ne
De-us, A-gnus De-i, Fi-li-us Pa-tris.
Qui tol-lis pec-ca-ta mun-di, mi-se-re-
re no-bis. Qui tol-lis pec-ca-ta mun-di, su-sci-pe
de-pre-ca-ti-o-nem no-stram. Qui se-des ad
dex-ter-am Pa-tris, mi-se-re-re no-bis. Quo-ni-am tu
so-lus San-ctus. Tu so-lus Do-mi-nus. Tu so-lus
Al-tis-si-mus, Je-su Chri-ste. Cum San-cto
Spi-ri-tu, in glo-ri-a De-i

Pa - tris. A - men.

LITURGY OF THE WORD

342 **THE FIRST READINGS**

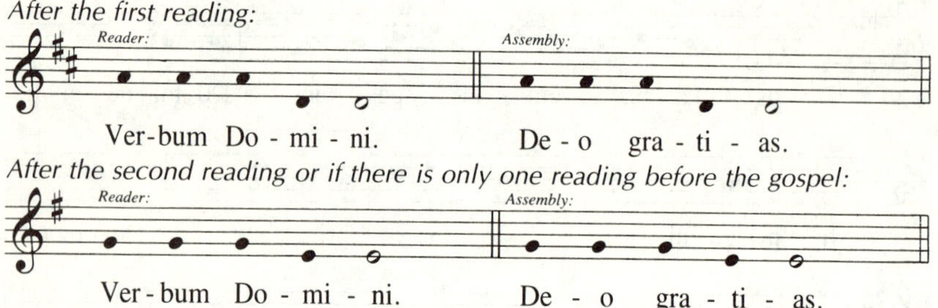
After the first reading:
Reader:
Assembly:
Ver-bum Do - mi - ni. De - o gra - ti - as.
After the second reading or if there is only one reading before the gospel:
Reader:
Assembly:
Ver-bum Do - mi - ni. De - o gra - ti - as.

343 **ALLELUIA**

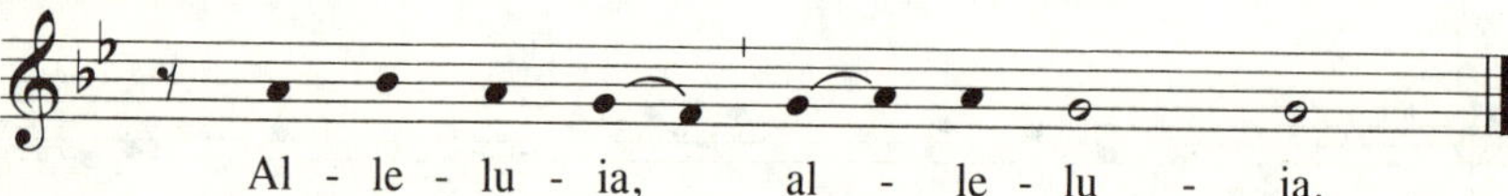
Al - le - lu - ia, al - le - lu - ia.

344 **GOSPEL**

Before the gospel:
Deacon or Priest:
Assembly:
Deacon:
Do-mi-nus vo-bis-cum. Et cum spi - ri - tu tu - o. Le-cti - o san-
Assembly:
cti E - van-ge - li - i se-cun-dum N... Glo - ri - a ti - bi, Do-mi-ne.
After the gospel:
Deacon:
Assembly:
Ver-bum Do - mi - ni. Laus ti - bi, Chri - ste.

345 **CREDO**

ed. Vat. III
Acc. by Gerard Farrell, OSB, 1985

Cre-do in u-num De - um, Pa - trem om - ni - po - ten-tem fa-

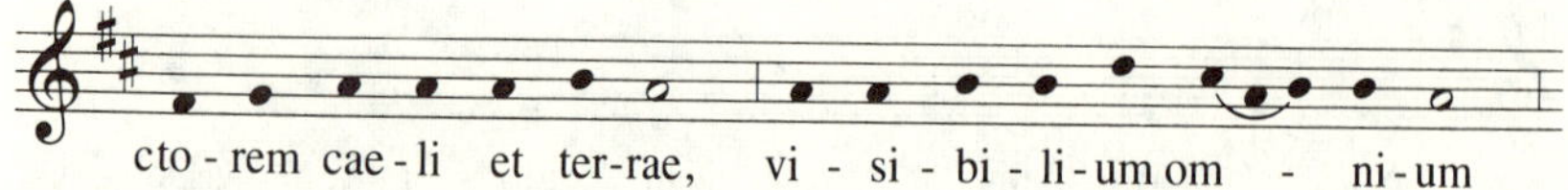
cto - rem cae - li et ter-rae, vi - si - bi - li-um om - ni-um

et in-vi-si-bi - li-um. Et in u-num Do-mi-num
Je-sum Chri-stum, Fi-li-um De-i u-ni-ge-ni-tum.
Et ex Pa-tre na - tum an-te om-ni-a sae - cu-la.
De-um de De-o, lu-men de lu-mi-ne, De-um ve-rum
de De-o ve - ro. Ge-ni-tum, non fa - ctum.
con-sub-stan-ti - a-lem Pa-tri: per quem om-ni-a fa-cta sunt.
Qui pro-pter nos ho-mi-nes et pro-pter nost-ram sa-lu-tem
de-scen-dit de cae-lis. Et in-car-na-tus est de Spi-ri-tu
San-cto ex Ma-ri-a Vir-gi-ne, et ho-mo fa-ctus est.
Cru-ci - fi - xus e-ti-am pro no - bis
sub Pon-ti-o Pi-la-to, pas-sus et se-pul - tus est.
Et re-sur-re-xit ter-ti-a di-e. se-cun-dum Scri-ptu-ras.

Et a - scen-dit in cae - lum, se-det ad dex - te-ram Pa - tris.
Et i - te-rum ven - tu - rus est cum glo - ri - a, ju - di - ca - re
vi - vos et mor - tu - os, cu - jus re - gni non e - rit fi - nis.
Et in Spi - ri - tum San-ctum, Do-mi-num et vi - vi - fi - can-tem:
qui ex Pa - tre Fi - li - o - que pro - ce - dit. Qui cum
Pa - tre et Fi - li - o si - mul a - do - ra - tur et con-glo-
ri - fi - ca - tur: qui lo - cu - tus est per pro - phe - tas.
Et u-nam, san-ctam, ca - tho - li - cam et a - po - sto - li-
cam Ec - cle - si - am. Con - fi - te - or u-num Ba - ptis - ma
in re - mis - si - o-nem pec - ca - to - rum. Et ex- - cto
re - sur-re - cti - o-nem mor - tu - o - rum. Et vi - tam ven-
tu - ri sae-cu-li. A - men.

GENERAL INTERCESSIONS 346

After each intention:

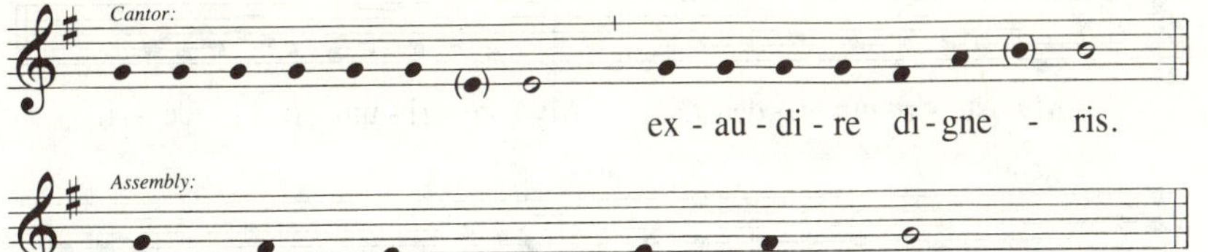
Cantor:
ex - au - di - re di - gne - ris.

Assembly:

Te ro - ga - mus, au - di - nos.

LITURGY OF THE EUCHARIST

PREFACE DIALOG 347

Presider: Do - mi - nus vo - bi - scum.

Assembly: Et cum Spir - i - tu tu - o.

Sur - sum cor - da.

Assembly: Ha - be - mus ad Do - mi - num.

Presider: Gra - ti - as a - ga - mus Do - mi - no De - o no - stro.

Assembly: Di - gnum et iu - stum est.

SANCTUS 348

ed. Vat. XVIII
Acc. by Gerard Farrell, OSB, 1985

San - ctus, San - ctus, San - ctus Do - mi - nus De - us Sa - ba - oth.

Ple - ni sunt cae - li et ter - ra glo - ri - a tu - a. Ho - san - na

in ex - cel - sis. Be - ne - di - ctus qui ve - nit in no - mi - ne

Do - mi - ni. Ho - san - na in ex - cel - sis.

349 MEMORIAL ACCLAMATION

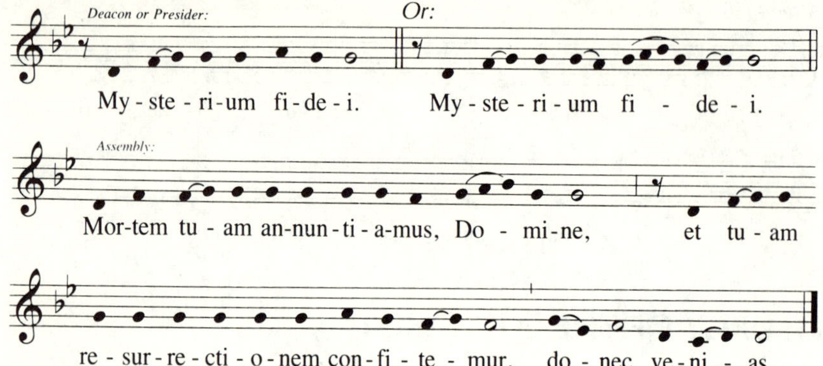
Deacon or Presider:
My - ste - ri - um fi - de - i.
Or:
My - ste - ri - um fi - de - i.
Assembly:
Mor-tem tu - am an-nun - ti - a-mus, Do - mi-ne, et tu - am
re - sur - re - cti - o - nem con - fi - te - mur, do - nec ve - ni - as.

350 AMEN

After the doxology:

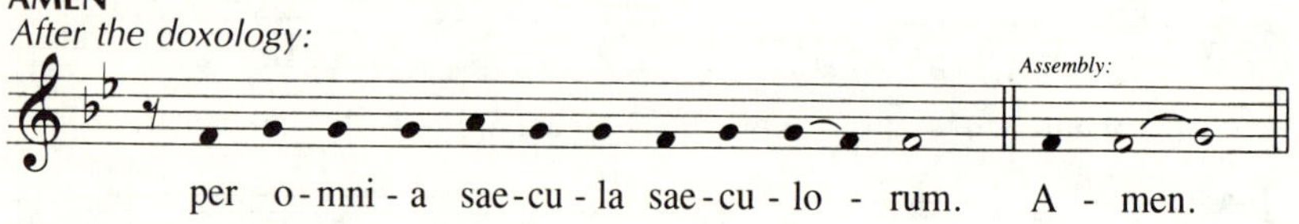
Assembly:
per o - mni - a sae - cu - la sae - cu - lo - rum. A - men.

COMMUNION RITE

351 LORD'S PRAYER

Presider:
Prae - ce - ptis sa - lu - ta - ri - bus mo - ni - ti, et di - vi - na
in - sti - tu - ti - o - ne for - ma - ti, au - de - mus di - ce - re:
All:
Acc. by Gerard Farrell, OSB, 1985
Pa - ter no - ster, qui es in cae - lis: san - cti - fi - ce - tur no - men
tu - um; ad - ve - ni - at re - gnum tu - um; fi - at vo - lun - tas
tu - a, si - cut in cae - lo, et in ter - ra. Pa - nem
no - strum co - ti - di - a - num da no - bis ho - di - e; et di - mit - te

no-bis de-bi-ta no-stra, si-cut et nos di-mit-ti-mus de-bi-
to-ri-bus no-stris; et ne nos in-du-cas in ten-ta-ti-
o - nem; sed li-be-ra nos a ma - lo.
After the prayer "Libera nos":
Qui-a tu-um est re-gnum, et po-te - stas,
et glo-ri-a in sae-cu-la.
SIGN OF PEACE
352
Presider:
Qui vivis et regnas in saecula sae-cu-lo - rum.
Assembly:
A - men.
Presider:
Pax Do - mi-ni sit sem-per
vo-bis - cum.
Assembly:
Et cum spi-ri-tu tu-o.
AGNUS DEI
353
ed. Vat. XVIII
Acc. by Gerard Farrell, OSB, 1985
A-gnus De-i, qui tol-lis pec-ca-ta mun-di: mi-se-re-re no-bis.
A-gnus De-i, qui tol-lis pec-ca-ta mun-di: mi-se-re-re no-bis.
A-gnus De-i, qui tol-lis pec-ca-ta mun-di: do-na no-bis pa-cem.

CONCLUDING RITE

354 **DISMISSAL**

Deacon or Presider:
Assembly:
I - te, mis - sa est. De - o gra - ti - as.

For Easter Sunday and the octave of Easter:

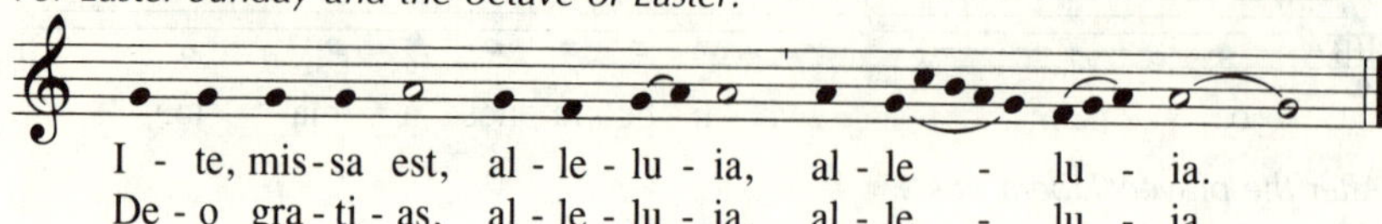
I - te, mis-sa est, al - le - lu - ia, al - le - lu - ia.
De - o gra - ti - as, al - le - lu - ia, al - le - lu - ia.

When the King Shall Come Again 355

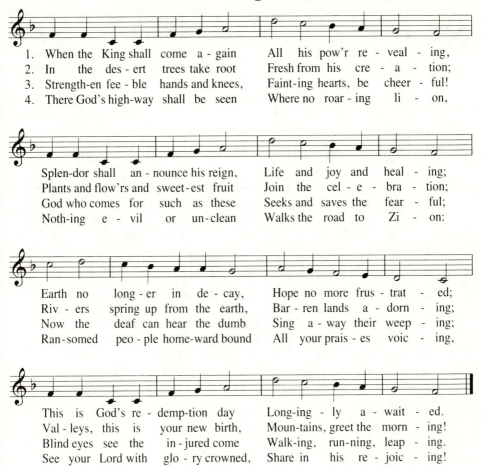

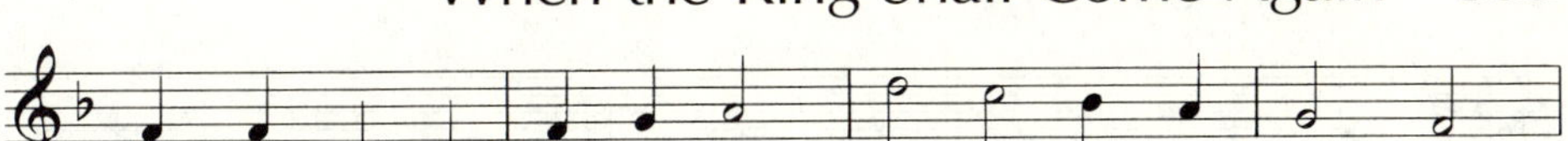

1. When the King shall come a - gain All his pow'r re - veal - ing,
2. In the des - ert trees take root Fresh from his cre - a - tion;
3. Strength-en fee - ble hands and knees, Faint-ing hearts, be cheer - ful!
4. There God's high-way shall be seen Where no roar - ing li - on,

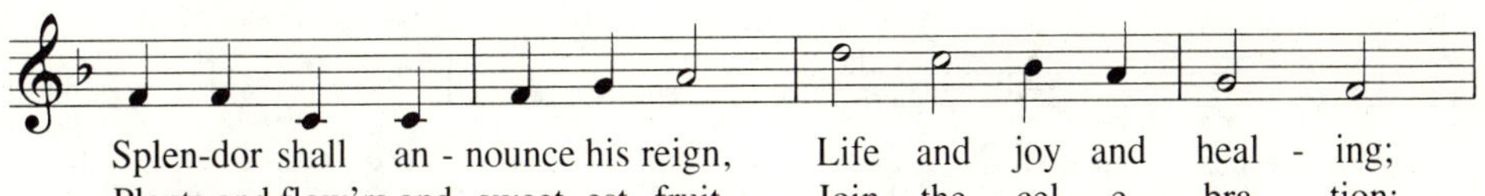

Splen-dor shall an - nounce his reign, Life and joy and heal - ing;
Plants and flow'rs and sweet-est fruit Join the cel - e - bra - tion;
God who comes for such as these Seeks and saves the fear - ful;
Noth-ing e - vil or un-clean Walks the road to Zi - on:

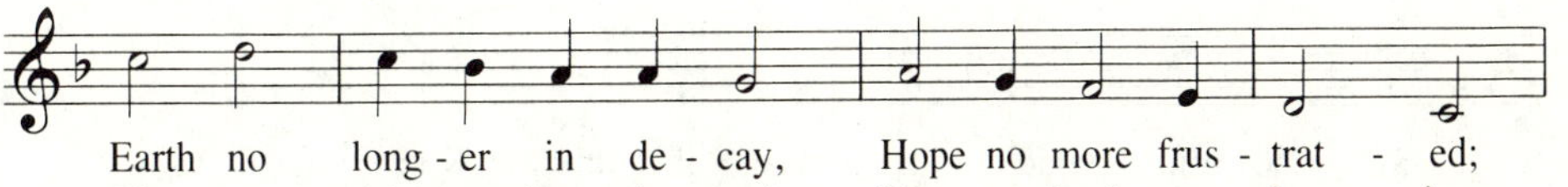

Earth no long - er in de - cay, Hope no more frus - trat - ed;
Riv - ers spring up from the earth, Bar - ren lands a - dorn - ing;
Now the deaf can hear the dumb Sing a - way their weep - ing;
Ran-somed peo - ple home-ward bound All your prais - es voic - ing,

This is God's re - demp-tion day Long-ing - ly a - wait - ed.
Val - leys, this is your new birth, Moun-tains, greet the morn - ing!
Blind eyes see the in - jured come Walk-ing, run-ning, leap - ing.
See your Lord with glo - ry crowned, Share in his re - joic - ing!

Text: Is. 35; Christopher Idle, b.1938,
Tune: GAUDEAMUS PARITER, 7 6 7 6 D; Johann Horn, c.1495-1547

356 On Jordan's Bank

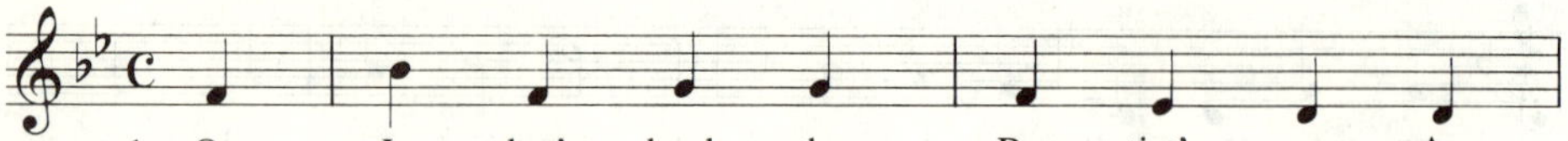

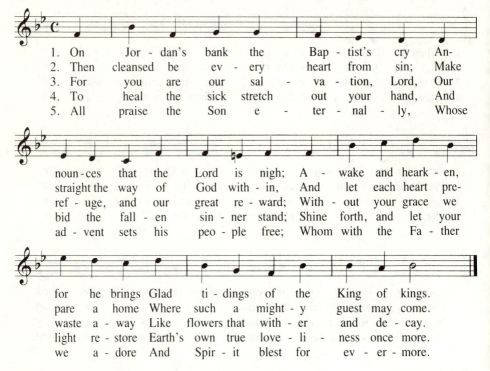

1. On Jor - dan's bank the Bap - tist's cry An-
2. Then cleansed be ev - ery heart from sin; Make
3. For you are our sal - va - tion, Lord, Our
4. To heal the sick stretch out your hand, And
5. All praise the Son e - ter - nal - ly, Whose

noun - ces that the Lord is nigh; A - wake and heark - en,
straight the way of God with - in, And let each heart pre-
ref - uge, and our great re - ward; With - out your grace we
bid the fall - en sin - ner stand; Shine forth, and let your
ad - vent sets his peo - ple free; Whom with the Fa - ther

for he brings Glad ti - dings of the King of kings.
pare a home Where such a might - y guest may come.
waste a - way Like flowers that with - er and de - cay.
light re - store Earth's own true love - li - ness once more.
we a - dore And Spir - it blest for ev - er - more.

Text: *Jordanis oras praevia;* Charles Coffin, 1676-1749; Tr. by John Chandler, 1806-1876
Tune: WINCHESTER NEW, LM; Adapt. from *Musikalisches Handbuch*, Hamburg, 1690

357 O Come, O Come, Emmanuel

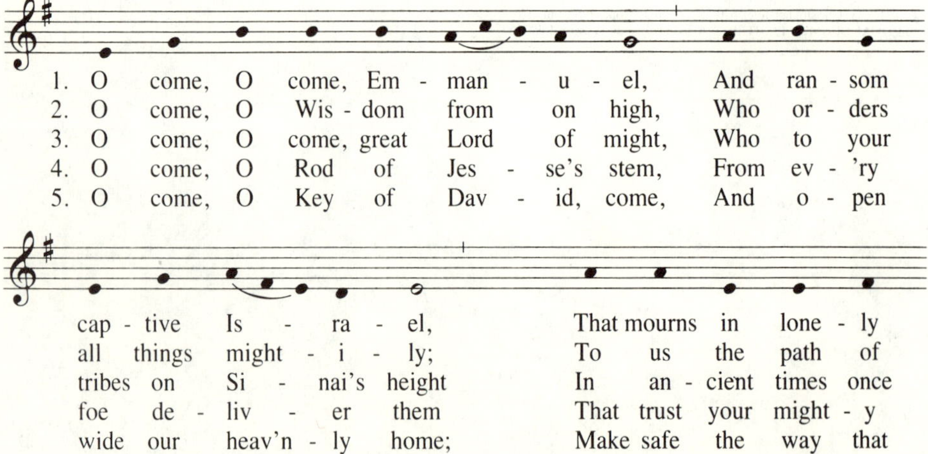
1. O come, O come, Em - man - u - el, And ran - som
2. O come, O Wis - dom from on high, Who or - ders
3. O come, O come, great Lord of might, Who to your
4. O come, O Rod of Jes - se's stem, From ev - 'ry
5. O come, O Key of Dav - id, come, And o - pen
cap - tive Is - ra - el, That mourns in lone - ly
all things might - i - ly; To us the path of
tribes on Si - nai's height In an - cient times once
foe de - liv - er them That trust your might - y
wide our heav'n - ly home; Make safe the way that

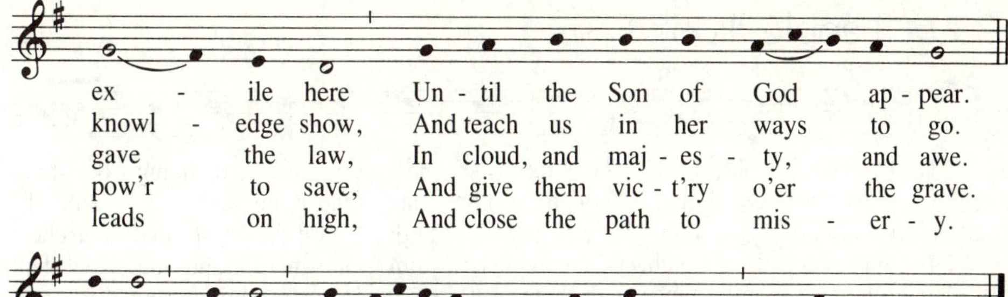
ex - ile here Un - til the Son of God ap - pear.
knowl - edge show, And teach us in her ways to go.
gave the law, In cloud, and maj - es - ty, and awe.
pow'r to save, And give them vic - t'ry o'er the grave.
leads on high, And close the path to mis - er - y.

Re-joice! Re-joice! Em - man - u - el Shall come to you, O Is - ra - el.

6. O come, O Dayspring from on high
And cheer us by your drawing nigh;
Disperse the gloomy clouds of night,
And death's dark shadow put to flight.

7. O come, Desire of nations, bind
In one the hearts of humankind;
O bid our sad divisions cease,
And be for us our King of Peace.

Text: *Veni, veni Emmanuel:* Latin 9th C.; Tr. by John M. Neale, 1818-1866, alt.
Tune: VENI, VENI EMMANUEL, LM with refrain; Mode I; Adapt. by Thomas Helmore, 1811-1890; Acc. by Richard Proulx, b.1937, © 1975, GIA Publications, Inc.

The Voice of God Goes Out through All the World 358

1. The voice of God goes out through all the world: God's glo - ry speaks a - cross the u - ni - verse. The great King's her - ald cries from star to star: With pow'r, with jus - tice, he will walk his way.
2. The Lord has said: "Re - ceive my mes - sen - ger, My prom - ise to the world, my pledge made flesh, A lamp to ev - 'ry na - tion, light from light: With pow'r, with jus - tice, he will walk his way."
3. The bro - ken reed he will not tram - ple down, Nor set his heel up - on the dy - ing flame, He binds the wounds, and health is in his hand: With pow'r, with jus - tice, he will walk his way.
4. A - noint - ed with the Spir - it and with power, He comes to crown with com - fort all the weak, To show the face of jus - tice to the poor: With pow'r, with jus - tice, he will walk his way.
5. His touch will bless the eyes that dark - ness held, The lame shall run, the halt - ing tongue shall sing, And pri - s'ners laugh in light and lib - er - ty: With pow'r, with jus - tice, he will walk his way.

Text: Luke Connaughton, 1919-1979, © 1970, Mayhew McCrimmon Ltd.
Tune: TOULON, 10 10 10 10; *Genevan Psalter,* 1551; Harm. by Louis Bourgeois, c.1510-1561

359 People, Look East

1. Peo - ple, look East. The time is near Of the crown-ing of the
2. Fur-rows, be glad. Though earth is bare, One more seed is plant-ed
3. Birds, though you long have ceased to build, Guard the nest that must be
4. Stars, keep the watch. When night is dim One more light the bowl shall
5. An - gels an - nounce with shouts of mirth Him who brings new life to

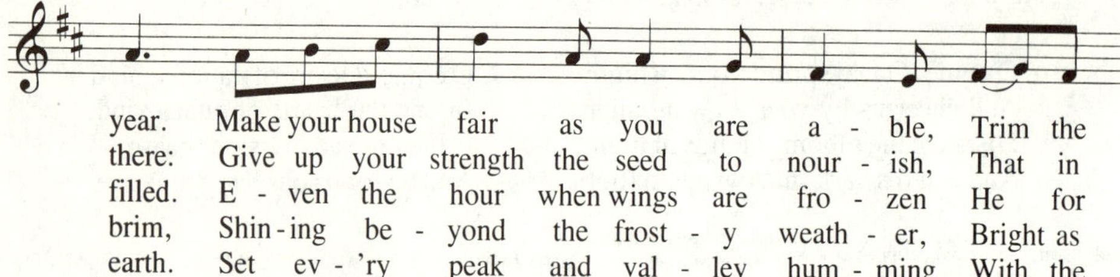

year. Make your house fair as you are a - ble, Trim the
there: Give up your strength the seed to nour - ish, That in
filled. E - ven the hour when wings are fro - zen He for
brim, Shin - ing be - yond the frost - y weath - er, Bright as
earth. Set ev - 'ry peak and val - ley hum - ming With the

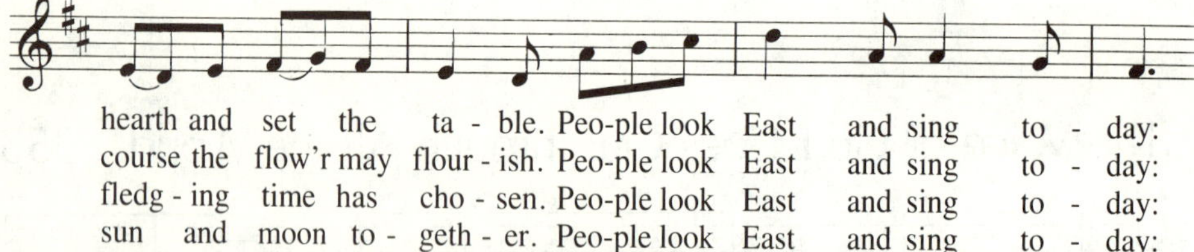

hearth and set the ta - ble. Peo-ple look East and sing to - day:
course the flow'r may flour - ish. Peo-ple look East and sing to - day:
fledg - ing time has cho - sen. Peo-ple look East and sing to - day:
sun and moon to - geth - er. Peo-ple look East and sing to - day:
word, the Lord is com - ing. Peo-ple look East and sing to - day:

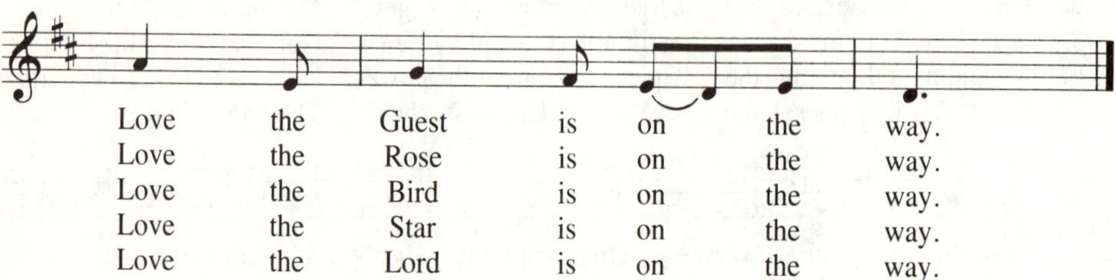

Love the Guest is on the way.
Love the Rose is on the way.
Love the Bird is on the way.
Love the Star is on the way.
Love the Lord is on the way.

Text: Eleanor Farjeon, 1881-1965, © David Higham Assoc. Ltd.
Tune: BESANCON, 87 98 87; French Traditional; Harm. by Martin Shaw, 1875-1958, © Oxford University Press

Awake! Awake, and Greet the New Morn 360

1. A - wake! a - wake, and greet the new morn, For
2. To us, to all in sor - row and fear, Em-
3. In dark - est night his com - ing shall be, When
4. Re - joice, re - joice, take heart in the night, Though

an - gels her - ald its dawn - ing, Sing out your joy, for
man - u - el comes a - sing - ing, His hum - ble song is
all the world is de - spair - ing, As morn - ing light so
dark the win - ter and cheer - less, The ris - ing sun shall

soon he is born, Be - hold! the Child of our long - ing.
qui - et and near, Yet fills the earth with its ring - ing;
qui - et and free, So warm and gen - tle and car - ing.
crown you with light, Be strong and lov - ing and fear - less;

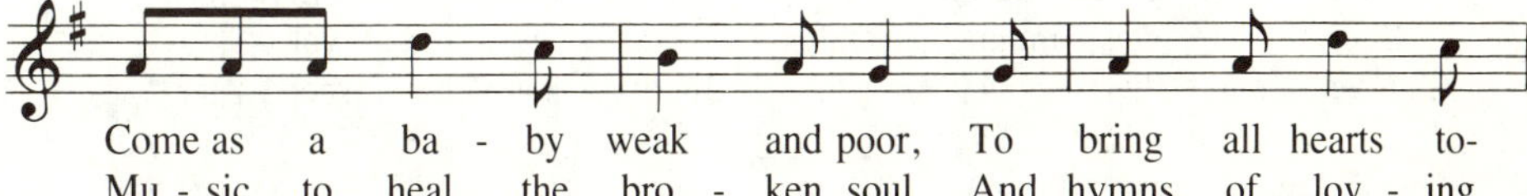

Come as a ba - by weak and poor, To bring all hearts to-
Mu - sic to heal the bro - ken soul And hymns of lov - ing
Then shall the mute break forth in song, The lame shall leap in
Love be our song and love our prayer, And love, our end - less

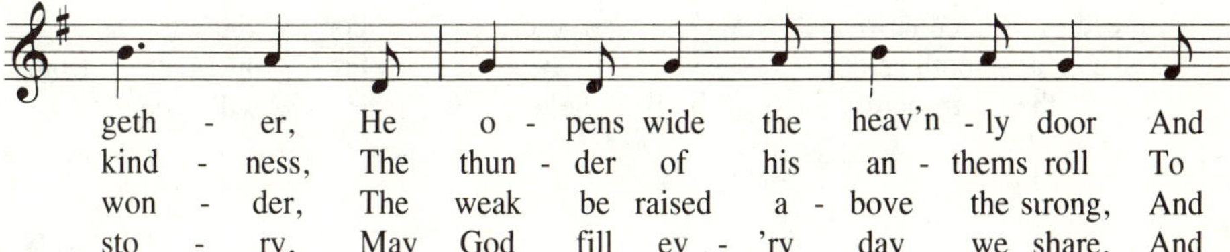

geth - er, He o - pens wide the heav'n - ly door And
kind - ness, The thun - der of his an - thems roll To
won - der, The weak be raised a - bove the strong, And
sto - ry, May God fill ev - 'ry day we share, And

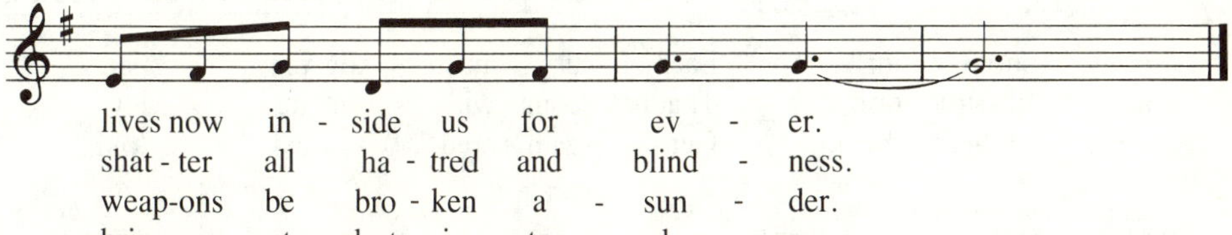

lives now in - side us for ev - er.
shat - ter all ha - tred and blind - ness.
weap-ons be bro - ken a - sun - der.
bring us at last in - to glo - ry.

Text: Marty Haugen, b.1952
Tune: REJOICE, REJOICE, 9 8 9 8 8 7 8 9; Marty Haugen, b.1952

361 Take Comfort, God's People

Take com - fort, God's peo - ple, take com - fort! The

prom - ised one is on the way. Sins are par-doned,

love has con-quered: Christ will come on Christ-mas day.

1. Shout the glad tid - ings high from the hill - tops;
2. Lev - el the moun - tains, fill in the val - leys;
3. Awe - some his pow - er, might - y his scep - ter

Spread the good news ev - 'ry - where. For the com - ing
Make a smooth and e - ven way. Free his path from
Yet the shep-herd's staff he'll hold. He will feed his

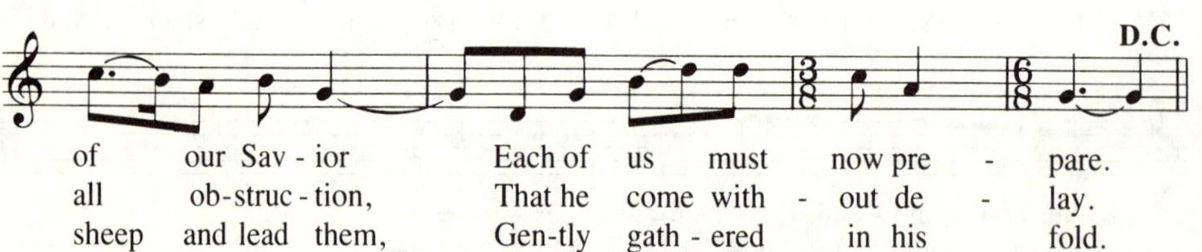
D.C.
of our Sav - ior Each of us must now pre - pare.
all ob-struc - tion, That he come with - out de - lay.
sheep and lead them, Gen-tly gath - ered in his fold.

Text: Is. 40:1-11; Omer Westendorf, b.1916
Tune: FIDDLER'S GREEN, 10 7 8 7 with refrain; Robert E. Kreutz, b.1922

City of God, Jerusalem 362

1. Cit - y of God, Je - ru - sa - lem, Where he has set his
2. Sing and be glad, Je - ru - sa - lem, For God does not for-
3. Sor - row no more, Je - ru - sa - lem, Dis - card your rags of
4. Look all a - round, Je - ru - sa - lem, Sur - vey from west to

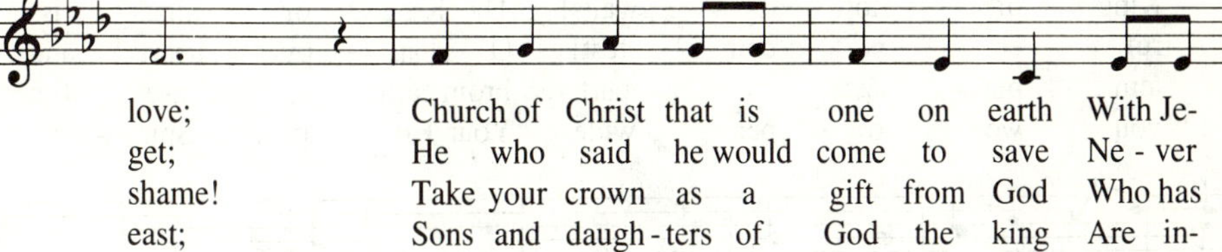

love; Church of Christ that is one on earth With Je-
get; He who said he would come to save Ne - ver
shame! Take your crown as a gift from God Who has
east; Sons and daugh - ters of God the king Are in-

ru - sa - lem a - bove: Here as we walk this chang-ing world
failed his peo - ple yet. Though we are tempt - ed by de-spair
called you by his name. Put off your sin, and wear the robe
vit - ed to his feast. Out of their ex - ile far a - way

Our joys are mixed with tears, But the day will be soon when the
And daunt-ed by de - feat, Our in - vin - ci - ble Lord will be
Of glo - ry in its place; You will shine in his light, you will
His scat-tered fam - ily come, And the streets will re-sound with the

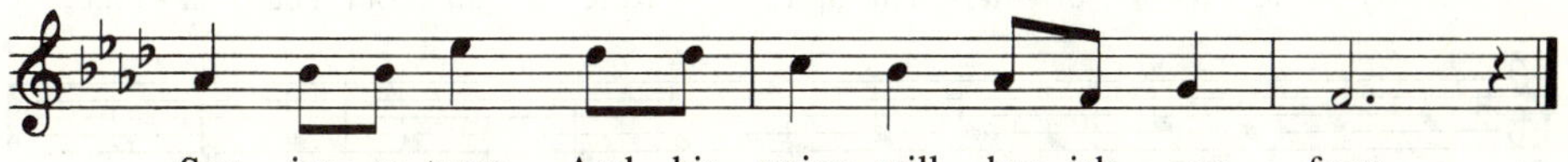

Sav - ior re-turns And his voice will ban-ish our fears.
seen in his strength, And his tri - umph will be com - plete.
share in his joy, You will praise his won-der - ful grace.
song of the saints When the Sav - ior wel-comes us home.

363 Lift Up Your Heads, O Mighty Gates

1. Lift up your heads, O might - y gates; Be - hold the
2. O blest the land, the cit - y blest, Where Christ the
3. Fling wide the por - tals of your heart; Make it a
4. Come, Sav - ior, come with us a - bide; Our hearts to
King of glo - ry waits! The King of kings is
rul - er is con - fest! O hap - py hearts and
tem - ple, set a - part From earth - ly use for
you we o - pen wide: Your Ho - ly Spir - it
draw - ing near; The Sa - vior of the world is here.
hap - py homes To whom this King of tri - umph comes!
heav'n's em - ploy, A - dorned with prayer and love and joy.
guide us on, Un - til our glo - rious goal is won.

Text: Based on Ps. 24; *Macht hoch die Tür;* George Weissel, 1590-1635; Tr. by Catherine Winkworth, 1827-1878, alt.
Tune: TRURO, LM, Williams' *Psalmodia Evangelica*, 1789

364 Come, O Long Expected Jesus

1. Come, O long ex - pect - ed Je - sus, Born to set your peo - ple free;
2. Is - rael's strength and con - so - la - tion, You, the hope of all the earth,
3. Born your peo - ple to de - liv - er; Born a child and yet a king!
4. By your own e - ter - nal Spir - it Rule in all our hearts a - lone;

From our fears and sins re - lease us; Free us from cap - tiv - i - ty.
Dear de - sire of ev - 'ry na - tion, Come, and save us by your birth.
Born to reign in us for ev - er, Now your gra-cious king-dom bring.
By your all suf - fi - cient mer - it Raise us to your glo-rious throne.

Text: Hag. 2:7; Charles Wesley, 1707-1788, alt.
Tune: STUTTGART, 8 7 8 7; Christian F. Witt, 1660-1716; Harm. by Kenneth D. Smith, b.1928, © National Christian Education Council

Hills of the North, Rejoice 365

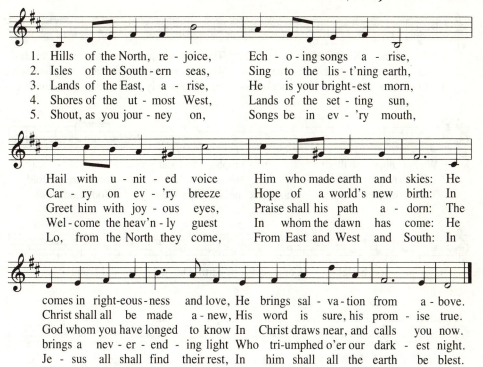

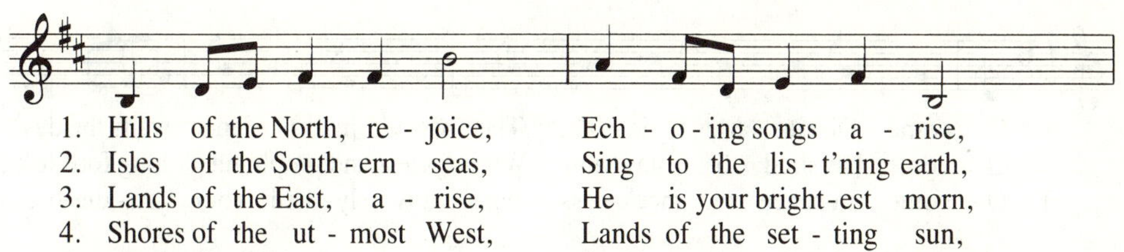

1. Hills of the North, re - joice, Ech - o - ing songs a - rise,
2. Isles of the South - ern seas, Sing to the lis - t'ning earth,
3. Lands of the East, a - rise, He is your bright - est morn,
4. Shores of the ut - most West, Lands of the set - ting sun,
5. Shout, as you jour - ney on, Songs be in ev - 'ry mouth,

Hail with u - nit - ed voice Him who made earth and skies: He
Car - ry on ev - 'ry breeze Hope of a world's new birth: In
Greet him with joy - ous eyes, Praise shall his path a - dorn: The
Wel - come the heav'n - ly guest In whom the dawn has come: He
Lo, from the North they come, From East and West and South: In

comes in right-eous - ness and love, He brings sal - va - tion from a - bove.
Christ shall all be made a - new, His word is sure, his prom - ise true.
God whom you have longed to know In Christ draws near, and calls you now.
brings a nev - er - end - ing light Who tri-umphed o'er our dark - est night.
Je - sus all shall find their rest, In him shall all the earth be blest.

Text: Editors of *English Praise*, Based on Charles E. Oakley, 1832-1865, © 1975, Oxford University Press
Tune: LITTLE CORNARD, 6 6 6 6 88; Martin Shaw, 1875-1958, © J. Curwen and Sons

Come, Lord, and Tarry Not 366

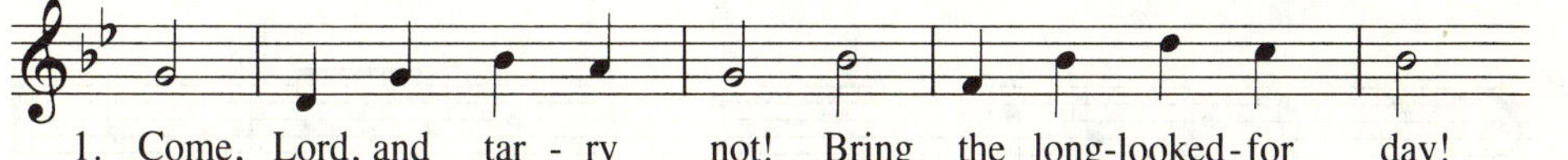

1. Come, Lord, and tar - ry not! Bring the long-looked - for day!
2. Come, for your saints still wait; Dai - ly as - cends their sigh;
3. Come, for cre - a - tion groans, Im - pa - tient of your stay,
4. Come, and make all things new, Build up this ru - ined earth;
5. Come, and be - gin your reign Of ev - er - last - ing peace;

O why these years of wait - ing here, These a - ges of de - lay?
The Spir - it and the Bride say, "Come!" Do you not hear the cry?
Worn out with these long years of ill, These a - ges of de - lay?
Re - store our fad - ed par - a - dise, Cre - a - tion's sec - ond birth.
Come, take the king-dom to your - self, Great King of right-eous - ness!

Text: Rev. 22:17, Attr. to Horatius Bonar, 1808-1889
Tune: ST. BRIDE, SM, Samuel Howard, 1710-1782

367 O Come, Divine Messiah

1. O come, Di-vine Mes - si - ah, The world in si - lence waits the day
2. O come, De-sired of na - tions, Whom priest and proph - et long fore-told,
3. O come, in peace and meek-ness, For low - ly will your cra - dle be:

When hope shall sing its tri - umph, And sad - ness flee a - way.
Will break the cap - tive fet - ters, Re-deem the long - lost fold.
Though clothed in hu - man weak - ness We shall your God-head see.

Dear Sav - ior, haste! Come, come to earth. Dis - pel the night and show your

face, And bid us hail the dawn of grace. O

come, Di-vine Mes - si - ah, The world in si - lence waits the day When

hope shall sing its tri - umph, And sad - ness flee a - way.

Text: *Venez, divin Messie;* Abbé Simon-Joseph Pellegrin, 1663-1745; Tr. by S. Mary of St. Philip, 1877
Tune: VENEZ, DIVIN MESSIE, 7 8 7 6 with refrain; French Noël, 16th C.; Harm. by Healey Willan, 1880-1968,

Creator of the Stars of Night 368

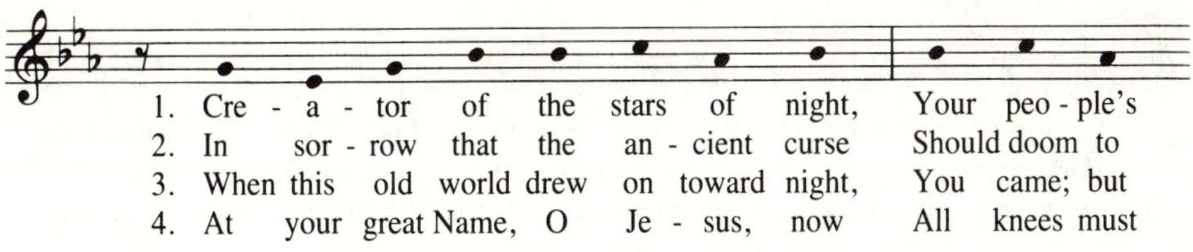
1. Cre - a - tor of the stars of night, Your peo - ple's
2. In sor - row that the an - cient curse Should doom to
3. When this old world drew on toward night, You came; but
4. At your great Name, O Je - sus, now All knees must

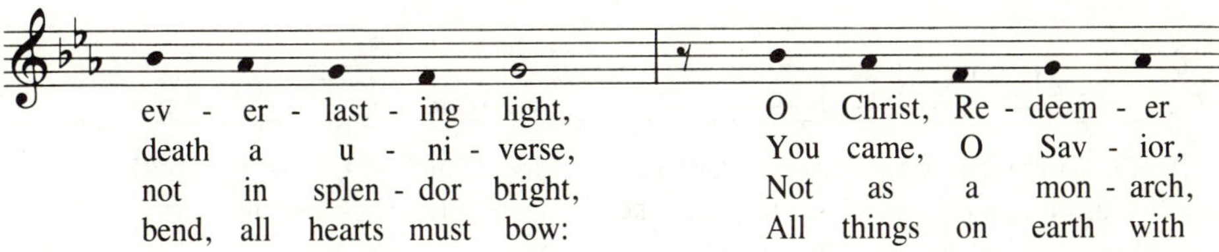
ev - er - last - ing light, O Christ, Re - deem - er
death a u - ni - verse, You came, O Sav - ior,
not in splen - dor bright, Not as a mon - arch,
bend, all hearts must bow: All things on earth with

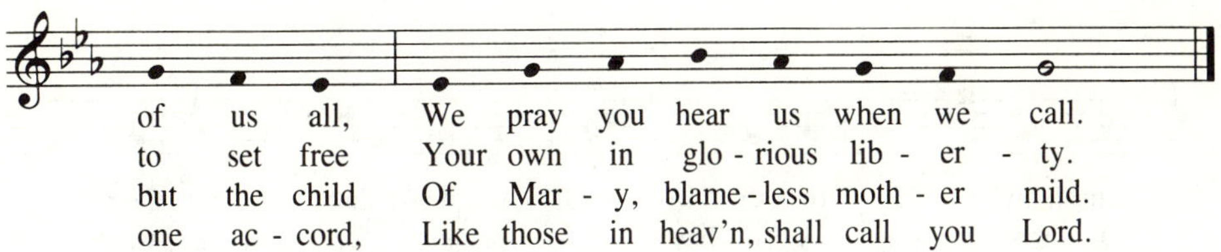
of us all, We pray you hear us when we call.
to set free Your own in glo - rious lib - er - ty.
but the child Of Mar - y, blame - less moth - er mild.
one ac - cord, Like those in heav'n, shall call you Lord.

5. Come in your holy might, we pray,
Redeem us for eternal day;
Defend us while we dwell below
From all assaults of our dread foe.

6. To God Creator, God the Son,
And God the Spirit, Three in One,
Praise, honor, might, and glory be
From age to age eternally.

Text: *Conditor alme siderum,* Latin 9th C.; Tr. *The Hymnal 1982,* © 1985, The Church Pension Fund
Tune: CONDITOR ALME SIDERUM, LM; Mode IV; Acc. by Gerard Farrell, OSB, b.1919, © 1986, GIA Publications, Inc.

Prepare the Way of the Lord 369

Canon

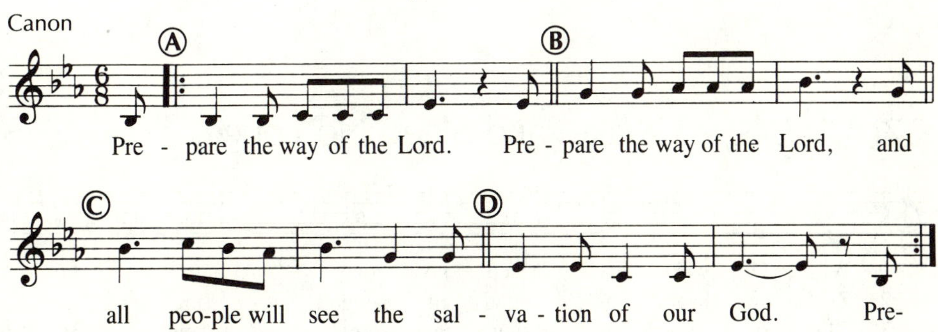
A
B
Pre - pare the way of the Lord. Pre - pare the way of the Lord, and
C
D
all peo-ple will see the sal - va - tion of our God. Pre-

Text: Luke 3:4,6; Taizé Community, 1984
Tune: Jacques Berthier, b.1923

370 Comfort, Comfort, O My People

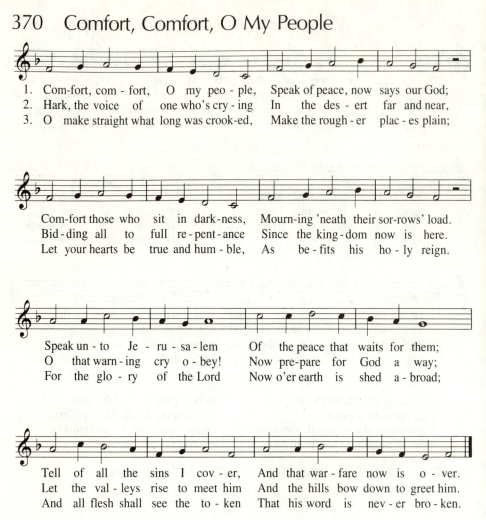

1. Com-fort, com - fort, O my peo - ple, Speak of peace, now says our God;
2. Hark, the voice of one who's cry - ing In the des - ert far and near,
3. O make straight what long was crook-ed, Make the rough - er plac - es plain;

Com-fort those who sit in dark-ness, Mourn-ing 'neath their sor-rows' load.
Bid-ding all to full re-pent-ance Since the king-dom now is here.
Let your hearts be true and hum - ble, As be - fits his ho - ly reign.

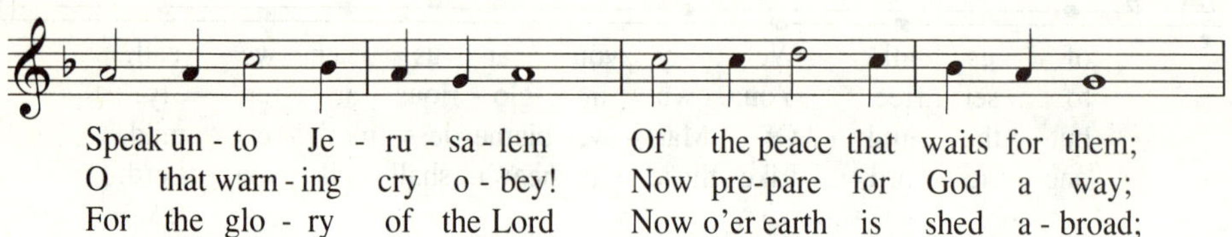

Speak un - to Je - ru - sa - lem Of the peace that waits for them;
O that warn - ing cry o - bey! Now pre-pare for God a way;
For the glo - ry of the Lord Now o'er earth is shed a - broad;

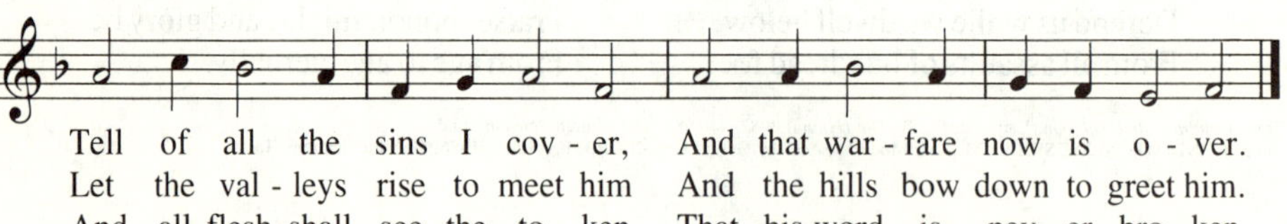

Tell of all the sins I cov - er, And that war - fare now is o - ver.
Let the val - leys rise to meet him And the hills bow down to greet him.
And all flesh shall see the to - ken That his word is nev - er bro - ken.

Text: Is. 40:1-8; *Tröstet, tröstet, meine Lieben;* Johann Olearius, 1611-1684; Tr. by Catherine Winkworth, 1827-1878, alt.
Tune: GENEVA 42, 8 7 8 7 77 88; *Genevan Psalter,* 1551; Harm. adapt. from Claude Goudimel, 1505-1572

371 Wake, O Wake, and Sleep No Longer

1. Wake, O wake, and sleep no long - er, For
2. Zi - on hears the sound of sing - ing; Our
3. Glo - ry, glo - ry, sing the an - gels, While

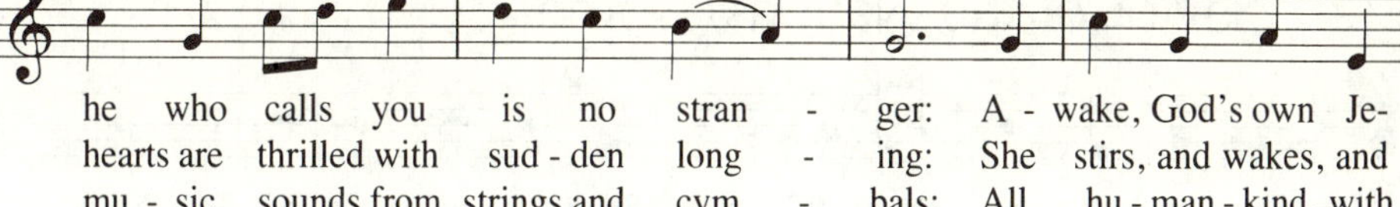

he who calls you is no stran - ger: A - wake, God's own Je-
hearts are thrilled with sud - den long - ing: She stirs, and wakes, and
mu - sic sounds from strings and cym - bals; All hu - man - kind, with

ru - sa - lem! Hear, the mid - night bells are chim - ing The
stands pre-pared. Christ, her friend, and lord, and lov - er, Her
songs a - rise! Twelve the gates in - to the cit - y, Each

sig - nal for his roy - al com - ing: Let voice to voice an-
star and sun and strong re - deem - er — At last his might - y
one a pearl of shin - ing beau - ty; The streets of gold ring

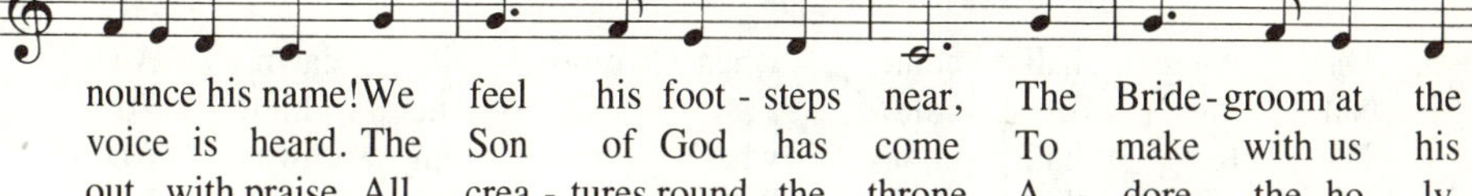

nounce his name! We feel his foot - steps near, The Bride - groom at the
voice is heard. The Son of God has come To make with us his
out with praise. All crea - tures round the throne A - dore the ho - ly

door — Al - le - lu - ia! The lamps will shine With
home: Sing Ho - san - na! The fight is won, The
One With re - joic - ing: A - men be sung By

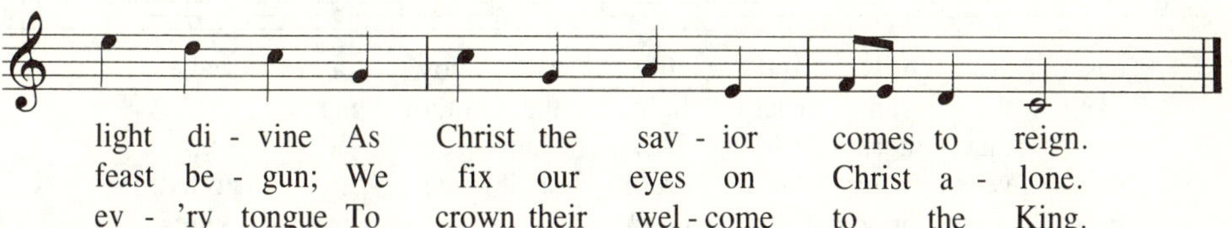

light di - vine As Christ the sav - ior comes to reign.
feast be - gun; We fix our eyes on Christ a - lone.
ev - 'ry tongue To crown their wel - come to the King.

Text: Matt. 25:1-13; *Wachet auf, ruft uns die Stimme,* Philipp Nicolai, 1556-1608; Tr. and adapt. by Christopher Idle, b.1938,
Tune: WACHET AUF, 89 8 89 8 66 4 44 8; Philipp Nicolai, 1556-1608; Harm. by J. S. Bach, 1685-1750

372 Savior of the Nations, Come

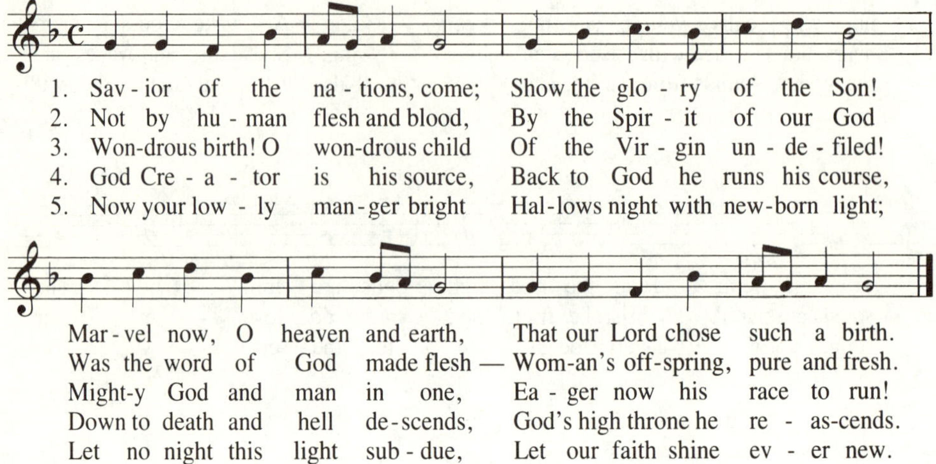
1. Sav - ior of the na - tions, come; Show the glo - ry of the Son!
2. Not by hu - man flesh and blood, By the Spir - it of our God
3. Won-drous birth! O won-drous child Of the Vir - gin un - de - filed!
4. God Cre - a - tor is his source, Back to God he runs his course,
5. Now your low - ly man - ger bright Hal-lows night with new-born light;
Mar - vel now, O heaven and earth, That our Lord chose such a birth.
Was the word of God made flesh — Wom-an's off-spring, pure and fresh.
Might-y God and man in one, Ea - ger now his race to run!
Down to death and hell de - scends, God's high throne he re - as-cends.
Let no night this light sub - due, Let our faith shine ev - er new.

Text: *Veni, Redemptor gentium;* Ascr. to St. Ambrose, 340-397; Tr. sts. 1-3a, William Reynolds, 1812-1876; Sts. 3b-5, Martin L. Seltz, 1909-1967, alt.
Tune: NUN KOMM DER HEIDEN HEILAND, 77 77; *Geystliche gesangk Buchleyn,* Wittenberg, 1524; Harm. by Melchior Vulpius, c.1560-1615

373 The King Shall Come When Morning Dawns

1. The King shall come when morn - ing dawns And light tri - um - phant breaks, When beau - ty gilds the east - ern hills And life to joy a - wakes.
2. Not, as of old, a lit - tle child, To suf - fer and to die, But crowned with glo - ry like the sun That lights the morn - ing sky.
3. The King shall come when morn - ing dawns And earth's dark night is past; O haste the ris - ing of that morn Whose day shall ev - er last.
4. And let the end - less bliss be - gin, By wea - ry saints fore - told, When right shall tri - umph o - ver wrong, And truth shall be ex - tolled.
5. The King shall come when morn - ing dawns And light and beau - ty brings. Hail, Christ, the Lord! your peo - ple pray: Come quick - ly, King of kings.

Text: John Brownlie, 1857-1925
Tune: ST. STEPHEN, CM; William Jones, 1726-1800

Lo, How a Rose E'er Blooming 374

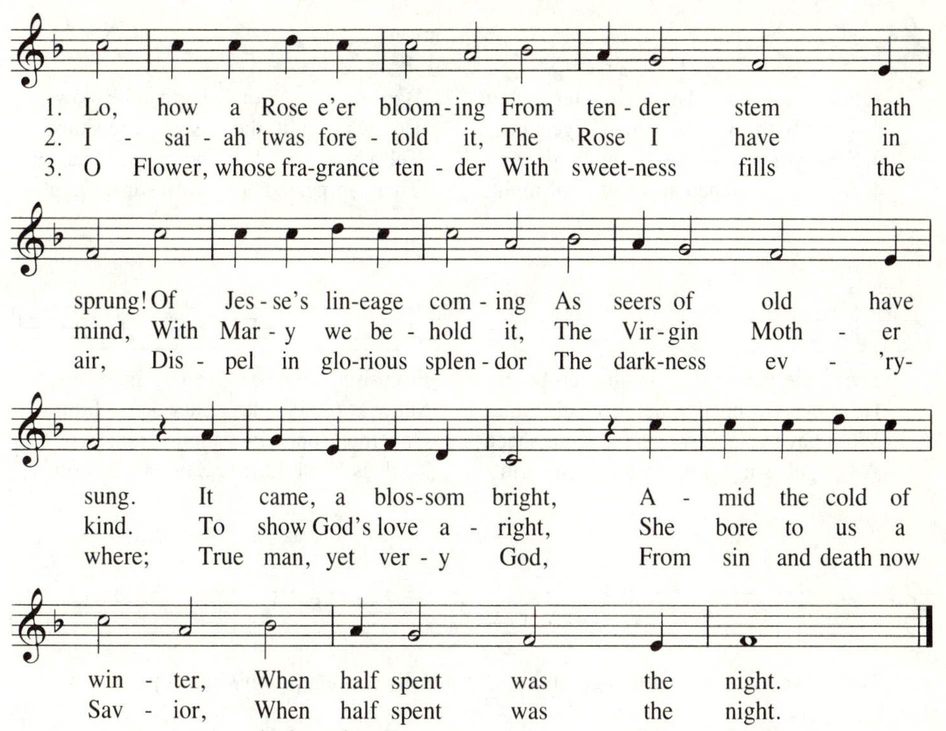
1. Lo, how a Rose e'er bloom-ing From ten-der stem hath
2. I - sai - ah 'twas fore - told it, The Rose I have in
3. O Flower, whose fra-grance ten - der With sweet-ness fills the
sprung! Of Jes - se's lin-eage com - ing As seers of old have
mind, With Mar - y we be - hold it, The Vir-gin Moth - er
air, Dis - pel in glo-rious splen - dor The dark-ness ev - 'ry-
sung. It came, a blos-som bright, A - mid the cold of
kind. To show God's love a - right, She bore to us a
where; True man, yet ver - y God, From sin and death now
win - ter, When half spent was the night.
Sav - ior, When half spent was the night.
save us, And share our ev - 'ry load.

Text: Is. 11:1; *Es ist ein' Ros' entsprungen; Speier Gebetbuch*, 1599; Tr. Sts. 1-2 by Theodore Baker, 1851-1934; St. 3, *The Hymnal*, 1940
Tune: ES IST EIN' ROS' ENTSPRUNGEN, 7 6 7 6 6 7 6; *Geistliche Kirchengesang*, Cologne, 1599; Harm. by Michael Praetorius, 1571-1621

375 See amid the Winter's Snow

1. See a-mid the win-ter's snow, Born for us on earth be-low,
2. There with-in a man-ger lies, He who built the star-ry skies,
3. Say, you ho-ly shep-herds, say, Tell your joy-ful news to-day,
4. As we watched at dead of night, There ap-peared a won-drous light;

See the gen-tle lamb ap-pears, Prom-ised from e-ter-nal years.
He who throned in heights sub-lime, Sits a-mid the cher-u-bim.
Why have you now left your sheep On the lone-ly moun-tain steep?
An-gels sing-ing peace on earth, Told us of the Sav-ior's birth.

Hail that ev-er bless-ed morn, Hail re-demp-tion's hap-py dawn,

Sing through all Je-ru-sa-lem: Christ is born in Beth-le-hem.

Text: Edward Caswall, 1814-1878
Tune: HUMILITY, 77 77 with refrain; John Goss, 1800-1880

Angels We Have Heard on High 376

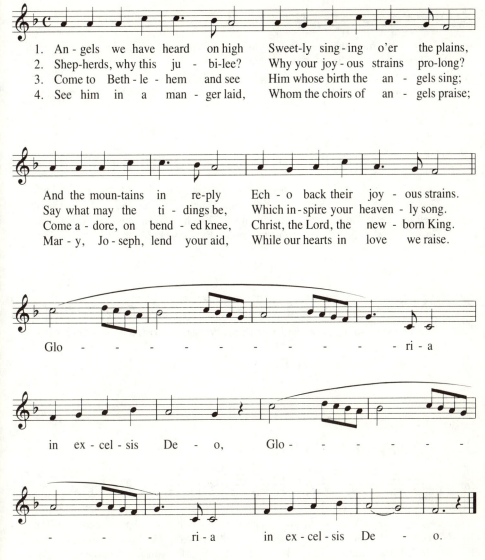

1. An - gels we have heard on high Sweet-ly sing - ing o'er the plains,
2. Shep-herds, why this ju - bi-lee? Why your joy - ous strains pro-long?
3. Come to Beth - le - hem and see Him whose birth the an - gels sing;
4. See him in a man - ger laid, Whom the choirs of an - gels praise;

And the moun-tains in re-ply Ech - o back their joy - ous strains.
Say what may the ti - dings be, Which in - spire your heaven - ly song.
Come a - dore, on bend - ed knee, Christ, the Lord, the new - born King.
Mar - y, Jo - seph, lend your aid, While our hearts in love we raise.

Glo - - - - - - - - - - ri - a

in ex - cel - sis De - o, Glo - - - - - -

- - - ri - a in ex - cel - sis De - o.

Text: *Les anges dans nos campagnes;* French, c.18th C.;Tr. from *Crown of Jesus Music*, London, 1862
Tune: GLORIA, 7 7 7 7 with refrain; French Traditional

377 Angels, from the Realms of Glory

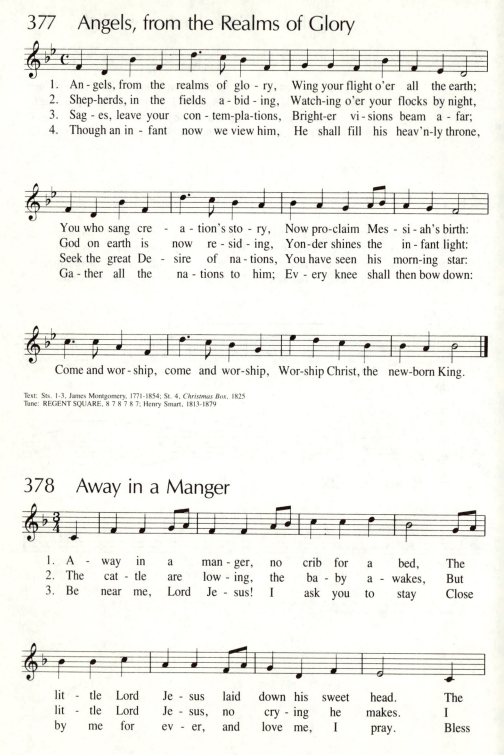

1. An - gels, from the realms of glo - ry, Wing your flight o'er all the earth;
2. Shep-herds, in the fields a - bid - ing, Watch-ing o'er your flocks by night,
3. Sag - es, leave your con - tem-pla-tions, Bright-er vi - sions beam a - far;
4. Though an in - fant now we view him, He shall fill his heav'n-ly throne,

You who sang cre - a - tion's sto - ry, Now pro-claim Mes - si - ah's birth:
God on earth is now re - sid - ing, Yon-der shines the in - fant light:
Seek the great De - sire of na - tions, You have seen his morn-ing star:
Ga - ther all the na - tions to him; Ev - ery knee shall then bow down:

Come and wor - ship, come and wor-ship, Wor-ship Christ, the new-born King.

Text: Sts. 1-3, James Montgomery, 1771-1854; St. 4, *Christmas Box*, 1825
Tune: REGENT SQUARE, 8 7 8 7 8 7; Henry Smart, 1813-1879

378 Away in a Manger

1. A - way in a man - ger, no crib for a bed, The
2. The cat - tle are low - ing, the ba - by a - wakes, But
3. Be near me, Lord Je - sus! I ask you to stay Close

lit - tle Lord Je - sus laid down his sweet head. The
lit - tle Lord Je - sus, no cry - ing he makes. I
by me for ev - er, and love me, I pray. Bless

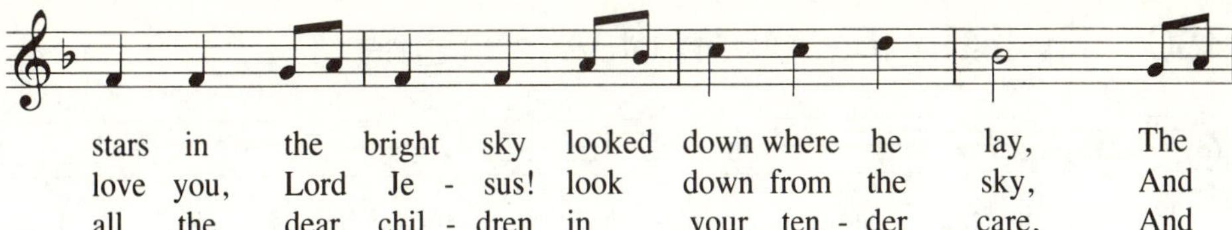
stars in the bright sky looked down where he lay, The
love you, Lord Je - sus! look down from the sky, And
all the dear chil - dren in your ten - der care, And

lit - tle Lord Je - sus, a - sleep on the hay.
stay by my cra - dle till morn - ing is nigh.
fit us for heav - en, to live with you there.

Text: Sts. 1-2, anonymous; St. 3, John T. McFarland, 1851-1913
Tune: CRADLE SONG, 11 11 11 11; William J. Kirkpatrick, 1838-1921; Harm. by David Willcocks, b.1919, © 1961, Oxford University Press

Silent Night, Holy Night 379

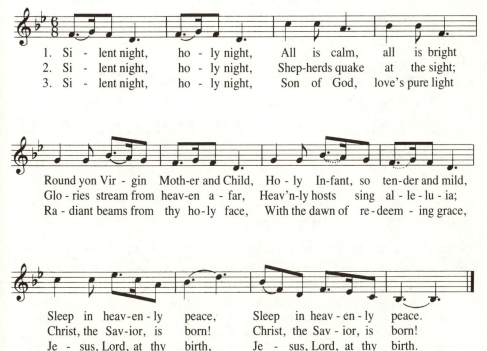

1. Si - lent night, ho - ly night, All is calm, all is bright
2. Si - lent night, ho - ly night, Shep-herds quake at the sight;
3. Si - lent night, ho - ly night, Son of God, love's pure light

Round yon Vir - gin Moth-er and Child, Ho - ly In-fant, so ten-der and mild,
Glo - ries stream from heav-en a - far, Heav'n-ly hosts sing al - le - lu - ia;
Ra - diant beams from thy ho-ly face, With the dawn of re - deem - ing grace,

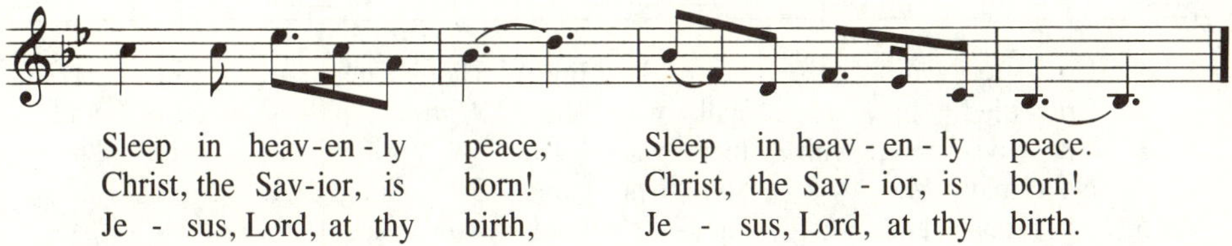
Sleep in heav-en - ly peace, Sleep in heav - en - ly peace.
Christ, the Sav-ior, is born! Christ, the Sav - ior, is born!
Je - sus, Lord, at thy birth, Je - sus, Lord, at thy birth.

Text: *Stille Nacht, heilige Nacht;* Joseph Mohr, 1792-1849; Tr. John F. Young, 1820-1885
Tune: STILLE NACHT, 66 89 66; Franz X. Gruber, 1787-1863

380 'Twas in the Moon of Wintertime

1. 'Twas in the moon of win - ter - time, When all the birds had fled, That
2. With - in a lodge of bro - ken bark The ten - der babe was found; A
3. The ear - liest moon of win - ter - time Is not so round and fair As
4. O chil - dren of the for - est free, The an - gel song is true; The

God the Lord of all the earth Sent an - gel choirs in - stead; Be-
rag - ged robe of rab - bit skin En - wrapped his beau - ty round; But
was the ring of glo - ry on The help - less in - fant there. The
ho - ly child of earth and heaven Is born to - day for you. Come

fore their light the stars grew dim, And won - d'ring hunt - ers heard the hymn:
as the hunt - er braves drew nigh, The an - gel song rang loud and high:
chiefs from far be - fore him knelt With gifts of fox and bea - ver pelt.
kneel be - fore the ra - diant boy, Who brings you beau - ty, peace, and joy.

Je - sus your king is born, Je - sus is born, in ex - cel - sis glo - ri - a.

Text: *Estennialon de tsonue Jesus ahatonhia;* St. Jean de Brebeuf, 1593-1649; Tr. by Jesse E. Middleton, 1872-1960, © Fredrick Harris Music Co. Ltd.
Tune: UNE JEUNE PUCELLE, 8 6 8 6 88 with refrain; French Melody; Harm. by Frederick F. Jackisch, b. 1922, © 1978, *Lutheran Book of Worship*

381 Unto Us a Boy Is Born

1. Un - to us a boy is born! The King of all cre-
2. Cra - dled in a stall was he With sleep - y cows and
3. Her - od then with fear was filled: "A prince," he said, "in
4. Now may Mar - y's son, who came So long a - go to
5. Al - pha and O - me - ga he! Now let the or - gan

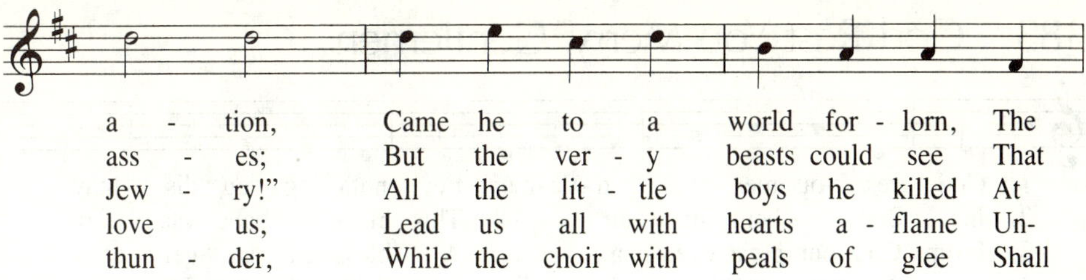
a - tion, Came he to a world for - lorn, The
ass - es; But the ver - y beasts could see That
Jew - ry!" All the lit - tle boys he killed At
love us; Lead us all with hearts a - flame Un-
thun - der, While the choir with peals of glee Shall

Lord of ev - 'ry na - - - - tion.
he the world sur - pass - - - - es.
Beth-lehem in his fu - - - - ry.
to the joys a - bove us.
rend the air a - sun - - - - der.

Text: *Puer nobis nascitur;* Latin, 15th C.; Tr. by Percy Dearmer, 1867-1936, © Oxford University Press
Tune: PUER NOBIS NASCITUR, 7 7 7 7; *Piae Cantiones*, 1582; Harm. by Geoffrey Shaw, 1879-1943, © A. R. Mowbray and Co. Ltd.

While Shepherds Watched 382

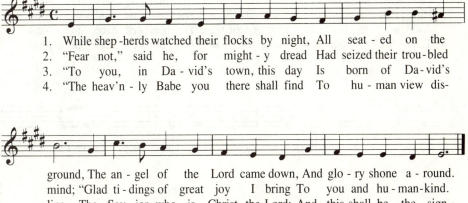

1. While shep - herds watched their flocks by night, All seat - ed on the
2. "Fear not," said he, for might - y dread Had seized their trou - bled
3. "To you, in Da - vid's town, this day Is born of Da - vid's
4. "The heav'n - ly Babe you there shall find To hu - man view dis-

ground, The an - gel of the Lord came down, And glo - ry shone a - round.
mind; "Glad ti - dings of great joy I bring To you and hu - man-kind.
line The Sav - ior, who is Christ the Lord; And this shall be the sign.
played, All mean - ly wrapped in swath - ing bands, And in a man - ger laid."

5. The angel spoke, and suddenly
Appeared a shining throng
Of angels praising God, who now
Begin their joyful song:

6. "All glory be to God on high
And on the earth be peace;
Good will henceforth from heav'n to all
Begin and never cease."

Text: Luke 2:8-14; Nahum Tate, 1652-1715
Tune: WINCHESTER OLD, CM; Christopher Tye, c.1500-c.1572; Harm. after George Kirby, fl. 1592

383 God Rest You Merry, Gentlemen

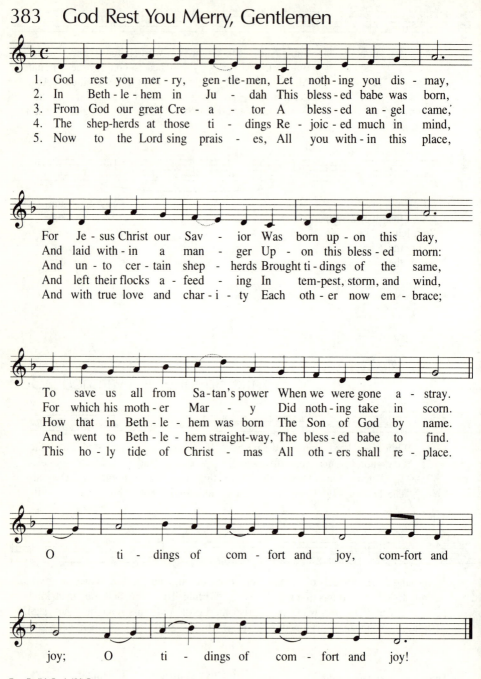

1. God rest you mer - ry, gen - tle - men, Let noth - ing you dis - may,
2. In Beth - le - hem in Ju - dah This bless - ed babe was born,
3. From God our great Cre - a - tor A bless - ed an - gel came,
4. The shep-herds at those ti - dings Re - joic - ed much in mind,
5. Now to the Lord sing prais - es, All you with - in this place,

For Je - sus Christ our Sav - ior Was born up - on this day,
And laid with - in a man - ger Up - on this bless - ed morn:
And un - to cer - tain shep - herds Brought ti - dings of the same,
And left their flocks a - feed - ing In tem-pest, storm, and wind,
And with true love and char - i - ty Each oth - er now em - brace;

To save us all from Sa - tan's power When we were gone a - stray.
For which his moth - er Mar - y Did noth - ing take in scorn.
How that in Beth - le - hem was born The Son of God by name.
And went to Beth - le - hem straight-way, The bless - ed babe to find.
This ho - ly tide of Christ - mas All oth - ers shall re - place.

O ti - dings of com - fort and joy, com-fort and

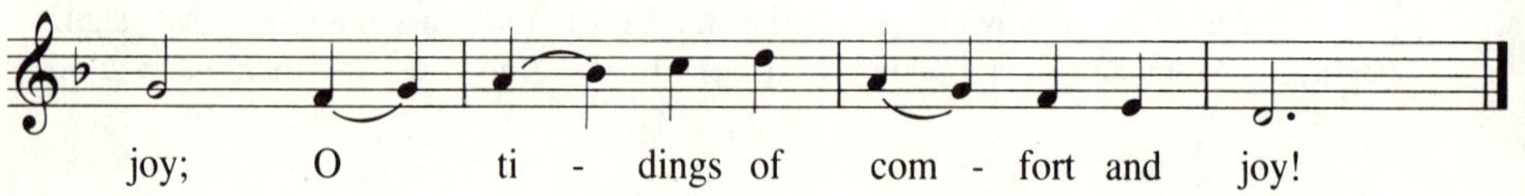

joy; O ti - dings of com - fort and joy!

Text: English Carol, 18th C.
Tune: GOD REST YOU MERRY, 8 6 8 6 8 6 with refrain; English 18th C.; Harm. by John Stainer, 1840-1901

A Child Is Born in Bethlehem 384

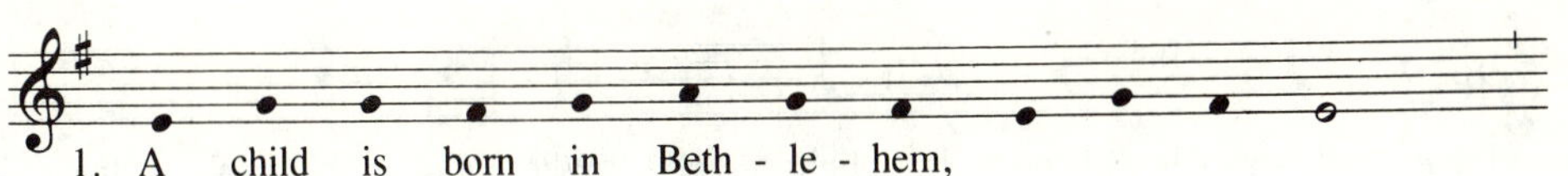
1. A child is born in Beth - le - hem,
2. The babe who lies up - on the straw, Al - le - lu - ia.
3. Up - on this joy - ful ho - ly night,
4. We praise you, Ho - ly Trin - i - ty,

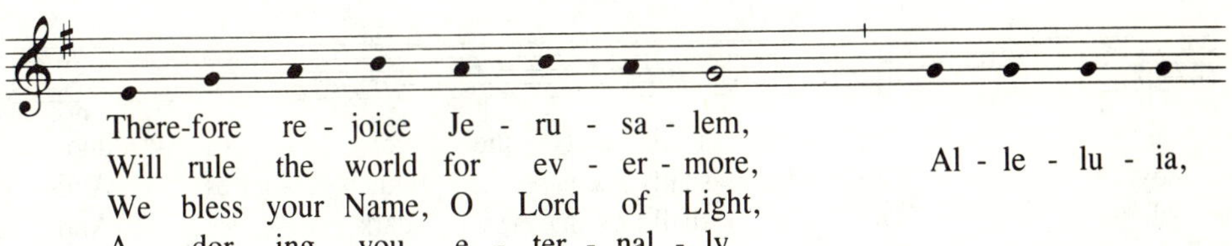
There-fore re - joice Je - ru - sa - lem,
Will rule the world for ev - er - more, Al - le - lu - ia,
We bless your Name, O Lord of Light,
A - dor - ing you e - ter - nal - ly.

al - le - lu - ia. Our joy - ful hearts we raise,

Christ is born, O come a - dore him In new-found songs of praise.

Text: *Puer natus in Bethlehem;* Latin 14th C.; Tr. by Ruth Fox Hume, b. 1922,
Tune: PUER NATUS, 8 8 with alleluias and refrain; Mode I; Acc. by Richard Proulx, b.1937,

385 A Stable Lamp Is Lighted

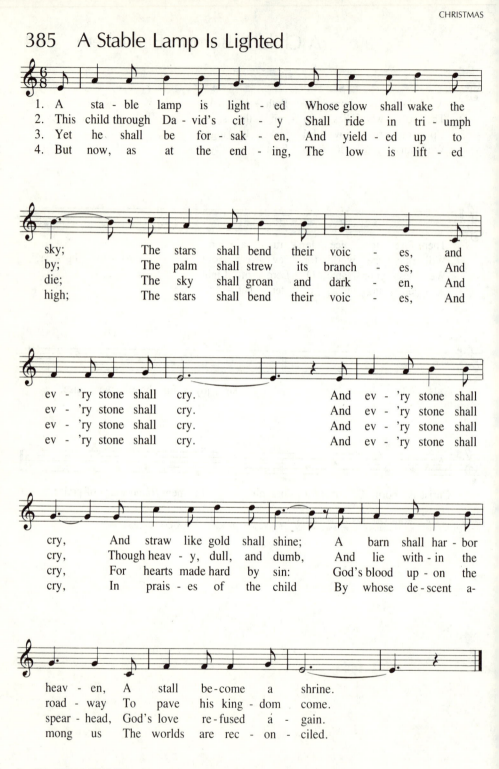

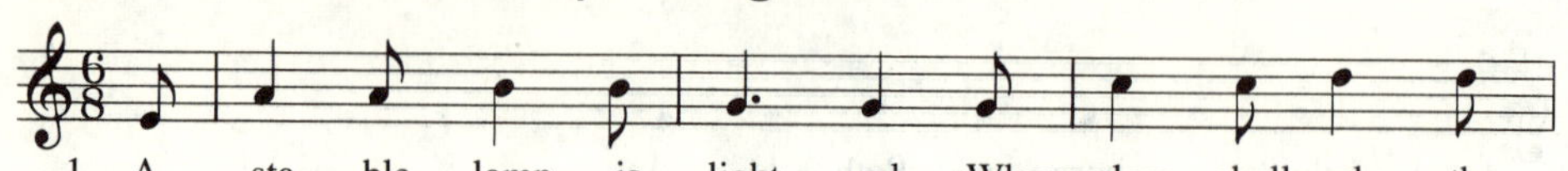

1. A sta - ble lamp is light - ed Whose glow shall wake the
2. This child through Da - vid's cit - y Shall ride in tri - umph
3. Yet he shall be for - sak - en, And yield - ed up to
4. But now, as at the end - ing, The low is lift - ed

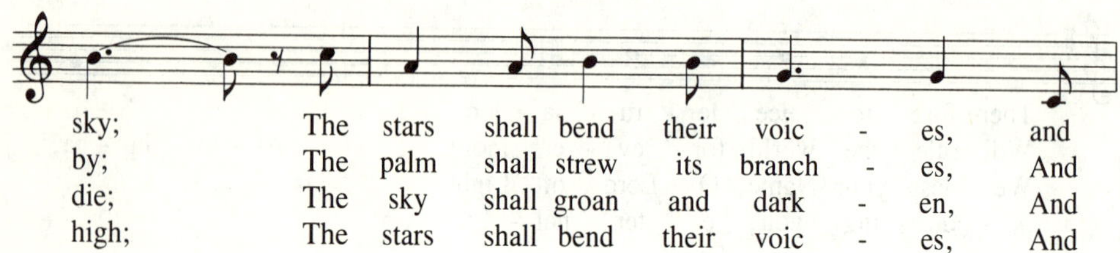
sky; The stars shall bend their voic - es, and
by; The palm shall strew its branch - es, And
die; The sky shall groan and dark - en, And
high; The stars shall bend their voic - es, And

ev - 'ry stone shall cry. And ev - 'ry stone shall
ev - 'ry stone shall cry. And ev - 'ry stone shall
ev - 'ry stone shall cry. And ev - 'ry stone shall
ev - 'ry stone shall cry. And ev - 'ry stone shall

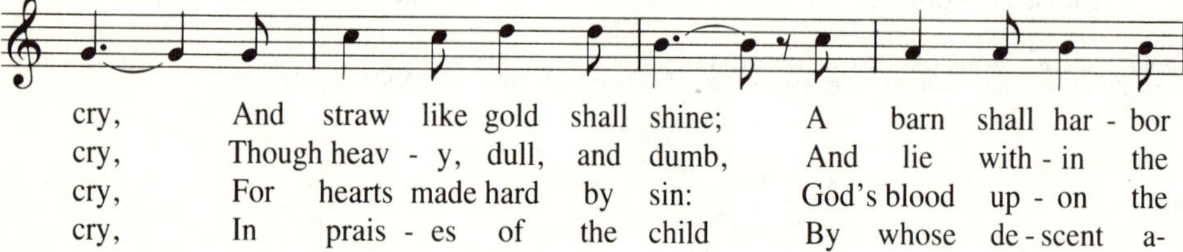
cry, And straw like gold shall shine; A barn shall har - bor
cry, Though heav - y, dull, and dumb, And lie with - in the
cry, For hearts made hard by sin: God's blood up - on the
cry, In prais - es of the child By whose de - scent a-

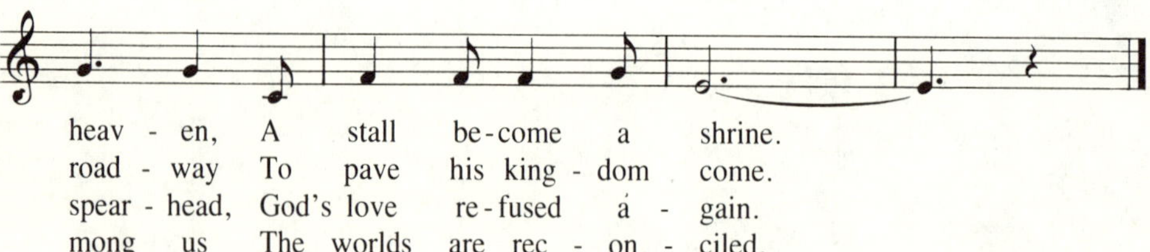
heav - en, A stall be - come a shrine.
road - way To pave his king - dom come.
spear - head, God's love re - fused a - gain.
mong us The worlds are rec - on - ciled.

Text: Richard Wilbur, b.1921, © 1961
Tune: ANDUJAR, 7 6 7 6 6 6 7 6; David Hurd, b.1950, © 1984, GIA Publications, Inc.

O Little Town of Bethlehem 386

1. O lit - tle town of Beth - le - hem, How still we see thee lie!
2. For Christ is born of Mar - y, And gath - ered all a - bove,
3. How si - lent - ly, how si - lent - ly, The won - drous gift is giv'n!
4. O ho - ly Child of Beth - le - hem! De - scend to us we pray;

A - bove thy deep and dream-less sleep The si - lent stars go by;
While mor - tals sleep, the an - gels keep Their watch of won-d'ring love.
So God im - parts to hu - man hearts The bless - ings of his heav'n.
Cast out our sin and en - ter in, Be born in us to - day.

Yet in the dark streets shin - eth The ev - er - last - ing Light;
O morn-ing stars, to - geth - er Pro - claim the ho - ly birth!
No ear may hear his com - ing, But in this world of sin,
We hear the Christ-mas an - gels The great glad ti - dings tell;

The hopes and fears of all the years Are met in thee to - night.
And prais - es sing to God the King, And peace to all on earth.
Where meek souls will re - ceive him, still The dear Christ en - ters in.
O come to us, a - bide with us, Our Lord Em - man - u - el!

Tune: Phillips Brooks, 1835-1893
Tune: ST. LOUIS, 8 6 8 6 7 6 8 6; Lewis H. Redner, 1831-1908

387 Hark! The Herald Angels Sing

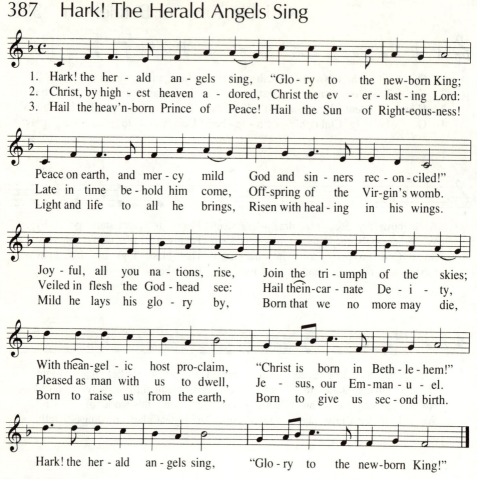

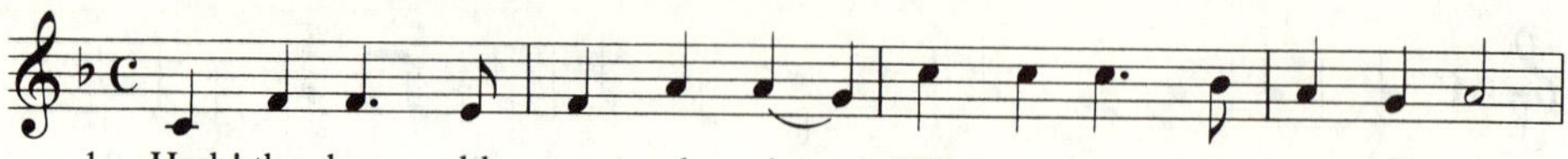

1. Hark! the her - ald an - gels sing, "Glo - ry to the new-born King;
2. Christ, by high - est heaven a - dored, Christ the ev - er - last - ing Lord:
3. Hail the heav'n-born Prince of Peace! Hail the Sun of Right-eous-ness!

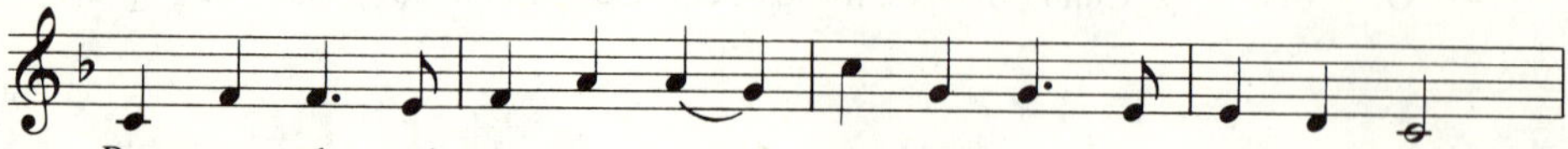

Peace on earth, and mer - cy mild God and sin - ners rec - on - ciled!"
Late in time be - hold him come, Off-spring of the Vir-gin's womb.
Light and life to all he brings, Risen with heal - ing in his wings.

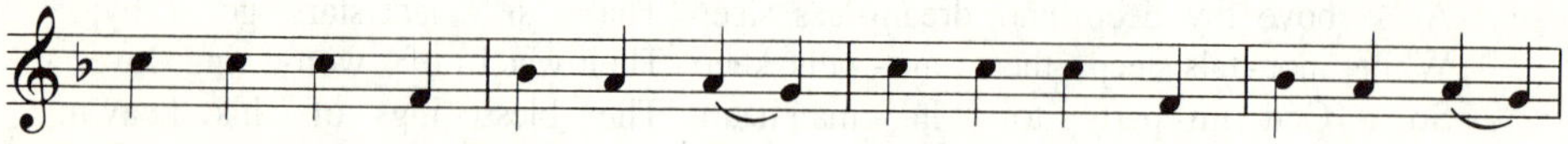

Joy - ful, all you na - tions, rise, Join the tri - umph of the skies;
Veiled in flesh the God - head see: Hail the in-car - nate De - i - ty,
Mild he lays his glo - ry by, Born that we no more may die,

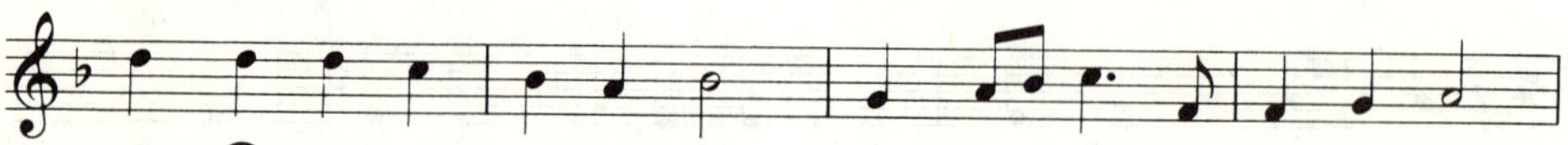

With the an-gel - ic host pro-claim, "Christ is born in Beth - le - hem!"
Pleased as man with us to dwell, Je - sus, our Em - man - u - el.
Born to raise us from the earth, Born to give us sec - ond birth.

Hark! the her - ald an - gels sing, "Glo - ry to the new-born King!"

Text: Charles Wesley, 1707-1788, alt.
Tune: MENDELSSOHN, 77 77 D with refrain; Felix Mendelssohn, 1809-1847; Descant with harm. by David Willcocks, b.1919,

From Heaven Above 388

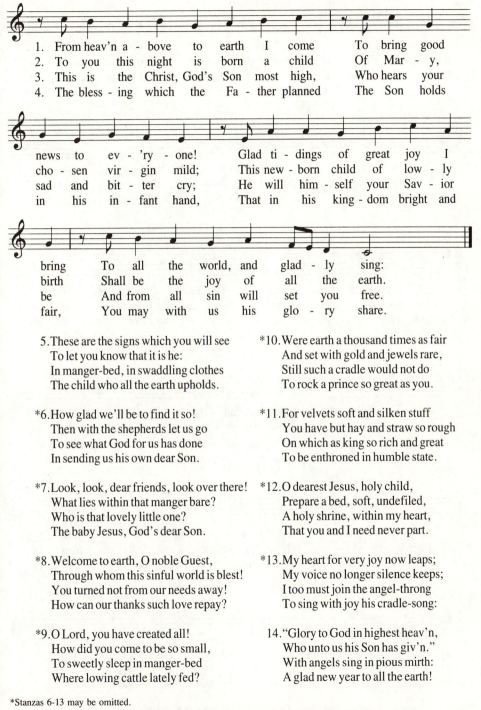

1. From heav'n a - bove to earth I come To bring good
2. To you this night is born a child Of Mar - y,
3. This is the Christ, God's Son most high, Who hears your
4. The bless - ing which the Fa - ther planned The Son holds
news to ev - 'ry - one! Glad ti - dings of great joy I
cho - sen vir - gin mild; This new - born child of low - ly
sad and bit - ter cry; He will him - self your Sav - ior
in his in - fant hand, That in his king - dom bright and
bring To all the world, and glad - ly sing:
birth Shall be the joy of all the earth.
be And from all sin will set you free.
fair, You may with us his glo - ry share.

5. These are the signs which you will see
To let you know that it is he:
In manger-bed, in swaddling clothes
The child who all the earth upholds.

*6. How glad we'll be to find it so!
Then with the shepherds let us go
To see what God for us has done
In sending us his own dear Son.

*7. Look, look, dear friends, look over there!
What lies within that manger bare?
Who is that lovely little one?
The baby Jesus, God's dear Son.

*8. Welcome to earth, O noble Guest,
Through whom this sinful world is blest!
You turned not from our needs away!
How can our thanks such love repay?

*9. O Lord, you have created all!
How did you come to be so small,
To sweetly sleep in manger-bed
Where lowing cattle lately fed?

*10. Were earth a thousand times as fair
And set with gold and jewels rare,
Still such a cradle would not do
To rock a prince so great as you.

*11. For velvets soft and silken stuff
You have but hay and straw so rough
On which as king so rich and great
To be enthroned in humble state.

*12. O dearest Jesus, holy child,
Prepare a bed, soft, undefiled,
A holy shrine, within my heart,
That you and I need never part.

*13. My heart for very joy now leaps;
My voice no longer silence keeps;
I too must join the angel-throng
To sing with joy his cradle-song:

14. "Glory to God in highest heav'n,
Who unto us his Son has giv'n."
With angels sing in pious mirth:
A glad new year to all the earth!

*Stanzas 6-13 may be omitted.

Text: Luke 2:1-18; *Vom Himmel hoch da komm ich her;* Martin Luther, 1483-1546; Tr. from *Lutheran Book of Worship,* 1978, ©
Tune: VOM HIMMEL HOCH, LM; Schumann's *Geistliche Lieder,* 1539; Harm. by Hans Leo Hassler, 1564-1612

389 How Brightly Beams the Morning Star

1. How bright - ly beams the morn-ing star! What sud-den ra-diance
2. Come, heav'n-ly bride-groom, light di - vine, And deep with - in our
3. O let the harps break forth in sound! Our joy be all with

from a - far A - glow with grace and mer - cy! Of Ja-
hearts now shine; There light a flame un - dy - ing! In your
mu - sic crowned, Our voic - es rich - ly blend - ing! For Christ

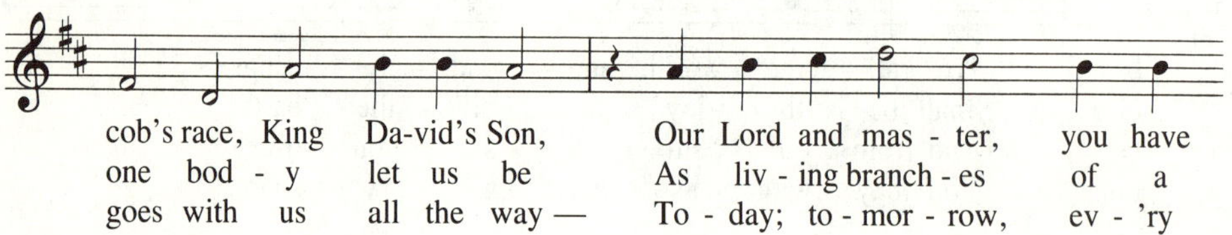

cob's race, King Da-vid's Son, Our Lord and mas - ter, you have
one bod - y let us be As liv - ing branch - es of a
goes with us all the way — To - day; to - mor - row, ev - 'ry

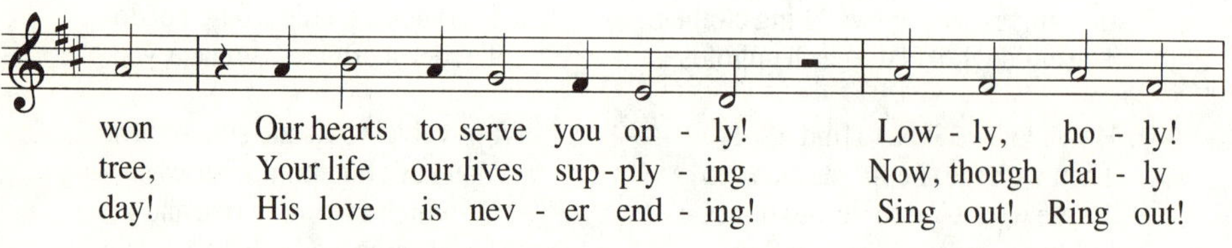

won Our hearts to serve you on - ly! Low - ly, ho - ly!
tree, Your life our lives sup-ply - ing. Now, though dai - ly
day! His love is nev - er end - ing! Sing out! Ring out!

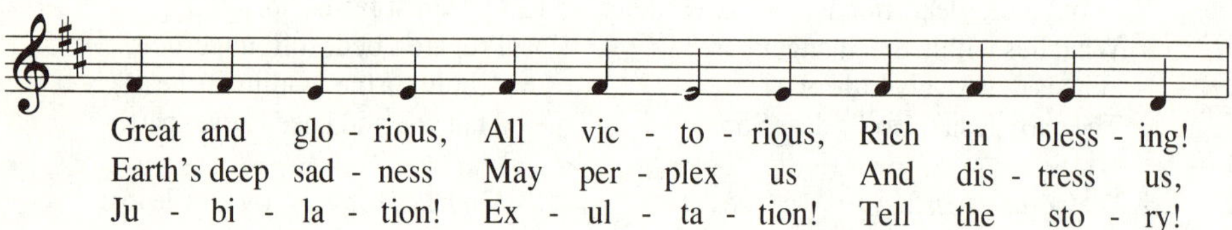

Great and glo - rious, All vic - to - rious, Rich in bless - ing!
Earth's deep sad - ness May per - plex us And dis - tress us,
Ju - bi - la - tion! Ex - ul - ta - tion! Tell the sto - ry!

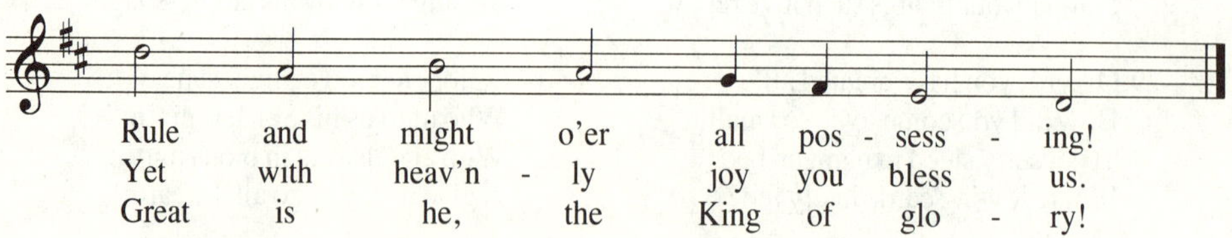

Rule and might o'er all pos - sess - ing!
Yet with heav'n - ly joy you bless us.
Great is he, the King of glo - ry!

Text: *Wie schön leuchtet der Morgenstern;* Philipp Nicolai, 1556-1608; Tr. from *Lutheran Book of Worship,* 1978, alt., ©
Tune: WIE SCHÖN LEUCHTET, 88 7 88 7 22 44 48; Philipp Nicolai, 1556-1608; Harm. by Johann H. Schein, 1586-1630

How Brightly Beams the Morning Star 390

1. How bright - ly beams the morn - ing star! What sud - den ra - diance
2. Come, heav'n-ly bride-groom, light di - vine, And deep with - in our
3. O let the harps break forth in sound! Our joy be all with

from a - far A - glow with grace and mer - cy! Of
hearts now shine; There light a flame un - dy - ing! In
mu - sic crowned, Our voic - es rich - ly blend - ing! For

Ja - cob's race, King Da - vid's Son, Our Lord and mas - ter,
your one bod - y let us be As liv - ing branch - es
Christ goes with us all the way—To - day, to - mor - row,

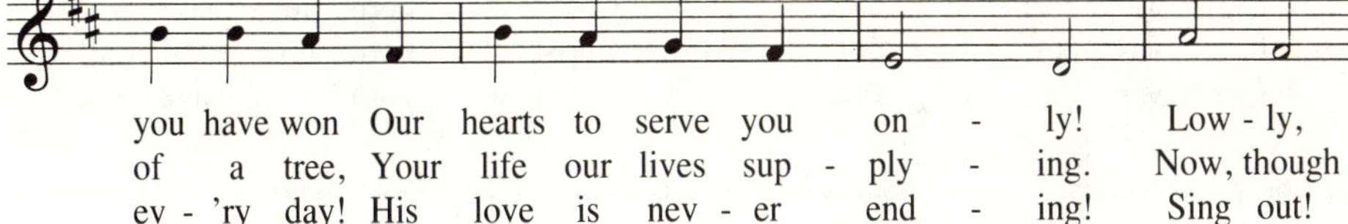
you have won Our hearts to serve you on - ly! Low - ly,
of a tree, Your life our lives sup - ply - ing. Now, though
ev - 'ry day! His love is nev - er end - ing! Sing out!

ho - ly! Great and glo - rious, All vic - to - rious, Rich in
dai - ly Earth's deep sad - ness May per-plex us And dis-
Ring out! Ju - bi - la - tion! Ex - ul - ta - tion! Tell the

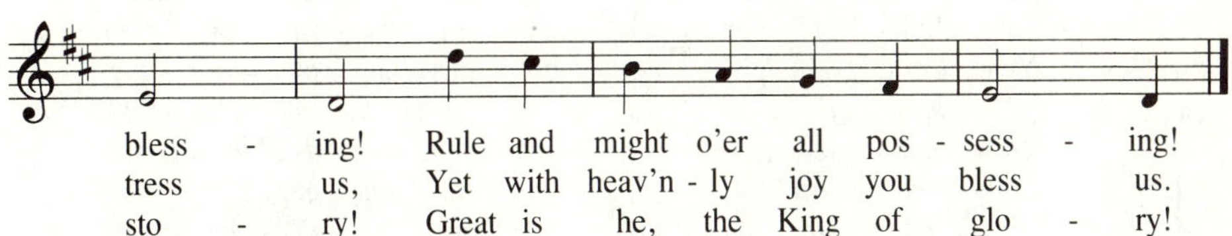
bless - ing! Rule and might o'er all pos - sess - ing!
tress us, Yet with heav'n - ly joy you bless us.
sto - ry! Great is he, the King of glo - ry!

Text: *Wie Schön leuchtet der Morgenstern;* Philipp Nicolai, 1556-1608; Tr. from *Lutheran Book of Worship*, 1978, alt., ©
Tune: WIE SCHÖN LEUCHTET, 88 7 88 7 22 44 48; Philipp Nicolai, 1556-1608; Harm. by J.S. Bach, 1685-1750

391 Good Christian Friends, Rejoice

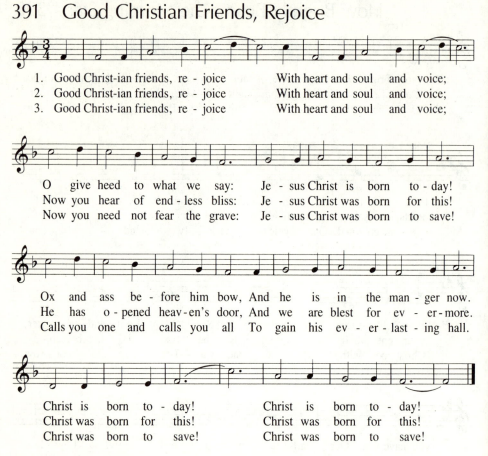

1. Good Christ-ian friends, re - joice With heart and soul and voice;
2. Good Christ-ian friends, re - joice With heart and soul and voice;
3. Good Christ-ian friends, re - joice With heart and soul and voice;

O give heed to what we say: Je - sus Christ is born to - day!
Now you hear of end - less bliss: Je - sus Christ was born for this!
Now you need not fear the grave: Je - sus Christ was born to save!

Ox and ass be - fore him bow, And he is in the man - ger now.
He has o - pened heav - en's door, And we are blest for ev - er - more.
Calls you one and calls you all To gain his ev - er - last - ing hall.

Christ is born to - day! Christ is born to - day!
Christ was born for this! Christ was born for this!
Christ was born to save! Christ was born to save!

Text: *In dulci jubilo;* Latin and German, 14th C.; Tr. by John M. Neal, 1818-1866
Tune: IN DULCI JUBILO, 66 77 77 55; Klug's *Geistliche Lieder,* Wittenberg, 1535; Harm. by Robert L. Pearsall, 1795-1856

392 O Come, All Ye Faithful/Adeste Fideles

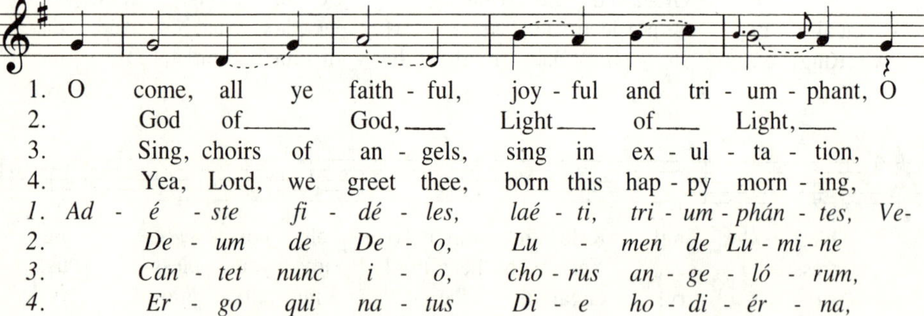
1. O come, all ye faith - ful, joy - ful and tri - um - phant, O
2. God of ___ God, ___ Light ___ of ___ Light, ___
3. Sing, choirs of an - gels, sing in ex - ul - ta - tion,
4. Yea, Lord, we greet thee, born this hap - py morn - ing,
1. Ad - é - ste fi - dé - les, laé - ti, tri - um - phán - tes, Ve-
2. De - um de De - o, Lu - men de Lu - mi - ne
3. Can - tet nunc i - o, cho - rus an - ge - ló - rum,
4. Er - go qui na - tus Di - e ho - di - ér - na,

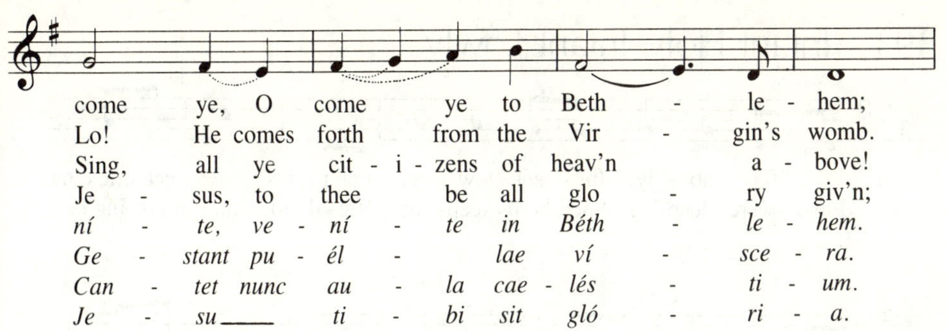
come ye, O come ye to Beth - le - hem;
Lo! He comes forth from the Vir - gin's womb.
Sing, all ye cit - i - zens of heav'n a - bove!
Je - sus, to thee be all glo - ry giv'n;
ní - te, ve - ní - te in Béth - le - hem.
Ge - stant pu - él - lae ví - sce - ra.
Can - tet nunc au - la cae - lés - ti - um.
Je - su ti - bi sit gló - ri - a.

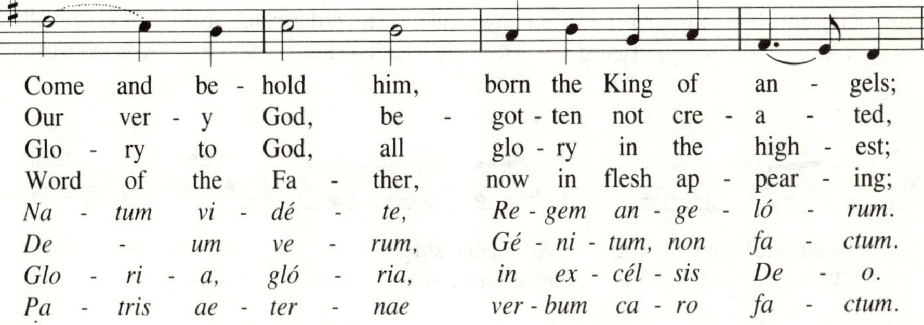
Come and be - hold him, born the King of an - gels;
Our ver - y God, be - got - ten not cre - a - ted,
Glo - ry to God, all glo - ry in the high - est;
Word of the Fa - ther, now in flesh ap - pear - ing;
Na - tum vi - dé - te, Re - gem an - ge - ló - rum.
De - um ve - rum, Gé - ni - tum, non fa - ctum.
Glo - ri - a, gló - ria, in ex - cél - sis De - o.
Pa - tris ae - ter - nae ver - bum ca - ro fa - ctum.

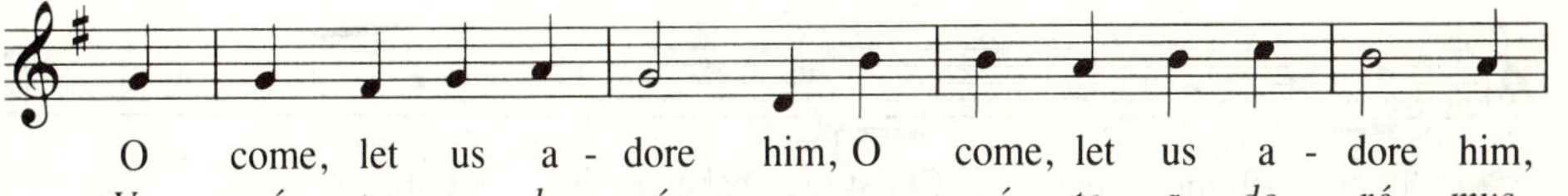
O come, let us a - dore him, O come, let us a - dore him,
Ve - ní - te a - do - ré - mus, ve - ní - te a - do - ré - mus,

O come, let us a - dore him, Christ, the Lord!
ve - ní - te a - do - ré - mus Dó - mi - num.

Text: *Adeste fideles;* John F. Wade, c.1711-1786; Tr. by Frederick Oakeley, 1802-1880, alt.
Tune: ADESTE FIDELES, Irr. with refrain; John F. Wade, c.1711-1786; Desc. with harm. by David Willcocks, b. 1919,

393 Infant Holy, Infant Lowly

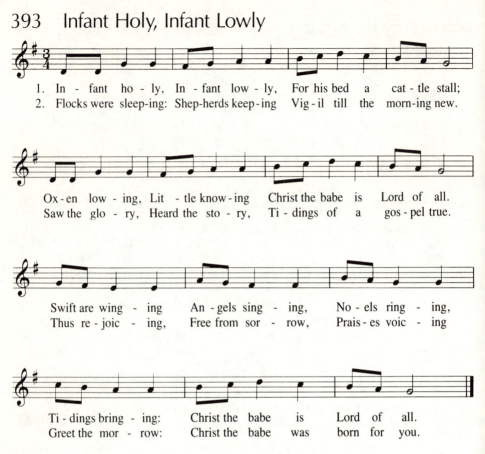

1. In - fant ho - ly, In - fant low - ly, For his bed a cat - tle stall;
2. Flocks were sleep-ing: Shep-herds keep - ing Vig - il till the morn-ing new.

Ox - en low - ing, Lit - tle know - ing Christ the babe is Lord of all.
Saw the glo - ry, Heard the sto - ry, Ti - dings of a gos - pel true.

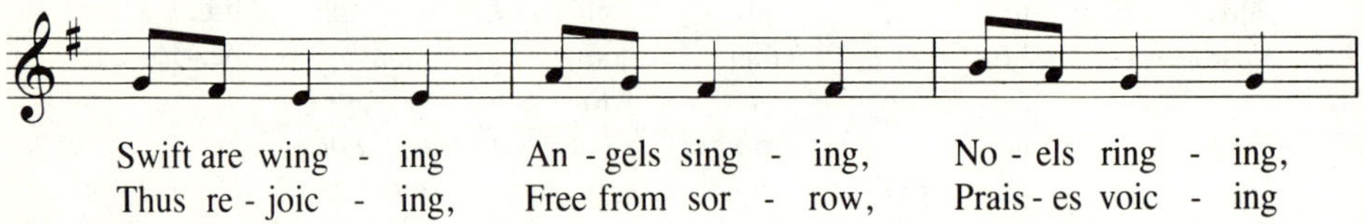

Swift are wing - ing An - gels sing - ing, No - els ring - ing,
Thus re - joic - ing, Free from sor - row, Prais - es voic - ing

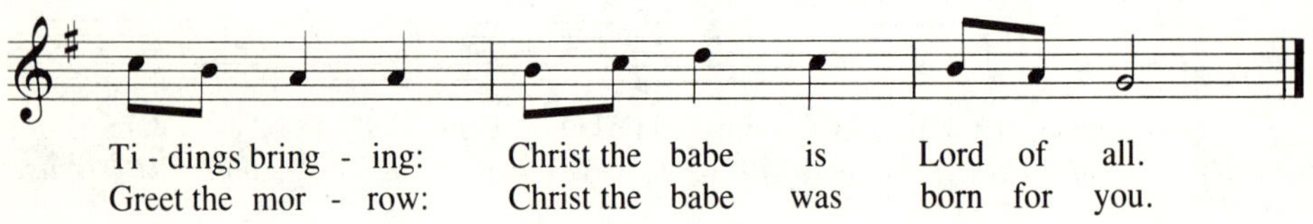

Ti - dings bring - ing: Christ the babe is Lord of all.
Greet the mor - row: Christ the babe was born for you.

Text: *W żłobie leży, któż pobieży*, Polish Carol; Para. by Edith M.G. Reed, 1885-1933
Tune: W ŻŁOBIE LEŻY, 44 7 44 7 4444 7; Polish Carol; Harm. by A.E. Rusbridge, 1917-1969,

394 Now Every Child That Dwells on Earth

1. Now ev-'ry child that dwells on earth, Stand up, stand up, and sing! The
2. Now ev-'ry star that dwells in sky, Look down, with shin - ing eyes: The

pass-ing night has giv - en birth Un - to the chil-dren's King. Sing
night has dropped in pass - ing by A star from par - a - dise. Sing

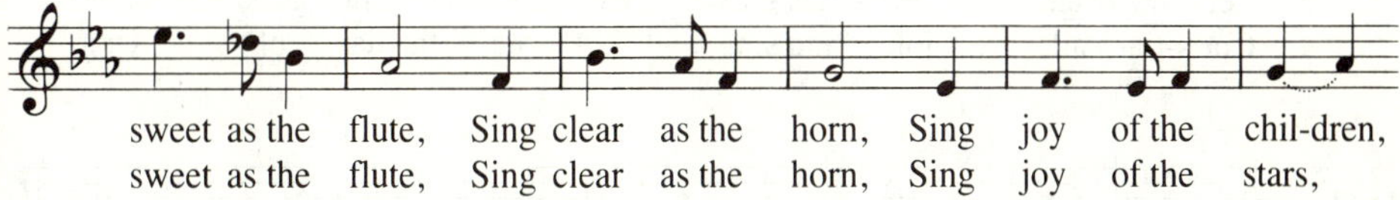
sweet as the flute, Sing clear as the horn, Sing joy of the chil-dren,
sweet as the flute, Sing clear as the horn, Sing joy of the stars,

Come Christ-mas the morn: Lit-tle Christ Je - sus our broth-er is born.
Come Christ-mas the morn: Lit-tle Christ Je - sus our broth-er is born.

Text: Eleanor Farjeon, 1881-1965, © 1927,1955, Harold Ober Associates
Tune: BERKELEY, Irregular; Leo Sowerby, 1895-1968, © The Estate of Leo Sowerby

Angels Voices Richly Blending 395

1. An - gel voic - es rich - ly blend-ing, Shep - herds
2. Lo! a star is bright - ly glow - ing! East - ern
3. To the man - ger come a - dor - ing, Hearts in

to the man - ger send-ing, Sing of peace from heav'n de-
Kings their gifts are show-ing To the King whose gifts pass
thank - ful - ness out - pour-ing To the child, true peace re-

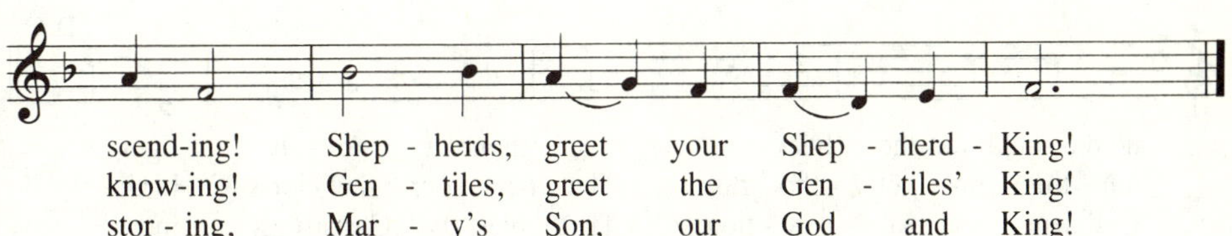
scend-ing! Shep - herds, greet your Shep - herd - King!
know-ing! Gen - tiles, greet the Gen - tiles' King!
stor - ing, Mar - y's Son, our God and King!

Text: *Quem pastores laudavere;* German Carol, 15th C.; Adapt. by James Quinn, SJ, b. 1919, © 1969
Tune: QUEM PASTORES, 888 7; German Carol, 15th C.

396 Christ Was Born on Christmas Day

1. Christ was born on Christ-mas day: Wreathe the hol - ly, twine the bay,
2. He is born to set us free, He is born our Lord to be,
3. Let the bright red ber - ries glow Ev - 'ry -where in good - ly show:
4. Chris-tians all, re - joice and sing, 'Tis the birth - day of a King,

Chri-stus na - tus ho - di - e: The Babe, the Son, the Ho - ly One of Mar-y.
Ex Ma - ri - a Vir - gi - ne: The God, the Lord, by all a-dored for ev-er.
Chri-stus na - tus ho - di - e: The Babe, the Son, the Ho - ly One of Mar-y.
Ex Ma - ri - a Vir - gi - ne: The God, the Lord, by all a-dored for ev-er.

Text: Traditional
Tune: RESONET IN LAUDIBUS, 777 11; German, 16th C.; Harm. by Ralph Vaughan Williams, 1872-1958, © Oxford University Press

397 Go Tell It on the Mountain

Go tell it on the moun - tain, O-ver the hills and ev - 'ry-where;

Go tell it on the moun - tain That Je - sus Christ is born!

1. While shep-herds kept their watch-ing O'er si - lent flocks by night, Be-
2. The shep-herds feared and trem-bled When lo! a - bove the earth Rang
3. Down in a low - ly man - ger The hum-ble Christ was born, And

D.C.

hold through-out the heav - ens There shone a ho - ly light.
out the an - gel cho - rus That hailed our Sav - ior's birth.
God sent us sal - va - tion That bless-ed Christ-mas morn.

Text: Afro-American Spiritual; Adapt. by John W. Work, Jr., 1871-1925, © Mrs. John W. Work III
Tune: GO TELL IT ON THE MOUNTAIN, 7 6 7 6 with refrain; Afro-American Spiritual; Harm. by Paul Sjolund, b. 1935, © Walton Music Corp.

Of the Father's Love Begotten 398

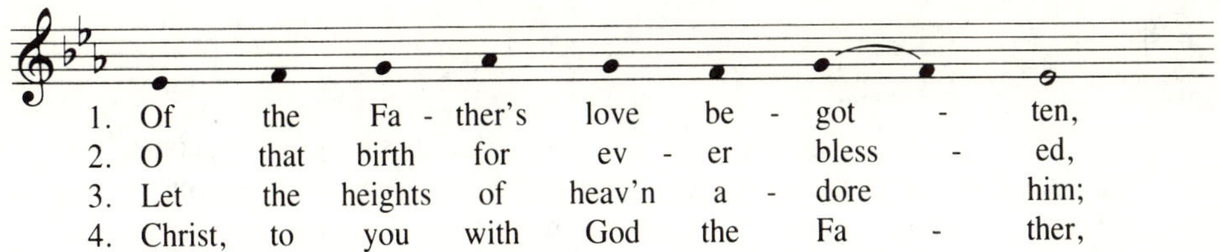
1. Of the Fa - ther's love be - got - ten,
2. O that birth for ev - er bless - ed,
3. Let the heights of heav'n a - dore him;
4. Christ, to you with God the Fa - ther,

Ere the worlds be - gan to be,
When the Vir - gin, full of grace,
An - gel hosts, his prais - es sing;
Spir - it blest e - ter - nal - ly,

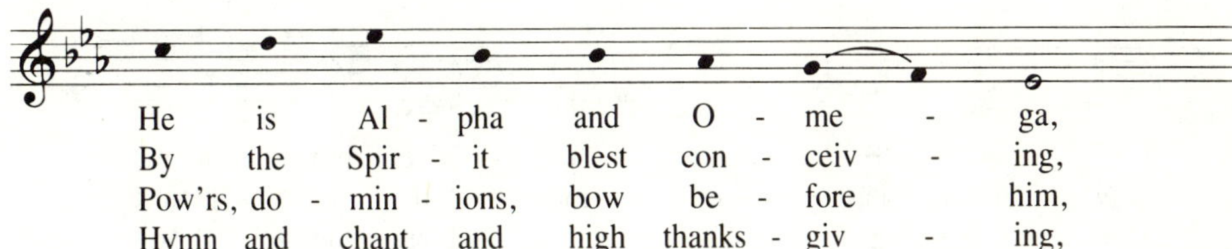
He is Al - pha and O - me - ga,
By the Spir - it blest con - ceiv - ing,
Pow'rs, do - min - ions, bow be - fore him,
Hymn and chant and high thanks - giv - ing,

He the source, the end - ing he,
Bore the Sav - ior of our race;
And ex - tol our God and King;
And un - end - ing prais - es be:

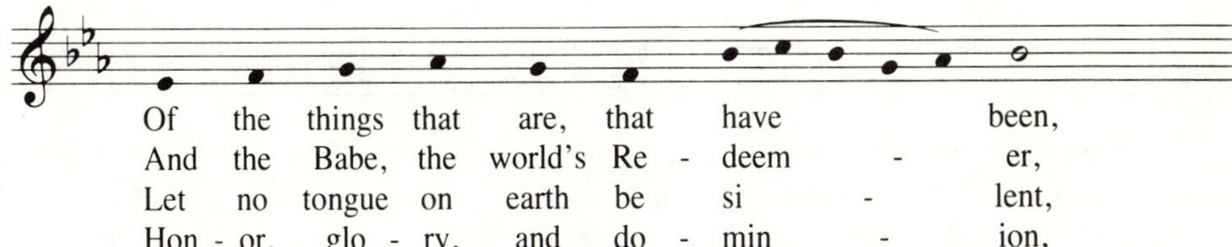
Of the things that are, that have been,
And the Babe, the world's Re - deem - er,
Let no tongue on earth be si - lent,
Hon - or, glo - ry, and do - min - ion,

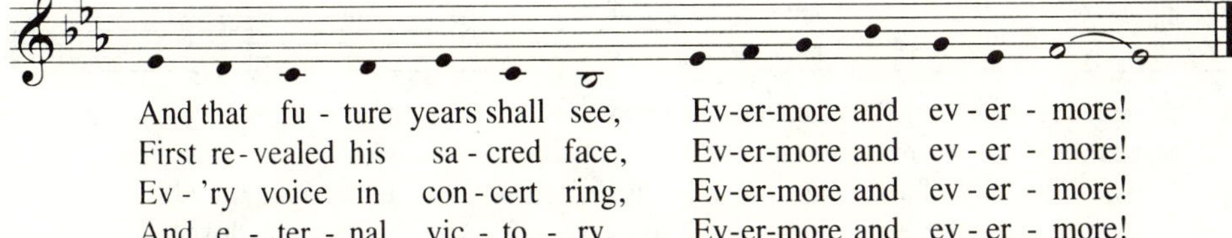
And that fu - ture years shall see, Ev-er-more and ev - er - more!
First re - vealed his sa - cred face, Ev-er-more and ev - er - more!
Ev - 'ry voice in con - cert ring, Ev-er-more and ev - er - more!
And e - ter - nal vic - to - ry, Ev-er-more and ev - er - more!

Text: *Corde natus ex Parentis;* Aurelius Prudentius, 348-413; Tr. by John M. Neale, 1818-1866 and Henry W. Baker, 1821-1877
Tune: DIVINUM MYSTERIUM, 8 7 8 7 8 7 7; 12th C.; Mode V; Acc. by Richard Proulx, b. 1937,

399 Joy to the World

1. Joy to the world! the Lord is come:
2. Joy to the world! the Sav - ior reigns:
3. No more let sin and sor - rows grow,
4. He rules the world with truth and grace,
Let earth re - ceive her King;
Let us, our songs em - ploy;
Nor thorns in - fest the ground;
And makes the na - tions prove
Let ev - 'ry heart pre - pare him room,
While fields and floods, rocks, hills, and plains;
He comes to make his bless - ings flow
The glo - ries of his right - eous - ness,
And heaven and na - ture sing, And
Re - peat the sound - ing joy, Re-
Far as the curse is found, Far
And won - ders of his love, And
heaven and na - ture sing, And
peat the sound - ing joy, Re-
as the curse is found, Far
won - ders of his love, And
heaven, and heaven and na - ture sing.
peat, re - peat the sound - ing joy.
as, far as the curse is found.
won - ders, won - ders of his love.

Text: Ps. 98; Isaac Watts, 1674-1748
Tune: ANTIOCH, CM; Arr. from George F. Handel, 1685-1759, in T. Hawkes' *Collection of Tunes*, 1833

It Came upon the Midnight Clear 400

1. It came up - on the mid-night clear, That glo - rious song of old,
2. Still through the clo - ven skies they come, With peace-ful wings un - furled,
3. Yet with the woes of sin and strife, The world has suf - fered long;
4. For, lo, the days are has-tening on, By proph-ets seen of old,

From an - gels bend-ing near the earth To touch their harps of gold:
And still their heav'n-ly mu - sic floats O'er all the wea - ry world:
Be - neath the heav'n-ly hymn have rolled Two thou-sand years of wrong;
When with the ev - er - cir-cling years Shall come the time fore - told,

"Peace on the earth, good will to all From heaven's all gra - cious King";
A - bove its sad and low - ly plains They bend on hov-'ring wing,
And war - ring hu - man - kind hears not The ti - dings which they bring;
When peace shall o - ver all the earth Its an - cient splen-dors fling,

The world in sol - emn still - ness lay, To hear the an - gels sing.
And ev - er o'er its Ba - bel sounds The bless - ed an - gels sing.
O hush the noise and cease your strife And hear the an - gels sing.
And all the world give back the song Which now the an - gels sing.

Text: Edmund H. Sears, 1810-1876, alt.
Tune: CAROL, CMD; Richard S. Willis, 1819-1900

Canon

Gloria, Gloria 401

A
B
Glo - ri - a, glo - ri - a, in ex - cel - sis De - o!
C
D
Glo - ri - a, glo - ri - a, al - le - lu - ia, al - le - lu - ia!

Text: Luke 2:14; Taizé Community, 1978
Tune: Jacques Berthier, b.1923

402 Once in Royal David's City

1. Once in roy - al Da - vid's cit - y Stood a low - ly cat - tle shed,
2. He came down to earth from heav - en Who is God and Lord of all,
3. And through all his won - drous child-hood He would hon - or and o - bey,
4. For he is our child - hood's pat - tern, Day by day like us he grew;
5. And our eyes at last shall see him, Thru his own re-deem-ing love;

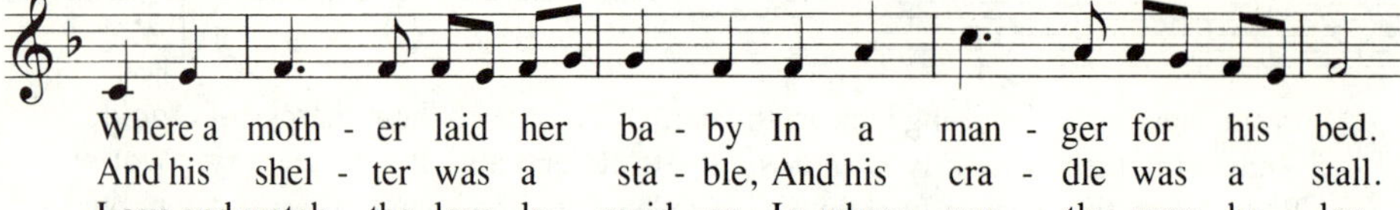

Where a moth - er laid her ba - by In a man - ger for his bed.
And his shel - ter was a sta - ble, And his cra - dle was a stall.
Love and watch the low - ly maid - en In whose gen - tle arms he lay.
He was lit - tle, weak, and help - less, Tears and smiles like us he knew:
For that child so dear and gen - tle Is our Lord in heav'n a - bove:

Mar - y was that moth-er mild, Je - sus Christ her lit - tle Child.
With the poor and mean and low-ly Lived on earth our Sav - ior ho - ly.
Chris-tian chil - dren all should be Kind, o - be - dient, good as he.
And he feels for all our sad-ness, And he shares in all our glad-ness.
And he leads his chil-dren on To the place where he has gone.

Text: Cecil Frances Alexander, 1818-1895
Tune: IRBY, 8 7 8 7 77; Henry J. Gauntlett, 1805-1876; Harm. by Arthur H. Mann, 1850-1929, © 1957, Novello and Co. Ltd.

403 Virgin-born, We Bow before You

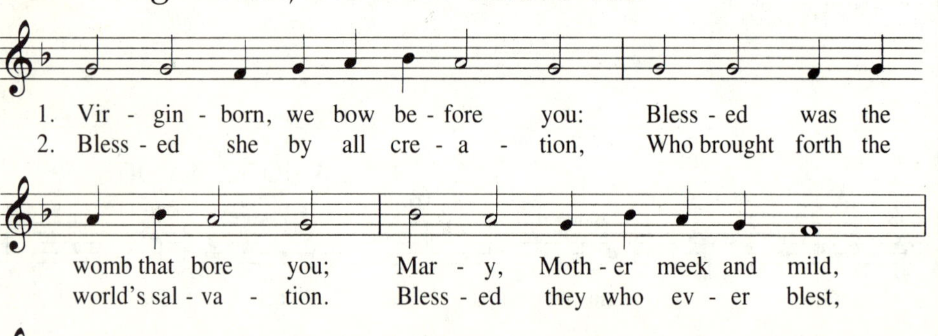

1. Vir - gin - born, we bow be - fore you: Bless - ed was the womb that bore you; Mar - y, Moth - er meek and mild,
2. Bless - ed she by all cre - a - tion, Who brought forth the world's sal - va - tion. Bless - ed they who ev - er blest,

Bless - ed was she in her Child. Bless - ed was the breast that
Love you most and serve you best. Vir - gin - born, we bow be-

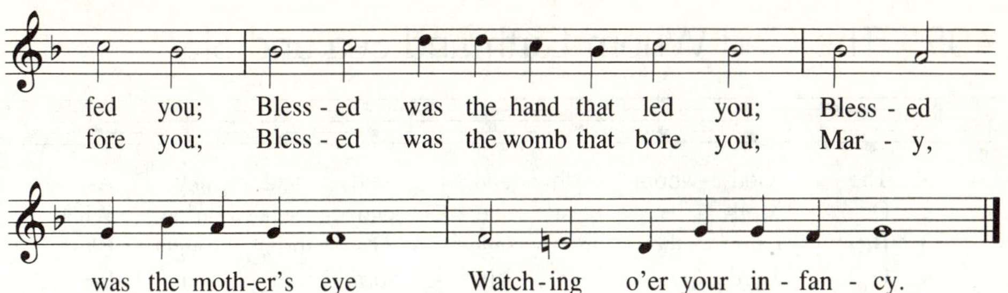

fed you; Bless - ed was the hand that led you; Bless - ed
fore you; Bless - ed was the womb that bore you; Mar - y,

was the moth-er's eye Watch - ing o'er your in - fan - cy.
Moth-er meek and mild, Bless - ed was she in her Child.

Text: Reginald Herber, 1783-1826, alt.
Tune: MON DIEU PRETE-MOI L'OREILLE, 88 77 D; Attr. to Louis Bourgeois, c.1510-1561; Harm. by Claude Goudimel, 1505-1572, alt.

Sing of Mary, Pure and Lowly 404

1. Sing of Mar - y, pure and low - ly, Vir - gin-moth - er un - de - filed,
2. Sing of Je - sus, son of Mar - y, In the home at Naz - a - reth.
3. Glo - ry be to God the Fa-ther; Glo - ry be to God the Son;

Sing of God's own Son most ho - ly, Who be-came her lit - tle child.
Toil and la - bor can-not wea - ry Love en - dur - ing un - to death.
Glo - ry be to God the Spir - it; Glo - ry to the Three in One.

Fair - est child of fair - est moth-er, God the Lord who came to earth,
Con - stant was the love he gave her, Though he went forth from her side,
From the heart of bless - ed Mar - y, From all saints the song as-cends,

Word made flesh, our ver - y broth-er, Takes our na - ture by his birth.
Forth to preach, and heal, and suf - fer, Till on Cal - va - ry he died.
And the church the strain re - ech - oes Un - to earth's re - mot-est ends.

Text: Roland F. Palmer, b.1891
Tune: PLEADING SAVIOR, 8 7 8 7 D; *Christian Lyre*, 1830; Harm. by Richard Proulx, b.1937,

405 The God Whom Earth and Sea and Sky

1. The God whom earth and sea and sky A-
2. O Moth - er blest! the cho - sen shrine Where-
3. Blest in the mes - sage Ga - briel brought; Blest
4. O Lord, the Vir - gin - born, to you E-

dore and praise and mag - ni - fy, Whose might they claim, whose
in the ar - chi - tect di - vine, Whose hand con - tains the
in the work the Spir - it wrought; Most blest, to bring to
ter - nal praise and laud are due, Whom with the Fa - ther

love they tell, In Mar - y's bod - y comes to dwell.
earth and sky, Has come in hu - man form to lie:
hu - man birth The long de - sired of all the earth.
we a - dore And Spir - it blest for ev - er - more.

Text: *Quem terra, pontus, aethera;* Venantius Fortunatus, c.530-609; Tr. by John M. Neale, 1818-1866, alt.
Tune: EISENACH, LM; John H. Schein, 1586-1630; Harm. by J. S. Bach, 1685-1750

406 We Three Kings of Orient Are

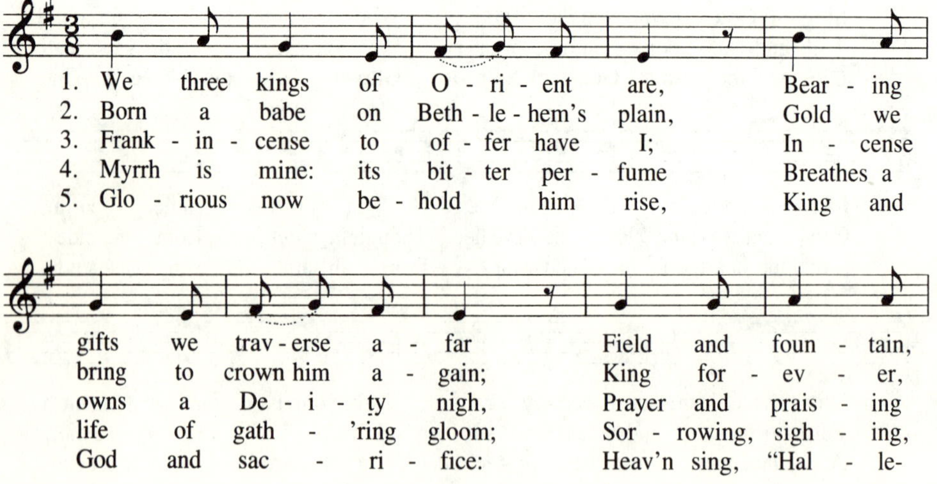
1. We three kings of O - ri - ent are, Bear - ing
2. Born a babe on Beth - le - hem's plain, Gold we
3. Frank - in - cense to of - fer have I; In - cense
4. Myrrh is mine: its bit - ter per - fume Breathes a
5. Glo - rious now be - hold him rise, King and
gifts we trav - erse a - far Field and foun - tain,
bring to crown him a - gain; King for - ev - er,
owns a De - i - ty nigh, Prayer and prais - ing
life of gath - 'ring gloom; Sor - rowing, sigh - ing,
God and sac - ri - fice: Heav'n sing, "Hal - le-

Moor and moun - tain, Fol - low - ing yon - der star.
Ceas - ing nev - er, O - ver us all to reign.
Glad - ly rais - ing, Wor-ship - ing God on high.
Bleed - ing, dy - ing, Sealed in the stone cold tomb.
lu - jah!" "Hal - le - lu - jah!" earth re - plies.

O star of won - der, star of night, Star with roy - al beau - ty

bright, West-ward lead-ing, still pro-ceed-ing, Guide us to the per-fect Light.

Text: Mt. 2:1-11; John H. Hopkins, Jr., 1820-1891
Tune: KINGS OF ORIENT, 88 44 6 with refrain; John H. Hopkins, Jr., 1820-1891

What Star Is This 407

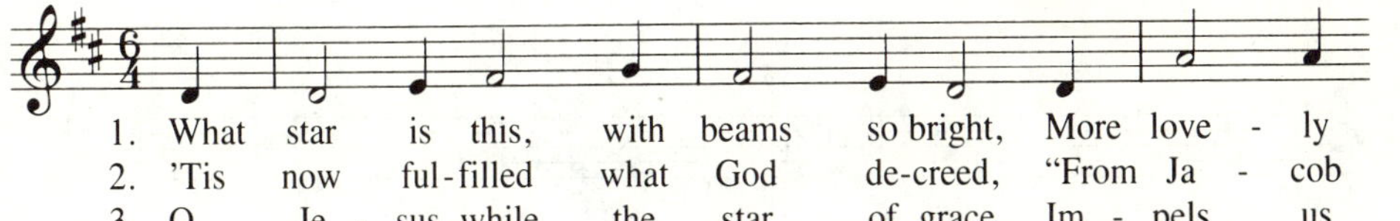
1. What star is this, with beams so bright, More love - ly
2. 'Tis now ful-filled what God de-creed, "From Ja - cob
3. O Je - sus, while the star of grace Im - pels us
4. To God Cre - a - tor, heav'n - ly light, To Christ, re-

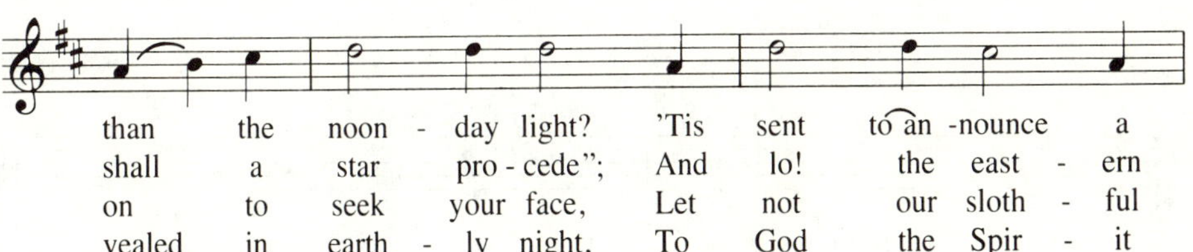
than the noon - day light? 'Tis sent to an - nounce a
shall a star pro - cede"; And lo! the east - ern
on to seek your face, Let not our sloth - ful
vealed in earth - ly night, To God the Spir - it

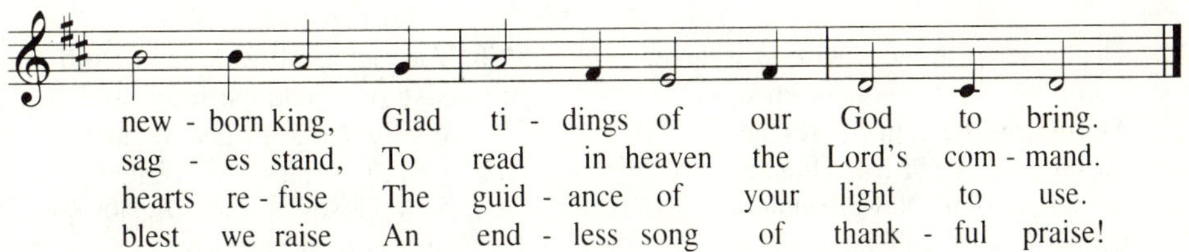
new - born king, Glad ti - dings of our God to bring.
sag - es stand, To read in heaven the Lord's com - mand.
hearts re - fuse The guid - ance of your light to use.
blest we raise An end - less song of thank - ful praise!

Text: *Quem stella sole pulchrior*, Charles Coffin, 1676-1749; Tr. by John Chandler, 1806-1876, alt.
Tune: PUER NOBIS, LM; Adapt. by Michael Praetorius, 1571-1621

408 The First Nowell

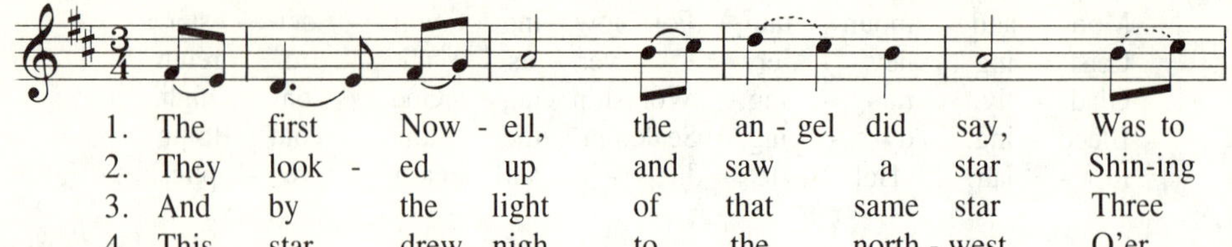
1. The first Now - ell, the an - gel did say, Was to
2. They look - ed up and saw a star Shin-ing
3. And by the light of that same star Three
4. This star drew nigh to the north - west, O'er

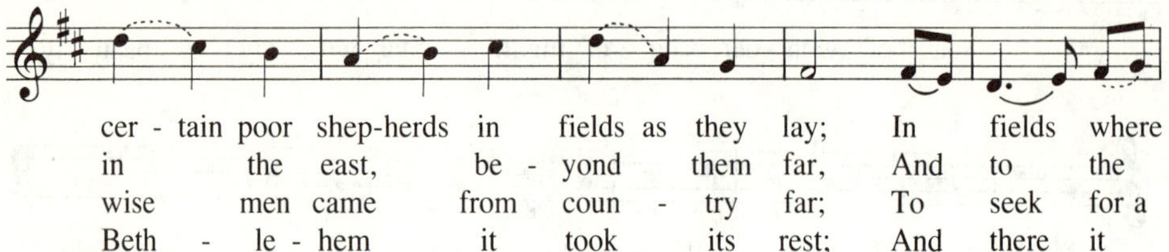
cer - tain poor shep-herds in fields as they lay; In fields where
in the east, be - yond them far, And to the
wise men came from coun - try far; To seek for a
Beth - le - hem it took its rest; And there it

they lay keep - ing their sheep, On a cold win - ter's night that
earth it gave great light, And so it con - tin-ued both
king was their in - tent, And to fol - low the star where-
did both stop and stay, Right o - ver the place where

was so deep.
day and night. Now - ell, Now - ell, Now - ell, Now-
ev - er it went.
Je - sus lay.

ell, Born is the King of Is - ra - el.

5. Then entered in those wise men three,
Full rev'rently upon their knee,
And offered there, in his presence,
Their gold and myrrh and frankincense.
Nowell, Nowell, Nowell, Nowell,
Born is the King of Israel.

6. Then let us all with one accord
Sing praises to our heav'nly Lord;
Who with the Father we adore
And Spirit blest for evermore.
Nowell, Nowell, Nowell, Nowell,
Born is the King of Israel.

Text: English Carol, 17th C.
Tune: THE FIRST NOWELL, Irregular; English Melody; Harm. by David Willcocks, b.1919,

As with Gladness Men of Old 409

1. As with glad - ness men of old Did the guid - ing star be - hold;
2. As with joy - ful steps they sped To that low - ly man - ger - bed,
3. As they of - fered gifts most rare At that man - ger crude and bare;
4. Christ Re - deem - er, with us stay, Help us live your ho - ly way;
5. In the heaven - ly cit - y bright None shall need cre - a - ted light;

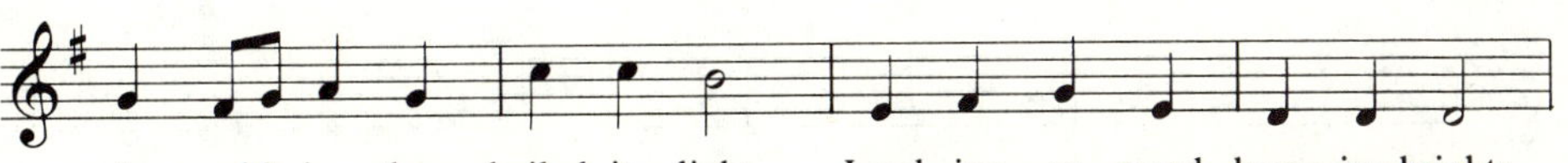

As with joy they hailed its light, Lead - ing on - ward, beam-ing bright;
There to bend the knee be - fore Christ whom heaven and earth a - dore;
So may we this ho - ly day, Drawn to you with - out de - lay,
And when earth - ly things are past, Bring our ran-somed souls at last
You, its light, its joy, its crown, You, its sun which goes not down;

So, most gra-cious Lord, may we Ev - er - more your splen - dor see.
So may we with hur - ried pace Run to seek your throne of grace.
All our cost - liest treas - ures bring, Christ, to you, our heaven - ly King.
Where they need no star to guide, Where no clouds your glo - ry hide.
There for ev - er may we sing Al - le - lu - ias to our King.

Text: William C. Dix, 1837-1898
Tune: DIX, 77 77 77; Arr. from Conrad Kocher, 1786-1872, by William H. Monk, 1823-1889

410 Songs of Thankfulness and Praise

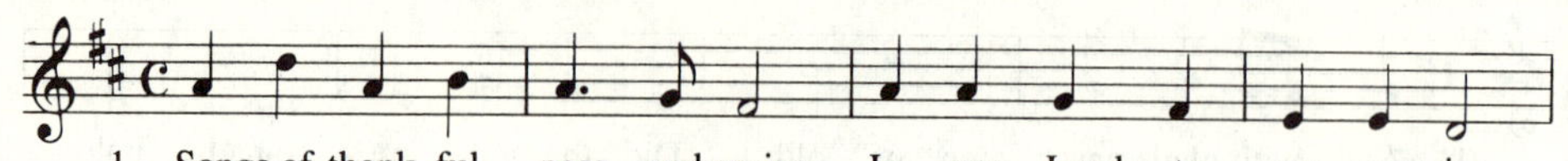

1. Songs of thank-ful - ness and praise, Je - sus, Lord, to you we raise,
2. Man - i - fest at Jor - dan's stream, Proph-et, Priest, and King su-preme;
3. Man - i - fest in mak - ing whole Pal - sied limbs and faint - ing soul;
4. Grant us grace to see you, Lord, Mir-rored in your ho - ly word;

Man - i - fest - ed by the star To the sag - es from a - far;
And at Ca - na, wed - ding guest, In your God-head man - i - fest;
Man - i - fest in val - iant fight, Quell-ing all the dev - il's might;
May we im - i - tate you now, And on us your grace en - dow;

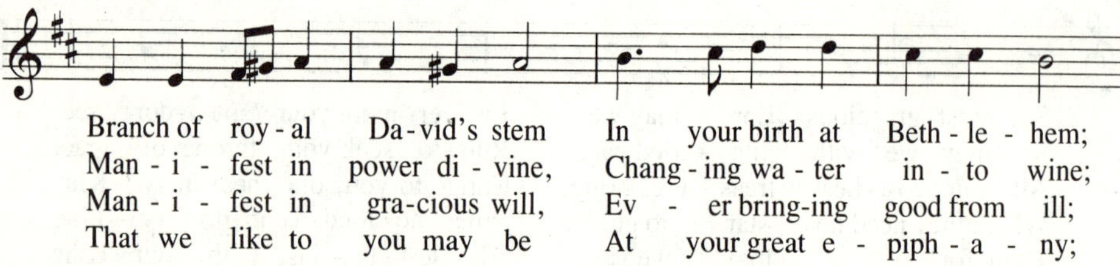

Branch of roy - al Da - vid's stem In your birth at Beth - le - hem;
Man - i - fest in power di - vine, Chang - ing wa - ter in - to wine;
Man - i - fest in gra-cious will, Ev - er bring-ing good from ill;
That we like to you may be At your great e - piph - a - ny;

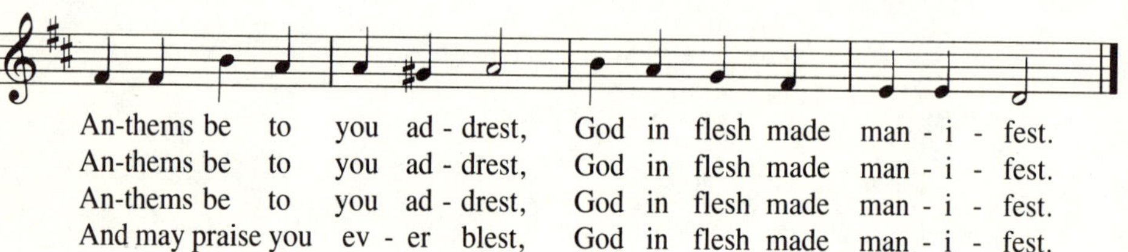

An-thems be to you ad - drest, God in flesh made man - i - fest.
An-thems be to you ad - drest, God in flesh made man - i - fest.
An-thems be to you ad - drest, God in flesh made man - i - fest.
And may praise you ev - er blest, God in flesh made man - i - fest.

Text: Christopher Wordsworth, 1807-1885
Tune: SALZBURG, 77 77 D; Jakob Hintze, 1622-1702, alt.; Harm. by J. S. Bach, 1685-1750

What Child Is This 411

1. What child is this, who, laid to rest, On
2. Why lies he in such mean es - tate Where
3. So bring him in - cense, gold, and myrrh, Come,

Mar - y's lap is sleep - ing? Whom an - gels greet with
ox and ass are feed - ing? Good Chris - tian, fear; for
peas - ant, king to own him; The King of kings sal-

an - thems sweet, While shep - herds watch are keep - ing?
sin - ners here The si - lent Word is plead - ing.
va - tion brings, Let lov - ing hearts en - throne him.

This, this is Christ the King, Whom shep-herds guard and an-gels sing;

Haste, haste to bring him laud, The babe, the son of Mar - y.

Text: William C. Dix, 1827-1898
Tune: GREENSLEEVES, 8 7 8 7 with refrain; English Melody, 16th C.; Harm. by John Stainer, 1840-1901

412 When John Baptized by Jordan's River

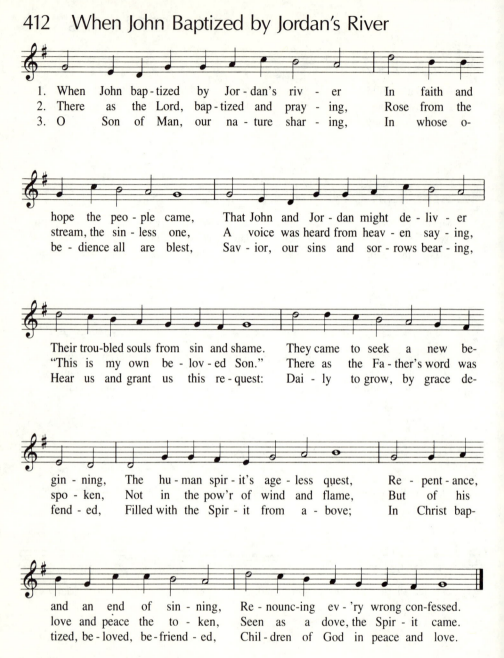

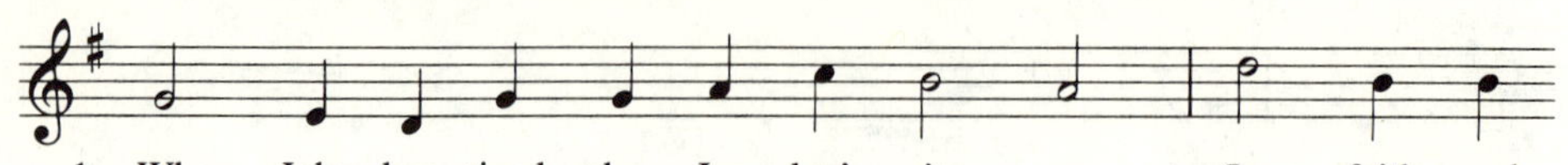

1. When John bap - tized by Jor - dan's riv - er In faith and
2. There as the Lord, bap - tized and pray - ing, Rose from the
3. O Son of Man, our na - ture shar - ing, In whose o-

hope the peo - ple came, That John and Jor - dan might de - liv - er
stream, the sin - less one, A voice was heard from heav - en say - ing,
be - dience all are blest, Sav - ior, our sins and sor - rows bear - ing,

Their trou-bled souls from sin and shame. They came to seek a new be-
"This is my own be - lov - ed Son." There as the Fa - ther's word was
Hear us and grant us this re - quest: Dai - ly to grow, by grace de-

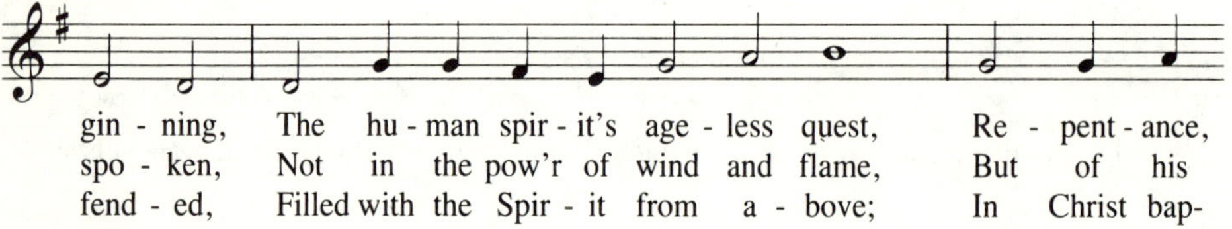

gin - ning, The hu - man spir - it's age - less quest, Re - pent - ance,
spo - ken, Not in the pow'r of wind and flame, But of his
fend - ed, Filled with the Spir - it from a - bove; In Christ bap-

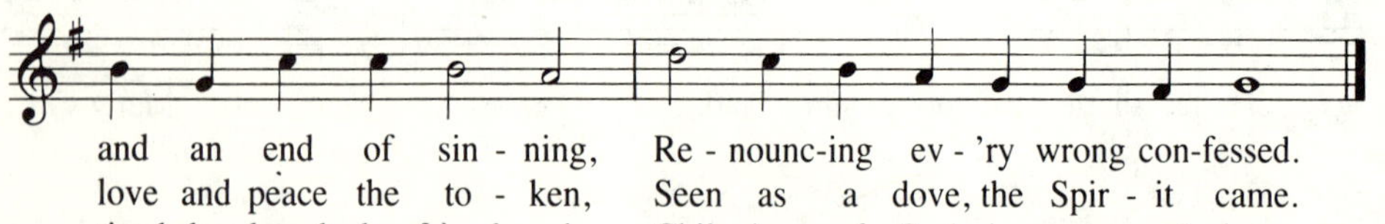

and an end of sin - ning, Re - nounc-ing ev - 'ry wrong con-fessed.
love and peace the to - ken, Seen as a dove, the Spir - it came.
tized, be - loved, be - friend - ed, Chil - dren of God in peace and love.

Text: Timothy Dudley-Smith, b.1926,
Tune: RENDEZ A DIEU, 9 8 9 8 D; Louis Bourgeois, c.1510-1561

Alleluia, Song of Gladness 413

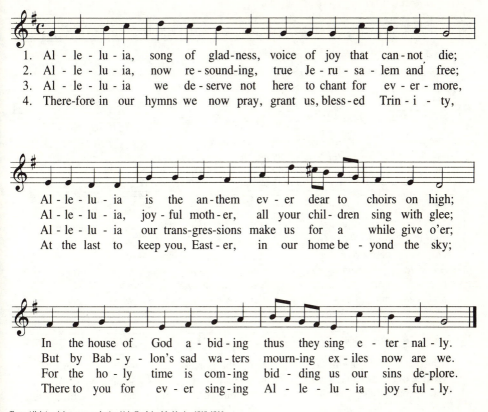

1. Al - le - lu - ia, song of glad-ness, voice of joy that can-not die;
2. Al - le - lu - ia, now re - sound-ing, true Je - ru - sa - lem and free;
3. Al - le - lu - ia we de - serve not here to chant for ev - er - more,
4. There-fore in our hymns we now pray, grant us, bless-ed Trin - i - ty,

Al - le - lu - ia is the an-them ev - er dear to choirs on high;
Al - le - lu - ia, joy - ful moth - er, all your chil- dren sing with glee;
Al - le - lu - ia our trans-gres-sions make us for a while give o'er;
At the last to keep you, East - er, in our home be - yond the sky;

In the house of God a - bid - ing thus they sing e - ter - nal - ly.
But by Bab - y - lon's sad wa - ters mourn-ing ex - iles now are we.
For the ho - ly time is com-ing bid - ding us our sins de-plore.
There to you for ev - er sing-ing Al - le - lu - ia joy - ful - ly.

Text: *Alleluia, dulce carmen;* Latin, 11th C.; John M. Neale, 1818-1866
Tune: DULCE CARMEN, 8 7 8 7 8 7; *Essay on the Church Plain Chant,* 1782

414 Hear Us, Almighty Lord/Attende Domine

Hear us, al - might - y Lord, show us your
At - tén - de Dó - mi - ne, et mi - se-
mer - cy Sin - ners we stand here be - fore you.
ré - re, Qui - a pec - cá - vi - mus ti - bi.
1. Je - sus our Sav - ior, Lord of all the na - tions,
2. Word of the Fa - ther, key - stone of God's build - ing,
3. God of com - pas - sion, Lord of might and splen - dor,
1. Ad te Rex sum - me, óm - ni - um re - dém - ptor,
2. Déx - te - ra Pa - tris, la - pis an - gu - lá - ris,
3. Ro - gá - mus, De - us, tu - am ma - je - stá - tem:
Christ our Re - deem - er, hear the prayers we of - fer,
Source of our glad - ness, gate - way to the King - dom,
Gra - cious - ly lis - ten, hear our cries of an - guish.
Ó - cu - los nó - stros sub - le - vá - mus flen - tes:
Vi - a sa - lú - tis já - nu - a cae - lé - stis,
Áu - ri - bus sa - cris gé - mi - tus ex - aú - di:
D.C.
Spare us and save us, com - fort us in sor - row.
Free us in mer - cy from the sins that bind us.
Touch us and heal us where our sins have wound - ed.
Ex - aú - di, Chri - ste, sup - pli - cán - tum pre - ces.
Áb - lu - e no - stri má - cu - las de - lí - cti.
Crí - mi - na no - stra plá - ci - dus in - dúl - ge.

4. Humbly confessing that we have offended,
Stripped of illusions, naked in our sorrow,
Pardon, Lord Jesus, those your blood has ransomed.

5. Innocent captive, you were led to slaughter,
Sentenced by sinners when they brought false witness.
Keep from damnation those your death has rescued.

4. *Tibi fatémur, crímina admíssa:*
Contríto corde pándimus occúlta:
Túa Redemptor, píetas ignóscat.

5. *Innocens captus, nec repúgnans ductus,*
Téstibus falsis, pro ímpiis damnátus:
Quos redemísti, tu consérva, Christe.

Text: Latin, 10th C.; Tr. by Ralph Wright, OSB, b.1938, © 1980, ICEL
Tune: ATTENDE DOMINE, 11 11 11 with refrain; Mode V; Acc. by Richard Proulx, b.1937, © 1975, GIA Publications, Inc.

Somebody's Knockin' at Your Door 415

Some-bod-y's knock-in' at your door; Some-bod-y's knock-in' at your door;
O sin - ner, why don't you an - swer? Some-bod-y's knock-in' at your
door.
Solo:
1. Knocks like Je - sus,
2. Can't you hear him?
3. Je - sus calls you,
4. Can't you trust him?
All:
Some-bod - y's knock-in' at your door;
Solo:
Knocks like Je - sus,
Can't you hear him?
Je - sus calls you,
Can't you trust him?
All:
Some-bod-y's knock-in' at your door. O
sin - ner, why don't you an-swer? Some-bod-y's knock-in' at your door.

Text: Afro-American Spiritual
Tune: SOMEBODY'S KNOCKIN', Irregular; Afro-American Spiritual; Harm. by Richard Proulx, b.1937, © 1986, GIA Publications, Inc.

416 Parce Domine

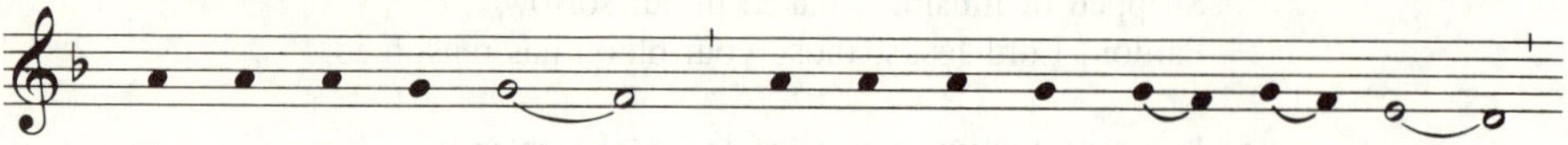

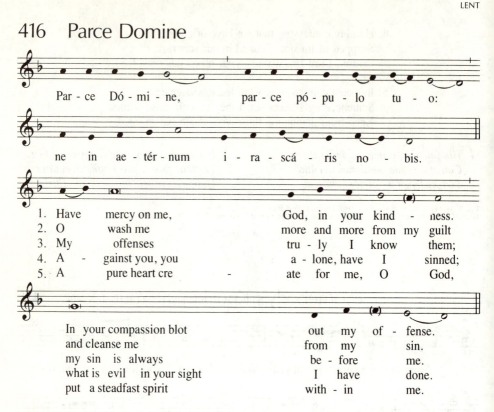

Par - ce Dó - mi - ne, par - ce pó - pu - lo tu - o: 
ne in ae - tér - num i - ra - scá - ris no - bis.

1. Have mercy on me, God, in your kind - ness. In your compassion blot out my of - fense.
2. O wash me more and more from my guilt and cleanse me from my sin.
3. My offenses tru - ly I know them; my sin is always be - fore me.
4. A - gainst you, you a - lone, have I sinned; what is evil in your sight I have done.
5. A pure heart cre - ate for me, O God, put a steadfast spirit with - in me.

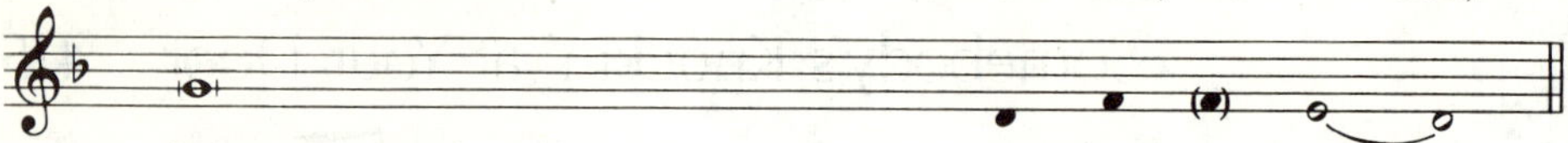

Text: Joel 2:17, Psalm 51:3-6,12; Tr. The Grail, 1963, © 1963, The Grail
Tune: PARCE DOMINE, Irregular; Mode I with Tonus Peregrinus; Acc. by Robert LeBlanc, b.1948, © 1986, GIA Publications, Inc.

417 Lord, Who throughout These Forty Days

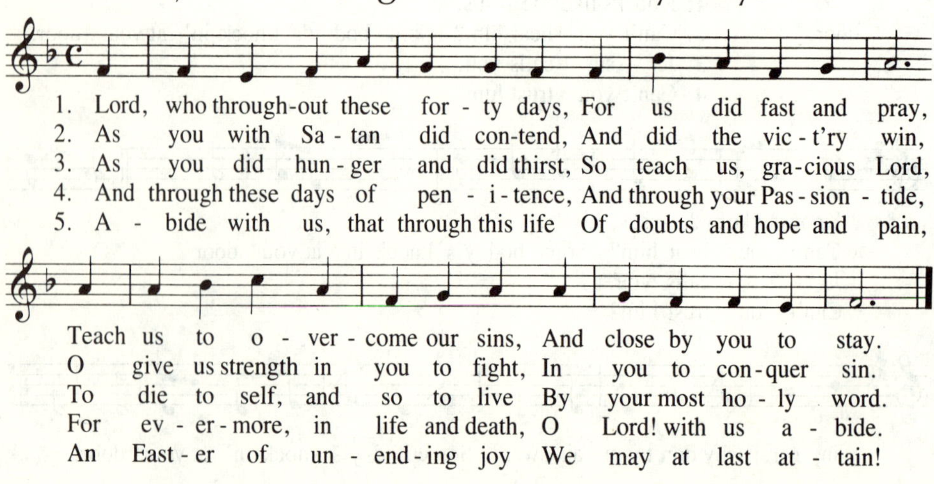
1. Lord, who through-out these for - ty days, For us did fast and pray,
2. As you with Sa - tan did con-tend, And did the vic - t'ry win,
3. As you did hun - ger and did thirst, So teach us, gra-cious Lord,
4. And through these days of pen - i - tence, And through your Pas - sion - tide,
5. A - bide with us, that through this life Of doubts and hope and pain,
Teach us to o - ver - come our sins, And close by you to stay.
O give us strength in you to fight, In you to con-quer sin.
To die to self, and so to live By your most ho - ly word.
For ev - er - more, in life and death, O Lord! with us a - bide.
An East - er of un - end - ing joy We may at last at - tain!

Text: Claudia F. Hernaman, 1838-1898, alt.
Tune: ST. FLAVIAN, CM; *John's Day Psalter,* 1562; Harm. based on the original *faux-bourdon* setting

Before the Fruit Is Ripened by the Sun 418

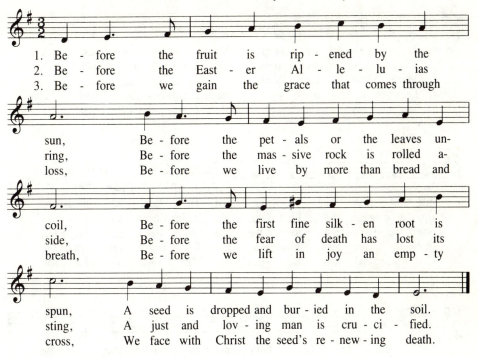

1. Be - fore the fruit is rip - ened by the
2. Be - fore the East - er Al - le - lu - ias
3. Be - fore we gain the grace that comes through

sun, Be - fore the pet - als or the leaves un-
ring, Be - fore the mas - sive rock is rolled a-
loss, Be - fore we live by more than bread and

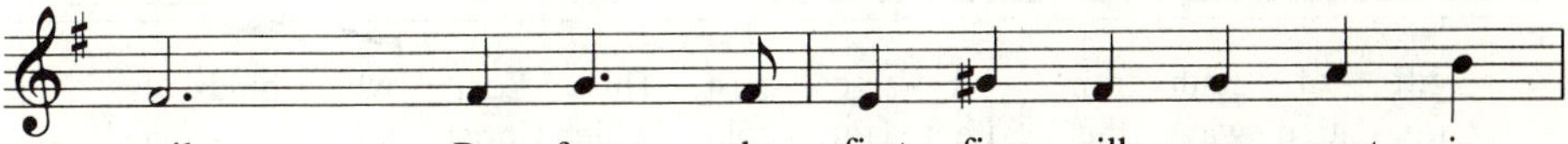

coil, Be - fore the first fine silk - en root is
side, Be - fore the fear of death has lost its
breath, Be - fore we lift in joy an emp - ty

spun, A seed is dropped and bur - ied in the soil.
sting, A just and lov - ing man is cru - ci - fied.
cross, We face with Christ the seed's re - new - ing death.

Text: John 12:20-33; Thomas H. Troeger, b.1945
Tune: RENEWING DEATH, 10 10 10 10; Carol Doran, b.1936

Forty Days and Forty Nights 419

1. For - ty days and for - ty nights You were fast - ing in the wild;
2. Shall not we your sor - row share And from world - ly joys ab - stain,
3. Then if Sa - tan on us press, Flesh or spir - it to as - sail,
4. So shall we have peace di - vine: Ho - lier glad - ness ours shall be;
5. Keep, O keep us, Sav - ior dear, Ev - er con - stant by your side;
For - ty days and for - ty nights Tempt - ed and yet un - de - filed.
Fast - ing with un - ceas - ing prayer, Strong with you to suf - fer pain?
Vic - tor in the wil - der - ness, Grant we may not faint nor fail!
Round us, too, shall an - gels shine, Such as served you faith - ful - ly.
That with you we may ap - pear At the e - ter - nal East - er - tide.

Text: George H. Smyttan, 1822-1870, alt.
Tune: HEINLEIN, 7 7 7 7; Attr. to Martin Herbst, 1654-1681; Harm. ascr. to J. S. Bach, 1685-1750

420 Again We Keep This Solemn Fast

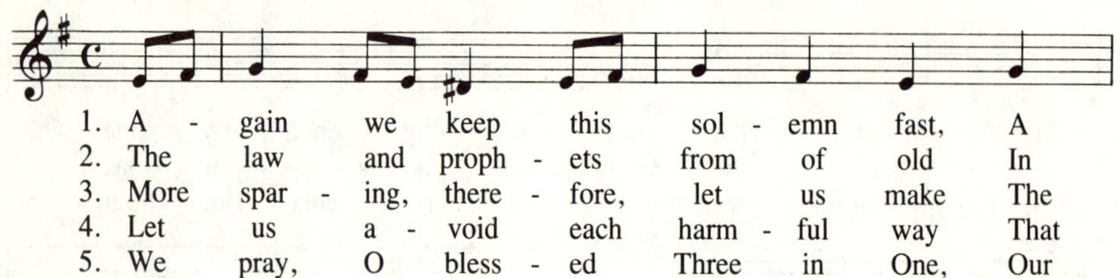
1. A - gain we keep this sol - emn fast, A
2. The law and proph - ets from of old In
3. More spar - ing, there - fore, let us make The
4. Let us a - void each harm - ful way That
5. We pray, O bless - ed Three in One, Our

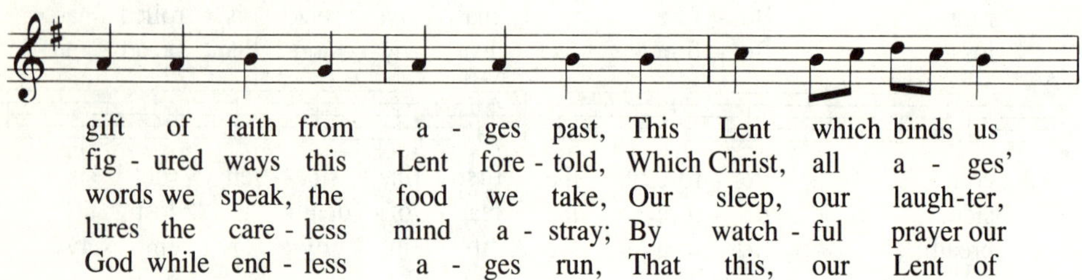
gift of faith from a - ges past, This Lent which binds us
fig - ured ways this Lent fore - told, Which Christ, all a - ges'
words we speak, the food we take, Our sleep, our laugh-ter,
lures the care - less mind a - stray; By watch - ful prayer our
God while end - less a - ges run, That this, our Lent of

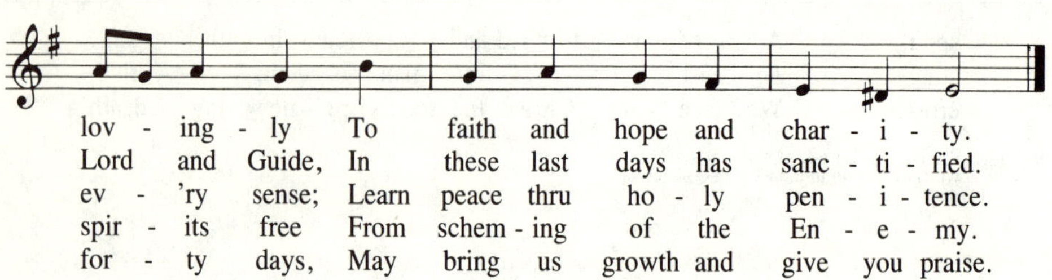
lov - ing - ly To faith and hope and char - i - ty.
Lord and Guide, In these last days has sanc - ti - fied.
ev - 'ry sense; Learn peace thru ho - ly pen - i - tence.
spir - its free From schem - ing of the En - e - my.
for - ty days, May bring us growth and give you praise.

Text: *Ex more docti mystico;* Ascr. to Gregory the Great, c.540-604; Tr. by Peter J. Scagnelli, b.1949, ©
Tune: ERHALT UNS HERR, LM; Klug's *Geistliche Lieder,* 1543; Harm. by J. S. Bach, 1685-1750

At the Cross Her Station Keeping 421

1. At the cross her sta - tion keep - ing, Mar - y stood in
2. While she wait - ed in her an - guish, See - ing Christ in
3. With what pain and de - so - la - tion, With what no - ble
4. Ev - er pa - tient in her yearn - ing, Though her tear - filled

sor - row, weep - ing, When her Son was cru - ci - fied.
tor - ment lan - guish, Bit - ter sor - row pierced her heart.
re - sig - na - tion, Mar - y watched her dy - ing Son.
eyes were burn - ing, Mar - y gazed up - on her Son.

5. Who, that sorrow contemplating,
On that passion meditating,
Would not share the Virgin's grief?

6. Christ she saw, for our salvation,
Scourged with cruel acclamation,
Bruised and beaten by the rod.

7. Christ she saw with life-blood failing,
All her anguish unavailing,
Saw him breathe his very last.

8. Mary, fount of love's devotion,
Let me share with true emotion
All the sorrow you endured.

9. Virgin, ever interceding,
Hear me in my fervent pleading:
Fire me with your love of Christ.

10. Mother, may this prayer be granted:
That Christ's love may be implanted
In the depths of my poor soul.

11. At the cross, your sorrow sharing,
All your grief and torment bearing,
Let me stand and mourn with you.

12. Fairest maid of all creation,
Queen of hope and consolation,
Let me feel your grief sublime.

13. Virgin, in your love befriend me,
At the Judgment Day defend me.
Help me by your constant prayer.

14. Savior, when my life shall leave me,
Through your mother's prayers receive me
With the fruits of victory.

15. Let me to your love be taken,
Let my soul in death awaken
To the joys of Paradise.

Text: *Stabat mater dolorosa;* Jacopone da Todi, 1230-1306; Tr. by Anthony G. Petti, 1932-1985,
Tune: STABAT MATER, 88 7; *Mainz Gesangbuch,* 1661; Harm. by Richard Proulx, b.1937,

422 The Glory of These Forty Days

1. The glo - ry of these for - ty days We
2. A - lone and fast - ing Mo - ses saw The
3. So Dan - iel trained his mys - tic sight, De-
4. Then grant that we like them be true, Con-

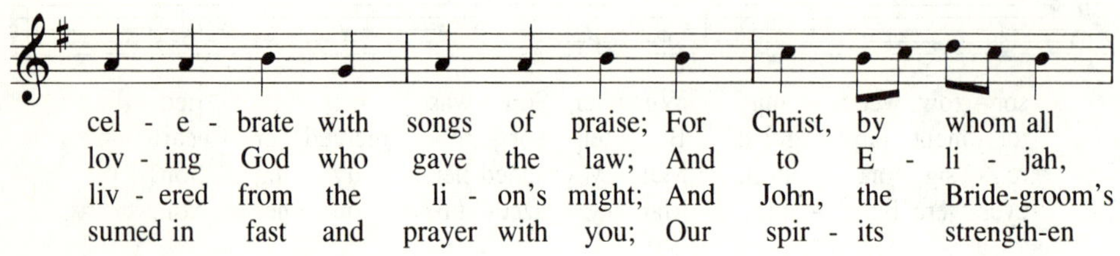
cel - e - brate with songs of praise; For Christ, by whom all
lov - ing God who gave the law; And to E - li - jah,
liv - ered from the li - on's might; And John, the Bride-groom's
sumed in fast and prayer with you; Our spir - its strength-en

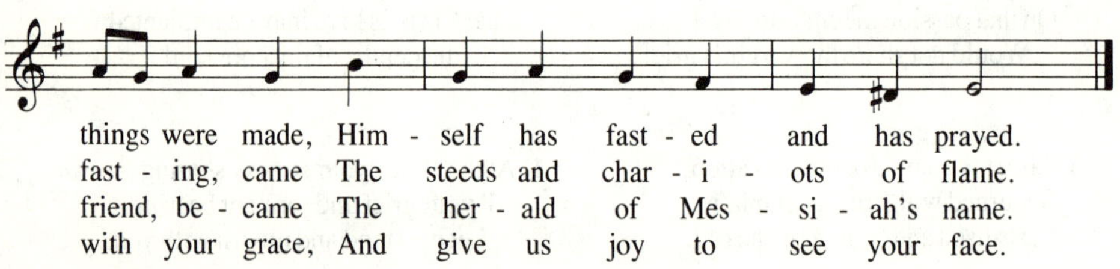
things were made, Him - self has fast - ed and has prayed.
fast - ing, came The steeds and char - i - ots of flame.
friend, be - came The her - ald of Mes - si - ah's name.
with your grace, And give us joy to see your face.

Text: *Clarum decus jejunii;* Gregory the Great, c.540-604; Tr. by Maurice F. Bell, 1862-1947
Tune: ERHALT UNS HERR, LM; Klug's *Geistliche Lieder,* 1543; Harm. by J. S. Bach, 1685-1750

423 Jesus, Remember Me

Je - sus, re - mem-ber me when you come in - to your King-dom.

Je - sus, re - mem-ber me when you come in - to your King-dom.

Text: Luke 23:42; Taizé Community, 1981
Tune: Jacques Berthier, b.1923

O Sun of Justice 424

1. O Sun of jus - tice, Je - sus Christ, Dis - pel the dark - ness
2. In this our "time ac - cept - a - ble" Touch ev - 'ry heart with
3. The day, your day, in beau - ty dawns When in your light earth
4. O lov - ing Trin - i - ty, our God, To you we bow through

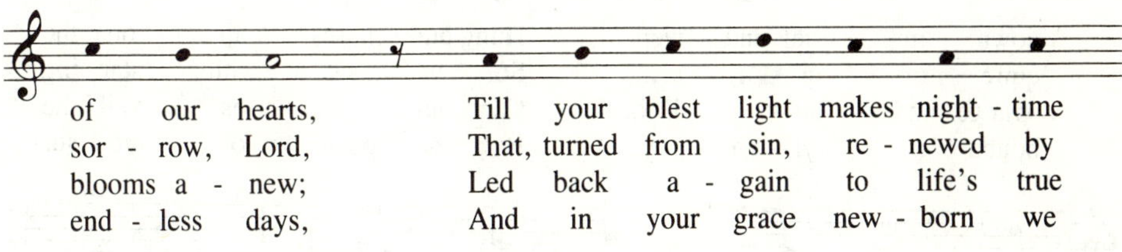
of our hearts, Till your blest light makes night - time
sor - row, Lord, That, turned from sin, re - newed by
blooms a - new; Led back a - gain to life's true
end - less days, And in your grace new - born we

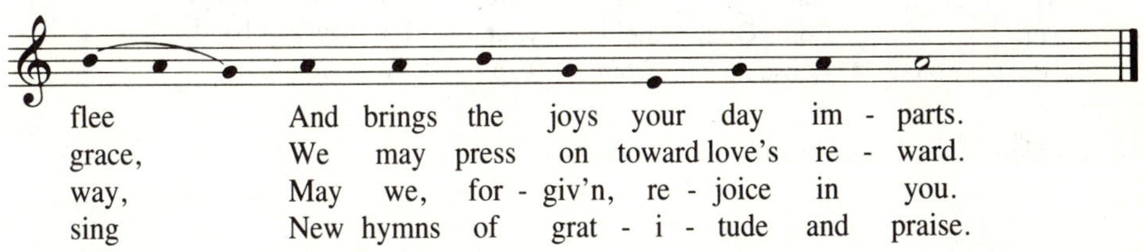
flee And brings the joys your day im - parts.
grace, We may press on toward love's re - ward.
way, May we, for - giv'n, re - joice in you.
sing New hymns of grat - i - tude and praise.

Text: *Jam Christe sol justitiae;* Latin, 6th C.; Tr. by Peter J. Scagnelli, b.1949, ©
Tune: JESU DULCIS MEMORIA, LM; Mode I; Acc. by Richard Proulx, b.1937, © 1975, GIA Publications, Inc.

Salvator Mundi 425

Canon

A
B
Sal - va-tor mun - di sal - va nos. Sal - va-tor mun - di sal - va nos.

C
D
Sal - va nos, sal - va nos. Sal - va-tor mun - di sal - va nos.

Text: *Savior of the world, save us;* Taizé Community, 1980
Tune: Jacques Berthier, b.1923

426 By the Babylonian Rivers

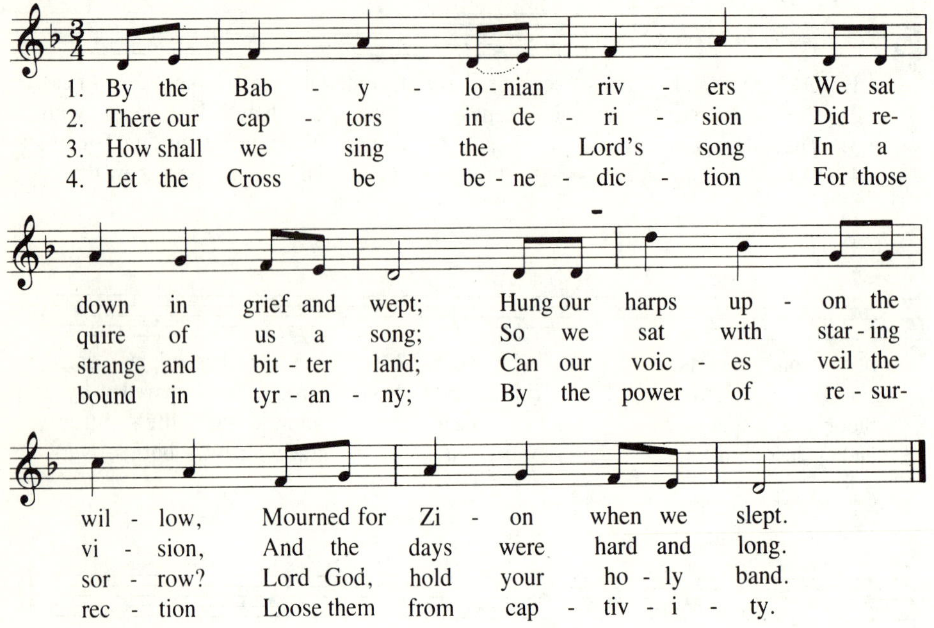
1. By the Bab - y - lo - nian riv - ers We sat down in grief and wept; Hung our harps up - on the wil - low, Mourned for Zi - on when we slept.
2. There our cap - tors in de - ri - sion Did re- quire of us a song; So we sat with star - ing vi - sion, And the days were hard and long.
3. How shall we sing the Lord's song In a strange and bit - ter land; Can our voic - es veil the sor - row? Lord God, hold your ho - ly band.
4. Let the Cross be be - ne - dic - tion For those bound in tyr - an - ny; By the power of re - sur- rec - tion Loose them from cap - tiv - i - ty.

Text: Ewald Bash, b.1924
Tune: KAS DZIEDAJA, 8 7 8 7; Latvian Folk Melody; Harm. by Geoffrey Laycock, b.1927, ©

427 Jesus Walked This Lonesome Valley

1. Je - sus walked this lone-some val - ley; He had to walk it by him - self. O no-bod-y else could walk it for him; He had to walk it by him - self.
2. We must walk this lone-some val - ley; We have to walk it by our - selves. O no-bod-y else can walk it for us; We have to walk it by our - selves.
3. You must go and stand your tri - al; You have to stand it by your - self. O no-bod-y else can stand it for you; You have to stand it by your - self.

Text: American Folk Hymn
Tune: LONESOME VALLEY, 8 8 10 8; American Folk Hymn; Harm. by Richard Proulx, b.1937, © 1975, GIA Publications, Inc.

All Glory, Laud, and Honor 428

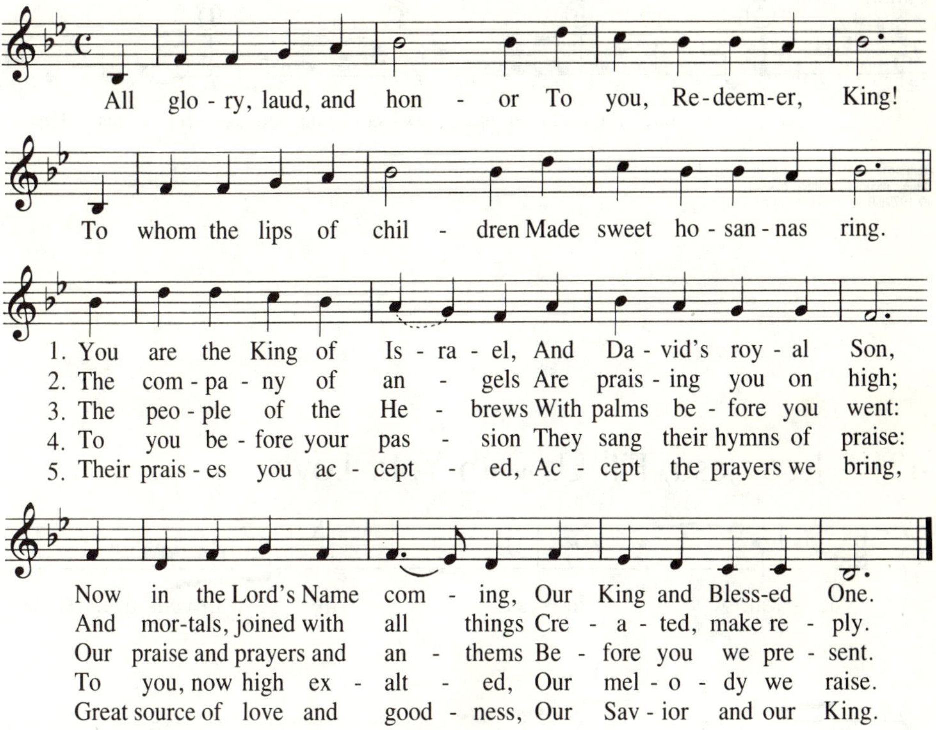

All glo - ry, laud, and hon - or To you, Re-deem-er, King!
To whom the lips of chil - dren Made sweet ho - san - nas ring.

1. You are the King of Is - ra - el, And Da - vid's roy - al Son,
Now in the Lord's Name com - ing, Our King and Bless-ed One.

2. The com - pa - ny of an - gels Are prais - ing you on high;
And mor-tals, joined with all things Cre - a - ted, make re - ply.

3. The peo - ple of the He - brews With palms be - fore you went:
Our praise and prayers and an - thems Be - fore you we pre - sent.

4. To you be - fore your pas - sion They sang their hymns of praise:
To you, now high ex - alt - ed, Our mel - o - dy we raise.

5. Their prais - es you ac - cept - ed, Ac - cept the prayers we bring,
Great source of love and good - ness, Our Sav - ior and our King.

Text: *Gloria, laus et honor;* Theodulph of Orleans, c.760-821; Tr. by John M. Neale, 1818-1866, alt.
Tune: ST. THEODULPH, 7 6 7 6 D; Melchior Teschner, 1584-1635

Benedictus Qui Venit 429

Canon
A
Be - ne - di - ctus qui ve - nit,
B
Be - ne - di - ctus qui ve - nit, in
C
no - mi - ne, in no - mi - ne,
D
in no - mi - ne Do - mi - ni.

Text: Mt. 21:9; Mt. 23:29; Mk. 11:9; Lk. 13:35; Ps. 118:26; Taizé Community, 1978
Tune: Jacques Berthier, b.1923

430 Hosanna in Excelsis

Canon

A
B
C
D
Ho - san - na, ho - san - na, ho - san - na in ex - cel - sis. Ho-

Text: Mt. 21.9; Mk. 11:10; Jn. 12:13; Taizé Community, 1978
Tune: Jacques Berthier, b.1923

431 Jesu, Jesu, Fill Us with Your Love

Je - su, Je - su, fill us with your love, show

us how to serve the neigh-bors we have from you.

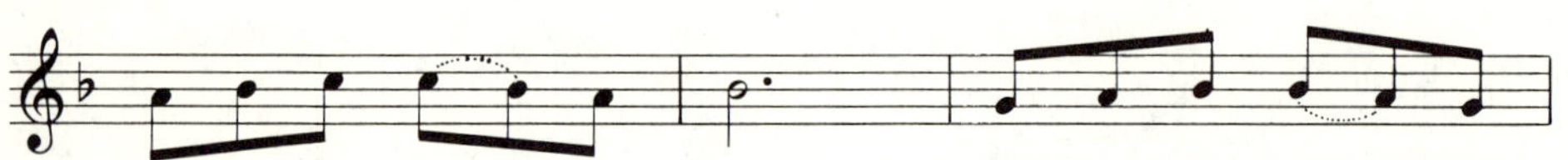
1. Kneels at the feet of his friends, Si - lent - ly wash - es their
2. Neigh-bors are rich and poor, Neigh-bors are black and
3. These are the ones we should serve, These are the ones we should
4. Kneel at the feet of our friends, Si - lent - ly wash-ing their

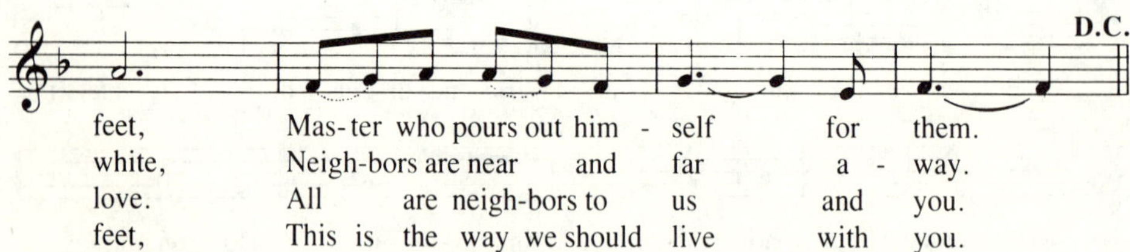
D.C.
feet, Mas- ter who pours out him - self for them.
white, Neigh-bors are near and far a - way.
love. All are neigh-bors to us and you.
feet, This is the way we should live with you.

Text: John 13:3-5; Ghana Folk Song; Tr. by Tom Colvin, b.1925
Tune: CHEREPONI, Irregular; Ghana Folk song; Acc. by Jane M. Marshall, b.1924, © 1982, Hope Publishing Co.

Jesus Took a Towel 432

Je - sus took a tow - el and he gird - ed him - self, Then he

washed my feet, yes, he washed my feet, Je - sus took a ba - sin and he

knelt him-self down, And he washed, yes, he washed my feet.

1. The heav - ens are the Lord's, and the earth is his, The
2. The hour had come, the Pasch was near;

clouds are his char - iot, glo - ry his cloak; He
Je - sus loved his own, loved them to the end. O

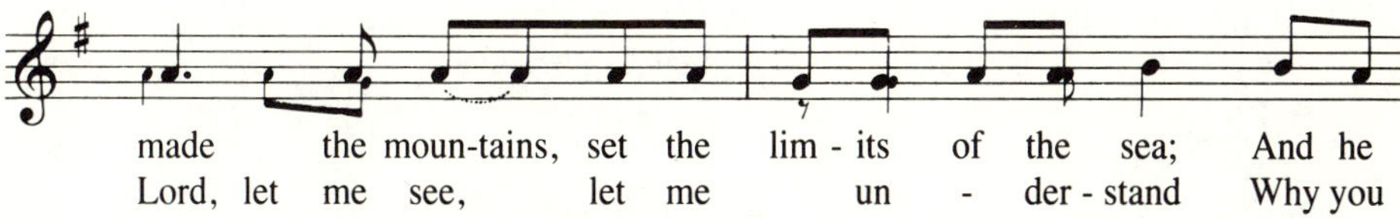
made the moun-tains, set the lim - its of the sea; And he
Lord, let me see, let me un - der - stand Why you

D.C.
stooped and washed my feet.
stooped and washed my feet.

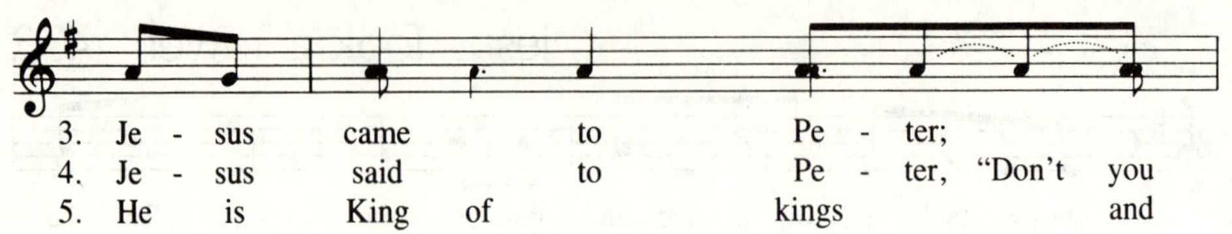
3. Je - sus came to Pe - ter;
4. Je - sus said to Pe - ter, "Don't you
5. He is King of kings and

Pe - ter said to him, "Do you wash my feet? Lord, do you
un - der - stand? If you want to be mine, I must
Lord of lords, Who dwells in light in - ac-

wash my feet?" Je - sus knelt down, but
wash your feet." "Then not just my feet, but my
- ces - si - ble; No one has seen him where he

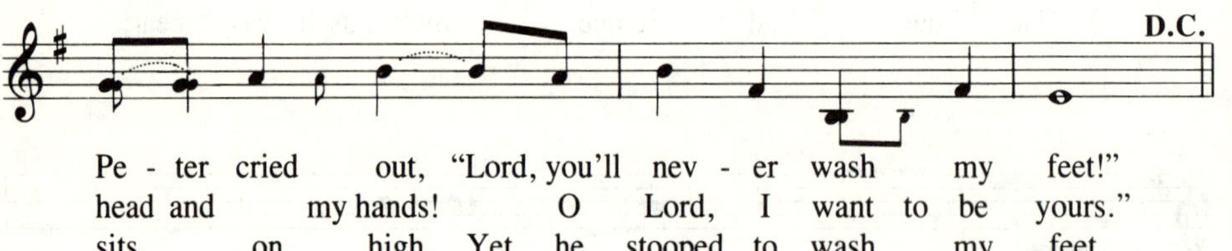
D.C.
Pe - ter cried out, "Lord, you'll nev - er wash my feet!"
head and my hands! O Lord, I want to be yours."
sits on high, Yet he stooped to wash my feet.

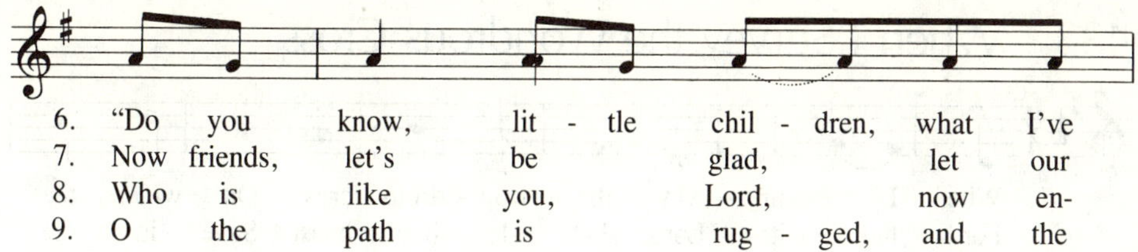
6. "Do you know, lit - tle chil - dren, what I've
7. Now friends, let's be glad, let our
8. Who is like you, Lord, now en-
9. O the path is rug - ged, and the

done for you? You call me Mas - ter, and you
joy be full. For God is love, and he a-
throned on high, Where you look up - on the heav - ens and the
go - ing is rough, The jour - ney is long to our

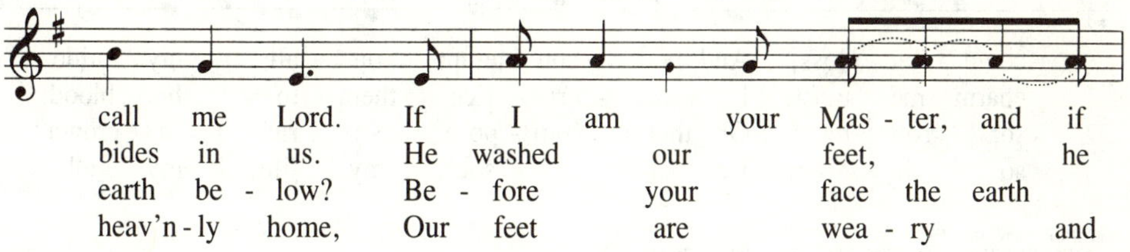
call me Lord. If I am your Mas - ter, and if
bides in us. He washed our feet, he
earth be - low? Be - fore your face the earth
heav'n - ly home, Our feet are wea - ry and

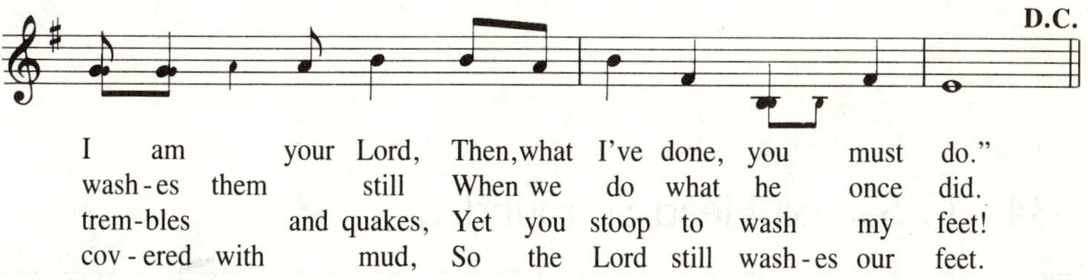
D.C.
I am your Lord, Then, what I've done, you must do."
wash - es them still When we do what he once did.
trem - bles and quakes, Yet you stoop to wash my feet!
cov - ered with mud, So the Lord still wash - es our feet.

Text: John 13; Chrysogonus Waddell, OCSO, b.1930
Tune: JESUS TOOK A TOWEL, Irregular; Chrysogonus Waddell, OCSO, b.1930

433 When I Survey the Wondrous Cross

1. When I sur - vey the won - drous cross On which the Prince of glo - ry died, My rich - est gain I count but loss, And pour con - tempt on all my pride.
2. For - bid it, Lord, that I should boast Save in the death of Christ, my God; All the vain things that charm me most, I sac - ri - fice them to his blood.
3. See, from his head, his hands, his feet, Sor - row and love flow min - gled down; Did e'er such love and sor - row meet, Or thorns com - pose so rich a crown?
4. Were the whole realm of na - ture mine, That were a pres - ent far too small: Love so a - maz - ing, so di - vine, De - mands my soul, my life, my all.

Text: Isaac Watts, 1674-1748
Tune: ROCKINGHAM, LM; Adapted by Edward Miller, 1735-1807

434 O Sacred Head Surrounded

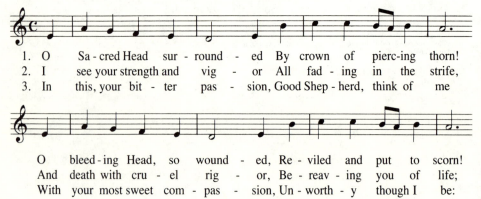

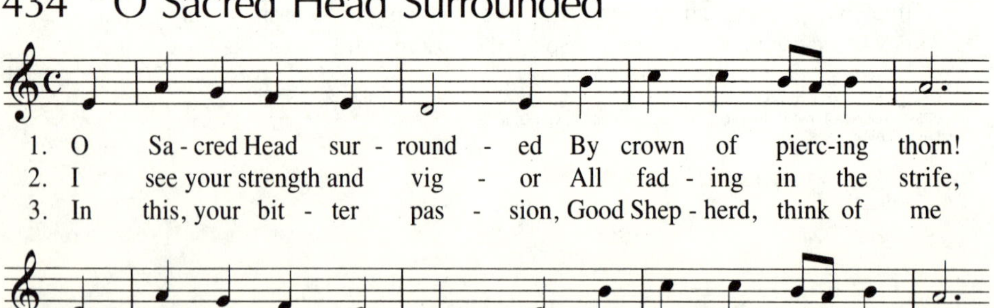
1. O Sa - cred Head sur - round - ed By crown of pierc-ing thorn!
2. I see your strength and vig - or All fad - ing in the strife,
3. In this, your bit - ter pas - sion, Good Shep - herd, think of me

O bleed - ing Head, so wound - ed, Re - viled and put to scorn!
And death with cru - el rig - or, Be - reav - ing you of life;
With your most sweet com - pas - sion, Un - worth - y though I be:

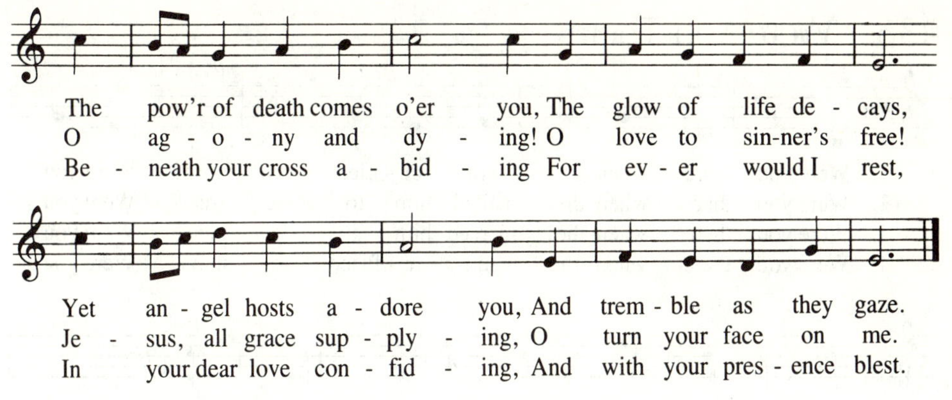
The pow'r of death comes o'er you, The glow of life de - cays,
O ag - o - ny and dy - ing! O love to sin-ner's free!
Be - neath your cross a - bid - ing For ev - er would I rest,
Yet an - gel hosts a - dore you, And trem - ble as they gaze.
Je - sus, all grace sup - ply - ing, O turn your face on me.
In your dear love con - fid - ing, And with your pres - ence blest.

Text: *Salve caput cruentatum;* Ascr. to Bernard of Clairvaux, 1091-1153; Tr. by Henry Baker, 1821-1877
Tune: PASSION CHORALE, 7 6 7 6 D; Hans Leo Hassler, 1564-1612; Harm. by J. S. Bach, 1685-1750

The Royal Banners Forward Go 435

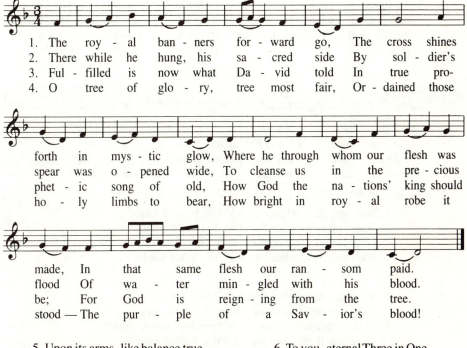

1. The roy - al ban - ners for - ward go, The cross shines forth in mys - tic glow, Where he through whom our flesh was made, In that same flesh our ran - som paid.
2. There while he hung, his sa - cred side By sol - dier's spear was o - pened wide, To cleanse us in the pre - cious flood Of wa - ter min - gled with his blood.
3. Ful - filled is now what Da - vid told In true pro - phet - ic song of old, How God the na - tions' king should be; For God is reign - ing from the tree.
4. O tree of glo - ry, tree most fair, Or - dained those ho - ly limbs to bear, How bright in roy - al robe it stood — The pur - ple of a Sav - ior's blood!

5. Upon its arms, like balance true,
He weighed the price for sinners due,
The price which none but he could pay,
And spoiled the spoiler of his prey.

6. To you, eternal Three in One,
Let homage due by all be done:
As by the cross you did restore,
So rule and guide us evermore.

Text: *Vexilla Regis prodeunt;* Venantius Fortunatus, c.530-609; Tr. by John M. Neale, 1818-1866, alt.
Tune: VEXILLA REGIS, LM; Mode I; Realization in modal rhythm by Schola Antiqua, 1983, ©; Acc. by David Hurd, b.1950, © 1985, GIA Publications, Inc.

436 Were You There

1. Were you there when they cru - ci - fied my Lord? Were you
2. Were you there when they nailed him to the tree? Were you
3. Were you there when they pierced him in the side? Were you
4. Were you there when the sun re - fused to shine? Were you

there when they cru - ci - fied my Lord? O!
there when they nailed him to the tree? O!
there when they pierced him in the side? O!
there when the sun re - fused to shine? O!

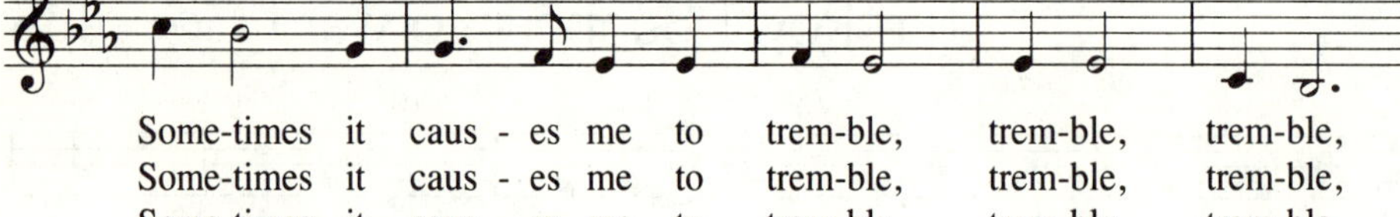

Some-times it caus - es me to trem-ble, trem-ble, trem-ble,
Some-times it caus - es me to trem-ble, trem-ble, trem-ble,
Some-times it caus - es me to trem-ble, trem-ble, trem-ble,
Some-times it caus - es me to trem-ble, trem-ble, trem-ble,

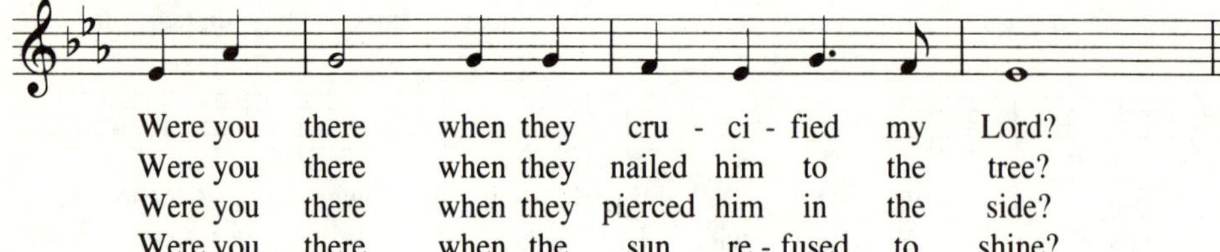

Were you there when they cru - ci - fied my Lord?
Were you there when they nailed him to the tree?
Were you there when they pierced him in the side?
Were you there when the sun re - fused to shine?

5. Were you there when they laid him in the tomb?
Were you there when they laid him in the tomb?
O! Sometimes it causes me to tremble, tremble, tremble,
Were you there when they laid him in the tomb?

6. Were you there when they rolled the stone away?
Were you there when they rolled the stone away?
O! Sometimes it causes me to tremble, tremble, tremble,
Were you there when they rolled the stone away?

Text: Afro-American Spiritual
Tune: WERE YOU THERE, 10 10 with refrain; Afro-American Spiritual; Harm. by C. Winfred Douglas, 1867-1944,

Sing, My Tongue, the Song of Triumph 437

1. Sing, my tongue, the song of tri - umph,
2. He en - dured the nails, the spit - ting,
3. Faith - ful Cross, a - bove all oth - er,
4. Bend your boughs, O Tree of glo - ry!
Tell the sto - ry far and wide;
Vin - e - gar and spear and reed;
One and on - ly no - ble tree,
All your rig - id branch - es, bend!
Tell of dread and fi - nal bat - tle,
From that ho - ly bod - y bro - ken
None in fo - liage, none in blos - som,
For a while the an - cient tem - per
Sing of Sav - ior cru - ci - fied;
Blood and wa - ter forth pro - ceed:
None in fruit your peer may be;
That your birth be - stowed, sus - pend;
How up - on the cross a vic-
Earth and stars and sky and o-
Sweet the wood and sweet the i-
And the King of earth and heav-
tim Van-quish - ing in death he died.
cean By that flood from stain are freed.
ron And your load, most sweet is he.
en Gent - ly on your bos - om tend.

Text: *Pange, lingua, gloriosi lauream certaminis;* Venantius Fortunatus, c.530-609; Tr. from *The Three Days*, 1981
Tune: PICARDY, 8 7 8 7 8 7; French Carol; Harm. by Richard Proulx, b.1937, © 1986, GIA Publications, Inc.

438 Lord Christ, When First You Came to Earth

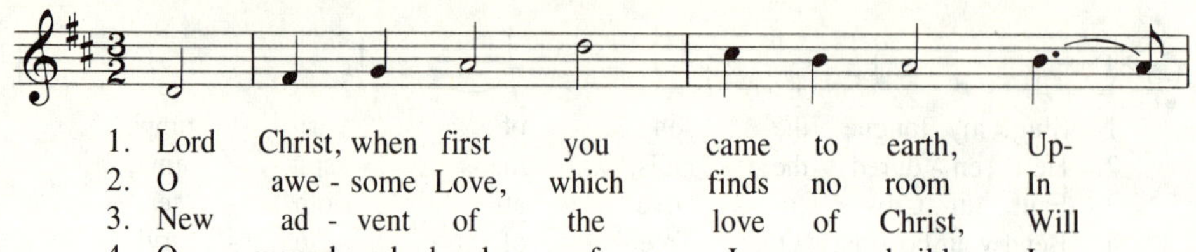
1. Lord Christ, when first you came to earth, Up-
2. O awe - some Love, which finds no room In
3. New ad - vent of the love of Christ, Will
4. O wound - ed hands of Je - sus, build In

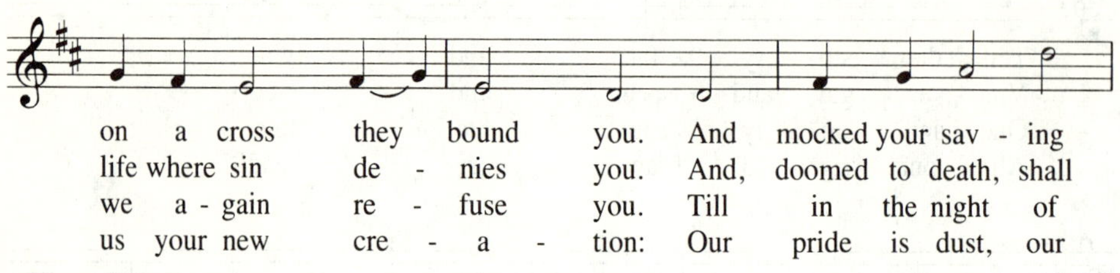
on a cross they bound you. And mocked your sav - ing
life where sin de - nies you. And, doomed to death, shall
we a - gain re - fuse you. Till in the night of
us your new cre - a - tion: Our pride is dust, our

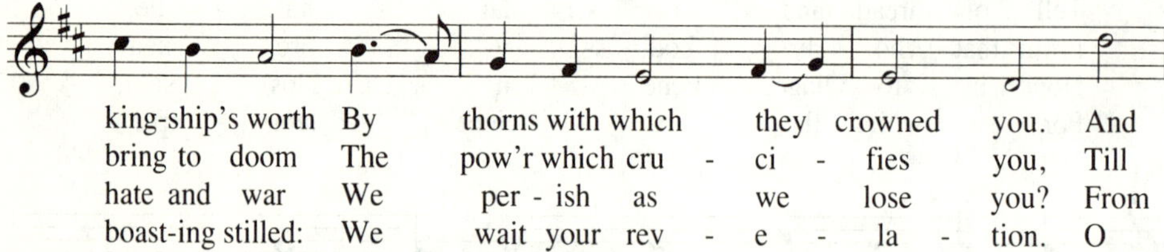
king-ship's worth By thorns with which they crowned you. And
bring to doom The pow'r which cru - ci - fies you, Till
hate and war We per - ish as we lose you? From
boast-ing stilled: We wait your rev - e - la - tion. O

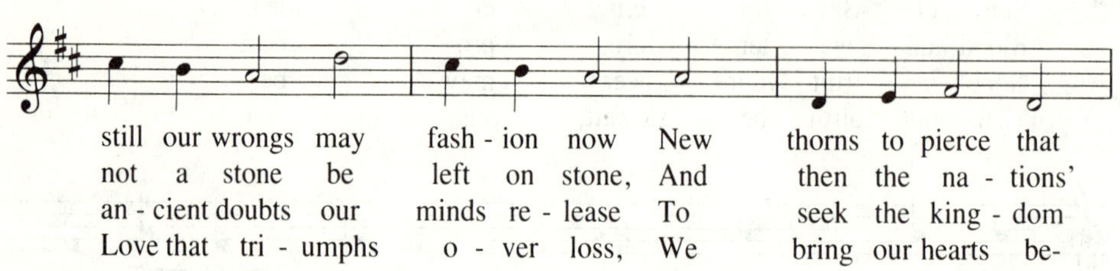
still our wrongs may fash - ion now New thorns to pierce that
not a stone be left on stone, And then the na - tions'
an - cient doubts our minds re - lease To seek the king - dom
Love that tri - umphs o - ver loss, We bring our hearts be-

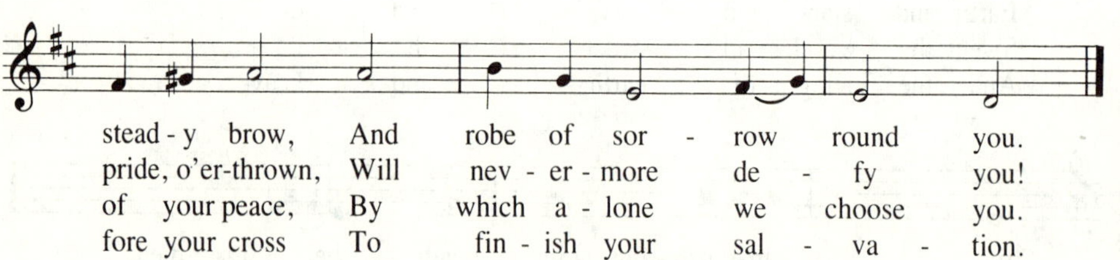
stead - y brow, And robe of sor - row round you.
pride, o'er-thrown, Will nev - er - more de - fy you!
of your peace, By which a - lone we choose you.
fore your cross To fin - ish your sal - va - tion.

Text: W. Russell Bowie, 1882-1969, alt., ©
Tune: MIT FREUDEN ZART, 8 7 8 7 88 7; Bohemian Brethren's *Kirchengesange*, 1566

My Song Is Love Unknown 439

1. My song is love un - known, My Sav - ior's love for
2. He came from his blest throne, Sal - va - tion to be-
3. Here might I stay and sing, No sto - ry so di-

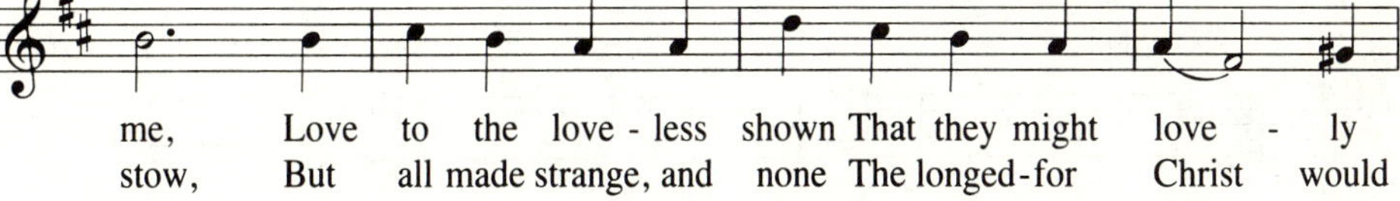

me, Love to the love - less shown That they might love - ly
stow, But all made strange, and none The longed-for Christ would
vine: Nev - er was love, dear King, Nev - er was grief like

be. O who am I That for my sake My
know. But O my friend, My friend in - deed, Who
thine. This is my friend, In whose sweet praise I

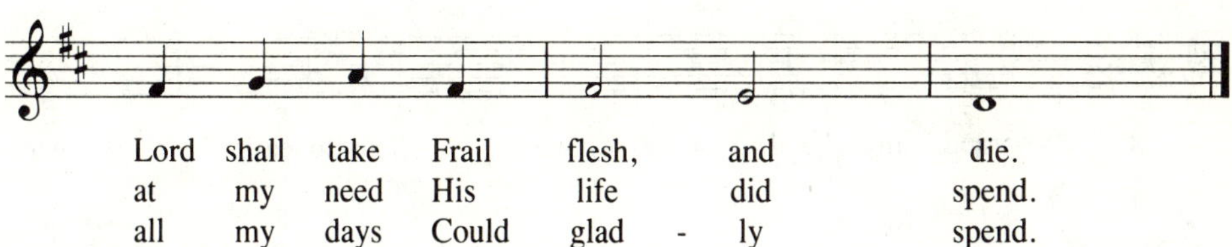

Lord shall take Frail flesh, and die.
at my need His life did spend.
all my days Could glad - ly spend.

Text: Samuel Crossman, c.1624-1683
Tune: LOVE UNKNOWN, 6 6 6 6 4 44 4; John Ireland, 1879-1962,

440 All You Who Pass This Way

Refrain
All you who pass this way, look and see.
Verses
1. Is an - y sor - row like the sor - row that af - flicts me? All
2. Wo-men of Je - ru - sa - lem! Do not weep for
me, but for your - selves, and for your chil - dren. All
3. Fa - ther, for - give them! they know not what they do. All
4. My God, my God, why have you a - ban-doned me? All
5. To - day you will be with me in par - a - dise. All
6. I am thirst - y. All
7. Fa - ther, in - to your hands I com - mend my spir - it. All

Text: From the Passion Gospels; Taizé Community, 1984
Tune: Jacques Berthier, b.1923

Alleluia, Alleluia, Give Thanks 441

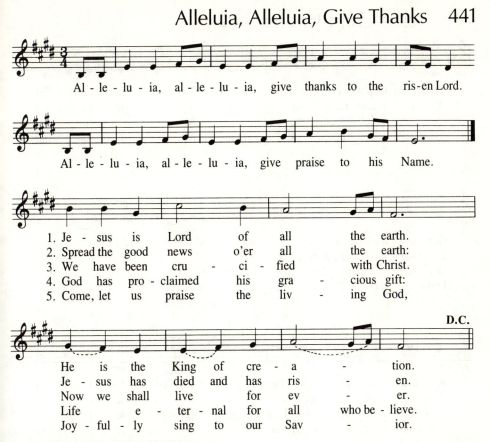

Al - le - lu - ia, al - le - lu - ia, give thanks to the ris-en Lord.

Al - le - lu - ia, al - le - lu - ia, give praise to his Name.

1. Je - sus is Lord of all the earth.
2. Spread the good news o'er all the earth:
3. We have been cru - ci - fied with Christ.
4. God has pro - claimed his gra - cious gift:
5. Come, let us praise the liv - ing God,

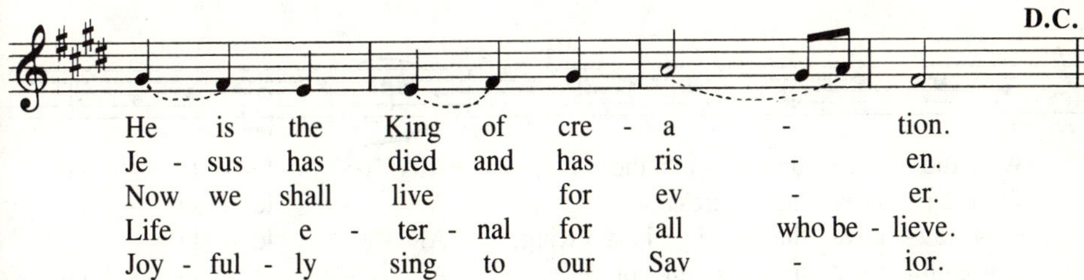
D.C.
He is the King of cre - a - tion.
Je - sus has died and has ris - en.
Now we shall live for ev - er.
Life e - ter - nal for all who be - lieve.
Joy - ful - ly sing to our Sav - ior.

Text: Donald Fishel, b.1950, © 1973, Word of God Music
Tune: ALLELUIA NO. 1, 8 8 with refrain; Donald Fishel, b.1950, © 1973, Word of God Music; Harm. by Betty Pulkingham, b.1929, Charles Mallory, b.1953, and George Mims, b.1938, © 1979, Celebration

442 Jesus Christ Is Risen Today

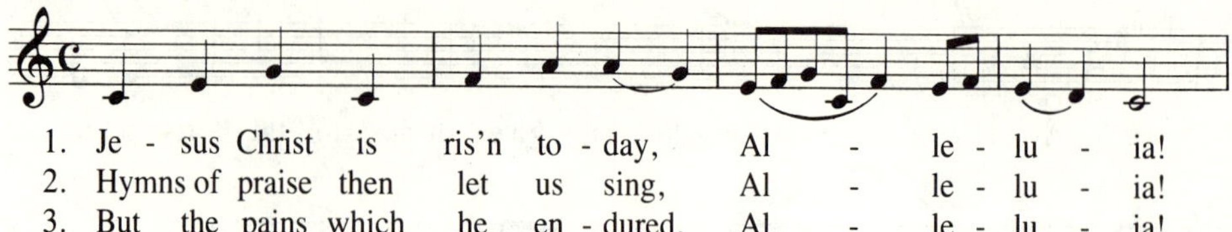

1. Je - sus Christ is ris'n to - day, Al - le - lu - ia!
2. Hymns of praise then let us sing, Al - le - lu - ia!
3. But the pains which he en - dured, Al - le - lu - ia!
4. Sing we to our God a - bove, Al - le - lu - ia!

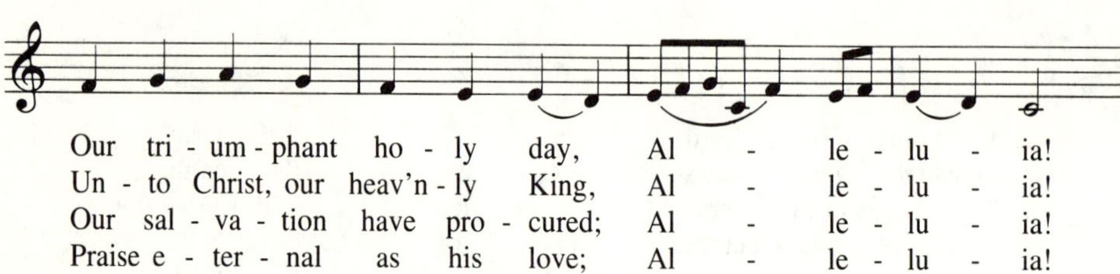

Our tri - um - phant ho - ly day, Al - le - lu - ia!
Un - to Christ, our heav'n - ly King, Al - le - lu - ia!
Our sal - va - tion have pro - cured; Al - le - lu - ia!
Praise e - ter - nal as his love; Al - le - lu - ia!

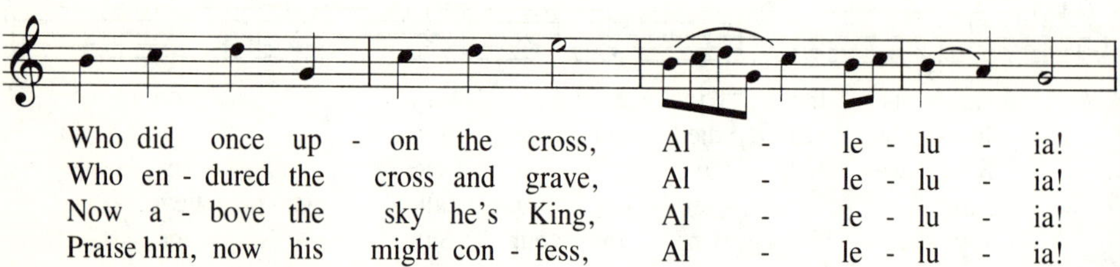

Who did once up - on the cross, Al - le - lu - ia!
Who en - dured the cross and grave, Al - le - lu - ia!
Now a - bove the sky he's King, Al - le - lu - ia!
Praise him, now his might con - fess, Al - le - lu - ia!

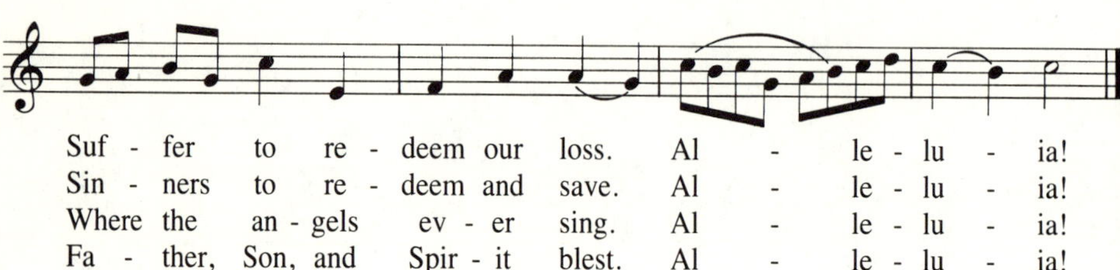

Suf - fer to re - deem our loss. Al - le - lu - ia!
Sin - ners to re - deem and save. Al - le - lu - ia!
Where the an - gels ev - er sing. Al - le - lu - ia!
Fa - ther, Son, and Spir - it blest. Al - le - lu - ia!

Text: St. 1, *Surrexit Christus hodie*, Latin, 14th C.; Para. in *Lyra Davidica*, 1708, alt.; St. 2, 3, *The Compleat Psalmodist*, c.1750, alt.; St. 4, Charles Wesley, 1707-1788
Tune: EASTER HYMN, 77 77 with alleluias; *Lyra Davidica*, 1708

O Queen of Heaven/Regina Caeli 443

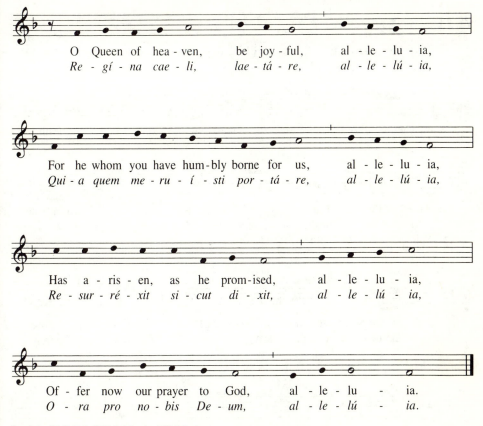

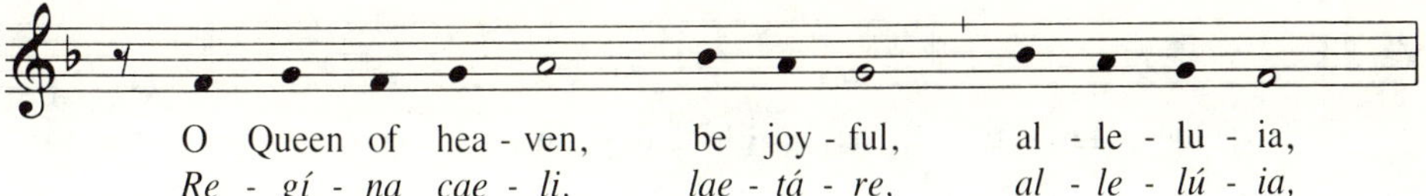

O Queen of hea - ven, be joy - ful, al - le - lu - ia,
Re - gí - na cae - li, lae - tá - re, al - le - lú - ia,

For he whom you have hum-bly borne for us, al - le - lu - ia,
Qui - a quem me - ru - í - sti por - tá - re, al - le - lú - ia,

Has a - ris - en, as he prom-ised, al - le - lu - ia,
Re - sur - ré - xit si - cut di - xit, al - le - lú - ia,

Of - fer now our prayer to God, al - le - lu - ia.
O - ra pro no - bis De - um, al - le - lú - ia.

Text: Latin, 12th C.; Tr. by C. Winfred Douglas, 1867-1944, alt.
Tune: REGINA CAELI, Irregular; Mode VI; Acc. by Robert LeBlanc, b.1948,

444 Hail Thee, Festival Day

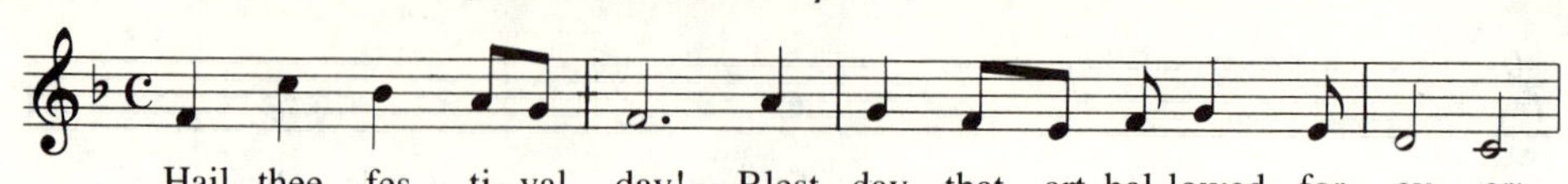

Hail thee, fes - ti - val day! Blest day that art hal-lowed for ev - er;

Day when our Lord was raised, break - ing the king - dom of death.

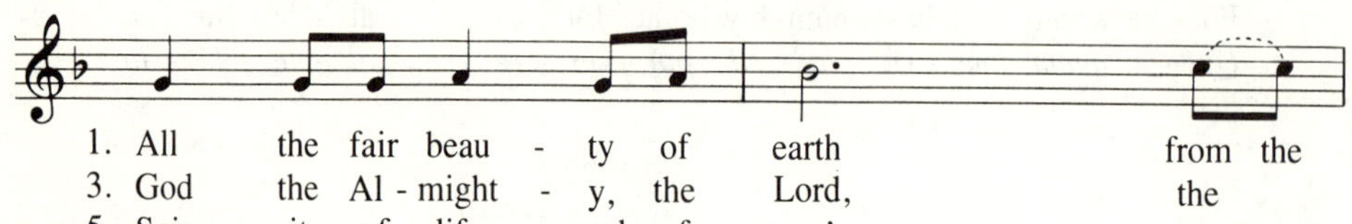

1. All the fair beau - ty of earth from the
3. God the Al - might - y, the Lord, the
5. Spir - it of life and of pow'r, now

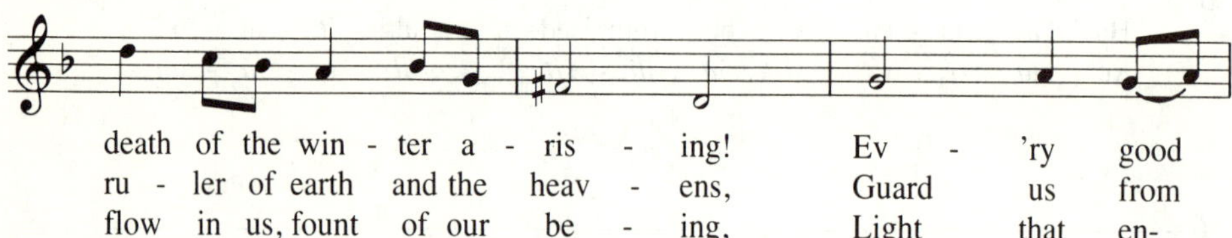

death of the win - ter a - ris - ing! Ev - 'ry good
ru - ler of earth and the heav - ens, Guard us from
flow in us, fount of our be - ing, Light that en-

D.C.

gift of the year now with its mas - ter re - turns.
harm with - out; cleanse us from ev - il with - in.
light - ens us all, life that in all may a - bide.

2. Rise from the grave now, O Lord, the au - thor of
4. Je - sus, the health of the world, en - light - en our
6. Praise to the giv - er of good! O Lov - er and

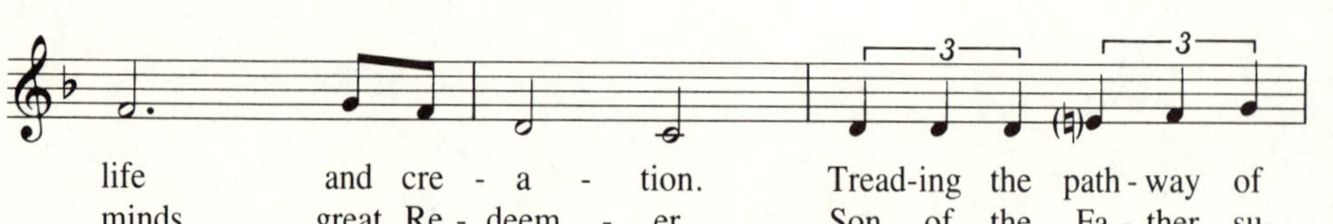

life and cre - a - tion. Tread-ing the path - way of
minds great Re - deem - er. Son of the Fa - ther su-
Au - thor of con - cord, Pour out your balm on our

EASTER

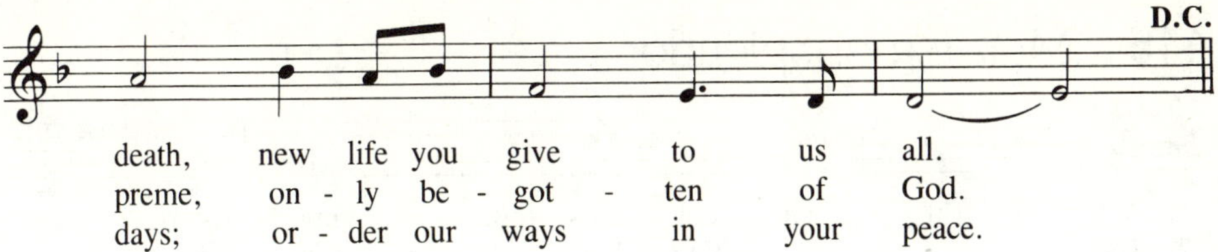
D.C.
death, new life you give to us all.
preme, on - ly be - got - ten of God.
days; or - der our ways in your peace.

Text: *Salve festa dies;* Venantius Fortunatus, c.530-609; Tr. composite
Tune: SALVE FESTA DIES, Irregular with refrain; Ralph Vaughan Williams, 1872-1958

I Know That My Redeemer Lives 445

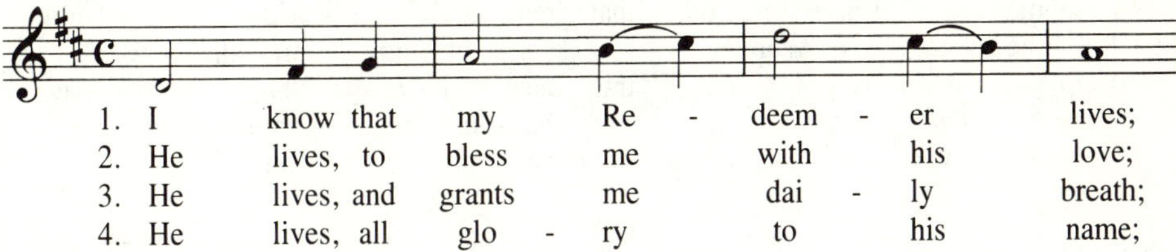
1. I know that my Re - deem - er lives;
2. He lives, to bless me with his love;
3. He lives, and grants me dai - ly breath;
4. He lives, all glo - ry to his name;

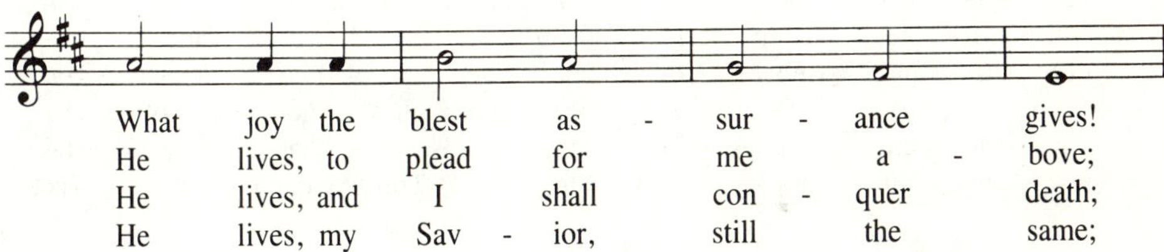
What joy the blest as - sur - ance gives!
He lives, to plead for me a - bove;
He lives, and I shall con - quer death;
He lives, my Sav - ior, still the same;

He lives, he lives, who once was dead;
He lives, my hun - gry soul to feed;
He lives, my man - sion to pre - pare;
What joy the blest as - sur - ance gives;

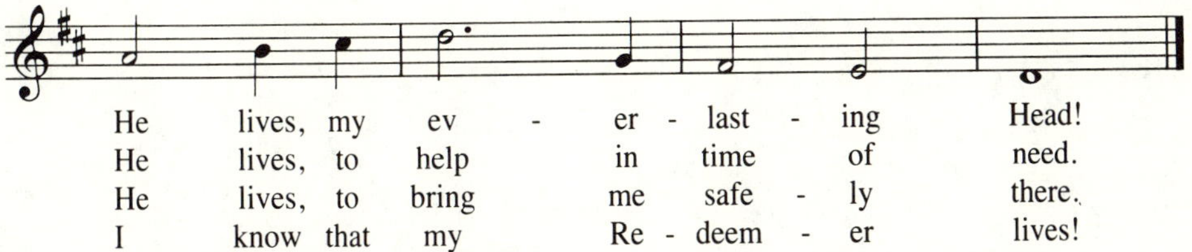
He lives, my ev - er - last - ing Head!
He lives, to help in time of need.
He lives, to bring me safe - ly there.
I know that my Re - deem - er lives!

Text: Samuel Medley, 1738-1799
Tune: DUKE STREET, LM; John Hatton, c.1710-1793

446 Morning of Splendor

1. Morn - ing of splen - dor, burst forth in my heart;
2. Day of sal - va - tion, burst forth in my mind;
3. Day of God's pur - pose, en - vel - op my soul;
4. Glo - ri - ous morn - ing, a - wak - en my voice;
5. Ra - diance this morn - ing, my spir - it con - sume;
6. Rise, Lord of life, and re - sound through my all;
Rise, sun of East - er that sig - nals to all That
Give me a sense of that great act of God Through
Fill me with ec - sta - cy, keep in my thought That
Help me to sing on this mar - vel - ous day That
That by his ris - ing, my be - ing might shine Be-
Vic - to - ry o - ver our na - ture in sin Is
Je - sus has died once a death for all sin And
which full re - demp - tion from sin is a - vailed To
ul - ti - mate show of God's in - fi - nite love: His
Je - sus is ris - en and death has no grasp On
fore all cre - a - tion to wit - ness that God Has
giv - en, all prais - es to God, Three in One, That
shat - tered for ev - er the pow - ers of doom.
those who be - lieve and who prac - tice his love.
Son, our Lord Je - sus' death on the cross.
those who would rise with him, strong in the faith.
giv - en us life, by his grace, through his Son.
we may show forth this great gift to the world.

Text: David Hurd, b.1950
Tune: MORNING OF SPLENDOR, 10 10 11 11; David Hurd, b.1950

O Sons and Daughters 447

Al - le - lu - ia, al - le - lu - ia, al - le - lu - ia.

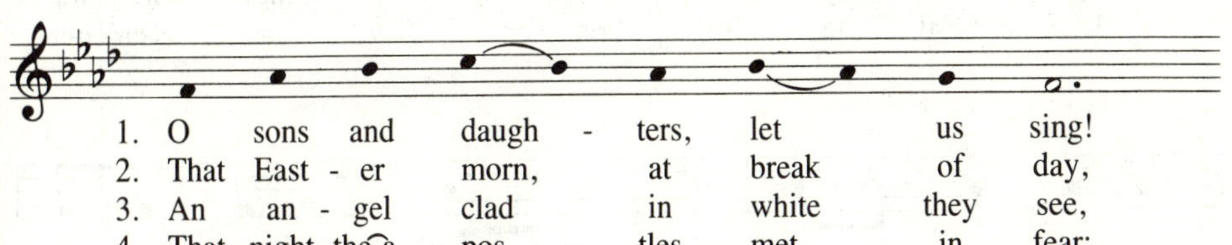

1. O sons and daugh - ters, let us sing!
2. That East - er morn, at break of day,
3. An an - gel clad in white they see,
4. That night the a - pos - tles met in fear;
5. When Thom - as, first the ti - dings heard,

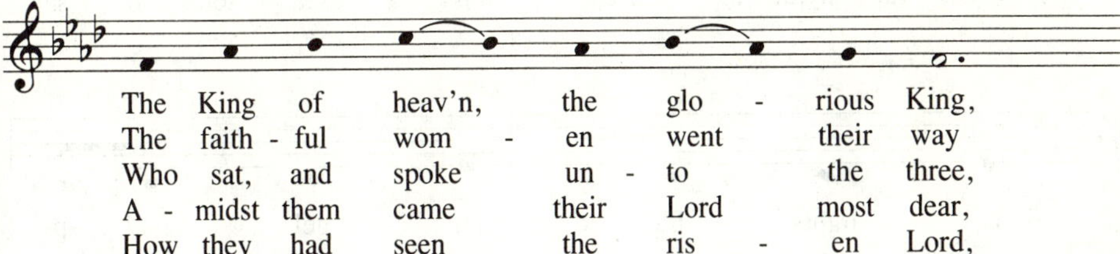

The King of heav'n, the glo - rious King,
The faith - ful wom - en went their way
Who sat, and spoke un - to the three,
A - midst them came their Lord most dear,
How they had seen the ris - en Lord,

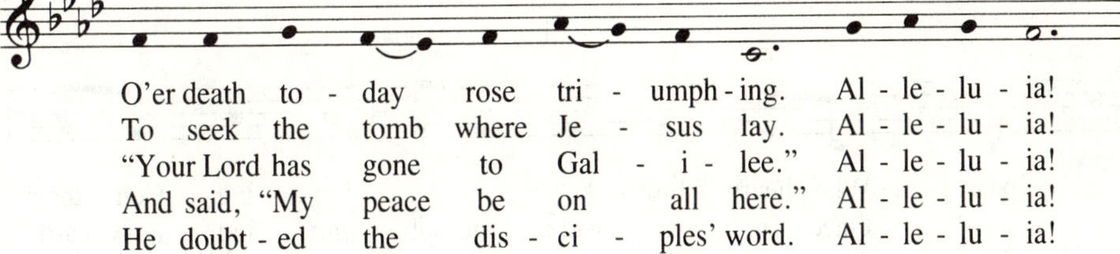

D.C.

O'er death to - day rose tri - umph - ing. Al - le - lu - ia!
To seek the tomb where Je - sus lay. Al - le - lu - ia!
"Your Lord has gone to Gal - i - lee." Al - le - lu - ia!
And said, "My peace be on all here." Al - le - lu - ia!
He doubt - ed the dis - ci - ples' word. Al - le - lu - ia!

6. "My wounded side, O Thomas, see;
Behold my hands, my feet," said he,
"Not faithless, but believing be." Alleluia!

7. No longer Thomas then denied,
He saw the feet, the hands, the side;
"You are my Lord and God," he cried. Alleluia!

8. How blest are they who have not seen,
And yet whose faith has constant been,
For they eternal life shall win. Alleluia!

9. On this most holy day of days,
To God your hearts and voices raise,
In laud, and jubilee and praise. Alleluia!

Text: *O filii et filae;* Jean Tisserand, d.1494; Tr. by John M. Neale, 1818-1866, alt.
Tune: O FILII ET FILIAE, 888 with alleluias; Mode II; Acc. by Richard Proulx, b.1937,

448 Daylight Fades

1. Day - light fades in days when death - less Light has
2. Won-drous mys - t'ry of love's giv - ing! Our for-
3. O Lord Je - sus, ris - en Sav - ior, Hear our

robbed earth's night of fear; On the edge of all our
giv - ing Fa - ther's Son. Crushed in sor - row, raised to
joy - ful hymn of praise; Grant a sea - son of sal-

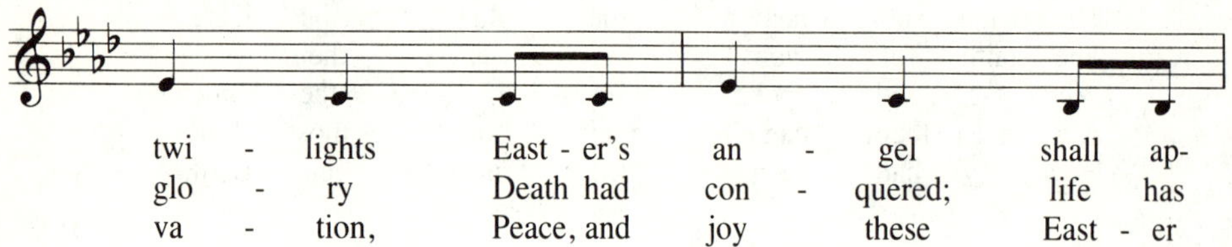

twi - lights East - er's an - gel shall ap-
glo - ry Death had con - quered; life has
va - tion, Peace, and joy these East - er

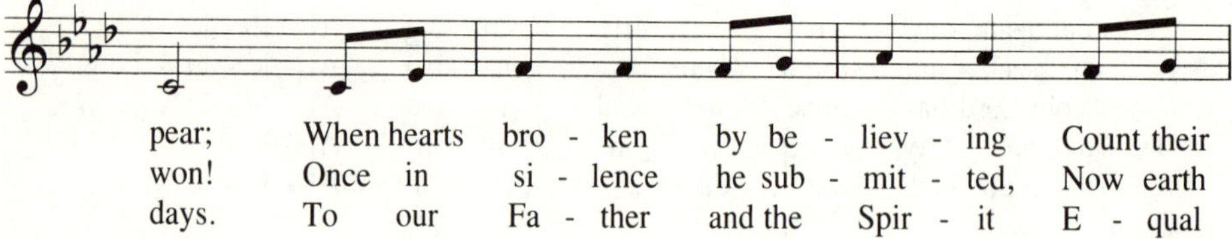

pear; When hearts bro - ken by be - liev - ing Count their
won! Once in si - lence he sub - mit - ted, Now earth
days. To our Fa - ther and the Spir - it E - qual

faith and hope as dead, Christ will greet them in each
sings to him, our King; Fear will ev - er flee de-
prais - es ev - er be; Born a - gain, we sing God's

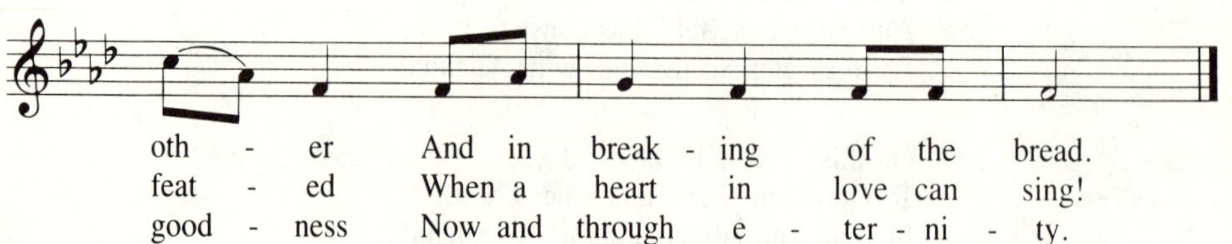

oth - er And in break - ing of the bread.
feat - ed When a heart in love can sing!
good - ness Now and through e - ter - ni - ty.

Text: Lk. 24:28-35; Peter J. Scagnelli, b.1949, ©
Tune: DOMHNACH TRIONOIDE, 8 7 8 7 D; Gaelic Melody; Harm. by Richard Proulx, b.1937, © 1975, GIA Publications, Inc.

This Joyful Eastertide 449

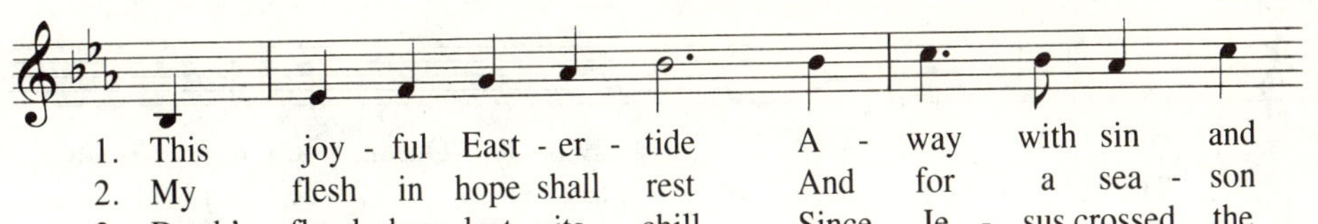
1. This joy - ful East - er - tide A - way with sin and
2. My flesh in hope shall rest And for a sea - son
3. Death's flood has lost its chill Since Je - sus crossed the

sor - row! My love, the Cru - ci - fied,
slum - ber Till trump from east to west
riv - er; Lov - er of souls, from ill

Has sprung to life this mor - row:
Shall wake the dead in num - ber:
My pass - ing soul de - liv - er:

Had Christ, who once was slain, Not burst his three-day pris - on,

Our faith had been in vain: But now has Christ a - ris - en, a-

ris - en, a - ris - en; But now has Christ a - ris - en!

Text: George R. Woodward, 1848-1934
Tune: VRUECHTEN, 6 7 6 7 D; Melody in Oudaen's *David's Psalmen*, 1685; Harm. by Paul G. Bunjes, b.1914,

450 Be Joyful, Mary

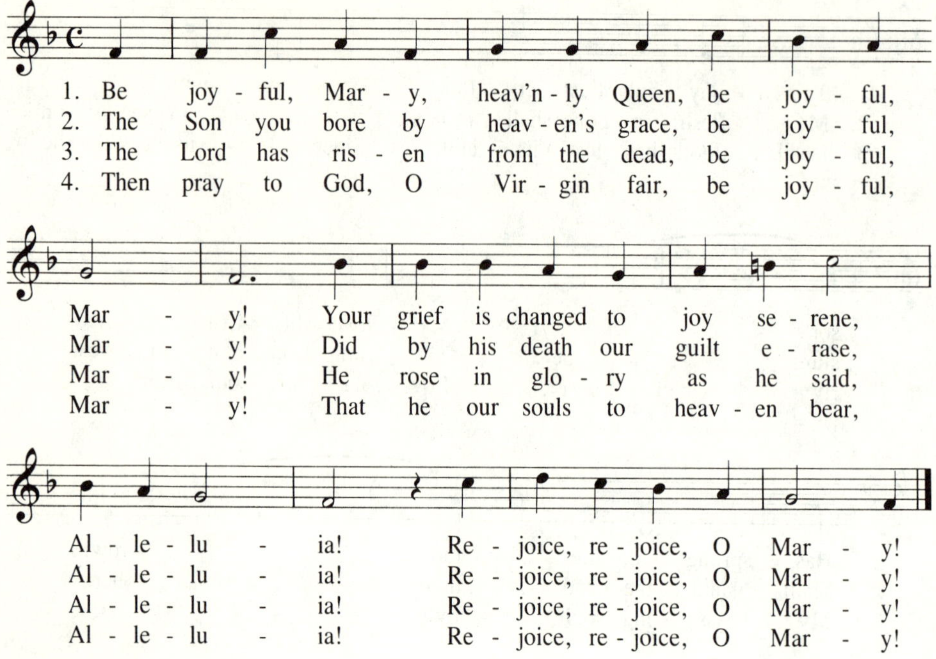
1. Be joy - ful, Mar - y, heav'n - ly Queen, be joy - ful,
2. The Son you bore by heav - en's grace, be joy - ful,
3. The Lord has ris - en from the dead, be joy - ful,
4. Then pray to God, O Vir - gin fair, be joy - ful,
Mar - y! Your grief is changed to joy se - rene,
Mar - y! Did by his death our guilt e - rase,
Mar - y! He rose in glo - ry as he said,
Mar - y! That he our souls to heav - en bear,
Al - le - lu - ia! Re - joice, re - joice, O Mar - y!
Al - le - lu - ia! Re - joice, re - joice, O Mar - y!
Al - le - lu - ia! Re - joice, re - joice, O Mar - y!
Al - le - lu - ia! Re - joice, re - joice, O Mar - y!

Text: *Regina Caeli, jubila;* Latin, 17th C.; Tr. anon. in *Psallite,* 1901
Tune: REGINA CAELI, 8 5 8 4 7; Leisentritt's *Gesangbuch,* 1584, alt.

451 The Strife Is O'er

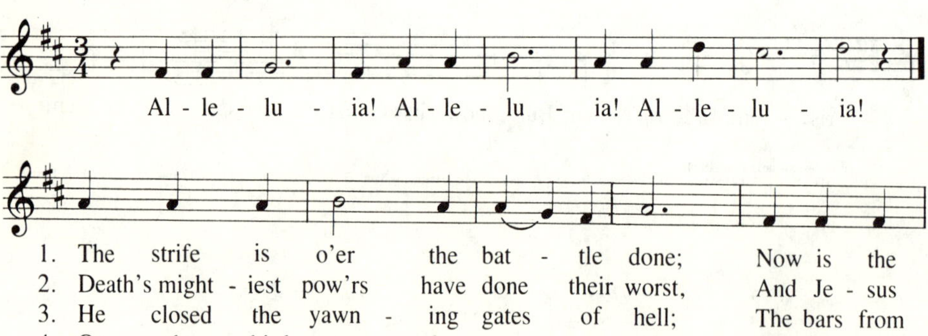
Al - le - lu - ia! Al - le - lu - ia! Al - le - lu - ia!
1. The strife is o'er the bat - tle done; Now is the
2. Death's might - iest pow'rs have done their worst, And Je - sus
3. He closed the yawn - ing gates of hell; The bars from
4. On the third morn he rose a gain Glo-rious in

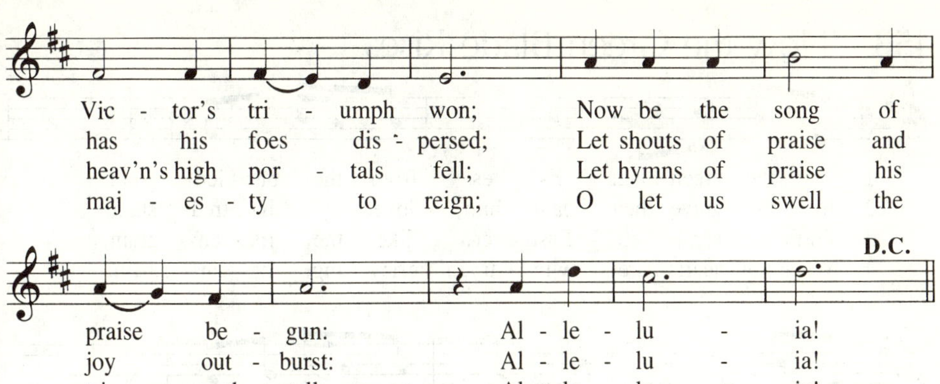

Vic - tor's tri - umph won; Now be the song of praise be - gun: Al - le - lu - ia!
has his foes dis - persed; Let shouts of praise and joy out - burst: Al - le - lu - ia!
heav'n's high por - tals fell; Let hymns of praise his tri - umph tell: Al - le - lu - ia!
maj - es - ty to reign; O let us swell the joy - ful strain: Al - le - lu - ia!

D.C.

Text: *Finita iam sunt praelia;* Latin, 12th C.; Tr. by Francis Pott; 1832-1909, alt.
Tune: VICTORY, 888 with alleluias; Giovanni da Palestrina, 1525-1594; Adapt. by William H. Monk, 1823-1889

Christ the Lord Is Risen Today 452

1. Christ the Lord is ris'n to - day; Chris-tians, haste your vows to pay; Make your joy and prais - es known; At the Pas - chal Vic - tim's throne.
2. For the sheep the Lamb has bled, Sin - less in the sin - ner's stead; Christ the Lord is ris'n on high; Now he lives no more to die.
3. Christ, the Vic - tim un - de-filed, God and sin - ners re - con-ciled, When in fierce and blood - y strife Met to - geth - er death and life.
4. Chris-tians, on this hap - py day, Raise your hearts with joy and say: Christ the Lord is ris'n on high; Now he lives no more to die.
5. Hal-lowed, cho - sen dawn of praise, East - er, queen of all our days: Zi - on's chil - dren now come forth; East to west and south to north.

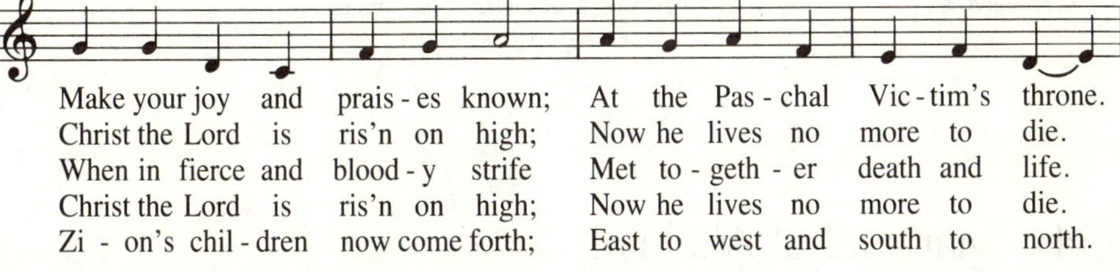

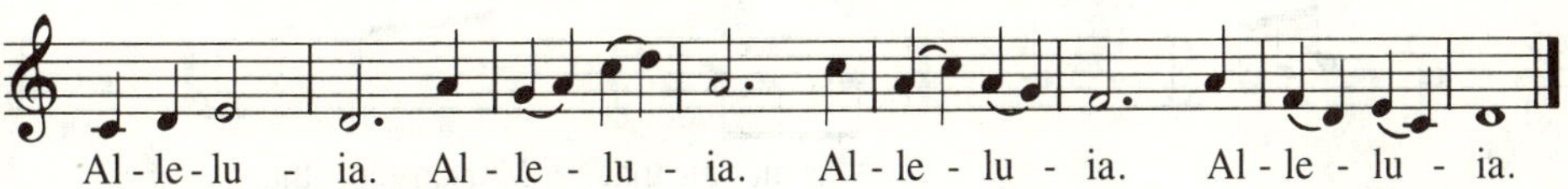

Al - le - lu - ia. Al - le - lu - ia. Al - le - lu - ia. Al - le - lu - ia.

6. Let the people praise you, Lord,
Be, by all that is adored:
Let the nations shout and sing;
Glory to their Paschal King.

7. Hymns of glory, songs of praise,
God on high, to you we raise:
Risen Lord, we now adore,
With the Spirit ever more.

Text: *Victimae paschali laudes;* Ascr. to Wipo of Burgundy, d.1048; Tr. by Jane E. Leeson, 1809-1881, alt.
Tune: SURGIT IN HAEC DIES, 77 77 with alleluias; 12th C.; Acc. by Richard Proulx, b.1937,

453 Now the Green Blade Rises

1. Now the green blade ris - es from the bur - ied grain,
2. In the grave they laid him, love by ha - tred slain,
3. Forth he came at East - er, like the ris - en grain,
4. When our hearts are win - try, griev - ing, or in pain,

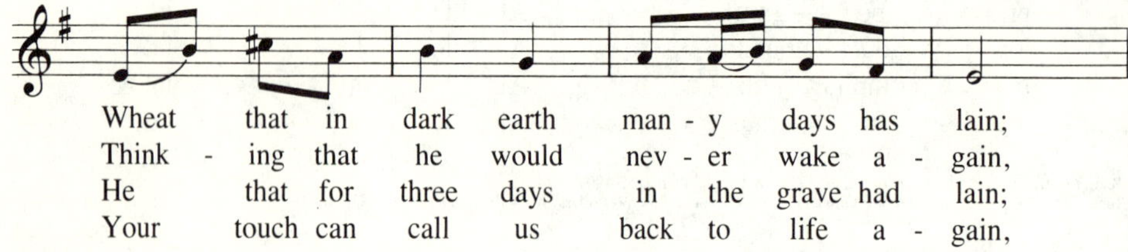

Wheat that in dark earth man - y days has lain;
Think - ing that he would nev - er wake a - gain,
He that for three days in the grave had lain;
Your touch can call us back to life a - gain,

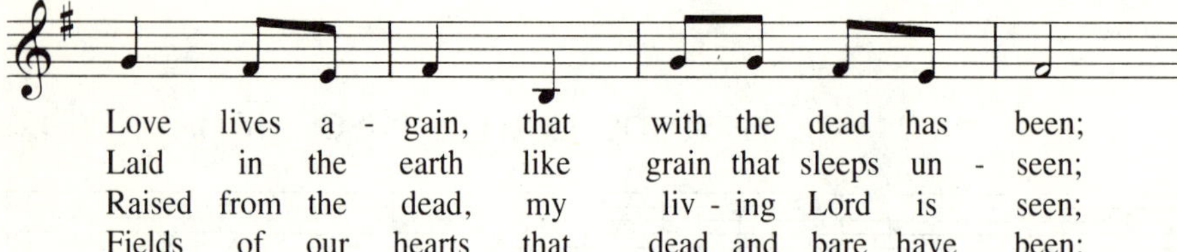

Love lives a - gain, that with the dead has been;
Laid in the earth like grain that sleeps un - seen;
Raised from the dead, my liv - ing Lord is seen;
Fields of our hearts that dead and bare have been;

Love is come a - gain like wheat a - ris - ing green.

Test: John M.C. Crum, 1872-1958, © Oxford University Press
Tune: NOËL NOUVELET, 11 10 11 10; French Carol; Harm. by Thomas Foster, b.1938, © 1986, GIA Publications, Inc.

454 Maranatha! Alleluia!

f
Mar-an - a - tha, Mar-an - a - tha!

f
Al - le - lu - ia, al - le - lu - ia! (Al-)

Text: 1 Cor. 16:22, Rev. 22:20; Taizé Community, 1978
Tune: Jacques Berthier, b.1923
© 1979, Les Presses de Taizé

Rejoice, Angelic Choirs 455

1. Re - joice, an - gel - ic choirs, re - joice! Re-
2. O earth, ex - ult in ra - diance bright, Il-
3. Let all who gath - er round this flame, The
joice now, all cre - a - tion! Let trum - pets loud - ly
lu - mined by Christ's splen - dor! Your dark - ness now is
sign of Christ's a - ris - ing, The death - less light of
raise their voice To hail the Lord's sal - va - tion; Let
put to flight; To him due prais - es ren - der! Be
Christ ac - claim, His sav - ing mer - cy priz - ing; That
all Christ's ho - ly peo - ple sing The tri - umph of their
glad, O Church! Sing out your songs! Your tem - ples fill with
all may live by faith in him Who con-quered death, de-
might-y king In fes - tal cel - e - bra - tion!
shout-ing throngs To hail the glo - rious vic - tor!
spair, and sin To make us his for ev - er.

Text: *Exsultet jam angelica;* Latin, 4th C.; Tr. by Joel W. Lundeen, b.1918, © 1978, *Lutheran Book of Worship*
Tune: MIT FREUDEN ZART, 8 7 8 7 88 7; Bohemian Brethren's *Kirchengesange*, 1556

456 Come, Ye Faithful, Raise the Strain

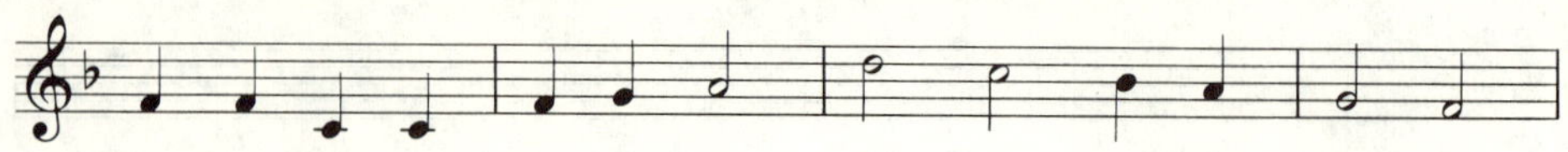

1. Come, ye faith - ful raise the strain Of tri - um - phant glad - ness;
2. 'Tis the spring of souls to - day; Christ has burst the pris - on,
3. Now the queen of sea-sons, bright With the day of splen - dor,
4. Nei - ther could the gates of death, Nor the tomb's dark por - tal,
5. "Al - le - lu - ia!" now we cry To our King im - mor - tal,

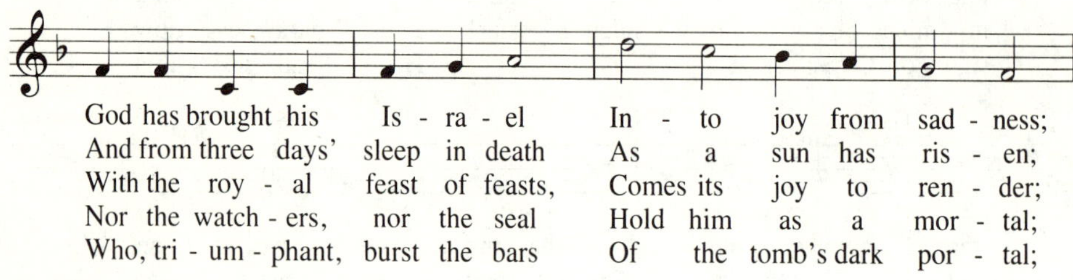

God has brought his Is - ra - el In - to joy from sad - ness;
And from three days' sleep in death As a sun has ris - en;
With the roy - al feast of feasts, Comes its joy to ren - der;
Nor the watch - ers, nor the seal Hold him as a mor - tal;
Who, tri - um - phant, burst the bars Of the tomb's dark por - tal;

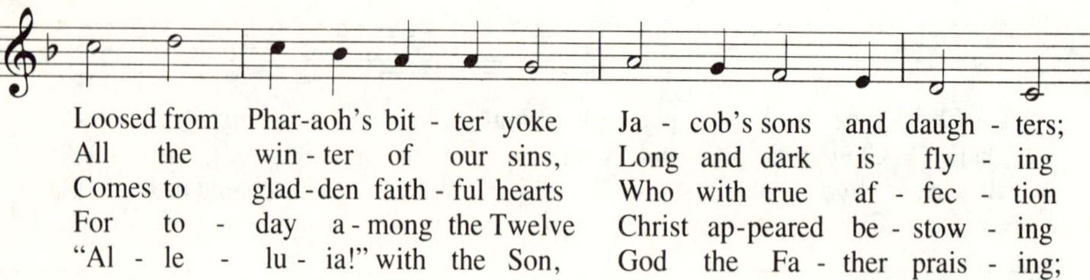

Loosed from Phar-aoh's bit - ter yoke Ja - cob's sons and daugh - ters;
All the win - ter of our sins, Long and dark is fly - ing
Comes to glad - den faith - ful hearts Who with true af - fec - tion
For to - day a - mong the Twelve Christ ap-peared be - stow - ing
"Al - le - lu - ia!" with the Son, God the Fa - ther prais - ing;

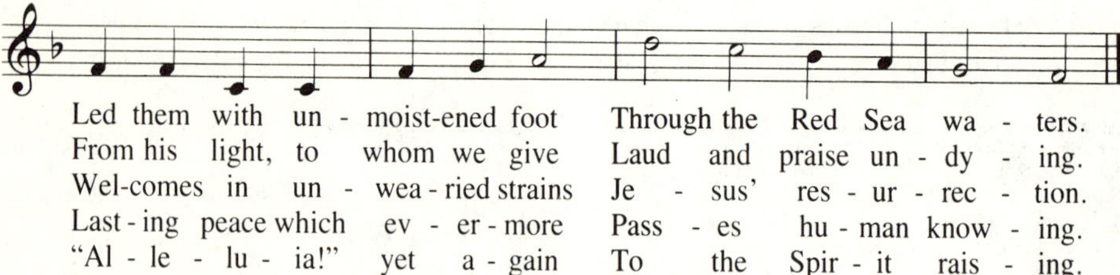

Led them with un - moist-ened foot Through the Red Sea wa - ters.
From his light, to whom we give Laud and praise un - dy - ing.
Wel-comes in un - wea - ried strains Je - sus' res - ur - rec - tion.
Last - ing peace which ev - er - more Pass - es hu - man know - ing.
"Al - le - lu - ia!" yet a - gain To the Spir - it rais - ing.

Text: Ex. 15; Ἄσωμεν πάντεζ λαοί; John of Damascus, c.675-c.749; Tr. by John M. Neale, 1818-1866, alt.
Tune: GAUDEAMUS PARITER, 7 6 7 6 D; Johann Horn, c.1495-1547

That Easter Day with Joy Was Bright 457

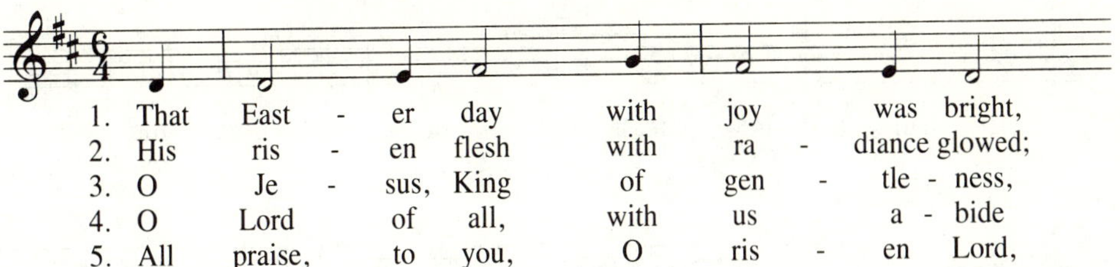
1. That East - er day with joy was bright,
2. His ris - en flesh with ra - diance glowed;
3. O Je - sus, King of gen - tle - ness,
4. O Lord of all, with us a - bide
5. All praise, to you, O ris - en Lord,

The sun shone out with fair - er light,
His wound - ed hands and feet he showed;
Who with your grace our hearts pos - sess
In this our joy - ful East - er - tide;
Now both by heaven and earth a - dored;

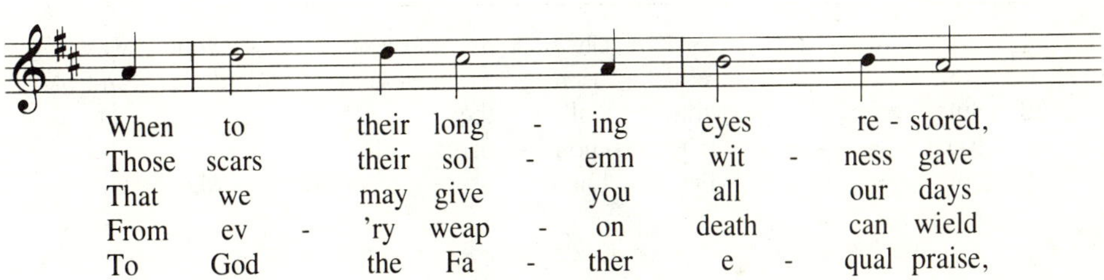
When to their long - ing eyes re - stored,
Those scars their sol - emn wit - ness gave
That we may give you all our days
From ev - 'ry weap - on death can wield
To God the Fa - ther e - qual praise,

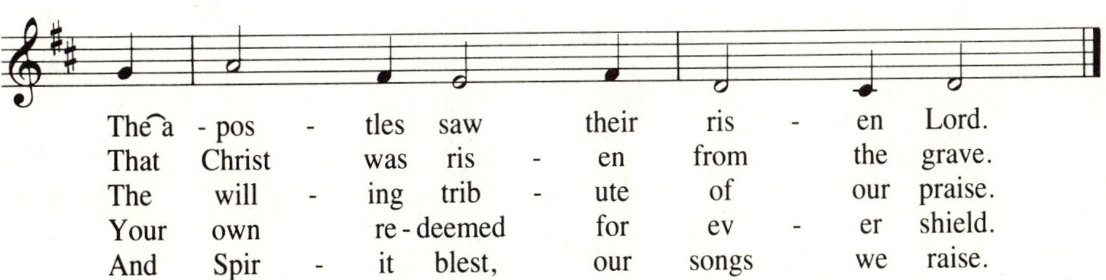
The a - pos - tles saw their ris - en Lord.
That Christ was ris - en from the grave.
The will - ing trib - ute of our praise.
Your own re - deemed for ev - er shield.
And Spir - it blest, our songs we raise.

Text: *Claro paschali gaudio;* Latin 5th C.; Tr. by John M. Neale, 1818-1866, alt.
Tune: PUER NOBIS, LM; Adapt. by Michael Praetorius, 1571-1621

458 This Is the Feast of Victory

This is the feast of vic-to-ry for our

God. Al-le-lu-ia, al-le-lu-ia, al-

To verses
Last time
le-lu-ia. lu-ia.

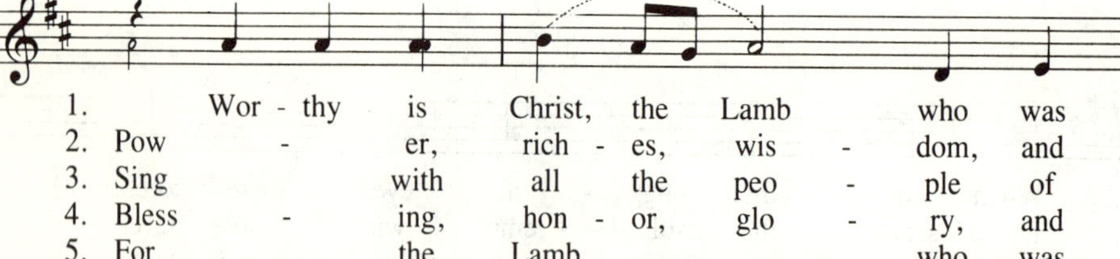
1. Wor-thy is Christ, the Lamb who was
2. Pow-er, rich-es, wis-dom, and
3. Sing with all the peo-ple of
4. Bless-ing, hon-or, glo-ry, and
5. For the Lamb who was

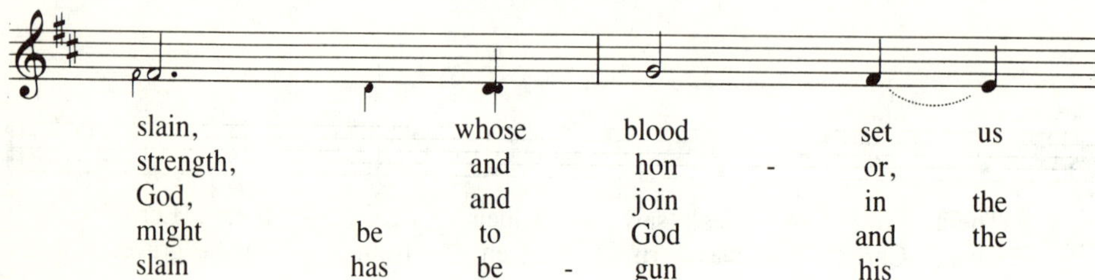
slain, whose blood set us
strength, and hon-or,
God, and join in the
might be to God and the
slain has be-gun his

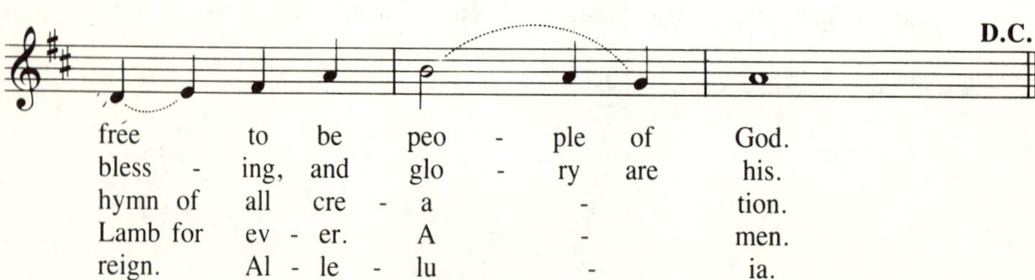
D.C.
free to be peo-ple of God.
bless-ing, and glo-ry are his.
hymn of all cre-a-tion.
Lamb for ev-er. A-men.
reign. Al-le-lu-ia.

Text: Based on Revelations 5, © 1978, *Lutheran Book of Worship*
Tune: FESTIVAL CANTICLE, Irregular; Richard Hillert, b.1923, © 1975, Richard Hillert, Harm: © 1978, *Lutheran Book of Worship*

At the Lamb's High Feast We Sing 459

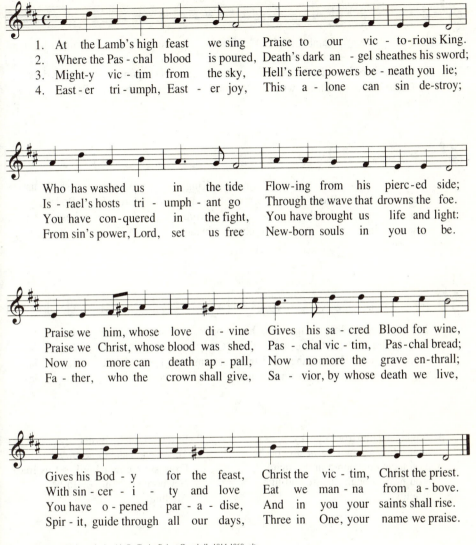

1. At the Lamb's high feast we sing Praise to our vic - to-rious King.
2. Where the Pas - chal blood is poured, Death's dark an - gel sheathes his sword;
3. Might-y vic - tim from the sky, Hell's fierce powers be - neath you lie;
4. East - er tri - umph, East - er joy, This a - lone can sin de-stroy;

Who has washed us in the tide Flow-ing from his pierc-ed side;
Is - rael's hosts tri - umph - ant go Through the wave that drowns the foe.
You have con-quered in the fight, You have brought us life and light:
From sin's power, Lord, set us free New-born souls in you to be.

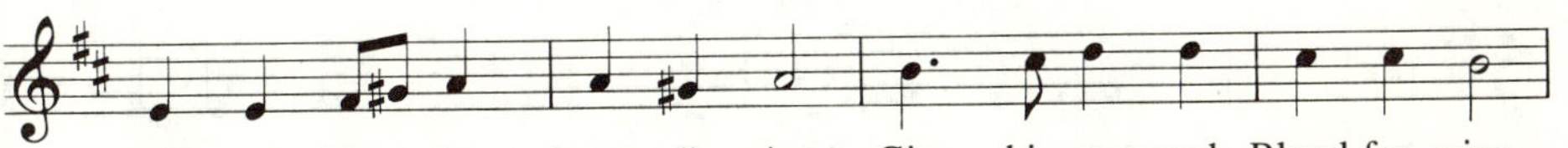

Praise we him, whose love di - vine Gives his sa - cred Blood for wine,
Praise we Christ, whose blood was shed, Pas - chal vic - tim, Pas-chal bread;
Now no more can death ap - pall, Now no more the grave en-thrall;
Fa - ther, who the crown shall give, Sa - vior, by whose death we live,

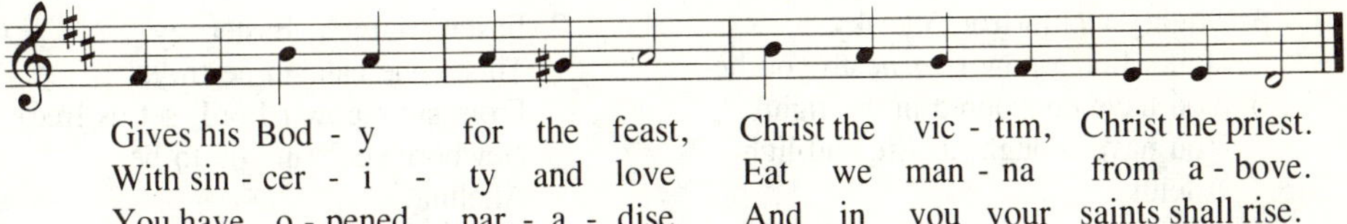

Gives his Bod - y for the feast, Christ the vic - tim, Christ the priest.
With sin - cer - i - ty and love Eat we man - na from a - bove.
You have o - pened par - a - dise, And in you your saints shall rise.
Spir - it, guide through all our days, Three in One, your name we praise.

Text: *Ad regias agni dapes;* Latin, 4th C.; Tr. by Robert Campbell, 1814-1868, alt.
Tune: SALZBURG, 77 77 D; Jakob Hintze, 1622-1702; Harm. by J.S. Bach, 1685-1750

460 At the Lamb's High Feast We Sing

1. At the Lamb's high feast we sing Praise to
2. Praise we him, whose love di - vine Gives his
3. Where the Pas - chal blood is poured, Death's dark
4. Praise we Christ, whose blood was shed, Pas - chal

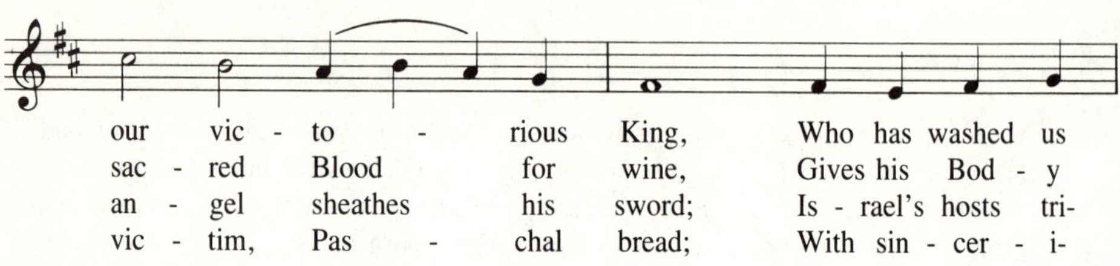
our vic - to - rious King, Who has washed us
sac - red Blood for wine, Gives his Bod - y
an - gel sheathes his sword; Is - rael's hosts tri-
vic - tim, Pas - chal bread; With sin - cer - i-

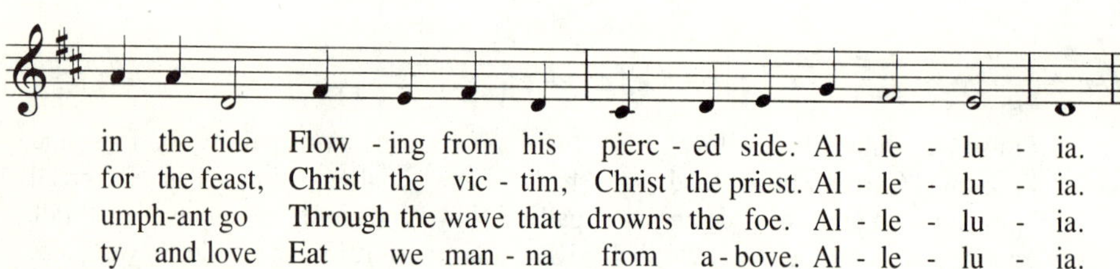
in the tide Flow - ing from his pierc - ed side. Al - le - lu - ia.
for the feast, Christ the vic - tim, Christ the priest. Al - le - lu - ia.
umph-ant go Through the wave that drowns the foe. Al - le - lu - ia.
ty and love Eat we man - na from a - bove. Al - le - lu - ia.

5. Mighty victim from the sky,
Hell's fierce pow'rs beneath you lie;
You have conquered in the fight,
You have brought us life and light.
Alleluia.

6. Now no more can death appall,
Now no more the grave enthrall;
You have opened paradise,
And in you your saints shall rise.
Alleluia.

7. Easter triumph, Easter joy,
This alone can sin destroy;
From sin's pow'r Lord, set us free
Newborn souls in you to be.
Alleluia.

8. Father, who the crown shall give,
Savior, by whose death we live,
Spirit, guide through all our days,
Three in One, your name we praise.
Alleluia.

Text: *Ad regias agni dapes;* Latin, 4th C.; Tr. by Robert Campbell, 1814-1868, alt.
Tune: SONNE DER GERECHTIGKEIT, 77 77 with alleluias; Bohemian Brethern's *Kirchengesange*, 1566

Christ the Lord Is Risen Today 461

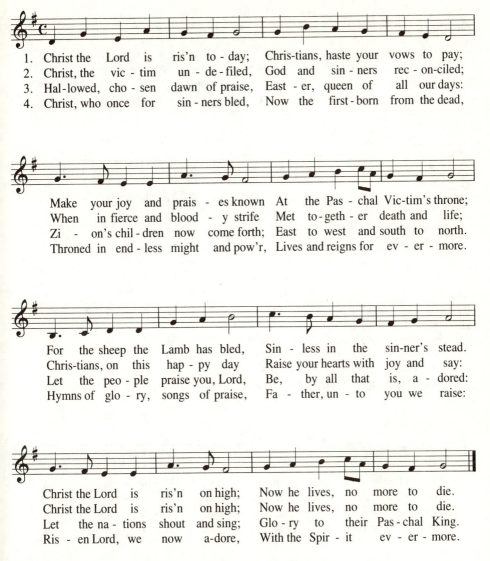

1. Christ the Lord is ris'n to - day; Chris-tians, haste your vows to pay;
2. Christ, the vic - tim un - de - filed, God and sin - ners rec - on-ciled;
3. Hal-lowed, cho - sen dawn of praise, East - er, queen of all our days:
4. Christ, who once for sin - ners bled, Now the first - born from the dead,

Make your joy and prais - es known At the Pas - chal Vic-tim's throne;
When in fierce and blood - y strife Met to-geth - er death and life;
Zi - on's chil - dren now come forth; East to west and south to north.
Throned in end - less might and pow'r, Lives and reigns for ev - er - more.

For the sheep the Lamb has bled, Sin - less in the sin-ner's stead.
Chris-tians, on this hap - py day Raise your hearts with joy and say:
Let the peo - ple praise you, Lord, Be, by all that is, a - dored:
Hymns of glo - ry, songs of praise, Fa - ther, un - to you we raise:

Christ the Lord is ris'n on high; Now he lives, no more to die.
Christ the Lord is ris'n on high; Now he lives, no more to die.
Let the na - tions shout and sing; Glo - ry to their Pas - chal King.
Ris - en Lord, we now a-dore, With the Spir - it ev - er - more.

Text: *Victimae paschali laudes;* Ascr. to Wipo of Burgundy, d.1048; Tr. by Jane E. Leeson, 1809-1881, alt.
Tune: VICTIMAE PASCHALI, 77 77 D; Würth's *Katholisches Gesangbuch,* 1859; Revised in *Catholic Youth's Hymn Book,* 1871

462 Christ the Lord Is Risen Today

1. Christ the Lord is ris'n to - day, Al - le - lu - ia!
2. Lives a - gain our glo - rious King; Al - le - lu - ia!
3. Love's re - deem - ing work is done, Al - le - lu - ia!
4. Soar we now where Christ has led, Al - le - lu - ia!

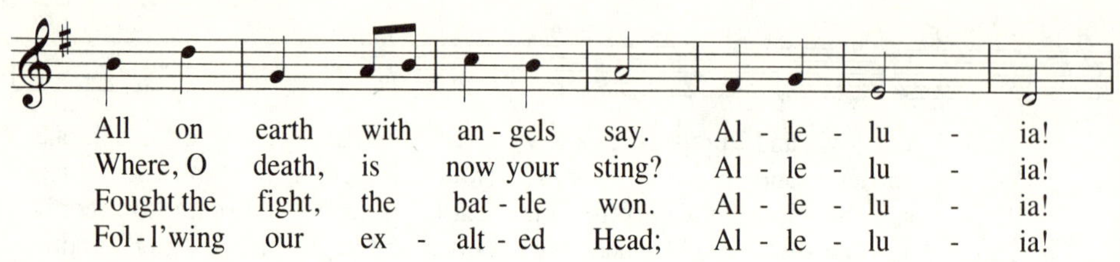
All on earth with an - gels say. Al - le - lu - ia!
Where, O death, is now your sting? Al - le - lu - ia!
Fought the fight, the bat - tle won. Al - le - lu - ia!
Fol - l'wing our ex - alt - ed Head; Al - le - lu - ia!

Raise your joys and tri - umphs high, Al - le - lu - ia!
Once he died our souls to save, Al - le - lu - ia!
Death in vain for - bids him rise; Al - le - lu - ia!
Made like him, like him we rise, Al - le - lu - ia!

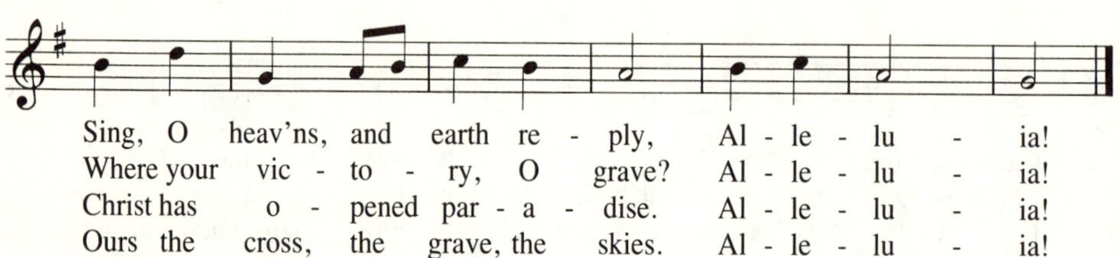
Sing, O heav'ns, and earth re - ply, Al - le - lu - ia!
Where your vic - to - ry, O grave? Al - le - lu - ia!
Christ has o - pened par - a - dise. Al - le - lu - ia!
Ours the cross, the grave, the skies. Al - le - lu - ia!

Text: Charles Wesley, 1707-1788
Tune: GWALCHMAI, 77 77 with alleluias; Joseph D. Jones, 1827-1870

Christ the Lord Is Risen Today 463

1. Christ the Lord is ris'n to - day, Al - le - lu - ia!
2. Lives a - gain our glo - rious King; Al - le - lu - ia!
3. Love's re - deem - ing work is done, Al - le - lu - ia!
4. Soar we now where Christ has led, Al - le - lu - ia!

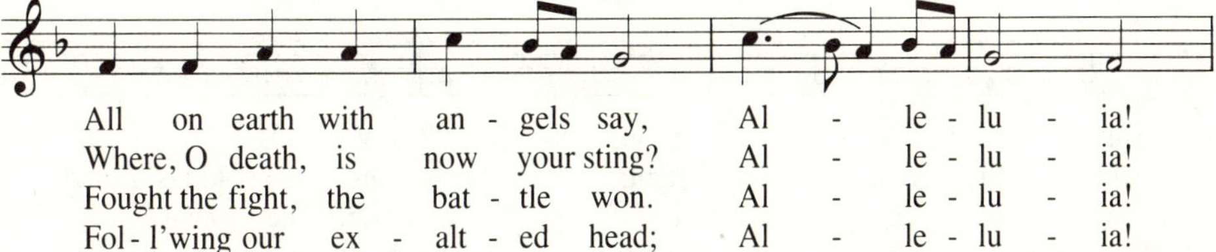

All on earth with an - gels say, Al - le - lu - ia!
Where, O death, is now your sting? Al - le - lu - ia!
Fought the fight, the bat - tle won. Al - le - lu - ia!
Fol - l'wing our ex - alt - ed head; Al - le - lu - ia!

Raise your joys and tri - umphs high, Al - le - lu - ia!
Once he died our souls to save, Al - le - lu - ia!
Death in vain for - bids him rise; Al - le - lu - ia!
Made like him, like him we rise, Al - le - lu - ia!

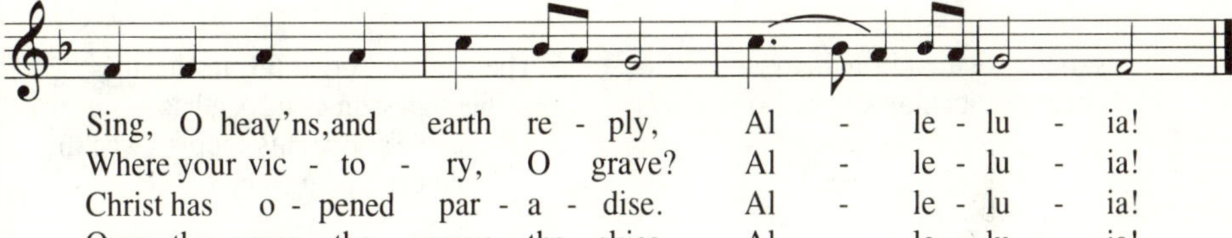

Sing, O heav'ns, and earth re - ply, Al - le - lu - ia!
Where your vic - to - ry, O grave? Al - le - lu - ia!
Christ has o - pened par - a - dise. Al - le - lu - ia!
Ours the cross, the grave, the skies. Al - le - lu - ia!

Text: Charles Wesley, 1707-1788
Tune: LLANFAIR, 77 77 with alleluias; Robert Williams, 1781-1821

464 The Head That Once Was Crowned with Thorns

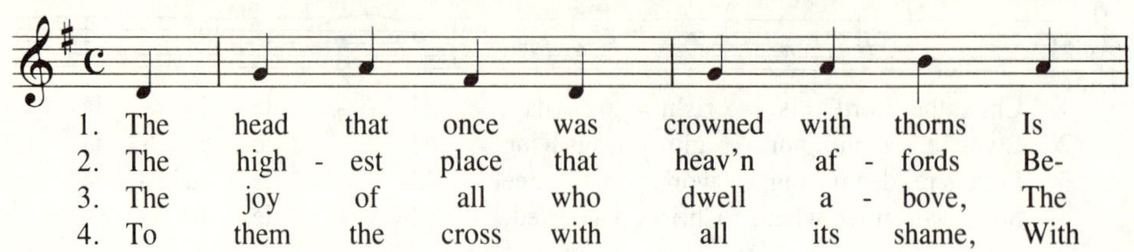
1. The head that once was crowned with thorns Is
2. The high - est place that heav'n af - fords Be-
3. The joy of all who dwell a - bove, The
4. To them the cross with all its shame, With

crowned with glo - ry now; A roy - al di - a-
longs to him by right; The King of kings, and
joy of all be - low, To whom he man - i-
all its grace, is giv'n; Their name an ev - er-

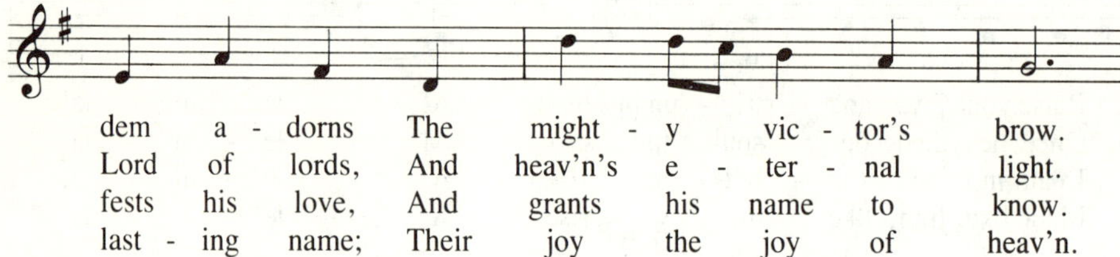
dem a - dorns The might - y vic - tor's brow.
Lord of lords, And heav'n's e - ter - nal light.
fests his love, And grants his name to know.
last - ing name; Their joy the joy of heav'n.

5. They suffer with their Lord below;
They reign with him above;
Their profit and their joy to know
The myst'ry of his love.

6. The cross he bore is life and health,
Though shame and death to him,
His people's hope, his people's wealth,
Their everlasting theme.

Text: Heb. 2:9-10; Thomas Kelly, 1769-1855
Tune: ST. MAGNUS, CM; Jeremiah Clarke, 1670-1707

465 Christus Resurrexit

(hum) Chri-stus re - sur - re - xit, Chri-stus re - sur - re - xit!
(hum) Al - le - lu - ia, al - le - lu - ia!

Text: *Christ is risen;* Psalm 118: 1,5,6,19,21,24; Tr. composite; Taizé Community, 1982
Tune: Jacques Berthier, b.1923

Christ Is Alive! 466

1. Christ is a - live! Let Chris - tians sing. His cross stands emp - ty to the sky. Let streets and homes with prais - es ring. His love in death shall nev - er die.
2. Christ is a - live! No long - er bound To dis - tant years in Pal - es - tine, He comes to claim the here and now And con - quer ev - 'ry place and time.
3. Not throned a - bove, re - mote - ly high, Un - touched, un - moved by hu - man pains, But dai - ly, in the midst of life, Our Sav - ior with the Fa - ther reigns.
4. In ev - 'ry in - sult, rift, and war Where col - or, scorn or wealth di - vide, He suf - fers still, yet loves the more, And lives, though ev - er cru - ci - fied.
5. Christ is a - live! His Spir - it burns Through this and ev - 'ry fu - ture age, Till all cre - a - tion lives and learns His joy, his jus - tice, love and praise.

Text: Rom. 6:5-11; Brian Wren, b.1936, © 1975, Hope Publishing Co.
Tune: TRURO, LM; Williams' *Psalmodia Evangelica,* 1789

467 Sing with All the Saints in Glory

1. Sing with all the saints in glo - ry, Sing the res - ur-
2. O what glo - ry, far ex - ceed - ing All that eye has
3. Life e - ter - nal! heav'n re - joic - es: Je - sus lives who
4. Life e - ter - nal! O what won - ders Crowd on faith; what
rec - tion song! Death and sor - row, earth's dark sto - ry,
yet per-ceived! Ho - liest hearts for a - ges plead - ing,
once was dead; Shout with joy, O death - less voic - es!
joy un-known, When, a - midst earth's clos - ing thun - ders,
To the for - mer days be - long. All a - round the
Nev - er that full joy con-ceived. God has prom - ised,
Child of God, lift up your head! Pa - tri - archs from
Saints shall stand be - fore the throne! O to en - ter
clouds are break - ing, Soon the storms of time shall cease;
Christ pre - pares it, There on high our wel - come waits;
dis - tant a - ges, Saints all long - ing for their heaven,
that bright por - tal, See that glow - ing fir - ma - ment,
In God's like - ness, we a - wak - en, Know-ing ev - er - last-ing peace.
Ev - 'ry hum - ble spir - it shares it, Christ has passed the e - ter - nal gates.
Proph-ets, psalm-ists, seers, and sag - es, All a - wait the glo - ry giv'n.
Know, with you, O God im - mor - tal, "Je - sus Christ whom you have sent!"

Text: 1 Cor. 15:20; William J. Irons, 1812-1883, alt.
Tune: HYMN TO JOY, 8 7 8 7 D; Arr. from Ludwig van Beethoven, 1770-1827, by Edward Hodges, 1796-1867

Look, O Look, the Sight Is Glorious 468

1. Look, O look, the sight is glo - rious, See the man of sor - rows now; From the fight re - turned vic - to - rious, Ev - 'ry knee to him shall bow.
2. Crown the Sav - ior! An - gels crown him! Rich the tro - phies Je - sus brings; On the seat of pow'r en - throne him While the vault of heav - en rings.
3. Sin - ners in de - ri - sion crowned him, Mock - ing thus the Sav - ior's claim; Saints and an - gels crowd a - round him, Own his ti - tle, praise his name.
4. Hark! those bursts of ac - cla - ma - tion! Hark! those loud tri - um - phant chords! Je - sus takes the high - est sta - tion; Oh, what joy the sight af - fords!
Crown him, crown him! Crown him, crown him! Crown him, Crown him!
Crowns be - come the vic - tor's brow. Crowns be - come the vic - tor's brow.
Crown the Sav - ior, King of kings. Crown the Sav - ior, King of kings.
Spread a - broad the vic - tor's fame! Spread a - broad the vic - tor's fame!
King of kings and Lord of lords! King of kings and Lord of lords!
rit.
a tempo

Text: Rev. 7:9-15; Thomas Kelly, 1769-1855, alt.
Tune: BRYN CALFARIA, 8 7 8 7 444 77; William Owen, 1814-1893

469 A Hymn of Glory Let Us Sing

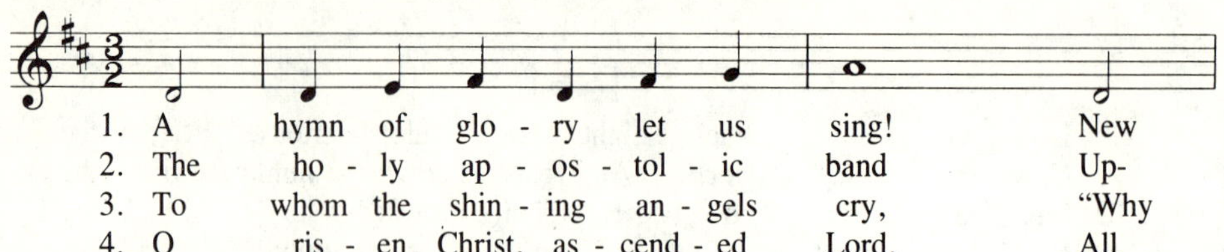
1. A hymn of glo - ry let us sing! New
2. The ho - ly ap - os - tol - ic band Up-
3. To whom the shin - ing an - gels cry, "Why
4. O ris - en Christ, as - cend - ed Lord, All

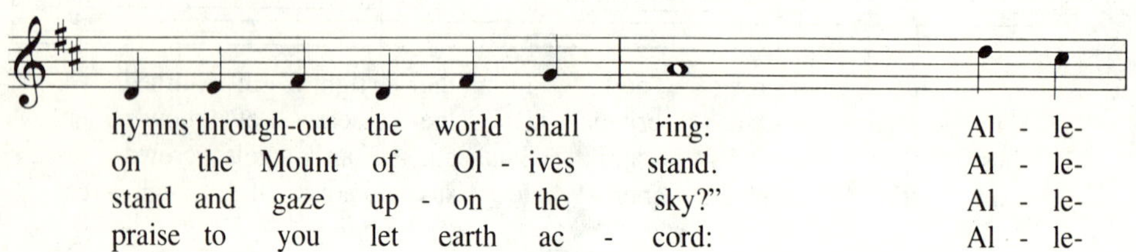
hymns through-out the world shall ring: Al - le-
on the Mount of Ol - ives stand. Al - le-
stand and gaze up - on the sky?" Al - le-
praise to you let earth ac - cord: Al - le-

lu - ia! Al - le - lu - ia! Christ, by a road be - fore un-
lu - ia! Al - le - lu - ia! And with his faith - ful fol-l'wers
lu - ia! Al - le - lu - ia! "This is the Sav - ior!" Thus they
lu - ia! Al - le - lu - ia! You are, while end - less a - ges

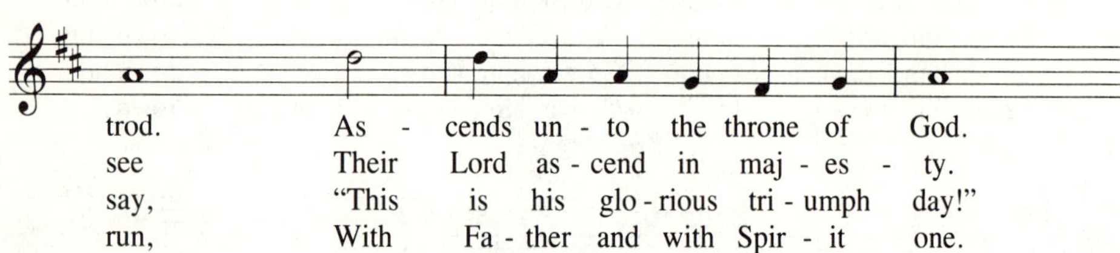
trod. As - cends un - to the throne of God.
see Their Lord as - cend in maj - es - ty.
say, "This is his glo - rious tri - umph day!"
run, With Fa - ther and with Spir - it one.

Al - le - lu - ia! Al - le - lu - ia! Al - le - lu - ia,

Al - le - lu - ia, Al - le - lu - ia!

Text: *Hymnum canamus gloria;* Venerable Bede, 673-735; Tr. *Lutheran Book of Worship*, 1978
Tune: LASST UNS ERFREUEN, LM; with alleluias; *Geistliche Kirchengesange*, Cologne, 1623; Harm. by Ralph Vaughan Williams, 1872-1958,

Lord, You Give the Great Commission 470

1. Lord, you give the great com - mis-sion: "Heal the
2. Lord, you call us to your ser - vice: "In my
3. Lord, you make the com - mon ho - ly: "This my
4. Lord, you show us love's true meas-ure: "Fa - ther,
5. Lord, you bless with words as - sur - ing: "I am
sick and preach the word." Lest the Church ne-
name bap - tize and teach." That the world may
bod - y, this my blood." Let us all, for
what they do, for - give." Yet we hoard as
with you to the end." Faith and hope and
glect its mis-sion, And the Gos - pel go un-
trust your pro-mise, Life a - bun - dant meant for
earth's true glo - ry, Dai - ly lift life heav - en-
pri - vate treas-ure All that you so free - ly
love re - stor - ing, May we serve as you in-
heard, Help us wit - ness to your pur - pose
each, Give us all new fer - vor, draw us
ward, Ask - ing that the world a - round us
give. May your care and mer - cy lead us
tend, And, a - mid the cares that claim us,
With re - newed in - teg - ri - ty;
Clos - er in com - mun - i - ty;
Share your chil - dren's lib - er - ty; With the
To a just so - ci - e - ty;
Hold in mind e - ter - ni - ty;
Spir - it's gifts em - power us For the work of min - is - try.

Text: Jeffrey Rowthorn, b.1934, © 1978
Tune: ABBOT'S LEIGH, 8 7 8 7 D; Cyril V. Taylor, b.1907, © 1942, 1970, Hope Publishing Co.

471 Hail the Day That Sees Him Rise

1. Hail the day that sees him rise Al - le - lu - ia!
2. There for him high tri - umph waits; Al - le - lu - ia!
3. High-est heav'n its Lord re - ceives, Al - le - lu - ia!
4. See, he lifts his hands a - bove. Al - le - lu - ia!

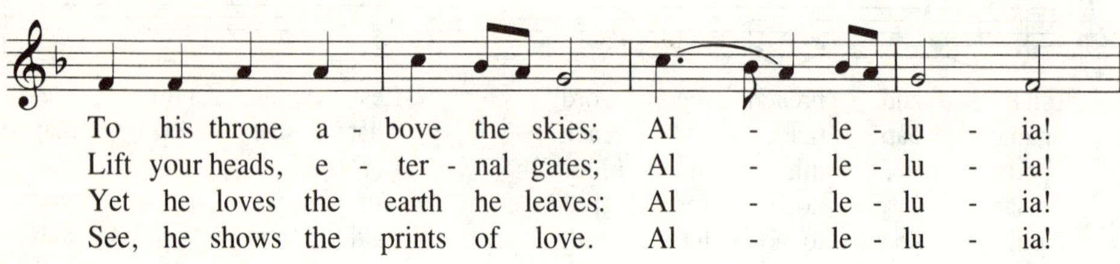
To his throne a - bove the skies; Al - le - lu - ia!
Lift your heads, e - ter - nal gates; Al - le - lu - ia!
Yet he loves the earth he leaves: Al - le - lu - ia!
See, he shows the prints of love. Al - le - lu - ia!

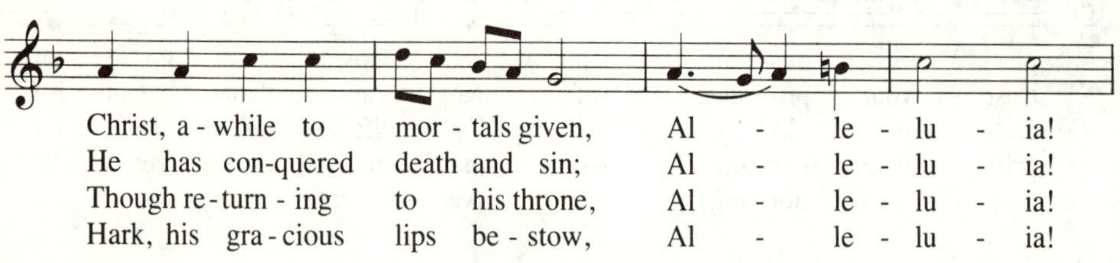
Christ, a - while to mor - tals given, Al - le - lu - ia!
He has con-quered death and sin; Al - le - lu - ia!
Though re - turn - ing to his throne, Al - le - lu - ia!
Hark, his gra - cious lips be - stow, Al - le - lu - ia!

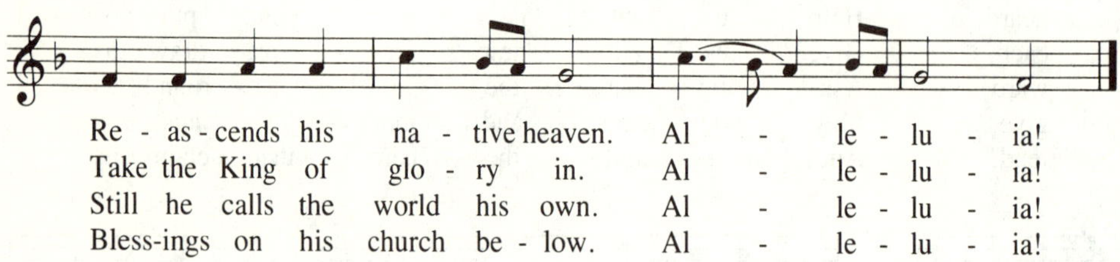
Re - as - cends his na - tive heaven. Al - le - lu - ia!
Take the King of glo - ry in. Al - le - lu - ia!
Still he calls the world his own. Al - le - lu - ia!
Bless-ings on his church be - low. Al - le - lu - ia!

5. Still for us he intercedes, Alleluia!
His prevailing death he pleads, Alleluia!
Near himself prepares our place, Alleluia!
He the first fruits of our race. Alleluia!

6. There we shall with him remain, Alleluia!
Partners of his endless reign; Alleluia!
There his face unclouded see, Alleluia!
Live with him eternally. Alleluia!

Text: Charles Wesley, 1707-1788, alt.
Tune: LLANFAIR, 77 77 with alleluias; Robert Williams, 1781-1821

Come Down, O Love Divine 472

1. Come down, O Love di - vine, Seek now this soul of
2. O let it free - ly burn, Till earth - ly pas - sions
3. And so the yearn - ing strong, With which the soul will

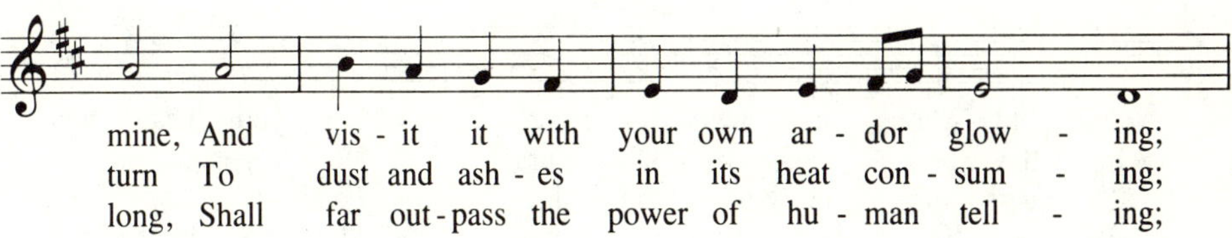
mine, And vis - it it with your own ar - dor glow - ing;
turn To dust and ash - es in its heat con - sum - ing;
long, Shall far out - pass the power of hu - man tell - ing;

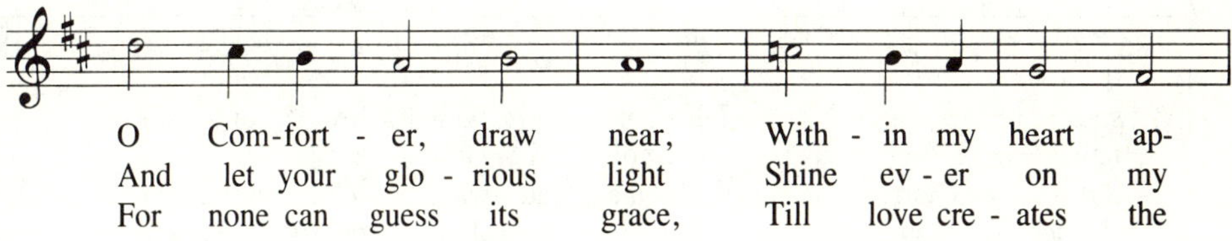
O Com-fort - er, draw near, With - in my heart ap-
And let your glo - rious light Shine ev - er on my
For none can guess its grace, Till love cre - ates the

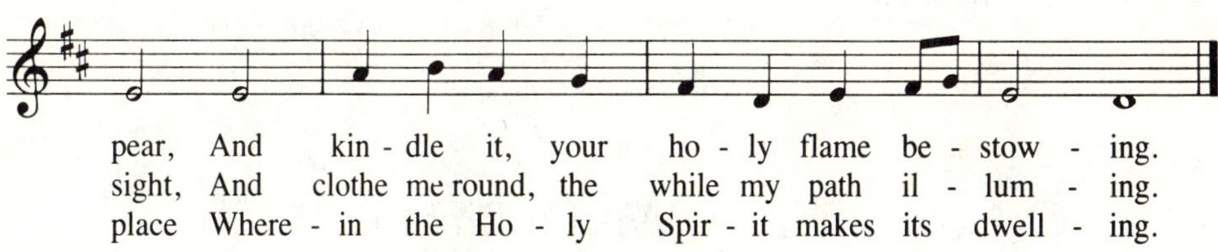
pear, And kin - dle it, your ho - ly flame be - stow - ing.
sight, And clothe me round, the while my path il - lum - ing.
place Where - in the Ho - ly Spir - it makes its dwell - ing.

Text: *Discendi, Amor Santo;* Bianco da Siena, d. c.1434; Tr. by Richard F. Littledale, 1833-1890
Tune: DOWN AMPNEY, 66 11 D; Ralph Vaughan Williams, 1872-1958,

Veni Sancte Spiritus 473

Ve - ni San - cte Spi - ri - tus.

Text: *Come Holy Spirit;* Verses drawn from the Pentecost Sequence; Taizé Community, 1978
Tune: Jacques Berthier, b.1923

474 Fire of God, Undying Flame

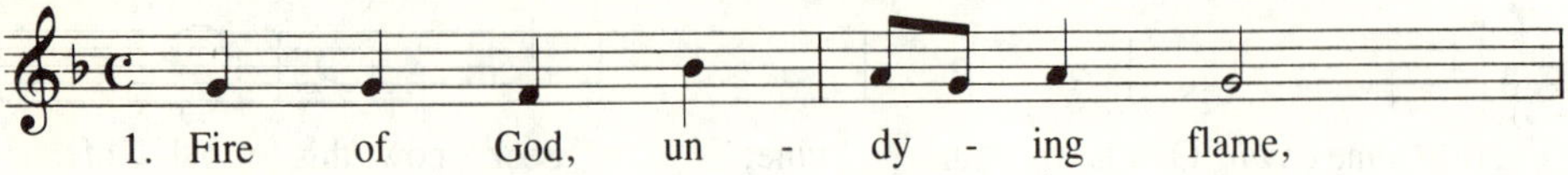

1. Fire of God, un - dy - ing flame,
2. Breath of God, that swept in power
3. Strength of God, your might with - in
4. Truth of God, your pierc - ing rays
5. Love of God, your grace pro - found

Spir - it who in splen - dor came, Let your heat my
In the Pen - te - cos - tal hour, Ho - ly breath, be
Con - quers sor - row, pain and sin; For - ti - fy from
Pen - e - trate my se - cret ways, May the light that
Knows not ei - ther age or bound; Come, my heart's own

soul re - fine, Till it glows with love di - vine.
now in me Source of vi - tal en - er - gy.
e - vil art All the gate - ways of my heart.
shames my sin Guide me ho - lier paths to win.
guest to be, Dwell for ev - er - more in me.

Text: Albert F. Bayly, 1901-1984, alt. © Oxford University Press
Tune: NUN KOMM DER HEIDEN HEILAND, 77 77; *Geystliche Gesank Buchleyn,* Wittenberg, 1524; Harm. by Melchior Vulpius, c.1560-1616

475 O Holy Spirit, by Whose Breath

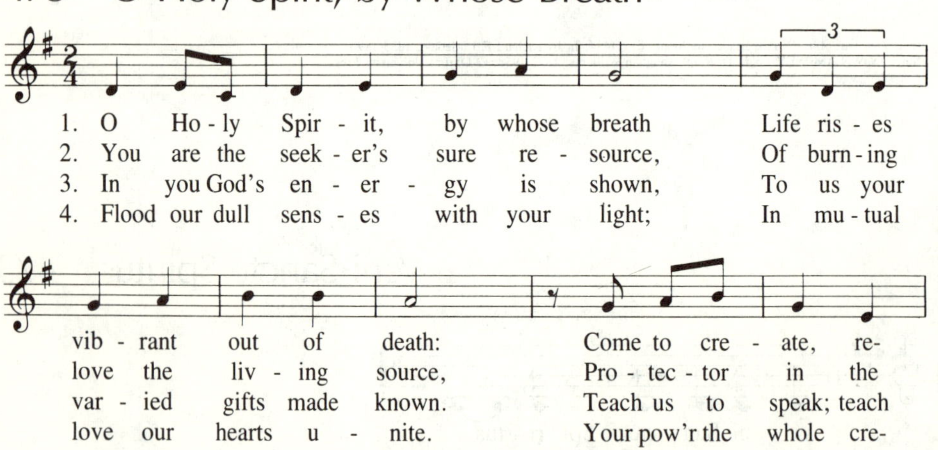
3
1. O Ho - ly Spir - it, by whose breath Life ris - es
2. You are the seek - er's sure re - source, Of burn - ing
3. In you God's en - er - gy is shown, To us your
4. Flood our dull sens - es with your light; In mu - tual
vib - rant out of death: Come to cre - ate, re-
love the liv - ing source, Pro - tec - tor in the
var - ied gifts made known. Teach us to speak; teach
love our hearts u - nite. Your pow'r the whole cre-

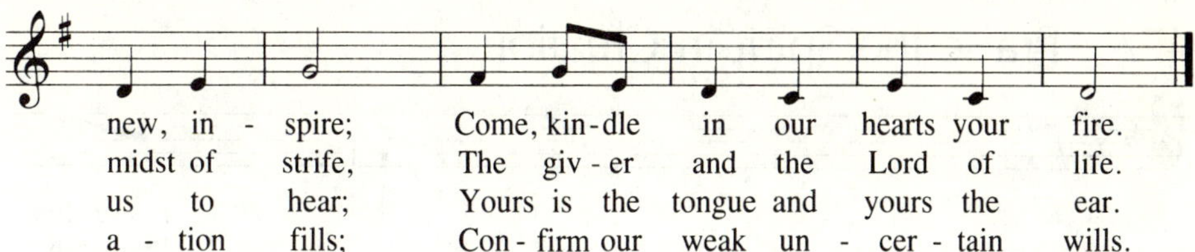
new, in - spire; Come, kin-dle in our hearts your fire.
midst of strife, The giv - er and the Lord of life.
us to hear; Yours is the tongue and yours the ear.
a - tion fills; Con - firm our weak un - cer - tain wills.

5. From inner strife grant us release;
Turn nations to the ways of peace.
To fuller life your people bring
That as one body we may sing:

6. Praise to the Father, Christ his Word,
And to the Spirit, God the Lord;
To whom all honor, glory be
Both now and for eternity.

Text: *Veni, Creator Spiritus;* Attr. to Rabanus Maurus, 776-865; Tr. by John W. Grant, b.1919,
Tune: VENI CREATOR SPIRITUS, LM; Mode VIII; Setting by Richard J. Wojcik, b.1923,

Spirit Divine, Accept Our Prayers 476

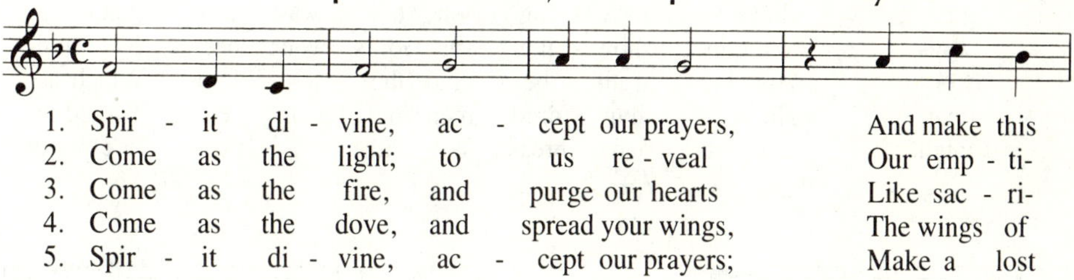

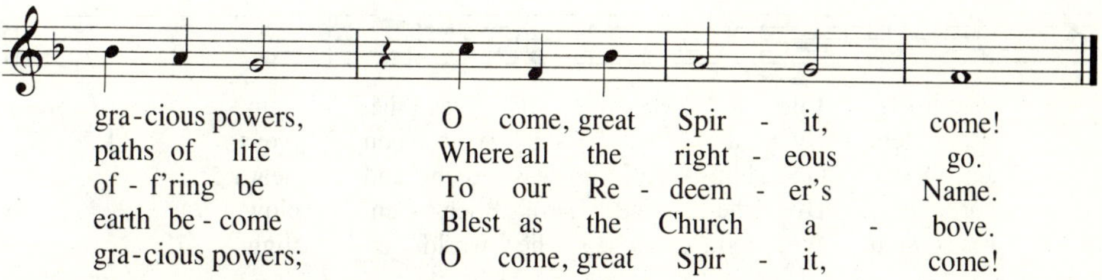

1. Spir - it di - vine, ac - cept our prayers, And make this
2. Come as the light; to us re - veal Our emp - ti-
3. Come as the fire, and purge our hearts Like sac - ri-
4. Come as the dove, and spread your wings, The wings of
5. Spir - it di - vine, ac - cept our prayers; Make a lost

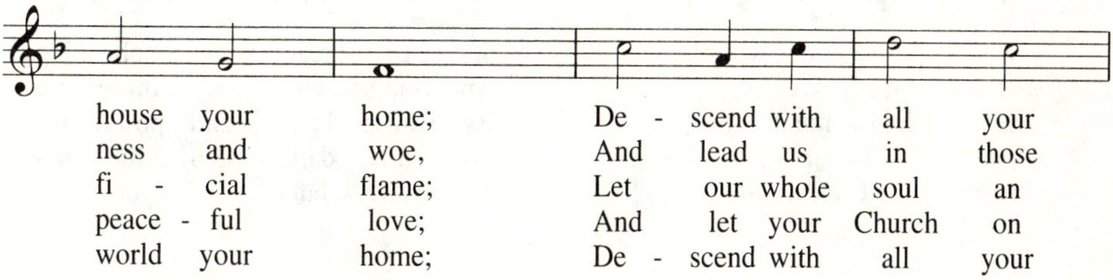

house your home; De - scend with all your
ness and woe, And lead us in those
fi - cial flame; Let our whole soul an
peace - ful love; And let your Church on
world your home; De - scend with all your

gra-cious powers, O come, great Spir - it, come!
paths of life Where all the right - eous go.
of - f'ring be To our Re - deem - er's Name.
earth be - come Blest as the Church a - bove.
gra-cious powers; O come, great Spir - it, come!

Text: Andrew Reed, 1788-1862, alt.
Tune: GRAEFENBERG, CM; Johann Crüger, 1598-1662

477 Praise the Spirit in Creation

1. Praise the
2. Praise the
3. Praise the
4. Tell of
5. Pray we

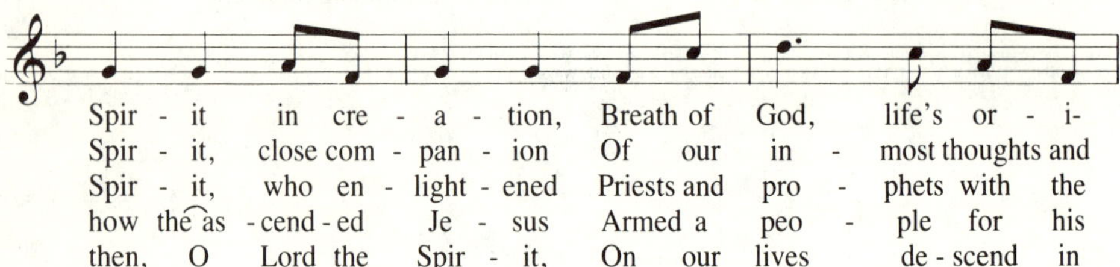
Spir - it in cre - a - tion, Breath of God, life's or - i-
Spir - it, close com - pan - ion Of our in - most thoughts and
Spir - it, who en - light - ened Priests and pro - phets with the
how the as - cend - ed Je - sus Armed a peo - ple for his
then, O Lord the Spir - it, On our lives de - scend in

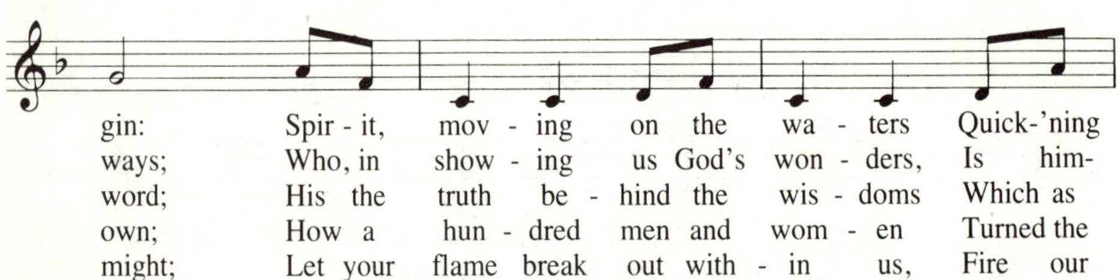
gin: Spir - it, mov - ing on the wa - ters Quick-'ning
ways; Who, in show - ing us God's won - ders, Is him-
word; His the truth be - hind the wis - doms Which as
own; How a hun - dred men and wom - en Turned the
might; Let your flame break out with - in us, Fire our

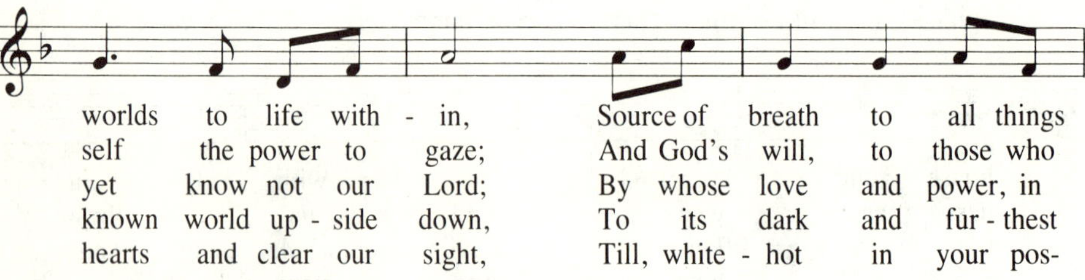
worlds to life with - in, Source of breath to all things
self the power to gaze; And God's will, to those who
yet know not our Lord; By whose love and power, in
known world up - side down, To its dark and fur - thest
hearts and clear our sight, Till, white - hot in your pos-

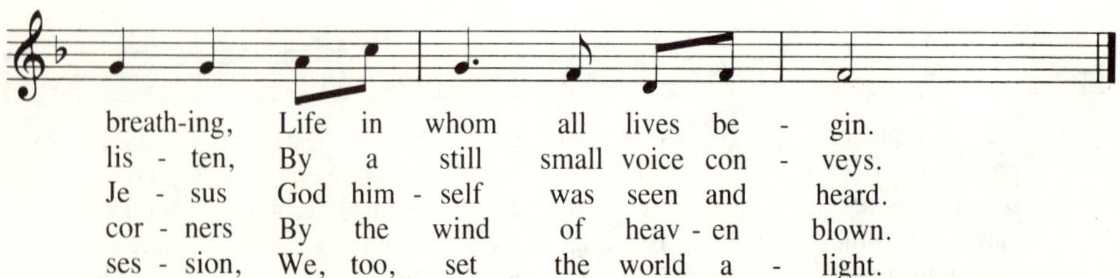
breath-ing, Life in whom all lives be - gin.
lis - ten, By a still small voice con - veys.
Je - sus God him - self was seen and heard.
cor - ners By the wind of heav - en blown.
ses - sion, We, too, set the world a - light.

Fire of God, Titanic Spirit 478

1. Fire of God, ti - tan - ic - Spir - it, Burn with-
2. Wind of God, dy - nam - ic Spir - it, Breathe up-
3. Voice of God, pro - phet - ic Spir - it, Speak to

in our hearts to - day; Cleanse our sin — may we ex-
on our hearts to - day; That we may your power in-
ev - 'ry heart to - day To en - cour - age or pro-

hib - it Ho - li - ness in ev - 'ry way:
her - it Hear us, Spir - it, as we pray:
hib - it, Urg - ing ac - tion or de - lay:

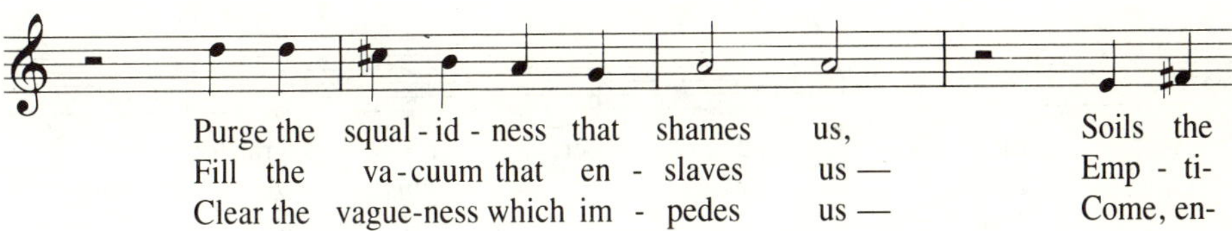
Purge the squal - id - ness that shames us, Soils the
Fill the va - cuum that en - slaves us — Emp - ti-
Clear the vague-ness which im - pedes us — Come, en-

bod - y, taints the soul; And, through Je - sus Christ who
ness of heart and soul; And, through Je - sus Christ who
light - en mind and soul; And, through Je - sus Christ who

claims us, Pu - ri - fy us, make us whole.
saves us, Give us life and make us whole.
leads us, Teach the truth that makes us whole.

Text: Michael Saward, b.1932.
Tune: FIRE OF GOD, 8 7 8 7 D; David G. Wilson, b.1940.

479 Veni Creator Spiritus

1. Ve - ni Cre - á - tor Spí - ri - tus,
2. Qui dí - ce - ris Pa - rá - cli - tus,
3. Tu se - pti - fór - mis mú - ne - re,
4. Ac - cén - de lu - men sén - si - bus,
5. Hó - stem re - pél - las lón - gi - us,
6. Per te sci - á - mus da Pa - trem,
7. De - o Pa - tri sit gló - ri - a,

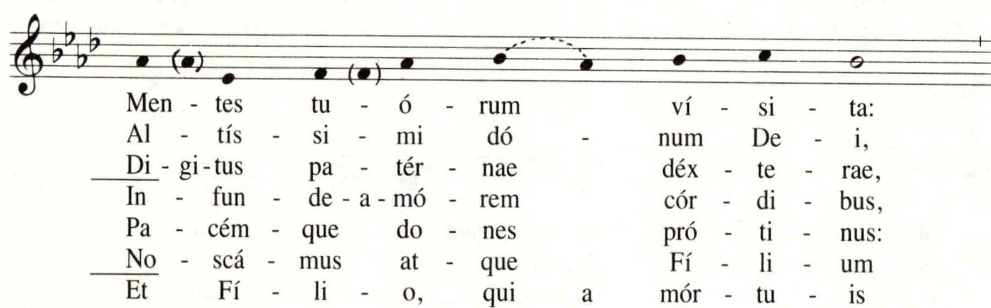
Men - tes tu - ó - rum ví - si - ta:
Al - tís - si - mi dó - num De - i,
Di - gi - tus pa - tér - nae déx - te - rae,
In - fun - de - a - mó - rem cór - di - bus,
Pa - cém - que do - nes pró - ti - nus:
No - scá - mus at - que Fí - li - um
Et Fí - li - o, qui a mór - tu - is

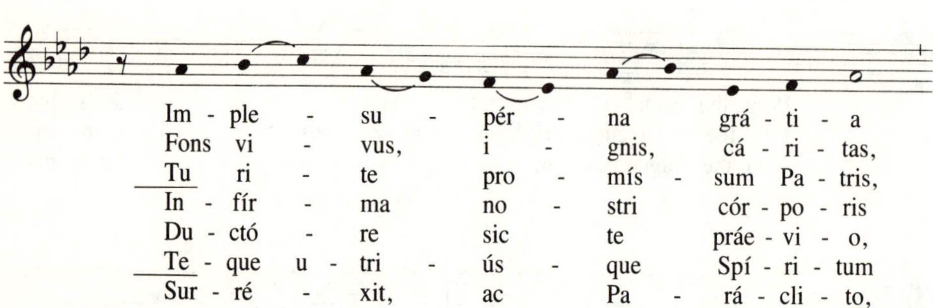
Im - ple - su - pér - na grá - ti - a
Fons vi - vus, i - gnis, cá - ri - tas,
Tu ri - te pro - mís - sum Pa - tris,
In - fír - ma no - stri cór - po - ris
Du - ctó - re sic te práe - vi - o,
Te - que u - tri - ús - que Spí - ri - tum
Sur - ré - xit, ac Pa - rá - cli - to,

Quae tu cre - á - sti pé - cto - ra.
Et spi - ri - tá - lis ún - cti - o.
Ser - mó - ne di - tans gút - tu - ra.
Vir - tú - te fír - mans pér - pe - ti.
Vi - té - mus om - ne nó - xi - um.
Cre - dá - mus om - ni tém - po - re.
In sae - cu - ló - rum sáe - cu - la. A - men.

Text: Attr. to Rabanus Maurus, 776-856
Tune: VENI CREATOR SPIRITUS, LM; Mode VIII; Acc. by Richard Proulx, b.1937,

Spirit of God within Me 480

1. Spir - it of God with - in me, Pos-
2. Spir - it of truth with - in me, Pos-
3. Spir - it of love with - in me, Pos-
4. Spir - it of life with - in me, Possess my hu - man frame; Fan the dull em - bers of my
sess my thought and mind; Light - en a - new the in - ward
sess my hands and heart; Break through the bonds of self - con-
sess this life of mine; Come as the wind of heav - en's
heart, Stir up the liv - ing flame:
eye By Sa - tan ren - dered blind:
cern That seeks to stand a - part:
breath, Come as the fire di - vine!
Strive till that im - age A - dam lost, New
Shine on the words that wis - dom speaks And
Grant me the love that suf - fers long, That
Spir - it of Christ, the liv - ing Lord, Reign
mint - ed and re - stored, In shin - ing splen - dor
grant me pow'r to see The truth made known to
hopes, be - lieves and bears; The love ful - filled in
in this house of clay, Till from its dust with
bright - ly bears The like - ness of the Lord.
all in Christ, And in that truth be free.
sac - ri - fice, That cares as Je - sus cares.
Christ I rise To ev - er - last - ing day.

Text: Timothy Dudley-Smith, b.1926,
Tune: ESCAMBIA, 7 6 8 6 8 6 8 6; Randolph Currie, b.1943,

481 When God the Spirit Came

1. When God the Spir - it came Up - on his church out-
2. What cour - age, pow'r and grace That youth - ful church dis-
3. They saw God's Word pre - vail, His king - dom still in-
4. Their theme was Christ a - lone, The Lord who lived and
5. So to this pre - sent hour Our task is still the

poured In sound of wind and sign of flame They
played! To those of ev - 'ry tribe and race They
crease, No part of all his pur - pose fail, No
died, Who rose to his e - ter - nal throne At
same, In pen - te - cost - al love and pow'r His

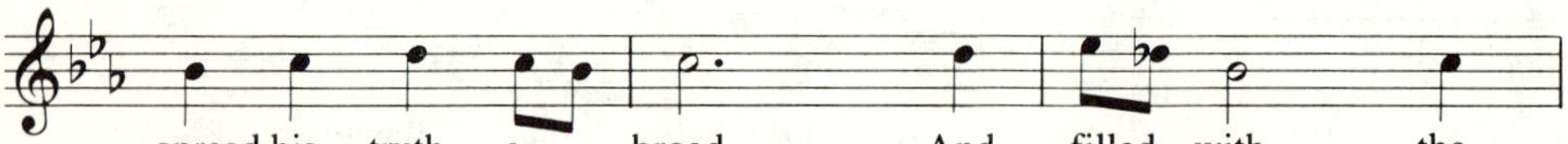

spread his truth a - broad, And filled with the
wit - nessed un - a - fraid, And filled with the
prom - ised bless - ing cease, And filled with the
God the Fa - ther's side; And filled with the
gos - pel to pro - claim, And filled with the

Spir - it Pro - claimed that Christ is Lord.
Spir - it They broke their bread and prayed.
Spir - it Knew love and joy and peace.
Spir - it The church was mul - ti - plied.
Spir - it, Re - joice in Je - sus' Name.

Text: Acts 2; Timothy Dudley-Smith, b.1926, © 1984, Hope Publishing Co.
Tune: VINEYARD HAVEN, 6 6 8 6 6 6; Richard Dirksen, b.1921, © 1974, 1986, Harold Flammer, Inc.

482 Come, Holy Ghost

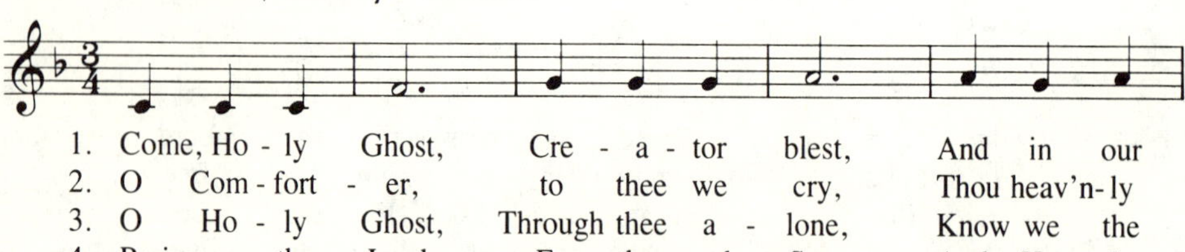

1. Come, Ho - ly Ghost, Cre - a - tor blest, And in our
2. O Com - fort - er, to thee we cry, Thou heav'n - ly
3. O Ho - ly Ghost, Through thee a - lone, Know we the
4. Praise we the Lord, Fa - ther and Son, And Ho - ly

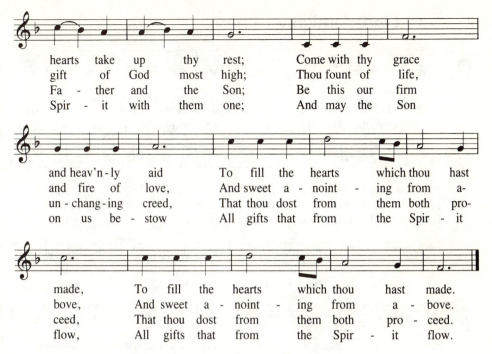

hearts take up thy rest; Come with thy grace and heav'n-ly aid To fill the hearts which thou hast made, To fill the hearts which thou hast made.
gift of God most high; Thou fount of life, and fire of love, And sweet a-noint-ing from a-bove, And sweet a-noint-ing from a-bove.
Fa-ther and the Son; Be this our firm un-chang-ing creed, That thou dost from them both pro-ceed, That thou dost from them both pro-ceed.
Spir-it with them one; And may the Son on us be-stow All gifts that from the Spir-it flow, All gifts that from the Spir-it flow.

Text: *Veni, Creator Spiritus;* Attr. to Rabanus Maurus, 776-856; Tr. by Edward Caswall, 1814-1878, alt.
Tune: LAMBILLOTTE, LM; with repeat; Louis Lambillotte, SJ, 1796-1855; Harm. by Richard Proulx, b.1937,

Over the Chaos of the Empty Waters 483

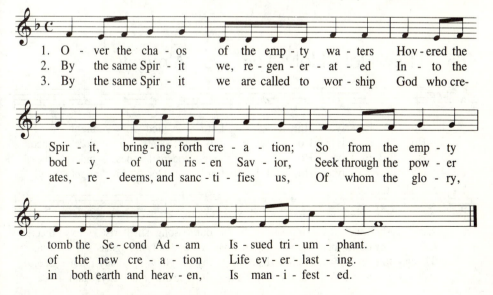

1. O-ver the cha-os of the emp-ty wa-ters Hov-ered the Spir-it, bring-ing forth cre-a-tion; So from the emp-ty tomb the Se-cond Ad-am Is-sued tri-um-phant.
2. By the same Spir-it we, re-gen-er-at-ed In-to the bod-y of our ris-en Sav-ior, Seek through the pow-er of the new cre-a-tion Life ev-er-last-ing.
3. By the same Spir-it we are called to wor-ship God who cre-ates, re-deems, and sanc-ti-fies us, Of whom the glo-ry, in both earth and heav-en, Is man-i-fest-ed.

Text: St. 1, 2, *A Monastic Breviary,* 1976, alt.; © Order of the Holy Cross; St. 3, *The Hymnal 1982*
Tune: BICKFORD, 11 11 11 5; Hank Beebe, b.1926, © 1983

484 O God, Almighty Father

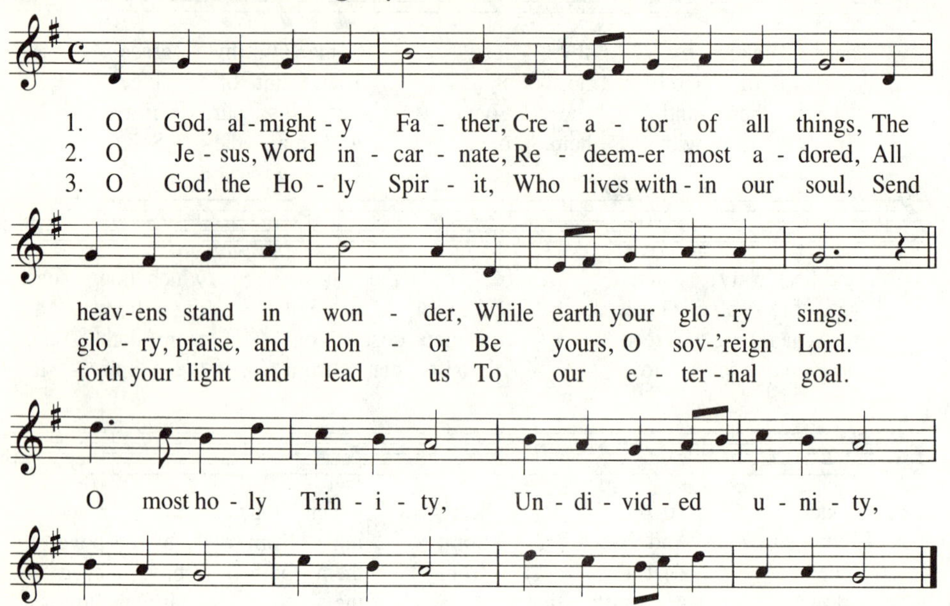
1. O God, al-might-y Fa-ther, Cre-a-tor of all things, The
2. O Je-sus, Word in-car-nate, Re-deem-er most a-dored, All
3. O God, the Ho-ly Spir-it, Who lives with-in our soul, Send
heav-ens stand in won-der, While earth your glo-ry sings.
glo-ry, praise, and hon-or Be yours, O sov-'reign Lord.
forth your light and lead us To our e-ter-nal goal.
O most ho-ly Trin-i-ty, Un-di-vid-ed u-ni-ty,
Ho-ly God, might-y God, God im-mor-tal be a-dored!

Text: *Gott Vater sei gepriesen;* Anon; Tr. by Irvin Udulutsch, OFM Cap., fl.1959, alt. © 1959, The Liturgical Press
Tune: GOTT VATER SEI GEPRIESEN, 76 76 with refrain; *Limburg Gesangbuch,* 1838; Harm. by Healey Willan, 1880-1968, © 1958, Ralph Jusko Publications, Inc.

485 Holy, Holy, Holy! Lord God Almighty

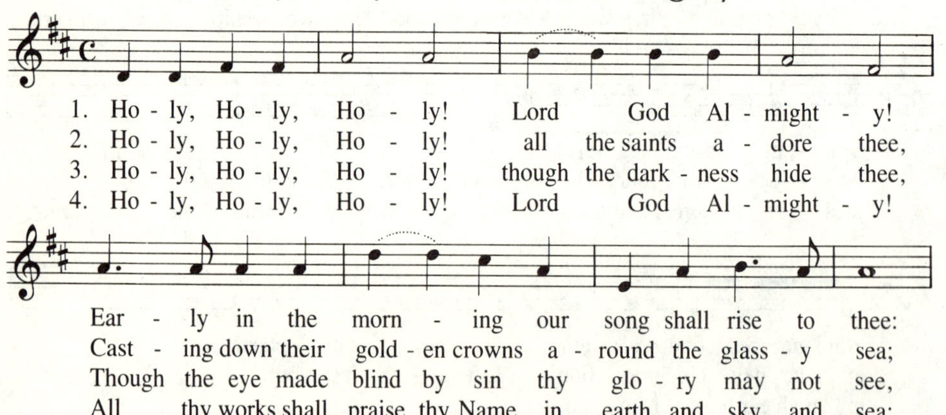
1. Ho-ly, Ho-ly, Ho-ly! Lord God Al-might-y!
2. Ho-ly, Ho-ly, Ho-ly! all the saints a-dore thee,
3. Ho-ly, Ho-ly, Ho-ly! though the dark-ness hide thee,
4. Ho-ly, Ho-ly, Ho-ly! Lord God Al-might-y!
Ear-ly in the morn-ing our song shall rise to thee:
Cast-ing down their gold-en crowns a-round the glass-y sea;
Though the eye made blind by sin thy glo-ry may not see,
All thy works shall praise thy Name in earth, and sky, and sea;

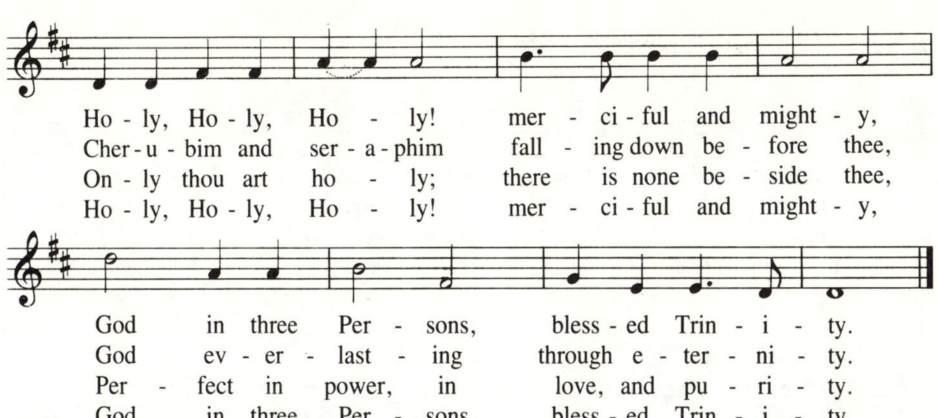
Ho - ly, Ho - ly, Ho - ly! mer - ci - ful and might - y,
Cher - u - bim and ser - a - phim fall - ing down be - fore thee,
On - ly thou art ho - ly; there is none be - side thee,
Ho - ly, Ho - ly, Ho - ly! mer - ci - ful and might - y,
God in three Per - sons, bless - ed Trin - i - ty.
God ev - er - last - ing through e - ter - ni - ty.
Per - fect in power, in love, and pu - ri - ty.
God in three Per - sons, bless - ed Trin - i - ty.

Text: Reginald Heber, 1783-1826, alt.
Tune: NICAEA, 11 12 12 10; John B. Dykes, 1823-1876

God, Whose Almighty Word 486

1. God, whose al - might - y word
2. Sav - ior, you came to give
3. Spir - it of truth and love,
4. Gra - cious and ho - ly Three,

Cha - os and dark - ness heard,
Those who in dark - ness live
Life - giv - ing, ho - ly dove,
Glo - ri - ous Trin - i - ty,

And took their flight:
Heal - ing and sight,
Speed on your flight!
Wis - dom, love, might:

Hear us, we hum - bly pray, And where the gos - pel - day
Health to the sick in mind, Sight to the in - ward blind:
Move on the wa - ter's face Bear - ing the lamp of grace
Bound-less as o - cean's tide Roll - ing in full - est pride

Sheds not its glo - rious ray, Let there be light!
Now to all hu - man-kind Let there be light!
And, in earth's dark - est place, Let there be light!
Through the world far and wide, Let there be light!

Text: John Marriott, 1780-1825, alt.
Tune: ITALIAN HYMN, 66 4 666 4; Felice de Giardini, 1716-1796

487 Come, Now Almighty King

1. Come, now al - might - y King, Help us your
2. Come, now In - car - nate Son, Your life in
3. Come, ho - ly Com - fort - er, Your sa - cred
4. To the great One in Three E - ter - nal

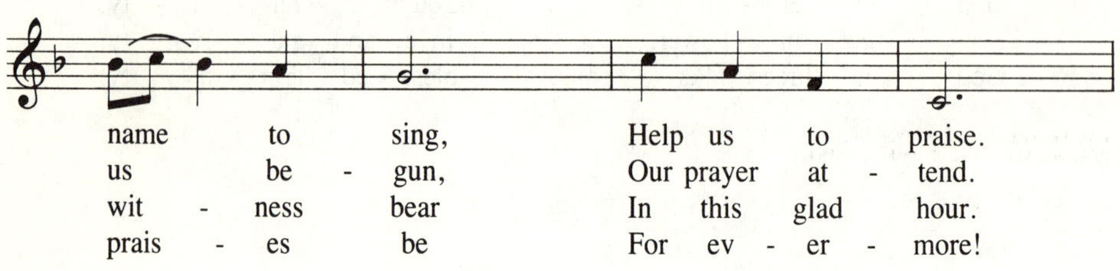
name to sing, Help us to praise.
us be - gun, Our prayer at - tend.
wit - ness bear In this glad hour.
prais - es be For ev - er - more!

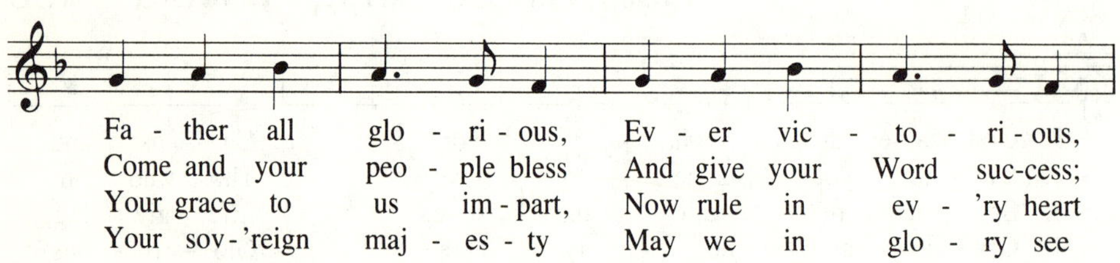
Fa - ther all glo - ri - ous, Ev - er vic - to - ri - ous,
Come and your peo - ple bless And give your Word suc-cess;
Your grace to us im - part, Now rule in ev - 'ry heart
Your sov-'reign maj - es - ty May we in glo - ry see

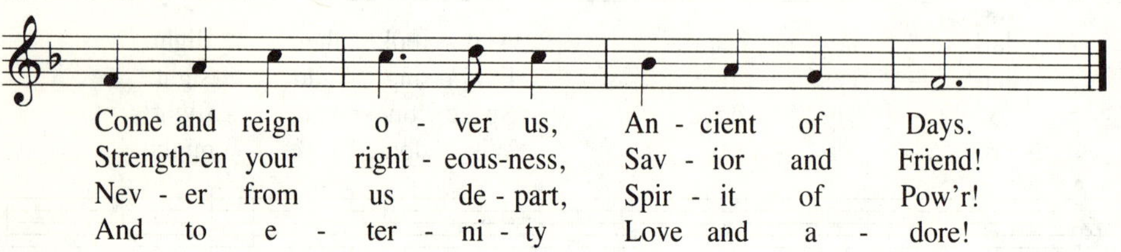
Come and reign o - ver us, An - cient of Days.
Strength-en your right - eous-ness, Sav - ior and Friend!
Nev - er from us de - part, Spir - it of Pow'r!
And to e - ter - ni - ty Love and a - dore!

Text: Anon. c.1757
Tune: ITALIAN HYMN, 66 4 666 4; Felice de Giardini, 1716-1796

Jesus, My Lord, My God, My All 488

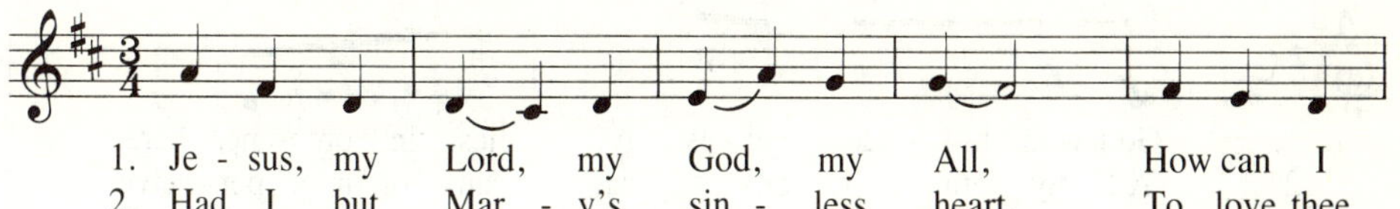

1. Je - sus, my Lord, my God, my All, How can I
2. Had I but Mar - y's sin - less heart, To love thee
3. O! see up - on the al - tar placed The vic - tim

love thee as I ought? And how re - vere this
with, my dear - est King; O! with what bursts of
of di - vin - est love! Let all the earth be-

won - drous gift, So far sur - pass - ing hope or thought?
fer - vent praise, Thy good-ness, Je - sus would I sing.
low a - dore, And join the choirs of heav'n a - bove.

Sweet Sac-ra - ment, we thee a - dore! O make us love thee

more and more! O make us love thee more and more.

Text: St. 1-2, Frederick W. Faber, 1814-1863; St. 3, *Mediator Dei Hymnal,* 1955,
Tune: SWEET SACRAMENT, LM; with refrain; *Romischkatholisches Gesangbuchlein,* 1826

489 God with Hidden Majesty/Adoro Te Devote

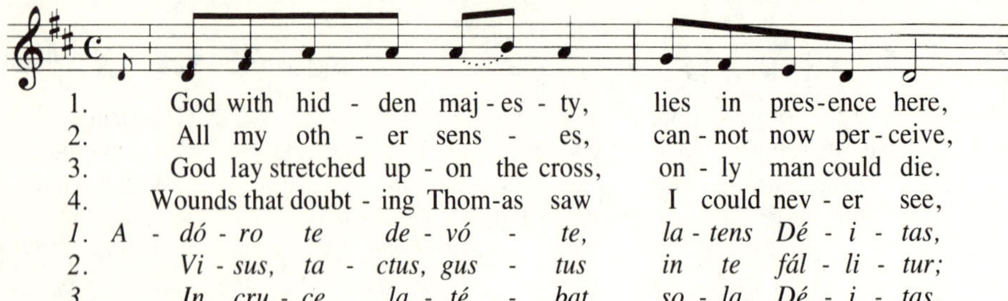

1. God with hid - den maj - es - ty, lies in pres - ence here,
2. All my oth - er sens - es, can - not now per - ceive,
3. God lay stretched up - on the cross, on - ly man could die.
4. Wounds that doubt - ing Thom - as saw I could nev - er see,
1. A - dó - ro te de - vó - te, la - tens Dé - i - tas,
2. Vi - sus, ta - ctus, gus - tus in te fál - li - tur;
3. In cru - ce la - té - bat so - la, Dé - i - tas,
4. Pla - gas, si - cut Tho - mas, non in - tú - e - or

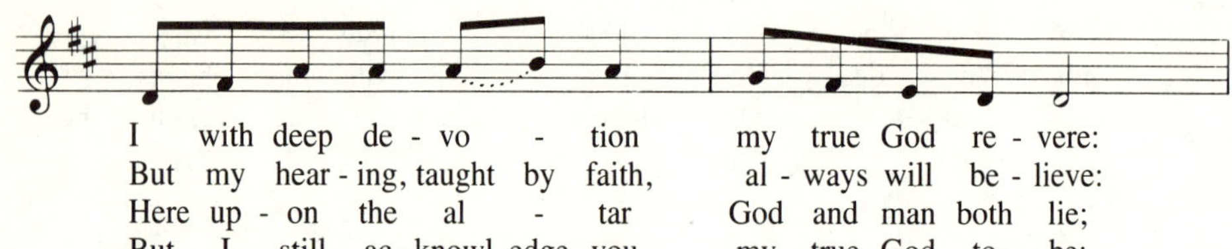

I with deep de - vo - tion my true God re - vere:
But my hear - ing, taught by faith, al - ways will be - lieve:
Here up - on the al - tar God and man both lie;
But I still ac - knowl - edge you my true God to be;
Quae sub his fi - gú - ris ve - re lá - ti - tas:
Sed au - dí - tu so - lo tu - to cré - di - tur:
At hic la - tet si - mul et hu - ma - ni - tas:
De - um ta - men me - um te con - fí - te - or:

Whom this out - ward shape and form se - cret - ly con - tains,
I ac - cept what - ev - er God the Son has said:
This I firm - ly hold as true, this is my be - lief,
Grant that I shall al - ways keep strong in faith and trust,
Ti - bi se cor me - um to - tum súb - ji - cit,
Cre - do quid - quid di - xit De - i Fí - li - us:
Am - bo ta - men cre - dens at - que cón - fi - tens
Fac me ti - bi sem - per ma - gis cré - de - re,

Christ in his di - vin - i - ty man - hood still re - tains.
Those who hear the word of God, by the truth are fed.
And I seek sal - va - tion, like the dy - ing thief.
Guid - ed by my Sav - ior, mer - ci - ful and just.
Qui - a te con - tém - plans to - tum dé - fi - cit.
Nil hoc ver - bo ve - ri - tá - tis ve - ri - us.
Pe - to quod pe - tí - vit la - tro paé - ni - tens.
In te spem ha - bé - re, te di - lí - ge - re.

5. Blest reminder of the death suffered for the world,
Sacrament of living bread, health to every mind,
Let my soul approach you, live within your grace,
Let me taste the perfect joys time shall not efface.

5. *O memoriále mortis Dómini,*
Panis vivus vitam praestans hómini,
Praesta meae menti de te vívere,
Et te illi semper dulce sápere.

6. *Pie pellicáne, Iesu Dómine,*
Me immúndum munda tuo sánguine,
Cuius una stilla salvum fácere,
Tótum múndum quit ab omni scélere.

7. *Iesu, quem velátum nunc aspício,*
Oro fiat illud quod tam sítio:
Ut te reveláta cernens fácie,
Vísu sim beátus tuae glóriae.

Text: Ascr. to Thomas Aquinas, 1227-1274; Tr. by Anthony G. Petti, b. 1932
Tune: ADORO TE DEVOTE 11 11 11 11; Mode V; Acc. by Richard Proulx, b. 1937

490 All You Who Seek a Comfort Sure

1. All you who seek a com - fort sure In sad - ness and dis - tress,
2. Now hear him as he speaks to us Those words for ev - er blest:

What - ev - er sor - row bur - dens you, What - ev - er griefs op - press:
"All you who la - bor, come to me, And I will give you rest."

When Je - sus gave him - self for us And died up - on the tree,
O heart a - dored by saints on high, And hope of sin - ners here,

His heart was pierced for love of us; He died to set us free.
We place our ev - 'ry trust in you And lift to you our prayer.

Text: *Quicumque certum quaeritis;* Latin, 18th C.; Tr. by Edward Caswall, 1814-1878, alt.
Tune: KINGSFOLD, CMD; English Traditional; Harm. by Ralph Vaughan Williams, 1872-1958, © Oxford University Press

491 To Christ, the Prince of Peace

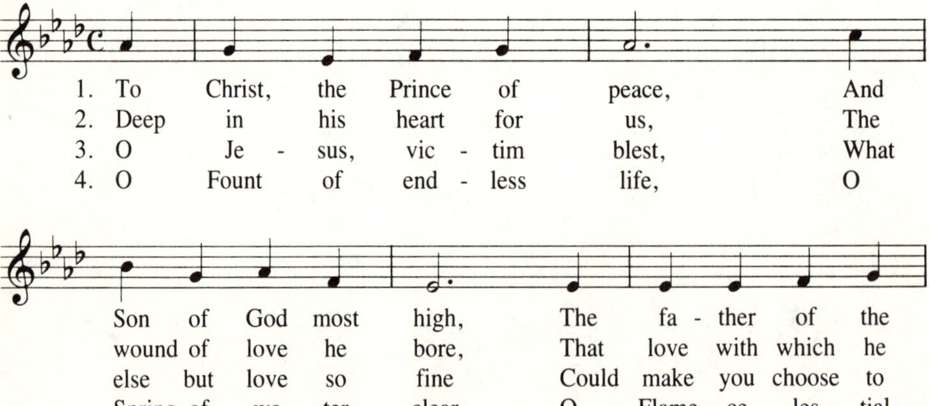
1. To Christ, the Prince of peace, And
2. Deep in his heart for us, The
3. O Je - sus, vic - tim blest, What
4. O Fount of end - less life, O
Son of God most high, The fa - ther of the
wound of love he bore, That love with which he
else but love so fine Could make you choose to
Spring of wa - ter clear, O Flame ce - les - tial,

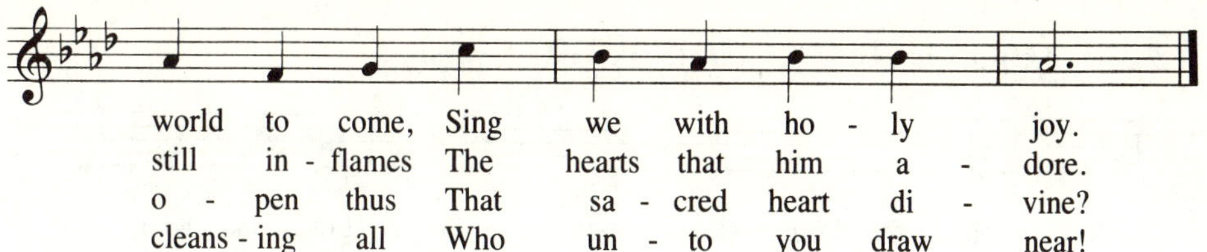
world to come, Sing we with ho - ly joy.
still in - flames The hearts that him a - dore.
o - pen thus That sa - cred heart di - vine?
cleans - ing all Who un - to you draw near!

Text: *Summi parentis filio; Paris Breviary,* 1736; Tr. by Edward Caswall, 1814-1876, alt.
Tune: NARENZA, SM; Liesentritt's *Catholicum Hymnologium Germanicum,* 1584; Adapt. by William H. Havergal, 1793-1870

Jesus Shall Reign 492

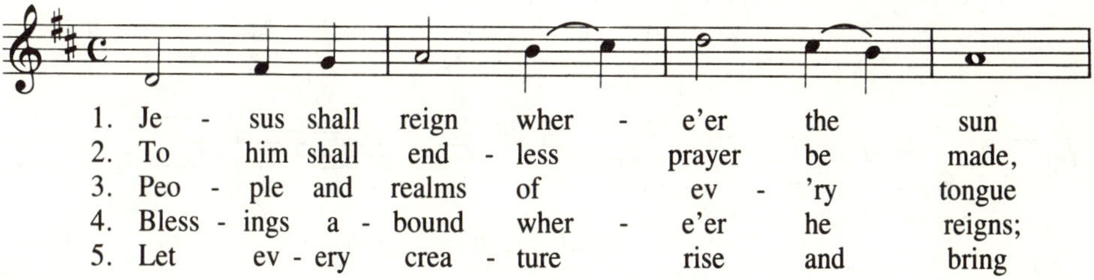

1. Je - sus shall reign wher - e'er the sun
2. To him shall end - less prayer be made,
3. Peo - ple and realms of ev - 'ry tongue
4. Bless - ings a - bound wher - e'er he reigns;
5. Let ev - ery crea - ture rise and bring

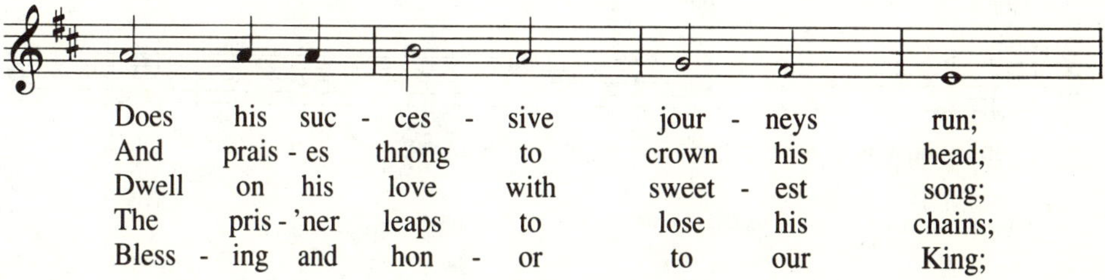

Does his suc - ces - sive jour - neys run;
And prais - es throng to crown his head;
Dwell on his love with sweet - est song;
The pris - 'ner leaps to lose his chains;
Bless - ing and hon - or to our King;

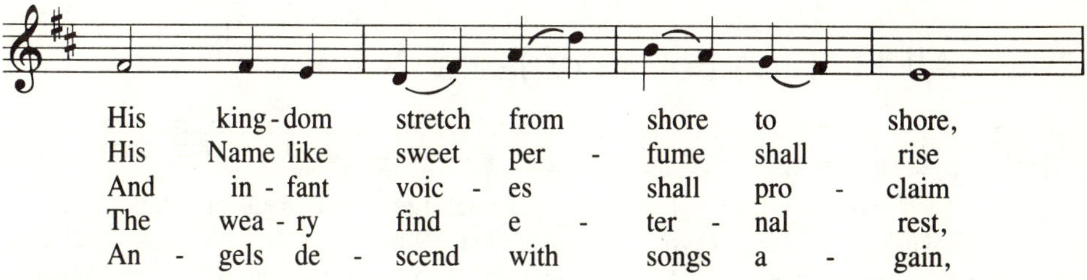

His king - dom stretch from shore to shore,
His Name like sweet per - fume shall rise
And in - fant voic - es shall pro - claim
The wea - ry find e - ter - nal rest,
An - gels de - scend with songs a - gain,

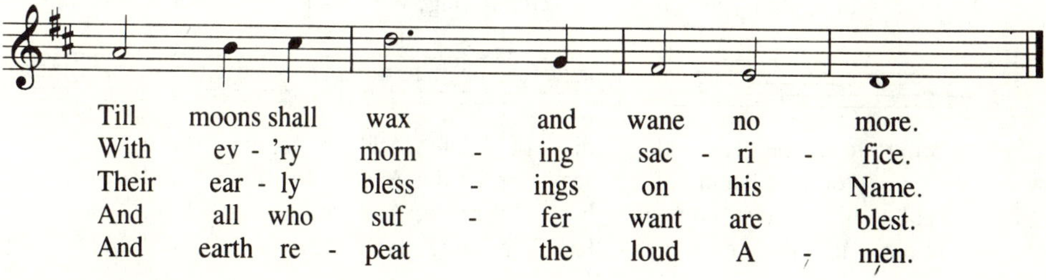

Till moons shall wax and wane no more.
With ev - 'ry morn - ing sac - ri - fice.
Their ear - ly bless - ings on his Name.
And all who suf - fer want are blest.
And earth re - peat the loud A - men.

Text: Isaac Watts, 1674-1748, alt.
Tune: DUKE STREET, LM; John Hatton, c.1710-1793

493 Rejoice, the Lord Is King

1. Re - joice, the Lord is King! Your Lord and King a-
2. The Lord, our Sav - ior, reigns, The God of truth and
3. His king - dom can - not fail, He rules o'er earth and
4. Re - joice in glo - rious hope! Our Lord the judge shall

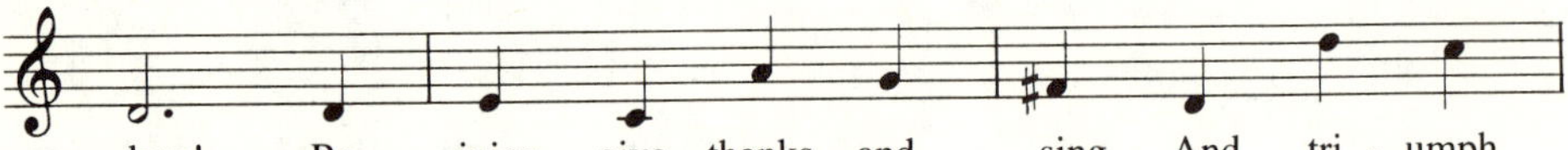

dore! Re - joice, give thanks, and sing, And tri - umph
love; When he had purged our sins, He took his
heav'n; The keys of death and hell Are to our
come And take his ser - vants up To their e-

ev - er - more:
seat a - bove: Lift up your heart, lift
Je - sus giv'n:
ter - nal home:

up your voice! Re - joice, a - gain I say, re - joice!

Text: Charles Wesley, 1707-1788
Tune: DARWALL'S 148TH, 6 6 6 6 88; John Darwall, 1731-1789; Harm. from *The Hymnal 1940*

494 All Hail the Power of Jesus' Name

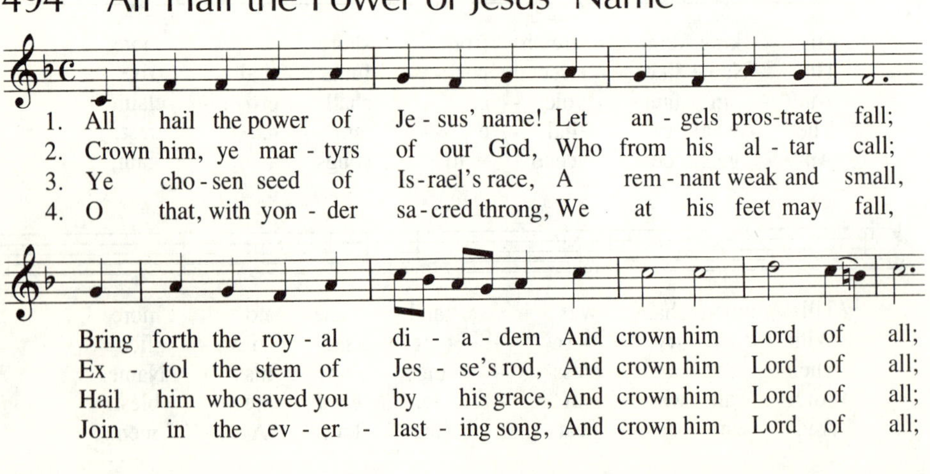
1. All hail the power of Je - sus' name! Let an - gels pros-trate fall;
2. Crown him, ye mar - tyrs of our God, Who from his al - tar call;
3. Ye cho - sen seed of Is-rael's race, A rem - nant weak and small,
4. O that, with yon - der sa-cred throng, We at his feet may fall,
Bring forth the roy - al di - a - dem And crown him Lord of all;
Ex - tol the stem of Jes - se's rod, And crown him Lord of all;
Hail him who saved you by his grace, And crown him Lord of all;
Join in the ev - er - last - ing song, And crown him Lord of all;

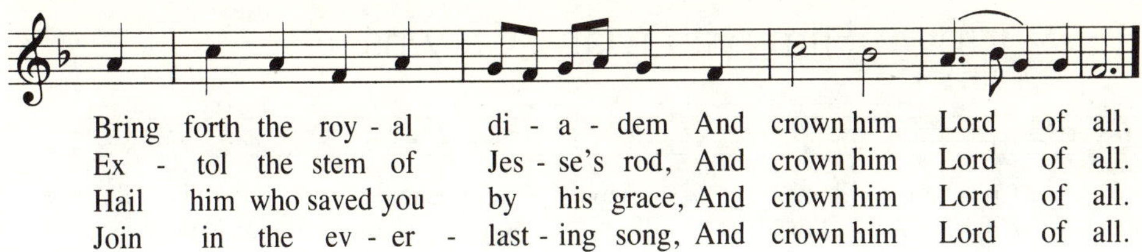
Bring forth the roy - al di - a - dem And crown him Lord of all.
Ex - tol the stem of Jes - se's rod, And crown him Lord of all.
Hail him who saved you by his grace, And crown him Lord of all.
Join in the ev - er - last - ing song, And crown him Lord of all.

Text: Edward Perronet, 1726-1792; Alt. by John Rippon, 1751-1836, alt.
Tune: CORONATION, CM with repeat; Oliver Holden, 1765-1844

All Hail the Power of Jesus' Name 495

1. All hail the pow'r of Je - sus' name! Let an - gels pros - trate
2. Crown him, ye mar - tyrs of our God, Who from his al - tar
3. Ye cho - sen seed of Is - rael's race, A rem - nant weak and
4. O that, with yon - der sa - cred throng, We at his feet may

fall; Bring forth the roy - al di - a - dem, And
call; Ex - tol the stem of Jes - se's rod, And
small, Hail him who saved you by his grace, And
fall, Join in the ev - er - last - ing song, And

crown him Lord of all, And crown him Lord of
crown him Lord of all, And crown him Lord of
crown him Lord of all, And crown him Lord of
crown him Lord of all, And crown him Lord of

all, And crown him Lord of all. Bring
all, And crown him Lord of all. Ex-
all, And crown him Lord of all. Hail
all, And crown him Lord of all. Join

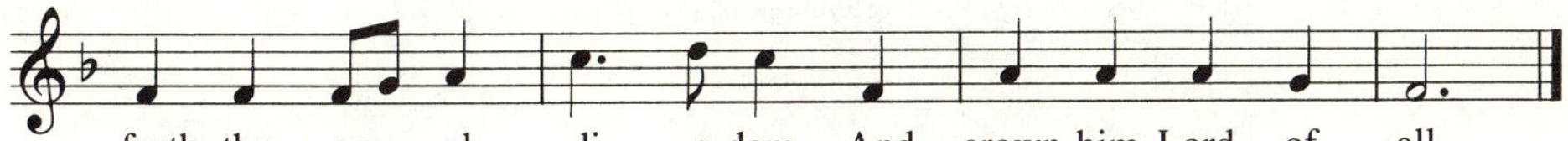

forth the roy - al di - a-dem, And crown him Lord of all.
tol the stem of Jes - se's rod, And crown him Lord of all.
him who saved you by his grace, And crown him Lord of all.
in the ev - er - last - ing song, And crown him Lord of all.

Text: Edward Perronet, 1726-1792; Alt. by John Rippon, 1751-1836, alt .
Tune: DIADEM, CM with repeats; From the *Primitive Baptist Hymn and Tune Book*, 1902; Harm. by Richard Proulx, b.1937,

496 Crown Him with Many Crowns

1. Crown him with man - y crowns, The Lamb up - on his throne;
2. Crown him the Lord of life, Who tri-umphed o'er the grave,
3. Crown him the Lord of love, Be - hold his hands and side,
4. Crown him the Lord of peace, Whose power a scep - ter sways
5. Crown him the Lord of years, The ris - en Lord sub - lime,

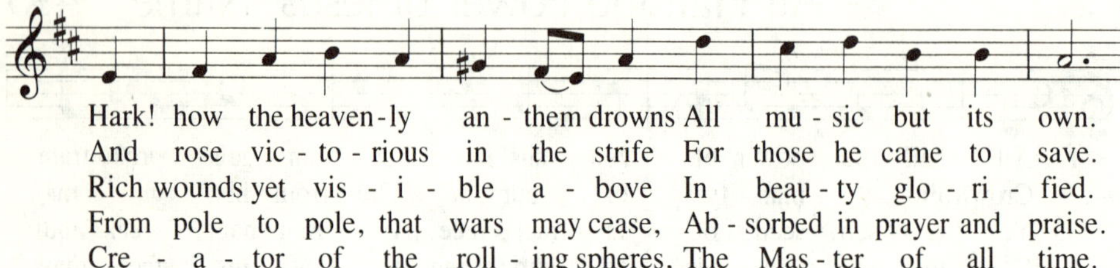

Hark! how the heaven-ly an - them drowns All mu - sic but its own.
And rose vic - to - rious in the strife For those he came to save.
Rich wounds yet vis - i - ble a - bove In beau - ty glo - ri - fied.
From pole to pole, that wars may cease, Ab - sorbed in prayer and praise.
Cre - a - tor of the roll - ing spheres, The Mas - ter of all time.

A - wake, my soul, and sing Of him who set us free,
His glo - ries now we sing, Who died and rose on high,
No an - gel in the sky Can full - y bear that sight,
His reign shall know no end, And round his pierc - ed feet
All hail, Re - deem - er, hail! For you have died for me;

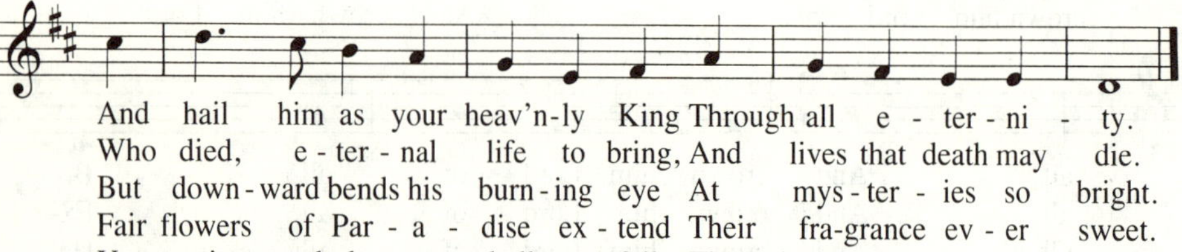

And hail him as your heav'n-ly King Through all e - ter - ni - ty.
Who died, e - ter - nal life to bring, And lives that death may die.
But down-ward bends his burn-ing eye At mys - ter - ies so bright.
Fair flowers of Par - a - dise ex - tend Their fra-grance ev - er sweet.
Your praise and glo - ry shall not fail Through-out e - ter - ni - ty.

Text: Rev. 19:12; St. 1, 3-5, Matthew Bridges, 1800-1894; St. 2, Godfrey Thring, 1823-1903
Tune: DIADEMATA, SMD.; George J. Elvey, 1816-1893

To Jesus Christ, Our Sovereign King 497

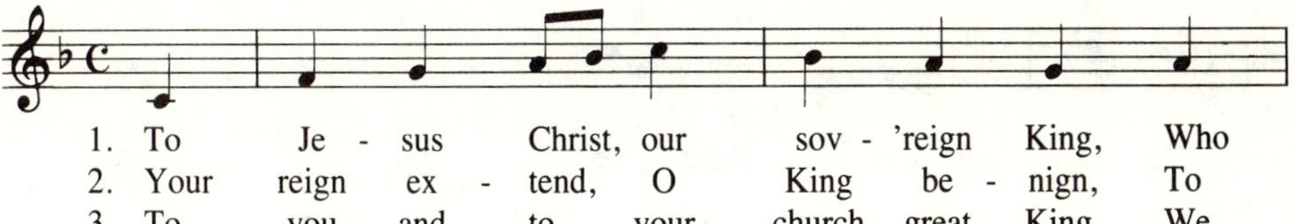
1. To Je - sus Christ, our sov - 'reign King, Who
2. Your reign ex - tend, O King be - nign, To
3. To you, and to your church, great King, We

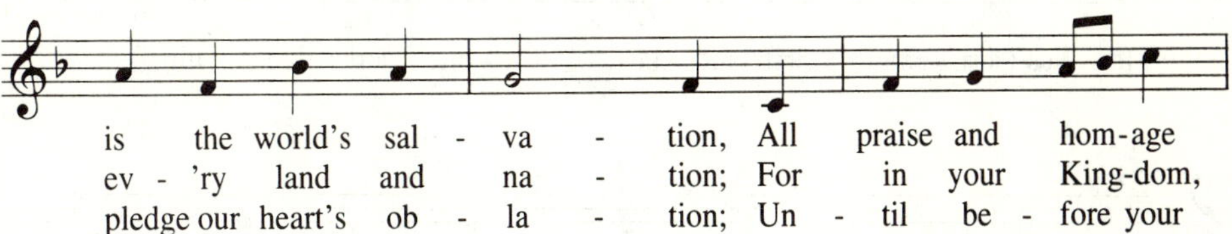
is the world's sal - va - tion, All praise and hom-age
ev - 'ry land and na - tion; For in your King-dom,
pledge our heart's ob - la - tion; Un - til be - fore your

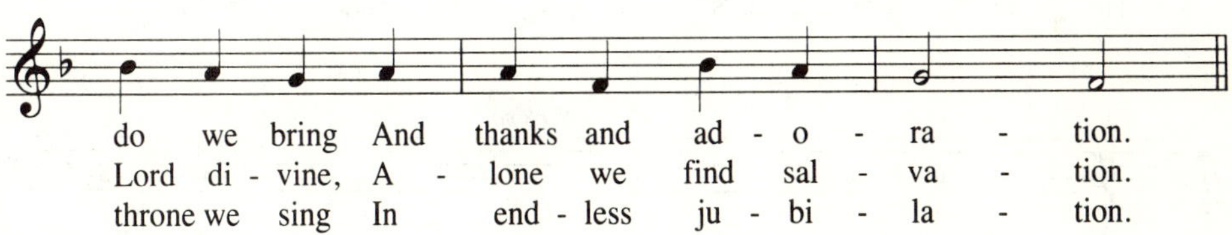
do we bring And thanks and ad - o - ra - tion.
Lord di - vine, A - lone we find sal - va - tion.
throne we sing In end - less ju - bi - la - tion.

Christ Je - sus, Vic - tor! Christ Je - sus, Ru - ler!

Christ Je - sus, Lord and Re - deem - er!

Text: Martin B. Hellrigel, 1891-1981, alt., © 1941, Irene C. Mueller
Tune: ICH GLAUB AN GOTT, 8 7 8 7 with refrain; *Mainz Gesangbuch*, 1870; Harm. by Richard Proulx, b.1937, © 1986, GIA Publications, Inc.

498 He Is King of Kings

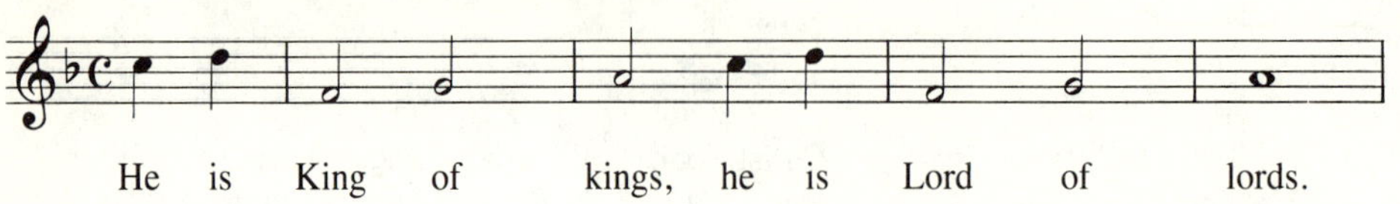
He is King of kings, he is Lord of lords.

Je - sus Christ the first and last, no one works like him.

Solo:
1. He built his throne up in the air,
2. He pitched his tents on Ca - naan's ground,

All:
Solo:
No one works like him. And called his saints from
No one works like him. And broke the Ro - man

All:
D.C.
ev - 'ry - where, No one works like him.
king - dom down, No one works like him.

Text: Afro-American Spiritual; Ed. by John W. Work, III, 1901-1967
Tune: HE IS KING, Irregular; Afro-American Spiritual; Ed. by John W. Work, III, 1901-1967

At the Name of Jesus 499

1. At the name of Je - sus Ev - 'ry knee shall bow,
2. Hum-bled for a sea - son To re - ceive a name
3. Bore it up tri - umph - ant With its hu - man light,
4. Name him, Chris-tians, name him— Strong your love as death —

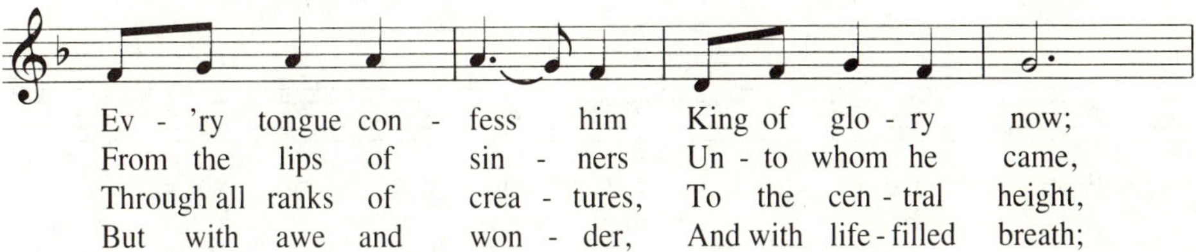

Ev - 'ry tongue con - fess him King of glo - ry now;
From the lips of sin - ners Un - to whom he came,
Through all ranks of crea - tures, To the cen - tral height,
But with awe and won - der, And with life - filled breath;

'Tis the Fa - ther's plea - sure We should call him Lord,
Faith-ful - ly he bore it, Spot-less to the last,
To the throne of God - head, To the Fa - ther's breast;
He is God the Sav - ior, He is Christ the Lord,

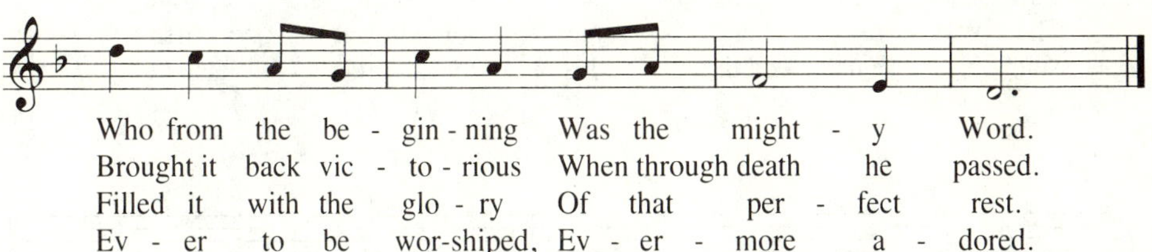

Who from the be - gin - ning Was the might - y Word.
Brought it back vic - to - rious When through death he passed.
Filled it with the glo - ry Of that per - fect rest.
Ev - er to be wor-shiped, Ev - er - more a - dored.

5. In your hearts enthrone him; There let him subdue
All that is not holy, All that is not true:
Crown him as your Captain In temptation's hour;
Let his will enfold you In its light and power.

6. Christians, this Lord Jesus Shall return again,
With his Father's glory O'er the earth to reign;
Love and faithful service We his people vow,
And our hearts confess him King of glory now.

Text: Phil. 2:5-7; Caroline M. Noel, 1817-1877, alt.
Tune: KING'S WESTON, 65 65 D; Ralph Vaughan Williams, 1872-1958, alt., © Oxford University Press

500 Christ Is the King

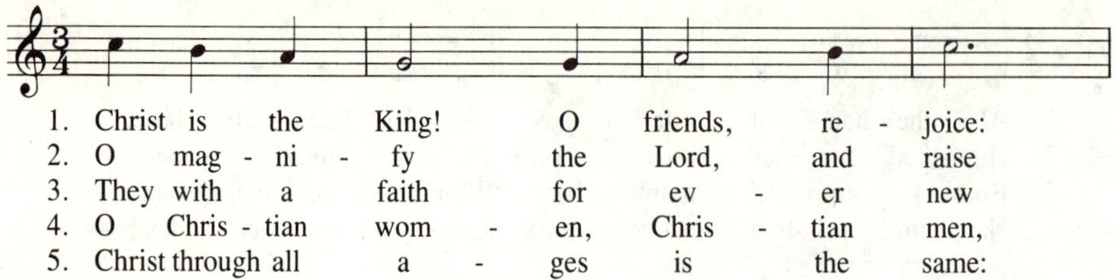
1. Christ is the King! O friends, re - joice:
2. O mag - ni - fy the Lord, and raise
3. They with a faith for ev - er new
4. O Chris - tian wom - en, Chris - tian men,
5. Christ through all a - ges is the same:

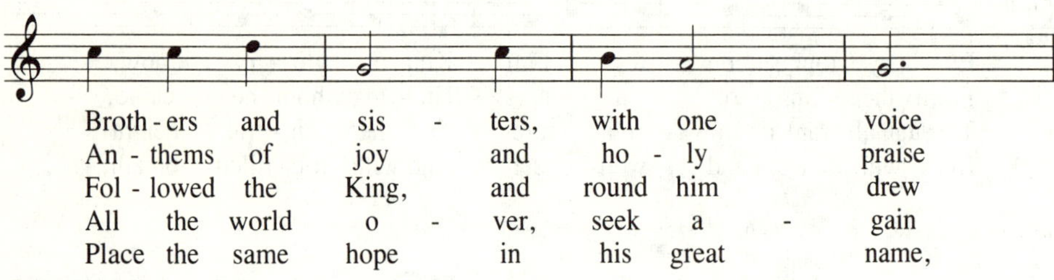
Broth - ers and sis - ters, with one voice
An - thems of joy and ho - ly praise
Fol - lowed the King, and round him drew
All the world o - ver, seek a - gain
Place the same hope in his great name,

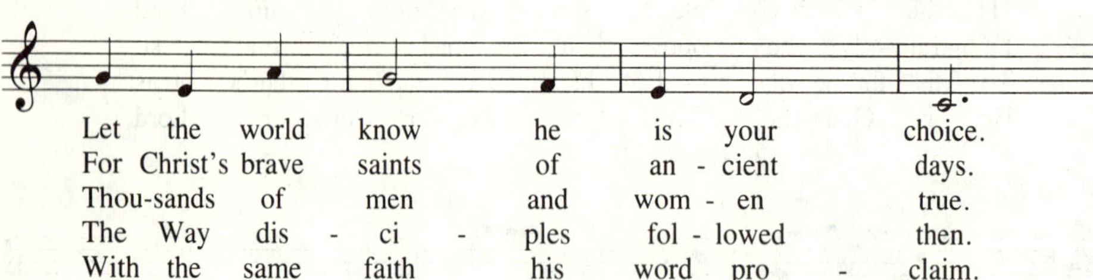
Let the world know he is your choice.
For Christ's brave saints of an - cient days.
Thou-sands of men and wom - en true.
The Way dis - ci - ples fol - lowed then.
With the same faith his word pro - claim.

Al - le - lu - ia, al - le - lu - ia, al - le - lu - ia.

6. Let love's all reconciling might
Your scattered companies unite
In service to the Lord of light.
Alleluia, alleluia, alleluia.

7. So shall God's will on earth be done,
New lamps be lit, new tasks begun,
And the whole Church at last be one.
Alleluia, alleluia, alleluia.

Text: George K. A. Bell, 1883-1958, alt., © Oxford University Press
Tune: GELOBT SEI GOTT, 888 with alleluias; Melchior Vulpius, c.1560-1616

The King of Glory 501

The King of glo - ry comes, the na - tion re - joic - es.

O - pen the gates be - fore him, lift up your voic - es.

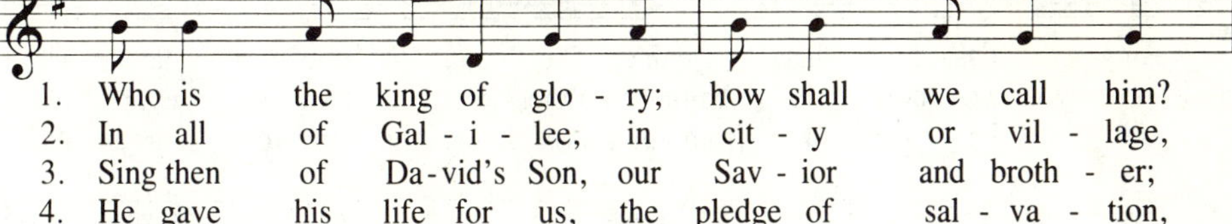
1. Who is the king of glo - ry; how shall we call him?
2. In all of Gal - i - lee, in cit - y or vil - lage,
3. Sing then of Da - vid's Son, our Sav - ior and broth - er;
4. He gave his life for us, the pledge of sal - va - tion,
5. He con - quered sin and death; he tru - ly has ris - en.

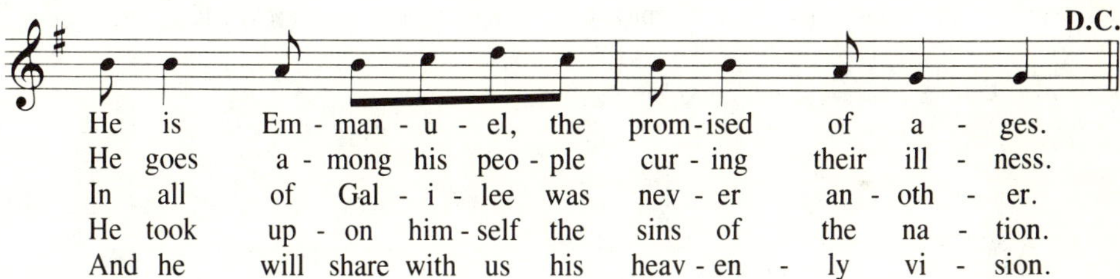
D.C.
He is Em - man - u - el, the prom - ised of a - ges.
He goes a - mong his peo - ple cur - ing their ill - ness.
In all of Gal - i - lee was nev - er an - oth - er.
He took up - on him - self the sins of the na - tion.
And he will share with us his heav - en - ly vi - sion.

Text: Willard F. Jabusch, b.1930, © 1966, 1984
Tune: KING OF GLORY, 12 12 with refrain; Israeli; Harm. by Richard Proulx, b.1937, © 1986, GIA Publications, Inc.

502 I Sing the Mighty Power of God

1. I sing the might - y pow'r of God That made the moun-tains rise, That
2. I sing the good-ness of the Lord That filled the earth with food; That
3. There's not a plant or flower be-low But makes your glo - ries known; And

spread the flow-ing seas a-broad, And built the loft - y skies. I
formed cre-a - tion with a word, And then pro-nounced it good. Lord,
clouds a - rise, and tem - pests blow, By or - der from your throne; While

sing the wis - dom that or-dained The sun to rule the day; The
how your won - ders are dis-played Wher - e'er I turn my eye; If
all that bor - rows life from you Is ev - er in your care, And

moon shines full at God's com-mand And all the stars o - bey.
I sur - vey the ground I tread, Or gaze up - on the sky!
ev - 'ry - where that I may be, O God, be pres - ent there.

Text: Isaac Watts, 1674-1748, alt.
Tune: MOZART, CMD; Attr. to Wolfgang A. Mozart, 1756-1791

503 Many and Great, O God, Are Your Works

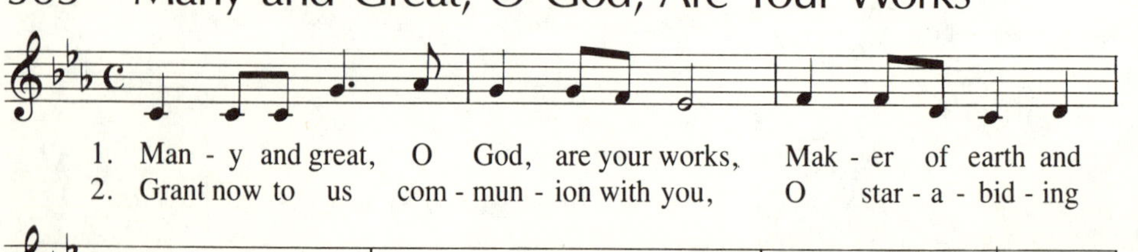
1. Man - y and great, O God, are your works, Mak - er of earth and
2. Grant now to us com - mun - ion with you, O star - a - bid - ing

sky; Your hands have set the heav - ens with stars;
one; Come now to us and dwell with us;

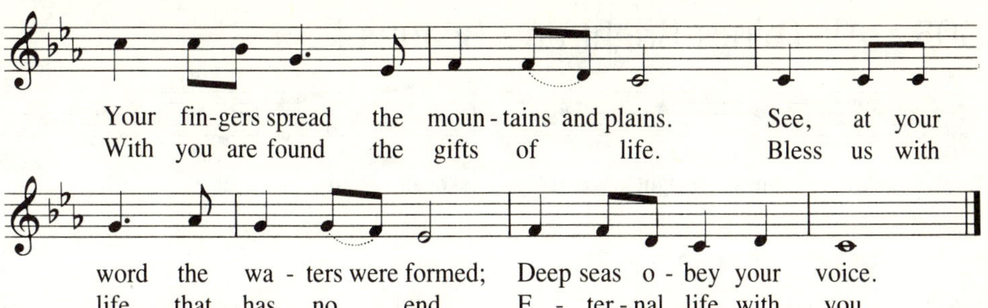
Your fin-gers spread the moun-tains and plains. See, at your
With you are found the gifts of life. Bless us with
word the wa - ters were formed; Deep seas o - bey your voice.
life that has no end, E - ter-nal life with you.

Text: *Wakantanka tuku nitawa;* Dakota Indian Hymn; Para. by Philip Frazier, 1892-1964, alt. © Walton Music Corp.
Tune: LACQUIPARLE, Irregular; *Dakota Odowan,* 1879; Setting by Richard Proulx, b.1937, © 1986, GIA Publications, Inc.

The Works of the Lord Are Created in Wisdom 504

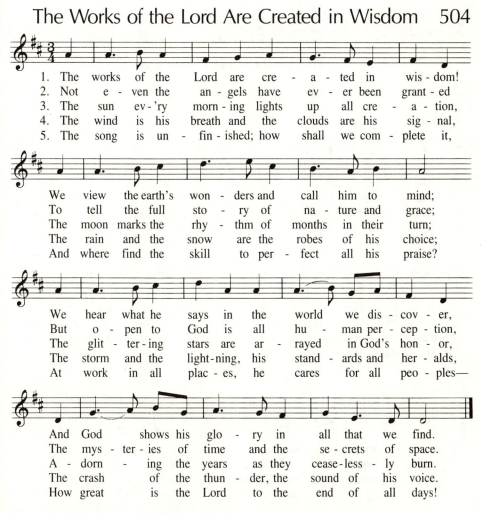

1. The works of the Lord are cre - a - ted in wis - dom!
We view the earth's won - ders and call him to mind;
We hear what he says in the world we dis - cov - er,
And God shows his glo - ry in all that we find.

2. Not e - ven the an - gels have ev - er been grant - ed
To tell the full sto - ry of na - ture and grace;
But o - pen to God is all hu - man per - cep - tion,
The mys - ter - ies of time and the se - crets of space.

3. The sun ev-'ry morn - ing lights up all cre - a - tion,
The moon marks the rhy - thm of months in their turn;
The glit - ter - ing stars are ar - rayed in God's hon - or,
A - dorn - ing the years as they cease-less - ly burn.

4. The wind is his breath and the clouds are his sig - nal,
The rain and the snow are the robes of his choice;
The storm and the light-ning, his stand - ards and her - alds,
The crash of the thun - der, the sound of his voice.

5. The song is un - fin - ished; how shall we com - plete it,
And where find the skill to per - fect all his praise?
At work in all plac - es, he cares for all peo - ples—
How great is the Lord to the end of all days!

Text: Eccles. 42-43; Christopher Idle, b.1938, © 1982, Hope Publishing Co.
Tune: KREMSER, 12 11 12 11; *Neder-landtsch Gedanckclanck,* 1626; Harm. by Edward Kremser, 1838-1914

505 All Things Bright and Beautiful

All things bright and beau - ti - ful, All

crea - tures great and small, All things wise and

won - der - ful, The Lord God made them all.

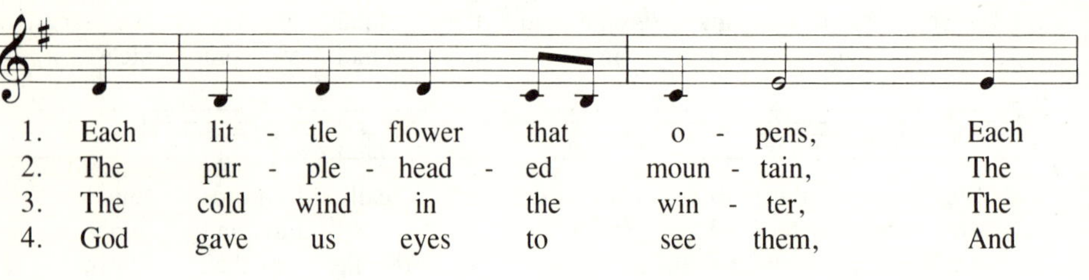
1. Each lit - tle flower that o - pens, Each
2. The pur - ple - head - ed moun - tain, The
3. The cold wind in the win - ter, The
4. God gave us eyes to see them, And

lit - tle bird that sings, God made their glow - ing
riv - er run - ning by, The sun - set, and the
plea - sant sum - mer sun, The ripe fruits in the
lips that we might tell How great is God Al-

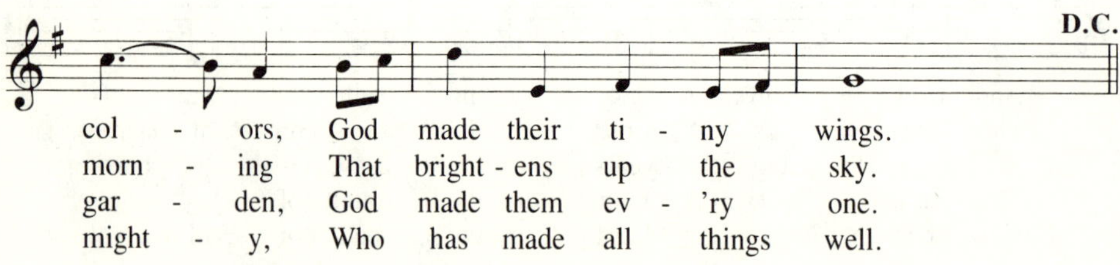
D.C.
col - ors, God made their ti - ny wings.
morn - ing That bright - ens up the sky.
gar - den, God made them ev - 'ry one.
might - y, Who has made all things well.

Text: Cecil F. Alexander, 1818-1895, alt.
Tune: ROYAL OAK, 7 6 7 6 with refrain; English Melody; Adapted by Martin Shaw, 1875-1958

The Stars Declare His Glory 506

1. The stars de - clare his glo - ry; The
2. The dawn re - turns in splen - dor, The
3. So shine the Lord's com - mand - ments To
4. So or - der too this life of mine, Di-

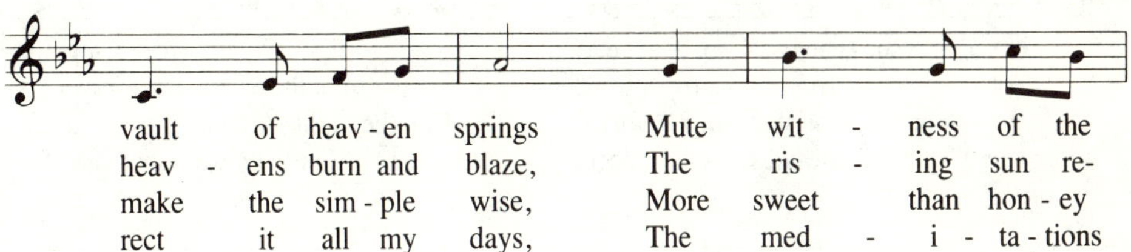
vault of heav - en springs Mute wit - ness of the
heav - ens burn and blaze, The ris - ing sun remake the sim - ple wise, More sweet than hon - ey
rect it all my days, The med - i - ta - tions

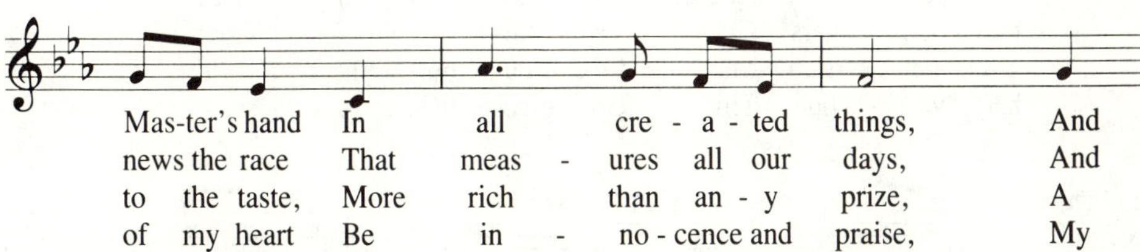
Mas-ter's hand In all cre - a - ted things, And
news the race That meas - ures all our days, And
to the taste, More rich than an - y prize, A
of my heart Be in - no - cence and praise, My

through the si - lenc - es of
writes in fire a - cross the
law of love with - in our
Rock, and my re - deem - ing

space Their sound - less mu - sic sings.
skies God's maj - es - ty and praise.
hearts, A light be - fore our eyes.
Lord, In all my words and ways.

Text: Psalm 19; Timothy Dudley-Smith, b.1926, © 1981, Hope Publishing Co.
Tune: ALDINE, 7 6 8 6 8 6; Richard Proulx, b.1937, © 1986, GIA Publications, Inc.

507 God Is Working His Purpose Out

1. God is work - ing his pur - pose out As
2. From ut - most east to ut - most west, Wher -
3. March we forth in the strength of God, With the
4. All we can do is worth - less toil Un -
year suc - ceeds to year: God is work - ing his
ev - er foot has trod, By the mouth of man - y
ban-ner of Christ un - furled, That the light of the glo - rious
less God bless-es the deed; Vain - ly we hope for the
pur - pose out, And the time is draw - ing near;
mes - sen - gers Goes forth the voice of God;
gos - pel of truth May shine through - out the world:
har - vest - tide Till God gives life to the seed; Yet
Near - er and near - er draws the time, The time that shall sure - ly
Give ear to me, you con - ti - nents, You isles, give ear to
Fight we the fight with sor-row and sin To set their cap - tives
near - er and near - er draws the time, The time that shall sure - ly
be, When the earth shall be filled with the glo - ry of God As the
me, That the earth may be filled with the glo - ry of God As the
free, That the earth may be filled with the glo - ry of God As the
be, When the earth shall be filled with the glo - ry of God As the
wa - ters cov - er the sea.
wa - ters cov - er the sea.
wa - ters cov - er the sea.
wa - ters cov - er the sea.
1.2.3.
4.

Text: Hab. 1:14; Arthur C. Ainger, 1841-1919, alt.
Tune: PURPOSE, Irregular; Martin Shaw, 1875-1958,

When Israel Was in Egypt's Land 508

1. When Is - rael was in E - gypt's land,
Let my peo - ple go;
Op - pressed so hard they could not stand,
Let my peo - ple go.

2. The Lord told Mo - ses what to do,
Let my peo - ple go;
To lead the chil - dren of Is - rael through,
Let my peo - ple go.

3. They jour - neyed on at God's com - mand,
Let my peo - ple go;
And came at length to Ca - naan's land,
Let my peo - ple go.

4. Oh, let us all from bond - age flee, 
Let my peo - ple go;
And let us all in Christ be free,
Let my peo - ple go.

Go down, Mo - ses, way down in E - gypt's land;

Tell old Phar - aoh to let my peo - ple go.

Text: Afro-American Spiritual
Tune: GO DOWN MOSES, Irregular; Afro-American Spiritual; Harm. from *English Praise*, 1975,

509 Who Can Measure Heaven and Earth

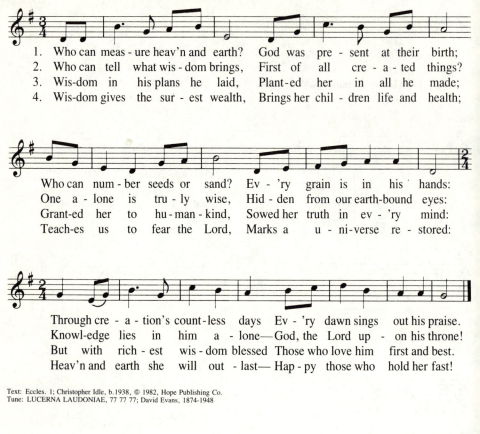

1. Who can meas - ure heav'n and earth? God was pre - sent at their birth;
2. Who can tell what wis - dom brings, First of all cre - a - ted things?
3. Wis-dom in his plans he laid, Plant-ed her in all he made;
4. Wis-dom gives the sur - est wealth, Brings her chil - dren life and health;

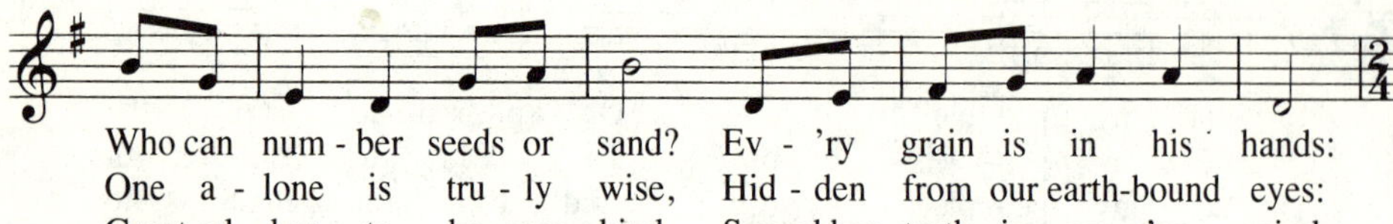

Who can num - ber seeds or sand? Ev - 'ry grain is in his hands:
One a - lone is tru - ly wise, Hid - den from our earth-bound eyes:
Grant-ed her to hu - man - kind, Sowed her truth in ev - 'ry mind:
Teach-es us to fear the Lord, Marks a u - ni-verse re - stored:

Through cre - a - tion's count-less days Ev - 'ry dawn sings out his praise.
Knowl-edge lies in him a - lone—God, the Lord up - on his throne!
But with rich - est wis - dom blessed Those who love him first and best.
Heav'n and earth she will out - last—Hap - py those who hold her fast!

Text: Eccles. 1; Christopher Idle, b.1938, © 1982, Hope Publishing Co.
Tune: LUCERNA LAUDONIAE, 77 77 77; David Evans, 1874-1948

510 I Want to Walk as a Child of the Light

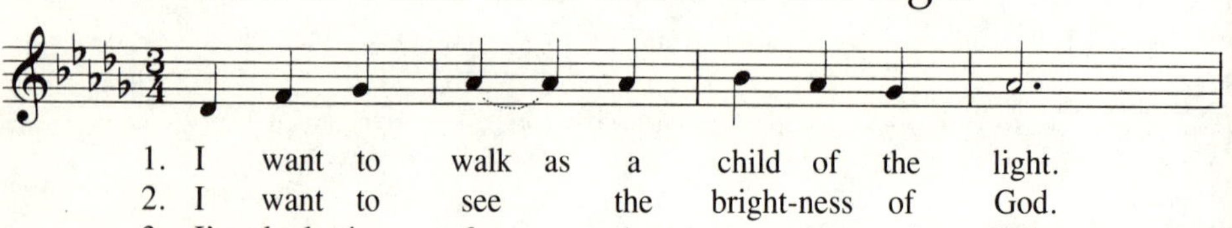

1. I want to walk as a child of the light.
2. I want to see the bright-ness of God.
3. I'm look - ing for the com - ing of Christ.

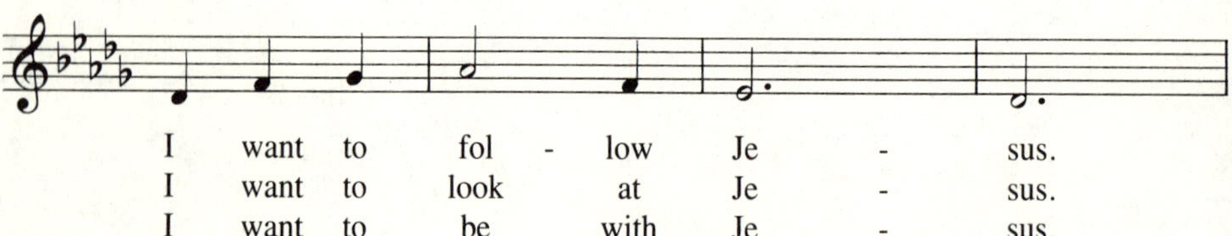

I want to fol - low Je - sus.
I want to look at Je - sus.
I want to be with Je - sus.

LIGHT

God set the stars to give light to the world. The star of my life is Je - sus.
Clear sun of right-eous-ness shine on my path, And show me the way to the Fa - ther.
When we have run with pa-tience the race, We shall know the joy of Je - sus.
In him there is no dark-ness at all. The night and the day are both a - like. The
Lamb is the light of the cit - y of God.

Shine in my heart, Lord Je - sus.

Text: Eph. 5:8-10; Rev. 21:23; Jn. 12:46; 1 Jn. 1:5; Heb. 12:1; Kathleen Thomerson, b.1934
Tune: HOUSTON, 10 7 10 8 9 9 10 7; Kathleen Thomerson, b.1934

511 Thy Strong Word Didst Cleave the Darkness

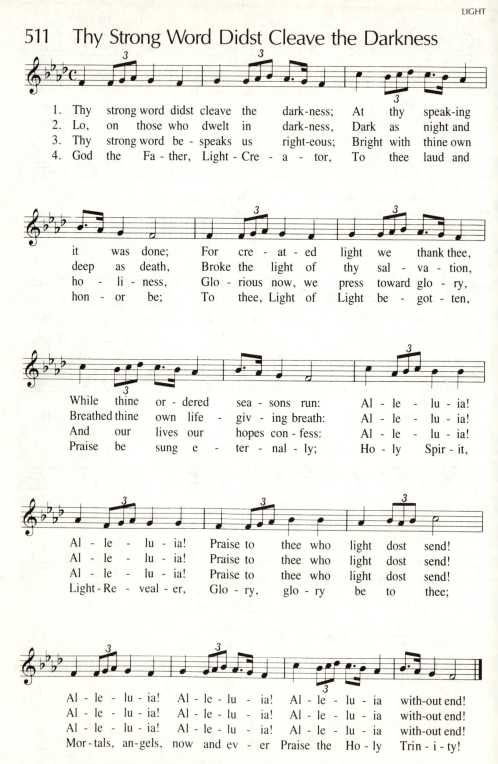

1. Thy strong word didst cleave the dark-ness; At thy speak-ing
2. Lo, on those who dwelt in dark-ness, Dark as night and
3. Thy strong word be - speaks us right-eous; Bright with thine own
4. God the Fa - ther, Light - Cre - a - tor, To thee laud and

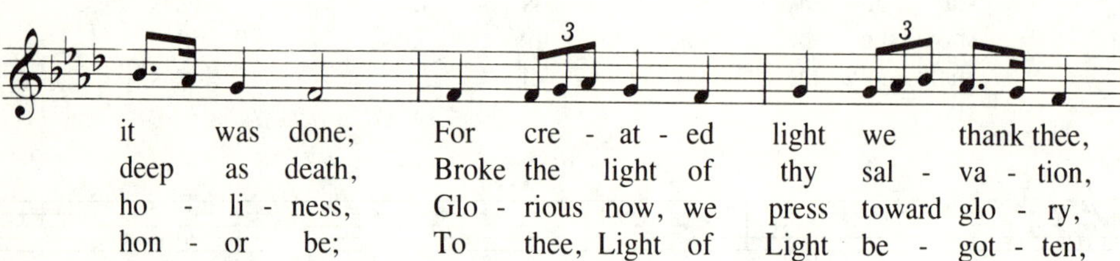

it was done; For cre - at - ed light we thank thee,
deep as death, Broke the light of thy sal - va - tion,
ho - li - ness, Glo - rious now, we press toward glo - ry,
hon - or be; To thee, Light of Light be - got - ten,

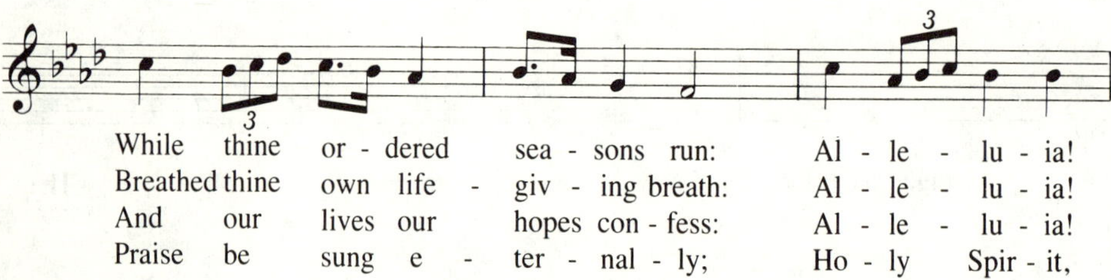

While thine or - dered sea - sons run: Al - le - lu - ia!
Breathed thine own life - giv - ing breath: Al - le - lu - ia!
And our lives our hopes con - fess: Al - le - lu - ia!
Praise be sung e - ter - nal - ly; Ho - ly Spir - it,

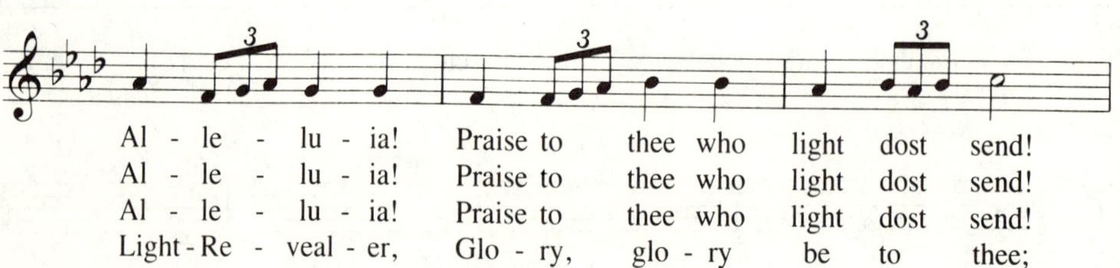

Al - le - lu - ia! Praise to thee who light dost send!
Al - le - lu - ia! Praise to thee who light dost send!
Al - le - lu - ia! Praise to thee who light dost send!
Light - Re - veal - er, Glo - ry, glo - ry be to thee;

Al - le - lu - ia! Al - le - lu - ia! Al - le - lu - ia with-out end!
Al - le - lu - ia! Al - le - lu - ia! Al - le - lu - ia with-out end!
Al - le - lu - ia! Al - le - lu - ia! Al - le - lu - ia with-out end!
Mor - tals, an - gels, now and ev - er Praise the Ho - ly Trin - i - ty!

Text: Martin H. Franzmann, 1907-1976, alt.,
Tune: EBENEZER, 8 7 8 7 D; Thomas J. Williams, 1869-1944

Immortal, Invisible, God Only Wise 512

1. Im - mor - tal, in - vis - i - ble, God on - ly wise,
2. Un - rest - ing, un - hast - ing, and si - lent as light,
3. Life - giv - ing Cre - a - tor, of both great and small;
4. Great Fa - ther of glo - ry, pure Fa - ther of light,

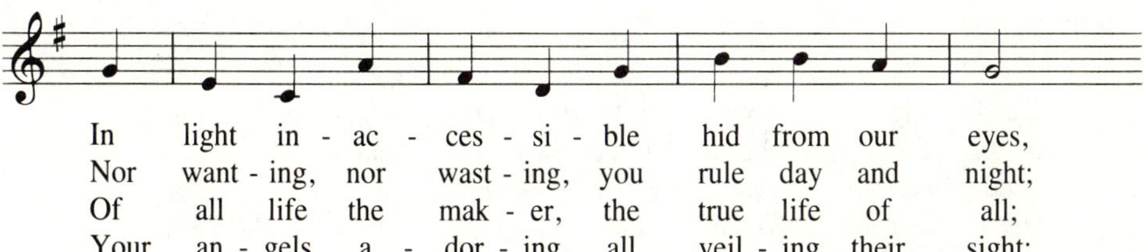

In light in - ac - ces - si - ble hid from our eyes,
Nor want - ing, nor wast - ing, you rule day and night;
Of all life the mak - er, the true life of all;
Your an - gels a - dor - ing, all veil - ing their sight;

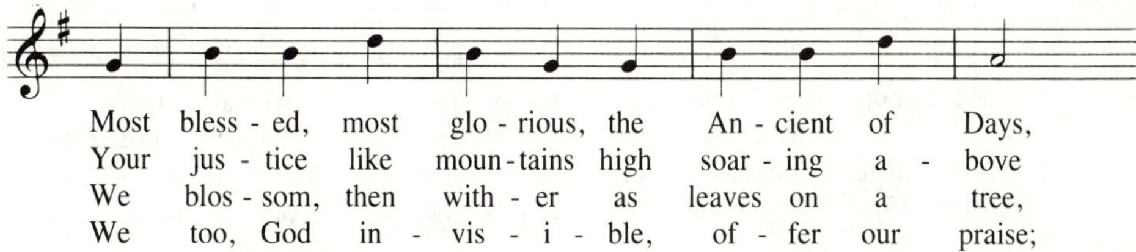

Most bless - ed, most glo - rious, the An - cient of Days,
Your jus - tice like moun - tains high soar - ing a - bove
We blos - som, then with - er as leaves on a tree,
We too, God in - vis - i - ble, of - fer our praise;

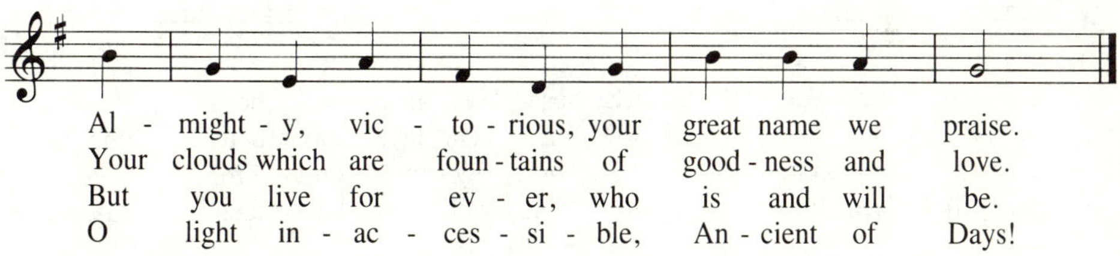

Al - might - y, vic - to - rious, your great name we praise.
Your clouds which are foun - tains of good - ness and love.
But you live for ev - er, who is and will be.
O light in - ac - ces - si - ble, An - cient of Days!

Text: 1 Tim. 1:17; Walter C. Smith, 1824-1908, alt.
Tune: ST DENIO, 11 11 11 11; Roberts' *Canaidau y Cyssegr*, 1839

513 Word of God, Come Down on Earth

1. Word of God, come down on earth, Liv - ing rain from heav'n de-
2. Word e - ter - nal, throned on high, Word that brought to life cre-
3. Word that caused blind eyes to see, Speak and heal our mor - tal
4. Word that speaks God's ten - der love, One with God be - yond all

scend - ing; Touch our hearts and bring to birth
a - tion, Word that came from heav'n to die,
blind - ness; Deaf we are: our heal - er be;
tell - ing, Word that sends us from a - bove,

Faith and hope and love un - end - ing. Word al - might - y,
Cru - ci - fied for our sal - va - tion, Sav - ing Word, the
Loose our tongues to tell your kind - ness. Be our Word in
God the Spir - it, with us dwell - ing, Word of truth, to

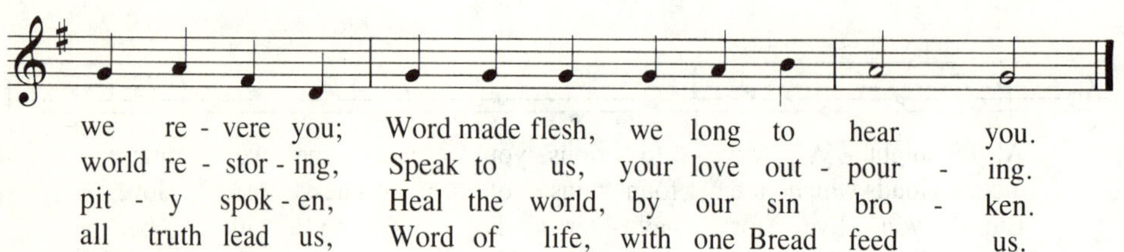

we re - vere you; Word made flesh, we long to hear you.
world re - stor - ing, Speak to us, your love out - pour - ing.
pit - y spok - en, Heal the world, by our sin bro - ken.
all truth lead us, Word of life, with one Bread feed us.

Text: James Quinn, SJ, b.1919, © 1969
Tune: LIEBSTER JESU, 7 8 7 8 88; Johann R. Ahle, 1625-1673; Harm. by George H. Palmer, 1846-1926

Thanks to God Whose Word Was Spoken 514

1. Thanks to God whose Word was spo - ken In the deed that
2. Thanks to God whose Word In - car - nate, Our new life in
3. Thanks to God whose Word is an - swered By the Spir - it's

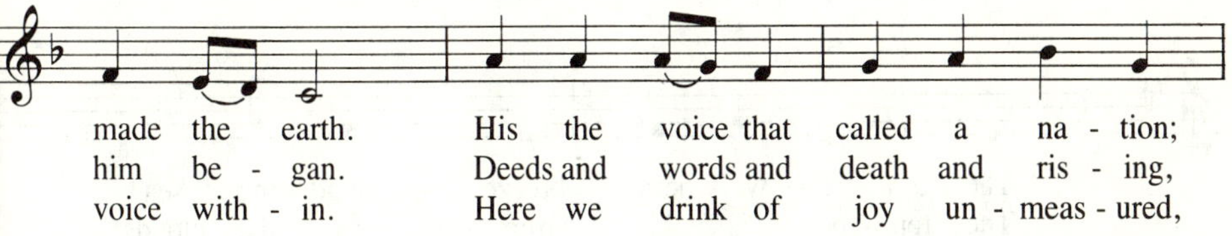

made the earth. His the voice that called a na - tion;
him be - gan. Deeds and words and death and ris - ing,
voice with - in. Here we drink of joy un - meas - ured,

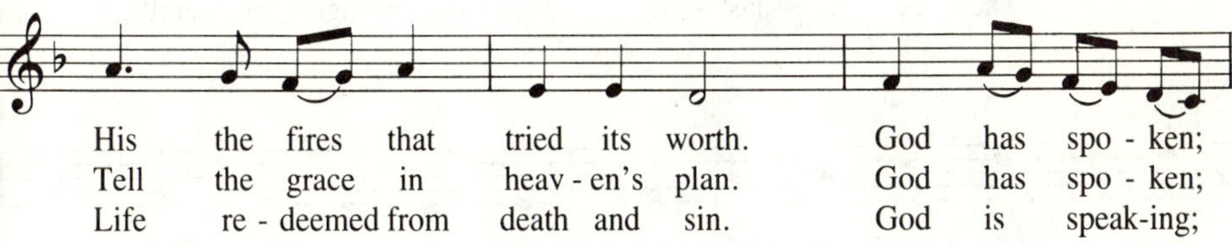

His the fires that tried its worth. God has spo - ken;
Tell the grace in heav - en's plan. God has spo - ken;
Life re - deemed from death and sin. God is speak-ing;

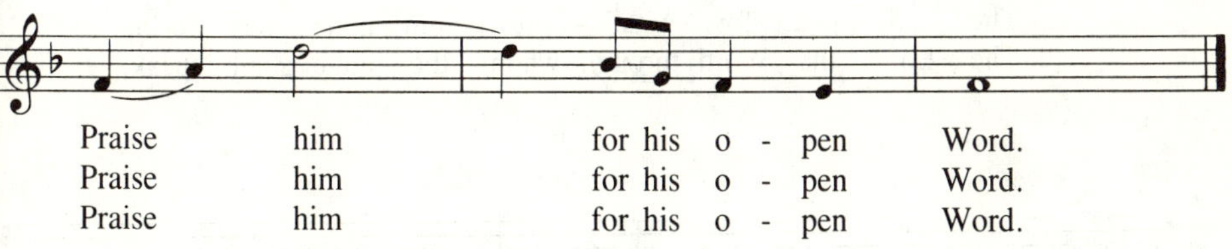

Praise him for his o - pen Word.
Praise him for his o - pen Word.
Praise him for his o - pen Word.

Text: R.T. Brooks, b.1918,
Tune: WYLDE GREEN, 8 7 8 7 4 7; Peter Cutts, b.1937,

515 His Voice Is in the Thunder, in the Storm

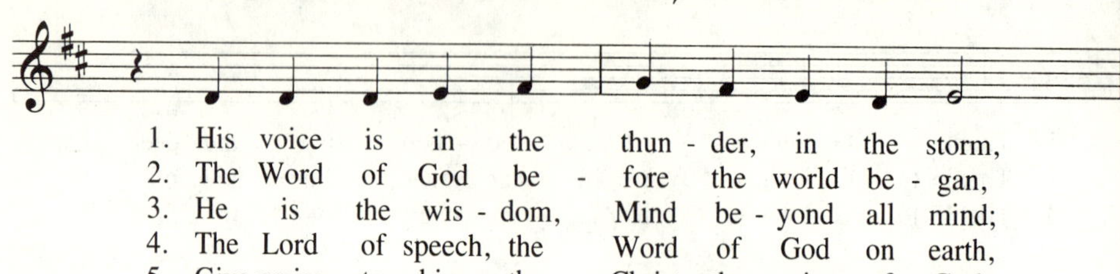
1. His voice is in the thun - der, in the storm,
2. The Word of God be - fore the world be - gan,
3. He is the wis - dom, Mind be - yond all mind;
4. The Lord of speech, the Word of God on earth,
5. Give praise to him, the Christ, the voice of God,

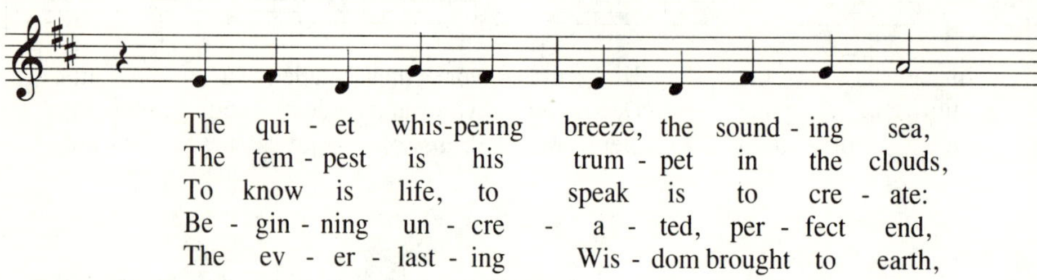
The qui - et whis-pering breeze, the sound - ing sea,
The tem - pest is his trum - pet in the clouds,
To know is life, to speak is to cre - ate:
Be - gin - ning un - cre - a - ted, per - fect end,
The ev - er - last - ing Wis - dom brought to earth,

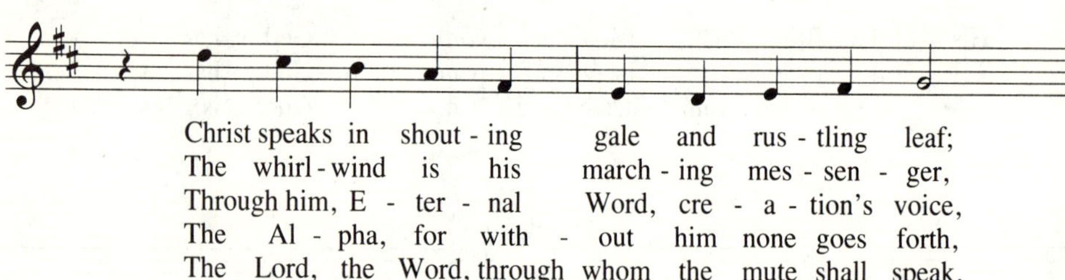
Christ speaks in shout - ing gale and rus - tling leaf;
The whirl - wind is his march - ing mes - sen - ger,
Through him, E - ter - nal Word, cre - a - tion's voice,
The Al - pha, for with - out him none goes forth,
The Lord, the Word, through whom the mute shall speak,

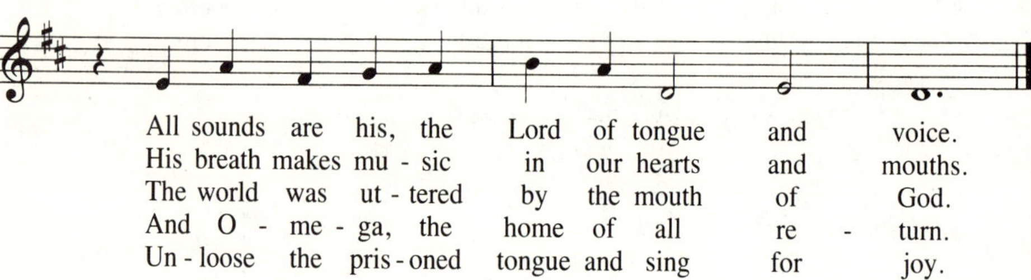
All sounds are his, the Lord of tongue and voice.
His breath makes mu - sic in our hearts and mouths.
The world was ut - tered by the mouth of God.
And O - me - ga, the home of all re - turn.
Un - loose the pris - oned tongue and sing for joy.

Text: Luke Connaughton, 1917-1979, alt.,
Tune: FLENTGE, 10 10 10 10; Carl Schalk, b.1929,

God Has Spoken by His Prophets 516

1. God has spo - ken by his proph - ets, Spo - ken
2. God has spo - ken by Christ Je - sus, Christ, the
3. God is speak - ing by his Spir - it, Speak - ing

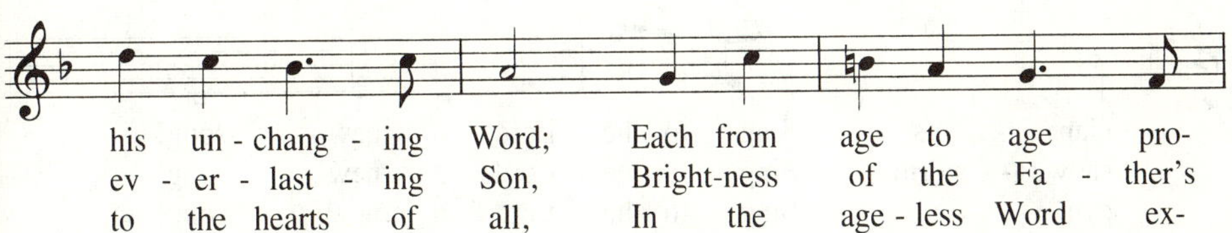
his un - chang - ing Word; Each from age to age pro-
ev - er - last - ing Son, Bright-ness of the Fa - ther's
to the hearts of all, In the age - less Word ex-

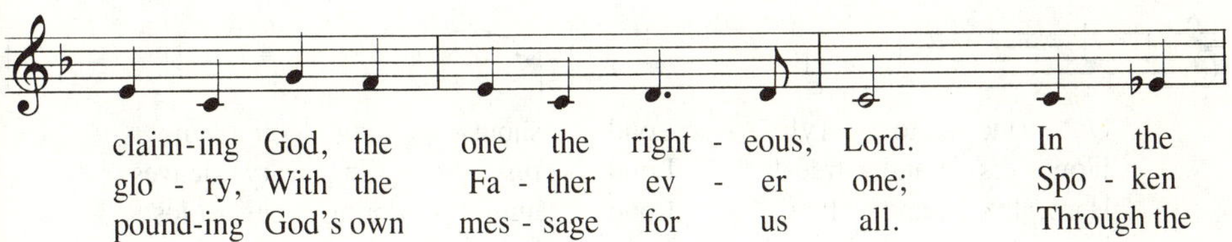
claim-ing God, the one the right - eous, Lord. In the
glo - ry, With the Fa - ther ev - er one; Spo - ken
pound-ing God's own mes - sage for us all. Through the

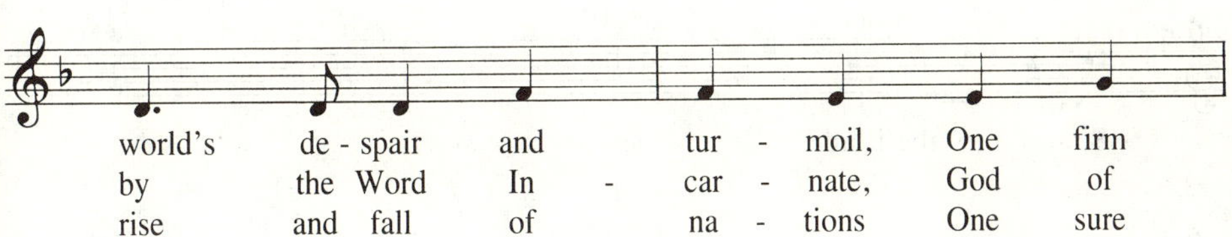
world's de - spair and tur - moil, One firm
by the Word In - car - nate, God of
rise and fall of na - tions One sure

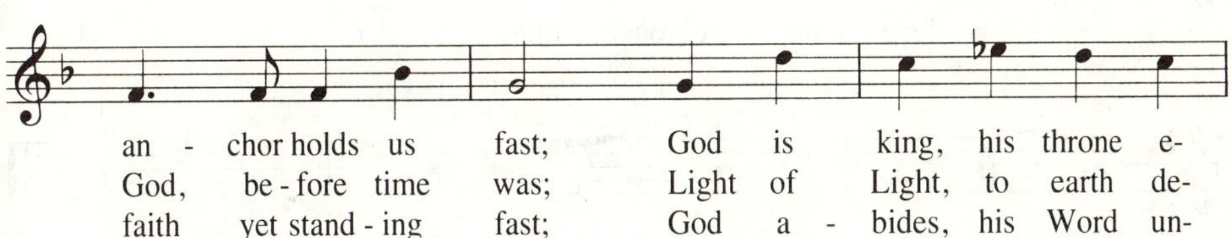
an - chor holds us fast; God is king, his throne e-
God, be - fore time was; Light of Light, to earth de-
faith yet stand - ing fast; God a - bides, his Word un-

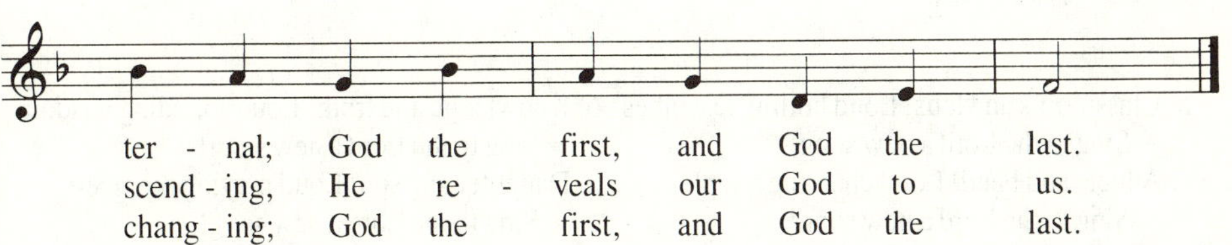
ter - nal; God the first, and God the last.
scend - ing, He re - veals our God to us.
chang - ing; God the first, and God the last.

Text: George W. Briggs, 1875-1959, alt.,
Tune: RUSTINGTON, 8 7 8 7 D; Charles H. H. Parry, 1848-1918

517 Earth and All Stars

1. Earth and all stars! Loud rush - ing plan - ets Sing to the Lord a new song!
2. Hail, wind and rain! Loud blow - ing snow - storm Sing to the Lord a new song!
3. Trum - pet and pipes! Loud clash - ing cym - bals Sing to the Lord a new song!
4. En - gines and steel! Loud pound - ing ham - mers Sing to the Lord a new song!
O vic - to - ry! Loud shout - ing ar - my
Flow - ers and trees! Loud rus - tling dry leaves
Harp, lute and lyre! Loud hum - ming cel - los
Lime-stone and beams! Loud build - ing work - ers
Sing to the Lord a new song!
God has done mar - vel - ous things. I too, I too sing prais - es with a new song!
indicates clapping of hands

5. Classrooms and labs! Loud boiling test tubes
Sing to the Lord a new song!
Athlete and band! Loud cheering people
Sing to the Lord a new song!

6. Knowledge and truth! Loud sounding wisdom
Sing to the Lord a new song!
Daughter and son! Loud praying members
Sing to the Lord a new song!

Text: Herbert Brokering, b.1926
Tune: EARTH AND ALL STARS, 4 5 7 D with refrain; Jan Bender, b.1909

Glory Be to God in Heaven 518

1. Glo - ry be to God in heav - en, Peace to those
2. On - ly Son of God the Fa - ther, Lamb who takes

who love him well; On the earth let all his
our sin a - way, Now with him in tri-umph

peo - ple Speak his grace, his won-ders tell:
seat - ed— For your mer - cy, Lord, we pray:

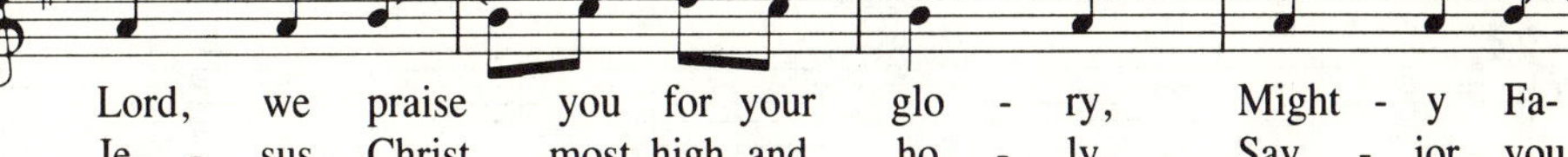

Lord, we praise you for your glo - ry, Might - y Fa-
Je - sus Christ, most high and ho - ly, Sav - ior, you

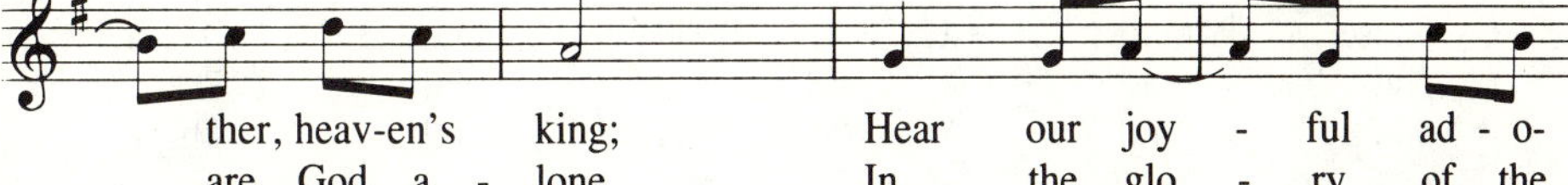

ther, heav-en's king; Hear our joy - ful ad - o-
are God a - lone In the glo - ry of the

ra - tion And ac - cept the thanks we bring.
Fa - ther With the Spir - it: Three in One!

Text: *Gloria in excelsis Deo;* Michael Perry, b.1942,
Tune: LADUE CHAPEL, 8 7 8 7 D; Ronald Arnatt, b.1930,

Laudate Dominum 519

Lau - da - te Do - mi - num, lau - da - te Do - mi - num
om - nes gen - tes, al - le - lu - ia. al - le - lu - ia.
1.
2.
D.C.

Tune: Psalm 117, Taizé Community, 1980
Tune: Jacques Berthier, b.1923

520 All Creatures of Our God and King

1. All crea - tures of our God and King, Lift
2. O rush - ing wind and breez - es soft, O
3. O flow - ing wa - ters, pure and clear, Make
4. Dear moth - er earth, who day by day Un-
5. O ev - 'ry one of ten - der heart, For-
up your voice and with us sing: Al - le
clouds that ride the winds a - loft: O
mu - sic for your Lord to hear. O
folds rich bless - ings on our way, O
giv - ing oth - ers, take your part, O
lu - ia! Al - le - lu - ia! O
praise him! Al - le - lu - ia! O
praise him! Al - le - lu - ia! O
praise him! Al - le - lu - ia! The
praise him! Al - le - lu - ia! All
burn - ing sun with gold - en beam And
ris - ing morn, in praise re - joice, O
fire so mas - ter - ful and bright, Pro-
fruits and flow'rs that ver - dant grow, Let
you who pain and sor - row bear, Praise
sil - ver moon with soft - er gleam:
lights of eve - ning, find a voice.
vid - ing us with warmth and light, O
them his praise a - bun - dant show.
God and lay on him your care.
praise him! O praise him! Al - le - lu - ia, al - le-

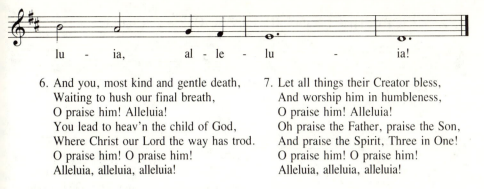

lu - ia, al - le - lu - ia!

6. And you, most kind and gentle death,
Waiting to hush our final breath,
O praise him! Alleluia!
You lead to heav'n the child of God,
Where Christ our Lord the way has trod.
O praise him! O praise him!
Alleluia, alleluia, alleluia!

7. Let all things their Creator bless,
And worship him in humbleness,
O praise him! Alleluia!
Oh praise the Father, praise the Son,
And praise the Spirit, Three in One!
O praise him! O praise him!
Alleluia, alleluia, alleluia!

Text: *Laudato si, mi Signor:* Francis of Assisi, 1182-1226; Tr. by William H. Draper, 1855-1933, alt., © J. Curwen and Sons
Tune: LASST UNS ERFREUEN, LM with alleluias; *Geistliche Kirchengesänge,* 1623; Harm. by Ralph Vaughan Williams, 1872-1958, © Oxford University Press

From All That Dwell below the Skies 521

1. From all that dwell be - low the skies,
2. E - ter - nal are your mer - cies, Lord;
3. Your loft - y themes, all mor - tals, bring;
4. In ev - ery land be - gin the song;

Let the Cre - a - tor's praise a - rise;
E - ter - nal truth at - tends your word:
In songs of praise di - vine - ly sing;
To ev - ery land the strains be - long;

Let the Re - deem - er's name be sung,
Your praise shall sound from shore to shore,
The great sal - va - tion loud pro - claim,
In cheer - ful sounds all voic - es raise,

Through ev - 'ry land by ev - 'ry tongue.
Till suns shall rise and set no more.
And shout for joy the Sav - ior's name.
And fill the world with loud - est praise.

Text: Psalm 117; St. 1-2; Isaac Watts, 1674-1748; St. 3-4, Anon.
Tune: DUKE STREET, LM; John Hatton, c.1710-1793

522 Heavenly Hosts in Ceaseless Worship

1. Heaven - ly hosts in cease - less wor - ship
2. All cre - a - tion, all re - demp - tion,
"Ho - ly, ho - ly, ho - ly" cry; "He who is, who
Join to sing the Sav - ior's worth; Lamb of God whose
was and will be, God, Al - might - y,
blood has bought us, Kings and priests, to
Lord most high." Praise and hon - or, power and glo - ry,
reign on earth. Wealth and wis - dom, power and glo - ry,
Be to Him who reigns a - lone; We, with all his
Hon - or, might, do - min - ion, praise, Now be his from
hands have fash - ioned, Fall be - fore the Fa - ther's throne.
all his crea - tures And to ev - er - last - ing days.

Text: Rev. 4-5; Timothy Dudley-Smith, b.1926, © 1975, Hope Publishing Co.
Tune: HEAVENLY HOSTS, 8 7 8 7 D; Noel H. Tredinnick, b.1949, © 1973, Hope Publishing Co.

Let All Mortal Flesh Keep Silence 523

1. Let all mor - tal flesh keep si - lence,
2. King of kings, yet born of Mar - y,
3. Rank on rank the host of heav - en
4. At his feet the six - winged ser - aph,
And with fear and trem - bling stand;
As of old on earth he stood,
Spreads its van - guard on the way,
Cher - u - bim with sleep - less eye,
Pon - der noth - ing earth - ly mind - ed,
Lord of lords in hu - man ves - ture,
As the Light of Light de - scend - ing
Veil their fac - es to the Pres - ence,
For with bless - ing in his hand
In the Bo - dy and the Blood
From the realms of end - less day,
As with cease - less voice they cry,
Christ our God to earth de - scend-
He will give to all the faith-
That the pow'rs of hell may van-
"Al - le - lu - ia, al - le - lu-
ing, Our full hom - age to de - mand.
ful His own self for heav'n - ly food.
ish As the dark - ness clears a - way.
ia, Al - le - lu - ia, Lord, most high!"

Text: Σιγησάτω Πᾶσα Σὰρξ Βροτεία; Liturgy of St. James 5th C.; Para. by Gerard Moultrie, 1829-1885
Tune: PICARDY, 8 7 8 7 8 7; French, 17th C.; Harm. by Russell Woolen, b.1923

524 Holy God, We Praise Thy Name

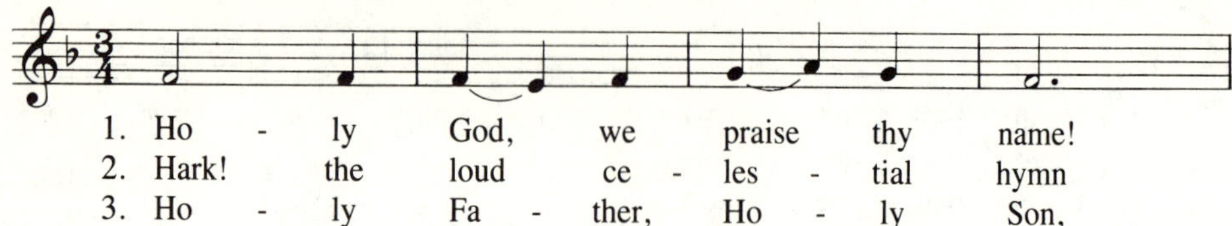
1. Ho - ly God, we praise thy name!
2. Hark! the loud ce - les - tial hymn
3. Ho - ly Fa - ther, Ho - ly Son,

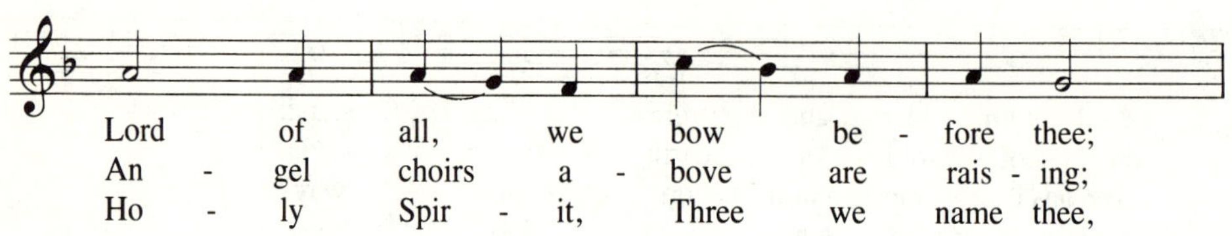
Lord of all, we bow be - fore thee;
An - gel choirs a - bove are rais - ing;
Ho - ly Spir - it, Three we name thee,

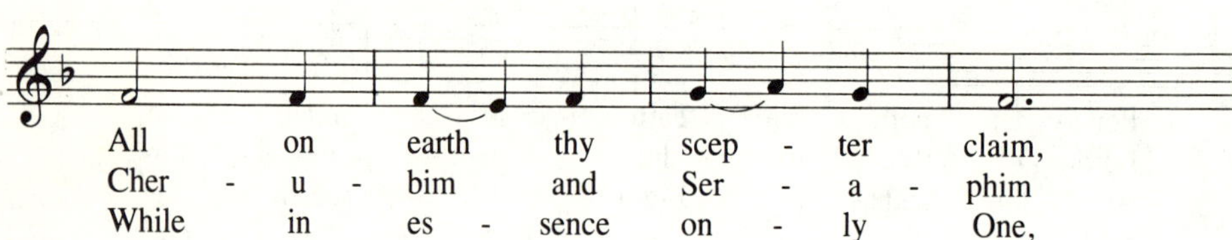
All on earth thy scep - ter claim,
Cher - u - bim and Ser - a - phim
While in es - sence on - ly One,

All in heav'n a - bove a - dore thee;
In un - ceas - ing cho - rus prais - ing,
Un - di - vid - ed God we claim thee,

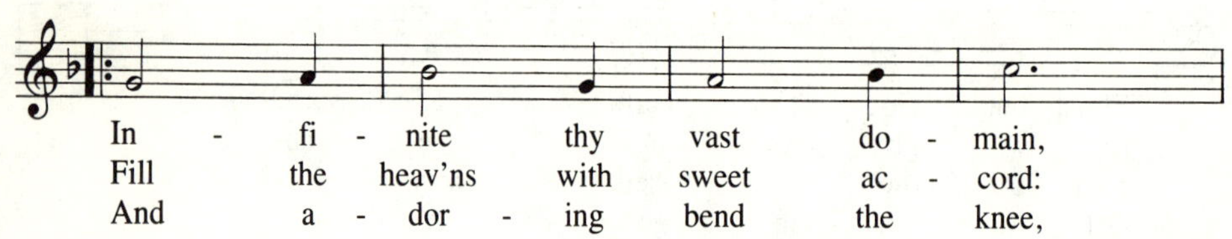
In - fi - nite thy vast do - main,
Fill the heav'ns with sweet ac - cord:
And a - dor - ing bend the knee,

Repeat ad lib
Ev - er - last - ing is thy reign.
Ho - ly, ho - ly, ho - ly Lord!
While we own the mys - ter - y.

Text: *Grosser Gott, wir loben dich;* Ascr. to Ignaz Franz, 1719-1790; Tr. by Clarence Walworth, 1820-1900
Tune: GROSSER GOTT, 7 8 7 8 77; *Katholisches Gesangbuch,* Vienna, c.1774

Joyful, Joyful, We Adore You 525

1. Joy-ful, joy-ful, we a-dore you, God of glo-ry, Lord of love;
2. All your works with joy sur-round you, Earth and heav'n re-flect your rays,
3. Al-ways giv-ing and for-giv-ing, Ev-er bless-ing, ev-er blest,
4. Mor-tals join the might-y cho-rus, Which the morn-ing stars be-gan;

Hearts un-fold like flowers be-fore you, Open-ing to the sun a-bove.
Stars and an-gels sing a-round you, Cen-ter of un-bro-ken praise;
Well-spring of the joy of liv-ing, O-cean depth of hap-py rest!
God's own love is reign-ing o'er us, Join-ing peo-ple hand in hand.

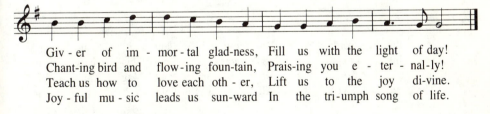

Melt the clouds of sin and sad-ness; Drive the dark of doubt a-way;
Field and for-est, vale and moun-tain, Flow-ery mead-ow, flash-ing sea,
Lov-ing Fa-ther, Christ our broth-er, Let your light up-on us shine;
Ev-er sing-ing, march we on-ward, Vic-tors in the midst of strife;

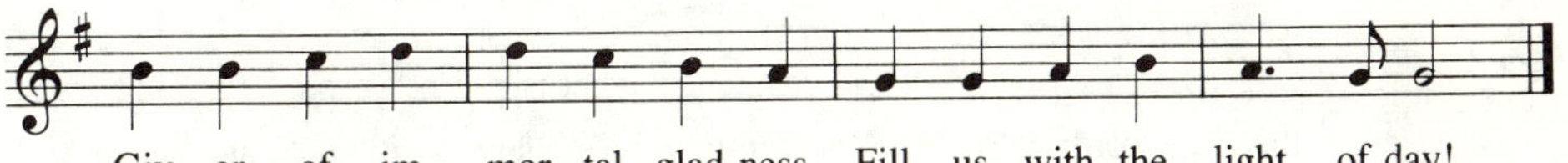

Giv-er of im-mor-tal glad-ness, Fill us with the light of day!
Chant-ing bird and flow-ing foun-tain, Prais-ing you e-ter-nal-ly!
Teach us how to love each oth-er, Lift us to the joy di-vine.
Joy-ful mu-sic leads us sun-ward In the tri-umph song of life.

Text: Henry van Dyke, 1852-1933, alt.,
Tune: HYMN TO JOY, 8 7 8 7 D; Arr. from Ludwig van Beethoven, 1770-1827, by Edward Hodges, 1796-1867

526 Thanks Be to God

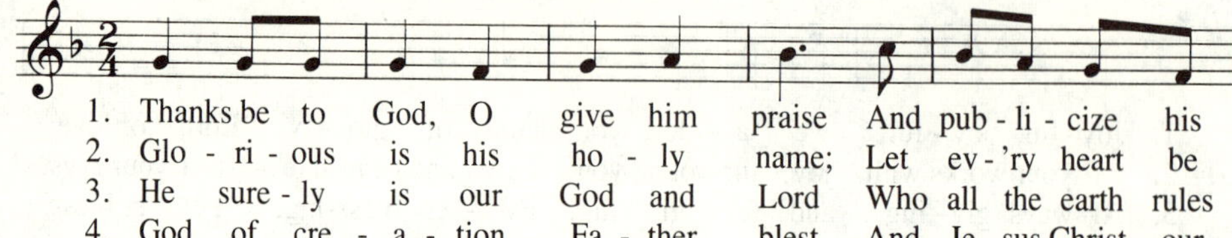
1. Thanks be to God, O give him praise And pub - li - cize his
2. Glo - ri - ous is his ho - ly name; Let ev - 'ry heart be
3. He sure - ly is our God and Lord Who all the earth rules
4. God of cre - a - tion, Fa - ther blest And Je - sus Christ, our

great - name. Shout out, pro - claim a - loud his deeds To
joy - ful. Cleansed they be - come through fear in faith Who
just - ly. His cov-'nant he will not for - get; It
Sav - ior, Spir - it of truth, our strength and pow'r, Who

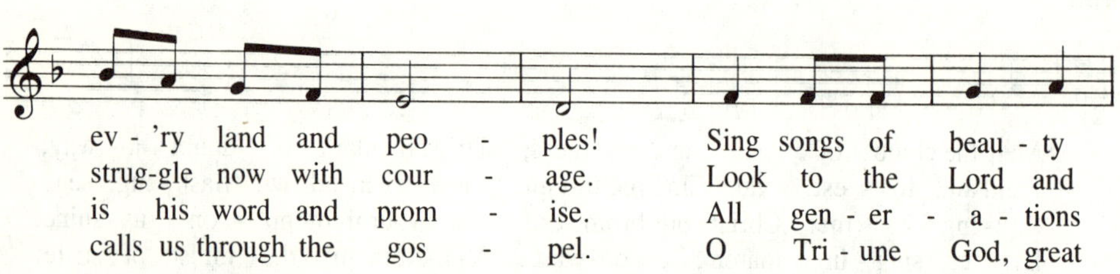
ev - 'ry land and peo - ples! Sing songs of beau - ty
strug-gle now with cour - age. Look to the Lord and
is his word and prom - ise. All gen - er - a - tions
calls us through the gos - pel. O Tri - une God, great

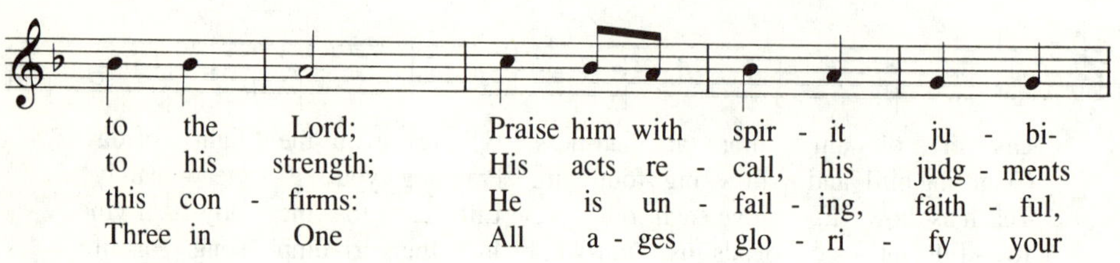
to the Lord; Praise him with spir - it ju - bi-
to his strength; His acts re - call, his judg - ments
this con - firms: He is un - fail - ing, faith - ful,
Three in One All a - ges glo - ri - fy your

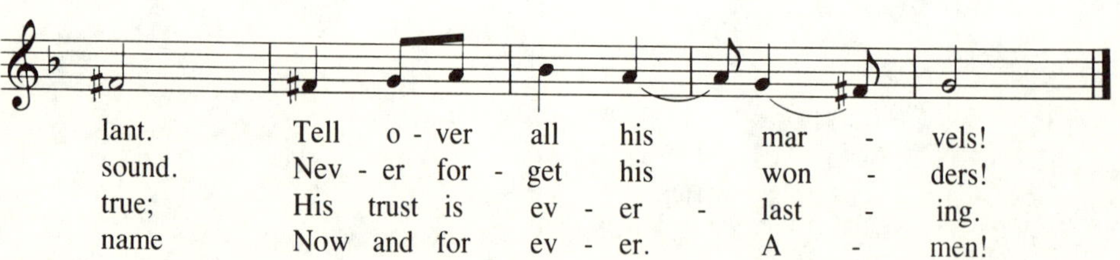
lant. Tell o - ver all his mar - vels!
sound. Nev - er for - get his won - ders!
true; His trust is ev - er - last - ing.
name Now and for ev - er. A - men!

Text: Psalm (104)105; *Danket dem Herren;* Cornelius Becker, 1561-1604; Tr. by Daniel G. Reuning, b.1935,
Tune: DANKET DEM HERREN, 8 7 8 7 8 8 7; Heinrich Schütz, 1585-1672

All Glory Be to God on High 527

1. All glo - ry be to God on high, And
2. O Lamb of God, Lord Je - sus Christ, Whom
3. You on - ly are the Ho - ly One, Who

peace on earth from heav - en, And God's good-will un-
God the Fa - ther gave us, Who for the world was
came for our sal - va - tion, And on - ly you are

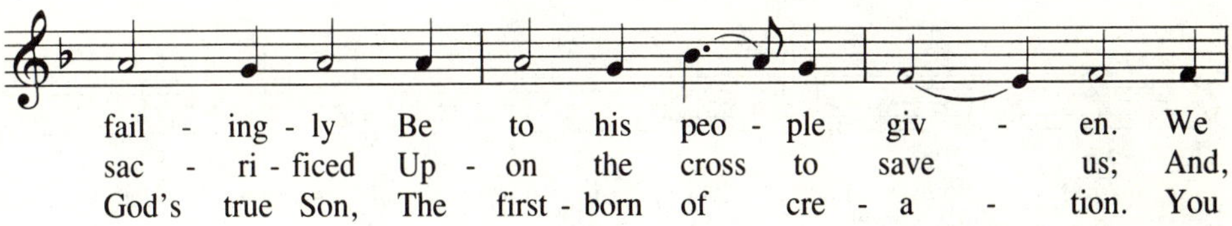
fail - ing - ly Be to his peo - ple giv - en. We
sac - ri - ficed Up - on the cross to save us; And,
God's true Son, The first - born of cre - a - tion. You

bless, we wor - ship you, we raise For your great glo - ry
as you sit at God's right hand, And we for judg - ment
on - ly, Christ, as Lord we own And, with the Spir - it,

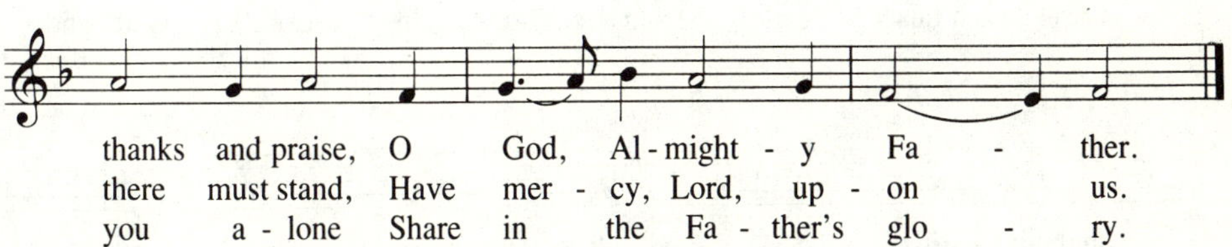
thanks and praise, O God, Al - might - y Fa - ther.
there must stand, Have mer - cy, Lord, up - on us.
you a - lone Share in the Fa - ther's glo - ry.

Text: *Allein Gott in der Hoh' sei Ehr' (Gloria in excelsis Deo);* Nikolaus Decius, c.1485-c.1546; Tr. by F. Bland Tucker, 1895-1984, © 1978, Church Pension Fund
Tune: ALLEIN GOTT IN DER HOH', 8 7 8 7 88 7; Attr. to Nikolaus Decius, c.1485-c.1546; Harm. from Michael Praetorius, 1571-1621

528 Sing Praise to God Who Reigns Above

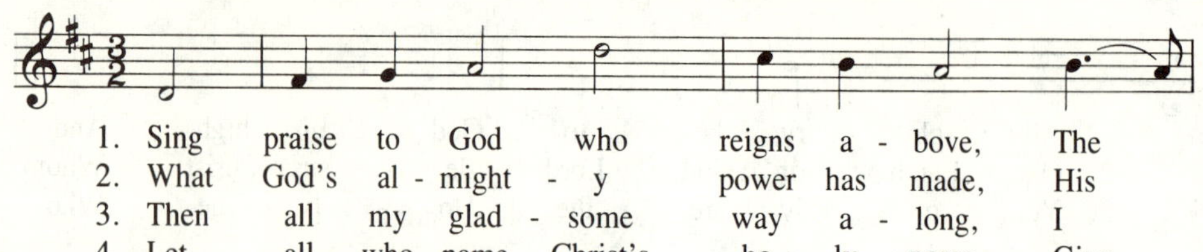
1. Sing praise to God who reigns a - bove, The
2. What God's al - might - y power has made, His
3. Then all my glad - some way a - long, I
4. Let all who name Christ's ho - ly name, Give

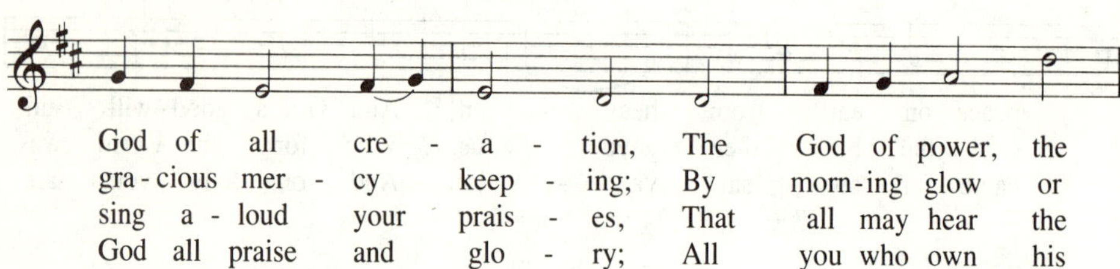
God of all cre - a - tion, The God of power, the
gra - cious mer - cy keep - ing; By morn - ing glow or
sing a - loud your prais - es, That all may hear the
God all praise and glo - ry; All you who own his

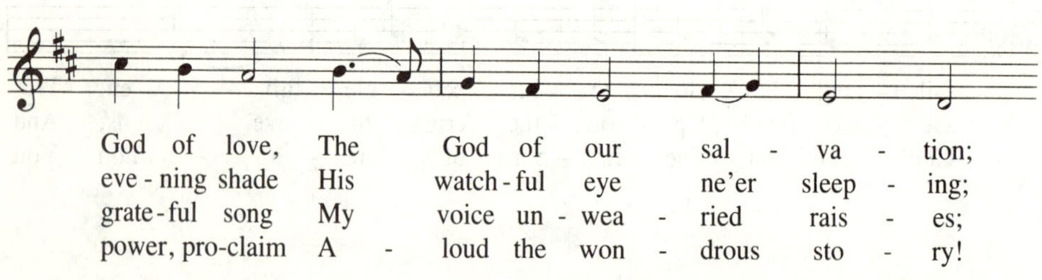
God of love, The God of our sal - va - tion;
eve - ning shade His watch - ful eye ne'er sleep - ing;
grate - ful song My voice un - wea - ried rais - es;
power, pro - claim A - loud the won - drous sto - ry!

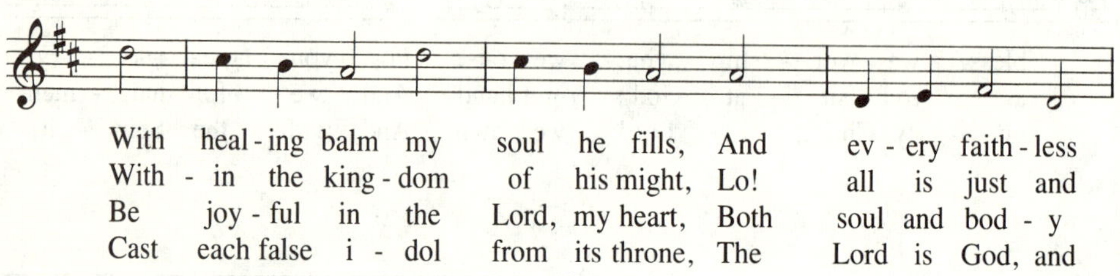
With heal - ing balm my soul he fills, And ev - ery faith - less
With - in the king - dom of his might, Lo! all is just and
Be joy - ful in the Lord, my heart, Both soul and bod - y
Cast each false i - dol from its throne, The Lord is God, and

mur - mur stills: To God all praise and glo - ry.
all is right: To God all praise and glo - ry.
sing your part: To God all praise and glo - ry.
he a - lone: To God all praise and glo - ry.

Text: *Sei Lob und Ehr' dem höchsten Gut;* Johann J. Schütz; 1640-1690; Tr. by Frances E. Cox, 1812-1897
Tune: MIT FREUDEN ZART, 8 7 8 7 88 7; Bohemian Brethern's *Kirchengesänge,* 1566

Praise the Lord! You Heavens, Adore Him 529

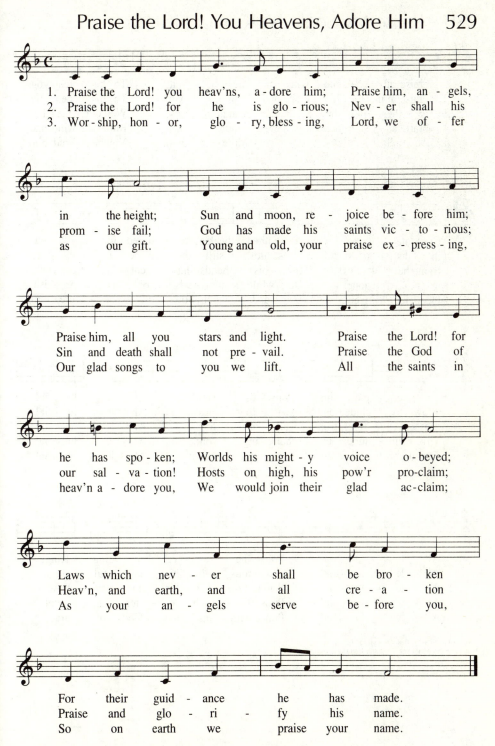

1. Praise the Lord! you heav'ns, a - dore him; Praise him, an - gels,
2. Praise the Lord! for he is glo - rious; Nev - er shall his
3. Wor - ship, hon - or, glo - ry, bless - ing, Lord, we of - fer

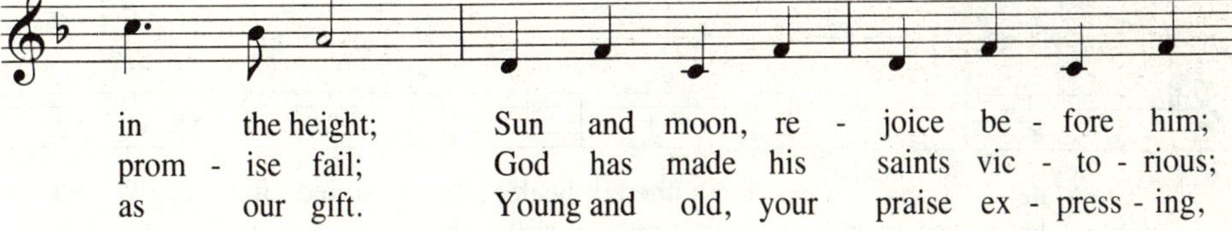
in the height; Sun and moon, re - joice be - fore him;
prom - ise fail; God has made his saints vic - to - rious;
as our gift. Young and old, your praise ex - press - ing,

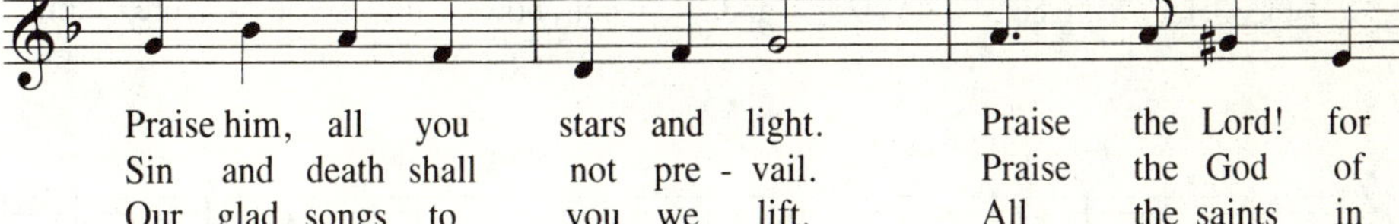
Praise him, all you stars and light. Praise the Lord! for
Sin and death shall not pre - vail. Praise the God of
Our glad songs to you we lift. All the saints in

he has spo - ken; Worlds his might - y voice o - beyed;
our sal - va - tion! Hosts on high, his pow'r pro-claim;
heav'n a - dore you, We would join their glad ac-claim;

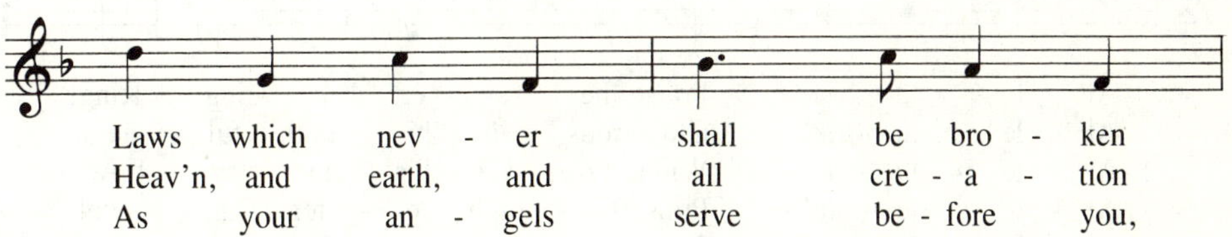
Laws which nev - er shall be bro - ken
Heav'n, and earth, and all cre - a - tion
As your an - gels serve be - fore you,

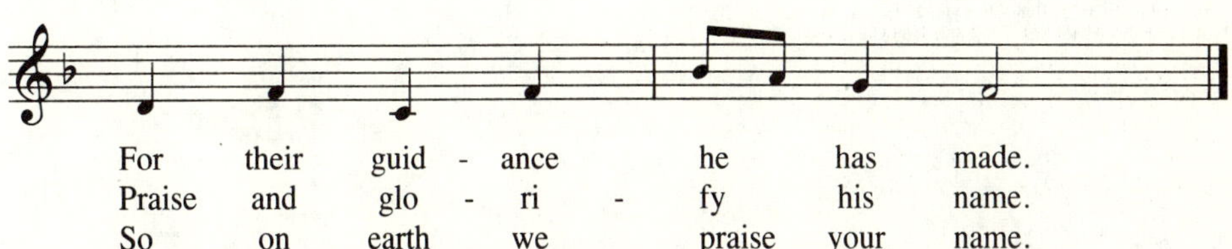
For their guid - ance he has made.
Praise and glo - ri - fy his name.
So on earth we praise your name.

Text: Psalm 148; St. 1-2, *Foundling Hospital Collection*, 1796; St. 3, Edward Osler, 1798-1863
Tune: HEAVENLY HOSTS, 8 7 8 7 D; Noel H. Tredinnick, b.1949,

530 Praise My Soul, the King of Heaven

1. Praise, my soul, the King of heav - en; To his feet your
2. Praise him for his grace and fa - vor To his peo - ple
3. Fa - ther - like he tends and spares us; Well our fee - ble
4. Frail as sum-mer's flow'r we flour - ish, Blows the wind and
5. An - gels, help us to a - dore him; You be - hold him

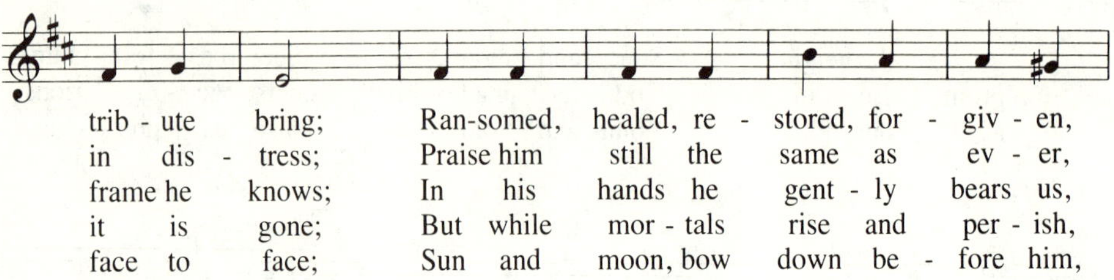

trib - ute bring; Ran-somed, healed, re - stored, for - giv - en,
in dis - tress; Praise him still the same as ev - er,
frame he knows; In his hands he gent - ly bears us,
it is gone; But while mor - tals rise and per - ish,
face to face; Sun and moon, bow down be - fore him,

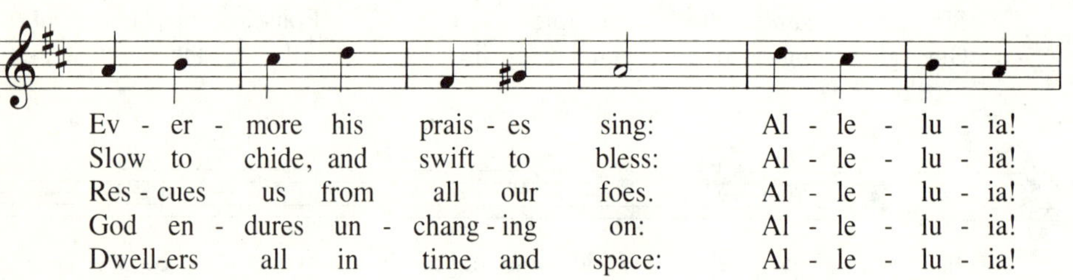

Ev - er - more his prais - es sing: Al - le - lu - ia!
Slow to chide, and swift to bless: Al - le - lu - ia!
Res - cues us from all our foes. Al - le - lu - ia!
God en - dures un - chang - ing on: Al - le - lu - ia!
Dwell-ers all in time and space: Al - le - lu - ia!

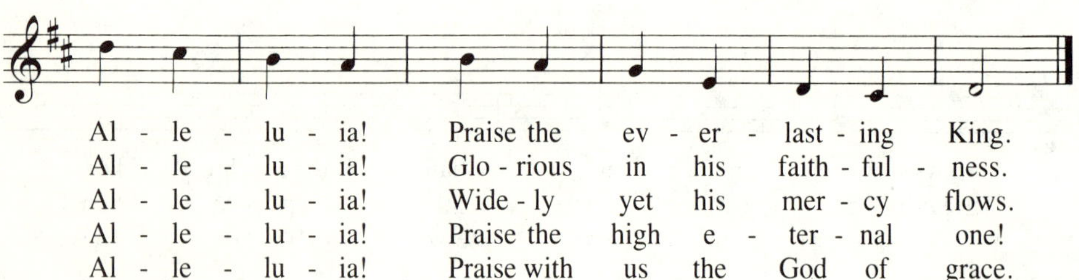

Al - le - lu - ia! Praise the ev - er - last - ing King.
Al - le - lu - ia! Glo - rious in his faith - ful - ness.
Al - le - lu - ia! Wide - ly yet his mer - cy flows.
Al - le - lu - ia! Praise the high e - ter - nal one!
Al - le - lu - ia! Praise with us the God of grace.

Text: Psalm (102)103; Henry F. Lyte, 1793-1847, alt.
Tune: LAUDA ANIMA, 8 7 8 7 8 7; John Goss, 1800-1880

There's a Spirit in the Air 531

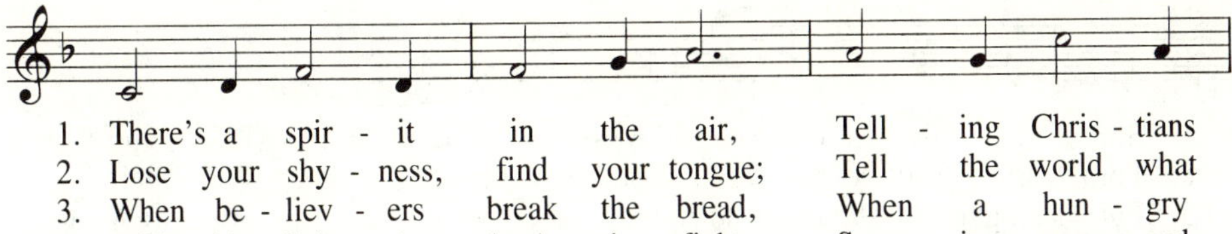

1. There's a spir - it in the air, Tell - ing Chris - tians
2. Lose your shy - ness, find your tongue; Tell the world what
3. When be - liev - ers break the bread, When a hun - gry
4. Still his Spir - it leads the fight, See - ing wrong and
5. When a strang - er's not a - lone, Where the home - less

ev - 'ry - where, "Praise the love that Christ re - vealed,
God has done: God in Christ has come to stay,
child is fed: Praise the love that Christ re - vealed,
set - ting right: God in Christ has come to stay,
find a home, Praise the love that Christ re - vealed,

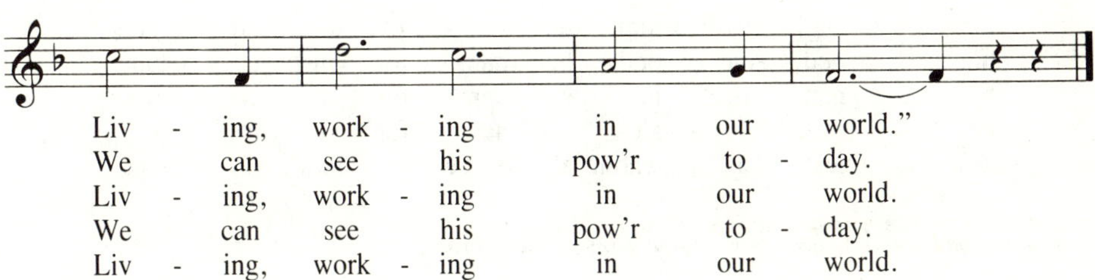

Liv - ing, work - ing in our world."
We can see his pow'r to - day.
Liv - ing, work - ing in our world.
We can see his pow'r to - day.
Liv - ing, work - ing in our world.

6. May his Spirit fill our praise,
Guide our thoughts and change our ways.
God in Christ has come to stay,
We can see his power today.

7. There's a Spirit in the air,
Calling people ev'rywhere;
Praise the love that Christ revealed:
Living, working in our world.

Text: Brian Wren, b.1936
Tune: LAUDS, 77 77; John W. Wilson, b.1905

532 Sing to the Lord a Joyful Song

1. Sing to the Lord a joy - ful song,
Lift up your hearts, your voic - es raise;
To us his gra - cious gifts be - long,
To him our songs of love and praise.

2. For life and love, for rest and food,
For dai - ly help and night - ly care,
Sing to the Lord, for he is good,
And praise his name, for it is fair.

3. For strength to those who on him wait
His truth to prove, his will to do,
Praise we our God, for he is great,
Trust in his name, for it is true.

4. For joys un - told, that from a - bove
Cheer those who love his sweet em - ploy,
Sing to our God, for he is love,
Ex - alt his name, for it is joy.

5. For he is Lord of heav'n and earth,
Whom an - gels serve and saints a - dore,
The Fa - ther, Son, and Spir - it blest,
To whom all praise be now con - fessed.

Text: Psalm 145:1-2; John S. B. Monsell, 1811-1875
Tune: GONFALON ROYAL, LM; Percy C. Buck, 1871-1947, © Oxford University Press

533 New Songs of Celebration

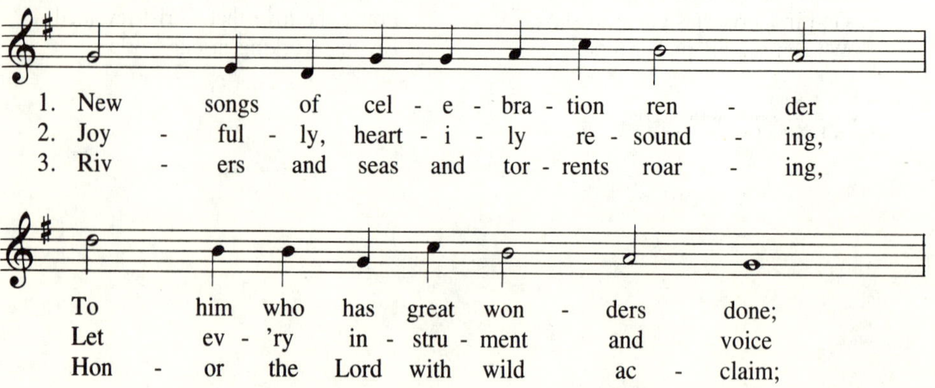
1. New songs of cel - e - bra - tion ren - der
2. Joy - ful - ly, heart - i - ly re - sound - ing,
3. Riv - ers and seas and tor - rents roar - ing,
To him who has great won - ders done;
Let ev - 'ry in - stru - ment and voice
Hon - or the Lord with wild ac - claim;

Awed by his pow'r his foes sur - ren - der
Peal out the praise of grace a - bound - ing,
Moun - tains and stones, look up a - dor - ing,
And fall be - fore the might - y One.
Call - ing the whole world to re - joice.
And find a voice to praise his name.
He has made known his great sal - va - tion
Trum - pets and or - gans set in mo - tion
Right - eous, com - mand - ing, ev - er glo - rious,
Which all his friends with joy con - fess.
Such sounds as make the heav - ens ring:
Prais - es be his that nev - er cease:
He has re - vealed to ev - 'ry na - tion
All things that live in earth and o - cean,
Just is our God, whose truth vic - to - rious
His ev - er - last - ing right - eous - ness.
Make mu - sic for your might - y King.
Es - tab - lish - es the world in peace.

Text: Psalm 98; Erik Routley, 1917-1982, © 1974, Hope Publishing Co.
Tune: RENDEZ À DIEU, 9 8 9 8 D; *Genevan Psalter,* 1551; Attr. to Louis Bourgeois, c.1510-1561; Harm. by Erik Routley, 1917-1982, ©1977 Hope Publishing Co.

534 Tell Out, My Soul, the Greatness of the Lord

1. Tell out, my soul, the great - ness of the Lord!
2. Tell out, my soul, the great - ness of his name!
3. Tell out, my soul, the great - ness of his might!
4. Tell out, my soul, the glo - ries of his word!
Un - num - bered bless-ings give my spir - it voice;
Make known his might, the deeds his arm has done;
Pow'rs and do - min - ions lay their glo - ry by;
Firm is his prom - ise, and his mer - cy sure.
Ten - der to me the prom - ise of his word;
His mer - cy sure, from age to age the same;
Proud hearts and stub - born wills are put to flight,
Tell out, my soul, the great-ness of the Lord
In God my Sav - ior shall my heart re - joice.
His ho - ly name—the Lord, the might - y One.
The hun - gry fed, the hum - ble lift - ed high.
To chil - dren's chil - dren and for ev - er - more!

Text: Luke 1:46-55; *Magnificat anima mea;* Timothy Dudley-Smith, b.1926, © 1962, Hope Publishing Co.
Tune: WOODLANDS, 10 10 10 10; Walter Greatorex, 1877-1949, © Oxford University Press

God, We Praise You 535

1. God, we praise you! God, we bless you! God, we
2. True a - pos - tles, faith - ful proph - ets, Saints who
3. Je - sus Christ, the king of glo - ry, Ev - er-
4. Christ, at God's right hand vic - to - rious, You will
name you sov-'reign Lord! Might-y King whom an - gels
set their world a - blaze, Mar - tyrs, once un - known, un-
last - ing Son of God, Hum-ble was your vir - gin
judge the world you made; Lord, in mer - cy help your
wor - ship, Fa - ther, by your church a - dored:
heed - ed, Join one grow - ing song of praise,
moth - er, Hard the lone - ly path you trod:
ser - vants For whose free - dom you have paid:
All cre - a - tion shows your glo - ry, Heav'n and
While your church on earth con - fess - es One ma-
By your cross is sin de - feat - ed, Hell con-
Raise us up from dust to glo - ry, Guard us
earth draw near your throne, Sing-ing "Ho - ly, ho - ly,
jes - tic Trin - i - ty: Fa - ther, Son, and Ho - ly
front - ed face to face, Heav-en o - pened to be-
from all sin to - day; King en - throned a - bove all
ho - ly, Lord of hosts, and God a - lone!"
Spir - it, God, our hope e - ter - nal - ly.
liev - ers, Sin - ners jus - ti - fied by grace.
prais - es, Save your peo - ple, God, we pray.

Text: Based on the *Te Deum;* Christopher Idle, b.1938, © 1982, Hope Publishing Co.
Tune: NETTLETON, 8 7 8 7 D; Wyeth's *Repository of Sacred Music, Pt. II, 1813*

536 Let All the World in Every Corner Sing

Let all the world in ev - 'ry cor - ner sing, My God and King! Let all the world in ev - 'ry cor - ner sing, My God and King! The heav'ns are not too high, His prais - es there may fly; The earth is not too low, His prais - es there may grow.
Let all the world in ev - 'ry cor - ner sing, My God and King! Let all the world in ev - 'ry cor - ner sing, My God and King! The Church with psalms must shout, No door can keep them out; But, a - bove all the heart Must bear the long - est part.
Let all the world in ev - 'ry cor - ner sing, My God and King.
Let all the world in ev - 'ry cor - ner sing, My God and
1.
2.
King. A - men.

Text: George Herbert, 1593-1632
Tune: MAC DOUGALL, 10 4 10 4 66 66 10 4; Calvin Hampton, 1938-1984,

The God of Abraham Praise 537

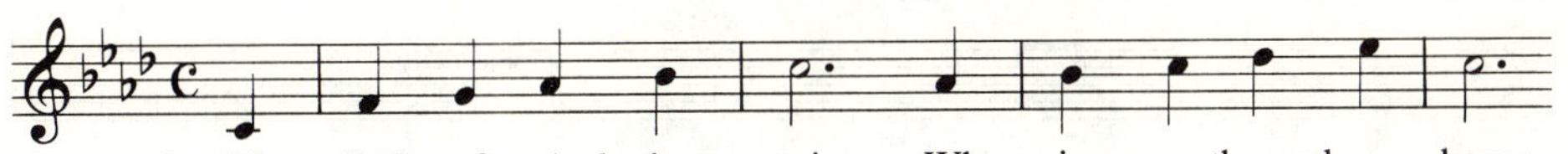

1. The God of A - braham praise, Who reigns en-throned a - bove;
2. He by him - self has sworn: I on his oath de - pend;
3. There dwells the Lord, our King, The Lord, our Right - eous - ness,
4. The God who reigns on high The great arch - an - gels sing,

An - cient of ev - er - last - ing days, And God of love;
I shall, on ea - gle - wings up-borne, To heav'n as - cend:
Tri - umph - ant o'er the world and sin, The Prince of Peace;
And "Ho - ly, Ho - ly, Ho - ly," cry, "Al - might - y King!

To him up - lift your voice, At whose su - preme com - mand
I shall be - hold his face, I shall his power a - dore,
On Zi - on's sa - cred height His king - dom he main - tains,
Who was, and is, the same, For all e - ter - ni - ty,

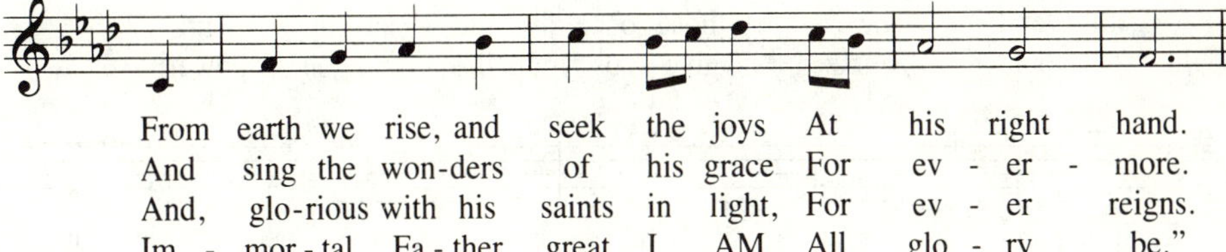

From earth we rise, and seek the joys At his right hand.
And sing the won-ders of his grace For ev - er - more.
And, glo-rious with his saints in light, For ev - er reigns.
Im - mor - tal Fa - ther, great I AM, All glo - ry be."

Text: *Yigdal Elohim Hai;* Ascr. to Daniel ben Judah Dayyan, fl.1400; Para. by Thomas Olivers, 1725-1799. alt.
Tune: LEONI, 6 6 8 4 D; From the *Yigdal;* Transcribed by Meyer Lyon, c.1751-1797

538 Christians, Lift Up Your Hearts

Chris-tians, lift up your hearts, and make this a day of re - joic - ing;
God is our strength and song; glo - ry and praise to his name!
1. This is the house of the Lord, where
3. Praise that his love o - ver - flowed in the
5. Come, Ho - ly Spir - it, to us, who
seek - ers and find - ers are wel - come; En - ter its
hearts of all who re - ceived him, Join - ing to -
live by your pres - ence with - in us, Come to di -
D.C.
gates with your praise, fill all its courts with your song:
geth - er in peace those once di - vid - ed by sin:
rect our course, give us your life and your power:
3
2. Strong and a - lert in his grace, God's peo - ple are
4. Those who are bur - dened with sin find here the
6. Al - might - y God, send us out to live to your
one in their wor - ship: Kept by his peace they de-
joy of for - give - ness, Lay - ing their sins be - fore
praise and your glo - ry; Yours is the pow'r and the
D.C.
part, read - y for serv - ing their Lord:
Christ, par - don and peace their re - ward:
might, ours be the cour - age and faith:

Text: John E. Bowers, b.1923, alt., © Canon John E. Bowers
Tune: SALVE FESTA DIES, Irregular with refrain; Ralph Vaughan Williams, 1872-1958, © Oxford University Press

Sing Praise to the Lord 539

1. Sing praise to the Lord! praise God in the height;
Re - joice in his word, you an - gels of light;
O heav - ens, a - dore him by whom you were made,
And wor - ship be - fore him in bright - ness ar - rayed.
2. Sing praise to the Lord! praise God up - on earth,
In tune - ful ac - cord, all you of new birth;
Praise him who has brought you his grace from a - bove,
Praise him who has taught you to sing of his love.
3. Sing praise to the Lord, all things that give sound;
Each ju - bi - lant chord re - ech - o a - round;
Loud or - gans, his glo - ry tell forth in deep tone,
And trum - pets, the sto - ry of what God has done.
4. Sing praise to the Lord! thanks - giv - ing and song
To him be out - poured all a - ges a - long;
For love in cre - a - tion, for heav - en re - stored,
For grace of sal - va - tion, sing praise to the Lord!

Text: Psalm 150; Henry W. Baker, 1821-1877, alt.
Tune: LAUDATE DOMINUM, 10 10 11 11; Charles H. H. Parry, 1840-1918

540 Shout for Joy, Loud and Long

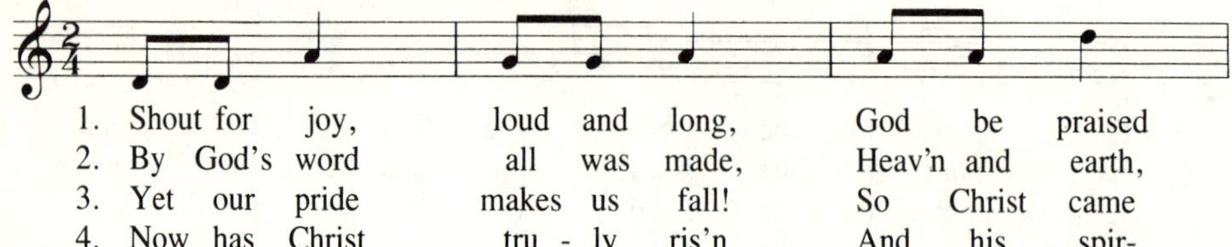
1. Shout for joy, loud and long, God be praised
2. By God's word all was made, Heav'n and earth,
3. Yet our pride makes us fall! So Christ came
4. Now has Christ tru - ly ris'n And his spir-

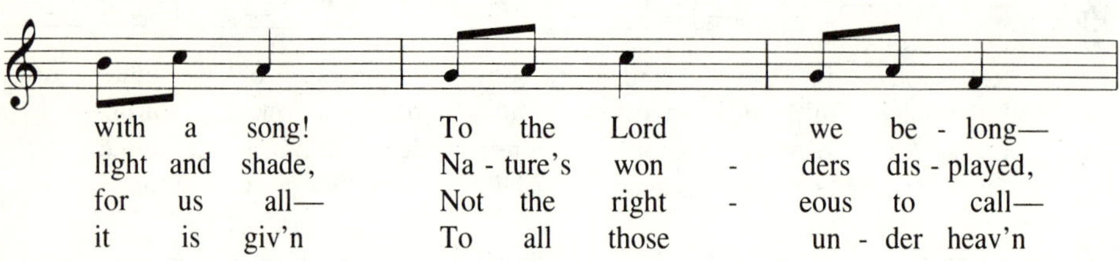
with a song! To the Lord we be - long—
light and shade, Na - ture's won - ders dis - played,
for us all— Not the right - eous to call—
it is giv'n To all those un - der heav'n

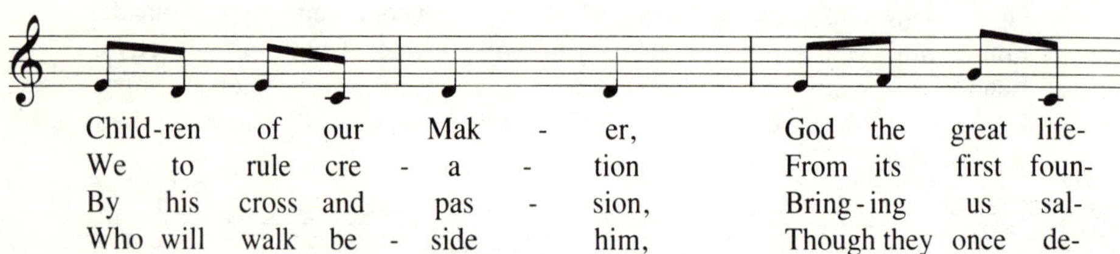
Child-ren of our Mak - er, God the great life-
We to rule cre - a - tion From its first foun-
By his cross and pas - sion, Bring-ing us sal-
Who will walk be - side him, Though they once de-

giv - er! Shout for joy, joy, joy! Shout for joy, joy, joy!
da - tion. Shout for joy, joy, joy! Shout for joy, joy, joy!
va - tion! Shout for joy, joy, joy! Shout for joy, joy, joy!
nied him! Shout for joy, joy, joy! Shout for joy, joy, joy!

God is love, God is light, God is ev - er - last - ing!
God is love, God is light, God is ev - er - last - ing!
God is love, God is light, God is ev - er - last - ing!
God is love, God is light, God is ev - er - last - ing!

Text: David Mowbray, b.1938, © 1982, Hope Publishing Co.
Tune: PERSONET HODIE, 666 66 with refrain; *Piae Cantiones*, 1582; Harm. by Richard Proulx, b.1937, © 1978, GIA Publications, Inc.

O God beyond All Praising 541

1. O God be-yond all prais-ing, We wor-ship you to - day
2. Then hear, O gra-cious Sav - ior, Ac - cept the love we bring,

And sing the love a - maz-ing That songs can - not re - pay;
That we who know your fa - vor May serve you as our king;

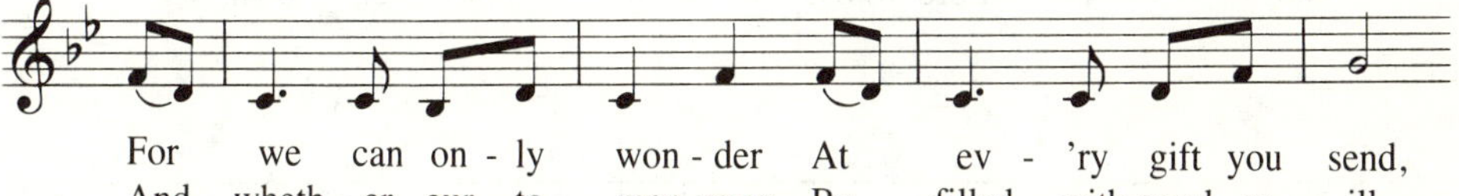

For we can on - ly won - der At ev - 'ry gift you send,
And wheth - er our to - mor - rows Be filled with good or ill,

At bless - ings with - out num - ber And mer-cies with - out end:
We'll tri-umph through our sor - rows And rise to bless you still:

We lift our hearts be - fore you And wait up - on your word,
To mar - vel at your beau - ty And glo - ry in your ways,

We hon - or and a - dore you, Our great and might - y Lord.
And make a joy - ful du - ty Our sac - ri - fice of praise.

Text: Michael Perry, b.1942, © 1982, Hope Publishing Co.
Tune: THAXTED, 13 13 13 13 13 13; Gustave Holst, 1874-1934

542 Glory to God in the Highest

1. Glo - ry to God in the
2. Wor - ship the Lord, the Al-
3. Je - sus, the Christ, the Re-
4. Christ and he on - ly is

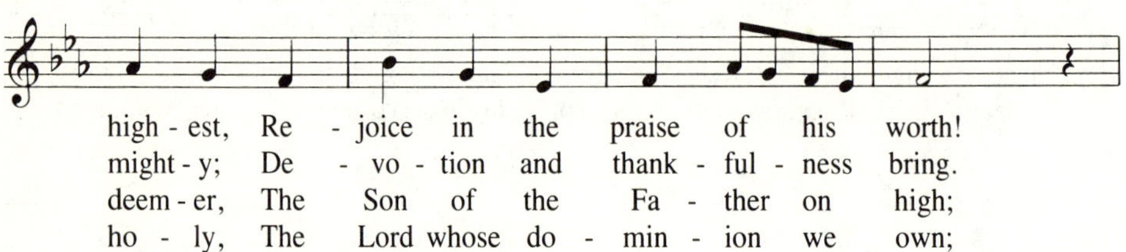
high - est, Re - joice in the praise of his worth!
might - y; De - vo - tion and thank - ful - ness bring.
deem - er, The Son of the Fa - ther on high;
ho - ly, The Lord whose do - min - ion we own;

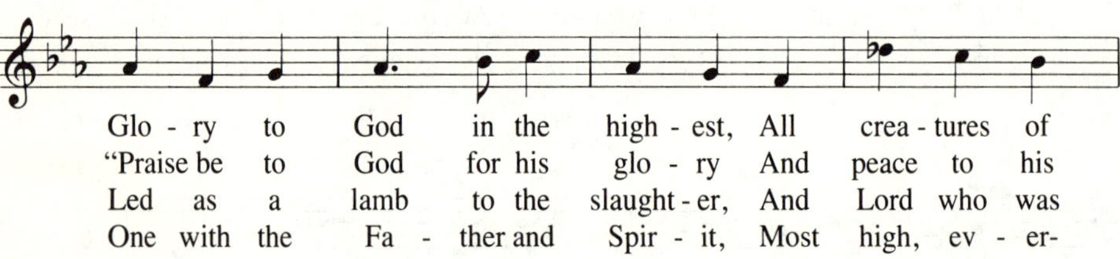
Glo - ry to God in the high - est, All crea - tures of
"Praise be to God for his glo - ry And peace to his
Led as a lamb to the slaught - er, And Lord who was
One with the Fa - ther and Spir - it, Most high, ev - er-

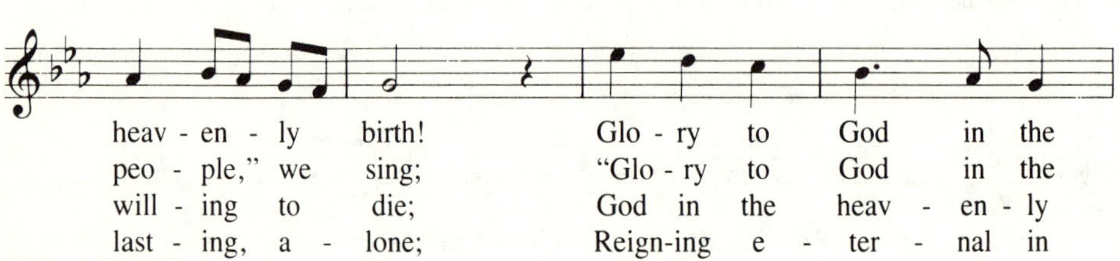
heav - en - ly birth! Glo - ry to God in the
peo - ple," we sing; "Glo - ry to God in the
will - ing to die; God in the heav - en - ly
last - ing, a - lone; Reign-ing e - ter - nal in

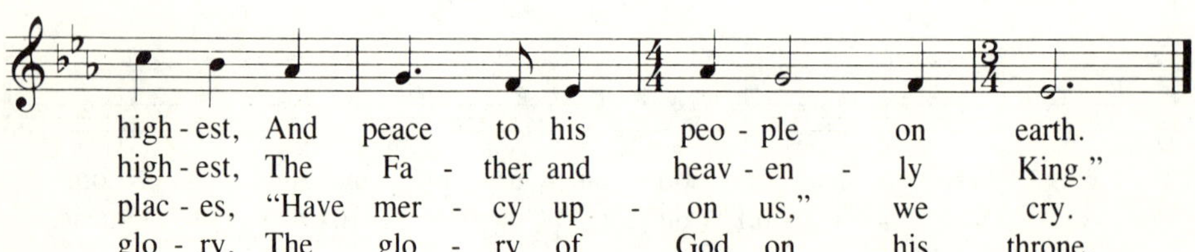
high - est, And peace to his peo - ple on earth.
high - est, The Fa - ther and heav - en - ly King."
plac - es, "Have mer - cy up - on us," we cry.
glo - ry, The glo - ry of God on his throne.

Text: *Gloria in excelsis Deo;* Timothy Dudley-Smith, b.1926, © 1980, Hope Publishing Co.
Tune: RUSSWIN, 8 8 8 8 8 8; Richard Proulx, b.1937, © 1980, GIA Publications, Inc.

Christ Is the World's Light 543

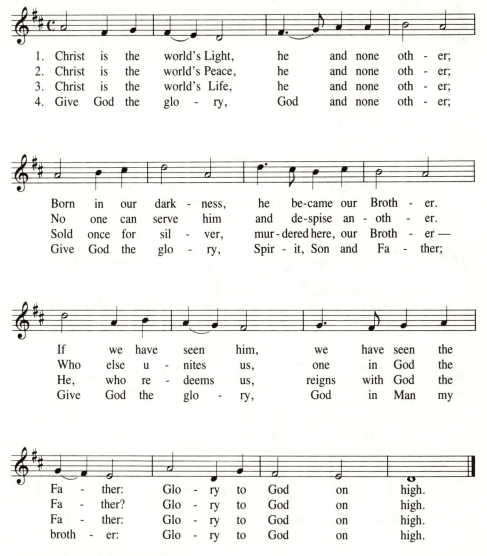

1. Christ is the world's Light, he and none oth - er;
2. Christ is the world's Peace, he and none oth - er;
3. Christ is the world's Life, he and none oth - er;
4. Give God the glo - ry, God and none oth - er;

Born in our dark - ness, he be-came our Broth - er.
No one can serve him and de-spise an - oth - er.
Sold once for sil - ver, mur-dered here, our Broth - er —
Give God the glo - ry, Spir - it, Son and Fa - ther;

If we have seen him, we have seen the
Who else u - nites us, one in God the
He, who re - deems us, reigns with God the
Give God the glo - ry, God in Man my

Fa - ther: Glo - ry to God on high.
Fa - ther? Glo - ry to God on high.
Fa - ther: Glo - ry to God on high.
broth - er: Glo - ry to God on high.

Text: Fred Pratt Green, b.1903,
Tune: CHRISTE SANCTORUM, 10 11 11 6; *Paris Antiphoner*, 1681

544 Reap Me the Earth

1. Reap me the earth as a
2. Go with your song and your
3. Glad - ness and pit - y and

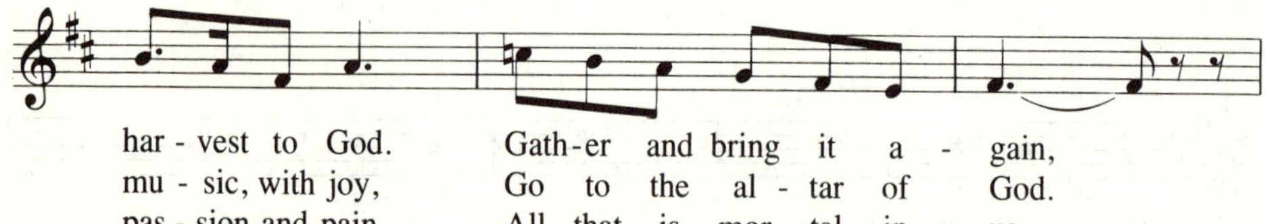
har - vest to God. Gath - er and bring it a - gain,
mu - sic, with joy, Go to the al - tar of God.
pas - sion and pain, All that is mor - tal in us,

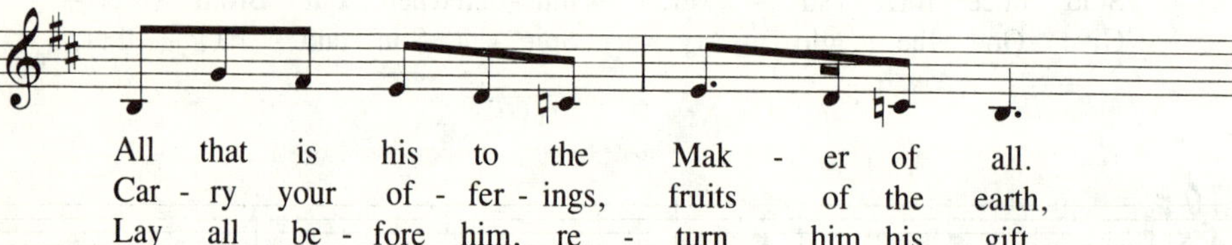
All that is his to the Mak - er of all.
Car - ry your of - fer - ings, fruits of the earth,
Lay all be - fore him, re - turn him his gift,

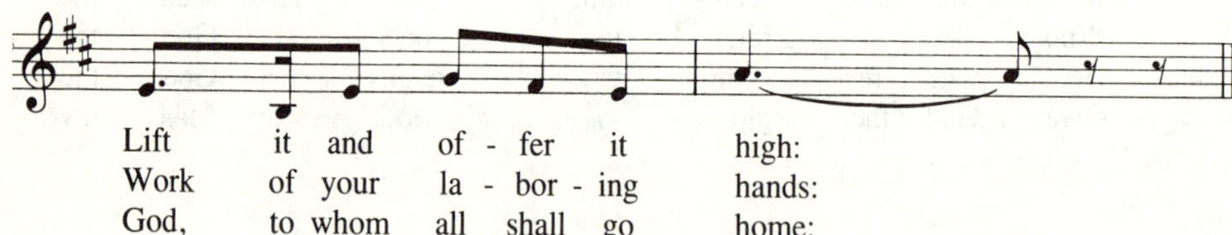
Lift it and of - fer it high:
Work of your la - bor - ing hands:
God, to whom all shall go home:

Bring bread, bring wine, give glo - ry to the Lord.

Whose is the earth but God's, whose is the praise but

his?

Text: Luke Connaughton, 1917-1979, © 1970, Mayhew McCrimmon Ltd.
Tune: BAY HALL, 10 7 10 7 with refrain; Michael Dawney, b.1942, ©

Praise Him 545

1. Praise him, praise him, praise him! pow'rs and dom - i - na-tions,
2. Praise him, praise him, praise him! o - cean depths and wa-ters,
3. Praise him, praise him, praise him! saints of God who fear him:
Praise his Name in glo - rious light, you crea - tures of the day!
El - e-ments of earth and heav'n, your sev - eral prais-es blend.
To the high - est Name of all, con - cert - ed an-thems raise —
Moon and stars ring prais - es through the con-stel - la - tions:
Birds and beasts and cat - tle, Ad - am's sons and daugh-ters,
Is - rael's sons and daugh-ters, ho - ly peo-ple near him,
Lord God, whose word shall nev - er pass a-
Wor - ship the King whose reign shall nev - er
Whom he ex - alts to power and crowns with
way.
end!
praise.

Text: Psalm 148; Michael A. Perry, b.1942
Tune: PRAISE HIM, 4 8 7 6 6 6 10; Norman L. Warren, b.1934

546 O That I Had a Thousand Voices

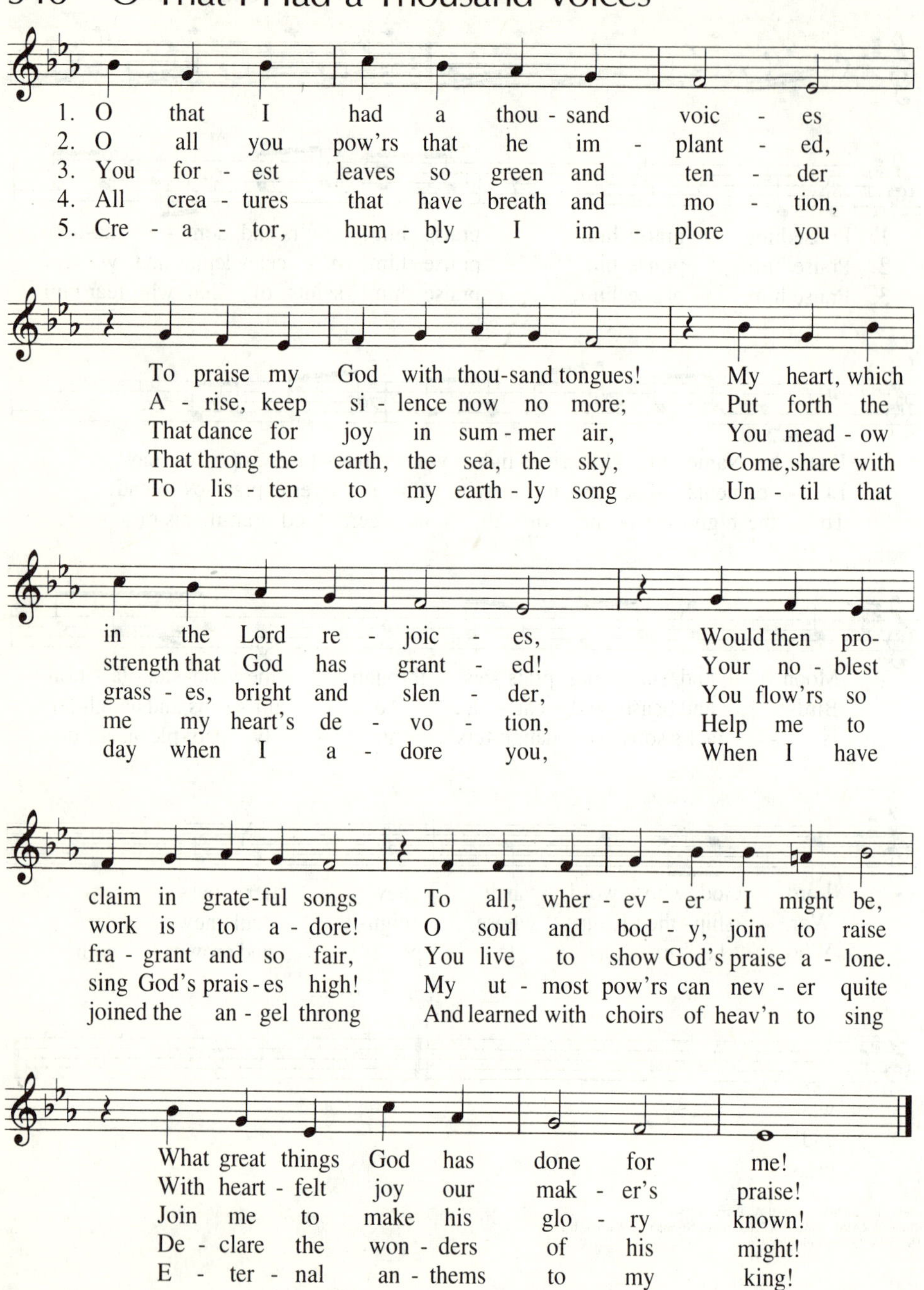
1. O that I had a thousand voices
To praise my God with thousand tongues!
My heart, which in the Lord rejoices,
Would then proclaim in grateful songs
To all, wherever I might be,
What great things God has done for me!
2. O all you pow'rs that he implanted,
Arise, keep silence now no more;
Put forth the strength that God has granted!
Your noblest work is to adore!
O soul and body, join to raise
With heartfelt joy our maker's praise!
3. You forest leaves so green and tender
That dance for joy in summer air,
You meadow grasses, bright and slender,
You flow'rs so fragrant and so fair,
You live to show God's praise alone.
Join me to make his glory known!
4. All creatures that have breath and motion,
That throng the earth, the sea, the sky,
Come, share with me my heart's devotion,
Help me to sing God's praises high!
My utmost pow'rs can never quite
Declare the wonders of his might!
5. Creator, humbly I implore you
To listen to my earthly song
Until that day when I adore you,
When I have joined the angel throng
And learned with choirs of heav'n to sing
Eternal anthems to my king!

Text: *O dass ich tausend Zungen hätte;* Johann Mentzer, 1658-1734; Tr. *The Lutheran Hymnal,* 1941, alt.
Tune: O DASS ICH TAUSEND ZUNGEN HÄTTE, 9 8 9 8 88; Attr. to Johann B. König, 1691-1758

Praise to the Lord, the Almighty 547

1. Praise to the Lord, the Al - might - y, the
2. Praise to the Lord, a - bove all things so
3. Praise to the Lord, who shall pros - per our
4. Praise to the Lord — O let all that is

king of cre - a - tion! O my soul,
might - i - ly reign - ing; Keep - ing us
work and de - fend us; Sure - ly his
in us a - dore him! All that has

praise him, for he is your health and sal-
safe at his side, and so gent - ly sus-
good - ness and mer - cy shall dai - ly at-
life and breath come now with prais - es be-

va - tion! Come, all who hear:
tain - ing. Have you not seen
tend us. Pon - der a - new
fore him! Let the "A - men!"

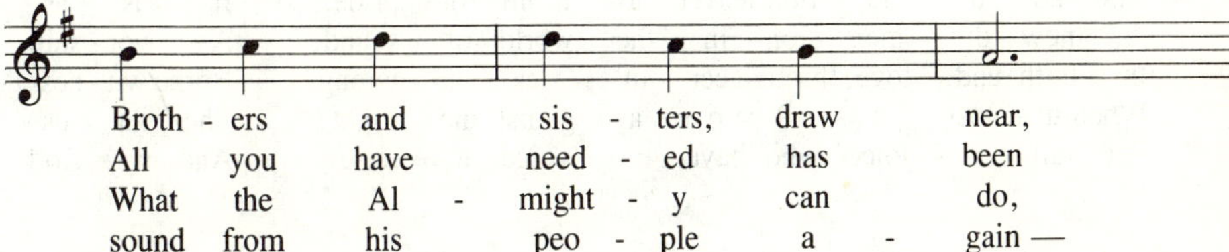
Broth - ers and sis - ters, draw near,
All you have need - ed has been
What the Al - might - y can do,
sound from his peo - ple a - gain —

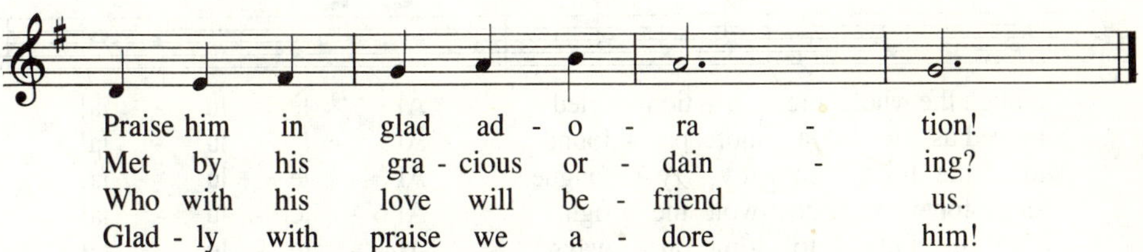
Praise him in glad ad - o - ra - tion!
Met by his gra - cious or - dain - ing?
Who with his love will be - friend us.
Glad - ly with praise we a - dore him!

Text: *Lobe den Herren, den mächtigen König;* Joachim Neander, 1650-1680; Tr. by Catherine Winkworth, 1827-1878, alt.
Tune: LOBE DEN HERREN, 14 14 47 8; Straslund Gesangbuch, 1665; Descant by C.S. Lang, 1891-1971,

548 Adoramus Te Domine

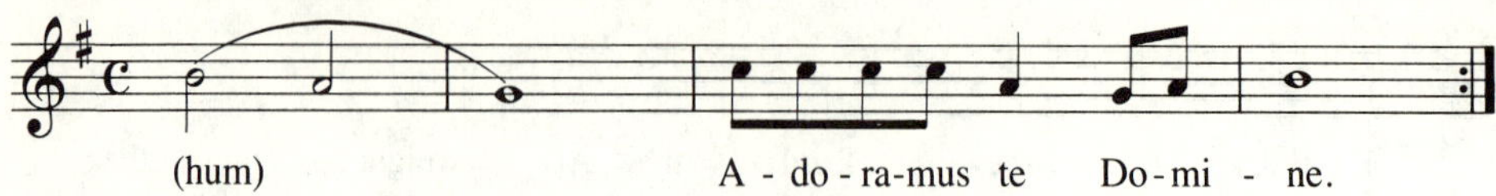
(hum)
A - do - ra-mus te Do - mi - ne.

Text: *We adore you, Lord;* Taizé Community, 1978
Tune: Jacques Berthier, b.1923

549 When in Our Music God Is Glorified

1. When in our mu - sic God is glo - ri - fied,
2. How of - ten, mak - ing mu - sic, we have found
3. So has the Church in lit - ur - gy and song,
4. And did not Je - sus sing a psalm that night
5. Let ev - 'ry in - stru-ment be tuned for praise!

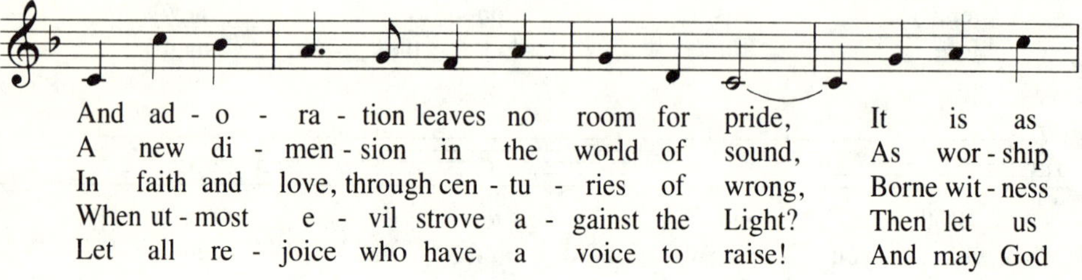
And ad - o - ra - tion leaves no room for pride, It is as
A new di - men - sion in the world of sound, As wor - ship
In faith and love, through cen - tu - ries of wrong, Borne wit - ness
When ut - most e - vil strove a - gainst the Light? Then let us
Let all re - joice who have a voice to raise! And may God

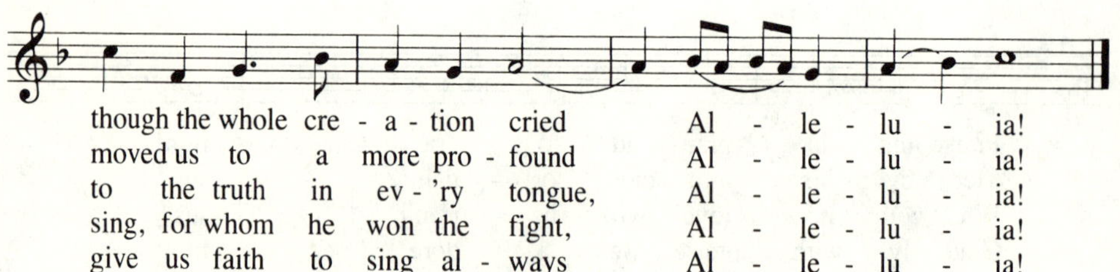
though the whole cre - a - tion cried Al - le - lu - ia!
moved us to a more pro - found Al - le - lu - ia!
to the truth in ev - 'ry tongue, Al - le - lu - ia!
sing, for whom he won the fight, Al - le - lu - ia!
give us faith to sing al - ways Al - le - lu - ia!

Text: Mark 14:26; Fred Pratt Green, b.1903, © 1972, Hope Publishing Co.
Tune: ENGELBERG, 10 10 10 with alleluia; Charles V. Stanford, 1852-1924

Sing a New Song to the Lord 550

1. Sing a new song to the Lord,
2. Now to the ends of the earth
3. Sing a new song and re - joice,
4. Join with the hills and the sea

He to whom won - ders be - long!
See his sal - va - tion is shown;
Pub - lish his prais - es a - broad!
Thun - ders of praise to pro - long!

Re - joice in his tri - umph and
And still he re - mem - bers his
Let voic - es in cho - rus, with
In judge - ment and jus - tice he

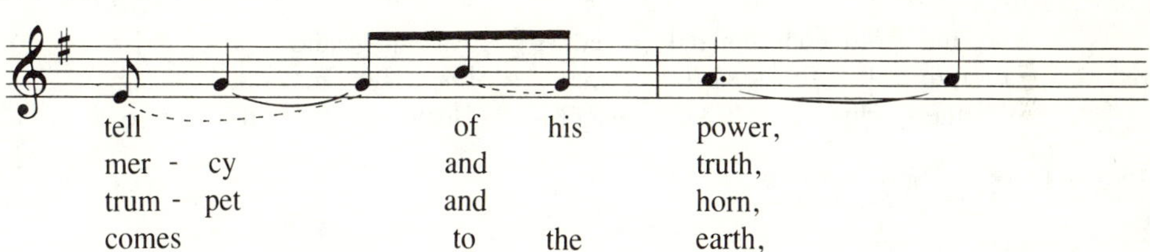
tell of his power,
mer - cy and truth,
trum - pet and horn,
comes to the earth,

O sing to the Lord a new song!
Un - chang - ing in love to his own.
Re - sound for the joy of the Lord!
O sing to the Lord a new song!

Text: Psalm 98; Timothy Dudley-Smith, b.1926,
Tune: CANTATE DOMINO, Irregular; David G. Wilson, b.1940,

551 Praise the Lord of Heaven

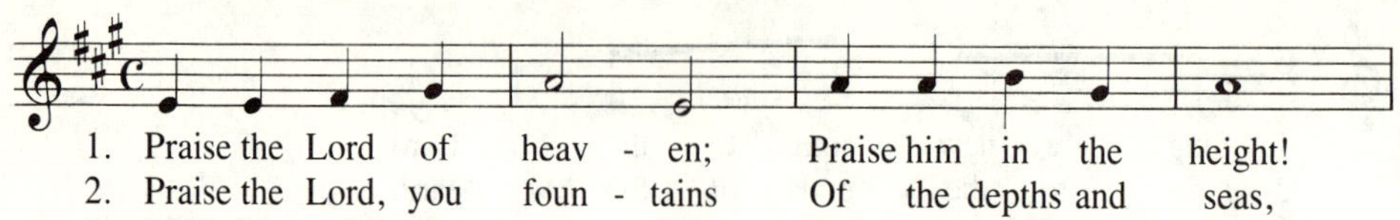
1. Praise the Lord of heav - en; Praise him in the height!
2. Praise the Lord, you foun - tains Of the depths and seas,
3. Praise him, all you na - tions, Rul - ers and all kings;

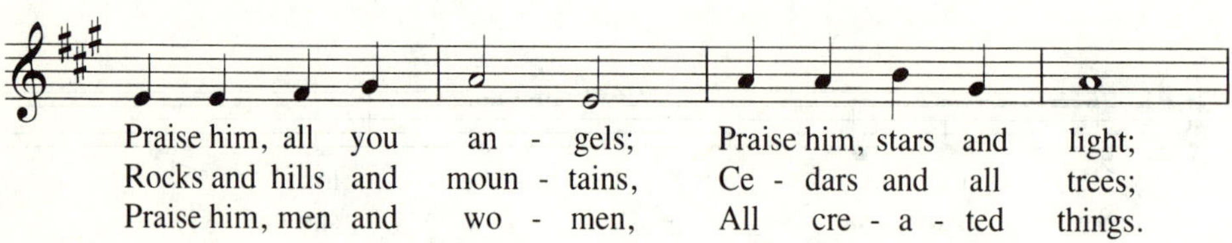
Praise him, all you an - gels; Praise him, stars and light;
Rocks and hills and moun - tains, Ce - dars and all trees;
Praise him, men and wo - men, All cre - a - ted things.

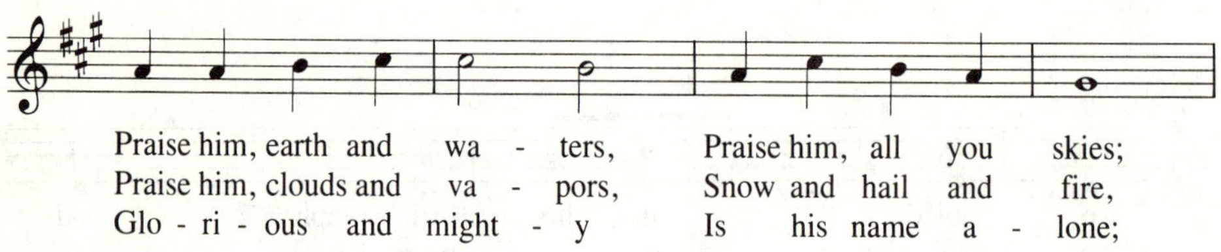
Praise him, earth and wa - ters, Praise him, all you skies;
Praise him, clouds and va - pors, Snow and hail and fire,
Glo - ri - ous and might - y Is his name a - lone;

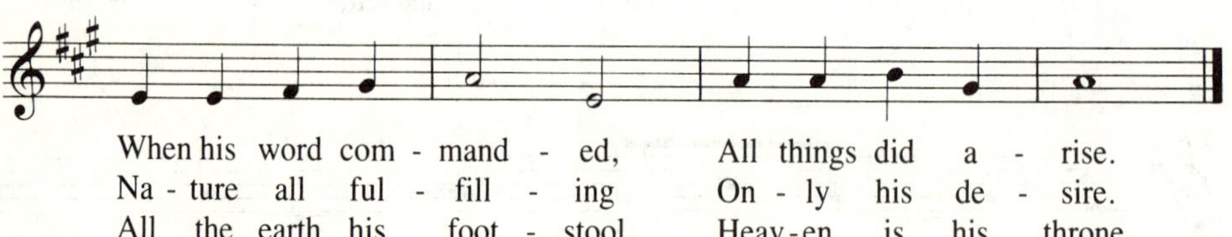
When his word com - mand - ed, All things did a - rise.
Na - ture all ful - fill - ing On - ly his de - sire.
All the earth his foot - stool, Heav - en is his throne.

Text: Psalm 148; Thomas B. Browne, 1805-1874, alt.
Tune: UNE VAINE CRAINTE, 6 5 6 5 D; French

552 Come, We That Love the Lord

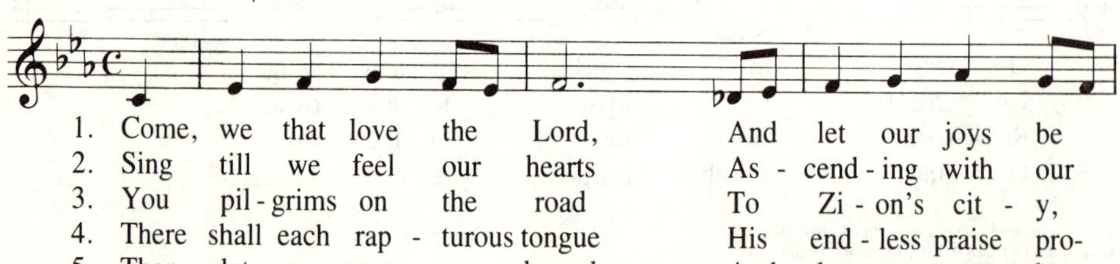
1. Come, we that love the Lord, And let our joys be
2. Sing till we feel our hearts As - cend - ing with our
3. You pil - grims on the road To Zi - on's cit - y,
4. There shall each rap - turous tongue His end - less praise pro-
5. Then let our songs a - bound And let our tears be

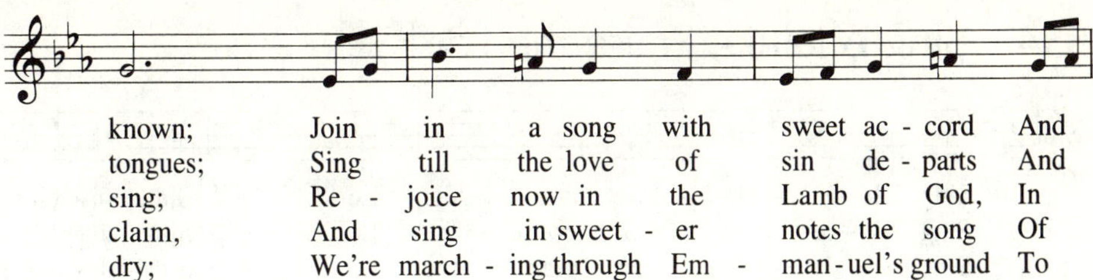
known; Join in a song with sweet ac - cord And
tongues; Sing till the love of sin de - parts And
sing; Re - joice now in the Lamb of God, In
claim, And sing in sweet - er notes the song Of
dry; We're march - ing through Em - man - uel's ground To

thus sur - round the throne.
grace in - spires our songs.
Christ, the e - ter - nal King. Ho - san - na, Ho-
Mo - ses and the Lamb.
fair - er worlds on high.

san - na, Re - joice, give thanks and sing.

Text: St. 1 & 5, Issac Watts, 1674-1748; St. 2-4, William Hammond, 1719-1783
Tune: VINEYARD HAVEN, SM with refrain; Richard Dirksen, b.1921, © 1974, 1986 Harold Flammer, Inc.

Canon

Magnificat 553

A
Ma - gni - fi - cat, ma - gni - fi - cat,
B
Ma - gni - fi - cat a - ni - ma
me - a Do - mi - num.
C
Ma - gni - fi - cat, ma - gni - fi - cat,
D
Ma - gni - fi - cat a - ni - ma me - a!

Text: Luke 1:46, *My soul magnifies the Lord;* Taizé Community, 1978
Tune: Jacques Berthier, b.1923

554 Sing Alleluia, Praise the Lord

1. Sing al - le - lu - ia, praise the Lord! Sing praise on earth, al - le - lu - ia. Sing praise in heav'n, de - clare his pow'r. Sing praise for all his might - y acts.
2. Sing al - le - lu - ia, praise the Lord! Sing al - le- lu - ia, praise his worth. Sing his a - chieve-ments, strength su- preme. Sing praise for his tran - scend-en - cy.
3. Sing al - le - lu - ia, praise the Lord! Sing al - le- lu - ia, praise with joy. Sing praise with psal - ter - y and harp. Sing praise with trum - pets blast-ing forth.
4. Sing al - le - lu - ia, praise the Lord! Sing praise with charm-ing reed and flute. Sing praise with danc - ing and with drums. Sing praise with strings most del - i - cate.

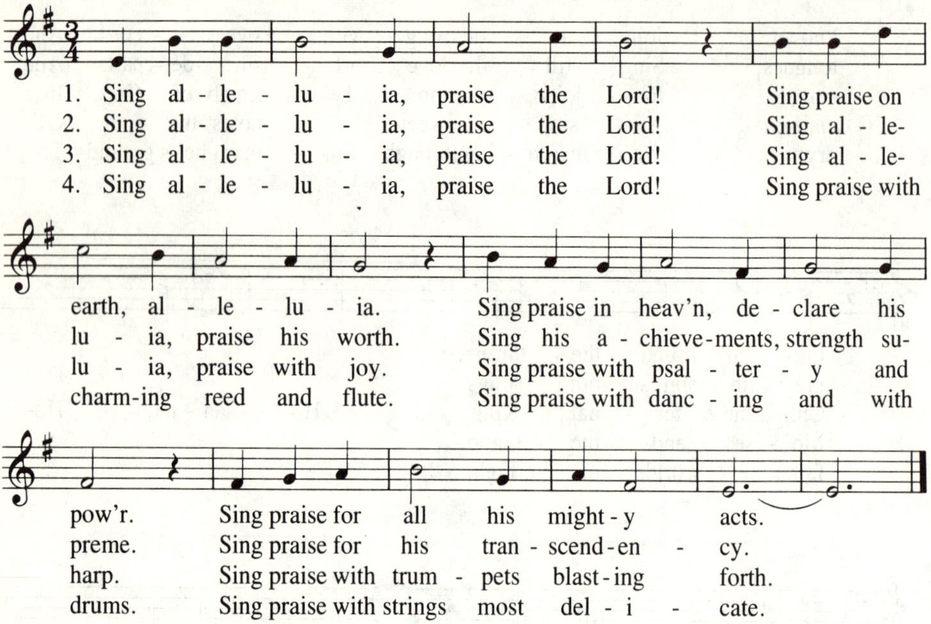

5. Sing alleluia, praise the Lord!
Sing alleluia, cymbals clash.
Sing alleluia, cymbals ring.
Sing all that breathe, alleluia!

6. Sing alleluia, praise the Lord!
All ages glorify his name.
Father and Son and Spirit, one;
Now and for evermore. Amen!

Text: Psalm 150 *Lobt Gott in seinem Heiligtum;* Cornelius Becker, 1561-1604; Tr. by Daniel G. Reuning, b.1935,
Tune: LOBT GOTT IN SEINEM HEILIGTUM, LM; Heinrich Schütz, 1585-1672

555 Jubilate Deo

Canon - *2 voices*

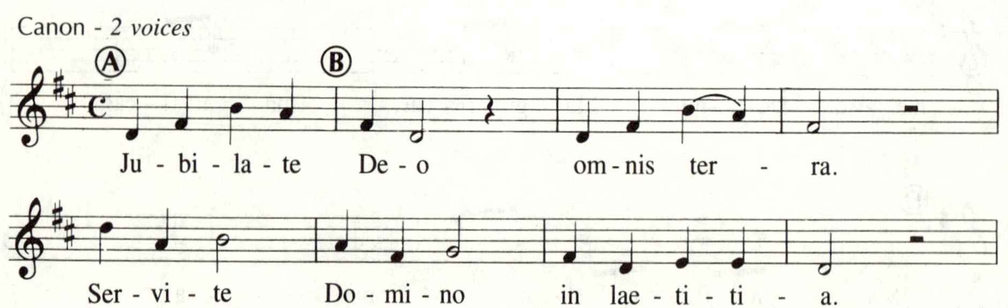
A
B
Ju - bi - la - te De - o om - nis ter - ra.
Ser - vi - te Do - mi - no in lae - ti - ti - a.

Al - le - lu - ia, al - le - lu - ia, in lae - ti - ti - a.
Al - le - lu - ia, al - le - lu - ia, in lae - ti - ti - a!

Text: Psalm 100, *Rejoice in God, all the earth. Serve the Lord with gladness;* Taizé Community, 1978
Tune: Jacques Berthier, b.1923

Lord of Our Growing Years 556

1. Lord of our grow - ing years, With us from in - fan - cy,
Laugh-ter and quick-dried tears, Fresh-ness and en - er - gy:
Your grace sur - rounds us all our days—
For all your gifts we bring our praise.

2. Lord of our strong - est years, Stretch-ing our youth - ful pow'rs,
Lov - ers and pi - o - neers When all the world seems ours:
Your grace sur - rounds us all our days—
For all your gifts we bring our praise.

3. Lord of our mid - dle years, Giv - er of stead - fast - ness,
Cour - age that per - se - veres When there is small suc - cess:
Your grace sur - rounds us all our days—
For all your gifts we bring our praise.

4. Lord of our old - er years, Steep though the road may be,
Rid us of fool - ish fears, Bring us se - ren - i - ty:
Your grace sur - rounds us all our days—
For all your gifts we bring our praise.

5. Lord of our clos - ing years, Al - ways your prom - ise stands;
Hold us when death ap - pears, Safe - ly with - in your hands:
Your grace sur - rounds us all our days—
For all your gifts we bring our praise.

Text: David Mowbray, b.1938, © 1982, Hope Publishing Co.
Tune: LITTLE CORNARD, 6 6 6 6 88; Martin Shaw, 1875-1958, © J. Curwen and Sons

557 For the Beauty of the Earth

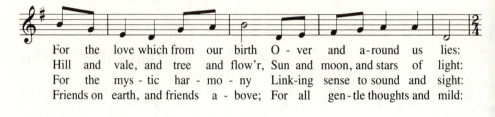

1. For the beau - ty of the earth, For the glo - ry of the skies,
2. For the beau - ty of each hour Of the day and of the night,
3. For the joy of ear and eye, For the heart and mind's de - light,
4. For the joy of hu-man love, Broth-er, sis - ter, par - ent, child,

For the love which from our birth O - ver and a-round us lies:
Hill and vale, and tree and flow'r, Sun and moon, and stars of light:
For the mys - tic har - mo - ny Link-ing sense to sound and sight:
Friends on earth, and friends a - bove; For all gen - tle thoughts and mild:

Lord of all, to you we raise This our hymn of grate - ful praise.

5. For your church, that evermore
Lifts its holy hands above,
Off'ring up on ev'ry shore
Its pure sacrifice of love:
Lord of all, to you we raise
This our hymn of grateful praise.

6. For, yourself, best Gift Divine!
To this world so freely giv'n;
Word Incarnate, God's design,
Peace on earth and joy in heav'n:
Lord of all, to you we raise
This our hymn of grateful praise.

Text: Folliot S. Pierpont, 1835-1917
Tune: LUCERNA LAUDONIAE, 7 7 7 7 77; David Evans, 1874-1948

Father, We Thank Thee, Who Hast Planted 558

1. Fa - ther, we thank thee, who hast plant - ed Thy ho - ly
2. Watch o'er thy Church, O Lord, in mer - cy, Save it from
Name with - in our hearts. Knowl-edge and faith and life im-
e - vil, guard it still, Per - fect it in thy love, u-
mor - tal Je - sus, thy Son, to us im - parts.
nite it, Cleansed and con-formed un - to thy will.
Thou, Lord, didst make all for thy plea - sure, Didst give us
As grain, once scat - ter'd on the hill - sides, Was in this
food for all our days, Giv - ing in Christ the Bread
bro - ken bread made one, So from all lands thy Church
e - ter - nal; Thine is the power, be thine the praise.
be gath - er'd In - to thy king - dom by thy Son.

Text: From the *Didache*, c.110; Tr. by F. Bland Tucker, 1895-1984, alt., © 1940, The Church Pension Fund
Tune: RENDEZ À DIEU, 9 8 9 8 D; *Genevan Psalter*, 1551; Attr. to Louis Bourgeois, c.1510-1561

559 Let All Things Now Living

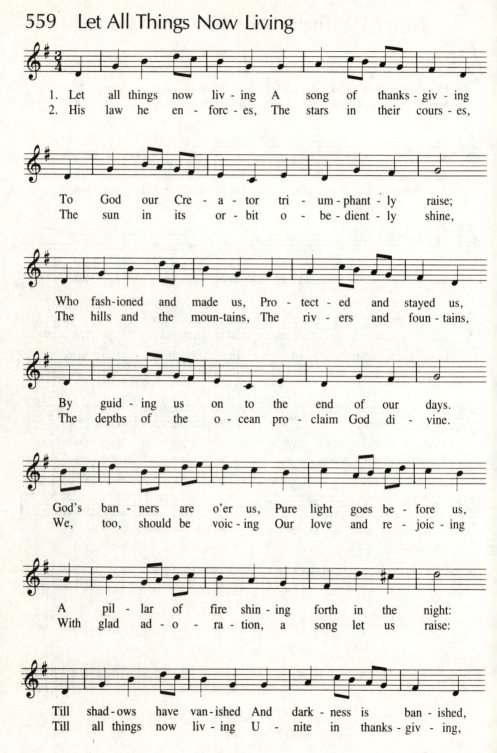

1. Let all things now liv - ing A song of thanks - giv - ing
2. His law he en - forc - es, The stars in their cours - es,

To God our Cre - a - tor tri - um - phant - ly raise;
The sun in its or - bit o - be - dient - ly shine,

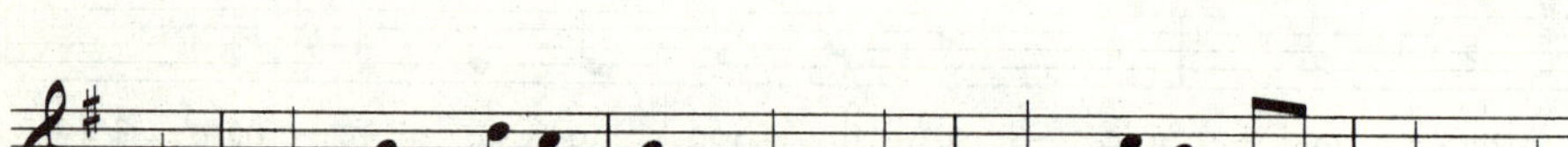

Who fash-ioned and made us, Pro - tect - ed and stayed us,
The hills and the moun-tains, The riv - ers and foun - tains,

By guid - ing us on to the end of our days.
The depths of the o - cean pro - claim God di - vine.

God's ban - ners are o'er us, Pure light goes be - fore us,
We, too, should be voic - ing Our love and re - joic - ing

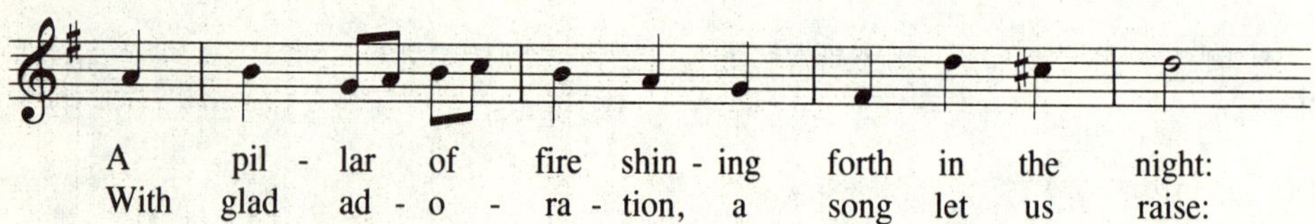

A pil - lar of fire shin - ing forth in the night:
With glad ad - o - ra - tion, a song let us raise:

Till shad - ows have van - ished And dark - ness is ban - ished,
Till all things now liv - ing U - nite in thanks - giv - ing,

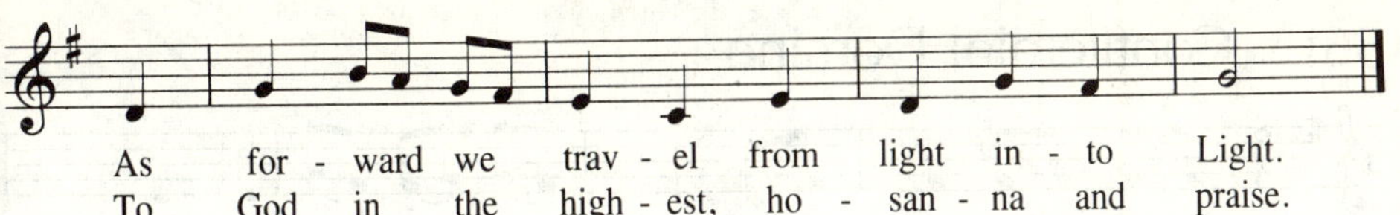

As for - ward we trav - el from light in - to Light.
To God in the high - est, ho - san - na and praise.

Text: Katherine K. Davis, 1892-1980, © 1939, E.C. Schirmer Music Co.
Tune: ASH GROVE, 66 11 66 11 D; Welsh; Harm. by Gerald H. Knight, 1908-1979, © The Royal School of Church Music

Now Thank We All Our God 560

1. Now thank we all our God With hearts and hands and voic - es,
2. O may this gra - cious God Through all our life be near us,
3. All praise and thanks to God The Fa - ther now be giv - en,

Who won-drous things has done, In whom his world re - joic - es;
With ev - er joy - ful hearts And bless - ed peace to cheer us;
The Son, and Spir - it blest, Who reigns in high - est heav - en,

Who, from our moth - ers' arms, Hath blessed us on our way
Pre - serve us in his grace, And guide us in dis - tress,
E - ter - nal, Tri - une God, Whom earth and heav'n a - dore;

With count-less gifts of love, And still is ours to - day.
And free us from all sin, Till heav - en we pos - sess.
For thus it was, is now, And shall be ev - er - more.

Text: *Nun danket alle Gott;* Martin Rinkart, 1586-1649; Tr. by Catherine Winkworth, 1827-1878, alt.
Tune: NUN DANKET, 6 7 6 7 6 6 6 6; Johann Crüger, 1598-1662; Harm. by A. Gregory Murray, OSB, b.1905

561 Confitemini Domino

Con-fi - te - mi - ni Do - mi - no quo - ni - am bo - nus.
Con-fi - te - mi - ni Do - mi - no, Al - le - lu - ia!

Text: Psalm 137, *Give thanks to the Lord for he is good;* Taizé Community, 1982
Tune: Jacques Berthier, b.1923

562 For the Fruits of This Creation

1. For the fruits of this cre - a - tion, Thanks be to God;
For the gifts to ev - 'ry na - tion, Thanks be to God;
For the plow - ing, sow - ing, reap - ing, Si - lent growth while we are sleep - ing,
Fu - ture needs in earth's safe keep - ing, Thanks be to God.

2. In the just re - ward of la - bor, God's will is done;
In the help we give our neigh - bor, God's will is done;
In our world - wide task of car - ing For the hun - gry and de - spair - ing,
In the har - vests we are shar - ing, God's will is done.

3. For the har - vests of the Spir - it, Thanks be to God;
For the good we all in - her - it, Thanks be to God;
For the won - ders that as - tound us, For the truths that still con - found us,
Most of all, that love has found us, Thanks be to God.

Text: Fred Pratt Green, b.1903,
Tune: EAST ACKLAM, 8 4 8 4 888 4; Francis Jackson, b.1917, ©

God, Omnipotent, Eternal 563

1. God, om - nip - o - tent, e - ter - nal,
2. In that dis - tant, wild be - gin - ning
3. "Si - lence this in - de - cent danc - ing,"
4. Lord, for - give us; Lord, re - store us,
5. Teach us to de - light in jus - tice,

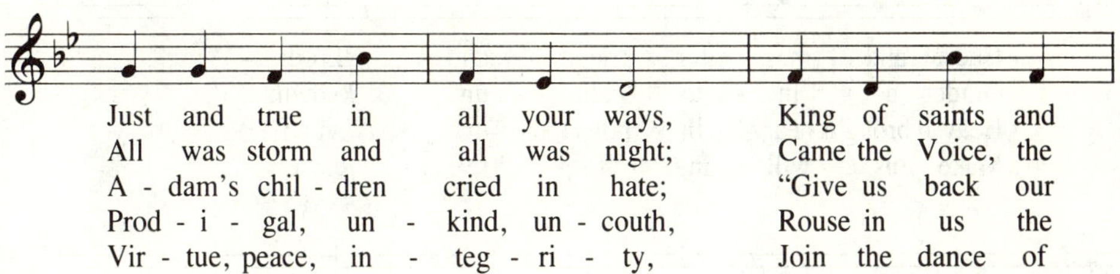
Just and true in all your ways,
All was storm and all was night;
A - dam's chil - dren cried in hate;
Prod - i - gal, un - kind, un - couth,
Vir - tue, peace, in - teg - ri - ty,
King of saints and
Came the Voice, the
"Give us back our
Rouse in us the
Join the dance of

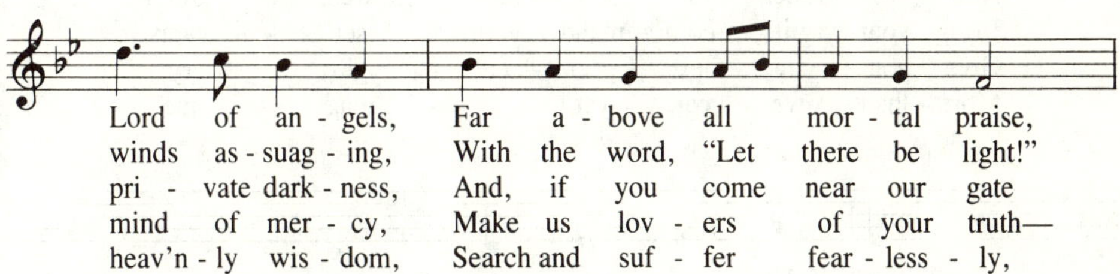
Lord of an - gels, Far a - bove all mor - tal praise,
winds as - suag - ing, With the word, "Let there be light!"
pri - vate dark - ness, And, if you come near our gate
mind of mer - cy, Make us lov - ers of your truth—
heav'n - ly wis - dom, Search and suf - fer fear - less - ly,

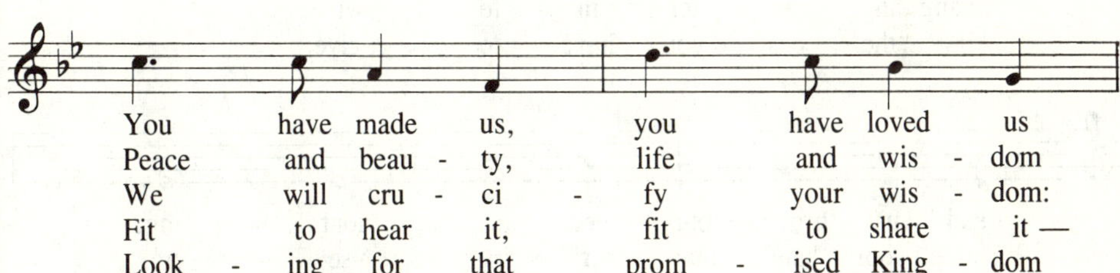
You have made us, you have loved us
Peace and beau - ty, life and wis - dom
We will cru - ci - fy your wis - dom:
Fit to hear it, fit to share it —
Look - ing for that prom - ised King - dom

Since those first re - bel - lious days.
Danced in their cre - a - tor's sight.
Leave our home in - vi - o - late!"
So re - new our pri - mal youth.
Where your truth shall make us free.

Text: Erik Routley, 1917-1982,
Tune: REGENT SQUARE, 8 7 8 7 8 7; Henry T. Smart, 1813-1879

564 Jesus, Come! For We Invite You

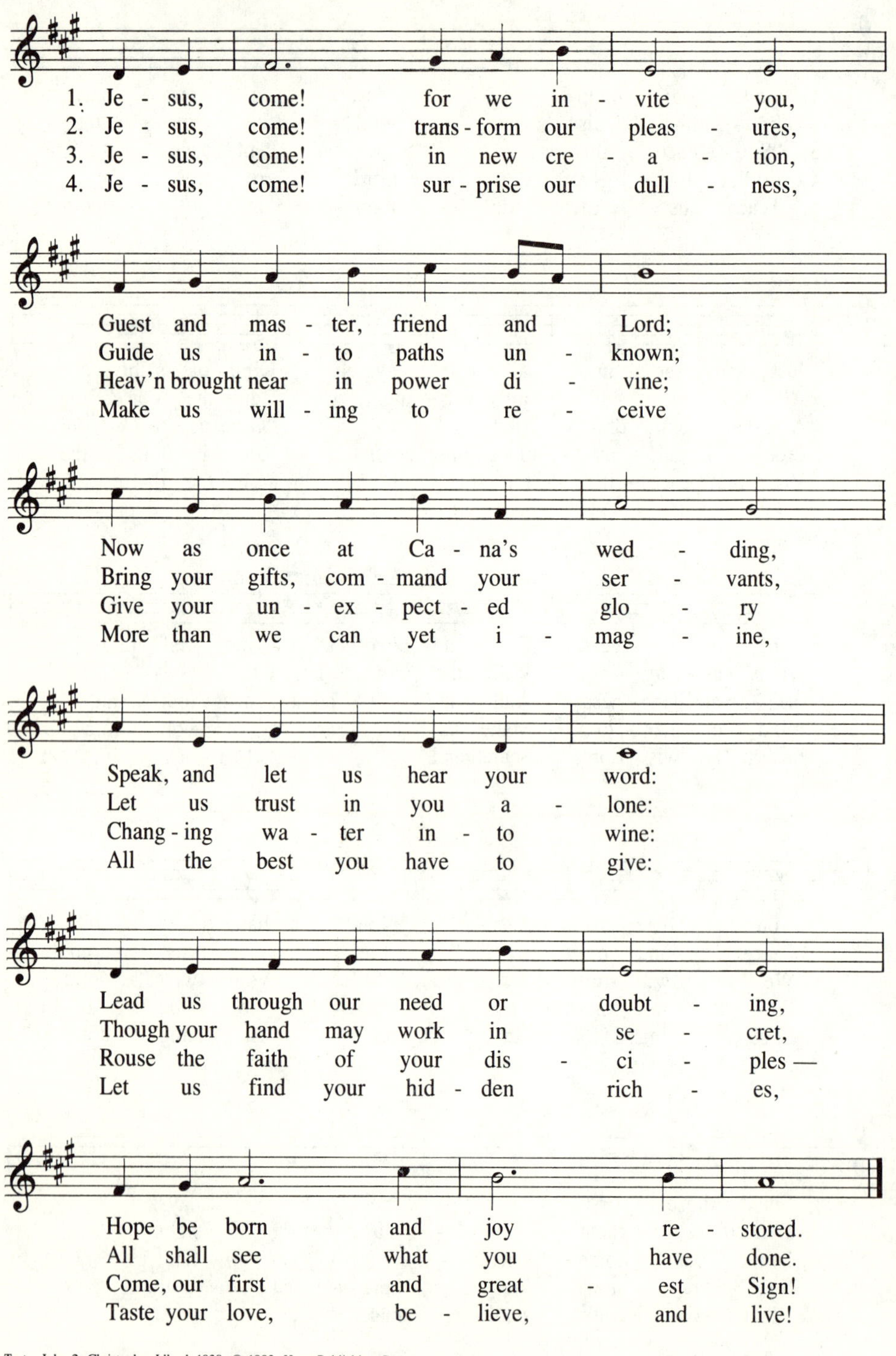
1. Je - sus, come! for we in - vite you,
2. Je - sus, come! trans - form our pleas - ures,
3. Je - sus, come! in new cre - a - tion,
4. Je - sus, come! sur - prise our dull - ness,
Guest and mas - ter, friend and Lord;
Guide us in - to paths un - known;
Heav'n brought near in power di - vine;
Make us will - ing to re - ceive
Now as once at Ca - na's wed - ding,
Bring your gifts, com - mand your ser - vants,
Give your un - ex - pect - ed glo - ry
More than we can yet i - mag - ine,
Speak, and let us hear your word:
Let us trust in you a - lone:
Chang - ing wa - ter in - to wine:
All the best you have to give:
Lead us through our need or doubt - ing,
Though your hand may work in se - cret,
Rouse the faith of your dis - ci - ples —
Let us find your hid - den rich - es,
Hope be born and joy re - stored.
All shall see what you have done.
Come, our first and great - est Sign!
Taste your love, be - lieve, and live!

Text: John 2; Christopher Idle, b.1938, © 1982, Hope Publishing Co.
Tune: BEST GIFT, 8 7 8 7 8 7; Ronald F. Krisman, b.1946, © 1986, GIA Publications, Inc.

Hope of the World 565

1. Hope of the world, O Christ of great com - pas - sion:
2. Hope of the world, God's gift from high - est heav - en,
3. Hope of the world, a - foot on dust - y high - ways,
4. Hope of the world, who by your cross did save us
5. Hope of the world, O Christ, o'er death vic - to - rious,
Speak to our fear - ful hearts by con - flict rent.
Bring - ing to hun - gry souls the bread of life:
Show - ing to wan - d'ring souls the path of light:
From death and dark de - spair, from sin and guilt:
Who by this sign did con - quer grief and pain:
Save us, your peo - ple, from con - sum - ing pas - sion,
Still let your Spir - it un - to us be giv - en
Walk now be - side us lest the tempt - ing by - ways
We ren - der back the love your mer - cy gave us;
We would be faith - ful to your gos - pel glo - rious;
Who by our own false hopes and aims are spent.
To heal earth's wounds and end our bit - ter strife.
Lure us a - way from you to end - less night.
Take now our lives and use them as you will.
You are our Lord! And you for ev - er reign!

Text: Georgia Harkness, 1891-1974, alt.,
Tune: DONNE SECOURS, 11 10 11 10; *Genevan Psalter*, 1551; Harm. by Claude Goudimel, c.1505-1572

566 Come to Us, Creative Spirit

1. Come to us, cre - a - tive Spir - it, In our
2. Po - et, paint - er, mu - sic - mak - er, All your
3. Word from God e - ter - nal spring - ing, Fill our
4. In all plac - es and for - ev - er Glo - ry

Fa - ther's house; Ev - 'ry hu - man tal - ent hal - low,
trea - sures bring; Crafts-man, ac - tor, grace-ful danc - er,
minds, we pray; And in all ar - tis - tic vi - sion
be ex - pressed To the Son, with God the Fa - ther

Hid - den skills a - rouse, That with- in your earth - ly
Make your of - fer - ing; Join your hands in cel - e-
Give in - te - gri - ty: May the flame with - in us
And the Spir - it blessed: In our wor - ship and our

tem - ple, Wise and sim - ple, may re - joice.
bra - tion: Let cre - a - tion shout and sing!
burn - ing Kin - dle yearn - ing day by day.
liv - ing Keep us striv - ing for the best.

Text: David Mowbray, b.1938, © Stainer and Bell Publications
Tune: CASTLEWOOD, 8 5 8 5 84 3; Richard Proulx, b.1937, © 1986, GIA Publications, Inc.

567 God Be in My Head

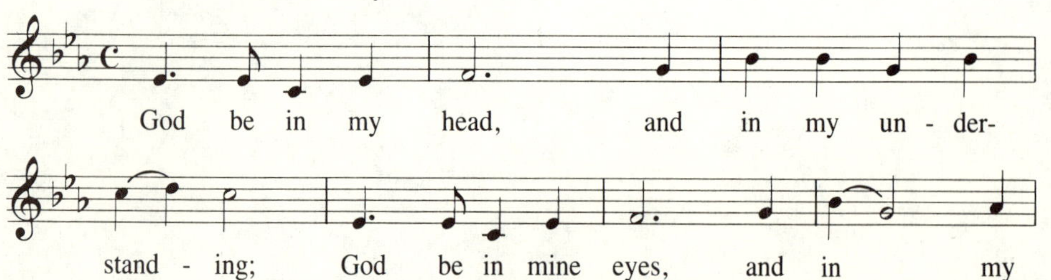
God be in my head, and in my un - der-
stand - ing; God be in mine eyes, and in my

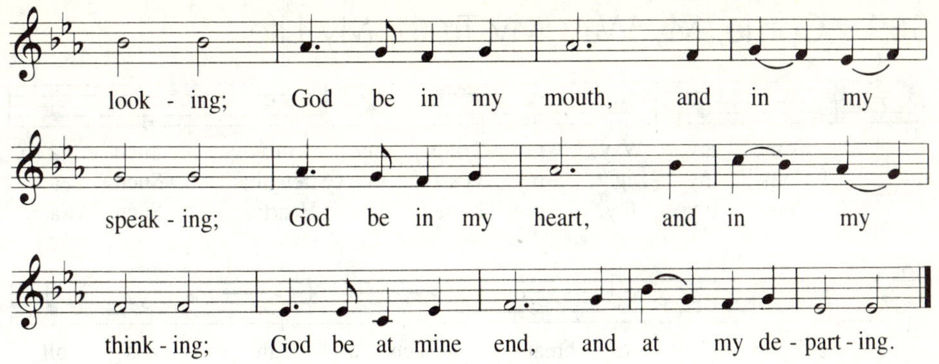
look - ing; God be in my mouth, and in my
speak - ing; God be in my heart, and in my
think - ing; God be at mine end, and at my de - part - ing.

Text: *Sarum Primer,* 1514
Tune: FIELD, Irregular; Keith Landis, b.1922; Harm. Jeffrey Rickard, b.1942, © 1986, Praise Publications

Lord of All Hopefulness 568

1. Lord of all hope - ful - ness, Lord of all joy,
2. Lord of all ea - ger - ness, Lord of all faith,
3. Lord of all kind - li - ness, Lord of all grace,
4. Lord of all gen - tle - ness, Lord of all calm,

Whose trust, e - ver child - like, no cares can de - stroy,
Whose strong hands were skilled at the plane and the lathe,
Your hands swift to wel - come, your arms to em - brace,
Whose voice is con - tent - ment, whose pres - ence is balm,

Be there at our wak - ing, and give us, we pray,
Be there at our la - bors, and give us, we pray,
Be there at our hom - ing, and give us, we pray,
Be there at our sleep - ing, and give us, we pray,

Your bliss in our hearts, Lord, at the break of the day.
Your strength in our hearts, Lord, at the noon of the day.
Your love in our hearts, Lord, at the eve of the day.
Your peace in our hearts, Lord, at the end of the day.

Text: Jan Struther, 1901-1953, © Oxford University Press
Tune: SLANE, 10 11 11 12; Gaelic; Harm. by Erik Routely, 1917-1982, © 1985, Hope Publishing Co.

569 Come, My Way, My Truth, My Life

1. Come, my Way, my Truth, my Life: Such a way as gives us breath; Such a truth as ends all strife; Such a life as kill - eth death.
2. Come, my Light, my Feast, my Strength: Such a light as shows a feast; Such a feast as mends in length; Such a strength as makes his guest.
3. Come, my Joy, my Love, my Heart: Such a joy as none can move; Such a love as none can part; Such a heart as joys in love.

Text: George Herbert, 1593-1632
Tune: THE CALL, 7 7 7 7; Ralph Vaughan Williams, 1872-1958, © Stainer and Bell Publications

570 Our Father, by Whose Name

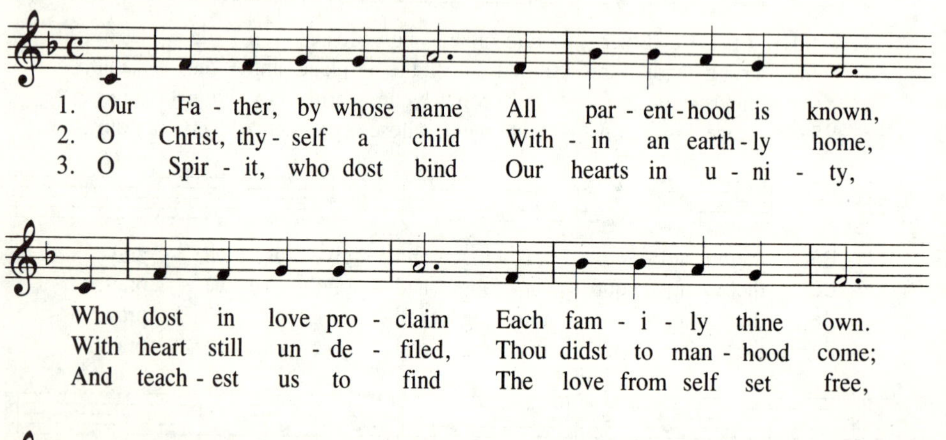
1. Our Fa - ther, by whose name All par - ent - hood is known, Who dost in love pro - claim Each fam - i - ly thine own.
2. O Christ, thy - self a child With - in an earth - ly home, With heart still un - de - filed, Thou didst to man - hood come;
3. O Spir - it, who dost bind Our hearts in u - ni - ty, And teach - est us to find The love from self set free,

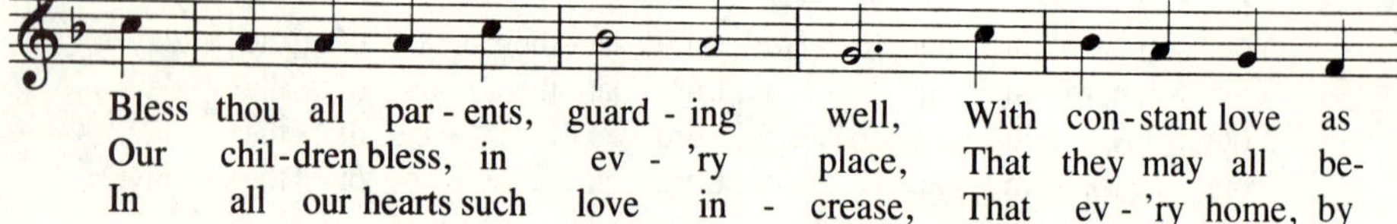
Bless thou all par - ents, guard - ing well, With con - stant love as
Our chil - dren bless, in ev - 'ry place, That they may all be -
In all our hearts such love in - crease, That ev - 'ry home, by

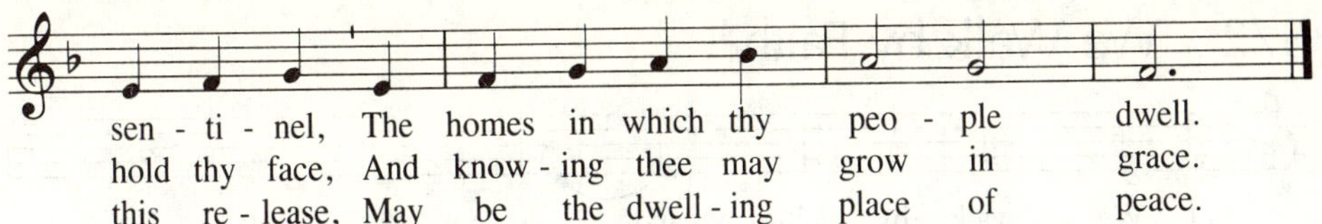
sen - ti - nel, The homes in which thy peo - ple dwell.
hold thy face, And know - ing thee may grow in grace.
this re - lease, May be the dwell - ing place of peace.

Text: F. Bland Tucker, 1895-1984, alt., © 1941, The Church Pension Fund
Tune: RHOSYMEDRE, 6 6 6 6 888; John Edwards, 1806-1885

Faith of Our Fathers 571

1. Faith of our fa - thers! liv - ing still In spite of dun-geon,
2. Our fa- thers, chained in pris - ons dark, Were still in heart and
3. Faith of our fa - thers! faith and pray'r Shall win all na - tions
4. Faith of our fa - thers! we will love Both friend and foe in

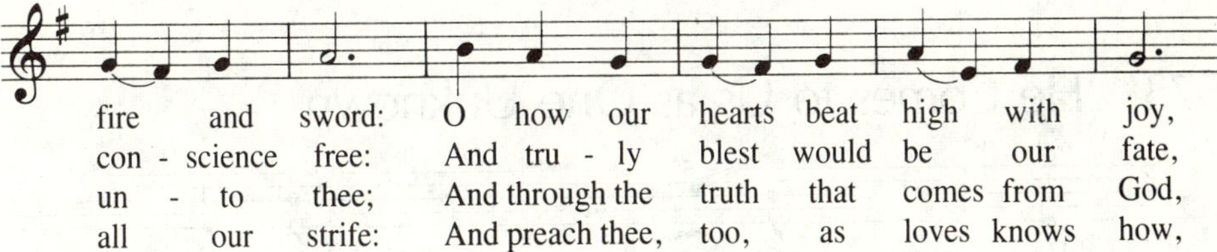
fire and sword: O how our hearts beat high with joy,
con - science free: And tru - ly blest would be our fate,
un - to thee; And through the truth that comes from God,
all our strife: And preach thee, too, as loves knows how,

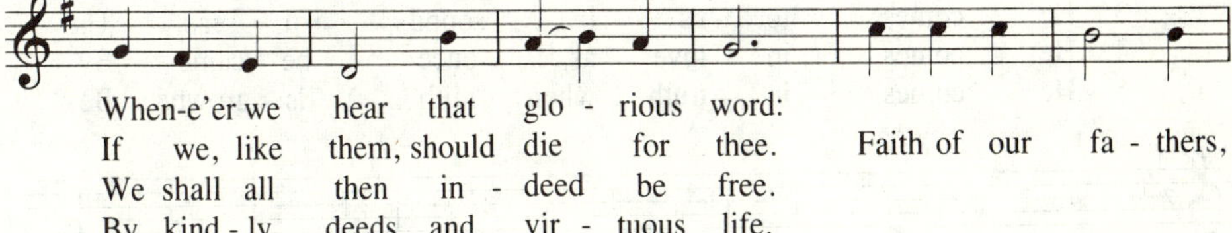
When-e'er we hear that glo - rious word:
If we, like them, should die for thee. Faith of our fa - thers,
We shall all then in - deed be free.
By kind - ly deeds and vir - tuous life.

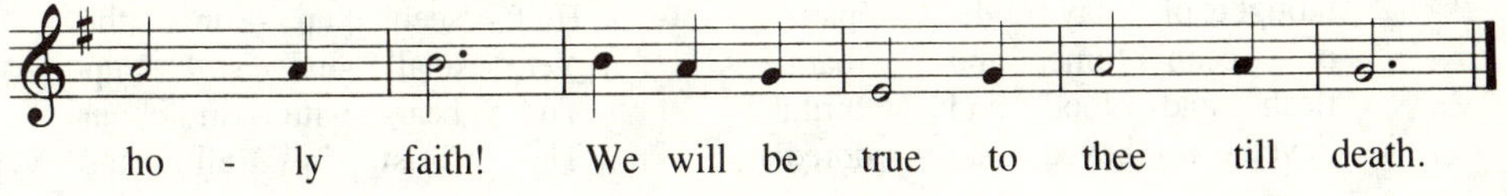
ho - ly faith! We will be true to thee till death.

Text: Frederick W. Faber, 1814-1863, alt.
Tune: ST. CATHERINE, LM with refrain; Henry F. Hemy, 1818-1888; Adapt. by James G. Walton, 1821-1905

572 We Walk by Faith

1. We walk by faith, and not by sight; No
2. We may not touch his hands and side, Nor
3. Help then, O Lord, our un - be - lief; And
4. That, when our life of faith is done, In
gra - cious words we hear From him who spoke as
fol - low where he trod; But in his prom - ise
may our faith a - bound, To call on you when
realms of clear - er light We may be - hold you
none e'er spoke; But we be - lieve him near.
we re - joice, And cry, "My Lord and God!"
you are near, And seek where you are found:
as you are, With full and end - less sight.

Text: Henry Alford, 1810-1871, alt.
Tune: DUNLAP'S CREEK, CM; Samuel McFarland, fl. 1816; Harm. by Richard Proulx, b.1937, © 1986, GIA Publications, Inc.

573 He Comes to Us as One Unknown

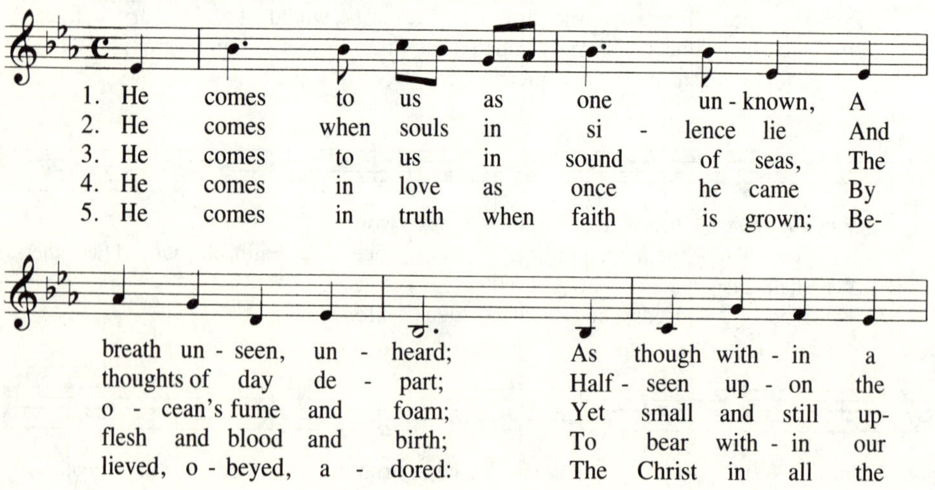
1. He comes to us as one un - known, A
2. He comes when souls in si - lence lie And
3. He comes to us in sound of seas, The
4. He comes in love as once he came By
5. He comes in truth when faith is grown; Be-
breath un - seen, un - heard; As though with - in a
thoughts of day de - part; Half - seen up - on the
o - cean's fume and foam; Yet small and still up-
flesh and blood and birth; To bear with - in our
lieved, o - beyed, a - dored: The Christ in all the

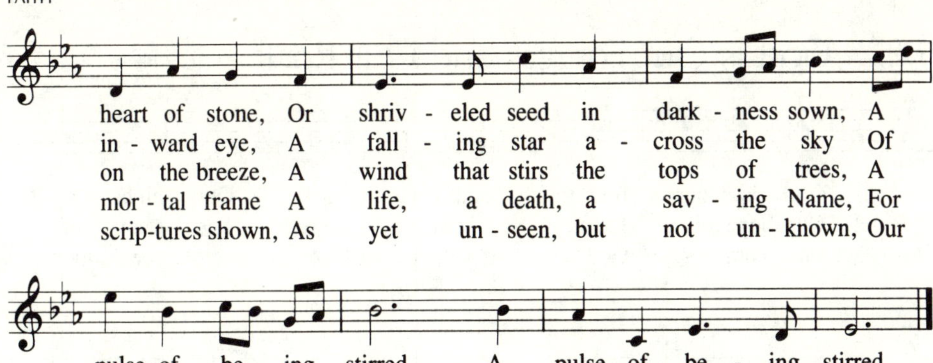
heart of stone, Or shriv - eled seed in dark - ness sown, A
in - ward eye, A fall - ing star a - cross the sky Of
on the breeze, A wind that stirs the tops of trees, A
mor - tal frame A life, a death, a sav - ing Name, For
scrip-tures shown, As yet un - seen, but not un - known, Our

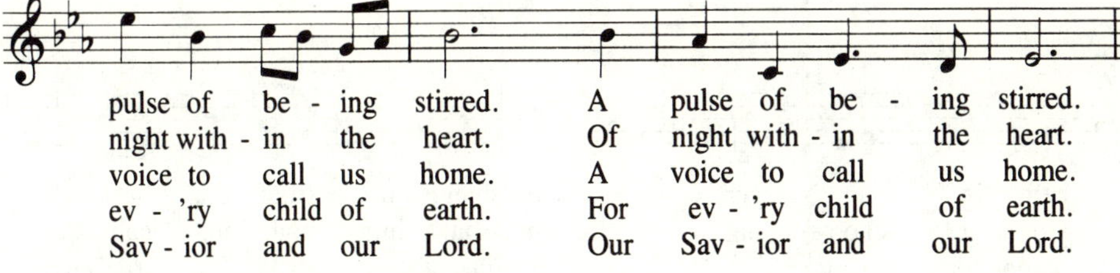
pulse of be - ing stirred. A pulse of be - ing stirred.
night with - in the heart. Of night with - in the heart.
voice to call us home. A voice to call us home.
ev - 'ry child of earth. For ev - 'ry child of earth.
Sav - ior and our Lord. Our Sav - ior and our Lord.

Text: Timothy Dudley-Smith, b.1926, © 1984, Hope Publishing Co.
Tune: REPTON, 8 6 88 6 with repeat; Charles H. H. Parry, 1848-1918

A Single Unmatched Stone 574

1. A sin - gle un-matched stone The build - ers hurled a - side Holds up the church a - lone Its cor - ner - stone and pride. The sym - me - try the build - ers planned Was al - tered by an - oth - er's hand.

2. A sin - gle faith - ful act That healed a man once lame The tem - ple priests at - tacked For bear-ing Je - sus' name. The right-eous heart, the rig - id mind To God's new work were deaf and blind.

3. A sin - gle deed or word Of truth or peace or grace Not seen be - fore or heard Is dif - fi - cult to face. Help us, O God, by faith to see What seems a threat may set us free.

Text: Acts 4:5-12; Thomas H. Troeger, b.1945
Tune: UNMATCHED STONE, 6 6 6 6 88; Carol Doran, b.1936

575 God Is Our Fortress and Our Rock

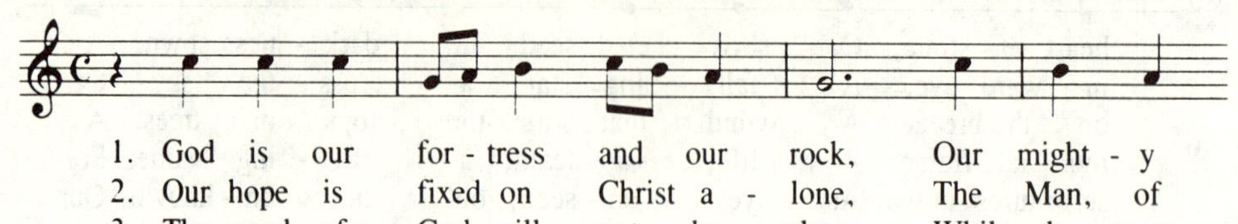
1. God is our for - tress and our rock, Our might - y
2. Our hope is fixed on Christ a - lone, The Man, of
3. The word of God will not be slow While de - mon

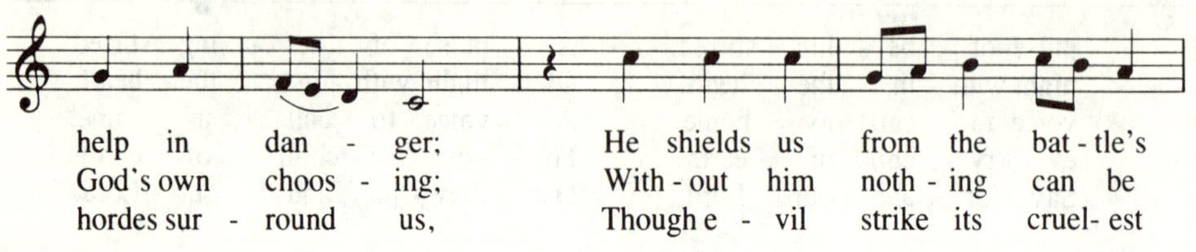
help in dan - ger; He shields us from the bat - tle's
God's own choos - ing; With - out him noth - ing can be
hordes sur - round us, Though e - vil strike its cruel- est

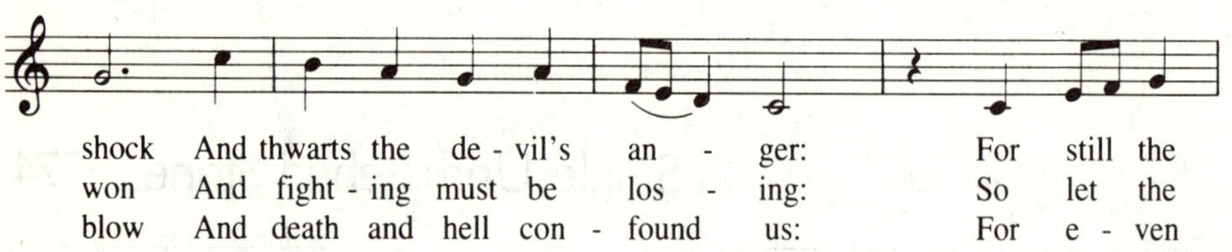
shock And thwarts the de - vil's an - ger: For still the
won And fight - ing must be los - ing: So let the
blow And death and hell con - found us: For e - ven

prince of night Pro - longs his e - vil fight;
pow'rs ac - cursed Come on and do their worst,
if dis - tress Should take all we pos - sess,

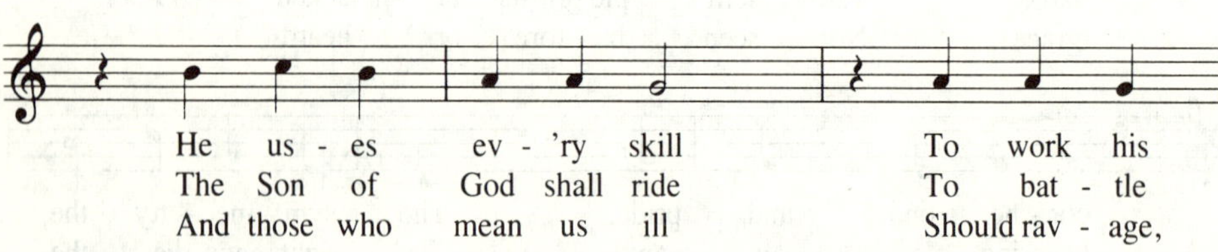
He us - es ev - 'ry skill To work his
The Son of God shall ride To bat - tle
And those who mean us ill Should rav - age,

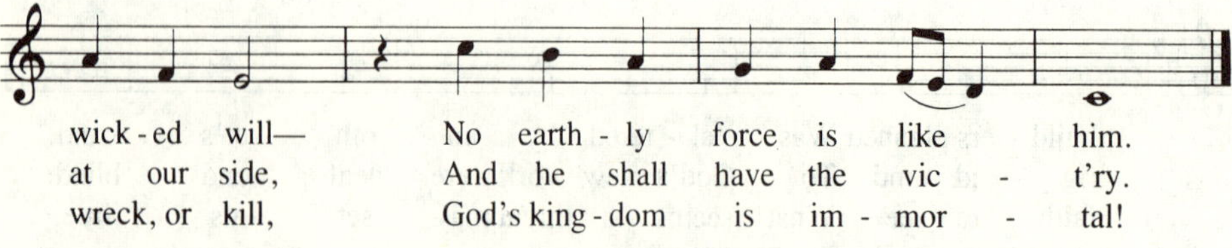
wick - ed will— No earth - ly force is like him.
at our side, And he shall have the vic - t'ry.
wreck, or kill, God's king - dom is im - mor - tal!

Text: Psalm (45)46; *Ein' feste Burg ist unser Gott;* Martin Luther, 1483-1546; Tr. by Michael Perry, b.1942,
Tune: EIN' FESTE BURG, 8 7 8 7 66 66 7; Martin Luther, 1483-1546; Harm. by J.S. Bach, 1685-1750

God Is Our Fortress and Our Rock 576

1. God is our for - tress and our rock,
2. Our hope is fixed on Christ a - lone,
3. The word of God will not be slow
Our might - y
The Man, of
While de - mon
help in dan - ger;
God's own choos - ing;
hordes sur - round us,
He shields us from the bat - tle's
With - out him noth - ing can be
Though e - vil strike its cruel - est
shock And thwarts the dev - il's an - ger:
won And fight - ing must be los - ing:
blow And death and hell con - found us:
For still the prince of night
So let the pow'rs ac - cursed
For e - ven if dis - tress
Pro - longs his e - vil fight; He us - es ev - 'ry skill
Come on and do their worst, The Son of God shall ride
Should take all we pos - sess, And those who mean us ill
To work his wick - ed will
To bat - tle at our side,
Should rav - age, wreck, or kill,
No earth - ly force is like him.
And he shall have the vic - t'ry.
God's king - dom is im - mor - tal!

Text: Psalm (45)46; *Ein' fest Burg ist unser Gott;* Martin Luther, 1483-1546; Tr. by Michael Perry, b.1942,
Tune: EIN' FESTE BURG, 8 7 8 7 66 66 7; Martin Luther, 1483-1546; Harm. based on Hans Leo Hassler, 1564-1612

577 By Gracious Powers

1. By gra-cious pow'rs so won-der-ful - ly shel - tered And con-
2. Yet is this heart by its old foe tor - ment - ed, Still e-
3. And when this cup you give is filled to brim - ming With bit-
4. Yet when a - gain, in this same world you give us The joy
fi - dent - ly wait - ing come what may, We know that
vil days bring bur - dens hard to bear; O give our
ter suf-fering, hard to un - der - stand, We take it
we had, the bright-ness of your sun, We shall re-
God is with us night and morn - ing And nev-
fright - ened souls the sure sal - va - tion For which,
thank - ful - ly and with - out trem - bling Out of
mem - ber all the days we lived through And our
er fails to greet us each new day.
O Lord, you taught us to pre - pare.
so good, and so be - loved a hand.
whole life shall then be yours a - lone.

Text: *Von guten Mächten;* Dietrich Bonhoeffer, 1906-1945; Tr. by Fred Pratt Green, b.1903, © 1974, Hope Publishing Co.
Tune: LE CÉNACLE, 11 10 11 10; Joseph Gelineau, SJ, b.1920, © SEFIM

God Spoke to Our Father Abraham 578

1. God spoke to our fa - ther A - bra - ham,
2. "We car - ry the wood, the fire, the knife,
3. A voice in the bra - zen wil - der - ness,
4. With wood on his shoul - der walked the boy,
5. His mem - o - ry, sealed in bread, in wine,
De - mand - ing death for I - saac the sin - less,
But where is found the vic - tim, my fa - ther,
The her - ald's voice, as bright as a trum - pet:
O - be - dient, bowed and meek to his fa - ther:
For strength and sav - ing, marks us dis - ci - ples;
Re - hears - ing the day when he would send
The lamb to be slain and of - fered up?"
"Look, there is the Lamb, the Lamb of God,
The Christ lifts his load, the wood of death,
In char - i - ty one, to set us free,
His on - ly Son to die for the world.
"O here, my son, for you are the lamb."
Whose death de - stroys the sin of the world!"
Sub - ject - ed to his Fa - ther's com - mand.
To lift our load, to crown us with life.
He res - cued his ser - vants who trust - ed in him:
He res - cued his ser - vants who trust - ed in him:
He res - cued his ser - vants who trust - ed in him:
He res - cued his ser - vants who trust - ed in him:
He res - cued his ser - vants who trust - ed in him:
From blood and from drown - ing he saved them.
From blood and from drown - ing he saved them.
From blood and from drown - ing he saved them.
From blood and from drown - ing he saved them.
From blood and from drown - ing he saved them.

Text: Gen. 22; Luke Connaughton, 1917-1979, © 1970, Mayhew McCrimmon Ltd.
Tune: SACRIFICE, 9 10 9 9 with refrain; John Schiavone, b.1947, © 1986, GIA Publications, Inc.

579 O God, Our Help in Ages Past

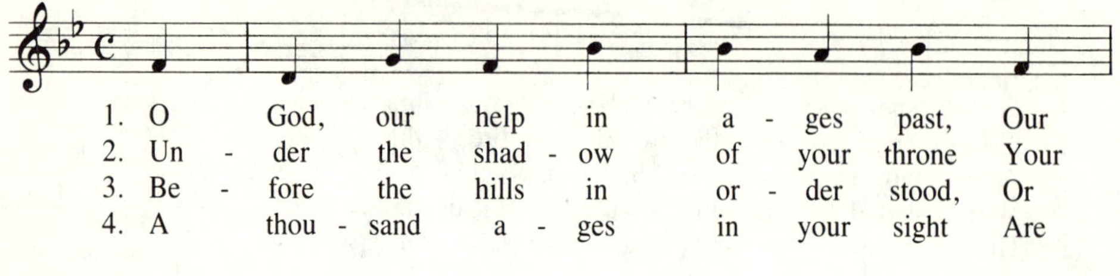
1. O God, our help in a - ges past, Our
2. Un - der the shad - ow of your throne Your
3. Be - fore the hills in or - der stood, Or
4. A thou - sand a - ges in your sight Are

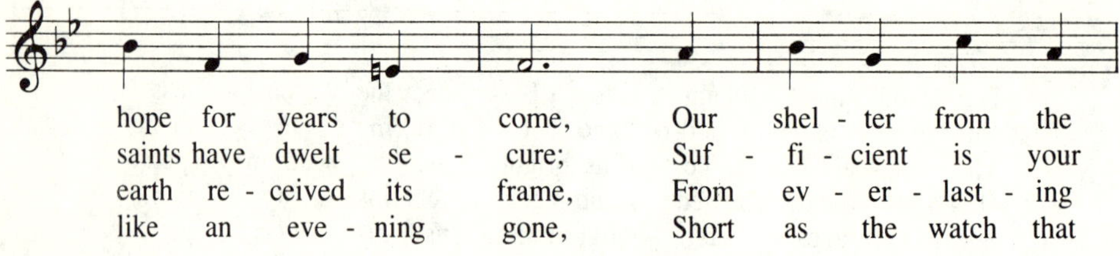
hope for years to come, Our shel - ter from the
saints have dwelt se - cure; Suf - fi - cient is your
earth re - ceived its frame, From ev - er - last - ing
like an eve - ning gone, Short as the watch that

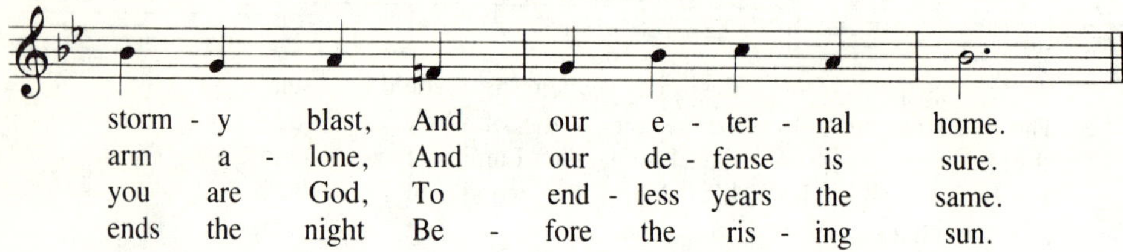
storm - y blast, And our e - ter - nal home.
arm a - lone, And our de - fense is sure.
you are God, To end - less years the same.
ends the night Be - fore the ris - ing sun.

5. Time, like an ever-rolling stream,
Soon bears us all away;
We fly forgotten, as a dream
Dies at the op'ning day.

6. O God, our help in ages past,
Our hope for years to come,
Still be our guard while troubles last,
And our eternal home.

Text: Psalm (89)90; Isaac Watts, 1674-1748
Tune: ST. ANNE, CM; Attr. to William Croft, 1678-1727; Harm. composite from 18th C. versions

580 Seek Ye First the Kingdom of God

1.
1. Seek ye first the king - dom of God and his right - eous-
2. Ask, and it shall be giv-en un - to you, seek, and ye shall
ness, and all these things shall be add - ed un - to you;
find, knock, and the door shall be o-pened un - to you;

2.
Al - le - lu, al - le - lu - ia. Al - le-
lu - ia, al - le - lu - ia, al - le-
lu - ia, al - le - lu, al - le - lu - ia.

Text: Mt. 6:33, 7:7; St. 1, adapt. by Karen Lafferty, b.1948; St. 2, anon.
Tune: SEEK YE FIRST, Irregular; Karen Lafferty, b.1948

God Is My Great Desire 581

1. God is my great de - sire, His face I seek the first;
2. God is my true de - light, My rich - est feast his praise,
3. God is my strong de - fense In ev - 'ry e - vil hour;

To him my heart and soul as - pire, For him I thirst.
Through si - lent watch - es of the night, Through all my days.
In him I face with con - fi - dence The temp - ter's power.

As one in des - ert lands, Whose ver - y flesh is flame,
To him my spir - it clings, On him my soul is cast;
I trust his mer - cy sure, With truth and tri - umph crowned:

In burn - ing love I lift my hands And bless his name.
Be - neath the shad - ow of his wings He holds me fast.
My hope and joy for ev - er - more In him are found.

Text: Psalm 63; Timothy Dudley-Smith, b.1926,
Tune: LEONI, 6 6 8 4 D; From the *Yigdal;* Transcribed by Meyer Lyon, c.1751-1797

582 This World, My God, Is Held within Your Hand

1. This world, my God, is held within your hand,
Though we forget your love and steadfast might
And in the changing day uncertain stand,
Disturbed by morning, and afraid of night.

2. From youthful confidence to careful age,
Help us each one to be your loving friend,
Rewarded by the faithful servant's wage,
God in Three Persons, reigning without end.

Text: Hamish Swanston, © 1971, Faber Music Ltd.
Tune: SURSUM CORDA, 10 10 10 10; Alfred M. Smith, 1879-1971, © Mrs. Alfred M. Smith

583 Amazing Grace

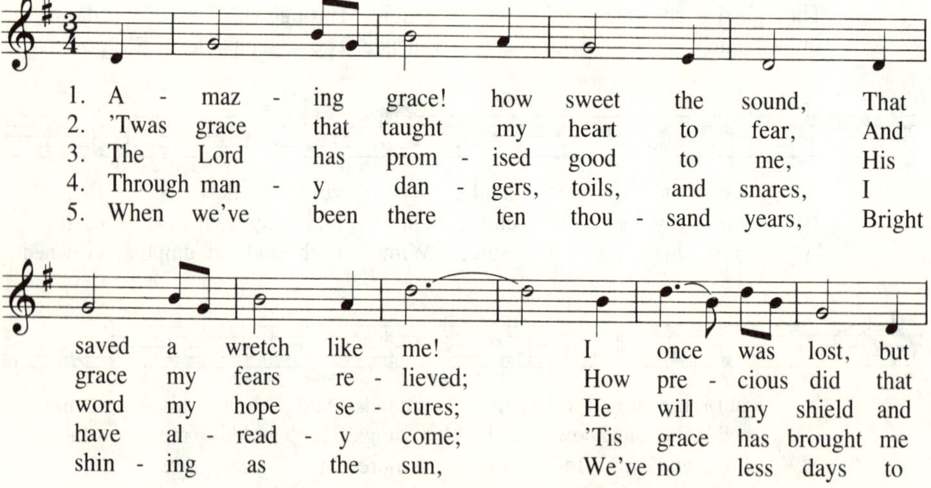
1. A - maz - ing grace! how sweet the sound, That saved a wretch like me! I once was lost, but
2. 'Twas grace that taught my heart to fear, And grace my fears re - lieved; How pre - cious did that
3. The Lord has prom - ised good to me, His word my hope se - cures; He will my shield and
4. Through man - y dan - gers, toils, and snares, I have al - read - y come; 'Tis grace has brought me
5. When we've been there ten thou - sand years, Bright shin - ing as the sun, We've no less days to

TRUST

now am found, Was blind, but now I see.
grace ap - pear The hour I first be - lieved!
por - tion be As long as life en - dures.
safe thus far, And grace will lead me home.
sing God's praise Than when we'd first be - gun.

Text: St. 1-4, John Newton, 1725-1807; St. 5, Ascr. to John Rees, fl.1859
Tune: NEW BRITAIN, CM; *Virginia Harmony*, 1831; Harm. by John Barnard, b.1948, © 1982, Hope Publishing Co.

Surely It Is God Who Saves Me 584

1. Sure - ly it is God who
2. Make his deeds known to the

saves me; Trust-ing him, I shall not fear. For the
peo - ples; Tell out his ex - alt - ed Name. Praise the

Lord de - fends and shields me And his sav - ing help is
Lord, who has done great things; All his works his might pro-

near. So re - joice as you draw wa - ter From sal-
claim. Zi - on, lift your voice in sing - ing; For with

va - tion's liv - ing spring; In the day of your de-
you has come to dwell, In your ver - y midst, the

liv - 'rance Thank the Lord, his mer - cies sing.
great and Ho - ly One of Is - ra - el.

Text: Is. 12:1-6; Carl P. Daw, Jr., b.1944, © 1982
Tune: RAQUEL, 8 7 8 7 D; Skinner Chávez-Melo, b.1944, ©

585 How Firm a Foundation

1. How firm a foundation, you saints of the Lord,
Is laid for your faith in his excellent Word!
What more can he say than to you he has said,
To you who for refuge to Jesus have fled?

2. "Fear not, I am with you, O be not dismayed,
For I am your God, and will still give you aid;
I'll strengthen you, help you, and cause you to stand,
Upheld by my righteous, omnipotent hand.

3. "When through the deep waters I call you to go,
The rivers of woe shall not you overflow;
For I will be with you, your troubles to bless,
And sanctify to you, your deepest distress.

4. "The soul that on Jesus still leans for repose,
I will not, I will not desert to its foes;
That soul, though all hell should endeavor to shake,
I'll never, no never, no never forsake!"

Text: 2 Peter 1:4; "K" in Rippon's *A Selection of Hymns,* 1787
Tune: FOUNDATION, 11 11 11 11; Funk's *Compilation of Genuine Church Music,* 1832; Harm. by Richard Proulx, b.1937, © 1975, GIA Publications, Inc.

586 Awake, O Sleeper, Rise from Death

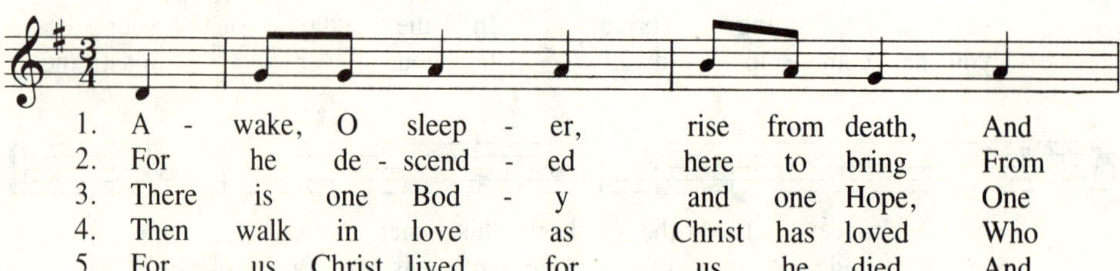
1. A - wake, O sleep - er, rise from death, And
2. For he de - scend - ed here to bring From
3. There is one Bod - y and one Hope, One
4. Then walk in love as Christ has loved Who
5. For us Christ lived, for us he died And

Christ shall give you light. So learn his love— its length and breadth, Its full - ness, depth and height.
sin and fears re - lease, To give the Spir - it's u - ni - ty, Which is the bond of peace.
Spir - it and one Call, One Lord, one Faith, and one Bap - tism, One Fa - ther of us all.
died that he might save; With kind and gen - tle hearts for - give As God in Christ for - gave.
con - quered in the strife. A - wake, a - rise, go forth in faith, And Christ shall give you life.

Text: Eph. 3-5; F. Bland Tucker, 1895-1984, alt., © 1980, Augsburg Publishing House
Tune: AZMON, CM; Carl G. Gläser, 1784-1829; Harm. by Lowell Mason, 1792-1872

Morning Glory, Starlit Sky 587

1. Morn - ing glo - ry, star - lit sky, Soar - ing mu - sic, schol - ars' truth, Flight of swal - lows, au - tumn leaves, Mem - ory's trea - sure, grace of youth:

2. O - pen are the gifts of God, Gifts of love to mind and sense; Hid - den is love's ag - o - ny, Love's en - deav - or, love's ex - pense.

3. Love that gives, gives ev - er more, Gives with zeal, with ea - ger hands, Spares not, keeps not, all out - pours, Ven - tures all, its all ex - pends.

4. Drained is love in mak - ing full, Bound in set - ting oth - ers free, Poor in mak - ing man - y rich, Weak in giv - ing pow'r to be.

5. Therefore he who shows us God
Helpless hangs upon the tree;
And the nails and crown of thorns
Tell of what God's love must be.

6. Here is God: no monarch he,
Throned in easy state to reign;
Here is God, whose arms of love
Aching, spent, the world sustain.

Text: W. H. Vanstone, b.1923. © J.W. Shore
Tune: BINGHAM, 7 7 7 7; Dorothy Sheets, b.1915, ©

588 Love Divine, All Loves Excelling

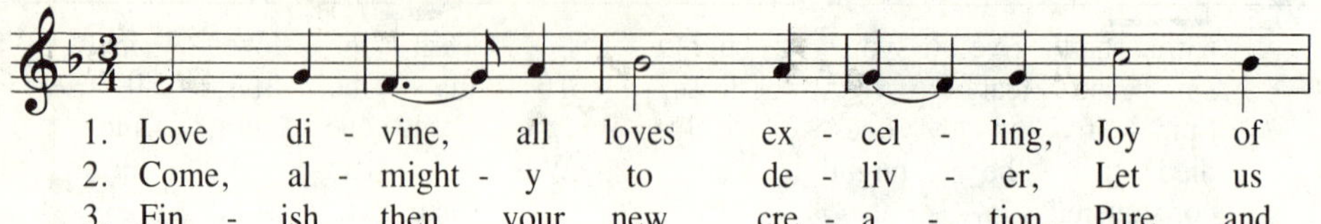
1. Love di - vine, all loves ex - cel - ling, Joy of
2. Come, al - might - y to de - liv - er, Let us
3. Fin - ish then your new cre - a - tion, Pure and

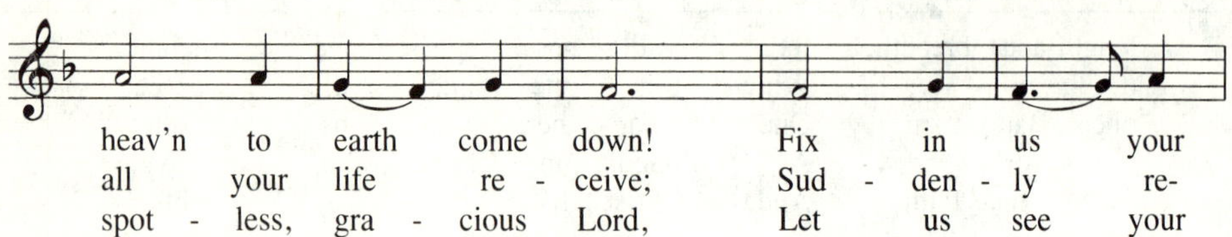
heav'n to earth come down! Fix in us your
all your life re - ceive; Sud - den - ly re-
spot - less, gra - cious Lord, Let us see your

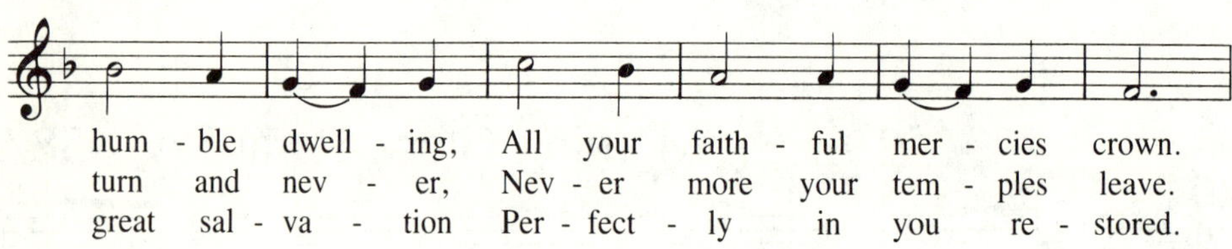
hum - ble dwell - ing, All your faith - ful mer - cies crown.
turn and nev - er, Nev - er more your tem - ples leave.
great sal - va - tion Per - fect - ly in you re - stored.

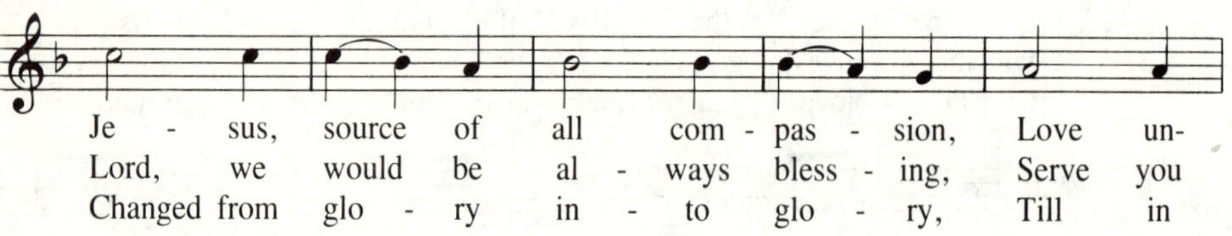
Je - sus, source of all com - pas - sion, Love un-
Lord, we would be al - ways bless - ing, Serve you
Changed from glo - ry in - to glo - ry, Till in

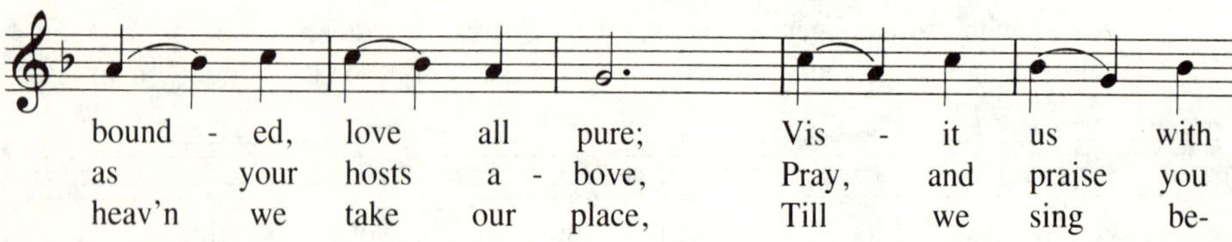
bound - ed, love all pure; Vis - it us with
as your hosts a - bove, Pray, and praise you
heav'n we take our place, Till we sing be-

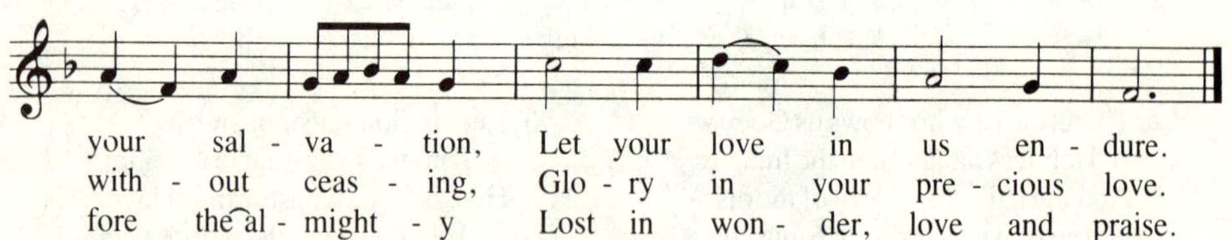
your sal - va - tion, Let your love in us en - dure.
with - out ceas - ing, Glo - ry in your pre - cious love.
fore the al - might - y Lost in won - der, love and praise.

Text: Charles Wesley, 1707-1788, alt.
Tune: HYFRYDOL, 8 7 8 7 D; Rowland H. Prichard, 1811-1887

Not for Tongues of Heaven's Angels 589

1. Not for tongues of heav - en's an - gels, Not for
2. Love is hum - ble, love is gen - tle, Love is
3. Nev - er jeal - ous, nev - er self - ish, Love will
4. Soon will fade the word of wis - dom, Faith and

wis - dom to dis - cern, Not for faith that mas - ters
ten - der, true and kind; Love is gra - cious, ev - er-
not re - joice in wrong; Nev - er boast - ful nor re-
hope be one day past: When we see our Sav - ior

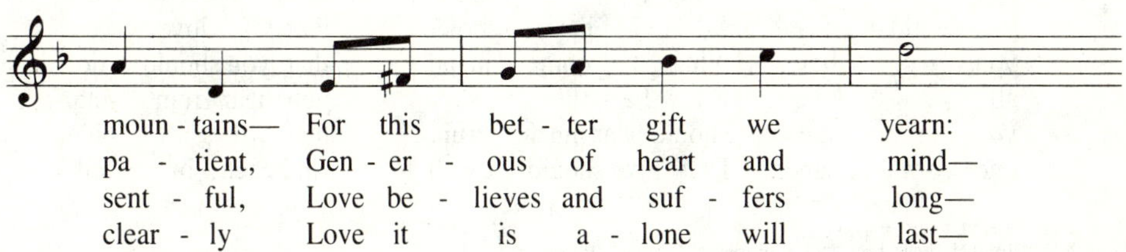

moun - tains— For this bet - ter gift we yearn:
pa - tient, Gen - er - ous of heart and mind—
sent - ful, Love be - lieves and suf - fers long—
clear - ly Love it is a - lone will last—

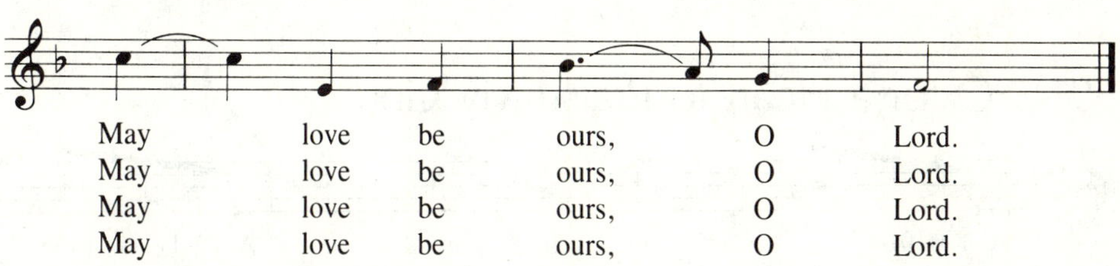

May love be ours, O Lord.
May love be ours, O Lord.
May love be ours, O Lord.
May love be ours, O Lord.

Text: I Cor. 13; Timothy Dudley-Smith, b.1926,
Tune: BRIDEGROOM, 8 7 8 7 6; Peter Cutts, b.1937,

590 This Is My Will

1. "This is my will, my one com - mand, That love should
2. "No great - er love that one can have Than that one
3. "I call you now no long - er slaves; No slave knows
4. "You chose not me, but I chose you, That you should
5. "All that you ask my Fa - ther dear For my name's

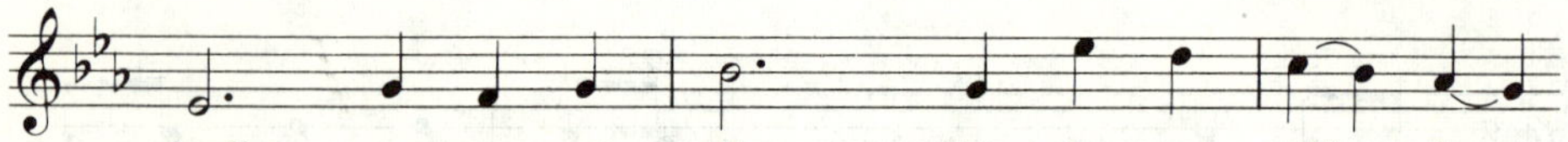

dwell a - mong you all. This is my will, that
die to save one's friends. You are my friends if
all the mas - ter does. I call you friends, for
go and bear much fruit. I chose you out that
sake you shall re - ceive. This is my will, my

you should love As I have shown that I love you.
you o - bey What I com - mand that you should do.
all I hear My Fa - ther say you hear from me.
you in me Should bear much fruit that will a - bide.
one com - mand, That love should dwell in each, in all."

Text: James Quinn, SJ, b.1919, © 1969
Tune: SUANTRAI, LM; Gaelic; Harm. by T.H. Weaving, © Estate of T.H. Weaving

591 O for a Heart to Praise My God

1. O for a heart to praise my God, A heart from
2. A heart, re - signed, sub - mis - sive, meek, My great Re-
3. A hum - ble, low - ly, con - trite heart, Be - liev - ing,
4. A heart in ev - 'ry thought re-newed, A heart whose
5. Your na - ture, gra - cious Lord, im - part; Come quick - ly
sin set free, A heart that al - ways
deem - er's throne, Where on - ly Christ is
true, and clean: Which nei - ther life nor
love en - dures; So per - fect, right, and
from a - bove, Write your new name up-

feels your blood So free - ly shed for me.
heard to speak, Where Je - sus reigns a - lone:
death can part From Him that dwells with - in:
pure, and good, A cop - y, Lord, of yours.
on my heart, Your new, best name of love.

Text: Psalm (50)51; Charles Wesley, 1707-1788, alt.
Tune: O FOR A HEART, CM; Malcolm Williamson, b.1943, © 1971, Josef Weinberger Ltd.

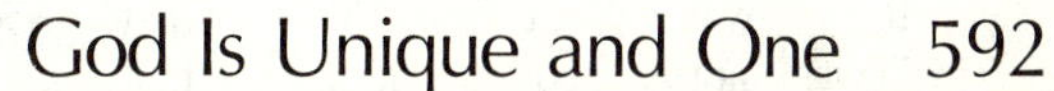

God Is Unique and One 592

1. God is u - nique and one: Mak - er, sus - tain - er, Lord!
2. Love came to earth in Christ, Our com-mon life to share,
3. The Ho - ly Spir - it moves Peo - ple to trace God's plan,
4. He shall for ev - er reign, Rul - er of time and space,

Pat - terns of life were spun By God's cre - a - tive
Choos-ing to be the least, Will - ing a cross to
This in - spi - ra - tion proves More than the mind can
God in the midst of life, Seen in the hu - man

word. Of God's in - ten - tion, love and
bear. He died, he rose, that we might
span. Each lis - tening heart is led to
face. We give ex - pres - sion to our

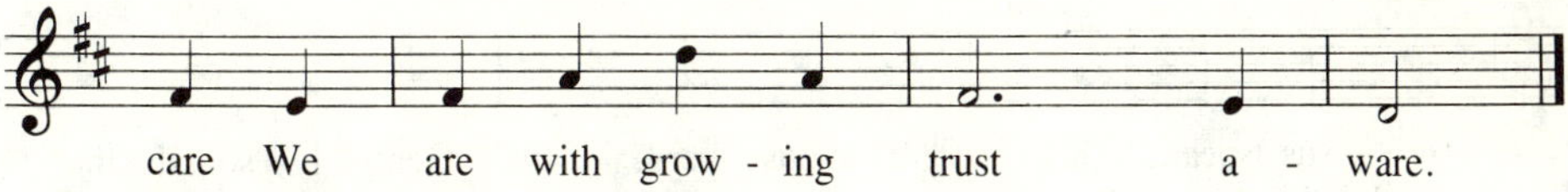

care We are with grow - ing trust a - ware.
live And all our love, re - spond - ing, give.
find The will of God for hu - man - kind.
creed By love in thought, in word and deed.

Text: Fred Kaan, b.1929, alt., © 1968, Hope Publishing Co.
Tune: LITTLE CORNARD, 6 6 6 6 88; Martin Shaw, 1875-1958, © J. Curwen and Sons

593 I Sought the Lord

1. I sought the Lord, and af - ter - ward I knew
2. Thou didst reach forth thy hand and mine en - fold,
3. I find, I walk, I love, but O the whole

He moved my soul to seek him, seek - ing me;
I walked and sank not on the storm-vexed sea;
Of love is but my an - swer, Lord, to thee!

It was not I that found, O Sav - ior true,
'Twas not so much that I on thee took hold
For thou wert long be - fore - hand with my soul;

No, I was found of thee.
As thou, dear Lord, on me.
Al - ways thou lov - edst me.

Text: Mt. 14:22-32; Anon. c.1878
Tune: FAITH, 10 10 10 6; J. Harold Moyer, b.1927,

594 Christian, Do You Hear the Lord

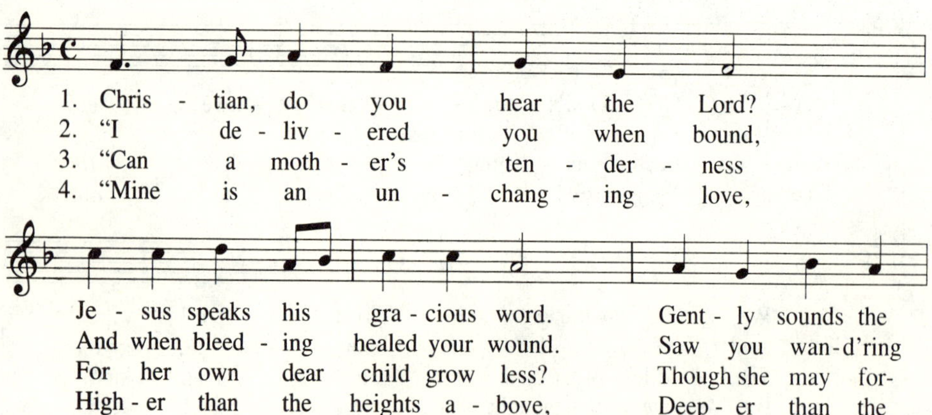
1. Chris - tian, do you hear the Lord?
2. "I de - liv - ered you when bound,
3. "Can a moth - er's ten - der - ness
4. "Mine is an un - chang - ing love,
Je - sus speaks his gra - cious word. Gent - ly sounds the
And when bleed - ing healed your wound. Saw you wan-d'ring
For her own dear child grow less? Though she may for-
High - er than the heights a - bove, Deep - er than the

Sav - ior's call, "Do you love me best of all?
set you right, Turned your dark - ness in - to light.
get - ful be, You are al - ways dear to me.
depths be - neath, Free and faith - ful, strong as death.

5. "You shall see my glory soon,
When the work of grace is done;
Crowned with splendor you shall be:
Christian, come and follow me!"

6. Lord, it is my chief complaint
That my love is weak and faint;
Yet I love you, and adore—
O for grace to love you more!

Text: William Cowper, 1731-1800, alt., © 1982, Hope Publishing Co.
Tune: ORIENTIS PARTIBUS, 77 77; Pierre de Corbiel, d.1222

There's a Wideness in God's Mercy 595

1. There's a wide-ness in God's mer-cy Like the wide - ness of the sea;
2. For the love of God is broad - er Than the meas - ures of our mind,
3. Trou - bled souls, why will you scat - ter Like a crowd of fright-ened sheep?

There's a kind - ness in God's jus-tice Which is more than lib - er - ty.
And the heart of the E - ter - nal Is most won - der - ful - ly kind.
Fool - ish hearts, why will you wan-der From a love so true and deep?

There is plen - ti - ful re - demp-tion In the blood that has been shed;
If our love were but more sim - ple We should take him at his word,
There is wel-come for the sin - ner And more grac - es for the good;

There is joy for all the mem-bers In the sor - rows of the Head.
And our lives would be thanks-giv-ing For the good - ness of our Lord.
There is mer - cy with the Sav - ior, There is heal - ing in his blood.

Text: Frederick W. Faber, 1814-1863, alt.
Tune: IN BABILONE, 8 7 8 7 D; *Oude en Nieuwe Hollanste Boerenlities*, c.1710

596 There's a Wideness in God's Mercy

1. There's a wide - ness in God's mer- cy Like the wide - ness of the sea; There's a kind - ness in God's jus- tice Which is more than lib - er - ty. There is plen - ti - ful re - demp - tion In the blood that has been shed; There is joy for all the mem - bers In the sor - rows of the Head.
2. For the love of God is broad- er Than the meas - ures of our mind, And the heart of the E - ter- nal Is most won - der - ful - ly kind. If our love were but more sim - ple We should take him at his word, And our lives would be thanks-giv - ing For the good-ness of our Lord.
3. Trou-bled souls, why will you scat- ter Like a crowd of fright - ened sheep? Fool - ish hearts, why will you wan- der From a love so true and deep? There is wel - come for the sin - ner And more grac- es for the good; There is mer - cy with the Sav - ior, There is heal - ing in his blood.
after last stanza - optional
A - men.

Text: Frederick W. Faber, 1814-1863, alt.
Tune: ST. HELENA, 8 7 8 7 D; Calvin Hampton, 1938-1984, © 1977, GIA Publications, Inc.

A Spendthrift Lover Is the Lord 597

1. A spend-thrift lov - er is the Lord Who nev - er
2. Still more is spent in blood and tears To win the
3. How shall we love this heart-strong God Who gives us
counts the cost Or asks if heav - en can af-
hu - man heart, To o - ver - come the vio - lent
ev - 'ry -thing, Whose ways to us are strange and
ford To woo a world that's lost.
fears That drive the world a - part.
odd, What can we give or bring?
Our lov - er toss - es coins of gold A - cross the
Be - hold the bruised and thorn-crowned face Of one who
Ac - cept - ance of the match-less gift Is gift e-
mid - night skies And stokes the sun a - gainst the
bears our scars And emp - ties out the wealth of
nough to give. The ver - y act will shake and
cold To warm us when we rise.
grace That's hint - ed by the stars.
shift The way we love and live.

Text: Jn. 3:14-21; Thomas Troeger, b.1945
Tune: SPENDTHRIFT LOVER, CMD; Carol Doran, b.1936, © 1983, Thomas H. Troeger and Carol Doran

598 Where True Love and Charity Are Found / Ubi Caritas

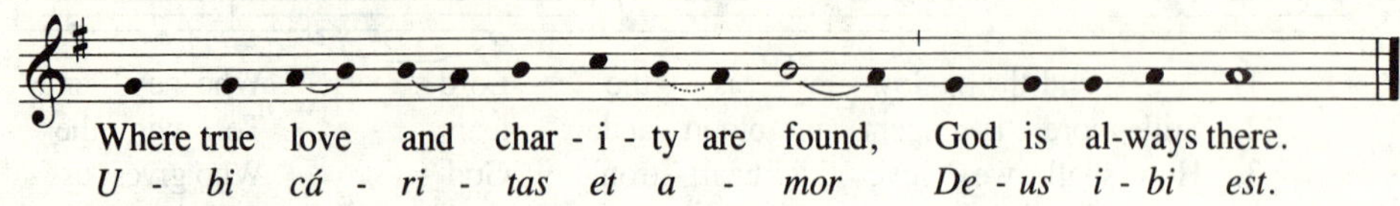
Where true love and char - i - ty are found, God is al-ways there.
U - bi cá - ri - tas et a - mor De - us i - bi est.

1. Since the love of Christ has brought us all to - geth - er,
2. There-fore when we gath - er as one in Christ Je - sus,
3. Bring us with your saints to be - hold your great beau - ty,
1. *Con - gre - gá - vit nos in u - num Chri - sti a - mor.*
2. *Si - mul er - go cum in u - num con - gre - gá - mur:*
3. *Si - mul quo - que cum be - á - tis vi - de - á - mus.*

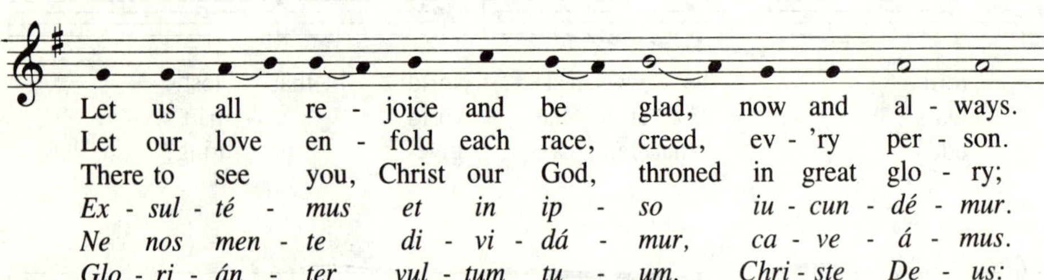
Let us all re - joice and be glad, now and al - ways.
Let our love en - fold each race, creed, ev - 'ry per - son.
There to see you, Christ our God, throned in great glo - ry;
Ex - sul - té - mus et in ip - so iu - cun - dé - mur.
Ne nos men - te di - vi - dá - mur, ca - ve - á - mus.
Glo - ri - án - ter vul - tum tu - um, Chri - ste De - us:

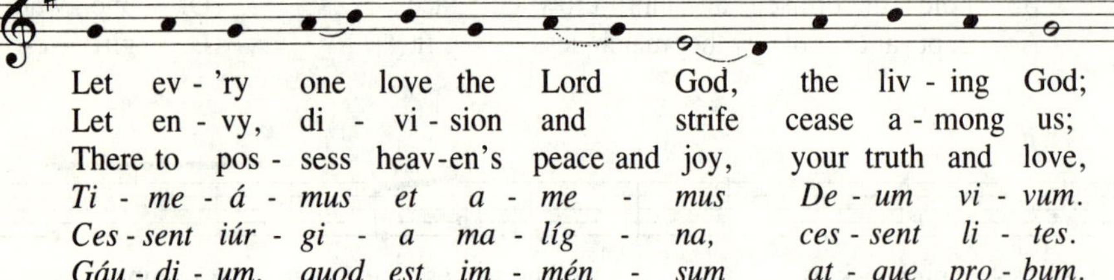
Let ev - 'ry one love the Lord God, the liv - ing God;
Let en - vy, di - vi - sion and strife cease a - mong us;
There to pos - sess heav-en's peace and joy, your truth and love,
Ti - me - á - mus et a - me - mus De - um vi - vum.
Ces - sent iúr - gi - a ma - líg - na, ces - sent li - tes.
Gáu - di - um, quod est im - mén - sum at - que pro - bum.

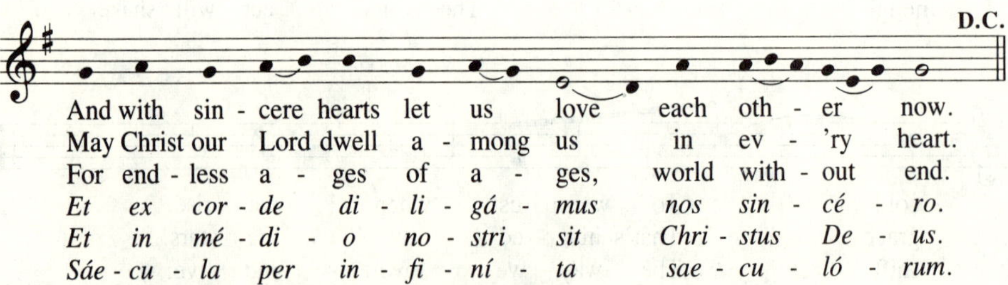
D.C.
And with sin - cere hearts let us love each oth - er now.
May Christ our Lord dwell a - mong us in ev - 'ry heart.
For end - less a - ges of a - ges, world with - out end.
Et ex cor - de di - li - gá - mus nos sin - cé - ro.
Et in mé - di - o no - stri sit Chri - stus De - us.
Sáe - cu - la per in - fi - ní - ta sae - cu - ló - rum.

Text: Latin, 9th C.; Tr. by Richard Proulx, b.1937, © 1975, 1986, GIA Publications, Inc.
Tune: UBI CARITAS, 12 12 12 12 with refrain; Mode VI; Acc. by Richard Proulx, b.1937, © 1986, GIA Publications, Inc.

Love Is His Word 599

1. Love is his word, love is his way. Feast-ing with all, fast - ing a - lone, Liv - ing and dy - ing, ris - ing a - gain. Love, on - ly love, is his way.
2. Love is his way, love is his mark. Shar - ing his last Pass - o - ver feast. Guest at his ta - ble, host to the Twelve, Love, on - ly love, is his mark.
3. Love is his mark, love is his sign. Bread for our strength, wine for our joy. "This is my bod - y, this is my blood." Love, on - ly love, is his sign.
4. Love is his sign, love is his news. "Do this," he said, "lest you for - get All my deep sor - row, all my dear blood." Love, on - ly love, is his news.
5. Love is his news, love is his name. We are his own, cho - sen and called, Fam - i - ly, breth - ren, cous-ins and kin. Love, on - ly love, is his name.
Rich - er than gold is the love of my Lord,
bet - ter than splen-dor and wealth. Rich - er than gold is the
love of my Lord, bet - ter than splen - dor and wealth.

6. Love is his name, love is his law.
Hear his command, all who are his:
"Love one another, I have loved you."
Love, only love, is his law.

7. Love is his law, love is his word:
Love of the Lord, Father and Word.
Love of the Spirit, God ev'ry one.
Love, only love, is his word.

600 What Wondrous Love Is This

1. What won-drous love is this, O my soul, O my soul?
2. To God and to the Lamb I will sing, I will sing;
3. And when from death I'm free, I'll sing on, I'll sing on;

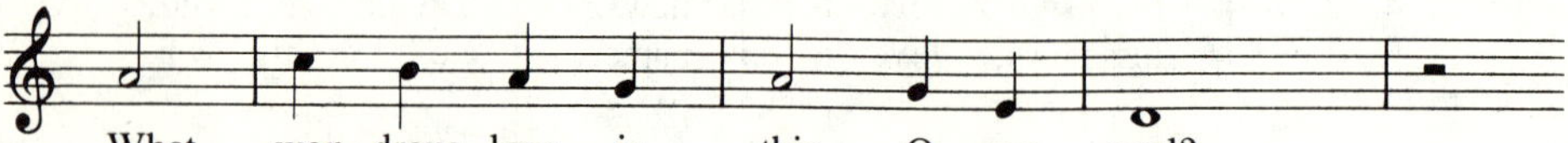

What won-drous love is this, O my soul?
To God and to the Lamb, I will sing;
And when from death I'm free, I'll sing on;

What won-drous love is this that caused the Lord of bliss
To God and to the Lamb who is the great I Am,
And when from death I'm free, I'll sing and joy - ful be,

To bear the dread - ful curse for my soul, for my soul;
While mil - lions join the theme, I will sing, I will sing;
And through e - ter - ni - ty I'll sing on, I'll sing on!

To bear the dread - ful curse for my soul?
While mil - lions join the theme, I will sing.
And through e - ter - ni - ty, I'll sing on.

Text: Alexander Means, 1801-1853
Tune: WONDROUS LOVE, 12 9 12 12 9; *Southern Harmony*, 1835; Harm. from *Cantate Domino, 1980*,

601 Beloved, Let Us Love

1. Be - lov - ed, let us love: for love is of God;
2. Be - lov - ed, let us love: for those who love,
3. Be - lov - ed, let us love: for love is rest,
4. Be - lov - ed, let us love: for love is light,
5. Be - lov - ed, let us love: for on - ly thus

In God a - lone love has its true a - bode.
They on - ly, are his chil - dren from a - bove.
And those who do not love can - not be blessed.
And those who do not love still live in night.
Shall we see God, the Lord, who first loved us.

Text: 1 Jn. 4, 7; Horatius Bonar, 1808-1889
Tune: SONG 46, 10 10; Orlando Gibbons, 1583-1625

Lord of All Nations, Grant Me Grace 602

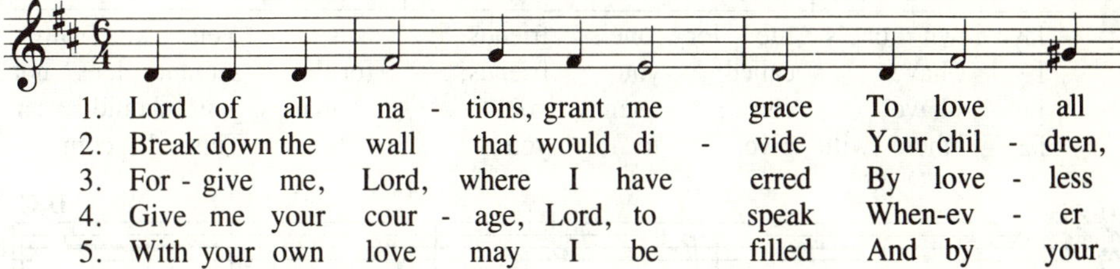
1. Lord of all na - tions, grant me grace To love all
2. Break down the wall that would di - vide Your chil - dren,
3. For - give me, Lord, where I have erred By love - less
4. Give me your cour - age, Lord, to speak When-ev - er
5. With your own love may I be filled And by your

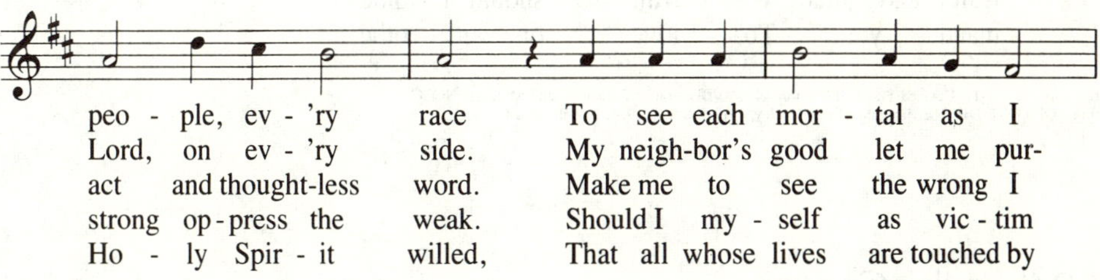
peo - ple, ev - 'ry race To see each mor - tal as I
Lord, on ev - 'ry side. My neigh-bor's good let me pur-
act and thought-less word. Make me to see the wrong I
strong op-press the weak. Should I my - self as vic - tim
Ho - ly Spir - it willed, That all whose lives are touched by

ought, My kin - dred, whom your love has bought.
sue, Let Chris - tian love bind warm and true.
do Will cru - ci - fy my Lord a - new.
live, Re - mem - b'ring you, may I for - give.
mine, May know your heal - ing touch di - vine.

Text: Phil. 2:1-18; Olive W. Spannaus, b.1916,
Tune: BEATUS VIR, LM; Slovak; Harm. by Richard Hillert, b.1923,

603 This Is My Commandment

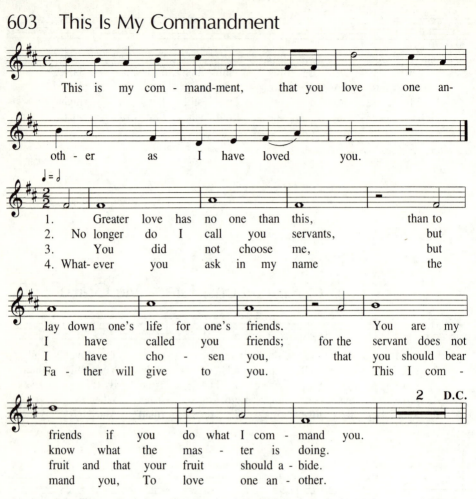

This is my com - mand-ment, that you love one an-
oth - er as I have loved you.

1. Greater love has no one than this, than to lay down one's life for one's friends. You are my friends if you do what I com - mand you.
2. No longer do I call you servants, but I have called you friends; for the servant does not know what the mas - ter is doing.
3. You did not choose me, but I have cho - sen you, that you should bear fruit and that your fruit should a - bide.
4. What-ever you ask in my name the Fa - ther will give to you. This I com - mand you, To love one an - other.

2 D.C.

Text: John 15:12-17; Revised Standard Version, alt., © Division of Education and Ministry, NCCC
Tune: OF LOVE DIVINE, Irregular; Erik Routley, 1917-1982, © 1974, Novello and Co. Ltd.

604 Ubi Caritas

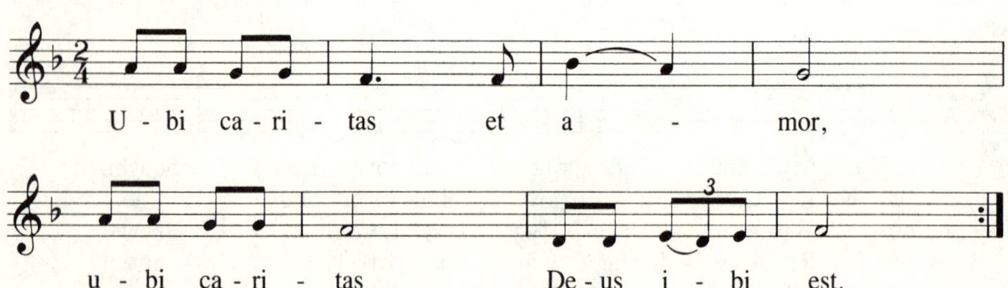
U - bi ca - ri - tas et a - mor,
u - bi ca - ri - tas De - us i - bi est.

Text: 1 Cor. 13: 2-8, *Where charity and love are found, God is there.* Taizé Community, 1978
Tune: Jacques Berthier, b.1923

O Jesus, Joy of Loving Hearts 605

1. O Je - sus, joy of lov - ing hearts, The fount of life and our true light, We seek the peace your love im - parts, And stand re - joic - ing in your sight.
2. We taste in you our liv - ing bread, And long to feast up - on you still; We drink of you, the foun - tain - head, Our thirst - ing souls to quench and fill.
3. For you our rest - less spir - its yearn Wher - e'er our chang - ing lot is cast; Glad, when your pres - ence we dis - cern, Blest, when our faith can hold you fast.
4. O Je - sus, ev - er with us stay; Make all our mo - ments calm and bright; O chase the night of sin a - way, Shed o'er the world your ho - ly light.

Text: *Jesu, delcedo cordium;* Attr. to Bernard of Clairvaux, 1091-1153; Para. by Ray Palmer, 1808-1887, alt.
Tune: WAREHAM, LM; William Knapp, 1698-1768

606 My Shepherd Will Supply My Need

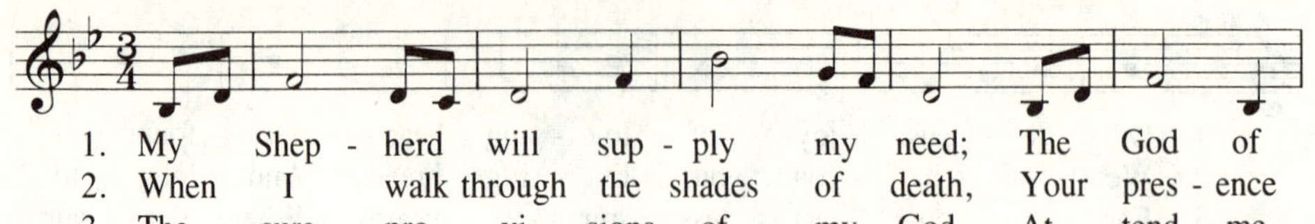
1. My Shep - herd will sup - ply my need; The God of
2. When I walk through the shades of death, Your pres - ence
3. The sure pro - vi - sions of my God At - tend me

love su - preme; In pas - tures green you
is my stay; One word of your sup-
all my days; O may your house be

make me feed, Be - side the liv - ing stream.
port - ing breath Drives all my fears a - way.
my a - bode, And all my work be praise!

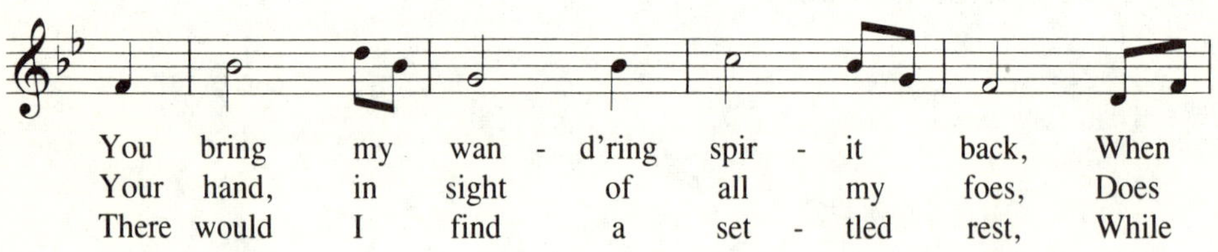
You bring my wan - d'ring spir - it back, When
Your hand, in sight of all my foes, Does
There would I find a set - tled rest, While

I for - sake your ways; And lead me for your
still my ta - ble spread; My cup with bless - ings
oth - ers go and come, No more a stran - ger

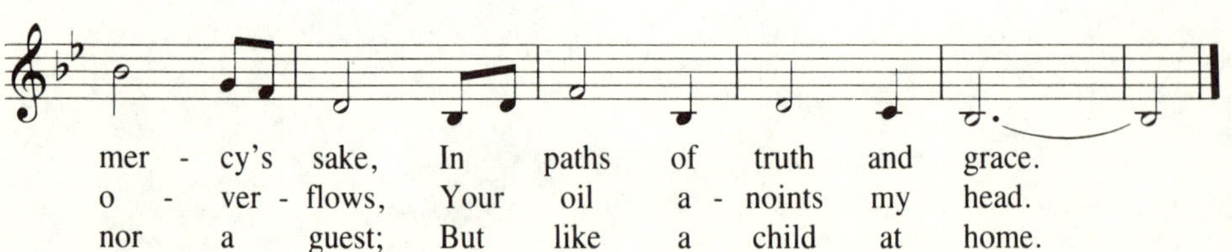
mer - cy's sake, In paths of truth and grace.
o - ver - flows, Your oil a - noints my head.
nor a guest; But like a child at home.

Text: Psalm (22)23; Isaac Watts, 1674-1748, alt.
Tune: RESIGNATION, CMD; Funk's *Compilation of Genuine Church Music*, 1832; Harm. by Richard Proulx, b.1937, © 1975, GIA Publications, Inc.

I Heard the Voice of Jesus Say 607

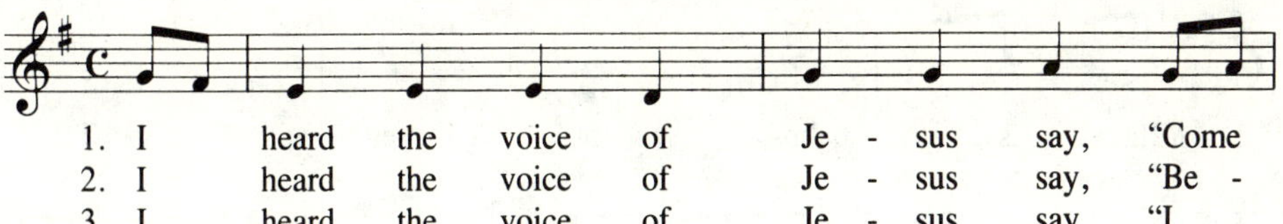

1. I heard the voice of Je - sus say, "Come
2. I heard the voice of Je - sus say, "Be -
3. I heard the voice of Je - sus say, "I

un - to me and rest; Lay down, O wear - y
hold, I free - ly give The liv - ing wa - ter;
am this dark world's light; Look un - to me, your

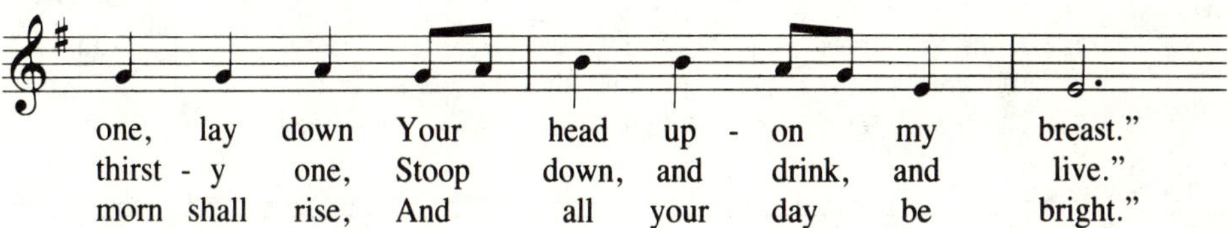

one, lay down Your head up - on my breast."
thirst - y one, Stoop down, and drink, and live."
morn shall rise, And all your day be bright."

I came to Je - sus as I was, So
I came to Je - sus, and I drank Of
I looked to Je - sus, and I found In

wea - ry worn and sad; I found in him a
that life - giv - ing stream; My thirst was quenched, my
him my star, my sun; And in that light of

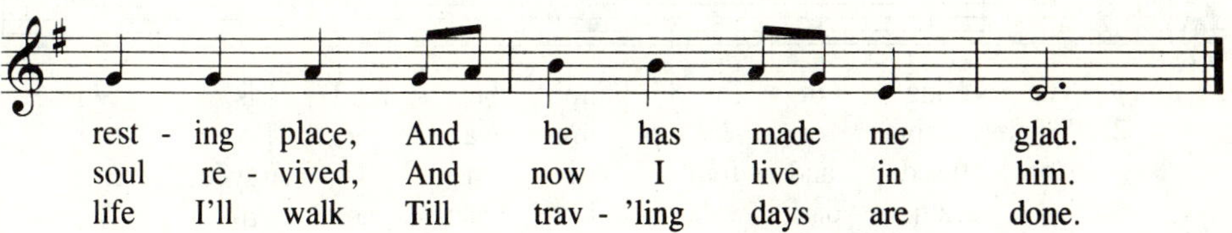

rest - ing place, And he has made me glad.
soul re - vived, And now I live in him.
life I'll walk Till trav - 'ling days are done.

Text: Horatius Bonar, 1808-1889
Tune: KINGSFOLD, CMD; English; Harm. by Ralph Vaughan Williams, 1872-1958, © Oxford University Press

608 There Is a Balm in Gilead

There is a balm in Gil - e - ad To
make the wound - ed whole, There is a balm in
Gil - e - ad to heal the sin - sick soul.

1. Some - times I feel dis - cour - aged And
think my work's in vain, But then the Ho - ly
Spir - it Re - vives my soul a - gain.

2. If you can - not preach like Pe - ter, If you
can - not pray like Paul, You can tell the love of
Je - sus, And say, "He died for all!"

3. Don't ev - er feel dis - cour - aged, For
Je - sus is your friend; And if you lack for
knowl-edge He'll ne'er re - fuse to lend.

D.C.

Text: Jer. 8:22, Afro-American Spiritual
Tune: BALM IN GILEAD, Irregular; Afro-American Spiritual; Harm. by David Hurd, b.1950, © 1985, GIA Publications, Inc.

609 The King of Love My Shepherd Is

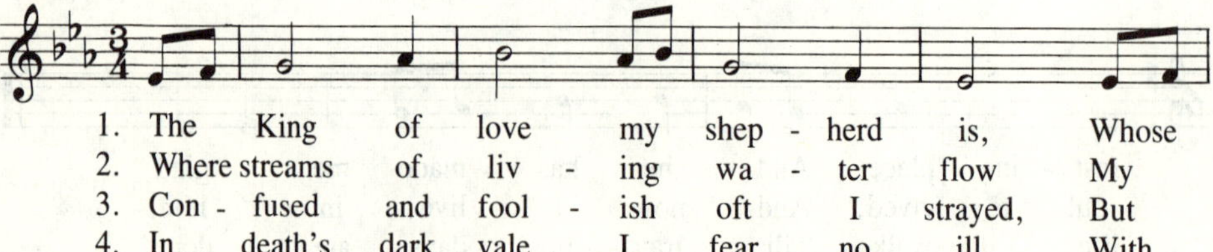
1. The King of love my shep - herd is, Whose
2. Where streams of liv - ing wa - ter flow My
3. Con - fused and fool - ish oft I strayed, But
4. In death's dark vale I fear no ill With

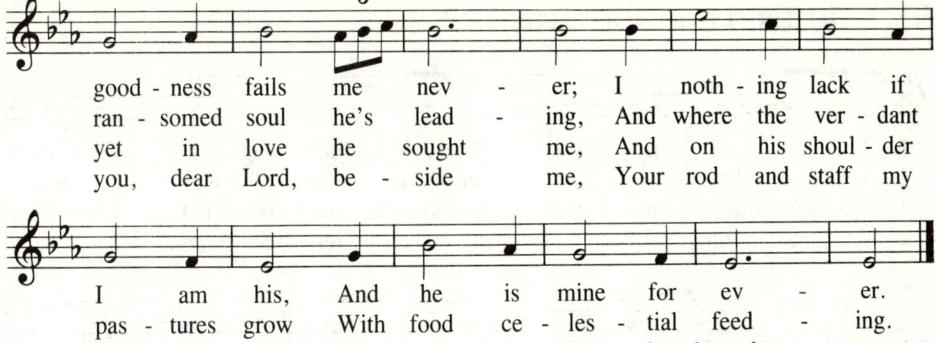
3
good - ness fails me nev - er; I noth - ing lack if
ran - somed soul he's lead - ing, And where the ver - dant
yet in love he sought me, And on his shoul - der
you, dear Lord, be - side me, Your rod and staff my
I am his, And he is mine for ev - er.
pas - tures grow With food ce - les - tial feed - ing.
gent - ly laid, And home, re - joic - ing, brought me.
com - fort still, Your cross be - fore to guide me.

5. You spread a table in my sight;
Your saving grace bestowing;
And O what transport of delight
From your pure chalice flowing!

6. And so through all the length of days
Your goodness fails me never;
Good Shepherd, may I sing your praise
Within your house for ever.

Text: Psalm (22)23; Henry W. Baker, 1821-1877, alt.
Tune: ST. COLUMBA, 8 7 8 7; Gaelic; Harm. by A. Gregory Murray, OSB, b.1905, ©

How Good the Name of Jesus Sounds 610

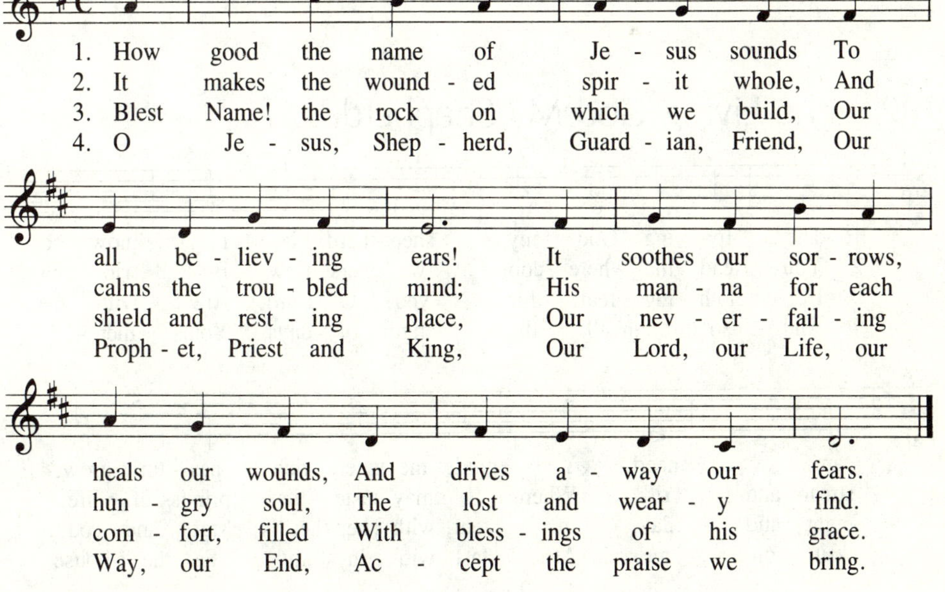
1. How good the name of Je - sus sounds To
2. It makes the wound - ed spir - it whole, And
3. Blest Name! the rock on which we build, Our
4. O Je - sus, Shep - herd, Guard - ian, Friend, Our
all be - liev - ing ears! It soothes our sor - rows,
calms the trou - bled mind; His man - na for each
shield and rest - ing place, Our nev - er - fail - ing
Proph - et, Priest and King, Our Lord, our Life, our
heals our wounds, And drives a - way our fears.
hun - gry soul, The lost and wear - y find.
com - fort, filled With bless - ings of his grace.
Way, our End, Ac - cept the praise we bring.

Text: John Newton, 1725-1807, alt.
Tune: ST. PETER, CM; Alexander R. Reinagle, 1799-1877

611 Jesus, Lead the Way

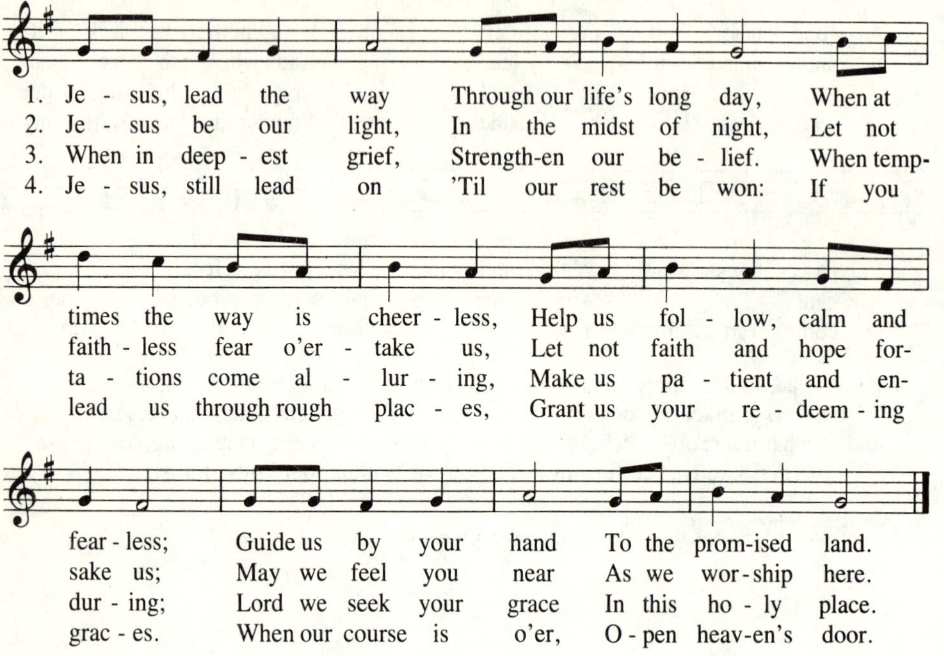
1. Je - sus, lead the way Through our life's long day, When at
2. Je - sus be our light, In the midst of night, Let not
3. When in deep - est grief, Strength-en our be - lief. When temp-
4. Je - sus, still lead on 'Til our rest be won: If you
times the way is cheer - less, Help us fol - low, calm and
faith - less fear o'er - take us, Let not faith and hope for-
ta - tions come al - lur - ing, Make us pa - tient and en-
lead us through rough plac - es, Grant us your re - deem - ing
fear - less; Guide us by your hand To the prom-ised land.
sake us; May we feel you near As we wor-ship here.
dur - ing; Lord we seek your grace In this ho - ly place.
grac - es. When our course is o'er, O - pen heav-en's door.

Text: *Jesu, geh voran;* Nicholas L. von Zinzendorf, 1700-1760; Tr. by Jane Borthwick, 1813-1897, alt.
Tune: ROCHELLE, 55 88 55; Adam Drese, 1620-1701; Harm. alt.

612 The Living God My Shepherd Is

1. The liv - ing God my shep - herd is, I know no
2. You lead me where cool wa - ters flow By rip - pling
3. I noth - ing fear; for you, O Lord, Are with me
4. And so through all the length of days, Your mer - cy
care or need. You guide me where rich pas - tures grow,
stream and rill, Where I may taste the springs of life,
night and day, In - tent, with shep-herd's staff and rod,
waits on me, At last with - in my Fa - ther's house

A - long the ver - dant mead, Where ev - 'ry day, by
My thirst - ing spir - it fill; You near me bide and
To guide me when I stray, And in the fold you
Your glo - ry I shall see; You ev - er - more will

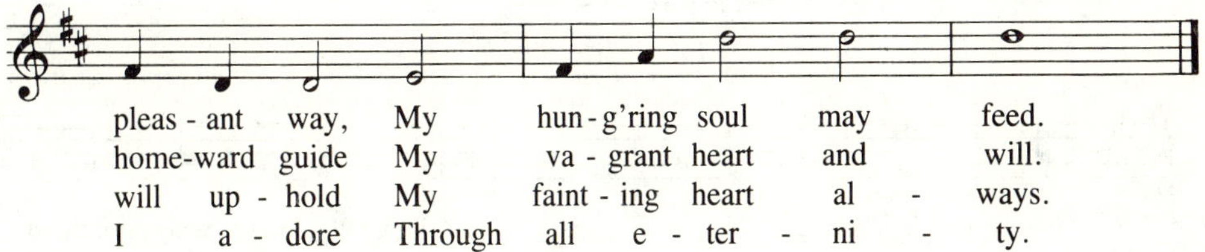
pleas - ant way, My hun - g'ring soul may feed.
home-ward guide My va - grant heart and will.
will up - hold My faint - ing heart al - ways.
I a - dore Through all e - ter - ni - ty.

Text: Psalm 23; J. Driscoll, SJ, 1946, © Peter Janson-Smith
Tune: BROTHER JAMES' AIR, 8 6 8 6 8 6; J. L. Macbeth Bain, c.1840-1925; Harm. by Gordon P. Jacob, 1895-1984, © Campbell, Thompson and McLaughlin, Ltd.

The Lord, the Lord, the Lord Is My Shepherd 613

1. The Lord, the Lord, the Lord is my shep - herd, The
2. He brings me rest in green, green, pas - tures, He
3. My fear is gone for he is with me, His

Lord, the Lord, the Lord is my shep - herd, The
leads me to the still, still wa - ters, He
rod and staff bring com - fort sure; His

Lord, the Lord, the Lord is my shep - herd, The
guides me a - long his own right way, The
good - ness and mer - cy shall fol - low me, The

Lord is my shep-herd and I shall not want.
Lord is my shep-herd and I shall not want.
Lord is my shep-herd and I shall not want.

Text: Afro-American Spiritual
Tune: THE LORD IS MY SHEPHERD, Irregular; Afro-American Spiritual; Harm. by Austin C. Lovelace, b.1919, © 1986, GIA Publications, Inc.

614 When Jesus Came Preaching the Kingdom of God

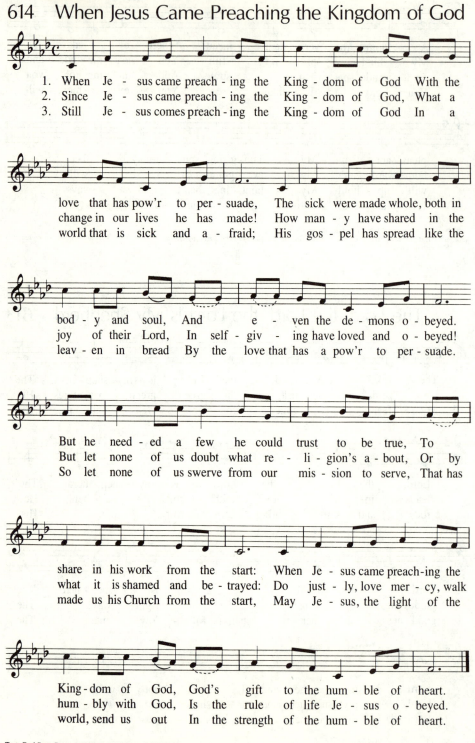

1. When Je - sus came preach - ing the King - dom of God With the
2. Since Je - sus came preach - ing the King - dom of God, What a
3. Still Je - sus comes preach - ing the King - dom of God In a

love that has pow'r to per - suade, The sick were made whole, both in
change in our lives he has made! How man - y have shared in the
world that is sick and a - fraid; His gos - pel has spread like the

bod - y and soul, And e - ven the de - mons o - beyed.
joy of their Lord, In self - giv - ing have loved and o - beyed!
leav - en in bread By the love that has a pow'r to per - suade.

But he need - ed a few he could trust to be true, To
But let none of us doubt what re - li - gion's a - bout, Or by
So let none of us swerve from our mis - sion to serve, That has

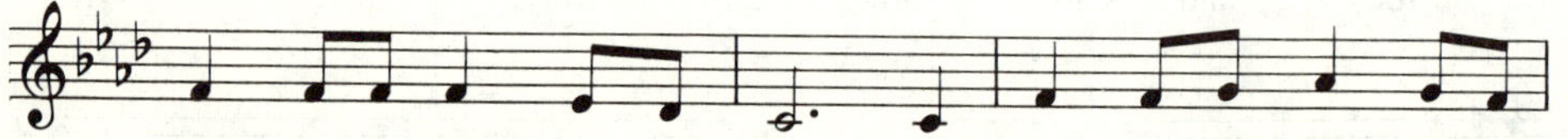

share in his work from the start: When Je - sus came preach-ing the
what it is shamed and be - trayed: Do just - ly, love mer - cy, walk
made us his Church from the start, May Je - sus, the light of the

King - dom of God, God's gift to the hum - ble of heart.
hum - bly with God, Is the rule of life Je - sus o - beyed.
world, send us out In the strength of the hum - ble of heart.

Text: Fred Pratt Green, b.1903, © 1974, Hope Publishing Co.
Tune: SAMANTHRA, 11 8 11 8 D; *Southern Harmony*, 1835; Harm. by Austin C. Lovelace, b.1919, © 1986, GIA Publications, Inc.

The Kingdom of God 615

1. The king - dom of God is jus - tice and joy;
2. The king - dom of God is mer - cy and grace;
3. The king - dom of God is chal - lenge and choice:
4. God's king - dom is come, the gift and the goal;

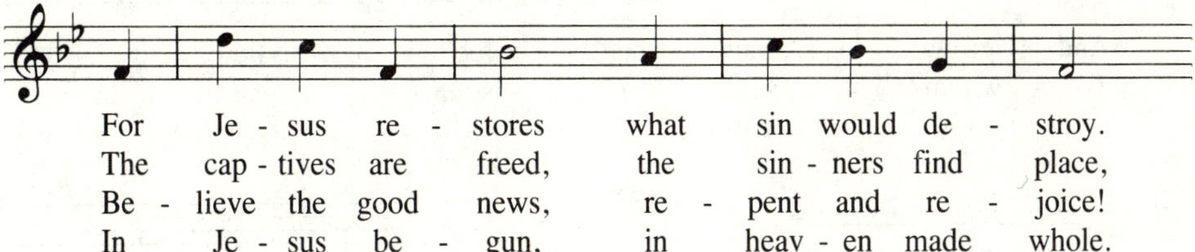
For Je - sus re - stores what sin would de - stroy.
The cap - tives are freed, the sin - ners find place,
Be - lieve the good news, re - pent and re - joice!
In Je - sus be - gun, in heav - en made whole.

God's pow - er and glo - ry in Je - sus we know;
The out - cast are wel - comed God's ban - quet to share;
God's love for us sin - ners brought Christ to his cross:
The heirs of the king - dom shall an - swer his call;

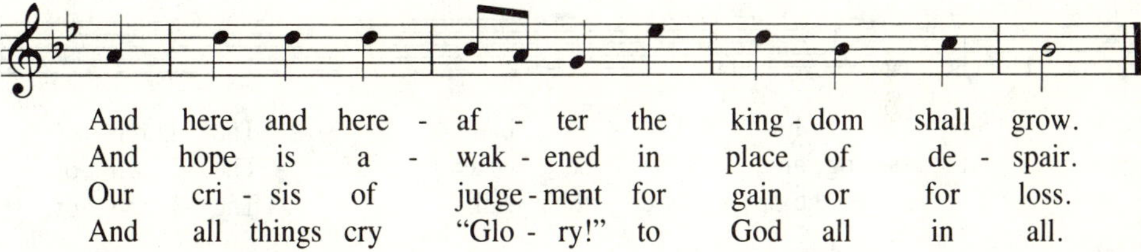
And here and here - af - ter the king - dom shall grow.
And hope is a - wak - ened in place of de - spair.
Our cri - sis of judge - ment for gain or for loss.
And all things cry "Glo - ry!" to God all in all.

Text: Bryn A. Rees, b.1911, © Mrs. M. Rees
Tune: LAUDATE DOMINUM, 10 10 11 11; Charles H. H. Parry, 1848-1918

616 Christ's Church Shall Glory in His Power

1. Christ's church shall glo - ry in his pow'r
2. Christ's peo - ple serve his way - ward world
3. Christ's liv - ing lamp shall bright - ly burn,
And grow to his per - fec - tion;
To whom he seems a stran - ger;
And to our earth - ly cit - y
He is our rock, our might - y tow'r
He knows its wel - come from of old,
For - got - ten beau - ty shall re - turn,
Our life, our res - ur - rec - tion:
He shares our joy, our dan - ger:
And pu - ri - ty and pit - y:
So by his skill - ful hand The church of
So strong, and yet so weak, The church of
To give the op - pressed their right The church of
Christ shall stand; The mas - ter - build - er's plan
Christ shall speak; His cross our great - est need,
Christ shall fight; And though the years seem long
He works, as he be - gan,
His word the vi - tal seed
He is our strength and song,

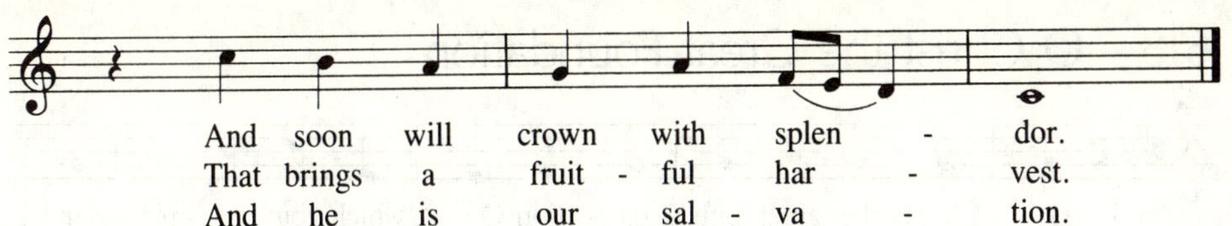
And soon will crown with splen - dor.
That brings a fruit - ful har - vest.
And he is our sal - va - tion.

Text: Christopher Idle, b.1938, © 1982, Hope Publishing Co.
Tune: EIN' FESTE BURG, 8 7 8 7 66 66 7; Martin Luther, 1483-1546; Harm. by J.S. Bach, 1685-1750

Christ Is Made the Sure Foundation 617

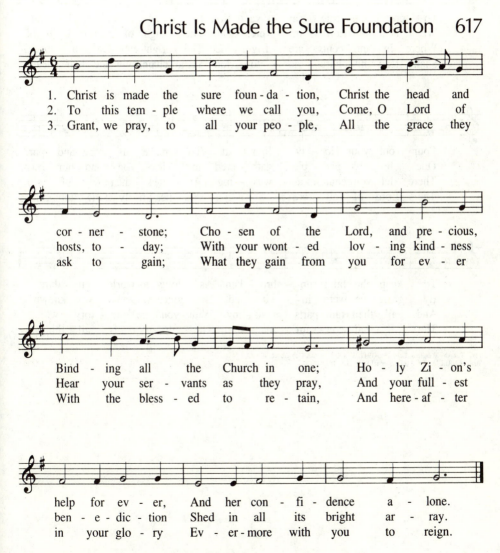

1. Christ is made the sure foun - da - tion, Christ the head and
2. To this tem - ple where we call you, Come, O Lord of
3. Grant, we pray, to all your peo - ple, All the grace they

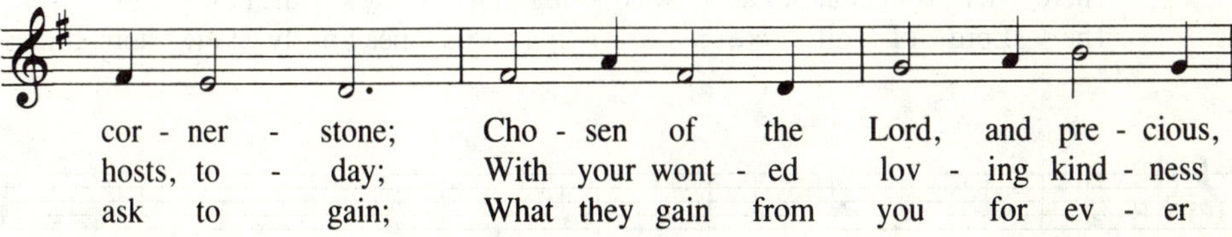
cor - ner - stone; Cho - sen of the Lord, and pre - cious,
hosts, to - day; With your wont - ed lov - ing kind - ness
ask to gain; What they gain from you for ev - er

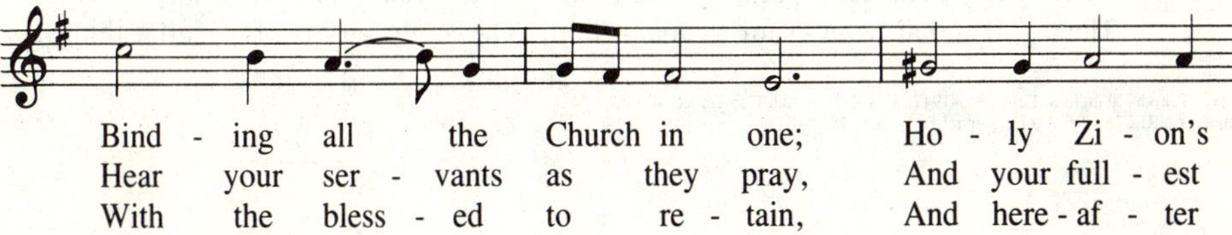
Bind - ing all the Church in one; Ho - ly Zi - on's
Hear your ser - vants as they pray, And your full - est
With the bless - ed to re - tain, And here - af - ter

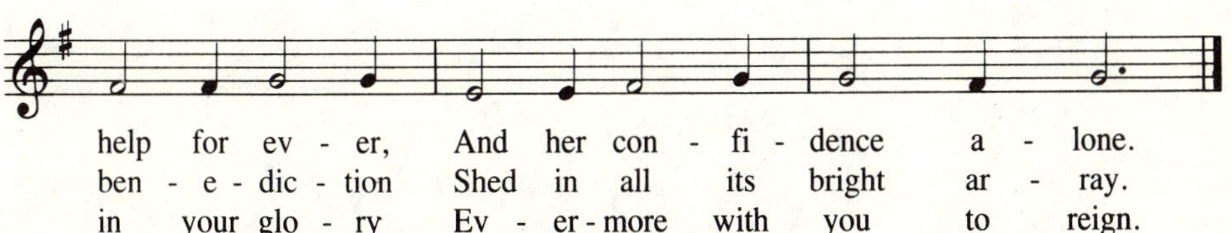
help for ev - er, And her con - fi - dence a - lone.
ben - e - dic - tion Shed in all its bright ar - ray.
in your glo - ry Ev - er - more with you to reign.

Text: *Angularis fundamentum;* 11th C.; Tr. by John M. Neale, 1818-1866, alt.
Tune: WESTMINSTER ABBEY, 8 7 8 7 8 7; Adapted from an anthem of Henry Purcell, 1659-1695

618 O Christ the Great Foundation

1. O Christ the great foun - da - tion On which your peo - ple stand
2. Bap - tized in one con - fes - sion, One church in all the earth,
3. Where ty - rants' hold is tight - ened, Where strong de - vour the weak,
4. This is the mo - ment glo - rious When he who once was dead

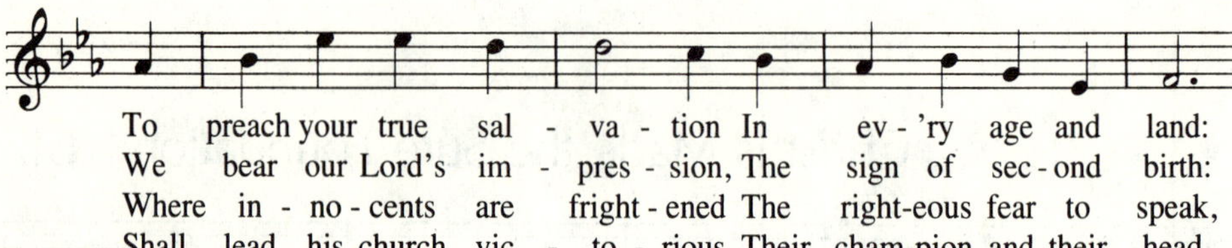

To preach your true sal - va - tion In ev - 'ry age and land:
We bear our Lord's im - pres - sion, The sign of sec - ond birth:
Where in - no - cents are fright - ened The right-eous fear to speak,
Shall lead his church vic - to - rious, Their cham-pion and their head.

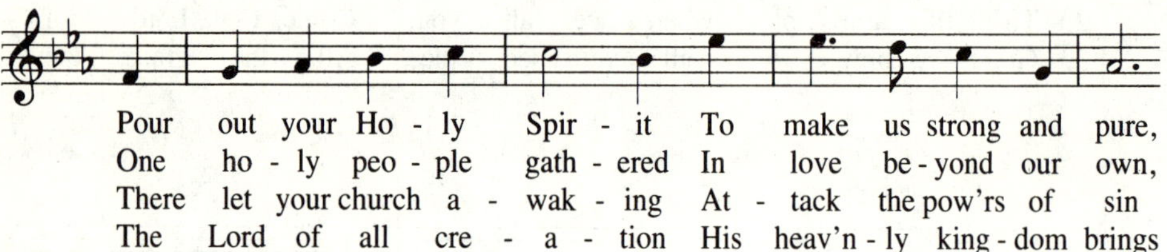

Pour out your Ho - ly Spir - it To make us strong and pure,
One ho - ly peo - ple gath - ered In love be - yond our own,
There let your church a - wak - ing At - tack the pow'rs of sin
The Lord of all cre - a - tion His heav'n - ly king - dom brings

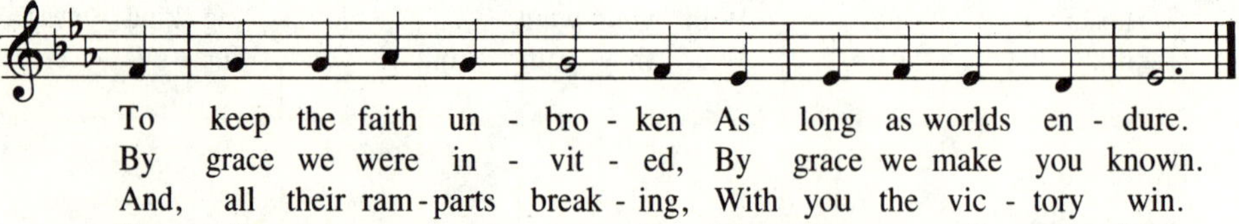

To keep the faith un - bro - ken As long as worlds en - dure.
By grace we were in - vit - ed, By grace we make you known.
And, all their ram - parts break - ing, With you the vic - tory win.
The fi - nal con - sum - ma - tion, The glo - ry of all things.

Text: Timothy T'ingfang Lew, 1891-1947, alt.,
Tune: AURELIA, 7 6 7 6 D; Samuel S. Wesley, 1810-1876

Glorious In Majesty 619

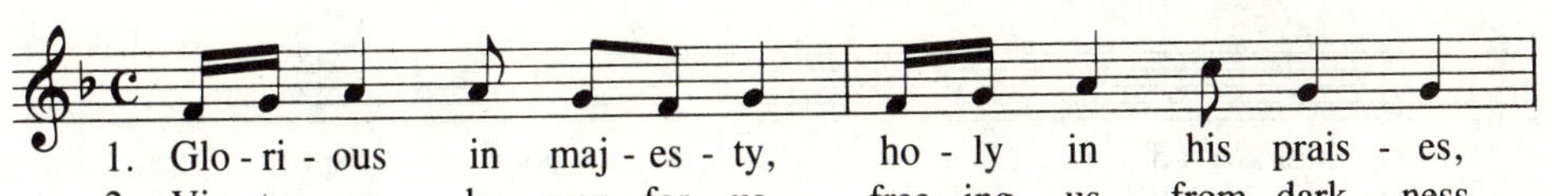
1. Glo - ri - ous in maj - es - ty, ho - ly in his prais - es,
2. Vic - to - ry he won for us, free - ing us from dark - ness,
3. One in love, as fam - i - ly, liv - ing with each oth - er,

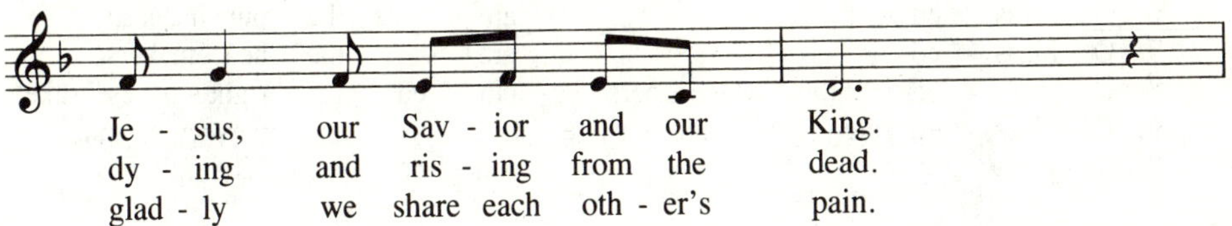
Je - sus, our Sav - ior and our King.
dy - ing and ris - ing from the dead.
glad - ly we share each oth - er's pain.

Born a man, yet God of old, let us all a - dore him:
Liv - ing with the Fa - ther now, yet he is a - mong us:
Yet he will not leave us so, soon he is re - turn - ing,

filled with his Spir - it, let us sing.
we are the bod - y, he the head.
tak - ing us back with him to reign.

Liv - ing is to love him, serv - ing him to know his free-dom.

Come a - long with us to join the praise of Je - sus.

Come to Je - sus now, Go to live his word re - joic - ing.

Text: Jeff Cothran, fl.1972
Tune: SHIBBOLET BASADEH, 7 6 8 D with refrain; Jewish; Harm. by Jeff Cothran, fl.1972

620 O Blessed Are the Poor in Spirit

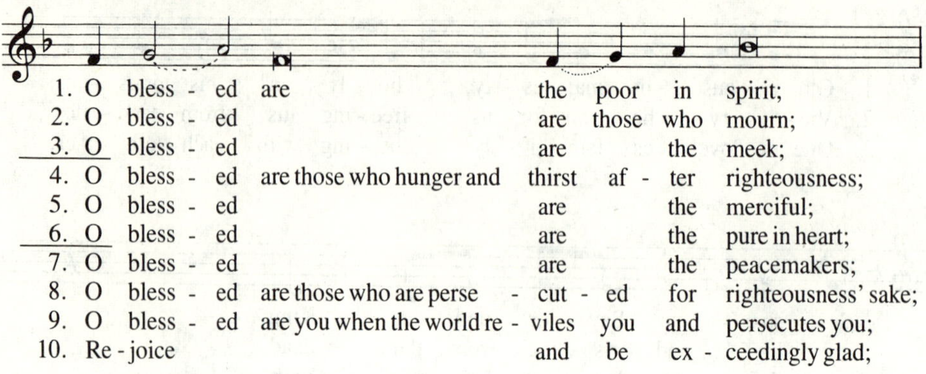
1. O bless - ed are the poor in spirit;
2. O bless - ed are those who mourn;
3. O bless - ed are the meek;
4. O bless - ed are those who hunger and thirst af - ter righteousness;
5. O bless - ed are the merciful;
6. O bless - ed are the pure in heart;
7. O bless - ed are the peacemakers;
8. O bless - ed are those who are perse - cut - ed for righteousness' sake;
9. O bless - ed are you when the world re - viles you and persecutes you;
10. Re - joice and be ex - ceedingly glad;

1. for theirs is the kingdom of heav - en.
2. for they shall be com - fort - ed.
3. for they shall in - her - it the earth.
4. for they shall be sat - is - fied.
5. for they shall obtain mer - cy.
6. for they shall see God.
7. for they shall be called the chil - dren of God.
8. for theirs is the kingdom of heav - en.
9. and utters all manner of evil against you falsely for my sake.
10. for great is your reward in heav - en.

Text: Matt. 5:3-12; *The Beatitudes*
Tune: KONTAKION, Irregular; Byzantine/Slavonic Chant, Adapt. by Richard Proulx, b.1937, © 1985, GIA Publications, Inc.

621 All Who Love and Serve Your City

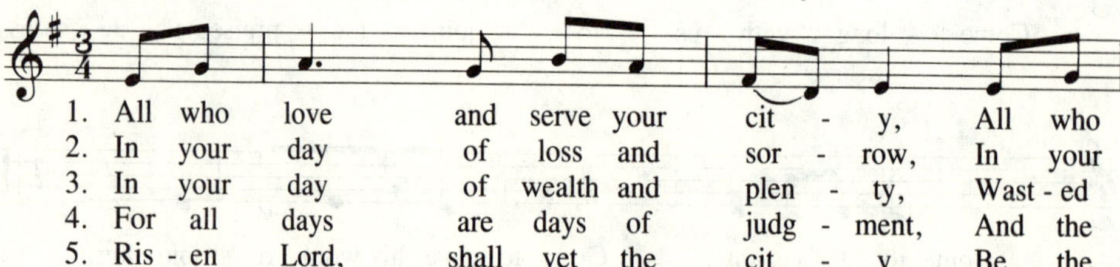
1. All who love and serve your cit - y, All who
2. In your day of loss and sor - row, In your
3. In your day of wealth and plen - ty, Wast - ed
4. For all days are days of judg - ment, And the
5. Ris - en Lord, shall yet the cit - y Be the

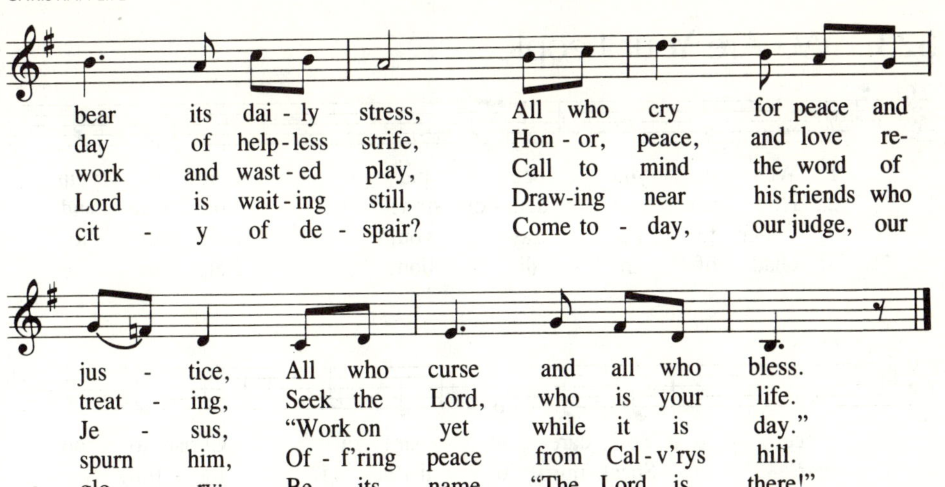
bear its dai - ly stress, All who cry for peace and
day of help-less strife, Hon - or, peace, and love re-
work and wast - ed play, Call to mind the word of
Lord is wait - ing still, Draw-ing near his friends who
cit - y of de - spair? Come to - day, our judge, our
jus - tice, All who curse and all who bless.
treat - ing, Seek the Lord, who is your life.
Je - sus, "Work on yet while it is day."
spurn him, Of - f'ring peace from Cal - v'rys hill.
glo - ry; Be its name "The Lord is there!"

Text: Erik Routley, 1917-1982, © Galliard Publications
Tune: BIRABUS, 8 7 8 7; Peter Cutts, b.1937, © 1969, Hope Publishing Co.

Where Temple Offerings Are Made 622

1. Where Tem-ple of - fer - ings are made, And know - ing he must
2. Some of - fer sil - ver, oth - ers gold, Some what they can af-
3. Name-less as shad - ows on a wall The poor - er come and
4. A wid - ow, pass - ing by, who scarce Can scrape e - nough to
5. How deep - ly moved he is by this, He leaves us in no

die, Our Mas - ter, rest - ing in the shade,
ford; Some give, in or - der to with-hold,
go; It is as if he knows them all,
live, She finds two pen - nies in her purse,
doubt: And he him - self will die for us,

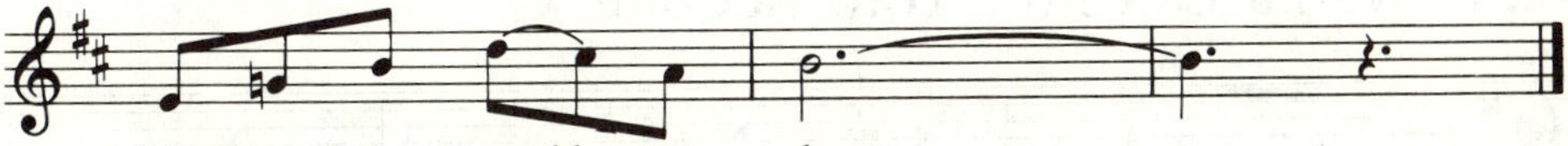

Watch-es the world go by.
And some to gain re - ward.
As on - ly God can know.
Gives all that she can give.
Be - fore the week is out.

Text: Mk. 12:41-44; Fred Pratt Green, b.1903, © 1982, Hope Publishing Co.
Tune: O FOR A HEART, CM; Malcolm Williamson, b.1943, © 1971, Josef Weinberger Ltd.

623 We Are Your People

1. We are your peo - ple: Lord, by your
2. How can we dem - on - strate Your love and
3. Called to por - tray you, Help us to
4. Glad of tra - di - tion, Help us to

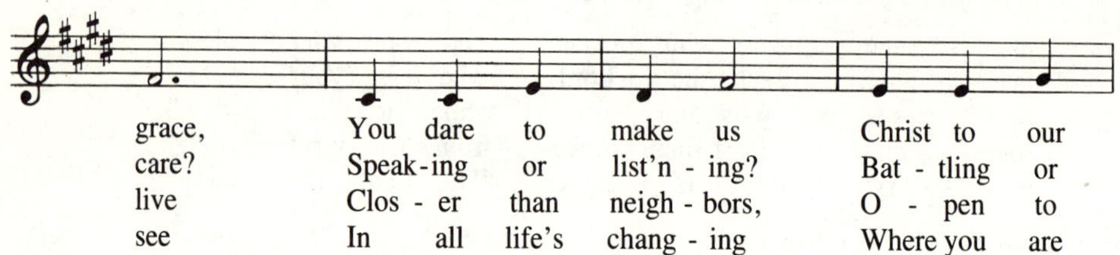
grace, You dare to make us Christ to our
care? Speak-ing or list'n - ing? Bat - tling or
live Clos - er than neigh - bors, O - pen to
see In all life's chang - ing Where you are

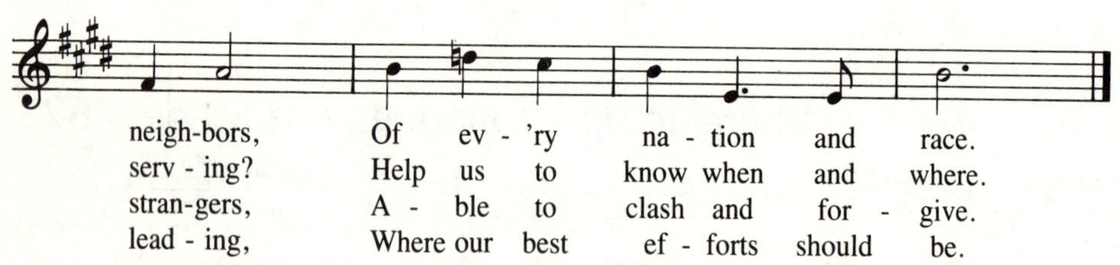
neigh-bors, Of ev - 'ry na - tion and race.
serv - ing? Help us to know when and where.
stran-gers, A - ble to clash and for - give.
lead - ing, Where our best ef - forts should be.

5. Joined in community,
   Breaking your bread,
May we discover
Gifts in each other,
   Willing to lead and be led.

6. Lord, as we minister
   In diff'rent ways,
May all we're doing
Show that you're living,
   Meeting your love with our praise.

Text: Brian Wren, b.1936, © 1975, Hope Publishing Co.
Tune: WHITFIELD, 5 4 5 5 7; John W. Wilson, b.1905, © 1980, Hope Publishing Co.

624 What Does the Lord Require

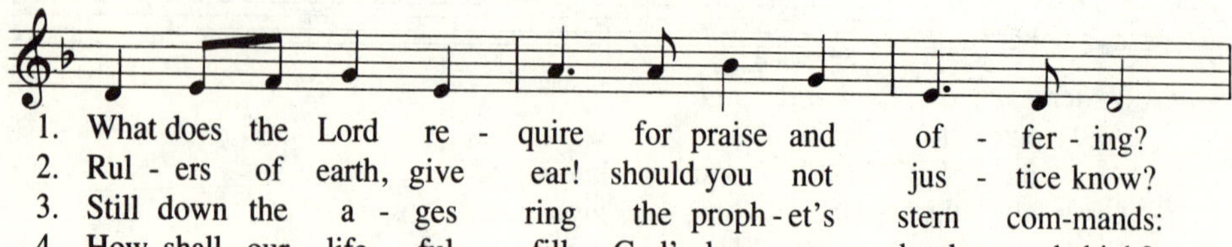
1. What does the Lord re - quire for praise and of - fer - ing?
2. Rul - ers of earth, give ear! should you not jus - tice know?
3. Still down the a - ges ring the proph - et's stern com-mands:
4. How shall our life ful - fill God's law so hard and high?

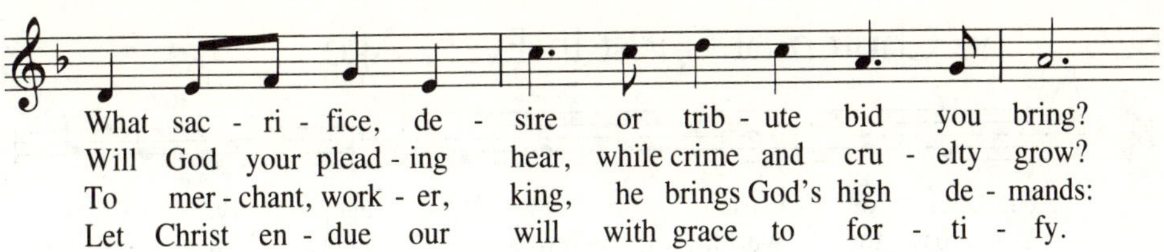
What sac - ri - fice, de - sire or trib - ute bid you bring?
Will God your plead - ing hear, while crime and cru - elty grow?
To mer - chant, work - er, king, he brings God's high de - mands:
Let Christ en - due our will with grace to for - ti - fy.

Do just - ly; Love mer - cy; Walk hum - bly with your God.
Do just - ly; Love mer - cy; Walk hum - bly with your God.
Do just - ly; Love mer - cy; Walk hum - bly with your God.
Then just - ly, In mer - cy, We'll hum - bly walk with God.

Text: Micah 6:6-8; Albert F. Bayly, 1901-1984, alt., © Oxford University Press
Tune: SHARPTHORNE, 6 6 6 6 33 6; Erik Routley, 1917-1982, © 1969, Hope Publishing Co.

Now Let Us from This Table Rise 625

1. Now let us from this ta - ble rise Re - newed in
2. With minds a - lert, up - held by grace, To spread the
3. To fill each hu - man house with love, It is the
4. Then grant us cour - age, car - ing God, To choose a-

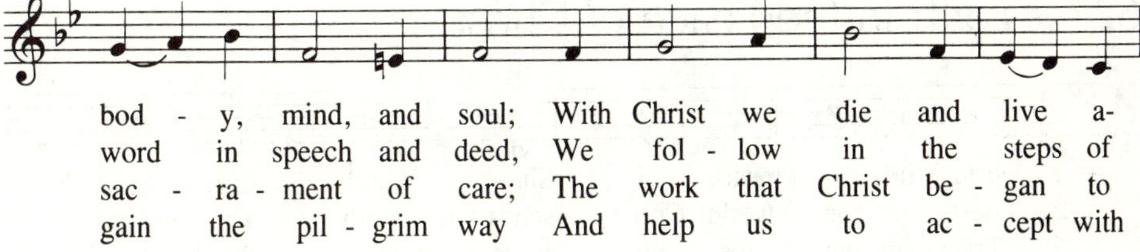
bod - y, mind, and soul; With Christ we die and live a-
word in speech and deed, We fol - low in the steps of
sac - ra - ment of care; The work that Christ be - gan to
gain the pil - grim way And help us to ac - cept with

gain, His self - less love has made us whole.
Christ, At one with us in hope and need.
do We hum - bly pledge our - selves to share.
joy The chal - lenge of to - mor - row's day.

Text: Fred Kaan, b.1929, © 1968, Hope Publishing Co.
Tune: DEUS TUORUM MILITUM, LM; *Grenoble Antiphoner,* 1753; Harm. by Basil Harwood, 1859-1949, © Executors of the late Dr. Basil Harwood

626 The Church of Christ in Every Age

1. The Church of Christ in ev - 'ry age Be - set by
2. A - cross the world, a - cross the street, The vic - tims
3. Then let the ser - vant Church a - rise, A car - ing
4. For he a - lone, whose blood was shed, Can cure the
5. We have no mis - sion but to serve In full o-

change but Spir - it led, Must claim and test its her - it-
of in - jus - tice cry For shel - ter and for bread to
Church that longs to be A part - ner in Christ's sac - ri-
fe - ver in our blood, And teach us how to share our
be - dience to our Lord: To care for all, with - out re-

age And keep on ris - ing from the dead.
eat, And nev - er live un - til they die.
fice, And clothed in Christ's hu - man - i - ty.
bread And feed the starv - ing mul - ti - tude.
serve, And spread his lib - er - at - ing Word.

Text: Fred Pratt Green, b.1903, © 1971, Hope Publishing Co.
Tune: DUNEDIN, LM; Vernon Griffiths, 1894-1985, ©

627 Forth in the Peace of Christ

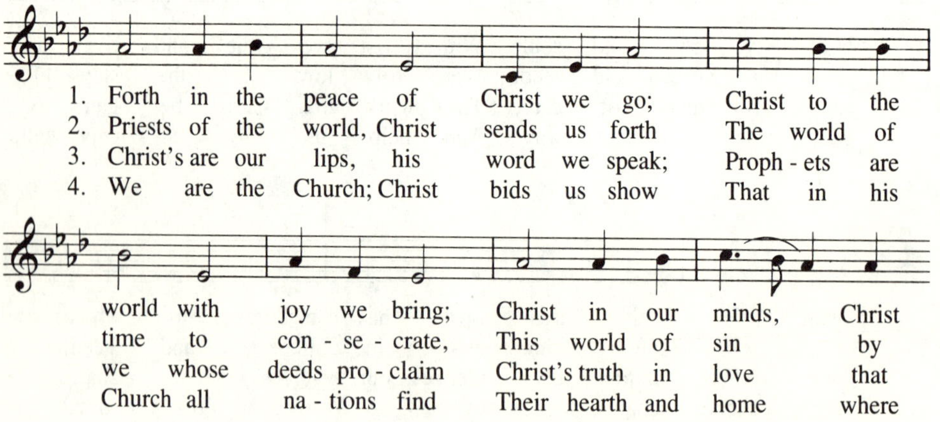
1. Forth in the peace of Christ we go; Christ to the
2. Priests of the world, Christ sends us forth The world of
3. Christ's are our lips, his word we speak; Proph - ets are
4. We are the Church; Christ bids us show That in his
world with joy we bring; Christ in our minds, Christ
time to con - se - crate, This world of sin by
we whose deeds pro - claim Christ's truth in love that
Church all na - tions find Their hearth and home where

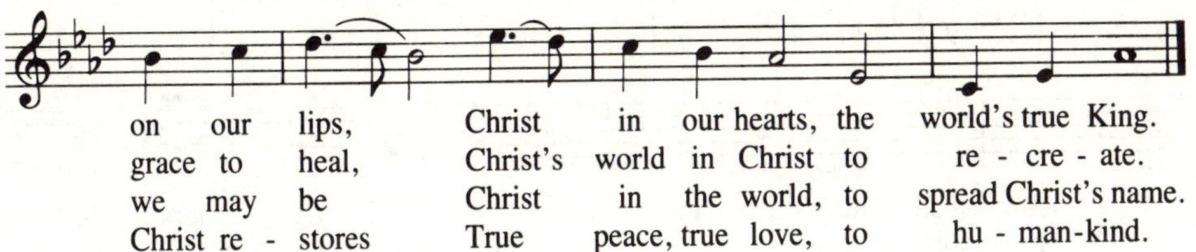
on our lips, Christ in our hearts, the world's true King.
grace to heal, Christ's world in Christ to re - cre - ate.
we may be Christ in the world, to spread Christ's name.
Christ re - stores True peace, true love, to hu - man-kind.

Text: James Quinn, SJ, b.1919, © 1969
Tune: LLEDROD, LM; Welsh; *Caniadan y Cyssegr,* 1839

Go Make of All Disciples 628

1. "Go make of all disciples": We hear the call, O Lord, That comes from you, our Father, In your eternal Word. Inspire our ways of learning Through earnest, fervent prayer, And let our daily living Reveal you everywhere.

2. "Go make of all disciples": Baptizing in the name Of Father, Son, and Spirit— From age to age the same. We call each new disciple To follow you, O Lord, Redeeming soul and body By water and the Word.

3. "Go make of all disciples": We at your feet would stay Until each life's vocation Accents your holy way. We cultivate the nature God plants in ev'ry heart, Revealing in our witness The Master Teacher's art.

4. "Go make of all disciples": We welcome your command; "Lo, I am with you always": We take your guiding hand. The task looms large before us— We follow without fear. In heav'n and earth your power Shall bring God's kingdom here.

Text: Matt. 28:19-20; Leon M. Adkins, b.1896, alt., © 1955,1964, Abingdon Press
Tune: ELLECOMBE, 76 76 D; *Gesangbuch der Herzogl,* Wirtemberg, 1784

629 How Shall They Hear the Word of God

1. How shall they hear the word of God Un - less the
2. How shall they call to God for help Un - less they
3. How shall the gos - pel be pro-claimed If her - alds
truth is told? How shall the sin - ful be set free,
have be - lieved? How shall the poor be giv - en hope,
are not sent? How shall the world find peace at last
The sor - row - ful con - soled? To all who speak the
The pris - on - er re - prieved? To those who help the
If we are neg - li - gent? So send us, Lord, for
truth to - day Im - part your Spir - it, Lord, we pray.
blind to see Give light and love and clar - i - ty.
we re - joice To speak of Christ with life and voice.

Text: Michael Perry, b.1942, © 1980, Hope Publishing Co.
Tune: AUCH JETZT MACHT GOTT, 8 6 8 6 88; Koch's *Choralbuch*, 1816

Lord, Whose Love in Humble Service 630

1. Lord, whose love in hum - ble ser - vice Bore the
2. Still your chil - dren wan - der home - less; Still the
3. As we wor - ship, grant us vi - sion, Till your
4. Called from wor - ship in - to ser - vice Forth in

weight of hu - man need, Who did on the
hun - gry cry for bread; Still the cap - tives
love's re - veal - ing light, Till the height and
your great name we go, To the child, the

Cross for - sak - en, Show us mer - cy's per - fect deed;
long for free - dom; Still in grief we mourn our dead.
depth and great - ness Dawns up - on our hu - man sight:
youth, the a - ged, Love in liv - ing deeds to show;

We, your ser - vants, bring the wor - ship Not of
As, O Lord, your deep com - pas - sion Healed the
Mak - ing known the needs and bur - dens Your com-
Hope and health, good - will and com - fort, Coun - cil,

voice a - lone, but heart: Con - se - crat - ing
sick and freed the soul, Use the love your
pas - sion bids us bear, Stir - ring us to
aid, and peace we give That your chil - dren,

to your pur - pose Ev - 'ry gift which you im - part.
Spir - it kin - dles Still to save and make us whole.
faith - ful ser - vice. Your a - bun - dant life to share.
Lord, in free - dom, May your mer - cy know and live.

Text: Albert F. Bayly, 1901-1984, © Oxford University Press
Tune: IN BABILONE 8 7 8 7 D; *Oude en Nieuwe Hollanste Boerenlities*, c.1710

631 God, Whose Giving Knows No Ending

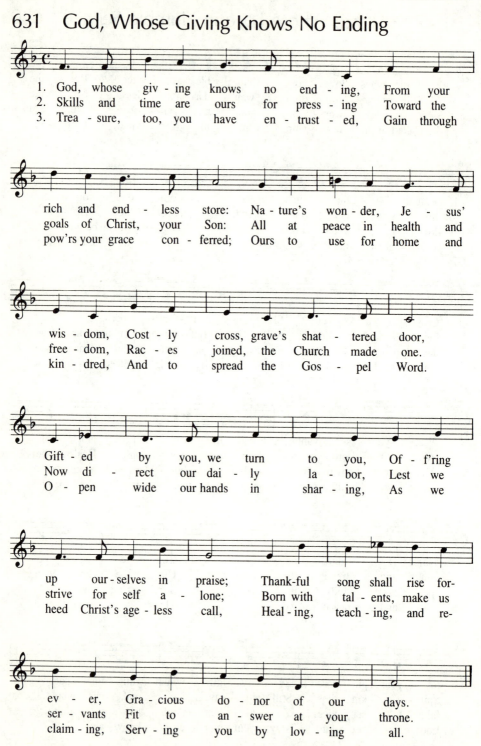

1. God, whose giv - ing knows no end - ing, From your
2. Skills and time are ours for press - ing Toward the
3. Trea - sure, too, you have en - trust - ed, Gain through

rich and end - less store: Na - ture's won - der, Je - sus'
goals of Christ, your Son: All at peace in health and
pow'rs your grace con - ferred; Ours to use for home and

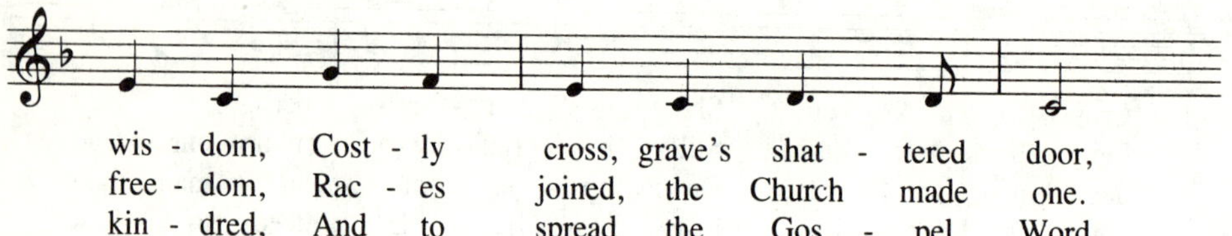
wis - dom, Cost - ly cross, grave's shat - tered door,
free - dom, Rac - es joined, the Church made one.
kin - dred, And to spread the Gos - pel Word.

Gift - ed by you, we turn to you, Of - f'ring
Now di - rect our dai - ly la - bor, Lest we
O - pen wide our hands in shar - ing, As we

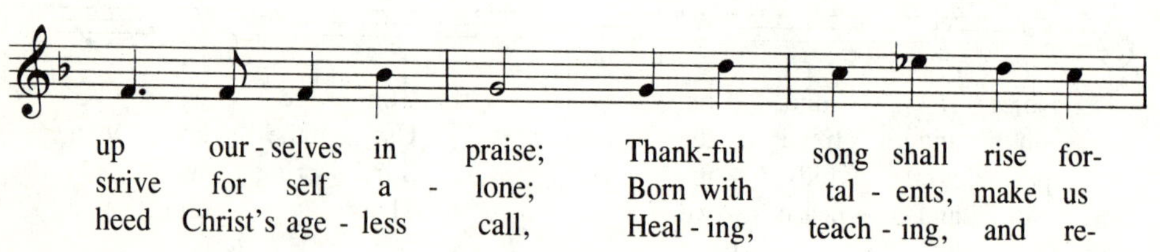
up our - selves in praise; Thank-ful song shall rise for-
strive for self a - lone; Born with tal - ents, make us
heed Christ's age - less call, Heal - ing, teach - ing, and re-

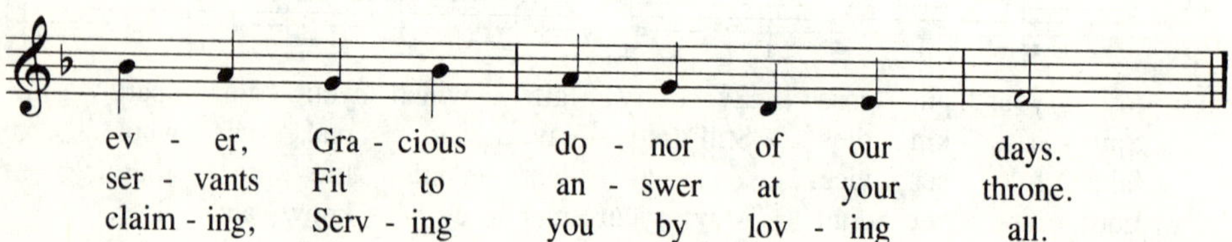
ev - er, Gra - cious do - nor of our days.
ser - vants Fit to an - swer at your throne.
claim - ing, Serv - ing you by lov - ing all.

Text: Robert L. Edwards, b.1915,
Tune: RUSTINGTON, 8 7 8 7 D; Charles H. H. Parry, 1848-1918

Those Who Love and Those Who Labor 632

1. Those who love and those who la - bor Fol - low
2. Where the man - y work to - geth - er, They with
3. Let the seek - er nev - er fal - ter Till the

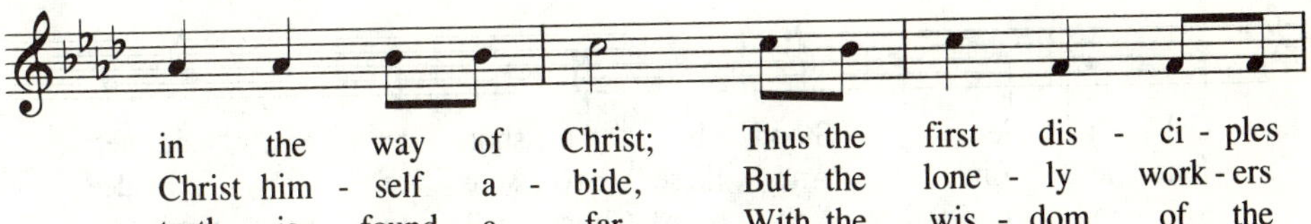

in the way of Christ; Thus the first dis - ci - ples
Christ him - self a - bide, But the lone - ly work - ers
truth is found a - far With the wis - dom of the

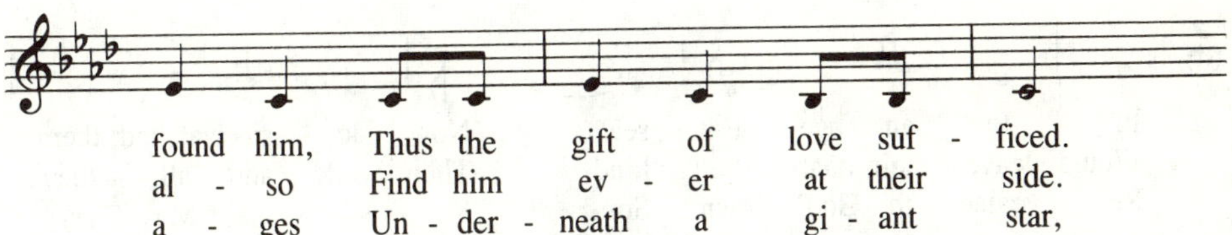

found him, Thus the gift of love suf - ficed.
al - so Find him ev - er at their side.
a - ges Un - der - neath a gi - ant star,

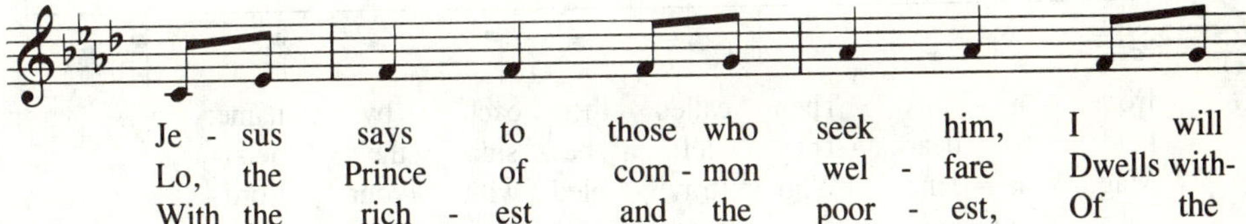

Je - sus says to those who seek him, I will
Lo, the Prince of com - mon wel - fare Dwells with-
With the rich - est and the poor - est, Of the

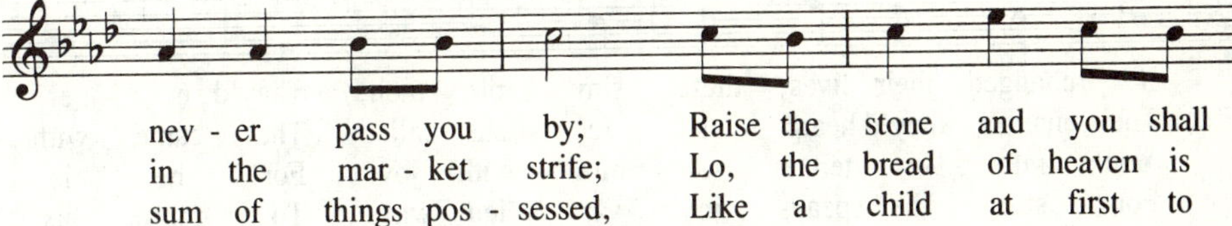

nev - er pass you by; Raise the stone and you shall
in the mar - ket strife; Lo, the bread of heaven is
sum of things pos - sessed, Like a child at first to

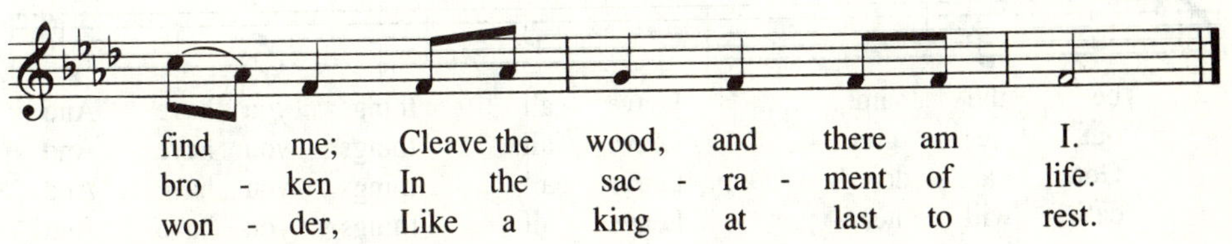

find me; Cleave the wood, and there am I.
bro - ken In the sac - ra - ment of life.
won - der, Like a king at last to rest.

Text: Geoffrey Dearmer, b.1893,
Tune: DOMHNACH TRIONOIDE, 8 7 8 7 D; Gaelic; Harm. by Richard Proulx, b.1937,

633 Two Fishermen

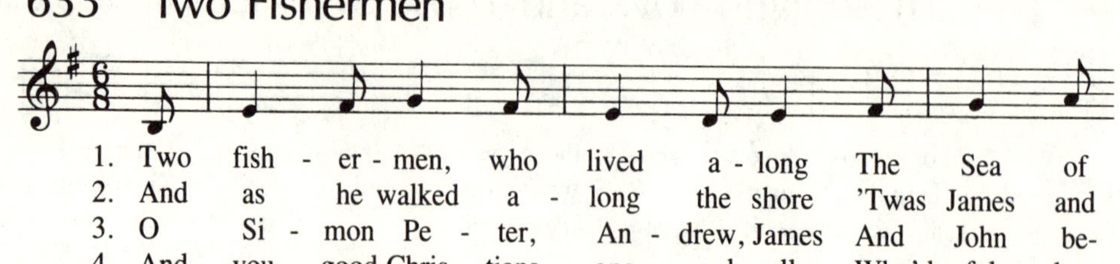
1. Two fish - er - men, who lived a - long The Sea of
2. And as he walked a - long the shore 'Twas James and
3. O Si - mon Pe - ter, An - drew, James And John be-
4. And you, good Chris - tians, one and all Who'd fol - low

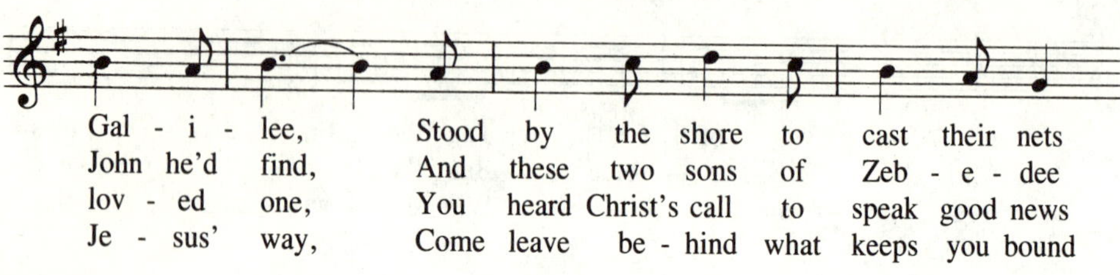
Gal - i - lee, Stood by the shore to cast their nets
John he'd find, And these two sons of Zeb - e - dee
lov - ed one, You heard Christ's call to speak good news
Je - sus' way, Come leave be - hind what keeps you bound

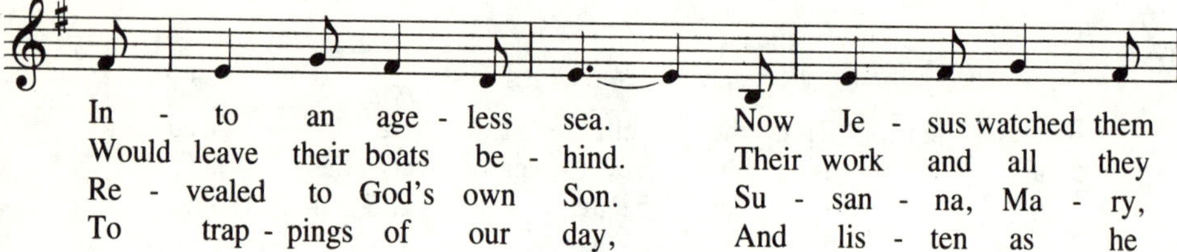
In - to an age - less sea. Now Je - sus watched them
Would leave their boats be - hind. Their work and all they
Re - vealed to God's own Son. Su - san - na, Ma - ry,
To trap - pings of our day, And lis - ten as he

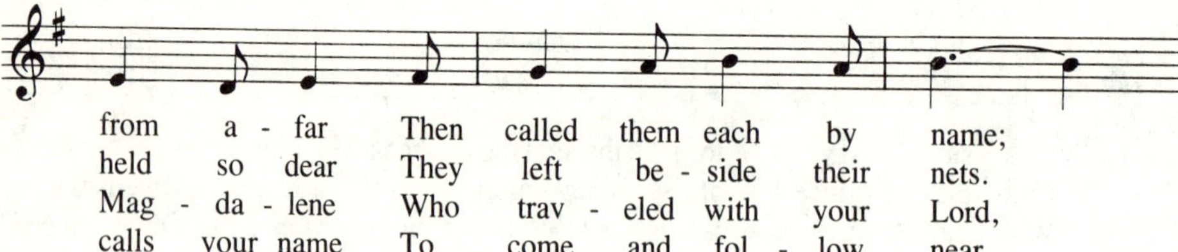
from a - far Then called them each by name;
held so dear They left be - side their nets.
Mag - da - lene Who trav - eled with your Lord,
calls your name To come and fol - low near,

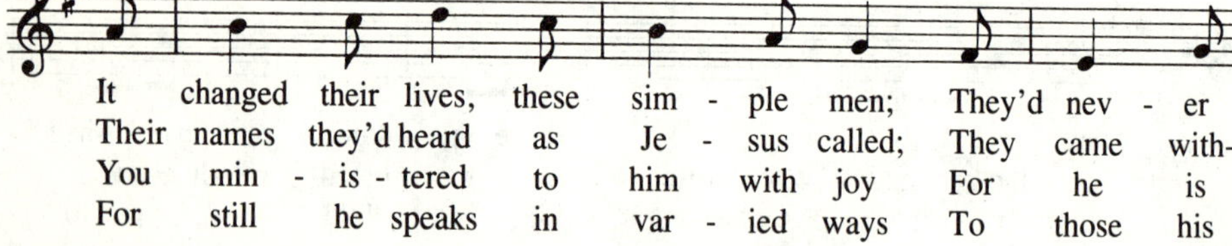
It changed their lives, these sim - ple men; They'd nev - er
Their names they'd heard as Je - sus called; They came with-
You min - is - tered to him with joy For he is
For still he speaks in var - ied ways To those his

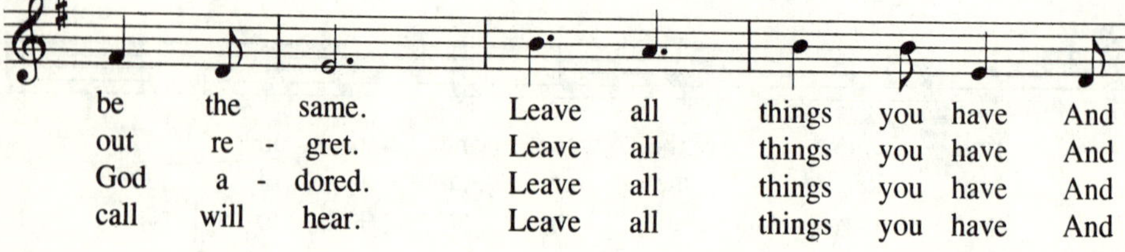
be the same. Leave all things you have And
out re - gret. Leave all things you have And
God a - dored. Leave all things you have And
call will hear. Leave all things you have And

come and fol - low me, And come and fol - low me.
come and fol - low me, And come and fol - low me.
come and fol - low me, And come and fol - low me.
come and fol - low me, And come and fol - low me.

Text: Suzanne Toolan, SM, B.1927, © 1986, GIA Publications, Inc.
Tune: LEAVE ALL THINGS, CMD with refrain; Suzanne Toolan, SM, b.1927, © 1970, GIA Publications, Inc.

Take Up Your Cross 634

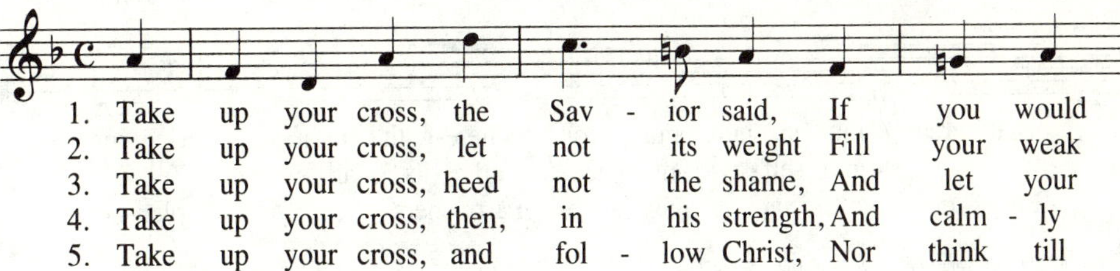
1. Take up your cross, the Sav - ior said, If you would
2. Take up your cross, let not its weight Fill your weak
3. Take up your cross, heed not the shame, And let your
4. Take up your cross, then, in his strength, And calm - ly
5. Take up your cross, and fol - low Christ, Nor think till

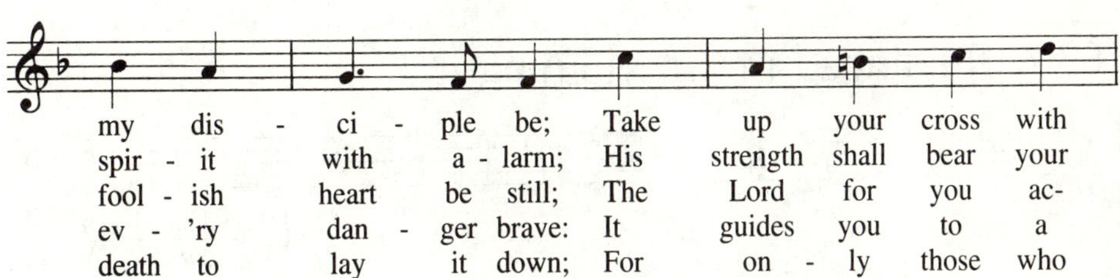
my dis - ci - ple be; Take up your cross with
spir - it with a - larm; His strength shall bear your
fool - ish heart be still; The Lord for you ac-
ev - 'ry dan - ger brave: It guides you to a
death to lay it down; For on - ly those who

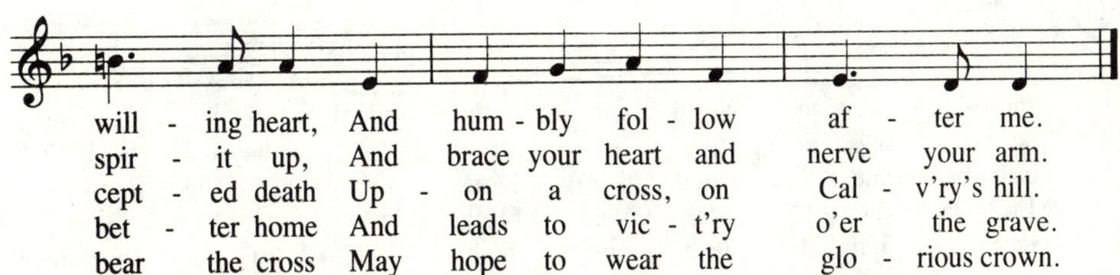
will - ing heart, And hum - bly fol - low af - ter me.
spir - it up, And brace your heart and nerve your arm.
cept - ed death Up - on a cross, on Cal - v'ry's hill.
bet - ter home And leads to vic - t'ry o'er the grave.
bear the cross May hope to wear the glo - rious crown.

Text: Charles W. Everest, 1814-1877, alt.
Tune: O JESU, MI DULCISSIME, LM; *Clausener Gesangbuch,* 1655

635 Weary of All Trumpeting

1. Wea - ry of all trum - pet - ing, Wea - ry of all kill - ing,
2. Bless - ed Sav - ior, low - ly Lord, Ser - vant King, your dy - ing
3. To the tri - umph of your cross Sum - mon all the liv - ing;

Wea - ry of all songs that sing Prom - ise, non - ful - fill - ing.
Asked us sheathe the fool - ish sword, Asked us cease de - ny - ing.
Sum - mon us to live by loss, Gain - ing all by giv - ing.

We would raise, O Christ, one song: We would join in sing - ing
Trum - pet with your Spir - it's breath Through each height and hol - low:
Suff'r - ing all, that we may see Tri - umph in sur - ren - der;

That great mu - sic pure and strong, Where - with heav'n is ring - ing.
In - to your self - giv - ing death, Call us all to fol - low.
Leav - ing all, that we may be Part - ners in your splen - dor.

Text: Martin Franzmann, 1907-1976, © Chantry Music Press
Tune: DISTLER, 7 6 7 6 D; Hugo Distler, 1908-1942, © Chantry Music Press; Harm. by Richard Proulx, b.1937, ©1975, GIA Publications, Inc.

636 I Danced in the Morning

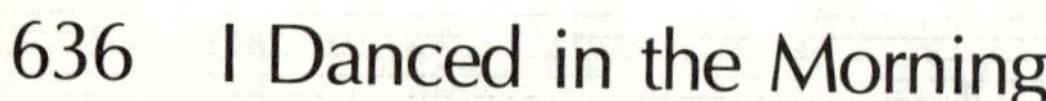

1. I danced in the
2. I danced for the
3. I danced on the
4. I danced on a
5. They cut me
morn - ing when the world was be - gun, And I danced in the
scribe and the phar - i - see, But they would - n't
Sab - bath and I cured the lame: The ho - ly peo - ple
Fri - day when the sky turned black; It's hard to
down and I leap up high; I am the

moon and the stars and the sun, And I
dance, and they would-n't fol-low me; I
said it was a shame. They
dance with the dev-il on your back. They
life that-'ll nev-er, nev-er die; I'll

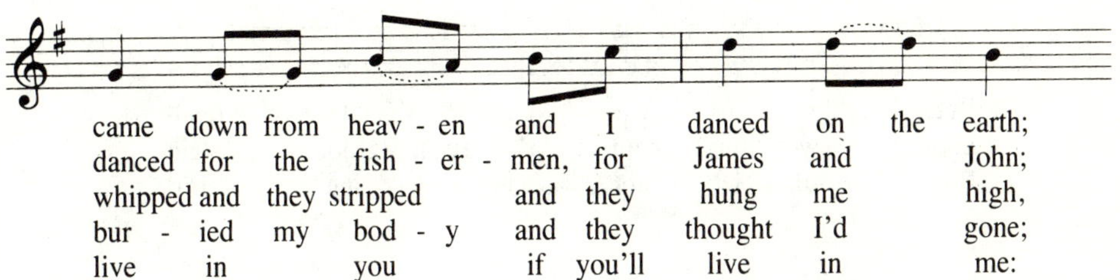
came down from heav-en and I danced on the earth;
danced for the fish-er-men, for James and John;
whipped and they stripped and they hung me high,
bur-ied my bod-y and they thought I'd gone;
live in you if you'll live in me:

At Beth-le-hem I had my birth.
They came with me and the dance went on.
And left me there on a cross to die.
But I am the dance and I still go on.
I am the Lord of the Dance, said he.

Dance then wher-ev-er you may be; I am the Lord of the

Dance, said he, And I'll lead you all, wher-ev-er you may be,

1.4.
5.
And I'll lead you all in the dance, said he. dance, said he.

Text: Sydney Carter, b.1915.
Tune: SHAKER SONG, Irregular; American Shaker; Harm. by Sydney Carter, b.1915.

637 It Shocked Them That the Master Did Not Fast

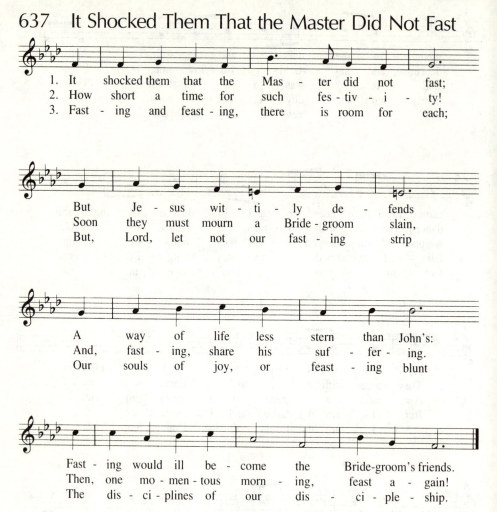

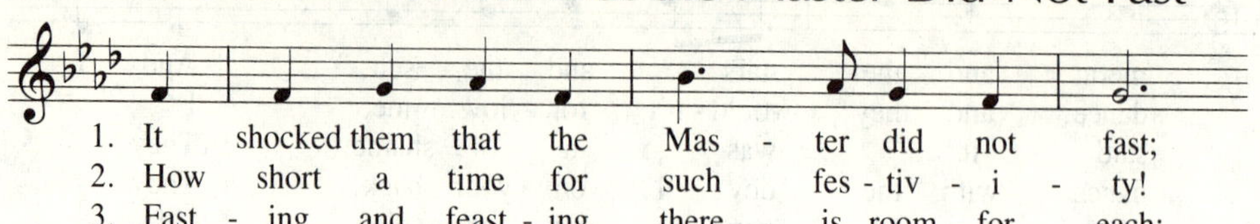
1. It shocked them that the Mas - ter did not fast;
2. How short a time for such fes - tiv - i - ty!
3. Fast - ing and feast - ing, there is room for each;

But Je - sus wit - ti - ly de - fends
Soon they must mourn a Bride - groom slain,
But, Lord, let not our fast - ing strip

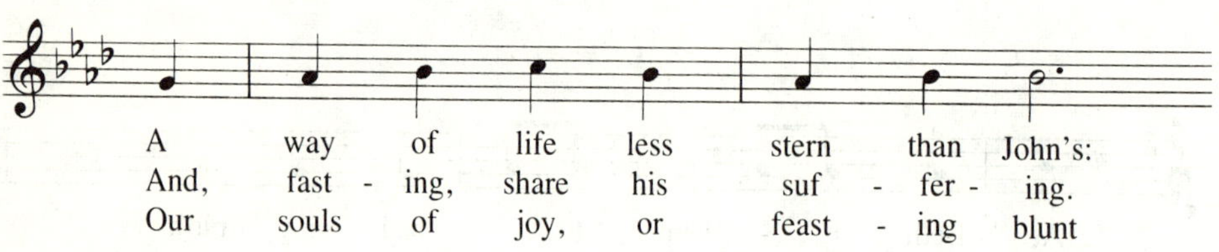
A way of life less stern than John's:
And, fast - ing, share his suf - fer - ing.
Our souls of joy, or feast - ing blunt

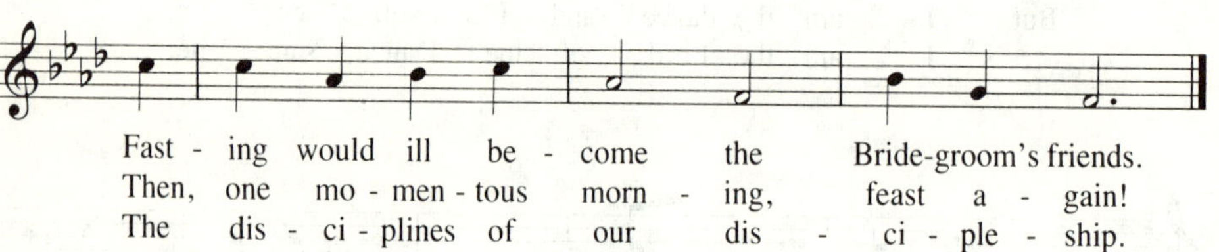
Fast - ing would ill be - come the Bride-groom's friends.
Then, one mo - men - tous morn - ing, feast a - gain!
The dis - ci - plines of our dis - ci - ple - ship.

Text: Fred Pratt Green, b.1903, © 1982, Hope Publishing Co.
Tune: MINTWOOD, 10 8 8 10; James J. Chepponis, b.1956, © 1986, GIA Publications, Inc.

Your Love, O God, Has All the World Created 638

1. Your love, O God, has all the world cre - a - ted,
2. We bring you, Lord, in fer - vent in - ter - ces - sion
3. From out the dark - ness of our hope's frus - tra - tion,
4. In pit - y look up - on your chil - dren's striv - ing
5. In - spire your church, mid earth's dis - cord - ant voic - es,

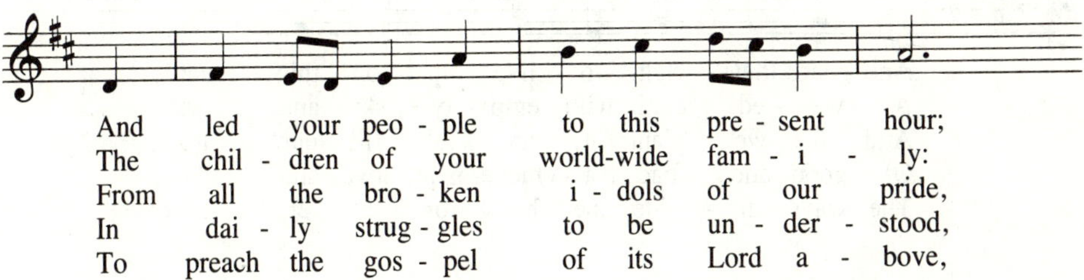

And led your peo - ple to this pre - sent hour;
The chil - dren of your world-wide fam - i - ly:
From all the bro - ken i - dols of our pride,
In dai - ly strug - gles to be un - der - stood,
To preach the gos - pel of its Lord a - bove,

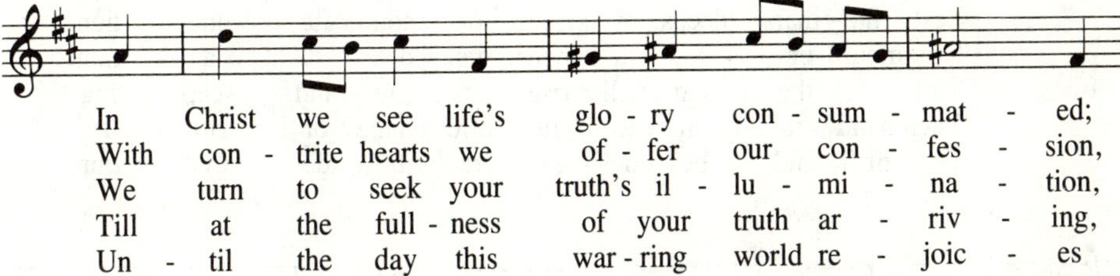

In Christ we see life's glo - ry con - sum - mat - ed;
With con - trite hearts we of - fer our con - fes - sion,
We turn to seek your truth's il - lu - mi - na - tion,
Till at the full - ness of your truth ar - riv - ing,
Un - til the day this war - ring world re - joic - es

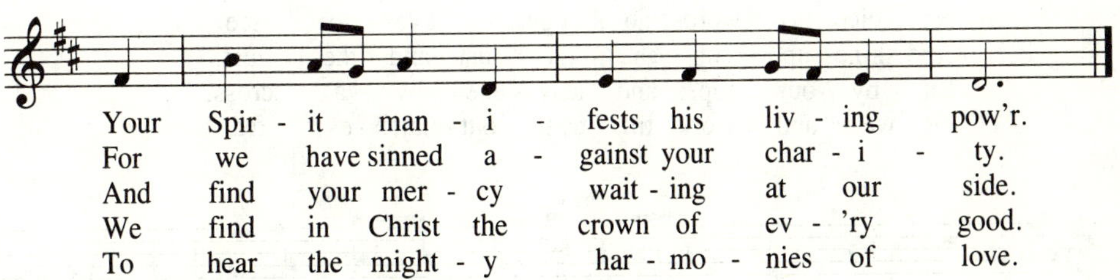

Your Spir - it man - i - fests his liv - ing pow'r.
For we have sinned a - gainst your char - i - ty.
And find your mer - cy wait - ing at our side.
We find in Christ the crown of ev - 'ry good.
To hear the might - y har - mo - nies of love.

Text: Albert F. Bayly, 1901-1984, alt.
Tune: NORTHBROOK, 11 10 11 10; Reginald S. Thatcher, 1888-1957,

639 Come, Let Us Love the Unborn Generations

1. Come, let us love the un - born gen - er - a - tions,
2. Come, con - tem - plate the sad - ness of ex - tinc - tion:
3. The pre - cious seed of life is in our keep - ing,
4. All we can do is live our hu - man sto - ry
5. We can - not sti - fle knowl - edge or in - ven - tion.

And guard their right to live up - on this earth,
A wast - ed earth, with emp - ty sky and sea;
And if we plant it, and ful - fill our trust,
Of good and bad, a - chieve - ment, love and loss,
The ways di - vide, the choice for ev - er clear:

Lest hu - man deeds, by stealth or con - fla - gra - tion,
No mourn - ers to la - ment its des - o - la - tion,
Still yet the sun will rise on joy and weep - ing,
Then hand it on to fu - ture shame or glo - ry,
To drift, and be de - liv - ered to de - struc - tion,

Snuff out all life and put an end to birth.
No voice, no words, no thought, no eyes to see.
And shine up - on the un - just and the just.
Lit by our hopes, and leav - ened by a cross.
Or wake, and work, till trust out - match - es fear.

6. Come, let us guard the gate - way to ex - ist - ence,

That thou - sands yet may stand where we have stood.

Give thanks for life, and prais - ing our per - sist - ence,

En - joy this love - ly earth, and call it good.

Text: Brian Wren, b.1936, © 1983, Hope Publishing Co.
Tune: LIFE ON EARTH, 11 10 11 10; Robert Leaf, b.1936, © 1986, GIA Publications, Inc.

God, Whose Purpose Is to Kindle 640

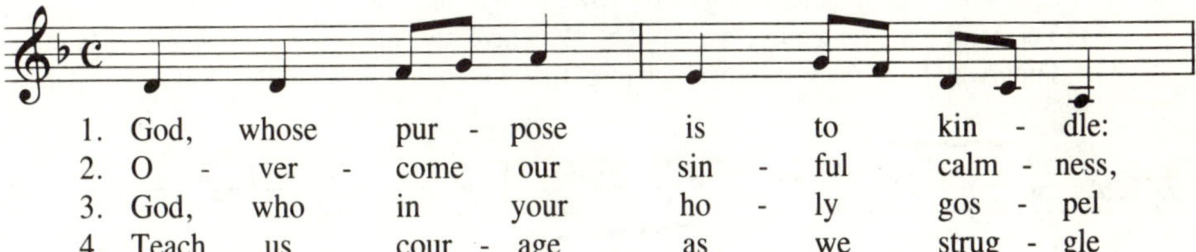
1. God, whose pur - pose is to kin - dle:
2. O - ver - come our sin - ful calm - ness,
3. God, who in your ho - ly gos - pel
4. Teach us cour - age as we strug - gle

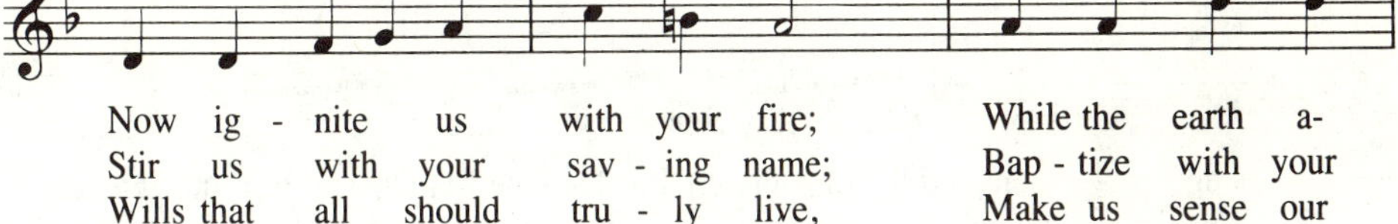
Now ig - nite us with your fire; While the earth a-
Stir us with your sav - ing name; Bap - tize with your
Wills that all should tru - ly live, Make us sense our
In all lib - er - at - ing strife; Lift the small - ness

waits your burn - ing, With your pas - sion us in - spire.
fi - ery Spir - it, Crown our lives with tongues of flame.
share of fail - ure, Our tran - quil - li - ty for - give.
of our vi - sion By your own a - bun - dant life.

5. God, who still a sword delivers
Rather than a placid peace,
With your sharpened word disturb us,
From complacency release!

6. Save us now from satisfaction,
When we privately are free,
Yet are undisturbed in spirit
By our neighbor's misery.

Text: Luke 12:49; David E. Trueblood, b.1900, © 1967, David Elton Trueblood
Tune: LIBERTY, 8 7 8 7; American; Harm. by Donald R. Riddle, b.1930, © 1975, Broadman Press

641 Lift Every Voice and Sing

1. Lift ev - 'ry voice and sing, Till earth and heav - en ring,
2. Ston - y the road we trod, Bit - ter the chas - t'ning rod,
3. God of our wea - ry years, God of our si - lent tears,
Ring with the har - mo - nies of lib - er - ty;
Felt in the days when hope un - born had died;
Thou who hast brought us thus far on the way;
Let our re - joic - ing rise High as the lis - t'ning skies,
Yet with a stead - y beat, Have not our wear - y feet
Thou who hast by thy might, Led us in - to the light,
Let it re - sound loud as the roll - ing sea.
Come to the place for which our peo - ple sighed?
Keep us for ev - er in the path, we pray.
Sing a song full of the faith that the dark past has taught us,
We have come o - ver a way that with tears has been wa - tered,
Lest our feet stray from the plac - es, our God, where we met thee,
Sing a song full of the hope that the pres - ent has brought
We have come, tread - ing our path thro' the blood of the slaugh-
Lest our hearts, drunk with the wine of the world, we for - get
us; Fac - ing the ris - ing sun Of our new day be-
tered; Out from the gloom - y past, Till now we stand at
thee; Shad-owed be - neath thy hand, May we for ev - er

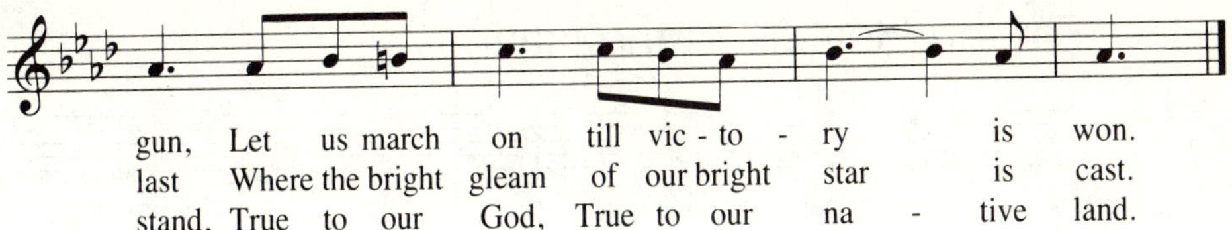
gun, Let us march on till vic - to - ry is won.
last Where the bright gleam of our bright star is cast.
stand, True to our God, True to our na - tive land.

Text: James W. Johnson, 1871-1938
Tune: ANTHEM, 66 10 66 10 14 14 66 10; J. Rosamund Johnson, 1873-1954

O God, Empower Us 642

1. O God, em - pow - er us to stem The ha - treds that di-
2. When neigh-bors feel dis - tress or grieve, Or sick - ness takes its
3. Though cold sus - pi - cion meet our warmth, We love at your com-

vide. En - a - ble us to bring an end To
toll, En - a - ble us to feel their pain, The
mand; And though not al - ways un - der - stood, We

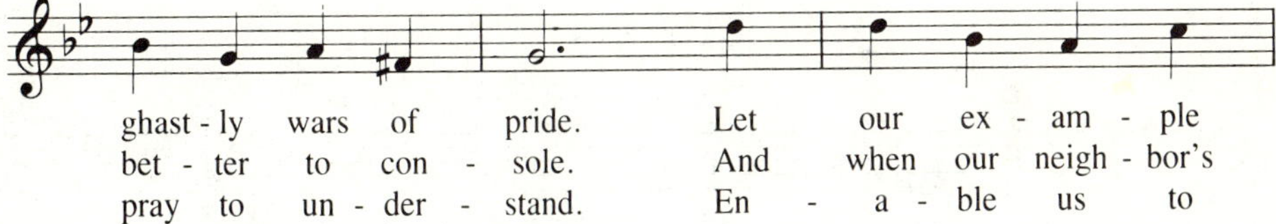
ghast - ly wars of pride. Let our ex - am - ple
bet - ter to con - sole. And when our neigh - bor's
pray to un - der - stand. En - a - ble us to

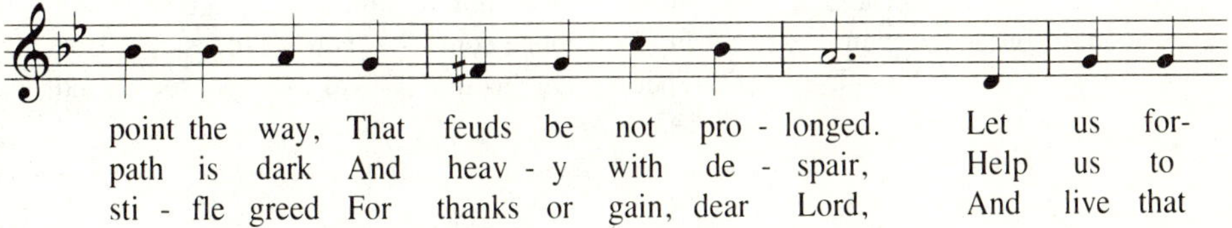
point the way, That feuds be not pro - longed. Let us for-
path is dark And heav - y with de - spair, Help us to
sti - fle greed For thanks or gain, dear Lord, And live that

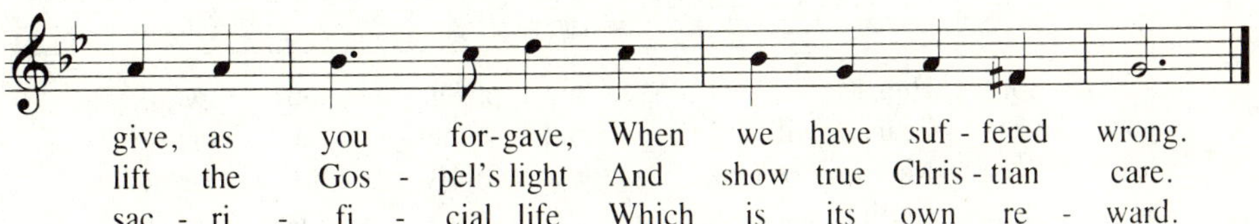
give, as you for-gave, When we have suf - fered wrong.
lift the Gos - pel's light And show true Chris - tian care.
sac - ri - fi - cial life Which is its own re - ward.

Text: Lee M. Baldwin, 1906-1982, ©
Tune: LLANGLOFFAN, CMD; Welsh

643 For the Healing of the Nations

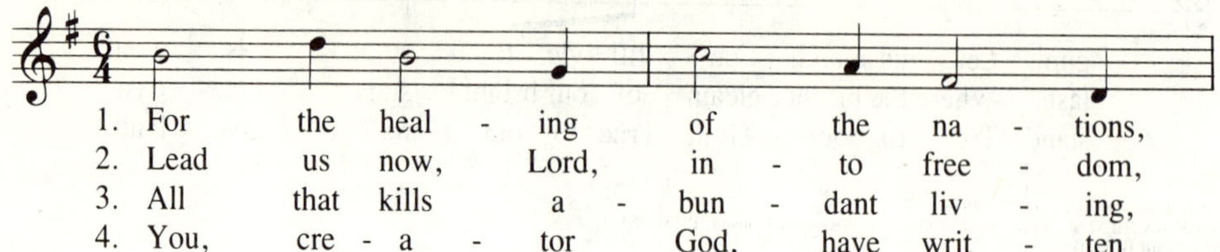
1. For the heal - ing of the na - tions,
2. Lead us now, Lord, in - to free - dom,
3. All that kills a - bun - dant liv - ing,
4. You, cre - a - tor God, have writ - ten

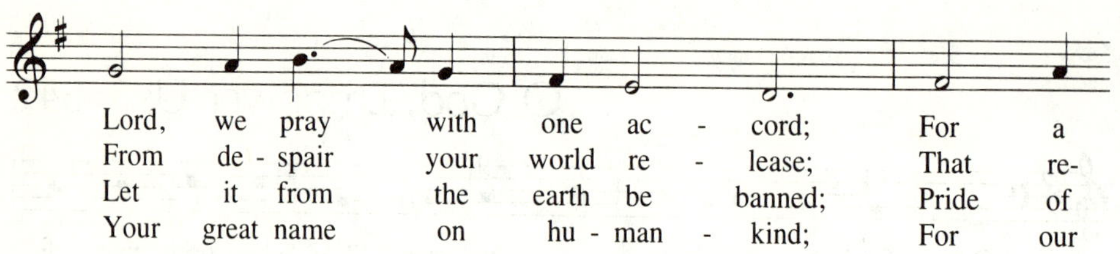
Lord, we pray with one ac - cord; For a
From de - spair your world re - lease; That re-
Let it from the earth be banned; Pride of
Your great name on hu - man - kind; For our

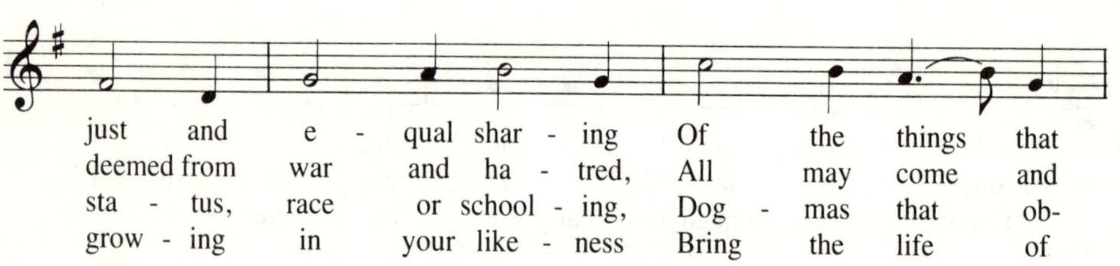
just and e - qual shar - ing Of the things that
deemed from war and ha - tred, All may come and
sta - tus, race or school - ing, Dog - mas that ob-
grow - ing in your like - ness Bring the life of

earth af - fords. To a life of love and
go in peace. Show us how through care and
scure your plan. In our com - mon quest for
Christ to mind: That by our re - sponse and

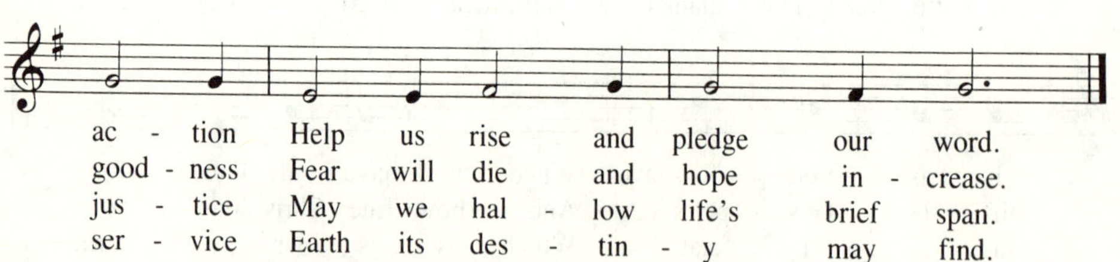
ac - tion Help us rise and pledge our word.
good - ness Fear will die and hope in - crease.
jus - tice May we hal - low life's brief span.
ser - vice Earth its des - tin - y may find.

Text: Fred Kaan, b.1929, alt., © 1968, Hope Publishing Co.
Tune: WESTMINSTER ABBEY, 8 7 8 7 8 7; Adapted from an anthem of Henry Purcell, c.1659-1695

Said Judas to Mary 644

1. Said Ju - das to Mar - y, "Now what will you do With your
2. "Oh Mar - y, O Mar - y, O think of the poor. This
3. "To - mor - row, to - mor - row, I'll think of the poor; To-
4. Said Je - sus to Mar - y, "Your love is so deep To-

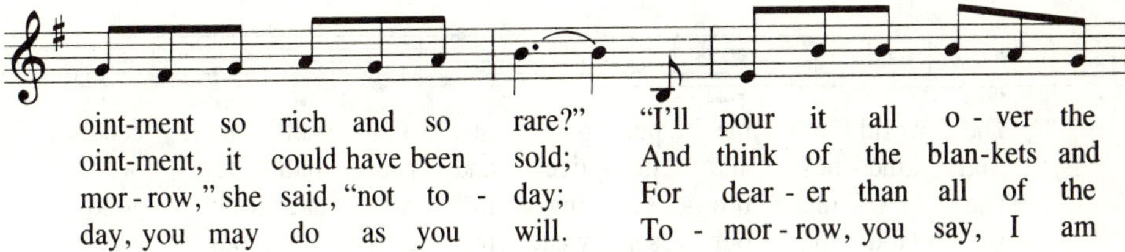
oint-ment so rich and so rare?" "I'll pour it all o - ver the
oint-ment, it could have been sold; And think of the blan-kets and
mor - row," she said, "not to - day; For dear - er than all of the
day, you may do as you will. To - mor - row, you say, I am

feet of the Lord, And I'll wipe it a - way with my
think of the bread You could buy with the sil - ver and
poor in the world Is my love who is go - ing a-
go - ing a - way, But my bod - y I leave with you

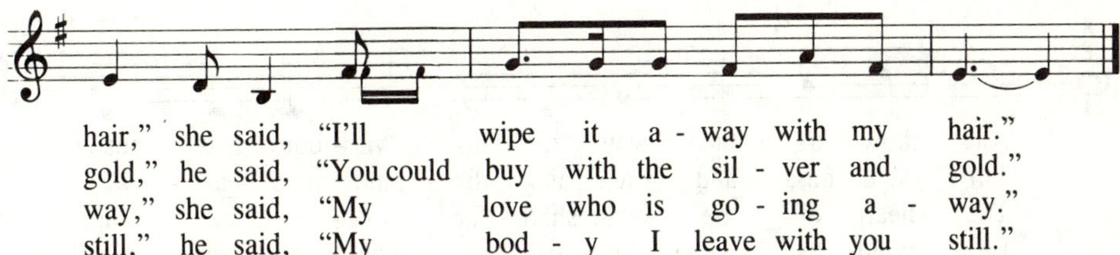
hair," she said, "I'll wipe it a - way with my hair."
gold," he said, "You could buy with the sil - ver and gold."
way," she said, "My love who is go - ing a - way."
still," he said, "My bod - y I leave with you still."

5. "The poor of the world are my body," he said,
"To the end of the world they shall be.
The bread and the blankets you give to the poor
You'll know you have given to me," he said,
"You'll know you have given to me."

6. "My body will hang on the cross of the world
Tomorrow," he said, "not today.
And Martha and Mary will find me again
And wash all my sorrow away," he said,
"And wash all my sorrow away."

Text: Sydney Carter, b.1915
Tune: JUDAS AND MARY, Irregular; Sydney Carter, b.1915

645 With Jesus for Hero

1. With Je - sus for he - ro, for teach - er and friend,
2. His King - dom is com - ing, God's will shall be done,
3. God's name shall be hal - lowed, his love un - der - stood,
4. To God be the glo - ry, to Christ be the praise,

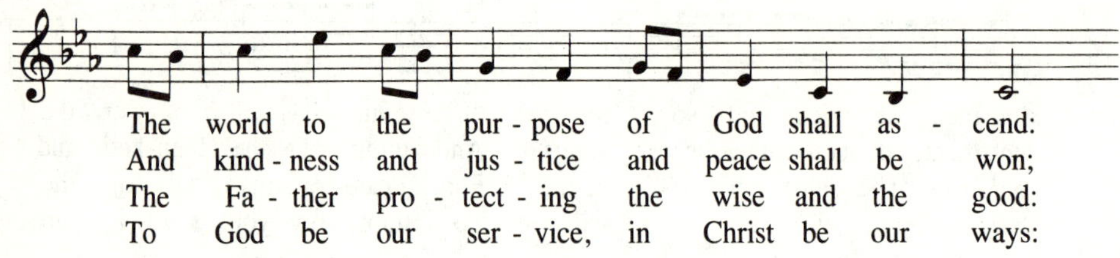

The world to the pur - pose of God shall as - cend:
And kind - ness and jus - tice and peace shall be won;
The Fa - ther pro - tect - ing the wise and the good:
To God be our ser - vice, in Christ be our ways:

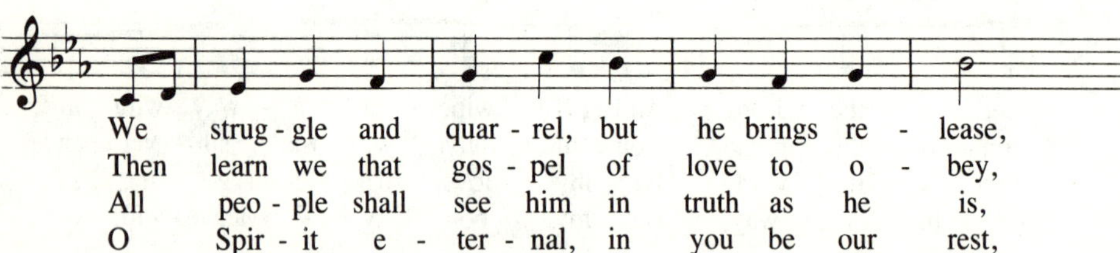

We strug - gle and quar - rel, but he brings re - lease,
Then learn we that gos - pel of love to o - bey,
All peo - ple shall see him in truth as he is,
O Spir - it e - ter - nal, in you be our rest,

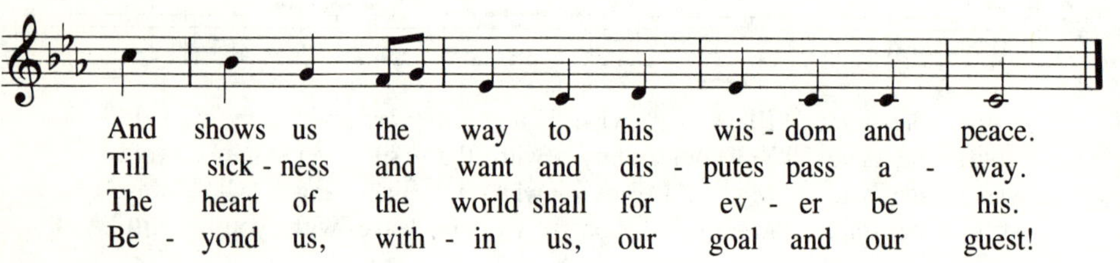

And shows us the way to his wis - dom and peace.
Till sick - ness and want and dis - putes pass a - way.
The heart of the world shall for ev - er be his.
Be - yond us, with - in us, our goal and our guest!

Text: Percy Dearmer, 1867-1936, © Oxford University Press
Tune: SIOBÁN NI LAOGHAIRE, 11 11 11 11; Gaelic; Harm. by Richard Proulx, b.1937, © 1975, GIA Publications, Inc.

O Jesus Christ, May Grateful Hymns Be Rising 646

1. O Je - sus Christ, may grate - ful hymns be ris - ing
2. Grant us new cour - age, sac - ri - fi - cial, hum - ble,
3. Show us your Spir - it, brood - ing o'er each cit - y

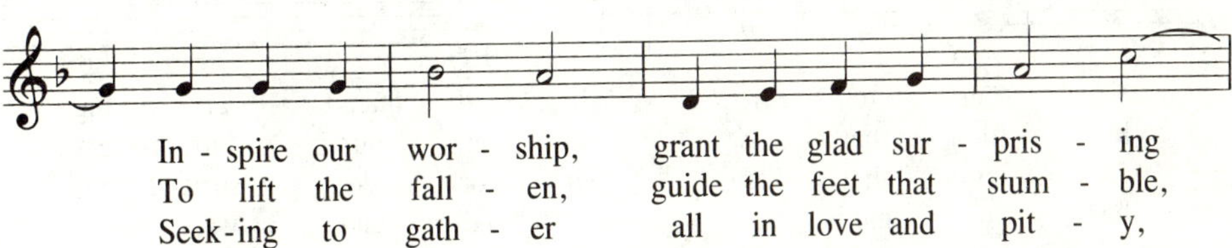

In ev - 'ry cit - y for your love and care:
Strong in your strength to ven - ture and to dare,
As you once wept a - bove Je - ru - sa - lem,

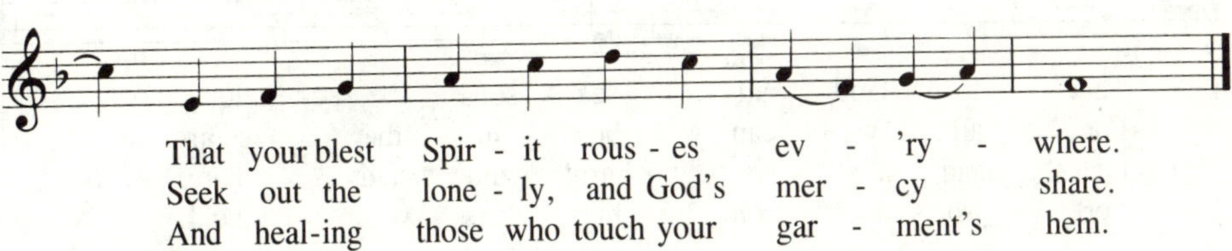

In - spire our wor - ship, grant the glad sur - pris - ing
To lift the fall - en, guide the feet that stum - ble,
Seek - ing to gath - er all in love and pit - y,

That your blest Spir - it rous - es ev - 'ry - where.
Seek out the lone - ly, and God's mer - cy share.
And heal - ing those who touch your gar - ment's hem.

647 Now Join We to Praise the Creator

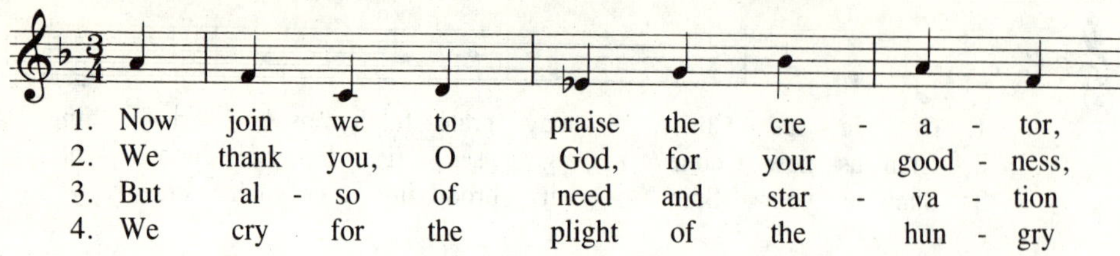
1. Now join we to praise the cre - a - tor,
2. We thank you, O God, for your good - ness,
3. But al - so of need and star - va - tion
4. We cry for the plight of the hun - gry

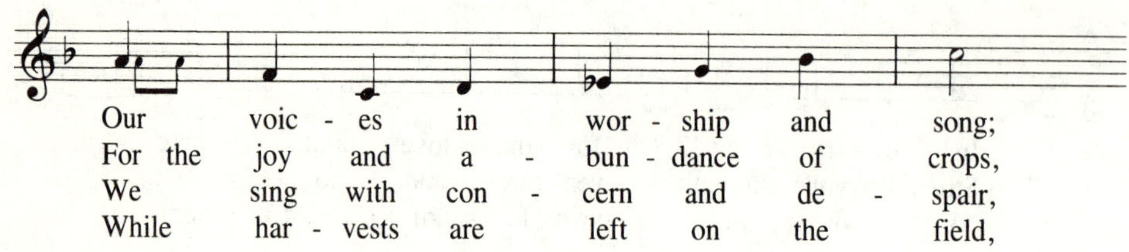
Our voic - es in wor - ship and song;
For the joy and a - bun - dance of crops,
We sing with con - cern and de - spair,
While har - vests are left on the field,

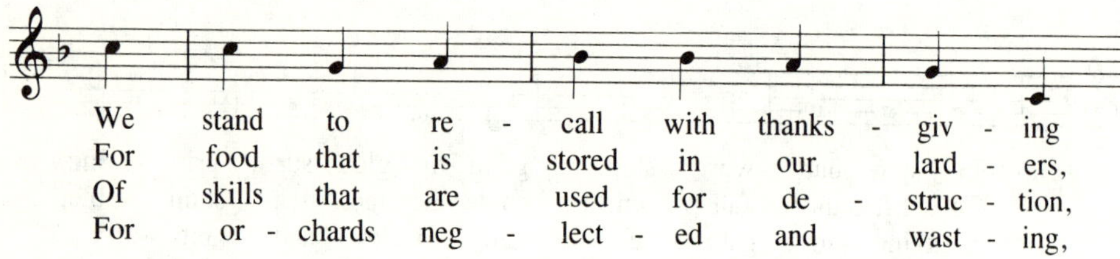
We stand to re - call with thanks - giv - ing
For food that is stored in our lard - ers,
Of skills that are used for de - struc - tion,
For or - chards neg - lect - ed and wast - ing,

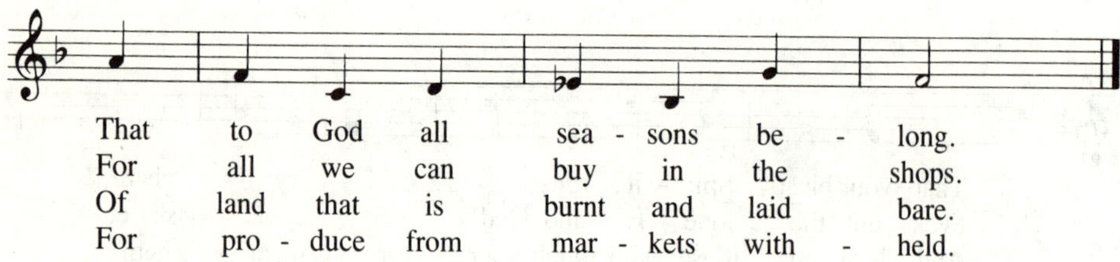
That to God all sea - sons be - long.
For all we can buy in the shops.
Of land that is burnt and laid bare.
For pro - duce from mar - kets with - held.

5. The song grows in depth and in wideness:
The earth and its people are one.
There can be no thanks without giving,
No words without deeds that are done.

6. Then teach us, O Lord of the harvest,
To be humble in all that we claim;
To share what we have with the nations,
To care for the world in your name.

Text: Fred Kaan, b.1929,
Tune: HARVEST, 9 8 9 8; Geoffrey Laycock, b.1927,

God, Who Stretched the Spangled Heavens 648

1. God, who stretched the span - gled heav - ens
2. Proud - ly rise our mod - ern cit - ies,
3. We have ven - tured worlds un - dreamed of
4. As each far ho - ri - zon beck - ons,

In - fi - nite in time and place, Flung the suns in
State - ly build - ings, row on row; Yet their win - dows,
Since the child - hood of our race; Known the ec - sta-
May it chal - lenge us a - new, Chil - dren of cre-

burn - ing ra - diance Through the si - lent fields of space;
blank, un - feel - ing, Stare on can - yoned streets be - low,
sy of wing - ing Through un - trav - eled realms of space;
a - tive pur - pose, Serv - ing oth - ers, hon - oring you.

We, your chil - dren, in your like - ness,
Where the lone - ly drift un - no - ticed
Probed the se - crets of the at - om,
May our dreams prove rich with prom - ise,

Share in - ven - tive pow'rs with you; Great Cre - a - tor,
In the cit - y's ebb and flow, Lost to pur - pose
Yield - ing un - i - mag - ined power, Fac - ing us with
Each en - deav - or, well be - gun: Great Cre - a - tor,

still cre - a - ting, Show us what we yet may do.
and to mean - ing, Scarce - ly car - ing where they go.
life's de - struc - tion Or our most tri - um - phant hour.
give us guid - ance Till our goals and yours are one.

Text: Catherine Cameron, b.1927, © 1967, Hope Publishing Co.
Tune: HOLY MANNA, 8 7 8 7 D; William Moore, fl.1830; Harm. by Charles Anders, b.1929, © 1969, Contemporary Worship I: Hymns

649 Jesus, Shepherd of Our Souls

1. Je - sus, shep - herd of our souls, Self - less in your
2. Je - sus, be our shep - herd still, Though the set - tings
3. Liv - ing Lord, re - new the charge At your ris - ing
4. May we with a shep - herd's heart Love the peo - ple

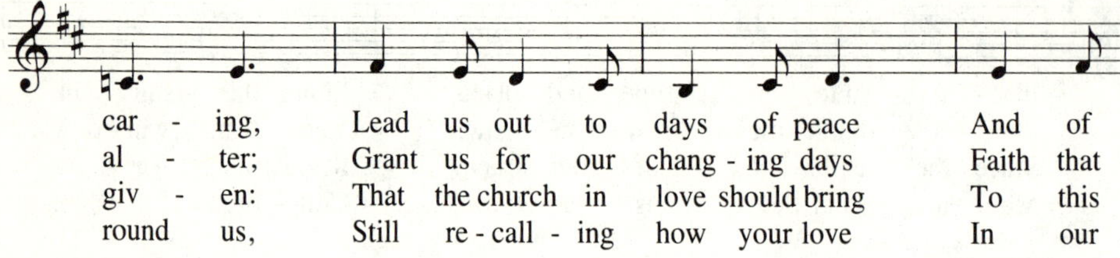
car - ing, Lead us out to days of peace And of
al - ter; Grant us for our chang - ing days Faith that
giv - en: That the church in love should bring To this
round us, Still re - call - ing how your love In our

thought-ful shar - ing. Free our life from ill and war;
will not fal - ter. Bless us in our mod - ern scene
earth your heav - en. Give us in - sight, show us how
stray - ing found us. Keep us, Lord, in hum - ble ways;

What is good in us re - store.
Of com-put - er and ma - chine.
Life is here the task is now.
Lead us clear - ly all our days.

Text: Fred Kaan, b.1929, © 1968, Hope Publishing Co.
Tune: GOOD SHEPHERD, 7 6 7 6 77; Alexander Peloquin, b.1918, © 1975, GIA Publications, Inc.

650 O God of Every Nation

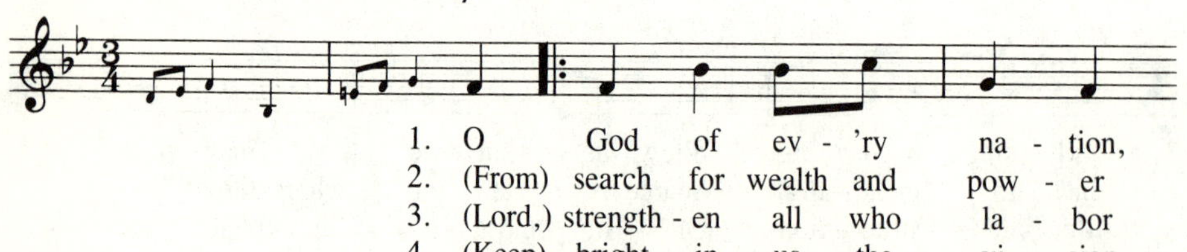
1. O God of ev - 'ry na - tion,
2. (From) search for wealth and pow - er
3. (Lord,) strength - en all who la - bor
4. (Keep) bright in us the vi - sion

PEACE
Of ev - 'ry race and land, Re-
And scorn of truth and right, From
That we may find re - lease From
Of days when wars shall cease, When
deem your whole cre - a - tion With your al - might - y
trust in bombs that show - er De - struc - tion through the
fear of rat - tling sa - ber, From dread of war's in-
ha - tred and di - vi - sion Give way to love and
hand; Where hate and fear di - vide us
night, From pride of race and sta - tion
crease; When hope and cour - age fal - ter,
peace, Till dawns the morn - ing glo - rious
And bit - ter threats are hurled, In
And blind - ness to your way, De-
Your still small voice be heard; With
When Christ a - lone shall reign And
love and mer - cy guide us And heal our strife - torn
liv - er ev - 'ry na - tion, E - ter - nal God, we
faith that none can al - ter, Up - hold us by your
he shall rule vic - to - rious O'er all the world's do-
1.,2.,3.
4.
world. From
pray. Lord,
word. Keep
main. A - men.

Text: William W. Reid, b.1923, alt., © 1958, Hymn Society of America
Tune: PIKE, 7 6 7 6 D; Calvin Hampton, 1938-1984, © 1975, GIA Publications, Inc.

651 Great God, Our Source and Lord of Space

1. Great God, our source and Lord of space, O
2. Great God of fire, in - car - nate flame, Through
3. Lord of the at - om, we praise your might, Ex -

Force of all by whose sheer pow'r The pri - mal
Christ in whom your love has burned And burns the
pressed in ter - ri - fy - ing light; Be - fore us

fires that flared and raged Were struck, blazed on, and
way for our dark pace On cos - mic routes with-
rise the flames as pyres, Or bursts of love—they

still are made: O save us, Lord, at this fierce
in us turned: Lead us be - yond a - tom - ic
blind our sight. Help us, our Lord, O help us

hour From threat - 'ning fires that we have laid.
night; Guide, Lord, in hope our bro - ken race.
see New forms of peace through suf - f'ring fires.

Text: George Utech, b.1931, ©
Tune: SALVA NOS, 8 8 8 8 8 8; John Schiavone, b.1947, © 1986, GIA Publications, Inc.

652 O God of Love, O King of Peace

1.
2.
3.
1. O God of love, O King of peace, Make
2. Whom shall we trust but you, O Lord? Where
3. Where saints and an - gels dwell a - bove, All

4.
wars through-out the world to cease; Our vio - lent ways help
rest but on your faith - ful word? None ev - er called on
hearts are joined in ho - ly love; O bind us in that
us con - tain; Give peace, O God, give peace a - gain!
you in vain; Give peace, O God, give peace a - gain!
heav'n-ly chain; Give peace, O God, give peace a - gain!

Text: Henry W. Baker, 1821-1877
Tune: TALLIS' CANON, LM; Thomas Tallis, d.1585

Let There Be Light 653

1. Let there be light,
2. O - pen our lips,
3. Per - ish the sword,
4. Hal - low our love,

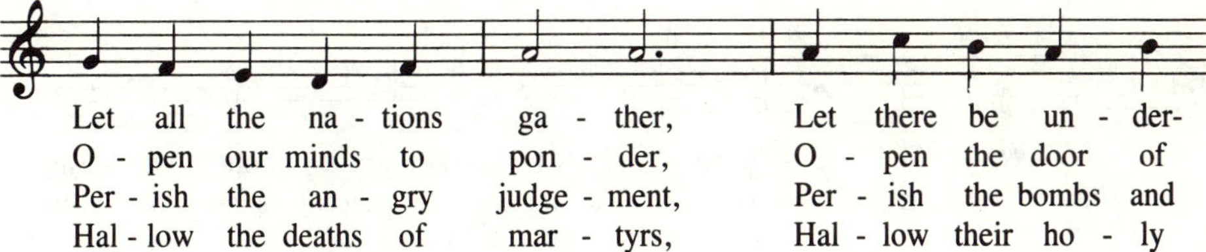
Let all the na - tions ga - ther, Let there be un - der-
O - pen our minds to pon - der, O - pen the door of
Per - ish the an - gry judge - ment, Per - ish the bombs and
Hal - low the deaths of mar - tyrs, Hal - low their ho - ly

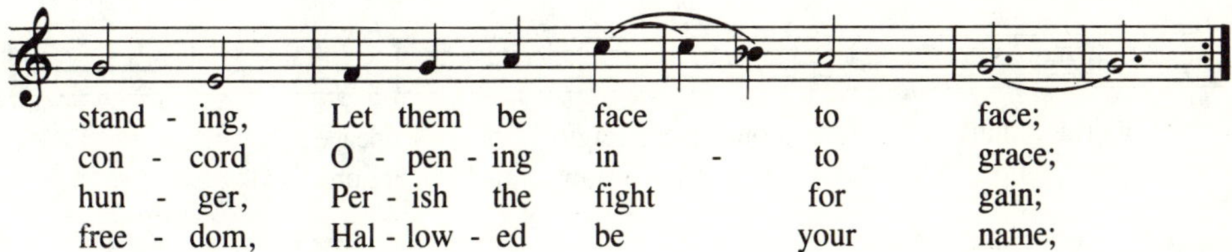
stand - ing, Let them be face to face;
con - cord O - pen - ing in - to grace;
hun - ger, Per - ish the fight for gain;
free - dom, Hal - low - ed be your name;

5. Your kingdom come,
Your spirit turn to language,
Your people speak together,
Your spirit never fade;

6. Let there be light,
Open our hearts to wonder,
Perish the way of terror,
Hallow the world God made.

Text: Frances W. Davis, b.1936, © American Peace Society
Tune: SPRAGUE, 4 7 7 6; David Hurd, b.1950, © 1985, GIA Publications, Inc.

654 O Day of Peace

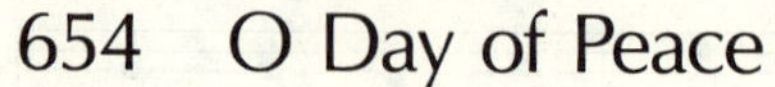

3
1. O day of peace that dim - ly
2. Then shall the wolf dwell with the

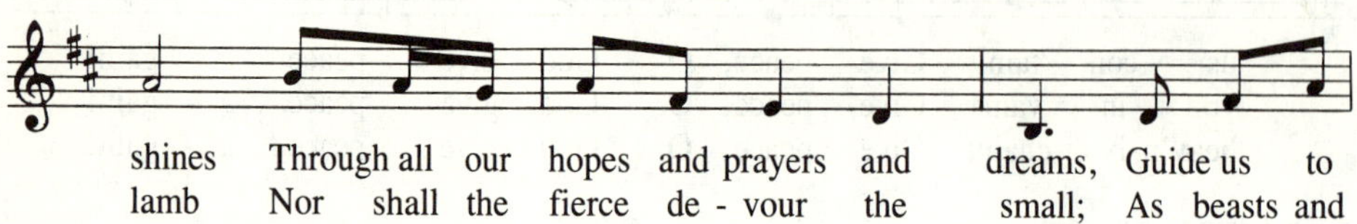
shines Through all our hopes and prayers and dreams, Guide us to
lamb Nor shall the fierce de - vour the small; As beasts and

jus - tice, truth and love; De - liv - ered from our self - ish
cat - tle calm - ly graze, A lit - tle child shall lead them

schemes. May swords of hate fall from our hands, Our hearts from
all. Then en - e - mies shall learn to love, All crea - tures

en - vy find re - lease, Till by God's grace our war - ring
find their true ac - cord; The hope of peace shall be ful-

2
world Shall see Christ's prom - ised reign of peace.
filled, For all the earth shall know the Lord.

Father, Lord of All Creation 655

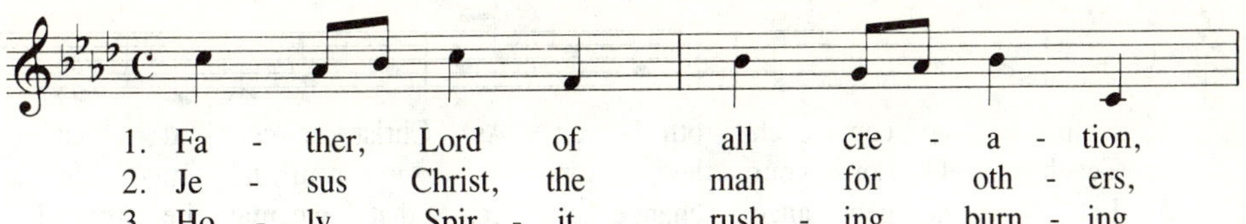
1. Fa - ther, Lord of all cre - a - tion,
2. Je - sus Christ, the man for oth - ers,
3. Ho - ly Spir - it, rush - ing, burn - ing

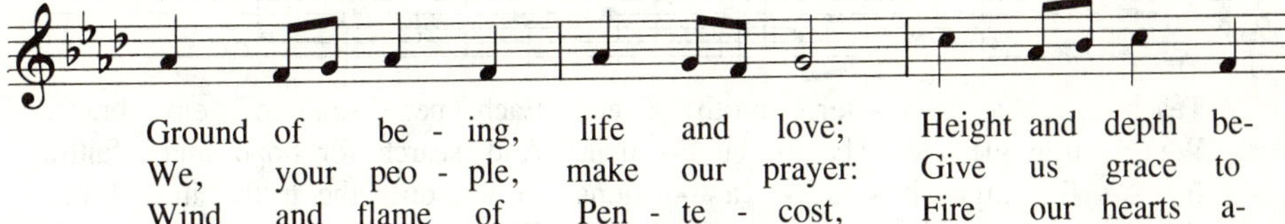
Ground of be - ing, life and love; Height and depth be-
We, your peo - ple, make our prayer: Give us grace to
Wind and flame of Pen - te - cost, Fire our hearts a-

yond de - scrip - tion On - ly life in you can prove:
love all oth - ers, Those whose bur - dens we can share.
fresh with yearn - ing To re - gain what we have lost.

You are mor - tal life's de - pen - dence:
Where your name binds us to - geth - er
May your love u - nite our ac - tion,

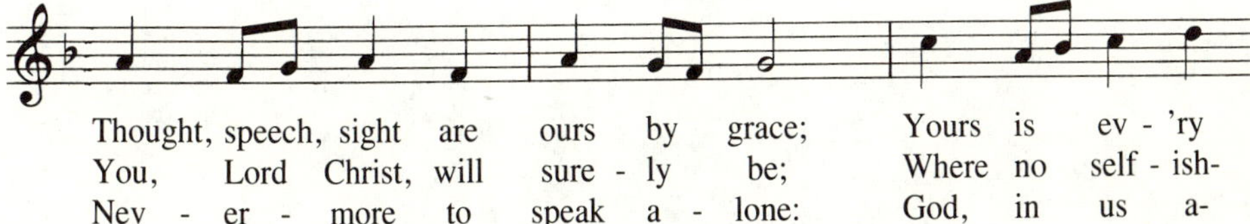
Thought, speech, sight are ours by grace; Yours is ev - 'ry
You, Lord Christ, will sure - ly be; Where no self - ish-
Nev - er - more to speak a - lone: God, in us a-

hour's ex - ist - ence, Sov - ereign Lord of time and space.
ness can sev - er, There your love we all may see.
bol - ish fac - tion, God, through us your love make known.

Text: Steward Cross, b.1928, ©
Tune: GENEVA, 8 7 8 7 D; George H. Day, 1883-1966, © 1942, The Church Pension Fund

656 Help Us Accept Each Other

1. Help us ac - cept each oth - er As Christ ac - cept - ed us;
2. Teach us, O Lord, your les - sons, As in our dai - ly life
3. Let your ac - cept - ance change us, So that we may be moved
4. Lord, for to - day's en - coun - ters With all who are in need,

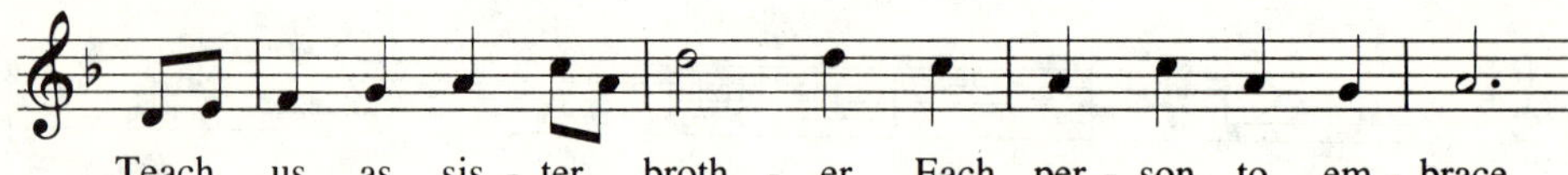

Teach us as sis - ter, broth - er, Each per - son to em - brace.
We strug - gle to be hu - man And search for hope and faith.
In liv - ing sit - u - a - tions To do the truth in love;
Who hun - ger for ac - cept - ance, For right - eous - ness and bread,

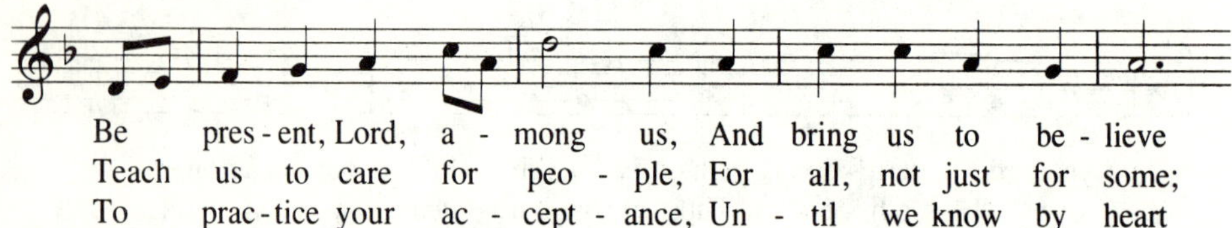

Be pres - ent, Lord, a - mong us, And bring us to be - lieve
Teach us to care for peo - ple, For all, not just for some;
To prac - tice your ac - cept - ance, Un - til we know by heart
We need new eyes for see - ing, New hands for hold - ing on;

We are our - selves ac - cept - ed And meant to love and live.
To love them as we find them, Or, as they may be - come.
The ta - ble of for - give - ness And laugh - ter's heal - ing art.
Re - new us with your Spir - it; Lord, free us, make us one!

Text: Jn. 15:12; Fred Kaan, b.1929,
Tune: KING'S LYNN, 7 6 7 6 D; English; Harm. by Ralph Vaughan Williams 1872-1958,

There Is One Lord 657

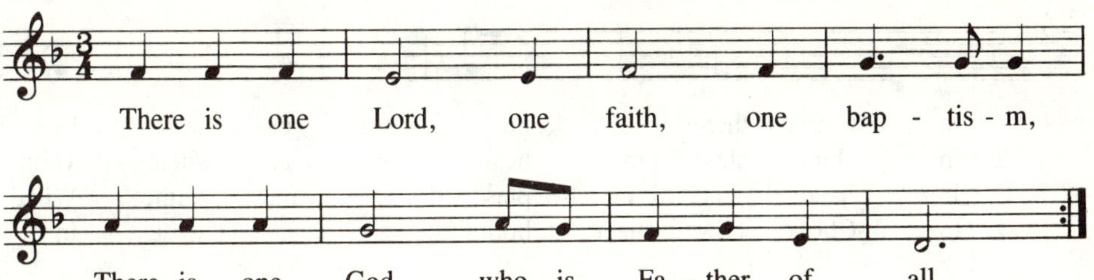
There is one Lord, one faith, one bap - tis - m,
There is one God who is Fa - ther of all.

Text: Eph. 4, Taizé Community, 1984
Tune: Jacques Berthier, b.1923

Lord Christ, the Father's Mighty Son 658

1. Lord Christ, the Fa - ther's might - y Son,
2. To make us one your prayers were said,
3. Lord Christ, for - give us, make us new!
4. We will not ques - tion or re - fuse

Whose work up - on the cross was done To
To make us one you broke the bread For
What our de - signs could nev - er do Your
The way you work, the means you choose, The

give and re - ceive, Make all our scat - tered
all to re - ceive; Its piec - es scat - ter
love can a - chieve. Our prayers, our work, we
pat - tern you weave; But rec - on - cile our

church-es one, That the world may be - lieve.
us in - stead: How can oth - ers be - lieve?
bring to you; That the world may be - lieve.
war - ring views, That the world may be - lieve.

Text: Brian Wren, b.1936
Tune: HAMPTON POYLE, 88 5 8 6; Peter Cutts, b.1937

659 In Christ There Is No East or West

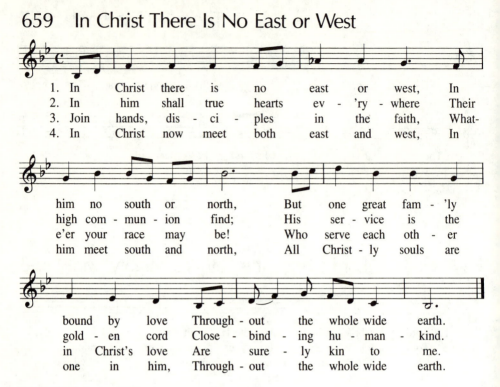

1. In Christ there is no east or west, In
2. In him shall true hearts ev - 'ry - where Their
3. Join hands, dis - ci - ples in the faith, What-
4. In Christ now meet both east and west, In

him no south or north, But one great fam - 'ly
high com - mun - ion find; His ser - vice is the
e'er your race may be! Who serve each oth - er
him meet south and north, All Christ - ly souls are

bound by love Through - out the whole wide earth.
gold - en cord Close - bind - ing hu - man - kind.
in Christ's love Are sure - ly kin to me.
one in him, Through - out the whole wide earth.

Text: Gal. 3:28; John Oxenham, 1852-1941, © American Tract Society
Tune: MC KEE, CM; Afro-American; Adapted by Harry T. Burleigh, 1866-1949

660 Peace with the Father

1. Peace with the Fa - ther, peace with Christ his Son,
2. Love of the Fa - ther, Love of Christ his Son,
3. Sin has di - vid - ed those whom Christ made one;
4. Send forth your Spir - it, Fa - ther, from a - bove
5. Chris - tians, for - give each oth - er from your heart;
Peace with the Spir - it, keep us ev - er one.
Love of the Spir - it, make all Christ - ians one.
Fa - ther, for - give us through your lov - ing Son.
On us, your chil - dren, one with Christ in love.
Christ be a - mong us, nev - er - more to part.

Text: James Quinn, SJ, b.1919, © 1969
Tune: SONG 46, 10 10; Orlando Gibbons, 1583-1625

Is This a Day of New Beginnings 661

1. Is this a day of new be - gin - nings,
2. How can the sea - sons of a plan - et
3. Yet thro' the life and death of Je - sus
4. Then let us with the Spir - it's dar - ing,
5. So let us gath - er 'round the ta - ble
Time to re - mem - ber and move on,
Mind - less - ly spin - ning 'round its sun
Love's might - y Spir - it, now as then,
Step from the past and leave be - hind
To taste and share what love can do.
Time to be - lieve what love is bring - ing,
With just a hu - man name and num - ber
Can make for us a world of dif - f'rence
Its dis - ap - point - ment, guilt, and griev - ing,
This is a day of new be - gin - nings—
Lay - ing to rest the pain that's gone?
Say that some new thing has be - gun?
As faith and hope are born a - gain.
Seek - ing new paths, and sure to find.
Our God is mak - ing all things new.

662 On This Day, the First of Days

1. On this day, the first of days,
2. On this day the e - ter - nal Son
3. Word - made - flesh, all prais - es be!
4. Ho - ly Spir - it, you im - part
5. God, the bless - ed Three in One,

God our Mak - er's name we praise; Who, cre - a - tion's
O - ver death his tri - umph won; On this day the
You from sin have set us free; And with you we
Gifts of love to ev - 'ry heart; Give us light and
May your ho - ly will be done; In your word our

Lord and Spring, Did the world from dark - ness bring.
Spir - it came With its gifts of liv - ing flame.
die and rise Un - to God in sac - ri - fice.
grace, we pray, Fill our hearts this ho - ly day.
souls are free, As we praise the Trin - i - ty.

Text: *Die parente temporum; Le Mans Breviary,* 1748; Tr. by Henry W. Baker, 1821-1877
Tune: LÜBECK, 77 77; *Freylinghausen's Gesangbuch,* 1704

663 This Is the Day When Light Was First Created

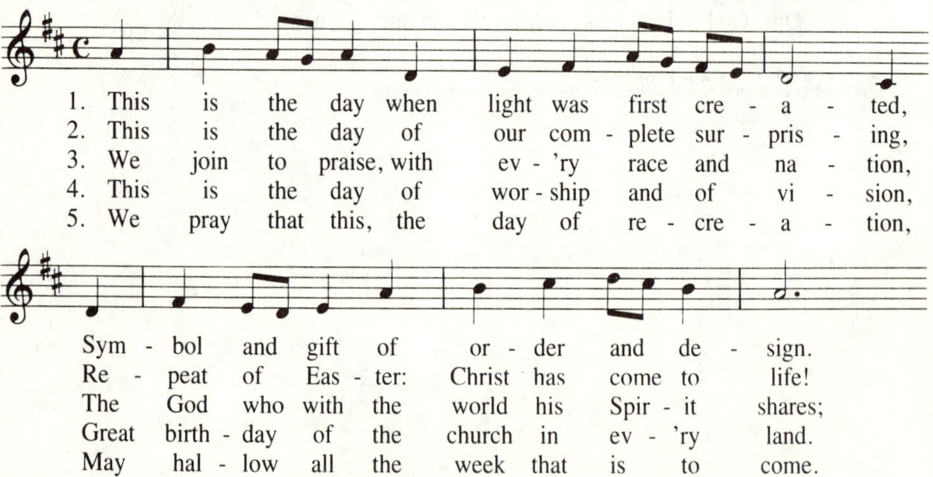
1. This is the day when light was first cre - a - ted,
2. This is the day of our com - plete sur - pris - ing,
3. We join to praise, with ev - 'ry race and na - tion,
4. This is the day of wor - ship and of vi - sion,
5. We pray that this, the day of re - cre - a - tion,
Sym - bol and gift of or - der and de - sign.
Re - peat of Eas - ter: Christ has come to life!
The God who with the world his Spir - it shares;
Great birth - day of the church in ev - 'ry land.
May hal - low all the week that is to come.

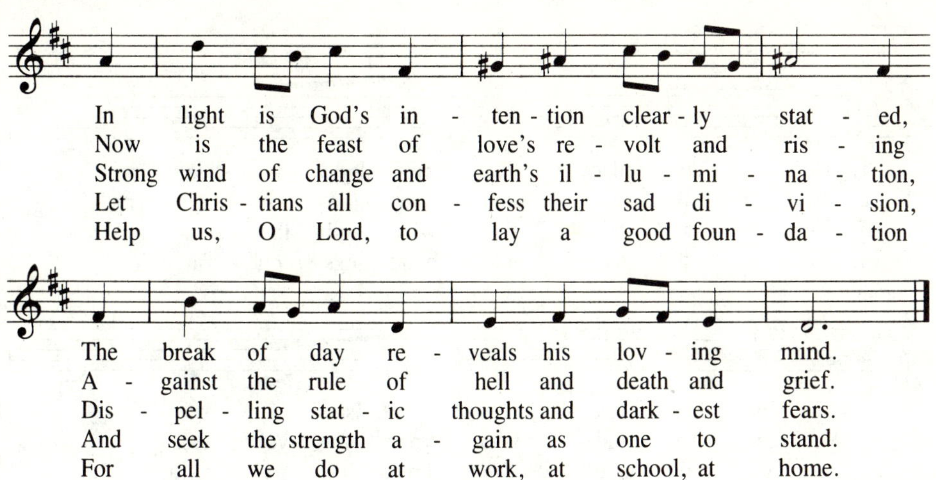
In light is God's in - ten - tion clear - ly stat - ed,
Now is the feast of love's re - volt and ris - ing
Strong wind of change and earth's il - lu - mi - na - tion,
Let Chris - tians all con - fess their sad di - vi - sion,
Help us, O Lord, to lay a good foun - da - tion
The break of day re - veals his lov - ing mind.
A - gainst the rule of hell and death and grief.
Dis - pel - ling stat - ic thoughts and dark - est fears.
And seek the strength a - gain as one to stand.
For all we do at work, at school, at home.

Text: Fred Kaan, b.1929, © 1968, Hope Publishing Co.
Tune: NORTHBROOK, 11 10 11 10; Reginald S. Thatcher, 1888-1957, © Oxford University Press

Come, Rejoice before Your Maker 664

1. Come, re - joice be - fore your Mak - er
2. Know for cer - tain, our Cre - a - tor
3. Come with grate - ful hearts be - fore him,
4. For the Lord our God is gra - cious
All you peo - ples of the earth; Serve the Lord your
Is the true and on - ly God; We are his, for
En - ter now his courts with praise; Show your thank - ful-
Ev - er - last - ing in his love, And to ev - 'ry
God with glad - ness, Come be - fore him with a song!
he has made us— We are sheep with - in his fold.
ness to - wards him, Give due hon - or to his name.
gen - er - a - tion His great faith - ful - ness en - dures.

Text: Psalm 100; Michael Baughen, b.1930
Tune: JUBILATE DEO, 8 7 8 7; Noel H. Tredinnick, b.1949

665 Gather Us In

1. Here in this place, new light is stream - ing,
2. We are the young— our lives are a mys - t'ry,
3. Here we will take the wine and the wa - ter,
4. Not in the dark of build - ings con - fin - ing,

Now is the dark - ness, van - ished a - way,
We are the old— who yearn for your face,
Here we will take the bread of new birth,
Not in some heav - en, light years a - way, But

See, in this space, our fears and our dream - ings,
We have been sung through - out all of his - t'ry,
Here you shall call your sons and your daugh - ters,
here in this place, the new light is shin - ing,

Brought here to you in the light of this
Called to be light to the whole hu - man
Call us a - new to be salt for the
Now is the King - dom, now is the

day. Gath - er us in— the
race. Gath - er us in— the
earth. Give us to drink the
day. Gath - er us in— and

lost and for - sak - en, Gath - er us in— the
rich and the haugh - ty, Gath - er us in— the
wine of com - pas - sion, Give us to eat the
hold us for ev - er, Gath - er us in— and

blind and the lame; Call to us now, and
proud and the strong; Give us a heart so
bread that is you; Nour - ish us well, and
make us your own; Gath - er us in— all
we shall a - wak - en, We shall a - rise at the
meek and so low - ly, Give us the cour - age to
teach us to fash - ion, Lives that are ho - ly and
peo - ples to - geth - er, Fire of love in our
sound of our name.
en - ter the song.
hearts that are true.
flesh and our bone.

Text: Marty Haugen, b.1952
Tune: GATHER US IN, 10 9 10 10 D (slightly irreg.); Marty Haugen, b.1952

666 Only-begotten, Word of God Eternal

1. On - ly - be - got - ten, Word of God e- ter - nal, Lord of cre - a - tion, mer - ci - ful and might - y, Hear now your ser - vants, when their tune - ful voic - es Rise to your pres - ence.
2. Ho - ly this tem - ple where our Lord is dwell - ing, This is none oth - er than the gate of heav - en; Stran - gers and pil - grims, seek - ing homes e- ter - nal, Pass through its por - tals.
3. Lord, we be - seech you, as we throng your tem - ple, By your past bless - ings, by your pres - ent boun - ty, Smile on your chil - dren, and with ten - der mer - cy Hear our pe - ti - tions.
4. God in Three Per - sons, Fa - ther ev - er- liv - ing, Son co - e - ter - nal, ev - er - bless - ed Spir - it, Yours be the glo - ry, praise and ad - or- a - tion, Now and for ev - er.

Text: *Christe cunctorum dominator alme;* Latin, 9th C.; Tr. by Maxwell J. Blacker, 1822-1888
Tune: ISTE CONFESSOR 11 11 11 5; Rouen Church Melody; Harm. by Carl Schalk, b.1929,

God Is Here! As We His People 667

1. God is here! As we his peo - ple, Meet to
2. Here are sym - bols to re - mind us Of our
3. Here our chil - dren find a wel-come In the
4. Lord of all, of church and king-dom, In an
of - fer praise and prayer, May we find in ful - ler
life - long need of grace; Here are ta - ble, font and
Shep - herd's flock and fold; Here, as bread and wine are
age of change and doubt, Keep us faith - ful to the
meas-ure What it is in Christ we share:
pul - pit, Here the cross has cen - tral place:
tak - en, Christ sus - tains us as of old:
gos - pel, Help us work your pur - pose out:
Here, as in the world a - round us, All our
Here in hon - es - ty of preach-ing, Here in
Here the ser - vants of the Ser - vant Seek in
Here, in this day's ded - i - ca - tion, All we
var - ied skills and arts Wait the com - ing
si - lence as in speech, Here in new - ness
wor - ship to ex - plore What it means in
have to give, re - ceive; We who can - not
of his Spir - it In - to o - pen minds and hearts.
and re - new - al God the Spir - it comes to each.
dai - ly liv - ing To be - lieve and to a - dore.
live with - out you, We a - dore you! We be - lieve!

668 Now the Silence

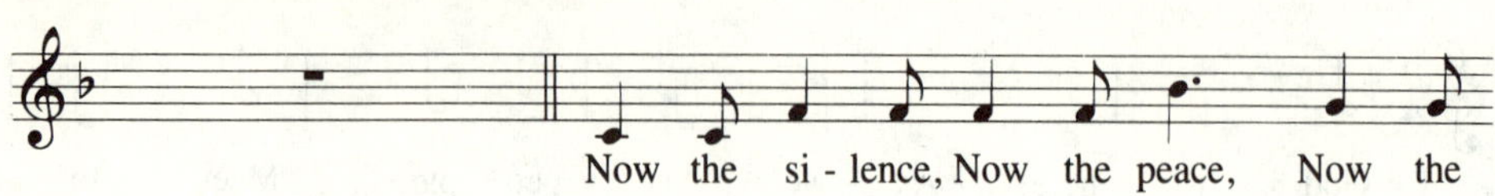
Now the si - lence, Now the peace, Now the

emp - ty hands up - lift - ed; Now the kneel - ing, Now the plea,

Now the Fa - ther's arms in wel - come; Now the hear - ing, Now the

pow'r, Now the ves - sel brimmed for pour - ing; Now the bod - y,

Now the blood, Now the joy - ful cel - e - bra - tion;

Now the wed - ding, Now the songs, Now the heart for - giv - en leap - ing;

Now the Spir - it's vis - i - ta - tion, Now the Son's e - piph - a - ny,

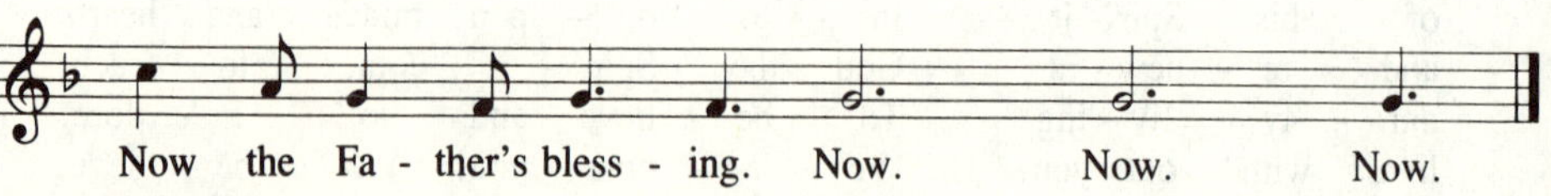
Now the Fa - ther's bless - ing. Now. Now. Now.

Text: Jaroslav J. Vajda, b.1919
Tune: NOW, 4 3 8 4 3 8 D with refrain; Carl Schalk, b.1929

All People That on Earth Do Dwell 669

1. All peo - ple that on earth do dwell,
2. Know that the Lord is God in - deed;
3. O en - ter then his gates with praise;
4. For why? the Lord our God is good:
5. To Fa - ther, Son, and Ho - ly Ghost,
* Praise God, from whom all bless - ings flow;

Sing to the Lord with cheer - ful voice;
With - out our aid he did us make;
Ap - proach with joy his courts un - to;
His mer - cy is for ev - er sure;
The God whom heaven and earth a - dore,
Praise Him, all crea - tures here be - low;

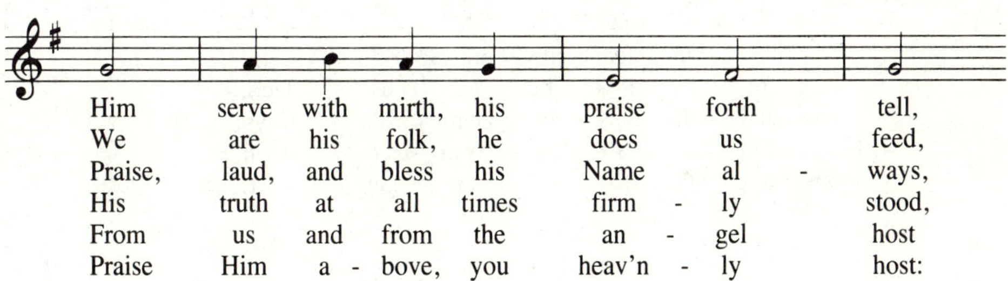
Him serve with mirth, his praise forth tell,
We are his folk, he does us feed,
Praise, laud, and bless his Name al - ways,
His truth at all times firm - ly stood,
From us and from the an - gel host
Praise Him a - bove, you heav'n - ly host:

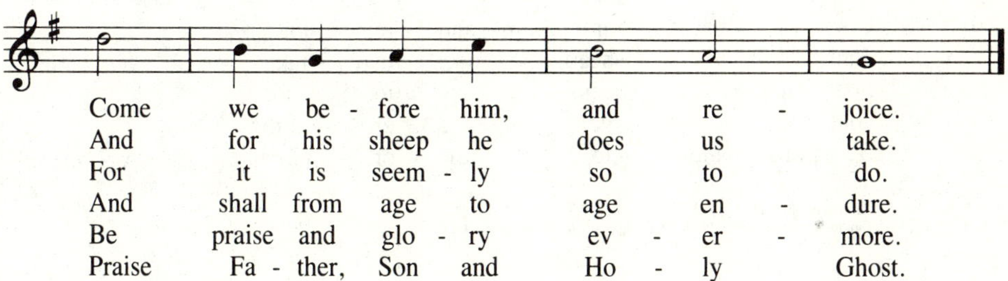
Come we be - fore him, and re - joice.
And for his sheep he does us take.
For it is seem - ly so to do.
And shall from age to age en - dure.
Be praise and glo - ry ev - er - more.
Praise Fa - ther, Son and Ho - ly Ghost.

*May be sung alone or as an alternate to stanza 5.

Text: Psalm (99)100; William Kethe, d. c.1593; Doxology, Thomas Ken, 1637-1711
Tune: OLD HUNDREDTH, LM; Louis Bourgeois, c.1510-1561; alt. harm. by John Dowland, 1562-1626

670 All People That on Earth Do Dwell

1. All peo - ple that on earth do dwell,
2. Know that the Lord is God in - deed;
3. O en - ter then his gates with praise,
4. For why? the Lord our God is good,
5. To Fa - ther, Son, and Ho - ly Ghost,

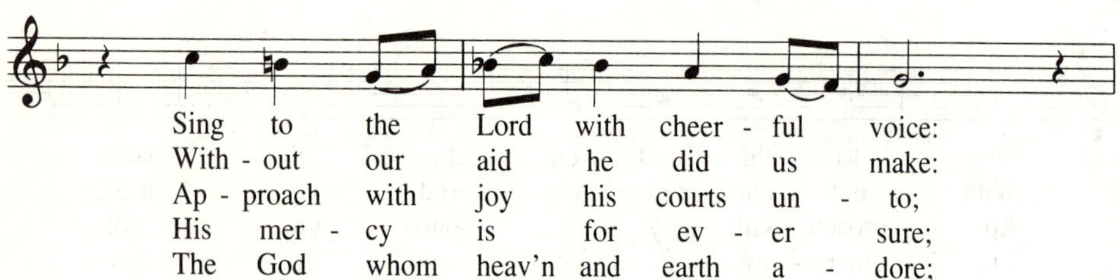
Sing to the Lord with cheer - ful voice:
With - out our aid he did us make:
Ap - proach with joy his courts un - to;
His mer - cy is for ev - er sure;
The God whom heav'n and earth a - dore;

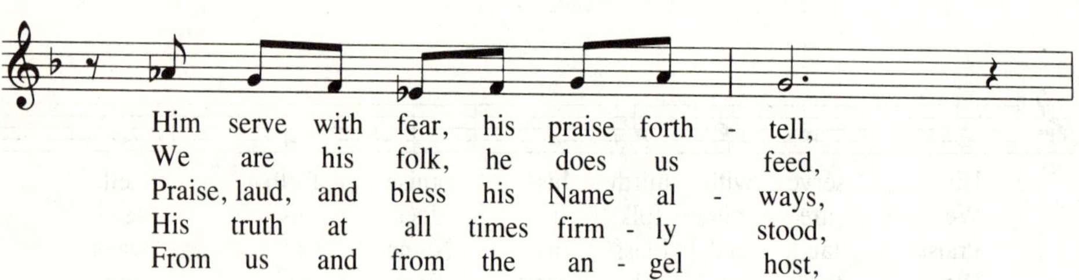
Him serve with fear, his praise forth - tell,
We are his folk, he does us feed,
Praise, laud, and bless his Name al - ways,
His truth at all times firm - ly stood,
From us and from the an - gel host,

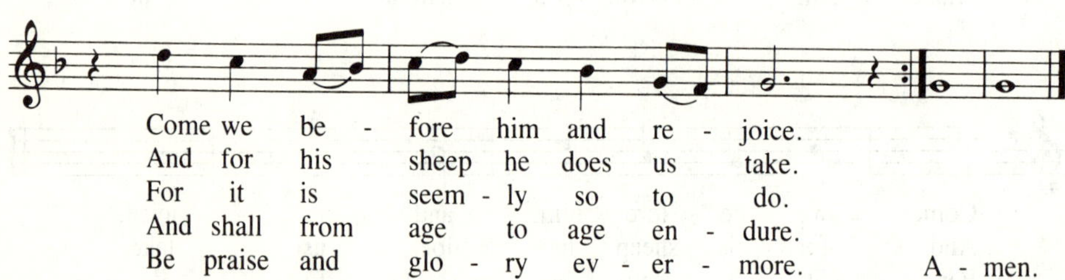
Come we be - fore him and re - joice.
And for his sheep he does us take.
For it is seem - ly so to do.
And shall from age to age en - dure.
Be praise and glo - ry ev - er - more. A - men.

Text: Psalm 100; William Kethe, d. c.1593
Tune: DE TAR, LM; Calvin Hampton,. 1938-1984, © 1973, Concordia Publishing House

I Sing As I Arise Today 671

1. I sing as I a - rise to - day! I
2. The word of God to be my speech, The
3. Al - le - lu - ia, al - le - lu - ia, Al-

call on my Cre - a - tor's might: The will of
hand of God to be my stay, The shield of
le - lu - ia, al - le - lu - ia, Al - le - lu-

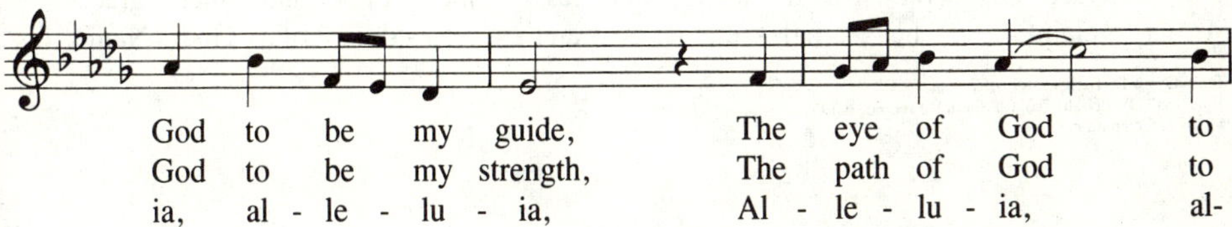
God to be my guide, The eye of God to
God to be my strength, The path of God to
ia, al - le - lu - ia, Al - le - lu - ia, al-

be my sight,
be my way.
le - lu - ia.

Text: Ascr. to St. Patrick, 372-466; Tr. Anonymous
Tune: KING, LM; David Hurd, b.1950,

672 How Beautiful the Morning and the Day

1. How beau - ti - ful the morn - ing and the day; My
2. How glo - ri - ous the morn - ing and the day; My
3. How boun - ti - ful the bless - ings that he brings Of
4. How mer - ci - ful the work - ings of God's grace; A-
5. How bar - ren was my life be - fore he came Sup-

heart a - bounds with mu - sic, My lips can on - ly
heart is still and lis - tens, My soul be - gins to
peace and joy and rap - ture That make my spir - it
rous - ing faith and ac - tion My soul would nev - er
ply - ing love and heal - ing; I live now to ac-

say How beau - ti - ful the morn - ing and the day.
pray To God who is the glo - ry of the day.
sing: How boun - ti - ful the bless - ings that he brings.
face With - out such match - less mer - cy and such grace.
claim The maj - es - ty and won - der of God's Name.

Text: Owen D. Barker, 1899-1974, alt.
Tune: ST. OWEN, 10 7 6 10; Sherrell Prebble, b.1951

673 This Day God Gives Me

1. This day God gives me Strength of high heav - en,
2. This day God sends me Strength as my guard - ian,
3. God's way is my way, God's shield is round me,
4. Ris - ing, I thank you, Might - y and strong One,
Sun and moon shin - ing, Flame in my hearth,
Might to up - hold me, Wis - dom as guide.
God's host de - fends me, Sav - ing from ill.
King of cre - a - tion, Giv - er of rest,

MORNING

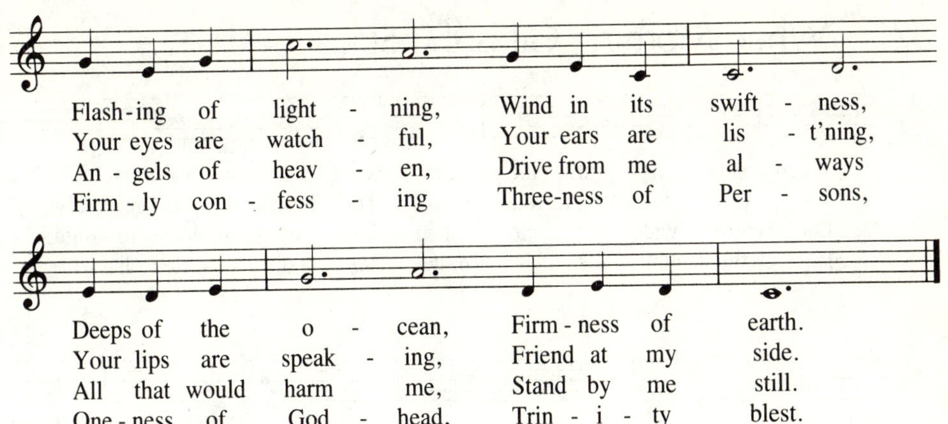
Flash-ing of light - ning, Wind in its swift - ness,
Your eyes are watch - ful, Your ears are lis - t'ning,
An - gels of heav - en, Drive from me al - ways
Firm - ly con - fess - ing Three-ness of Per - sons,
Deeps of the o - cean, Firm - ness of earth.
Your lips are speak - ing, Friend at my side.
All that would harm me, Stand by me still.
One - ness of God - head, Trin - i - ty blest.

Text: Ascr. to St. Patrick, 372-466; Adapted by James Quinn, SJ, b.1919, © 1969
Tune: BUNESSAN 5 5 5 4 D; Gaelic; Harm. by A. Gregory Murray, OSB, b.1905, ©

Morning Has Broken 674

Use previous tune

1. Morning has broken
   Like the first morning,
   Blackbird has spoken
   Like the first bird.
   Praise for the singing!
   Praise for the morning!
   Praise for them, springing
   Fresh from the Word!

2. Sweet the rain's new fall
   Sunlit from heaven,
   Like the first dewfall
   On the first grass.
   Praise for the sweetness
   Of the wet garden,
   Sprung in completeness
   Where his feet pass.

3. Mine is the sunlight!
   Mine is the morning
   Born of the one light
   Eden saw play!
   Praise with elation,
   Praise ev'ry morning,
   God's re-creation
   Of the new day!

Text: Eleanor Farjeon, 1881-1965, © David Higham Assoc. Ltd.

675 When Morning Gilds the Skies

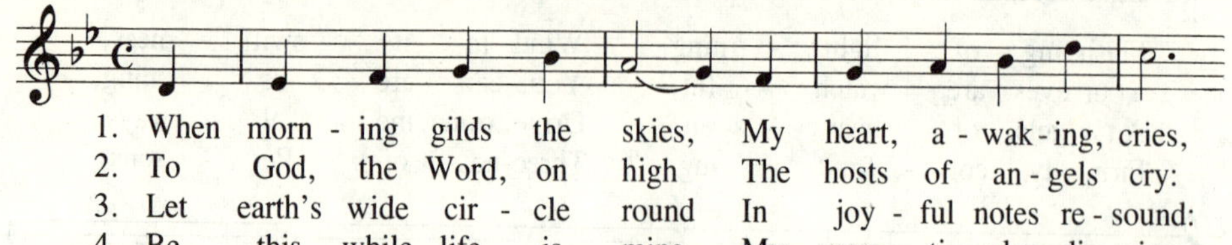
1. When morn - ing gilds the skies, My heart, a - wak - ing, cries,
2. To God, the Word, on high The hosts of an - gels cry:
3. Let earth's wide cir - cle round In joy - ful notes re - sound:
4. Be this while life is mine My can - ti - cle di - vine:

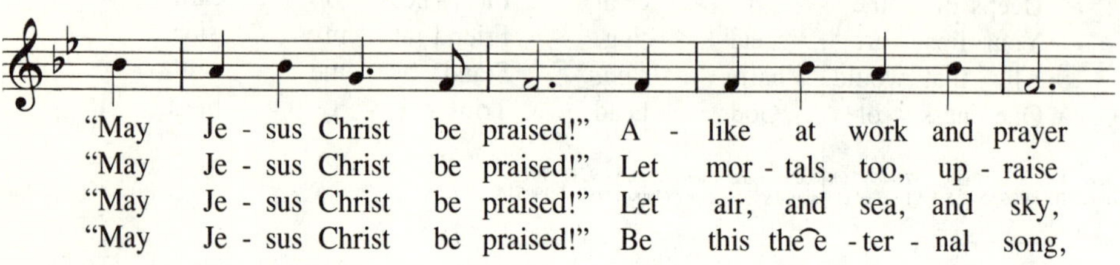
"May Je - sus Christ be praised!" A - like at work and prayer
"May Je - sus Christ be praised!" Let mor - tals, too, up - raise
"May Je - sus Christ be praised!" Let air, and sea, and sky,
"May Je - sus Christ be praised!" Be this the e - ter - nal song,

To Je - sus I re - pair: "May Je - sus Christ be praised!"
Their voice in hymns of praise: "May Je - sus Christ be praised!"
From depth to height, re - ply: "May Je - sus Christ be praised!"
Through all the a - ges long: "May Je - sus Christ be praised!"

Text: *Wach ich früh Morgens auf; Katholiches Gesangbuch,* 1828; Tr. by Edward Caswall, 1814-1878
Tune: LAUDES DOMINI, 66 6 D; Joseph Barnby, 1838-1896

Nunc Dimittis 676

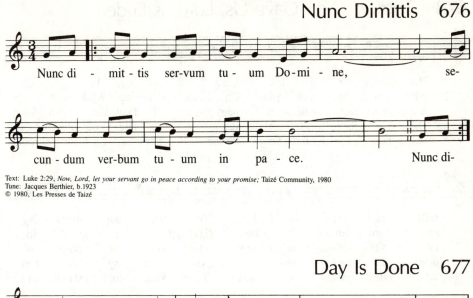

Nunc di - mit - tis ser-vum tu - um Do - mi - ne, se-

cun - dum ver-bum tu - um in pa - ce. Nunc di-

Text: Luke 2:29, *Now, Lord, let your servant go in peace according to your promise;* Taizé Community, 1980
Tune: Jacques Berthier, b.1923

Day Is Done 677

1. Day is done, but love un-fail - ing Dwells ev - er here;
2. Dark de-scends, but light un-end - ing Shines through our night;
3. Eyes will close, but you un-sleep - ing Watch by our side;

Shad - ows fall, but hope, pre-vail - ing, Calms ev - 'ry fear.
You are with us, ev - er lend - ing New strength to sight:
Death may come, in love's safe keep - ing Still we a - bide.

God, our Mak - er, none for - sak - ing, Take our hearts, of Love's own
One in love, your truth con - fess - ing, One in hope of heav - en's
God of love, all e - vil quell - ing, Sin for - giv - ing, fear dis-

mak-ing, Watch our sleep-ing, guard our wak-ing, Be al - ways near.
bless-ing, May we see, in love's pos-sess-ing, Love's end - less light!
pel - ling, Stay with us, our hearts in-dwell-ing, This e - ven - tide.

Text: James Quinn, SJ, b.1919, © 1969
Tune: AR HYD NOS, 8 4 8 4 888 4; Welsh

678 The Day You Gave Us, Lord, Is Ended

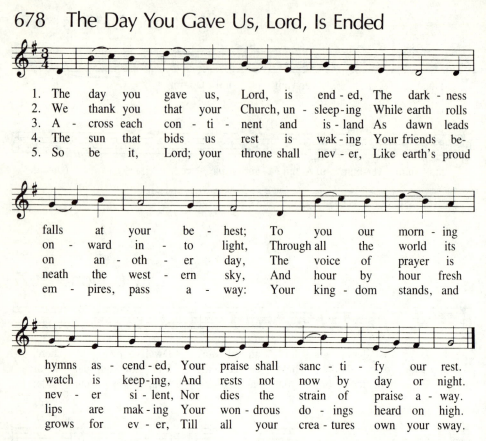

1. The day you gave us, Lord, is end - ed, The dark - ness
2. We thank you that your Church, un - sleep - ing While earth rolls
3. A - cross each con - ti - nent and is - land As dawn leads
4. The sun that bids us rest is wak - ing Your friends be-
5. So be it, Lord; your throne shall nev - er, Like earth's proud

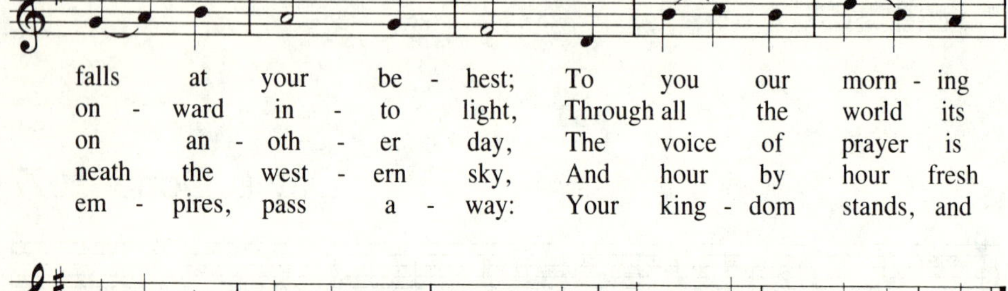

falls at your be - hest; To you our morn - ing
on - ward in - to light, Through all the world its
on an - oth - er day, The voice of prayer is
neath the west - ern sky, And hour by hour fresh
em - pires, pass a - way: Your king - dom stands, and

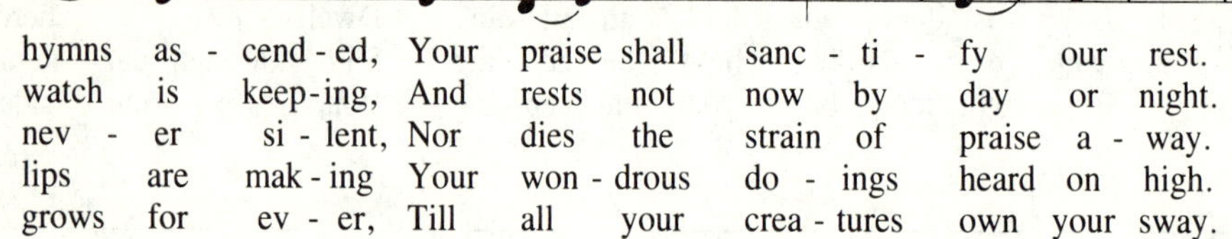

hymns as - cend - ed, Your praise shall sanc - ti - fy our rest.
watch is keep - ing, And rests not now by day or night.
nev - er si - lent, Nor dies the strain of praise a - way.
lips are mak - ing Your won - drous do - ings heard on high.
grows for ev - er, Till all your crea - tures own your sway.

Text: John Ellerton, 1826-1893, alt.
Tune: ST. CLEMENT, 9 8 9 8; Clement C. Scholefield, 1839-1904

679 O Gladsome Light

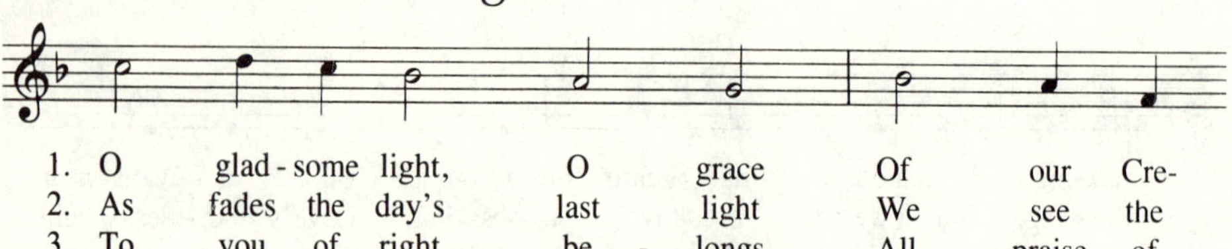

1. O glad - some light, O grace Of our Cre-
2. As fades the day's last light We see the
3. To you of right be - longs All praise of

a - tor's face, The e - ter - nal splen - dor wear - ing:
lamps of night, Our com - mon hymn out - pour - ing,
ho - ly songs, O Son of God, Life - giv - er;
Ce - les - tial, ho - ly blest, Our Sav - ior
O God of might un - known, You, the in-
You, there - fore, O Most High, The world does

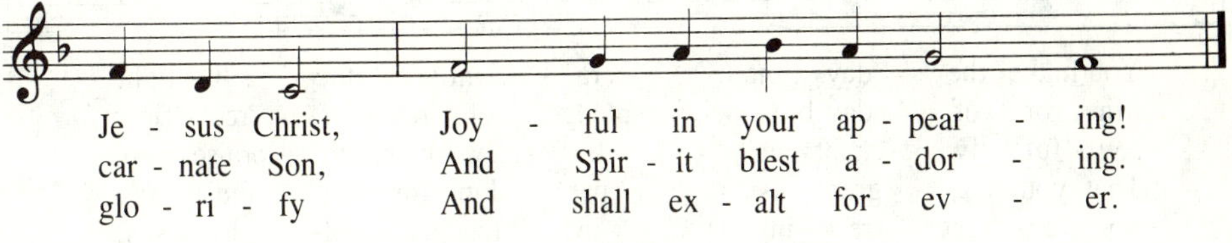
Je - sus Christ, Joy - ful in your ap - pear - ing!
car - nate Son, And Spir - it blest a - dor - ing.
glo - ri - fy And shall ex - alt for ev - er.

Text: Φωσ Ἱλαϱον; Greek, c.200; Tr. Robert S. Bridges, 1844-1930
Tune: NUNC DIMITTIS 66 7 66 7; *Genevan Psalter,* 1549; Harm. by Claude Goudimel, c.1505-1572

We Praise You, Father 680

1. We praise you, Father, for your gift
Of dusk and nightfall over earth,
Foreshadowing the mystery
Of death that leads to endless day.

2. Within your hands we rest secure;
In quiet sleep our strength renew;
Yet give your people hearts that wake
In love to you, unsleeping Lord.

3. Your glory may we ever seek
In rest, as in activity,
Until its fullness is revealed,
O Source of life, O Trinity.

Text: Benedictine Nuns of St. Mary's Abbey, West Malling, Kent, ©
Tune: WERNER, LM; Anthony Werner, fl.1863

681 Christ, Mighty Savior

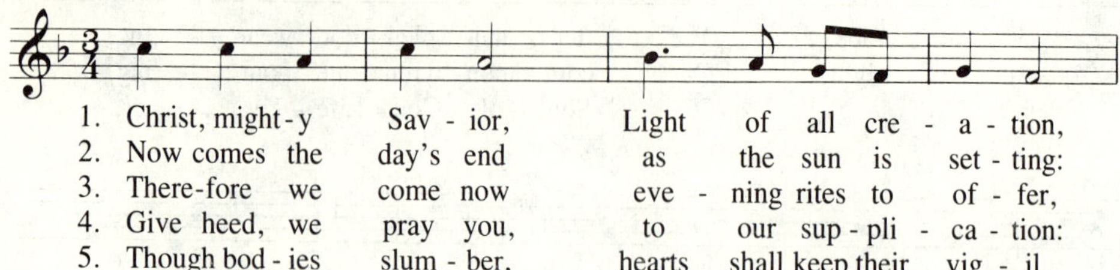
1. Christ, might-y Sav - ior, Light of all cre - a - tion,
2. Now comes the day's end as the sun is set - ting:
3. There-fore we come now eve - ning rites to of - fer,
4. Give heed, we pray you, to our sup - pli - ca - tion:
5. Though bod - ies slum - ber, hearts shall keep their vig - il,

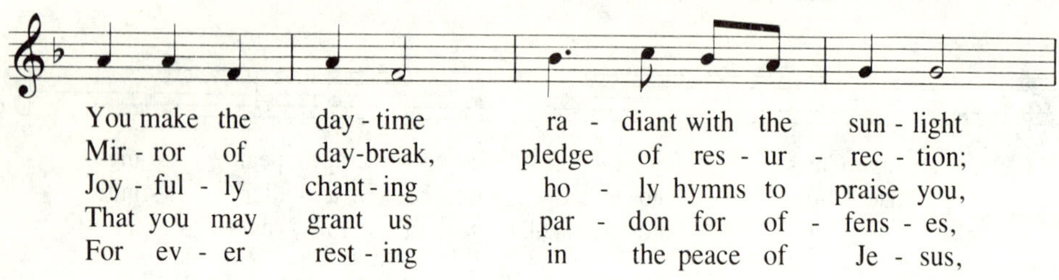
You make the day - time ra - diant with the sun - light
Mir - ror of day-break, pledge of res - ur - rec - tion;
Joy - ful - ly chant - ing ho - ly hymns to praise you,
That you may grant us par - don for of - fens - es,
For ev - er rest - ing in the peace of Je - sus,

And to the night give glit - ter - ing a - dorn-ment,
While in the heav - ens choirs of stars ap - pear - ing
With all cre - a - tion join - ing hearts and voic - es
Strength for our weak hearts, rest for ach - ing bod - ies,
In light or dark - ness wor - ship - ing our Sav - ior

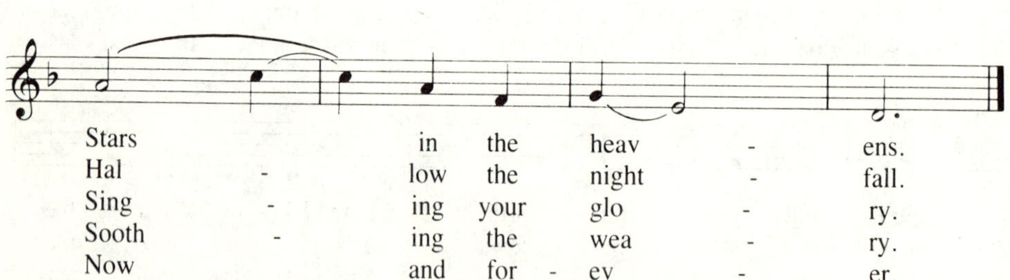
Stars in the heav - ens.
Hal - low the night - fall.
Sing - ing your glo - ry.
Sooth - ing the wea - ry.
Now and for - ev - er.

Text: *Christe, lux mundi;* Mozarabic Rite, 10th C.; Tr. by Alan G. McDougall, 1895-1964 Rev. by Anne K. LeCroy, b.1930, and others, ©
Tune: MIGHTY SAVIOR, 11 11 11 5; David Hurd, b.1950, © 1985, GIA Publications, Inc.

Praise and Thanksgiving 682

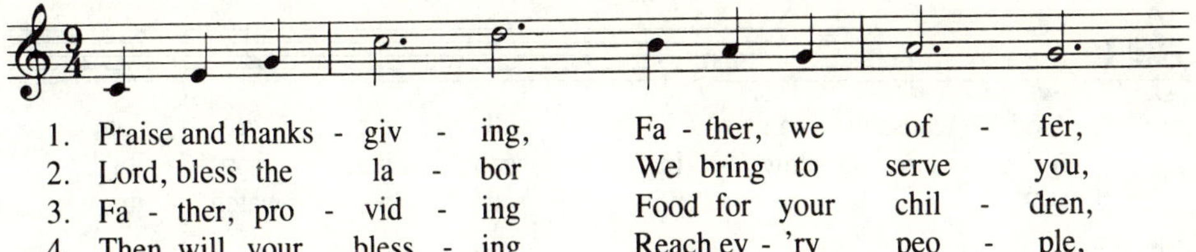
1. Praise and thanks - giv - ing, Fa - ther, we of - fer,
2. Lord, bless the la - bor We bring to serve you,
3. Fa - ther, pro - vid - ing Food for your chil - dren,
4. Then will your bless - ing Reach ev - 'ry peo - ple,

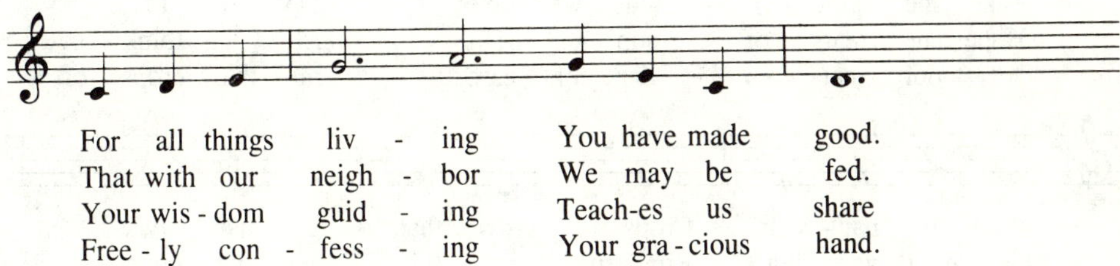
For all things liv - ing You have made good.
That with our neigh - bor We may be fed.
Your wis - dom guid - ing Teach-es us share
Free - ly con - fess - ing Your gra - cious hand.

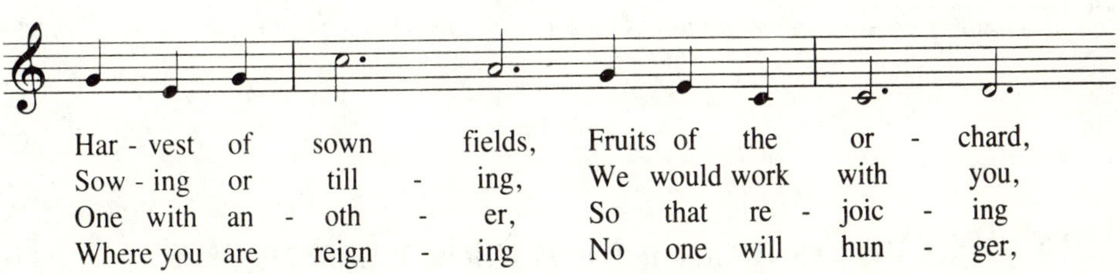
Har - vest of sown fields, Fruits of the or - chard,
Sow - ing or till - ing, We would work with you,
One with an - oth - er, So that re - joic - ing
Where you are reign - ing No one will hun - ger,

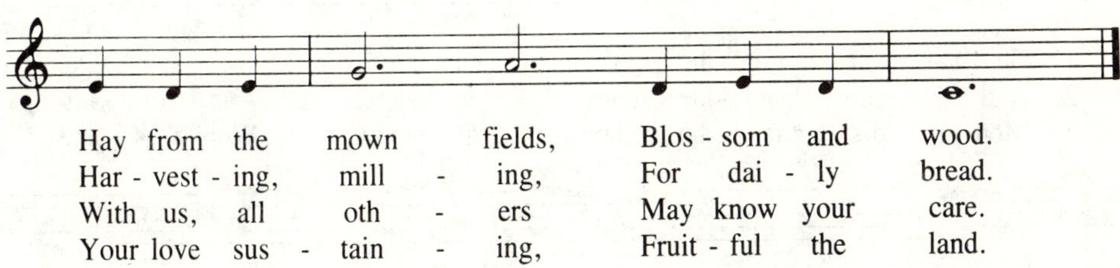
Hay from the mown fields, Blos - som and wood.
Har - vest - ing, mill - ing, For dai - ly bread.
With us, all oth - ers May know your care.
Your love sus - tain - ing, Fruit - ful the land.

Text: Albert F. Bayly, 1901-1984, © Oxford University Press
Tune: BUNESSAN, 5 5 5 4 D; Gaelic; Harm. by A. Gregory Murray, OSB, b.1905, ©

683 God, Whose Farm Is All Creation

1. God, whose farm is all cre - a - tion,
2. Take our plow - ing, seed - ing, reap - ing,
3. All our la - bor, all our watch - ing,
Take the grat - i - tude we give; Take the fin - est
Hopes and fears of sun and rain, All our think - ing,
All our cal - en - dar of care, In these crops of
of our har - vest, Crops we grow that all may live.
plan - ning, wait - ing, Rip - ened in this fruit and grain.
your cre - a - tion, Take, O God: they are our prayer.

Text: John Arlott, b.1914, © The Old Sun
Tune: STUTTGART, 8 7 8 7; Christian F. Witt, 1660-1716; Harm. by Kenneth D. Smith, b.1928, © National Christian Education Council

684 He Walks among the Golden Lamps

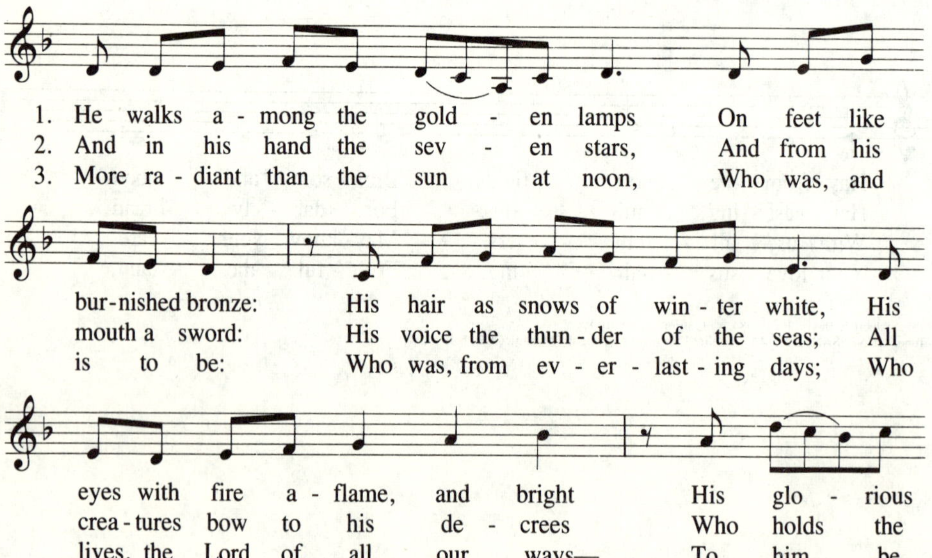
1. He walks a - mong the gold - en lamps On feet like
2. And in his hand the sev - en stars, And from his
3. More ra - diant than the sun at noon, Who was, and
bur - nished bronze: His hair as snows of win - ter white, His
mouth a sword: His voice the thun - der of the seas; All
is to be: Who was, from ev - er - last - ing days; Who
eyes with fire a - flame, and bright His glo - rious
crea - tures bow to his de - crees Who holds the
lives, the Lord of all our ways— To him be

robe of seam - less light Sur - pass - ing Sol - o - mon's.
ev - er - last - ing keys And reigns as sov - ereign Lord.
maj - es - ty and praise For all e - ter - ni - ty.

Text: Rev. 1:12-18; Timothy Dudley-Smith, b.1926, © 1973, Hope Publishing Co.
Tune: REVELATION, 8 6 888 6; Robert LeBlanc, b.1948, © 1986, GIA Publications, Inc.

O Holy City, Seen of John 685

1. O Ho - ly Cit - y, seen of John, Where Christ, the
2. O shame to us who rest con - tent While lust and
3. Give us, O God, the strength to build The Cit - y
4. Al - read - y in the mind of God That Cit - y

Lamb, does reign, With - in those four - square walls shall
greed for gain In street and shop and ten - e-
that has stood Too long a dream, whose laws are
ris - es fair: Lo, how its splen - dor chal - leng-

come No night, nor need, nor pain, And where the
ment Wring gold from hu - man pain, And bit - ter
love, Whose ways, the com - mon good, And where the
es The souls that great - ly dare: Yea, bids us

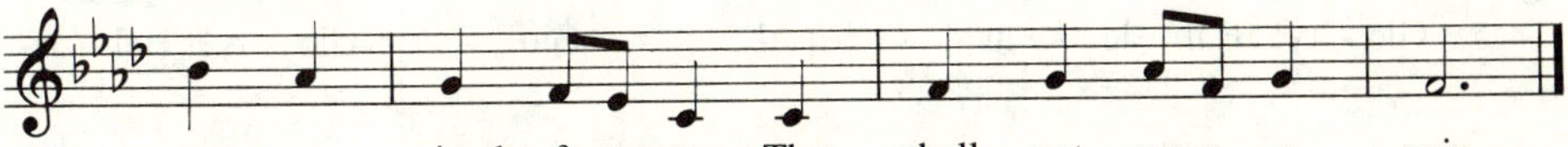

tears are wiped from eyes That shall not weep a - gain.
lips in blind de - spair Cry, "Christ has died in vain."
shin - ing sun be - comes God's grace for hu - man good.
seize the whole of life And build its glo - ry there.

Text: Rev.21; W. Russell Bowie, 1882-1969, © Harper and Row
Tune: MORNING SONG, 8 6 8 6 8 6; *Kentucky Harmony,* 1816; Harm. by C. Winfred Douglas, 1867-1944, © 1940, The Church Pension Fund

686 Mine Eyes Have Seen the Glory

1. Mine eyes have seen the glo - ry of the com - ing of the
2. I have seen him in the watch - fires of a hun - dred cir - cling
3. He has sound - ed forth the trum - pet that shall nev - er call re-
4. In the beau - ty of the lil - ies Christ was born a - cross the

Lord; He is tram-pling out the vin-tage where the grapes of wrath are
camps; They have build - ed him an al - tar in the eve - ning dews and
treat; He is sift - ing out all hu - man hearts be - fore his judg - ment
sea, With a glo - ry in his bos - om that trans - fig - ures you and

stored; He hath loosed the fate - ful light - ning of his ter - ri - ble swift
damps; I can read the right - eous sen - tence by the dim and flar - ing
seat; O be swift, my soul, to an - swer him; be ju - bi - lant, my
me; As he died to make us ho - ly, let us die that all be

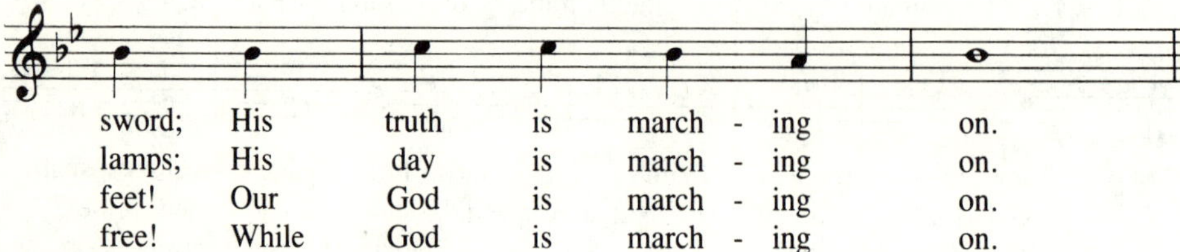

sword; His truth is march - ing on.
lamps; His day is march - ing on.
feet! Our God is march - ing on.
free! While God is march - ing on.

Glo - ry! Glo - ry! Hal - le - lu - jah! Glo - ry!

Glo - ry! Hal - le - lu - jah! Glo - ry! Glo - ry! Hal - le-

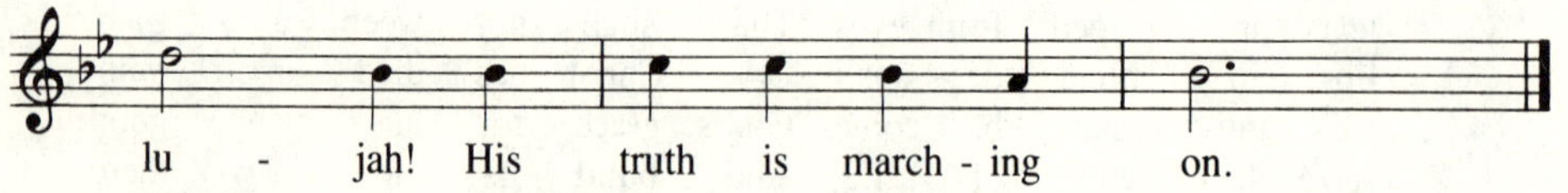

lu - jah! His truth is march - ing on.

Text: Julia W. Howe, 1819-1910
Tune: BATTLE HYMN OF THE REPUBLIC, 15 15 15 6 with refrain; Attr. to William Steffe, d.1911

Now the Day of the Lord Is at Hand 687

1. Now the day of the Lord is at hand, at hand;
2. Who would sigh for an old lost age of gold,

Its storms roll up the sky;
While the Lord of a - ges is here?

The na - tions sleep starv - ing on heaps of gold; All
True hearts then will leap at the trum - pet of God, And

dream - ers toss and sigh; The night is dark - est be-
those who suf - fer can dare. Each age of gold was an

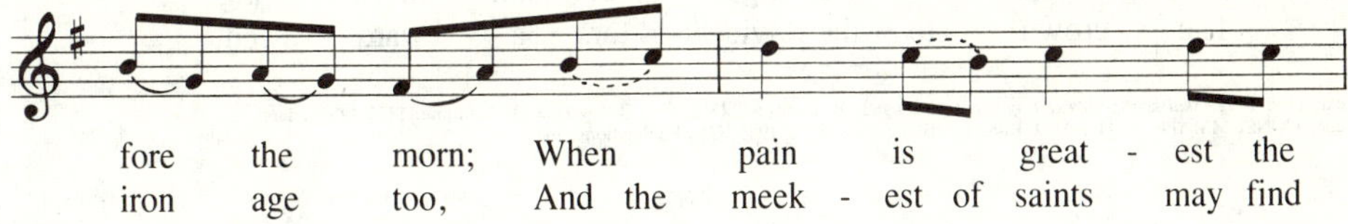

fore the morn; When pain is great - est the
iron age too, And the meek - est of saints may find

child is born, For the day of the Lord is at
work to do For the day of the Lord is at

hand, at hand, The day of the Lord is at hand.
hand, at hand, The day of the Lord is at hand.

Text: Based on Charles Kingsley, 1819-1875, by Richard Proulx, b.1937
Tune: REMEMBER THE POOR, Irregular; Gaelic; Alt. and harm. by Richard Proulx, b.1937,

688 A Multitude Comes from the East and the West

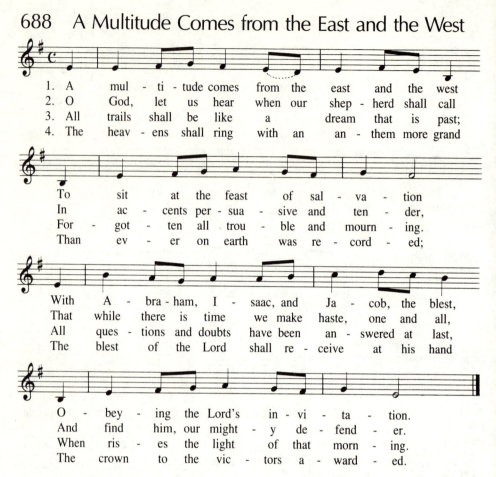

1. A mul - ti - tude comes from the east and the west
2. O God, let us hear when our shep - herd shall call
3. All trails shall be like a dream that is past;
4. The heav - ens shall ring with an an - them more grand

To sit at the feast of sal - va - tion
In ac - cents per - sua - sive and ten - der,
For - got - ten all trou - ble and mourn - ing.
Than ev - er on earth was re - cord - ed;

With A - bra - ham, I - saac, and Ja - cob, the blest,
That while there is time we make haste, one and all,
All ques - tions and doubts have been an - swered at last,
The blest of the Lord shall re - ceive at his hand

O - bey - ing the Lord's in - vi - ta - tion.
And find him, our might - y de - fend - er.
When ris - es the light of that morn - ing.
The crown to the vic - tors a - ward - ed.

Text: *Der Mange skal komme fra Öst og fra Vest;* Magnus B. Landstad, 1802-1880; Tr. by Peer O. Strömme, 1856-1951, adapt.
Tune: CONSUMMATION, 11 9 11 9; Robert LeBlanc, b.1948, © 1986, GIA Publications, Inc.

689 O the Beautiful Treasures

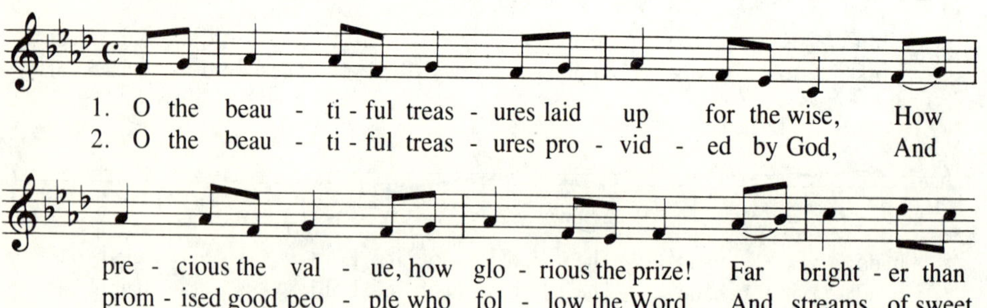
1. O the beau - ti - ful treas - ures laid up for the wise, How
2. O the beau - ti - ful treas - ures pro - vid - ed by God, And
pre - cious the val - ue, how glo - rious the prize! Far bright - er than
prom - ised good peo - ple who fol - low the Word. And streams of sweet

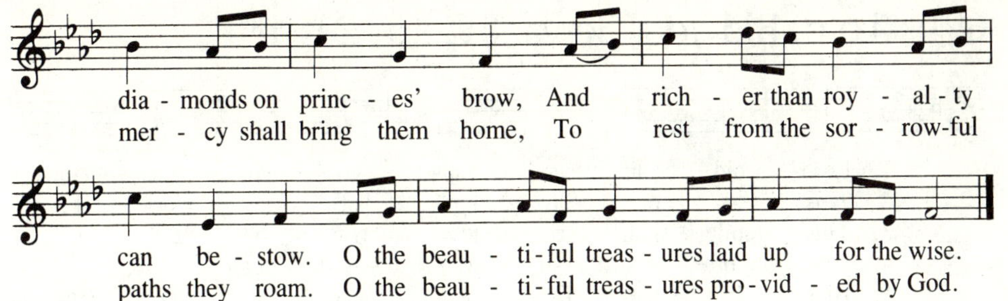
dia - monds on princ - es' brow, And rich - er than roy - al - ty
mer - cy shall bring them home, To rest from the sor - row-ful
can be - stow. O the beau - ti - ful treas - ures laid up for the wise.
paths they roam. O the beau - ti - ful treas - ures pro - vid - ed by God.

Text: Shaker
Tune: BEAUTIFUL TREASURES, 12 11 10 10 12; American Shaker Melody, 1849; Harm. by Richard Proulx, b.1937,

Jerusalem, My Happy Home 690

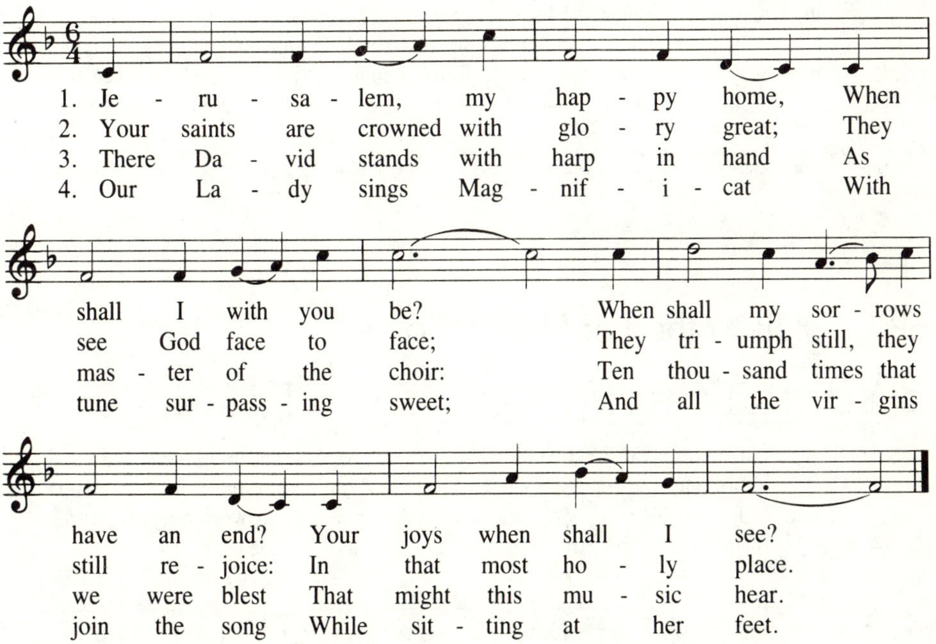

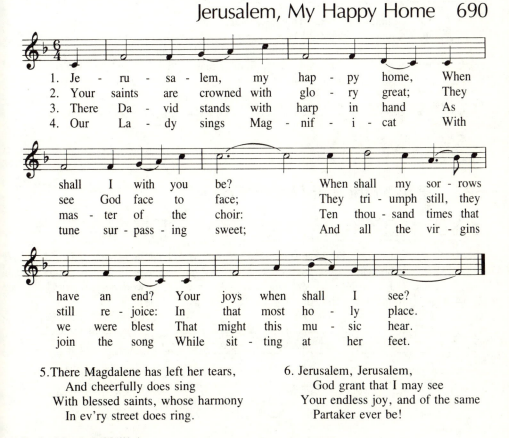

1. Je - ru - sa - lem, my hap - py home, When
2. Your saints are crowned with glo - ry great; They
3. There Da - vid stands with harp in hand As
4. Our La - dy sings Mag - nif - i - cat With

shall I with you be? When shall my sor - rows
see God face to face; They tri - umph still, they
mas - ter of the choir: Ten thou - sand times that
tune sur - pass - ing sweet; And all the vir - gins

have an end? Your joys when shall I see?
still re - joice: In that most ho - ly place.
we were blest That might this mu - sic hear.
join the song While sit - ting at her feet.

5. There Magdalene has left her tears,
And cheerfully does sing
With blessed saints, whose harmony
In ev'ry street does ring.

6. Jerusalem, Jerusalem,
God grant that I may see
Your endless joy, and of the same
Partaker ever be!

Text: Joseph Bromehead, 1747-1826, alt.
Tune: LAND OF REST, CM; American; Harm. by Richard Proulx, b.1937,

691 Lord, Bid Your Servant Go in Peace

1. Lord, bid your ser - vant go in peace, Your
2. This is the Sav - ior of the world, The
3. This child shall see the rise, the fall, Of
4. His moth - er's soul a sword shall pierce, Of
5. Blest be the Fa - ther, who has giv'n His

word is now ful - filled. These eyes have seen sal-
gen - tiles' prom - ised light, God's glo - ry dwell - ing
those in Is - ra - el, God's sign raised high for
sor - row keen and deep; And se - cret thoughts of
Son to be our Lord, Blest too that Son, and

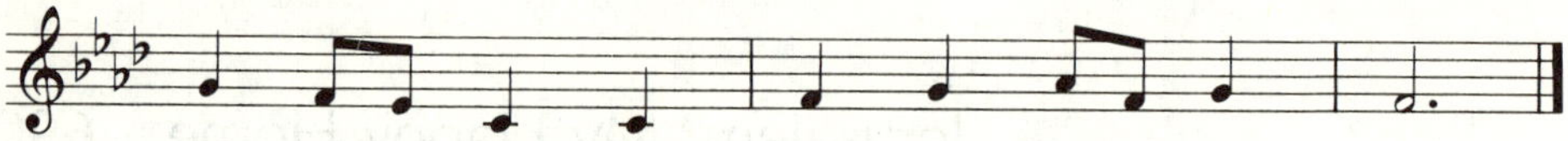

va - tion's dawn, This child so long fore - told.
in our midst, The joy of Is - ra - el.
all to see, Whom some shall yet de - ny.
man - y hearts Through him shall be re - vealed.
with them both The Spir - it of their love.

Text: Lk. 2:29-32, 34-35; *Nunc dimittis;* James Quinn, SJ, b.1919, alt., © 1969
Tune: MORNING SONG, CM; Wyeth's *Repository of Sacred Music,* 1813; Harm. by Richard Proulx, b.1937, © 1975, GIA Publications, Inc.

692 Hail to the Lord Who Comes

1. Hail to the Lord who comes, Comes to his tem - ple gate;
2. But, born up - on the throne Of Mar - y's gen - tle breast,
3. There Jo - seph at her side In rev - 'rent won - der stands;
4. O Light of all the earth, To us come hast - i - ly,
Not with his an - gel host, Not in his king - ly state;
Watched by her du - teous love, In her fond arms at rest,
And, filled with ho - ly joy, Old Sim - eon in his hands
Come to your tem - ples here, That we, from sin set free,

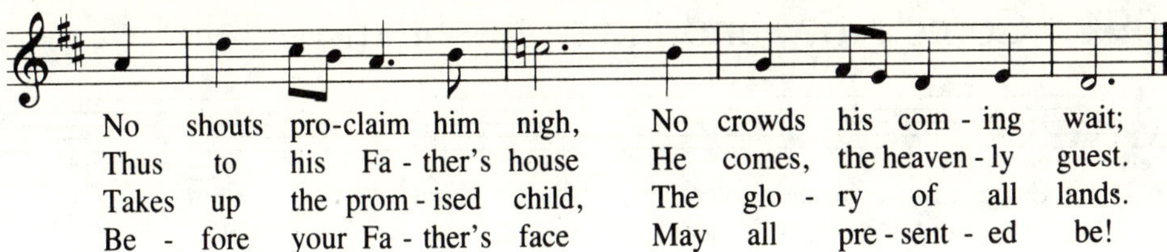
No shouts pro-claim him nigh, No crowds his com - ing wait;
Thus to his Fa - ther's house He comes, the heaven - ly guest.
Takes up the prom - ised child, The glo - ry of all lands.
Be - fore your Fa - ther's face May all pre - sent - ed be!

Text: John Ellerton, 1826-1893, alt.
Tune: PRESENTATION, 6 6 6 6 6 6; Sean Duggan, OSB, b.1954, © 1986, GIA Publications, Inc.

Joseph, Be Our Guide and Pattern 693

1. Jo - seph, be our guide and pat - tern, Faith - ful to your sa - cred trust, Strong pro - tec - tor of the Vir - gin And the in - fant, Je - sus Christ. Jo - seph, firm and faith - ful, guide us, Jo - seph walk the way with us.

2. Faith - ful to the guid - ing vi - sion, Lis - t'ning to the an - gel's word; Shield-ing Mar - y from all slan - der, Guard-ing Christ, both Son and Lord. Jo - seph, true and trust - ing, guide us, Jo - seph walk the way with us.

3. Lead - ing them through man - y dan - gers To the home in Naz - a - reth, Hum - bly for their needs pro - vid - ing In your wise and stead - fast faith. Jo - seph, brave, o- be - dient, guide us, Jo - seph walk the way with us.

4. Work-man skilled with saw and ham - mer, Strong to earn the dai - ly bread, From the gifts of God cre - at - ing Use - ful things for peo - ple's need. Jo - seph, strong and stead-fast, guide us, Jo - seph walk the way with us.

Text: Muriel Newton-White, b.1928, © 1972, Canadian Catholic Conference
Tune: ORIEL, 8 7 8 7 8 7; Ett's *Cantica Sacra,* 1840

694 Come Now, and Praise the Humble Saint

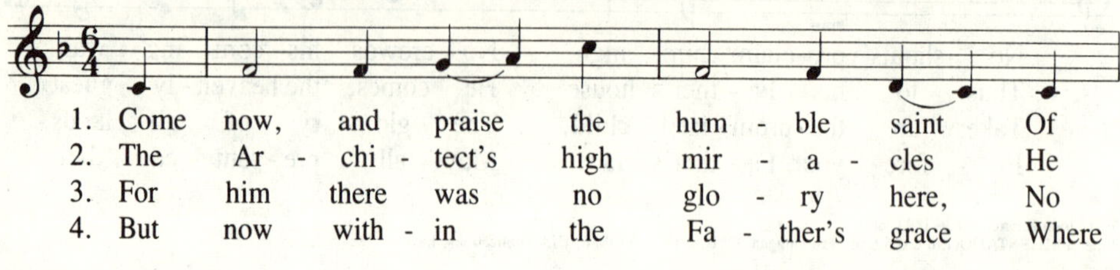
1. Come now, and praise the hum - ble saint Of
2. The Ar - chi - tect's high mir - a - cles He
3. For him there was no glo - ry here, No
4. But now with - in the Fa - ther's grace Where

Da - vid's house and line, The car - pen - ter whose
saw, and what was done, The Vir - gin's spouse, the
crown or mar - tyr's fame, For him there was the
saints and an - gel's throng, Be - side his spouse, be-

life ful - filled Our gra - cious God's de - sign.
guard - ian of Great Da - vid's great - er Son.
pa - tient life Of faith and hum - ble name.
fore the Son, He joins the heav'n - ly song.

Text: G. W. Williams, b.1922, © 1979, Hymn Society of America
Tune: LAND OF REST, CM; American; Harm. by Richard Proulx, b.1937, © 1975, GIA Publications, Inc.

695 The Angel Gabriel from Heaven Came

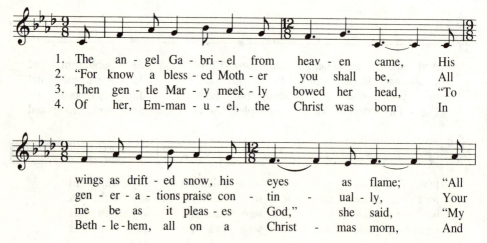

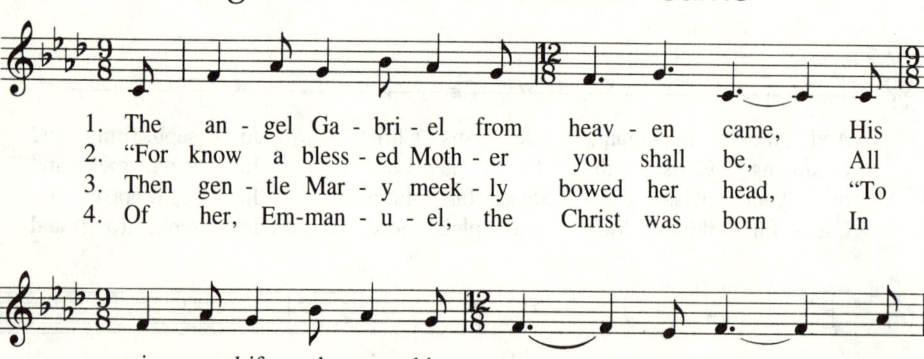
1. The an - gel Ga - bri - el from heav - en came, His
2. "For know a bless - ed Moth - er you shall be, All
3. Then gen - tle Mar - y meek - ly bowed her head, "To
4. Of her, Em-man - u - el, the Christ was born In

wings as drift - ed snow, his eyes as flame; "All
gen - er - a - tions praise con - tin - ual - ly, Your
me be as it pleas - es God," she said, "My
Beth - le - hem, all on a Christ - mas morn, And

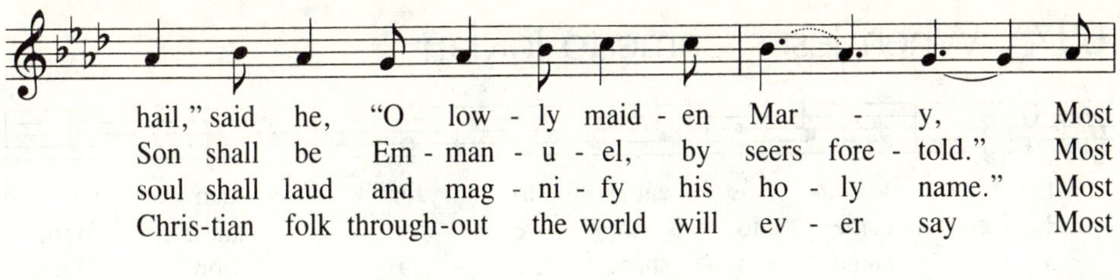
hail," said he, "O low - ly maid - en Mar - y, Most
Son shall be Em - man - u - el, by seers fore - told." Most
soul shall laud and mag - ni - fy his ho - ly name." Most
Chris-tian folk through-out the world will ev - er say Most

high - ly fa - vored la - dy," Glo - ri - a!

Text: Sabine Baring-Gould, 1834-1924
Tune: GABRIEL'S MESSAGE, 10 10 12 10; Basque Carol; Harm. by Charles E. Pettman, 1865-1943

Praise We the Lord This Day 696

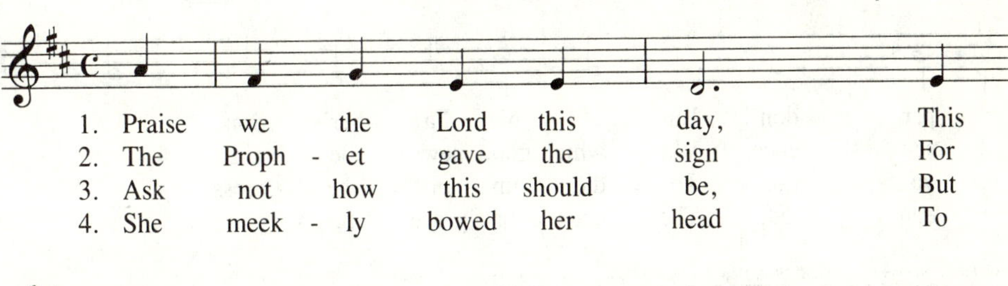
1. Praise we the Lord this day, This
2. The Proph - et gave the sign For
3. Ask not how this should be, But
4. She meek - ly bowed her head To
day so long fore - told, Whose prom - ise shone with
faith - ful folk to read: A vir - gin, born of
wor - ship and a - dore Like her whom God's own
hear the gra - cious word, Mar - y, the pure and

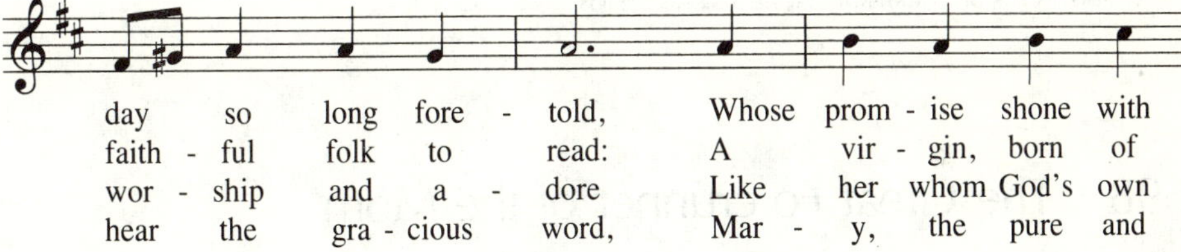
cheer - ing ray On wait - ing saints of old.
Da - vid's line, Shall bear the prom - ised Seed.
maj - es - ty Came down to shad - ow o'er.
low - ly maid, The fa - vored of the Lord.

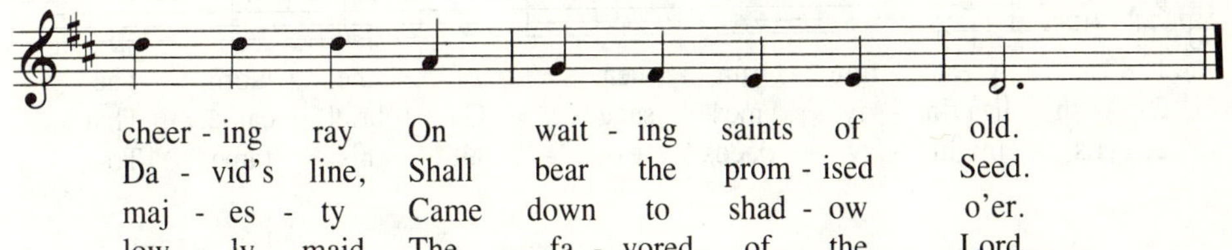

5. Blessèd shall be her name
In all the Church on earth
Through whom that wondrous mercy came,
The incarnate Savior's birth.

6. O Christ, the Virgin's Son,
We praise you and adore,
You are with God the Father One
And Spirit evermore.

Text: Matt. 1:23; *Hymns for the Festivals and Saints' Days,* 1846
Tune: SWABIA, SM; Johann M. Spiess, 1715-1772

697 When Jesus Came to Jordan

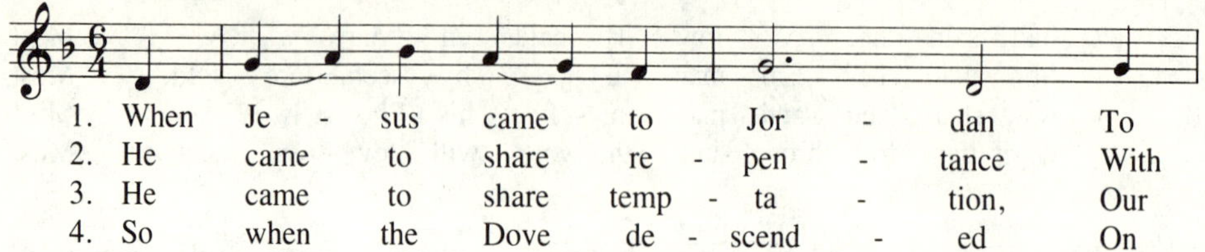
1. When Je - sus came to Jor - dan To
2. He came to share re - pen - tance With
3. He came to share temp - ta - tion, Our
4. So when the Dove de - scend - ed On

be bap - tized by John, He did not come for
all who mourn their sins, To speak the vi - tal
ut - most woe and loss; For us and our sal-
him, the Son of Man, The hid - den years had

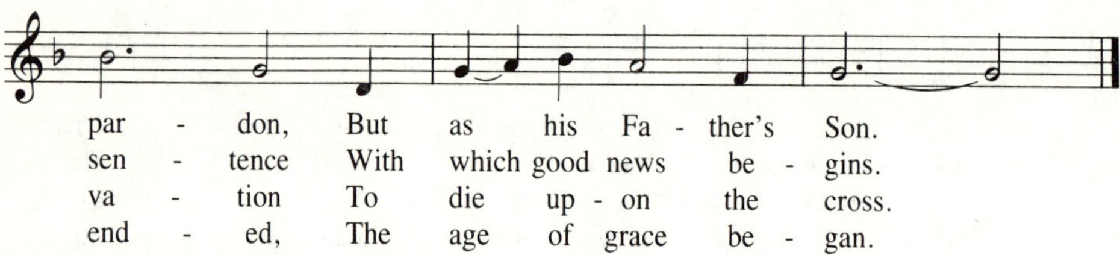
par - don, But as his Fa - ther's Son.
sen - tence With which good news be - gins.
va - tion To die up - on the cross.
end - ed, The age of grace be - gan.

Text: Fred Pratt Green, b.1903, © 1980, Hope Publishing Co.
Tune: DE EERSTEN ZIJN DE LAATSTEN, 7 6 7 6; Frits Mehrtens, 1922-1975, © Boekencentrum

698 The Great Forerunner of the Morn

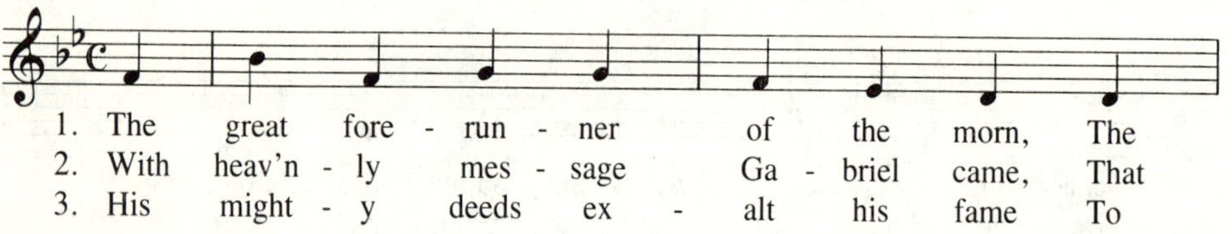
1. The great fore - run - ner of the morn, The
2. With heav'n - ly mes - sage Ga - briel came, That
3. His might - y deeds ex - alt his fame To

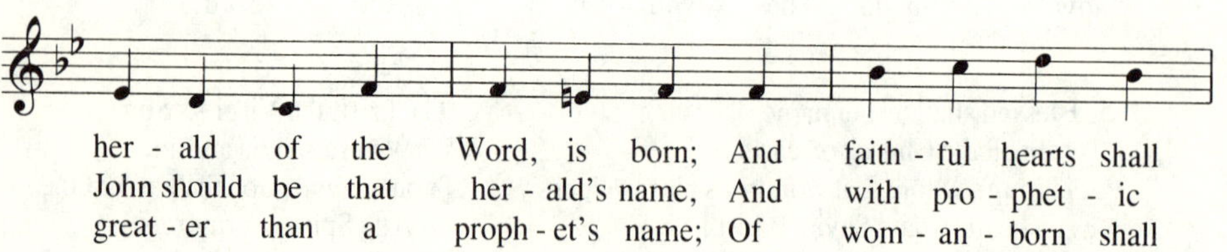
her - ald of the Word, is born; And faith - ful hearts shall
John should be that her - ald's name, And with pro - phet - ic
great - er than a proph - et's name; Of wom - an - born shall

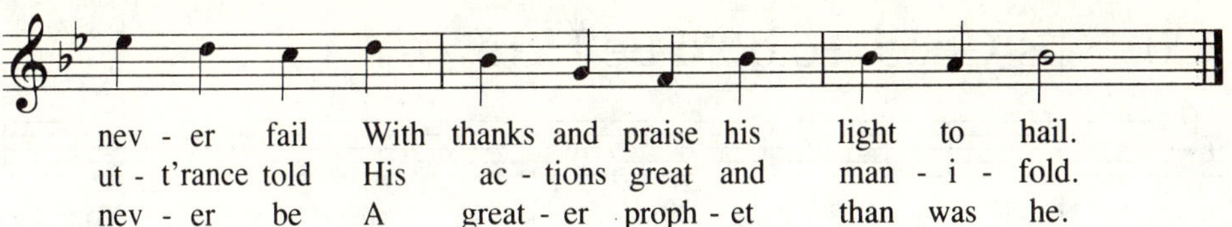
nev - er fail With thanks and praise his light to hail.
ut - t'rance told His ac - tions great and man - i - fold.
nev - er be A great - er proph - et than was he.

Text: *Praecursor altus luminis;* Venerable Bede, 673-735; Tr. by John M. Neale, 1818-1866, alt.
Tune: WINCHESTER NEW, LM; Ádapt. from *Musikalisches Handbuch,* Hamburg, 1690

Two Noble Saints 699

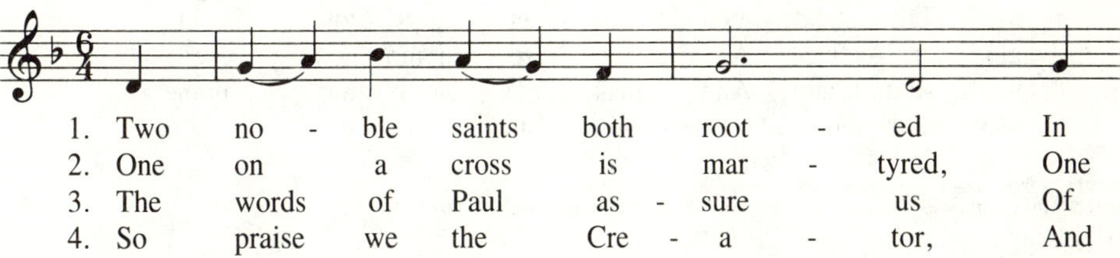
1. Two no - ble saints both root - ed In
2. One on a cross is mar - tyred, One
3. The words of Paul as - sure us Of
4. So praise we the Cre - a - tor, And

faith and ho - ly love, By hope of God u-
by the sword is slain; Both tri - umph in their
Christ's re - deem - ing word; The works of Pe - ter
praise we Christ the Son, Who with the Ho - ly

nit - ed They reach to heaven a - bove.
dy - ing, Both glo - rious saint - hood gain.
show us How we may serve the Lord.
Spir - it, Now reign, blest Three in One.

Text: Based on *Decora lux aeternitatis auream,* by Anne K. LeCroy, b.1930, ©
Tune: DE EERSTEN ZIJN DE LAASTEN, 7 6 7 6 Fritis Mehrtens, 1922-1975, © Boekencentrum

700 'Tis Good, Lord, to Be Here

1. 'Tis good, Lord, to be here! Your
2. 'Tis good, Lord, to be here, Your
3. Ful - fill - er of the past! Prom-
4. Be - fore we taste of death, We
5. 'Tis good, Lord, to be here! Yet

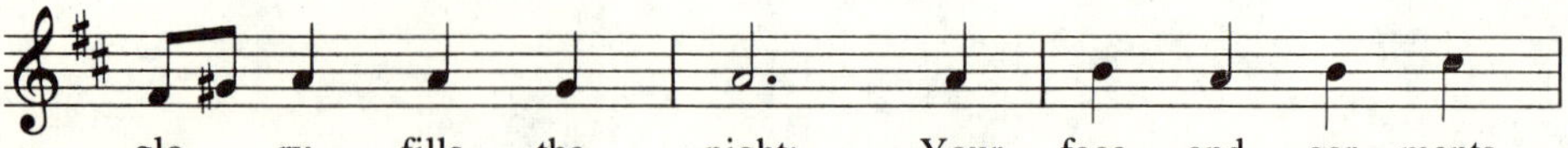

glo - ry fills the night; Your face and gar - ments,
beau - ty to be - hold, Where Mo - ses and E-
ise of things to be! We hail your bod - y
see your king - dom come; We long to hold the
we may not re - main; But since you bid us

like the sun, Shine with un - bor - rowed light.
li - jah stand, Your mes - sen - gers of old.
glo - ri - fied, And our re - demp - tion see.
vi - sion bright, And make this hill our home.
leave the mount, Come with us to the plain.

Text: Lk. 9:32-33; Joseph A. Robinson, 1858-1933, alt., © Esme. D. E. Bird
Tune: SWABIA, SM; Johann M. Speiss, 1715-1772; Adapt. by William H. Havergal, 1793-1870

701 Christ upon the Mountain Peak

1. Christ up - on the moun - tain peak Stands a - lone in
2. Trem-bling at his feet we saw Mo - ses and E-
3. Swift the cloud of glo - ry came: God pro - claim - ing
4. This is God's be - lov - ed Son! Law and proph - ets
glo - ry blaz - ing; Let us, if we dare to speak,
li - jah speak - ing. All the proph - ets and the law
in the thun - der Je - sus as his Son by name!
fade be - fore him; First and last and on - ly One,

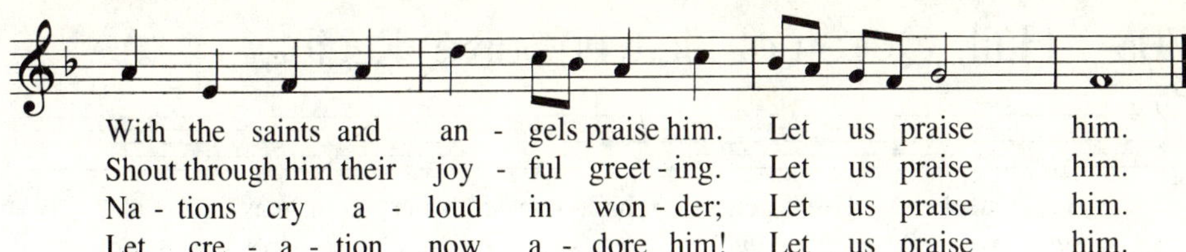
With the saints and an - gels praise him. Let us praise him.
Shout through him their joy - ful greet - ing. Let us praise him.
Na - tions cry a - loud in won - der; Let us praise him.
Let cre - a - tion now a - dore him! Let us praise him.

Text: Brian Wren, b.1936; © 1977, Hope Publishing Co.
Tune: MOWSLEY, 7 8 7 8 4; Cyril V. Taylor, b.1907; © 1985, Hope Publishing Co.

Hail, Holy Queen Enthroned Above 702

1. Hail, ho - ly Queen en - throned a - bove, O Ma-
2. The cause of joy to all be - low, O Ma-
3. O gen - tle, lov - ing, ho - ly one, O Ma-

ri - a. Hail, Queen of mer - cy and of love,
ri - a. The spring through which all grac - es flow,
ri - a. The God of light be - came your Son,

O Ma - ri - a. Tri - umph, all ye Cher - u - bim,
O Ma - ri - a. An - gels, all your prais - es bring,
O Ma - ri - a. Tri - umph, all ye Cher - u - bim,

Sing with us, ye Ser - a - phim, Heav'n and earth re - sound the
Earth and heav - en, with us sing, All cre - a - tion ech - o-
Sing with us, ye Ser - a - phim, Heav'n and earth re - sound the

hymn: Sal - ve, Sal - ve, Sal - ve, Re - gi - na.
ing: Sal - ve, Sal - ve, Sal - ve, Re - gi - na.
hymn: Sal - ve, Sal - ve, Sal - ve, Re - gi - na.

Text: *Salve, Regina, mater misericordia;* c.1080; Tr. *Roman Hymnal,* 1884; St. 2-3, adapt. by M. Owen Lee, CSB, b.1930
Tune: SALVE REGINA COELITUM, 8 4 8 4 777 4 5; *Choralmelodien zum Heiligen Gesänge,* 1808; Harm. by Healey Willan, 1880-1968, © Willis Music Co.

703 Hail, Queen of Heaven/Salve, Regina

Hail, Queen of Heav - en, hail, our Moth - er com - pas - sion - ate,
Sal - ve, Re - gí - na, ma - ter mi - se - ri - cór - di - ae:
True life and com - fort and our hope, we greet you!
Vi - ta, dul - cé - do et spes no - stra sal - ve.
To you we ex - iles, chil - dren of Eve, raise our voic - es.
Ad te cla - má - mus, éx - su - les fí - li - i He - vae.
We send up sighs to you, as mourn - ing and weep - ing,
Ad te sus - pi - rá - mus, ge - mén - tes et flen - tes
we pass through this vale of sor - row. Then turn to us,
in hac la - cri - má - rum val - le. E - ia er - go,
O most gra - cious Wom - an, those eyes of yours, so full of
ad - vo - cá - ta no - stra, il - los tu - os mi - se - ri-
love and ten - der - ness, so full of pit - y.
cór - des ó - cu - los ad nos con - vér - te.
And grant us af - ter these, our days of lone - ly
Et Je - sum, be - ne - dí - ctum fru - ctum ven - tris

ex - ile, the sight of your blest Son and Lord, Christ
tu - i, no - bis post hoc ex - sí - li - um o-
Je - sus. O gen - tle, O lov - ing,
stén - de. O cle - mens, O pi - a,
O ho - ly sweet Vir - gin Ma - ry.
O dul - cis Vir - go Ma - rí - a.

Text: Latin, c.1080; Tr. by John C. Selner, SS, b.1904, © 1954, GIA Publications, Inc.
Tune: SALVE REGINA, Irregular; Mode V; Acc. by Gerard Farrell, OSB, b.1919, © 1986, GIA Publications, Inc.

Lift High the Cross 704

Lift high the cross, the love of Christ pro - claim till
all the world a - dore his sa - cred name.

1. Come, Chris - tians, fol - low where the Mas - ter trod, our
2. Led on their way by this tri - um - phant sign, the
3. Each new - born fol - l'wer of the Cru - ci - fied bears
4. O Lord, once lift - ed on the glo - rious tree, your
5. So shall our song of tri - umph ev - er be: praise

D.C.

King vic - to - rious, Christ, the Son of God.
hosts of God in con - quering ranks com - bine.
on the brow the seal of him who died.
death has bought us life e - ter - nal - ly.
to the Cru - ci - fied for vic - to - ry!

Text: 1 Cor. 1:18; George W. Kitchen, 1827-1912, and Michael R. Newbolt, 1874-1956, alt.
Tune: CRUCIFER, 10 10 with refrain; Sydney H. Nicholson, 1875-1947, © by permission of Hymns Ancient and Modern, Ltd.

705 For All the Saints

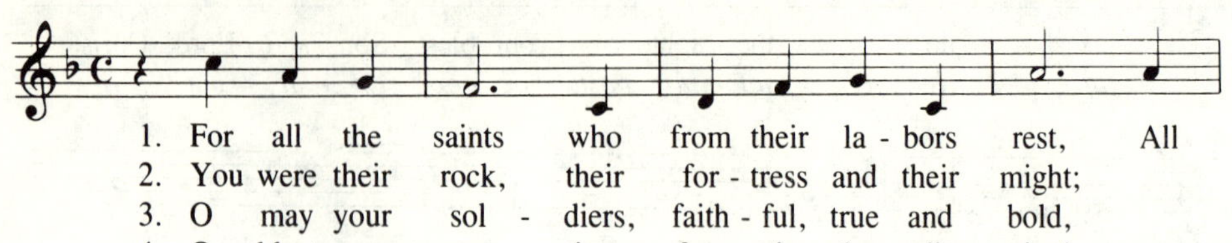
1. For all the saints who from their la - bors rest, All
2. You were their rock, their for - tress and their might;
3. O may your sol - diers, faith - ful, true and bold,
4. O blest com - mun - ion, fam - i - ly di - vine!

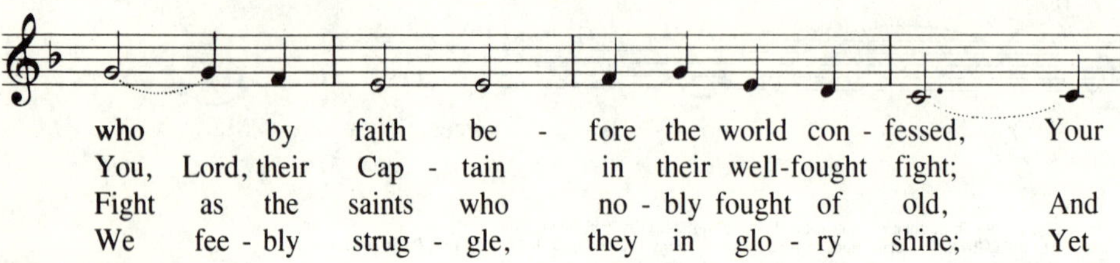
who by faith be - fore the world con - fessed, Your
You, Lord, their Cap - tain in their well-fought fight;
Fight as the saints who no - bly fought of old, And
We fee - bly strug - gle, they in glo - ry shine; Yet

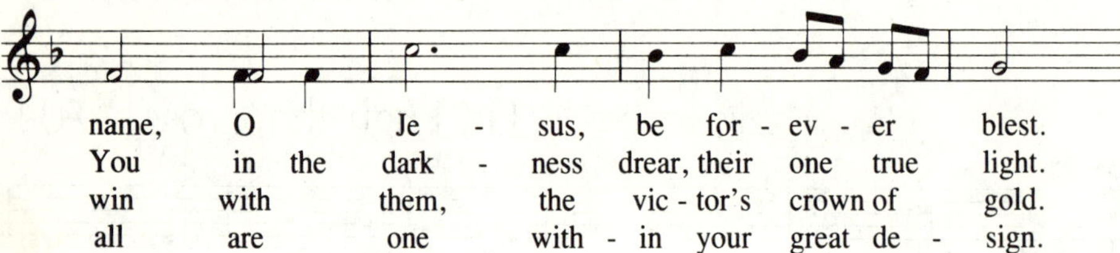
name, O Je - sus, be for - ev - er blest.
You in the dark - ness drear, their one true light.
win with them, the vic - tor's crown of gold.
all are one with - in your great de - sign.

Al - le - lu - ia! Al - le - lu - ia!

5. And when the strife is fierce, the warfare long,
Steals on the ear the distant triumph song,
And hearts are brave again, and arms are strong.

6. The golden evening brightens in the west;
Soon, soon to faithful warriors comes their rest;
Sweet is the calm of paradise the blest.

7. But then there breaks a yet more glorious day:
The saints triumphant rise in bright array;
The King of glory passes on his way.

8. From earth's wide bounds, from ocean's farthest coast,
Through gates of pearl streams in the countless host,
Singing to Father, Son, and Holy Ghost:

Text: William W. How, 1823-1897
Tune: SINE NOMINE, 10 10 10 with alleluias; Ralph Vaughan Williams, 1872-1958,

By All Your Saints Still Striving 706

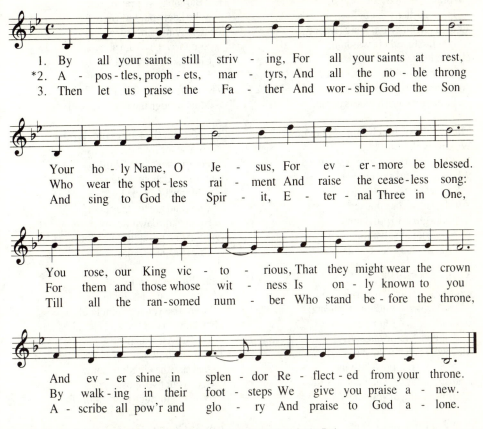

1. By all your saints still striv - ing, For all your saints at rest,
*2. A - pos - tles, proph - ets, mar - tyrs, And all the no - ble throng
3. Then let us praise the Fa - ther And wor - ship God the Son

Your ho - ly Name, O Je - sus, For ev - er - more be blessed.
Who wear the spot - less rai - ment And raise the cease - less song:
And sing to God the Spir - it, E - ter - nal Three in One,

You rose, our King vic - to - rious, That they might wear the crown
For them and those whose wit - ness Is on - ly known to you
Till all the ran - somed num - ber Who stand be - fore the throne,

And ev - er shine in splen - dor Re - flect - ed from your throne.
By walk - ing in their foot - steps We give you praise a - new.
A - scribe all pow'r and glo - ry And praise to God a - lone.

Text: Based on Horatio Nelson, 1823-1913, by Jerry D. Godwin, b.1944,
Tune: ST. THEODULPH, 7 6 7 6 D; Melchior Teschner, 1584-1635

*This stanza may be replaced by an appropriate stanza taken from the following pages.

January 25: Conversion of Paul
Praise for the light from heaven
And for the voice of awe:
Praise for the glorious vision
The persecutor saw.
O Lord, for Paul's conversion,
We bless your Name today.
Come shine within our darkness
And guide us in the Way.

February 22: Chair of Peter
We praise you, Lord, for Peter,
So eager and so bold:
Thrice falling, yet repentant,
Thrice charged to feed your fold.
Lord, make your pastors faithful
To guard your flock from harm
And hold them when they waver
With your almighty arm.

March 19: Joseph, Husband of Mary
All praise, O God, for Joseph,
The guardian of your Son,
Who saved him from King Herod,
When safety there was none.
He taught the trade of builder,
When they to Naz'reth came,
And Joseph's love made "Father"
To be, for Christ, God's name.

March 25: Annunciation of Our Lord
We sing with joy of Mary
Whose heart with awe was stirred
When, youthful and unready,
She heard the angel's word;
Yet she her voice upraises
God's glory to proclaim,
As once for our salvation
Your mother she became.

April 25: Mark
For Mark, O Lord, we praise you,
The weak by grace made strong:
His witness in his Gospel
Becomes victorious song.
May we, in all our weakness,
Receive your power divine,
And all, as faithful branches,
Grow strong in you, the Vine.

May 3: Philip and James
We praise you, Lord, for Philip,
Blest guide to Greek and Jew,
And for young James the faithful,
Who heard and followed you,
O grant us grace to know you,
The victor in the strife,
That we with all your servants
May wear the crown of life.

May 14: Matthias
For one in place of Judas,
The apostles sought God's choice:
The lot fell to Matthias
For whom we now rejoice.
May we like true apostles
Your holy Church defend,
And not betray our calling
But serve you to the end.

June 11: Barnabas
For Barnabas we praise you,
Who kept your law of love
And, leaving earthly treasures,
Sought riches from above.
O Christ, our Lord and Savior,
Let gifts of grace descend,
That your true consolation
May through the world extend.

June 24: Birth of John the Baptist
All praise for John the Baptist,
Forerunner of the Word,
Our true Elijah, making
A highway for the Lord.
The last and greatest prophet,
He saw the dawning ray
Of light that grows in splendor
Until the perfect day.

June 29: Peter and Paul
We praise you for Saint Peter;
We praise you for Saint Paul.
They taught both Jew and Gentile
That Christ is all in all.
To cross and sword they yielded
And saw the kingdom come:
O God, your two apostles
Won life through martyrdom.

July 3: Thomas
All praise, O Lord, for Thomas
Whose short-lived doubtings prove
Your perfect twofold nature,
The depth of your true love.
To all who live with questions
A steadfast faith afford;
And grant us grace to know you,
Made flesh, yet God and Lord.

July 22: Mary Magdalene
All praise for Mary Magdalene,
Whose wholeness was restored
By you, her faithful Master,
Her Savior and her Lord.
On Easter morning early,
A word from you sufficed:
Her faith was first to see you,
Her Lord, the risen Christ.

July 25: James
O Lord, for James, we praise you,
Who fell to Herod's sword.
He drank the cup of suff'ring
And thus fulfilled your word.
Lord, curb our vain impatience
For glory and for fame,
Equip us for such suff'rings
As glorify your Name.

August 24: Bartholomew
Praised for your blest apostle
Surnamed Bartholomew;
We know not his achievements
But know that he was true,
For he at the Ascension
Was an apostle still.
May we discern your presence
And seek, like him, your will.

September 21: Matthew
We praise you, Lord, for Matthew,
Whose gospel words declare
That, worldly gain forsaking,
Your path of life we share.
From all unrighteous mammon,
O raise our eyes anew,
That we, whate'er our station
May rise and follow you.

October 18: Luke
For Luke, beloved physician,
All praise; whose Gospel shows
The healer of the nations,
The one who shares our woes.
Your wine and oil, O Savior,
Upon our spirits pour,
And with true balm of Gilead
Anoint us evermore.

October 28: Simon and Jude
Praise, Lord, for your apostles,
Saint Simon and Saint Jude.
One love, one hope impelled them
To tread the way, renewed.
May we with zeal as earnest
The faith of Christ maintain,
Be bound in love together,
And life eternal gain.

November 30: Andrew
All praise, O Lord, for Andrew,
The first to follow you;
He witnessed to his brother,
"This is Messiah true."
You called him from his fishing
Upon Lake Galilee;
He rose to meet your challenge,
"Leave all and follow me."

December 26: Stephen
All praise, O Lord, for Stephen
Who, martyred, saw you stand
To help in time of torment,
To plead at God's right hand.
Like you, our suff'ring Savior,
His enemies he blessed,
With "Lord, receive my spirit,"
His faith, in death, confessed.

December 27: John
For John, your loved disciple,
Exiled to Patmos' shore,
And for his faithful record,
We praise you evermore;
Praise for the mystic vision
His words to us unfold.
Instill in us his longing,
Your glory to behold.

December 28: Holy Innocents
Praise for your infant martyrs,
Whom your mysterious love
Called early from life's conflicts
To share your peace above.
O Rachel, cease your weeping;
They're free from pain and cares.
Lord, grant us crowns as brilliant
And lives as pure as theirs.

707 Ye Watchers and Ye Holy Ones

1. Ye watch - ers and ye ho - ly ones,
2. O high - er than the cher - u - bim,
3. Re - spond, ye souls in end - less rest,
4. O friends, in glad - ness let us sing,
Bright ser - aphs, cher - u - bim, and thrones,
More glo - rious than the ser - a - phim,
Ye pa - tri - archs and proph - ets blest,
Su - per - nal an - thems ech - o - ing,
Raise the glad strain, Al - le - lu - ia!
Lead their prais - es, Al - le - lu - ia!
Al - le - lu - ia, Al - le - lu - ia!
Al - le - lu - ia, Al - le - lu - ia!
Cry out, do - min - ions, prince - doms, powers,
O bear - er of the e - ter - nal Word,
Ye ho - ly Twelve, ye mar - tyrs strong,
To God the Fa - ther, God the Son,
Vir - tues, arch - an - gels, an - gels' choirs,
Most gra - cious, mag - ni - fy the Lord,
All saints tri - um - phant, raise in song,
And God the Spir - it, Three in One,
Al - le - lu - ia, Al - le - lu - ia, Al - le - lu - ia,
Al - le - lu - ia, Al - le - lu - ia!

Text: John A. Riley, 1858-1945, © Oxford University Press
Tune: LASST UNS ERFREUEN, LM with alleluias; *Geistliche Kirchengesänge,* Cologne, 1623; Harm. by Ralph Vaughan Williams, 1872-1958, © Oxford University Press

Immaculate Mary 708

1. Im - ma - cu - late Mar - y, your prais - es we sing;
2. Pre - des - tined for Christ by e - ter - nal de - cree,
3. To you by an an - gel, the Lord God made known
4. Most blest of all wom - en, you heard and be - lieved,
5. The an - gels re - joiced when you brought forth God's Son;
You reign now in splen - dor with Je - sus our King.
God willed you both vir - gin and moth - er to be.
The grace of the Spir - it, the gift of the Son.
Most blest in the fruit of your womb then con - ceived.
Your joy is the joy of all a - ges to come.
A - ve, A - ve, A - ve, Ma - ri - a.
A - ve, A - ve, Ma - ri - a.

6. Your child is the Savior, all hope lies in him:
He gives us new life and redeems us from sin.

7. In glory for ever now close to your Son,
All ages will praise you for all God has done.

Text: St. 1, Jeremiah Cummings, 1814-1866, alt.; St. 2-7, Brian Foley, b.1919, © 1971, Faber Music Ltd.
Tune: LOURDES HYMN, 11 11 with refrain; Grenoble, 1882

709 What Is This Place

1. What is this place where we are meet - ing? On - ly a
2. Words from a - far, stars that are fall - ing, Sparks that are
3. And we ac - cept bread at his ta - ble, Bro - ken and

house, the earth its floor, Walls and a roof shel - ter - ing
sown in us like seed. Names for our God, dreams, signs, and
shared, a liv - ing sign. Here in this world, dy - ing and

peo - ple, Win - dows for light, an o - pen door.
won - ders Sent from the past are all we need.
liv - ing, We are each oth - er's bread and wine.

Yet it be-comes a bod - y that lives When we are
We in this place re - mem - ber and speak A - gain what
This is the place where we can re - ceive What we need

gath - ered here, And know our God is near.
we have heard: God's free re - deem - ing word.
to in - crease: God's jus - tice and God's peace.

Text: *Zomaar een dak boven wat hoofden;* Huub Oosterhuis, b.1933; Tr. by David Smith, b.1933, © 1984, TEAM Publications
Tune: KOMT NU MET ZANG, 9 8 9 8 9 66; Valerius' *Neder-landtsche gedenck-klanck,* 1626; Harm. by Adrian Engels, b.1906

710 How Blessed Is This Place

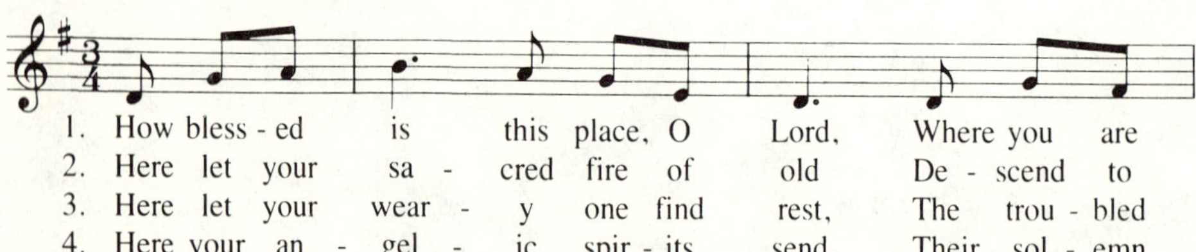
1. How bless - ed is this place, O Lord, Where you are
2. Here let your sa - cred fire of old De - scend to
3. Here let your wear - y one find rest, The trou - bled
4. Here your an - gel - ic spir - its send Their sol - emn

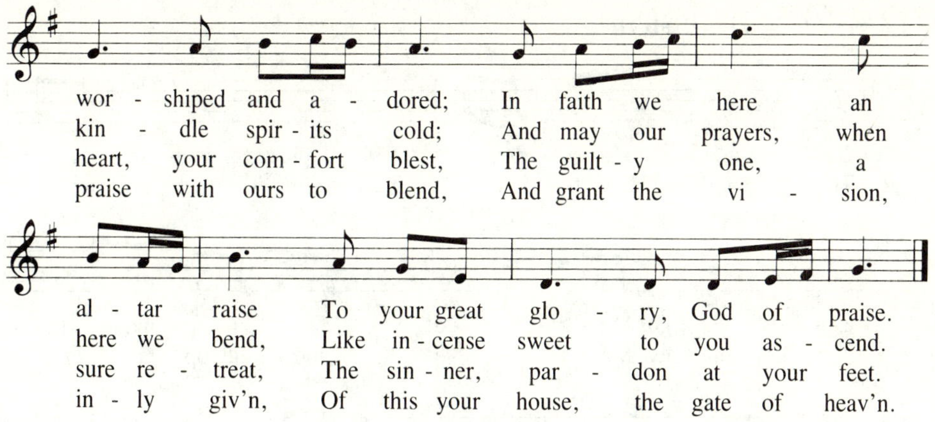
wor - shiped and a - dored; In faith we here an
kin - dle spir - its cold; And may our prayers, when
heart, your com - fort blest, The guilt - y one, a
praise with ours to blend, And grant the vi - sion,
al - tar raise To your great glo - ry, God of praise.
here we bend, Like in - cense sweet to you as - cend.
sure re - treat, The sin - ner, par - don at your feet.
in - ly giv'n, Of this your house, the gate of heav'n.

Text: Ernest E. Ryden, 1886-1981, alt., © Sts. 1-3, Lutheran Church in America, © St. 4, 1958, Service Book and Hymnal
Tune: O WALY WALY, LM; English; Harm. by Martin West, b.1929, © 1983, Hope Publishing Co.

Mary, How Lovely the Light of Your Glory 711

1. Mar - y, how love - ly the light of your glo - ry,
From Da - vid's house, roy - al daugh - ter you come,
Ho - li - er, high - er than an - gels in heav - en,
Ho - li - est, high - est through all God has done. 

2. Blest of all wom - en, both Vir - gin and Moth - er,
Fa - vored in grace for the Son whom you bore,
Christ is your Son whom all peo - ples must wor - ship,
Christ is your Son whom all an - gels a - dore.

3. Pray for us, plead for us, ex - iles in dark - ness,
Pray with us, pray - ing to Christ in our needs;
All pow'r is giv - en him here and in heav - en,
Christ ev - er lives for us and in - ter - cedes.

Text: Brian Foley, b.1919
Tune: CHANCE, 11 10 11 10; Colin Mawby, b.1936

712 O Sanctissima

1. O san - ctís - si - ma, O pi - ís - si - ma,
2. Tu so - lá - ti - um Et re - fú - gi - um,
Dul - cis vir - go Ma - rí - a! Ma - ter a - má - ta,
Vir - go ma - ter Ma - rí - a! Quid - quid op - tá - mus,
In - te - me - rá - ta, O - ra, o - ra pro no - bis.
Per te spe - rá - mus, O - ra, o - ra pro no - bis.

Text: St. 1, *Stimmen der Völker in Liedern,* 1807; St. 2, *Arundel Hymnal,* 1902
Tune: O DU FRÖLICHE, 55 7 55 7; Tattersall's *Improved Psalmody,* 1794

713 Ave Maria

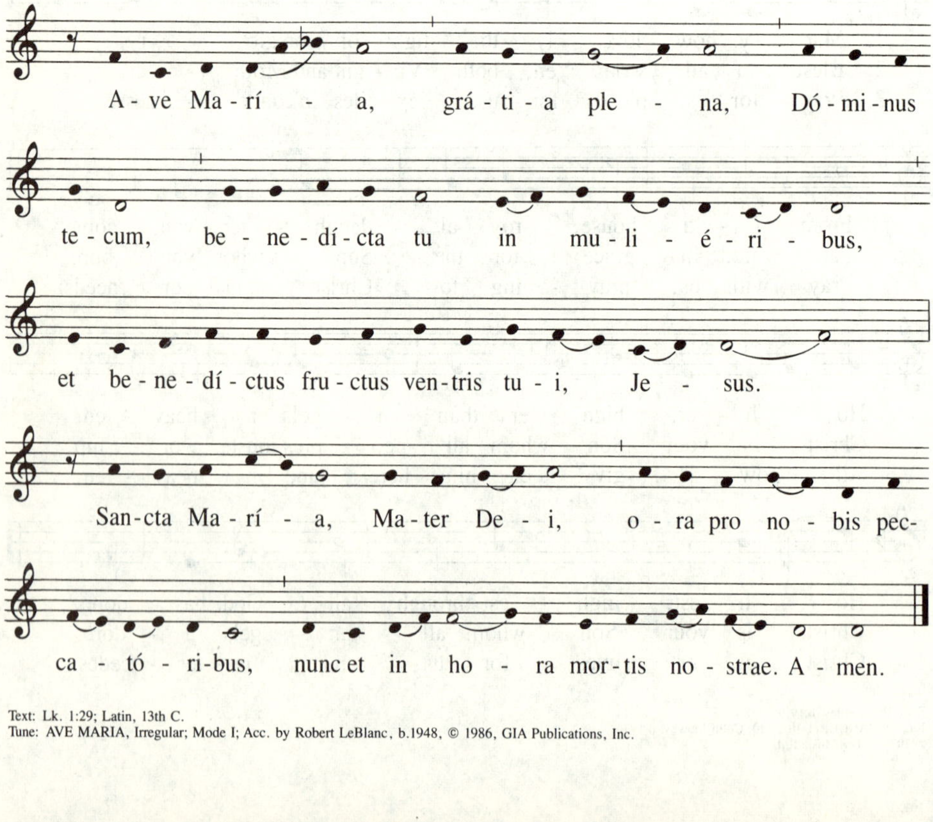

A - ve Ma - rí - a, grá - ti - a ple - na, Dó - mi - nus
te - cum, be - ne - dí - cta tu in mu - li - é - ri - bus,
et be - ne - dí - ctus fru - ctus ven - tris tu - i, Je - sus.
San - cta Ma - rí - a, Ma - ter De - i, o - ra pro no - bis pec-
ca - tó - ri - bus, nunc et in ho - ra mor - tis no - strae. A - men.

Text: Lk. 1:29; Latin, 13th C.
Tune: AVE MARIA, Irregular; Mode I; Acc. by Robert LeBlanc, b.1948, © 1986, GIA Publications, Inc.

Sing We of the Blessed Mother 714

1. Sing we of the bless - ed Moth - er
2. Sing we, too, of Mar - y's sor - rows,
3. Sing a - gain the joys of Mar - y
4. Sing the great - est joy of Mar - y

Who re - ceived the an - gel's word, And o - be - dient
Of the sword that pierced her through, When be - neath the
When she saw the ris - en Lord, And in prayer with
When on earth her work was done, And the Lord of

to the sum - mons Bore in love the in - fant Lord;
cross of Je - sus She his weight of suf - f'ring knew,
Christ's a - pos - tles, Wait - ed on his prom - ised word:
all cre - a - tion Brought her to his heav'n - ly home:

Sing we of the joys of Mar - y
Looked up - on her Son and Sav - ior
From on high the blaz - ing glo - ry
Vir - gin Moth - er, Mar - y bless - ed,

At whose breast that child was fed Who is Son of
Reign - ing from the aw - ful tree, Saw the price of
Of the Spir - it's pres - ence came, Heav'n - ly breath of
Raised on high and crowned with grace, May your Son, the

God e - ter - nal And the ev - er - last - ing Bread.
our re - demp - tion Paid to set the sin - ner free.
God's own be - ing, To - kened in the wind and flame.
world's re - deem - er, Grant us all to see his face.

Text: George B. Timms, b.1910, © 1975, Oxford University Press
Tune: OMNE DIE, 8 7 8 7 D; *Trier Gesängebuch,* 1695

715 Let Us with Joy Our Voices Raise

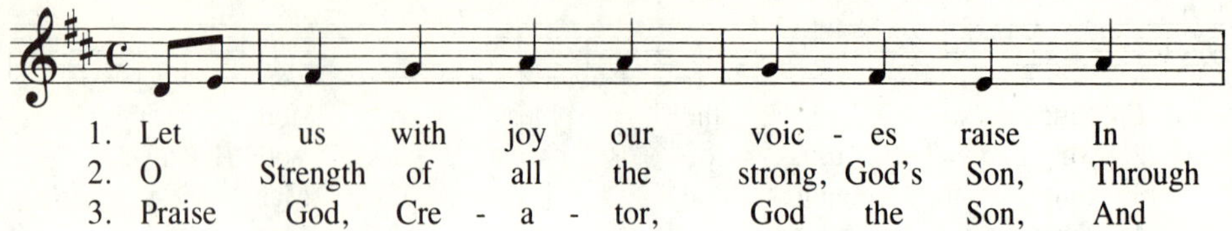
1. Let us with joy our voic - es raise In
2. O Strength of all the strong, God's Son, Through
3. Praise God, Cre - a - tor, God the Son, And

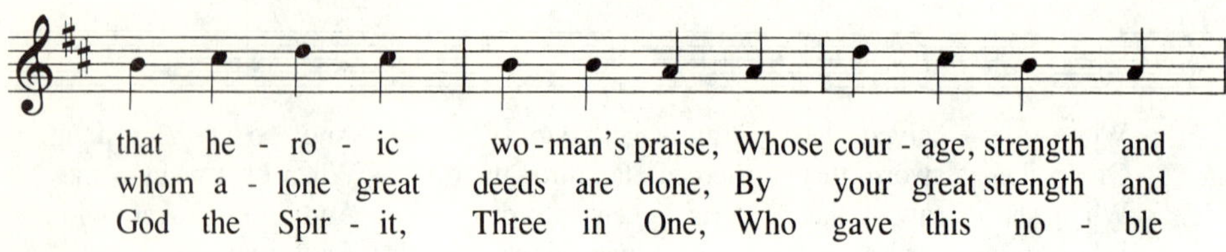
that he - ro - ic wo - man's praise, Whose cour - age, strength and
whom a - lone great deeds are done, By your great strength and
God the Spir - it, Three in One, Who gave this no - ble

ho - ly fame Have giv - en her an hon - ored name.
through her prayer May we bear wit - ness ev - 'ry - where.
wo - man grace A life of vir - tue to em - brace.

Text: *Fortem virili pectore;* Silvio Antoniano, 1540-1603; Tr. and St. 3 by Roger Nachtwey, b.1930, alt., © 1965, FEL Publications, Ltd.
Tune: EISENACH, LM; Johann H. Schein, 1586-1630; Harm. by J.S. Bach, 1685-1750

716 Let All on Earth Their Voices Raise

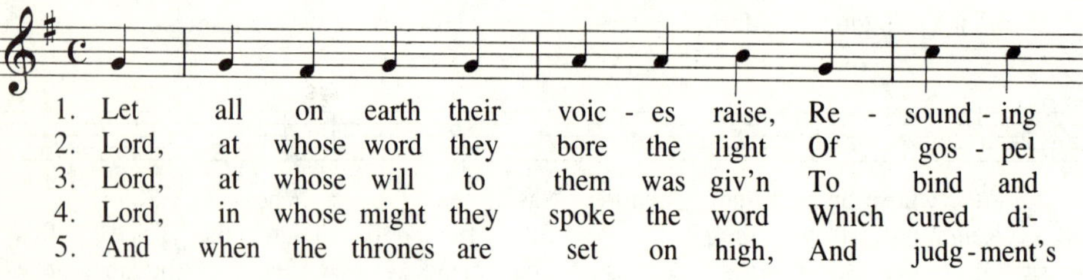
1. Let all on earth their voic - es raise, Re - sound - ing
2. Lord, at whose word they bore the light Of gos - pel
3. Lord, at whose will to them was giv'n To bind and
4. Lord, in whose might they spoke the word Which cured di-
5. And when the thrones are set on high, And judg - ment's

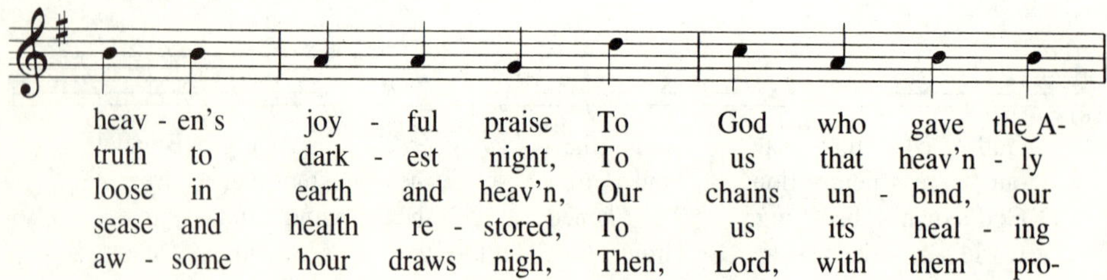
heav - en's joy - ful praise To God who gave the A-
truth to dark - est night, To us that heav'n - ly
loose in earth and heav'n, Our chains un - bind, our
sease and health re - stored, To us its heal - ing
aw - some hour draws nigh, Then, Lord, with them pro-

pos - tles grace To run on earth their glo - rious race.
light im - part, Make glad our eyes and cheer our heart.
sins un - do, And in our hearts your grace re - new.
pow'r pro - long, Sup - port the weak, con - firm the strong.
nounce us blest, And take us to your end - less rest.

Text: *Exsultet orbis gaudiis;* Latin, 10th C.; Tr. by Richard Mant, 1776-1848, alt.
Tune: TALLIS' CANON, LM; Thomas Tallis, c.1505-1585

This Is the Feast Day of the Lord's True Witness 717

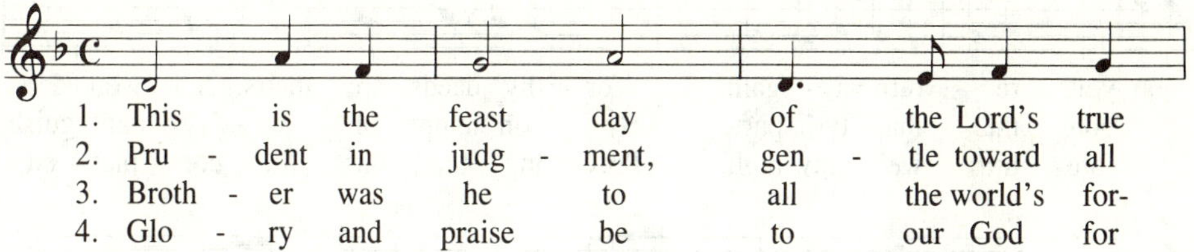
1. This is the feast day of the Lord's true
2. Pru - dent in judg - ment, gen - tle toward all
3. Broth - er was he to all the world's for-
4. Glo - ry and praise be to our God for

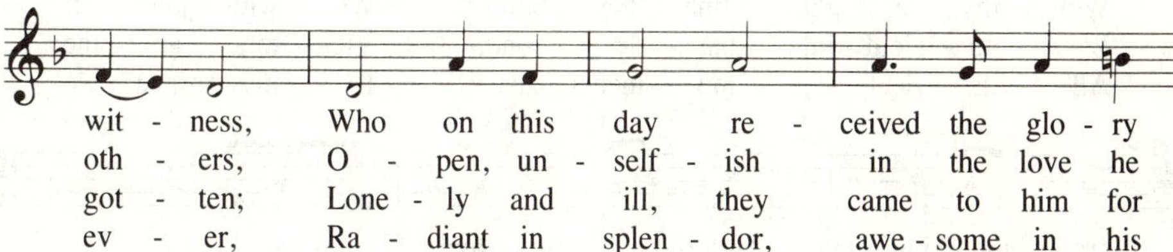
wit - ness, Who on this day re - ceived the glo - ry
oth - ers, O - pen, un - self - ish in the love he
got - ten; Lone - ly and ill, they came to him for
ev - er, Ra - diant in splen - dor, awe - some in his

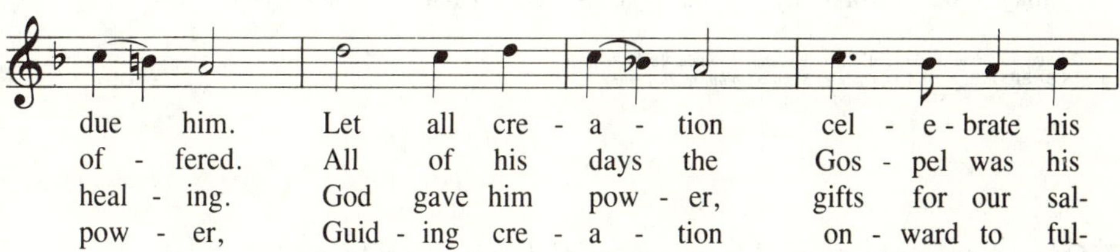
due him. Let all cre - a - tion cel - e - brate his
of - fered. All of his days the Gos - pel was his
heal - ing. God gave him pow - er, gifts for our sal-
pow - er, Guid - ing cre - a - tion on - ward to ful-

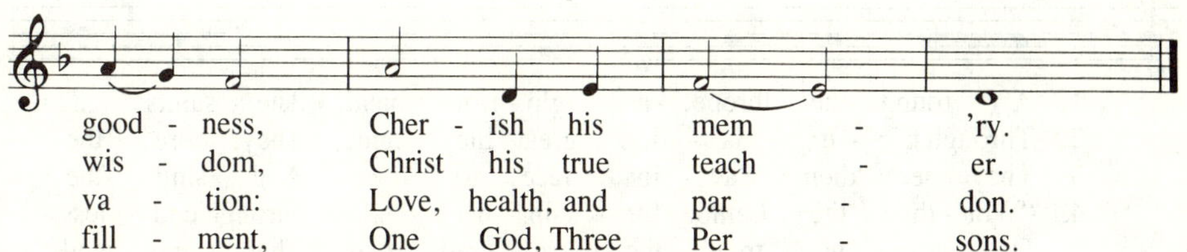
good - ness, Cher - ish his mem - 'ry.
wis - dom, Christ his true teach - er.
va - tion: Love, health, and par - don.
fill - ment, One God, Three Per - sons.

Text: *Iste confessor Domini, colentes;* Latin, 8th C.; Tr. by Peter J. Scagnelli, b.1949, ©
Tune: ISTE CONFESSOR, 11 11 11 5; Rouen Church Melody; Harm. by Carl Schalk, b.1929, © 1969, Condordia Publishing House

718 Blessed Feasts of Blessed Martyrs

1. Bless - ed feasts of bless - ed mar - tyrs, Ho - ly wom - en,
2. Faith pre - vail - ing, hope un - fail - ing, Lov - ing Christ with
3. There - fore, all that reign in glo - ry, Strong and sure with

ho - ly men, With our love and ad - mi - ra - tion, Greet we
sin - gle heart, Thus they, glo - rious and vic - to - rious, Brave - ly
Christ on high, Join to ours your sup - pli - ca - tion When be-

your re - turn a - gain. Wor - thy deeds are theirs, and won - ders,
bore the mar - tyr's part, By con - tempt of ev - 'ry an - guish,
fore him we draw nigh, Pray - ing that, this life com - plet - ed,

Wor - thy of the name they bore; We, with joy - ful
By un - yield - ing bat - tle done; Vic - tors at the
All its fleet - ing mo - ments past, By his grace we

praise and sing - ing, Hon - or them for ev - er - more.
last, they tri - umph, With the host of an - gels one.
may be wor - thy Of e - ter - nal bliss at last.

Text: *O beata beatorum;* Latin, 12th C.; Tr. by John M. Neale, 1818-1866, alt.
Tune: IN BABILONE, 8 7 8 7 D; *Oude en Nieuwe Hollanste Boerenlities,* c.1710

719 Around the Throne a Glorious Band

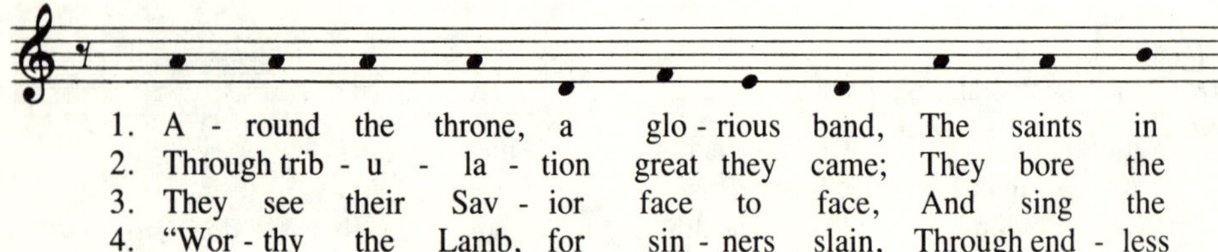

1. A - round the throne, a glo - rious band, The saints in
2. Through trib - u - la - tion great they came; They bore the
3. They see their Sav - ior face to face, And sing the
4. "Wor - thy the Lamb, for sin - ners slain, Through end - less
5. O may we tread the sa - cred road That saints and

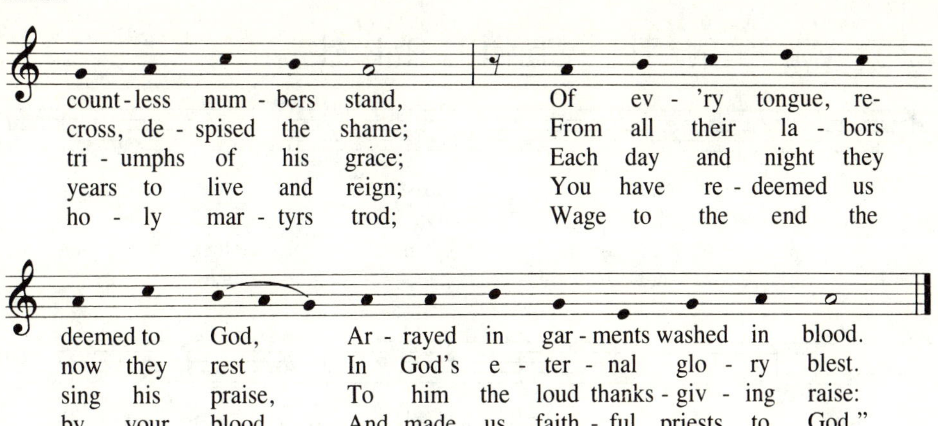
count-less num - bers stand, Of ev - 'ry tongue, re-
cross, de - spised the shame; From all their la - bors
tri - umphs of his grace; Each day and night they
years to live and reign; You have re - deemed us
ho - ly mar - tyrs trod; Wage to the end the
deemed to God, Ar - rayed in gar - ments washed in blood.
now they rest In God's e - ter - nal glo - ry blest.
sing his praise, To him the loud thanks - giv - ing raise:
by your blood, And made us faith - ful priests to God."
glo - rious strife And win, like them, a crown of life.

Text: Rowland Hill, 1744-1833
Tune: JESU DULCIS MEMORIA, LM; Model I; Acc. by Richard Proulx, b.1937, © 1975, GIA Publications, Inc.

Baptized in Water 720

1. Bap - tized in wa - ter, Sealed by the Spir - it,
2. Bap - tized in wa - ter, Sealed by the Spir - it,
3. Bap - tized in wa - ter, Sealed by the Spir - it,

Cleansed by the blood of Christ our King:
Dead in the tomb with Christ our King:
Marked with the sign of Christ our King:

Heirs of sal - va - tion, Trust-ing his prom - ise,
One with his ris - ing, Freed and for - giv - en,
Born of one Fa - ther, We are his chil - dren,

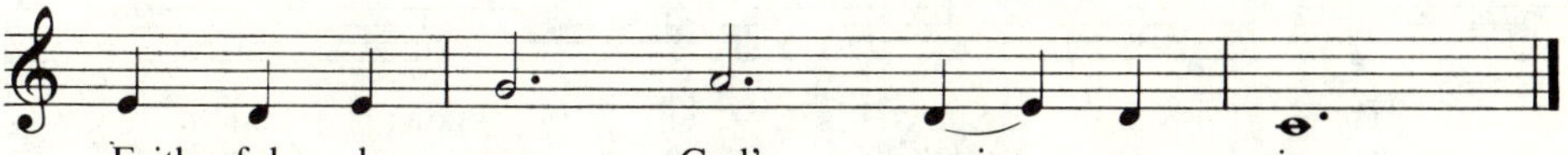

Faith - ful - ly now God's praise we sing.
Thank-ful - ly now God's praise we sing.
Joy - ful - ly now God's praise we sing.

Text: Michael A. Saward, b.1932, © 1982, Hope Publishing Co.
Tune: BUNESSAN, 5 5 8 D; Gaelic; Harm. by A. Gregory Murray, OSB, b.1905, ©

721 We Know That Christ Is Raised

1. We know that Christ is raised and
2. We share by wa - ter in his
3. The Fa - ther's splen - dor clothes the
4. A new cre - a - tion comes to

dies no more. Em - braced by death, he broke its
sav - ing death. Re - born, we share with him and
Son with life. The Spir - it's fis - sion shakes the
life and grows As Christ's new bod - y takes on

fear - ful hold, And our de - spair he turned to
East - er life As liv - ing mem - bers of our
Church of God. Bap - tized, we live with God the
flesh and blood. The u - ni - verse re - stored and

blaz - ing joy. Al - le - lu - ia!
Sav - ior Christ. Al - le - lu - ia!
Three in One. Al - le - lu - ia!
whole will sing: Al - le - lu - ia!

Text: Rom. 6:4,9; John B. Geyer, b.1932, ©
Tune: ENGELBERG, 10 10 10 with alleluia; Charles V. Stanford, 1852-1924

722 This Is the Spirit's Entry Now

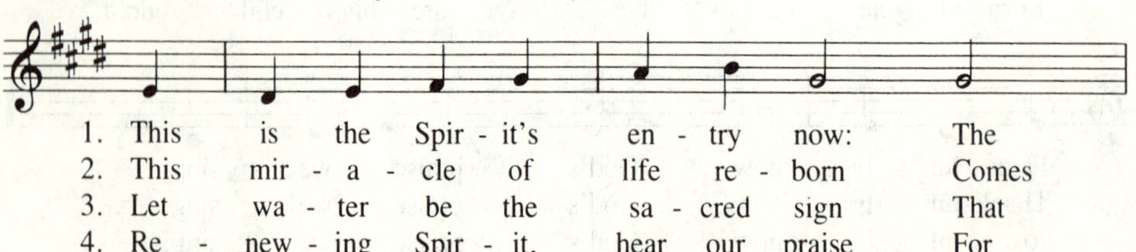
1. This is the Spir - it's en - try now: The
2. This mir - a - cle of life re - born Comes
3. Let wa - ter be the sa - cred sign That
4. Re - new - ing Spir - it, hear our praise For

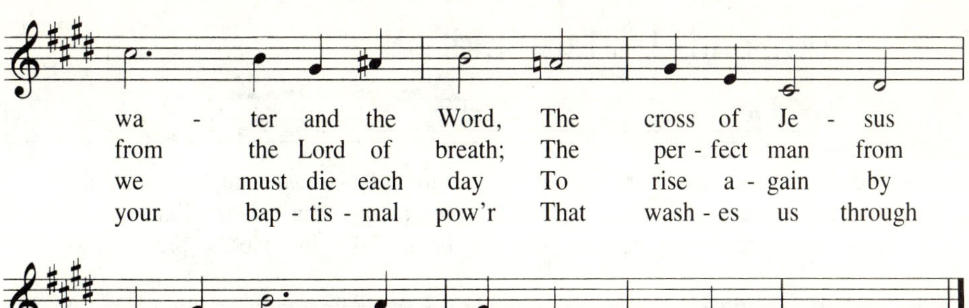
wa - ter and the Word, The cross of Je - sus
from the Lord of breath; The per - fect man from
we must die each day To rise a - gain by
your bap - tis - mal pow'r That wash - es us through

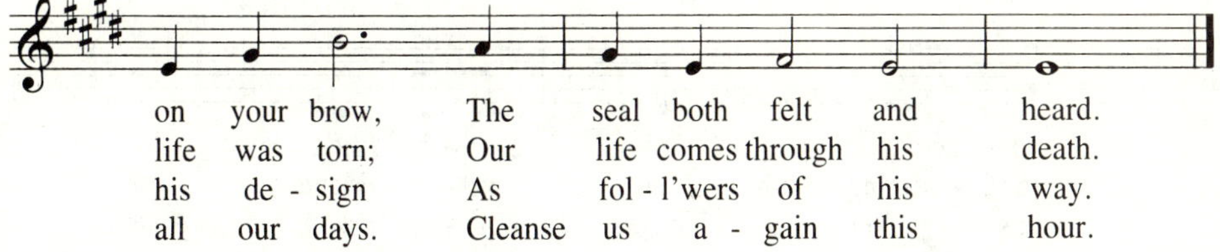
on your brow, The seal both felt and heard.
life was torn; Our life comes through his death.
his de - sign As fol - l'wers of his way.
all our days. Cleanse us a - gain this hour.

Text: Thomas E. Herbranson, b.1933, alt., © 1978
Tune: PERRY, CM; Leo Sowerby, 1895-1968, © 1964, Abingdon Press

Come and Let Us Drink of That New River 723

1. Come and let us drink of that new riv - er,
2. Now the world has bright il - lu - mi - na - tion,
3. Yes - ter - day with you in bur - ial ly - ing,

Not from bar - ren rock di - vine - ly poured,
Heav - en and all things up - on the earth:
Now with you in tri - umph I a - rise,

But the fount of life that springs for ev - er
Ris - en is the God of all cre - a - tion,
Yes - ter - day the part - ner of your dy - ing,

From the sa - cred bod - y of our Lord.
Christ the Lord who gave cre - a - tion birth.
Raise me with you far be - yond the skies.

Text: Δεῦτε Πόωα Πίωμεν; John of Damascus, c.675-746; Tr. by John M. Neale, 1818-1866, adapt. by Anthony G. Petti, 1932-1985, © 1971, Faber Music Ltd.
Tune: NEW RIVER 10 9 10 9; Kenneth D. Smith, b.1928

724 God Sends Us His Spirit

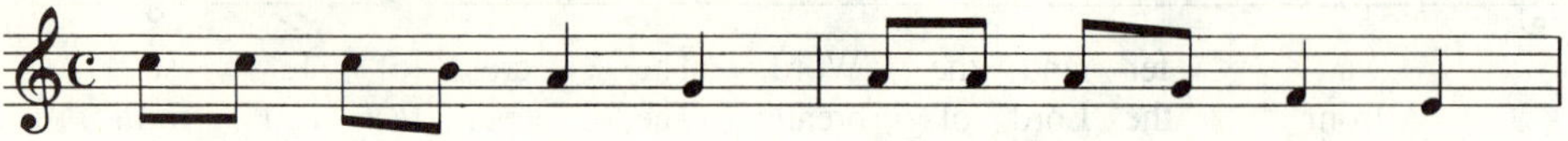

1. God sends us his Spir - it to be - friend and help us.
2. Dark-ened roads are clear - er, heav - y bur - dens light - er,
3. Now we are God's peo - ple, bond - ed by God's pres - ence,

Re - cre - ate and guide us, Spir - it - Friend.
When we're walk - ing with our Spir - it - Friend.
A - gents of God's pur - pose, Spir - it - Friend.

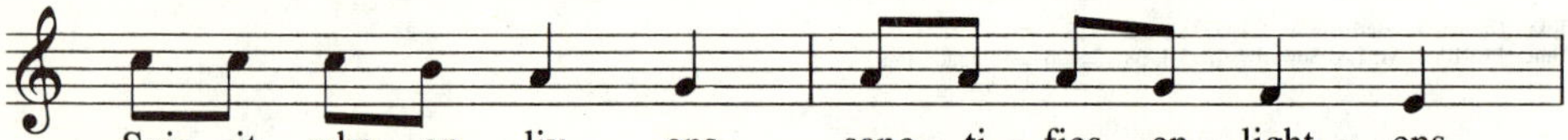

Spir - it who en - liv - ens, sanc - ti - fies, en - light - ens,
Now we need not fear the pow - ers of the dark - ness.
Lead us for - ward ev - er, slip - ping back-ward nev - er,

Sets us free, is now our Spir - it - Friend.
None can o - ver - come our Spir - it - Friend.
To your re - made world, our Spir - it - Friend.

Sung three times after each stanza. *Hand claps*

Spir - it of our Mak - er, Spir - it - Friend.
Spir - it of our Je - su, Spir - it - Friend.
Spir - it of God's peo - ple, Spir - it - Friend.

Text: Tom Colvin, b.1925
Tune: NATOMAH, 12 9 12 9 with refrain; Gonja Folk Song; Adapt. by Tom Colvin, b.1925

725 O Breathe on Me, O Breath of God

1. O breathe on me, O breath of God, Fill me
2. O breathe on me, O breath of God, Un - til
3. O breathe on me, O breath of God, My will
4. O breathe on me, O breath of God: So shall

3
with life a - new, That I may love the
my heart is pure; Un - til my will is
to yours in - cline, Un - til this self - ish
I nev - er die, But live with you the
things you love, And do what you would do.
one with yours, To do and to en - dure.
part of me Glows with your fire di - vine.
per - fect life Of your e - ter - ni - ty.

Text: Edwin Hatch, 1835-1889
Tune: ST. COLUMBA, CM; Gaelic; Harm. by A. Gregory Murray, OSB, b.1905, ©

I Come with Joy to Meet My Lord 726

1. I come with joy to meet my Lord, For-
2. I come with Chris - tians far and near To
3. As Christ breaks bread and bids us share Each
4. And thus with joy we meet our Lord. His
5. To - geth - er met, to - geth - er bound, We'll
giv - en, loved, and free, In awe and won - der
find, as all are fed, The new com - mu - ni-
proud di - vi - sion ends. The love that made us
pres - ence, al - ways near, Is in such friend - ship
go our dif - f'rent ways, And as his peo - ple
to re - call His life laid down for me.
ty of love In Christ's com - mu - nion bread.
makes us one, And strang - ers now are friends.
bet - ter known; We see and praise him here.
in the world, We'll live and speak his praise.

Text: Brian Wren, b.1936, © 1971, Hope Publishing Co.
Tune: LAND OF REST, CM; American; Harm. by Annabel M. Buchanan, b.1888, © 1938, 1966, J. Fisher and Bro.

727 Let Us Break Bread Together

1. Let us break bread to-geth-er on our knees;
Let us break bread to-geth-er on our knees;
When I fall on my knees, With my face to the ris-ing sun, O Lord, have mer-cy on me.

2. Let us drink wine to-geth-er on our knees;
Let us drink wine to-geth-er on our knees;

3. Let us praise God to-geth-er on our knees;
Let us praise God to-geth-er on our knees;

Text: American Folk Hymn
Tune: LET US BREAK BREAD, 10 10 6 8 7; American Folk Hymn; Harm. by David Hurd, b.1950,

728 Shepherd of Souls

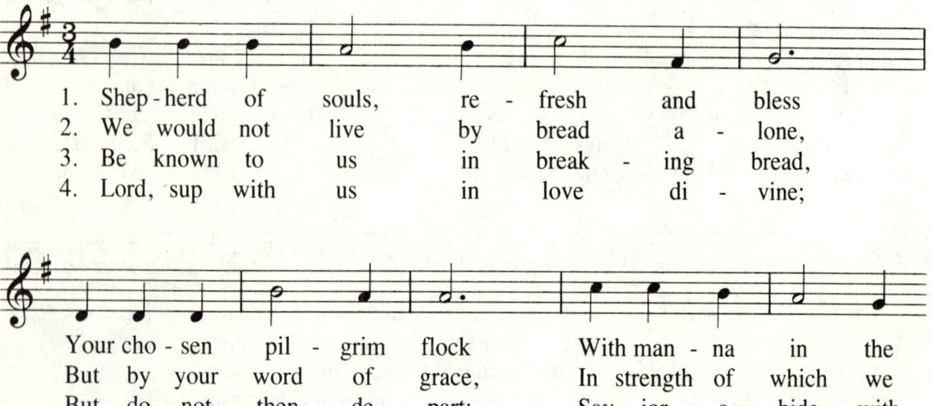
1. Shep-herd of souls, re-fresh and bless
2. We would not live by bread a-lone,
3. Be known to us in break-ing bread,
4. Lord, sup with us in love di-vine;
Your cho-sen pil-grim flock With man-na in the
But by your word of grace, In strength of which we
But do not then de-part; Sav-ior, a-bide with
Your Bod-y and your Blood, That liv-ing bread, that

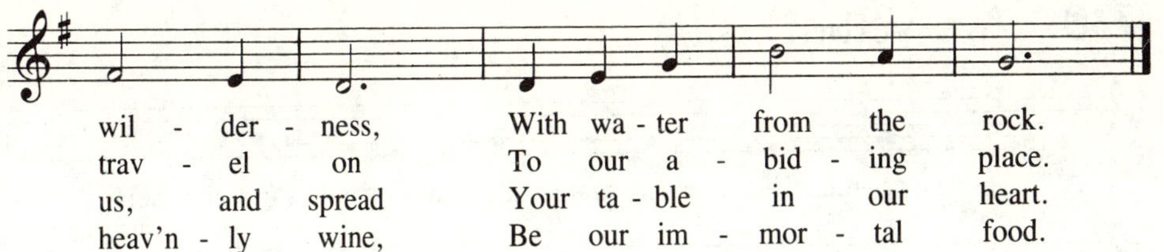
wil - der - ness, With wa - ter from the rock.
trav - el on To our a - bid - ing place.
us, and spread Your ta - ble in our heart.
heav'n - ly wine, Be our im - mor - tal food.

Text: James Montgomery, 1771-1854, alt.
Tune: ST. AGNES, CM; John B. Dykes, 1823-1876; Harm. by Richard Proulx, b.1937, © 1986, GIA Publications, Inc.

O Food of Exiles Lowly 729

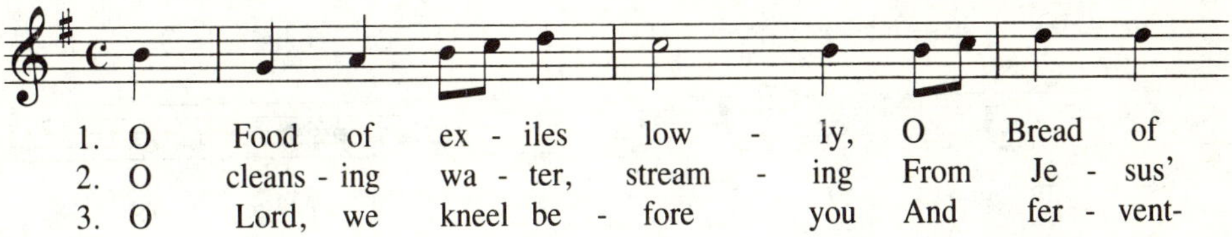

1. O Food of ex - iles low - ly, O Bread of
2. O cleans - ing wa - ter, stream - ing From Je - sus'
3. O Lord, we kneel be - fore you And fer - vent-

an - gels ho - ly, O Man - na from on high! We
side, re - deem - ing All those of A - dam's race! O
ly a - dore you, All hid be - neath this bread. But

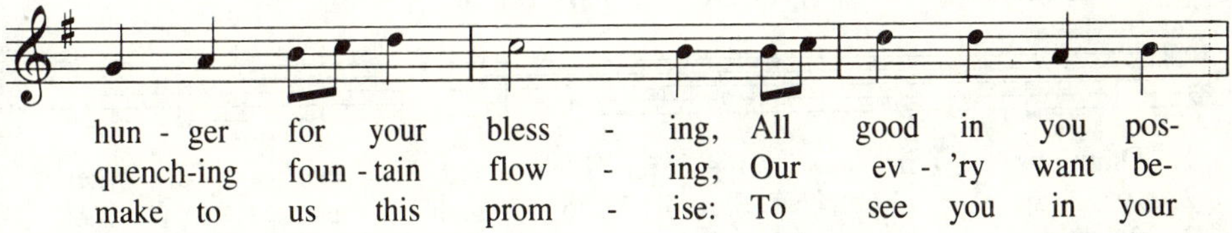

hun - ger for your bless - ing, All good in you pos-
quench-ing foun - tain flow - ing, Our ev - 'ry want be-
make to us this prom - ise: To see you in your

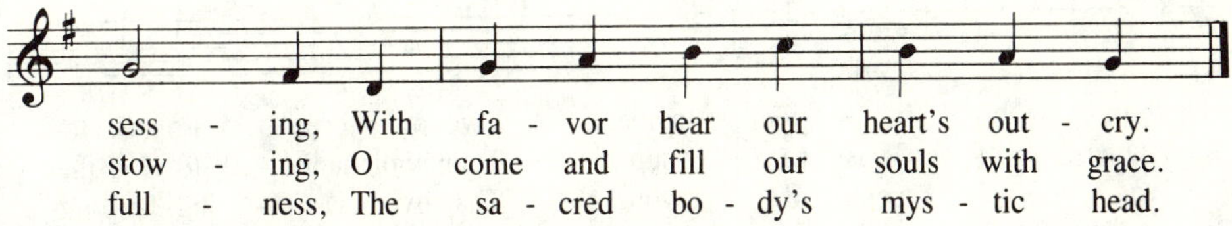

sess - ing, With fa - vor hear our heart's out - cry.
stow - ing, O come and fill our souls with grace.
full - ness, The sa - cred bo - dy's mys - tic head.

Text: *O esca viatorum; Mainz Gesangbuch,* 1661; Tr. by M. Owen Lee, CSB, b.1930
Tune: INNSBRUCK, 77 6 77 8; Heinrich Isaak, c.1460-c.1527; Harm. by J.S. Bach, 1685-1750

730 Ave Verum

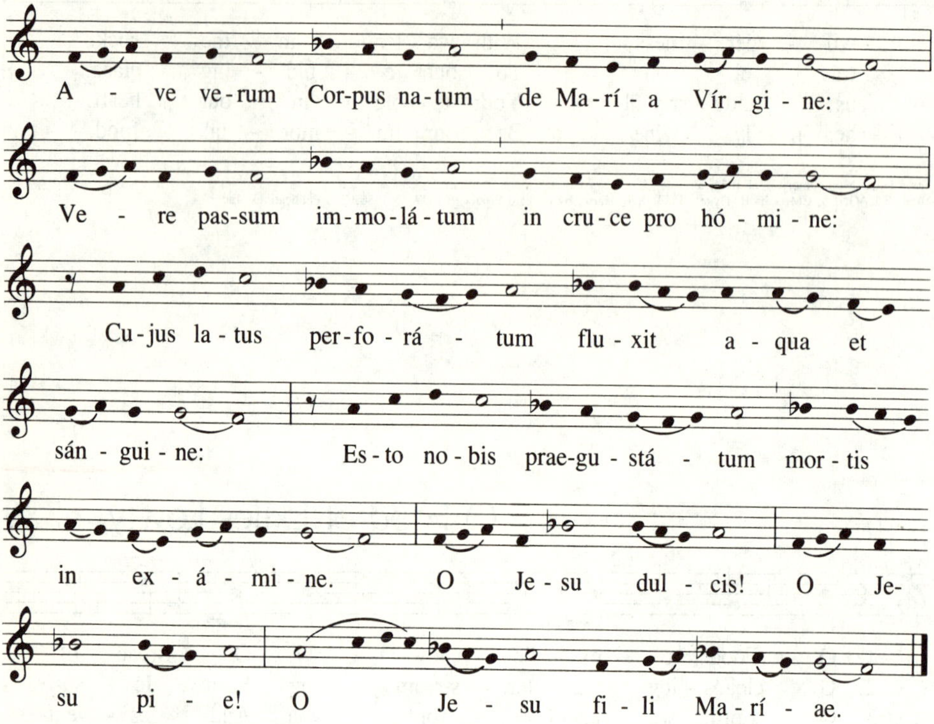

A - ve ve-rum Cor-pus na-tum de Ma-rí - a Vír - gi - ne:

Ve - re pas-sum im-mo-lá-tum in cru-ce pro hó - mi - ne:

Cu-jus la-tus per-fo - rá - tum flu - xit a - qua et

sán - gui - ne: Es-to no-bis prae-gu - stá - tum mor-tis

in ex - á - mi-ne. O Je - su dul - cis! O Je-

su pi - e! O Je - su fi - li Ma-rí - ae.

Text: Ascr. to Innocent VI, d.1362
Tune: AVE VERUM, Irregular; Mode VI; Acc. by Robert LeBlanc, b.1948,

731 Draw Us in the Spirit's Tether

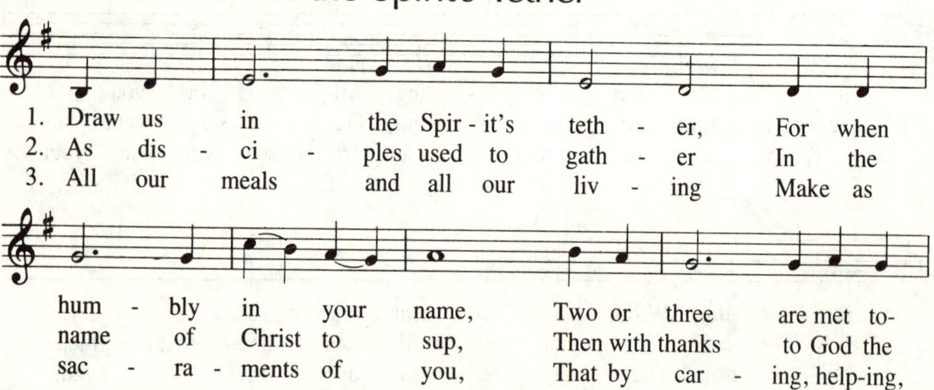
1. Draw us in the Spir - it's teth - er, For when
2. As dis - ci - ples used to gath - er In the
3. All our meals and all our liv - ing Make as
hum - bly in your name, Two or three are met to-
name of Christ to sup, Then with thanks to God the
sac - ra - ments of you, That by car - ing, help-ing,

geth - er, You are in the midst of them;
Fa - ther Break the bread and bless the cup,
giv - ing, We may be dis - ci - ples true.
Al - le - lu - ia! Al - le - lu - ia!
Al - le - lu - ia! Al - le - lu - ia!
Al - le - lu - ia! Al - le - lu - ia!
Touch we now your gar - ment's hem.
So now bind our friend - ship up.
We will serve with faith a - new.

Text: Percy Dearmer, 1867-1936, alt., © Oxford University Press
Tune: UNION SEMINARY, 8 7 8 7 44 7; Harold Friedell, 1905-1958, © 1957, H.W. Gray Co., Inc.; Harm. by Jet Turner, 1928-1984, © Christian Board of Education

Draw Near and Take the Body of Your Lord 732

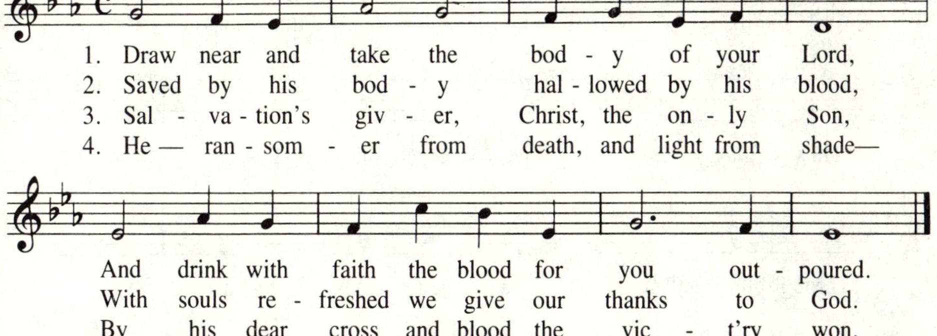
1. Draw near and take the bod - y of your Lord,
2. Saved by his bod - y hal - lowed by his blood,
3. Sal - va - tion's giv - er, Christ, the on - ly Son,
4. He — ran - som - er from death, and light from shade—
And drink with faith the blood for you out - poured.
With souls re - freshed we give our thanks to God.
By his dear cross and blood the vic - t'ry won.
Now gives his ho - ly grace his saints to aid.

5. Let us approach
 with faithful hearts sincere,
 And take the pledges
 of salvation here.

6. The Lord in this world
 rules his saints, and shields,
 To all believers
 life eternal yields:

7. With heav'nly bread makes
 those who hunger whole,
 Gives living waters
 to the thirsting soul.

8. Before your presence, Lord,
 all people bow.
 In this your feast of love
 be with us now.

Text: *Sancti, venite, Christe corpus sumite;* Latin, 7th C.; Tr. by John M. Neale, 1818-1866, alt.
Tune: COENA DOMINI, 10 10; Arthur S. Sullivan, 1842-1900

733 At That First Eucharist

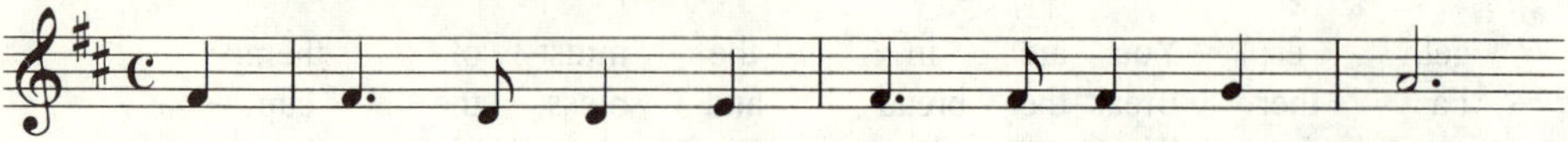

1. At that first Eu - cha - rist be - fore you died,
2. For all your church, O Lord, we in - ter - cede;
3. We pray for those who wan - der from the fold;

O Lord, you prayed that all be one in you;
O make our lack of char - i - ty to cease;
O bring them back, Good Shep - herd of the sheep,

At this our Eu - cha - rist a - gain pre - side,
Draw us the near - er each to each we plead,
Back to the faith which saints be - lieved of old,

And in our hearts your law of love re - new.
By draw - ing all to you, O Prince of Peace.
Back to the Church which still that faith does keep.

Thus may we all one Bread, one Bod - y be;
Through this blest Sac - ra - ment of U - ni - ty. 

Text: William H. Turton, 1859-1938, alt.
Tune: UNDE ET MEMORES, 10 10 10 10 with refrain; William H. Monk, 1823-1889, alt.

734 Eat This Bread

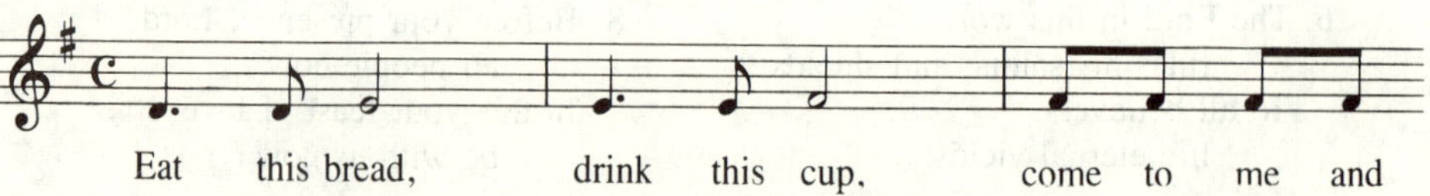
Eat this bread, drink this cup, come to me and

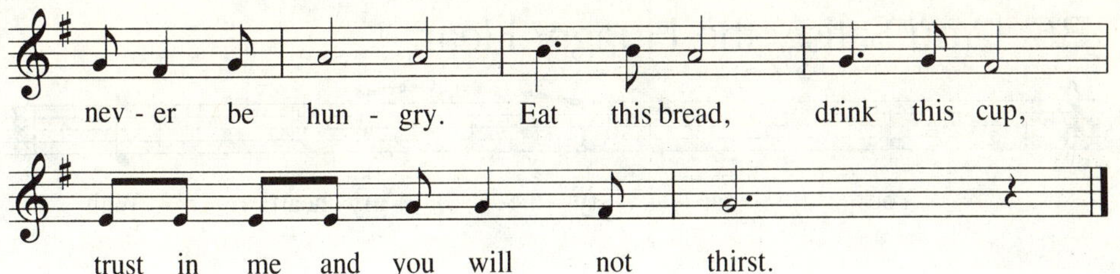
nev - er be hun - gry. Eat this bread, drink this cup,
trust in me and you will not thirst.

Text: John 6; Adapted by Robert J. Batastini, b.1942 and the Taizé Community, 1984
Tune: Jacques Berthier, b.1923

I Received the Living God 735

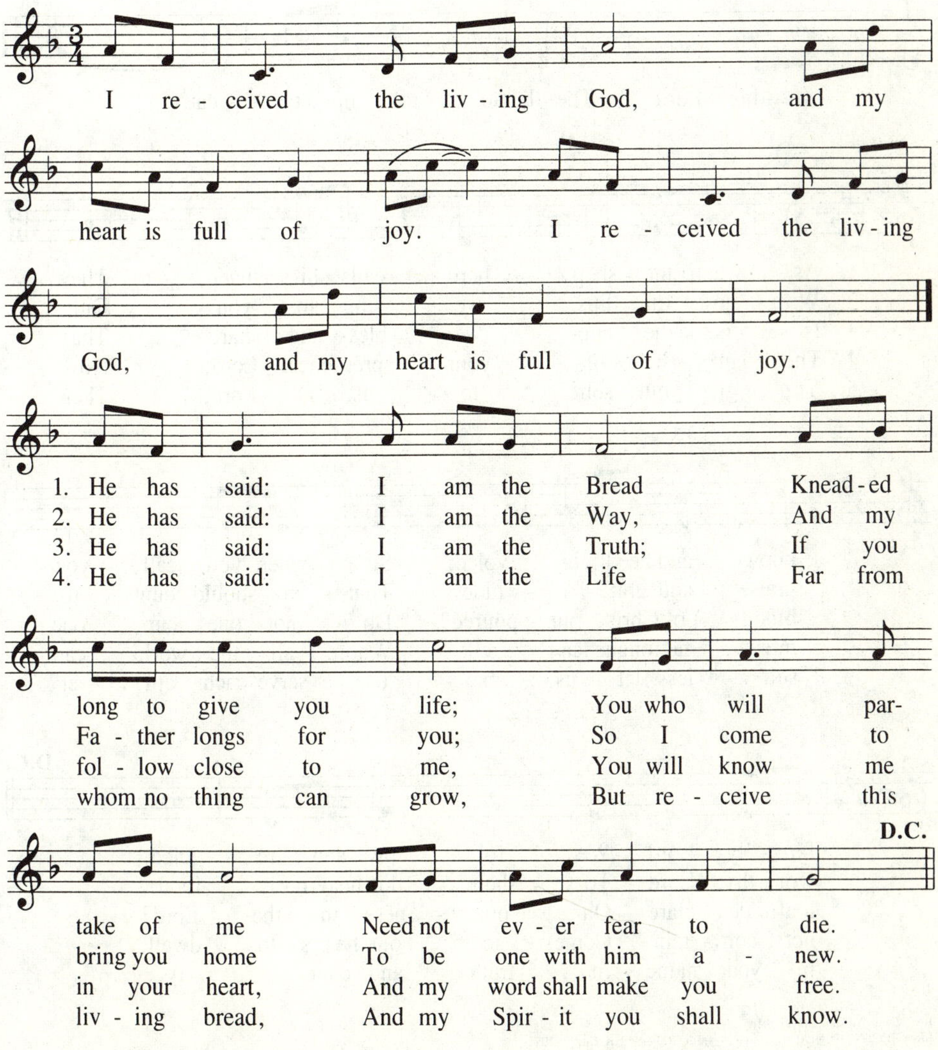

I re - ceived the liv - ing God, and my heart is full of joy. I re - ceived the liv - ing God, and my heart is full of joy.

1. He has said: I am the Bread Knead - ed long to give you life; You who will par- take of me Need not ev - er fear to die.
2. He has said: I am the Way, And my Fa - ther longs for you; So I come to bring you home To be one with him a - new.
3. He has said: I am the Truth; If you fol - low close to me, You will know me in your heart, And my word shall make you free.
4. He has said: I am the Life Far from whom no thing can grow, But re - ceive this liv - ing bread, And my Spir - it you shall know.

D.C.

Text: Anonymous
Tune: LIVING GOD, 7 7 7 7 with refrain; Anonymous; Harm. by Richard Proulx, b.1937,

736 You Satisfy the Hungry Heart

You sat - is - fy the hun - gry heart With

gift of fin - est wheat; Come give to us, O

sav - ing Lord, The bread of life to eat.

1. As when the shep - herd calls his sheep, They
2. With joy - ful lips we sing to you Our
3. Is not the cup we bless and share The
4. The mys - t'ry of your pres - ence, Lord, No
5. You give your - self to us, O Lord; Then

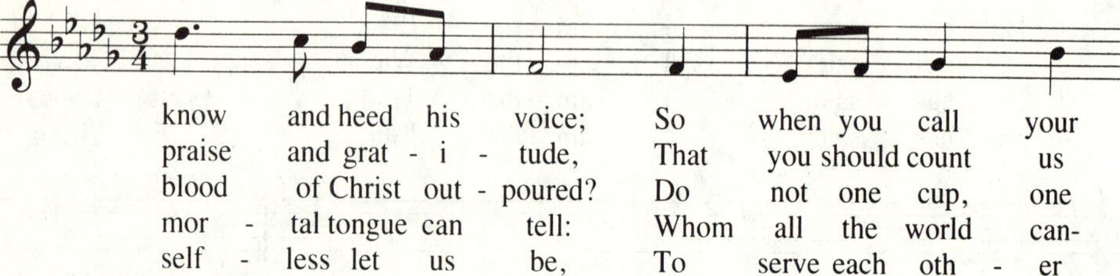
know and heed his voice; So when you call your
praise and grat - i - tude, That you should count us
blood of Christ out - poured? Do not one cup, one
mor - tal tongue can tell: Whom all the world can-
self - less let us be, To serve each oth - er

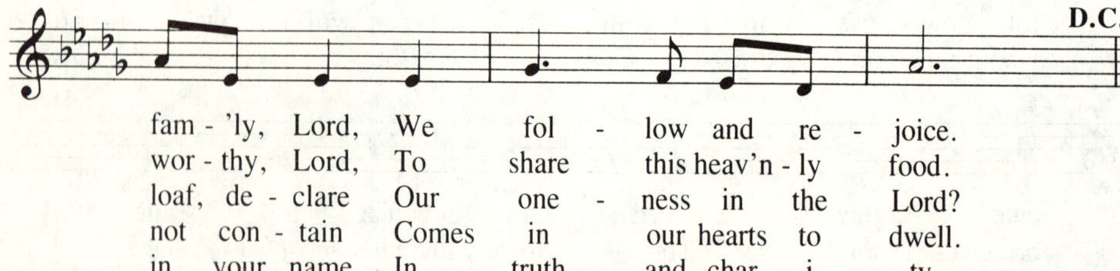
D.C.
fam - 'ly, Lord, We fol - low and re - joice.
wor - thy, Lord, To share this heav'n - ly food.
loaf, de - clare Our one - ness in the Lord?
not con - tain Comes in our hearts to dwell.
in your name In truth and char - i - ty.

Text: Omer Westendorf, b.1916
Tune: BICENTENNIAL, CM with refrain: Robert E. Kreutz, b.1922

Alleluia! Sing to Jesus 737

1. Al - le - lu - ia! sing to Je - sus! His the scep - ter, his the throne; Al - le - lu - ia! his the tri - umph, His the vic - to - ry a - lone; Hark! the songs of peace - ful Zi - on Thun - der like a might - y flood; Je - sus out of ev - 'ry na - tion Has re - deemed us by his blood.
2. Al - le - lu - ia! not as or - phans Are we left in sor - row now; Al - le - lu - ia! he is near us, Faith be - lieves, nor ques - tions how: Though the cloud from sight re - ceived him, When the for - ty days were o'er, Shall our hearts for- get his prom - ise, "I am with you ev - er - more"?
3. Al - le - lu - ia! Bread of An - gels, Here on earth our food, our stay! Al - le - lu - ia! here the sin - ful Flee to you from day to day: In - ter - ces - sor, friend of sin - ners, Earth's re- deem - er, plead for me, Where the songs of all the sin - less Sweep a - cross the crys - tal sea.
4. Al - le - lu - ia! King e - ter - nal, You the Lord of lords we own; Al - le - lu - ia! born of Ma - ry, Earth your foot stool, heav'n your throne: You, with - in the veil, have en - tered, Robed in flesh, our great high priest; Here on earth both priest and vic - tim In the eu - cha - ris - tic feast.

Text: Rev. 5:9; William C. Dix, 1837-1898
Tune: HYFRYDOL, 8 7 8 7 D; Rowland H. Prichard, 1811-1887

738 I Am the Bread of Life

1. I am the Bread of life. You who come to me shall not hunger; and who believe in me shall not thirst. No one can come to me unless the Father beckons.
2. The bread that I will give is my flesh for the life of the world, and if you eat of this bread, you shall live forever, you shall live for-ever.
3. Unless you eat of the flesh of the Son of Man and drink of his blood, and drink of his blood, you shall not have life within you.
4. I am the Resurrection, I am the life. If you believe in me, even though you die, you shall live for ever.
5. Yes, Lord, I believe that you are the Christ, the Son of God, Who have come into the world.
And I will raise you up, and I will raise you up, and I will raise you up on the last day.

Text: John 6; Suzanne Toolan, SM, b.1927
Tune: BREAD OF LIFE, Irregular with refrain; Suzanne Toolan, SM, b.1927, © 1966, GIA Publications, Inc.

Lord of the Living 739

1. Lord of the liv - ing, in your name as - sem - bled,
2. Help us to treas - ure all that will re - mind us
3. May we, when - ev - er tempt - ed to de - jec - tion,
4. Lord, you can lift us from the grave of sor - row
We join to thank you for the life re - mem - bered.
Of the en - rich - ment in the days be - hind us.
Strong - ly re - cap - ture thoughts of res - ur - rec - tion.
In - to the pres - ence of your own to - mor - row:
Fa - ther, have mer - cy, to your chil - dren giv - ing
Your love has set us in the gen - er - a - tions,
You gave us Je - sus to de - feat our sad - ness
Give to your peo - ple for the day's af - flic - tion
Hope in be - liev - ing.
God of cre - a - tion.
With East - er glad - ness.
Your ben - e - dic - tion.

Tune: CHRISTE SANCTORUM, 11 11 11 5; *Paris Antiphoner,* 1681

740 O Lord, You Died That All Might Live

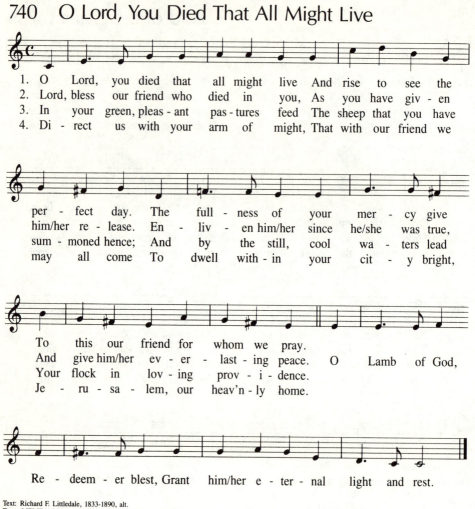

1. O Lord, you died that all might live And rise to see the
2. Lord, bless our friend who died in you, As you have giv - en
3. In your green, pleas - ant pas - tures feed The sheep that you have
4. Di - rect us with your arm of might, That with our friend we

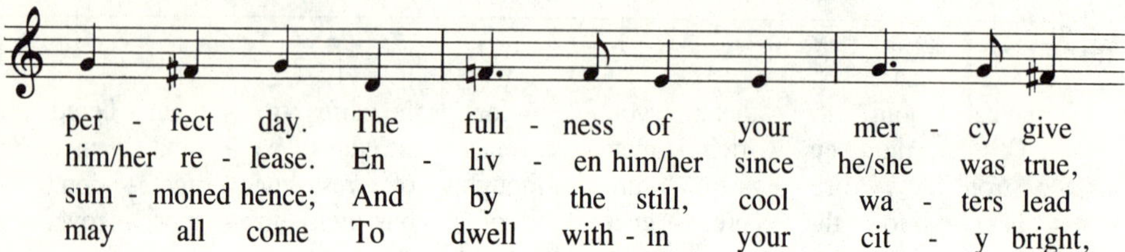

per - fect day. The full - ness of your mer - cy give
him/her re - lease. En - liv - en him/her since he/she was true,
sum - moned hence; And by the still, cool wa - ters lead
may all come To dwell with - in your cit - y bright,

To this our friend for whom we pray.
And give him/her ev - er - last - ing peace. O Lamb of God,
Your flock in lov - ing prov - i - dence.
Je - ru - sa - lem, our heav'n - ly home.

Re - deem - er blest, Grant him/her e - ter - nal light and rest.

Text: Richard F. Littledale, 1833-1890, alt.
Tune: MELITA, LM, with refrain; John B. Dykes, 1823-1876

741 Let Saints on Earth in Concert Sing

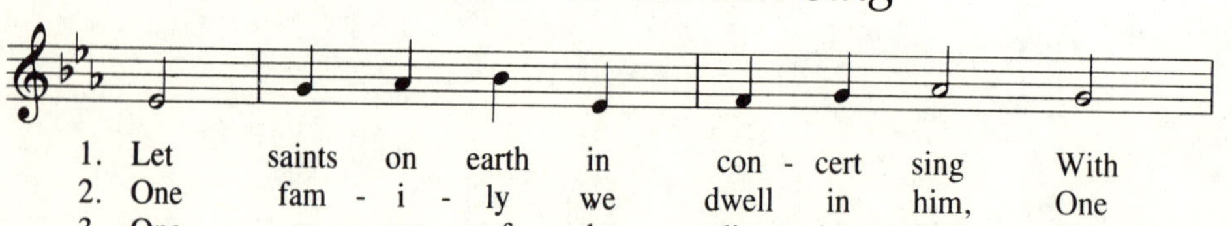

1. Let saints on earth in con - cert sing With
2. One fam - i - ly we dwell in him, One
3. One ar - my of the liv - ing God, To
4. E'en now by faith we join our hands With
5. Je - sus, be now our con - stant guide; Then,

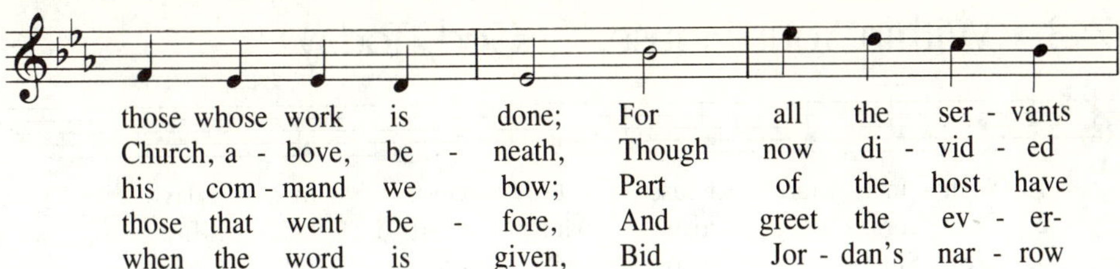
those whose work is done; For all the ser - vants
Church, a - bove, be - neath, Though now di - vid - ed
his com - mand we bow; Part of the host have
those that went be - fore, And greet the ev - er-
when the word is given, Bid Jor - dan's nar - row

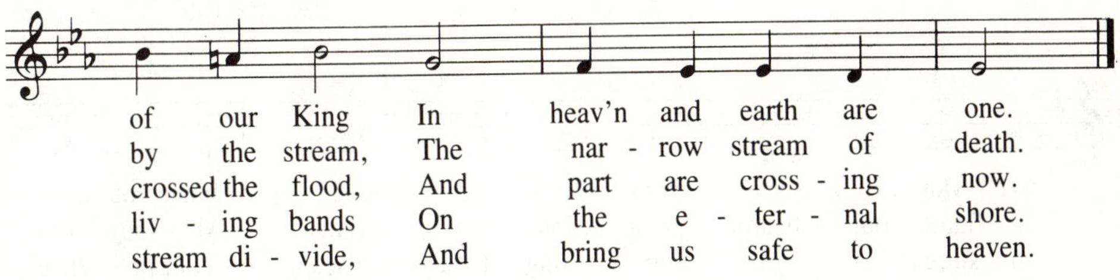
of our King In heav'n and earth are one.
by the stream, The nar - row stream of death.
crossed the flood, And part are cross - ing now.
liv - ing bands On the e - ter - nal shore.
stream di - vide, And bring us safe to heaven.

Text: Charles Wesley, 1707-1788
Tune: DUNDEE, CM; *Scottish Psalter, 1615*

May the Grace of Christ Our Savior 742

1. May the grace of Christ our Sav - ior And the
2. So they may a - bide in un - ion With each
3. Now with all the saints in heav - en Thanks and

Fa - ther's bound - less love, With the Ho - ly
oth - er and the Lord, And pos - sess, in
prais - es do we sing; Fa - ther, Son, and

Spir - it's fa - vor Rest up - on them from a - bove.
blest com - mun - ion, Joys which earth can - not af - ford.
Ho - ly Spir - it, Three in One, our Tri - une King.

Text: 2 Cor. 13-14; St. 1-2, John Newton, 1725-1807; St. 3, Adapt. by Carroll T. Andrews, b.1918, © 1971, GIA Publications, Inc.
Tune: STUTTGART, 8 7 8 7; Christian F. Witt, 1660-1716; Harm. by Kenneth D. Smith, b.1928, © National Christian Education Council

743 Within Your House, O God, Today

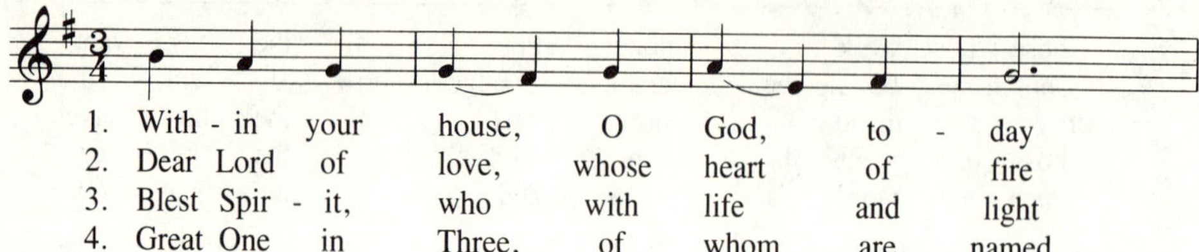
1. With - in your house, O God, to - day
2. Dear Lord of love, whose heart of fire
3. Blest Spir - it, who with life and light
4. Great One in Three, of whom are named

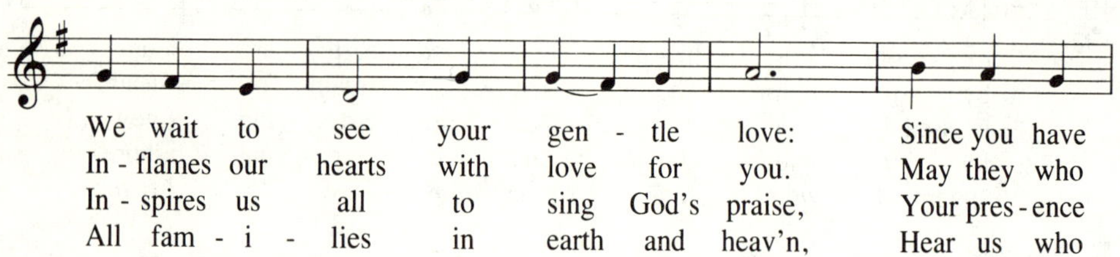
We wait to see your gen - tle love: Since you have
In - flames our hearts with love for you. May they who
In - spires us all to sing God's praise, Your pres - ence
All fam - i - lies in earth and heav'n, Hear us who

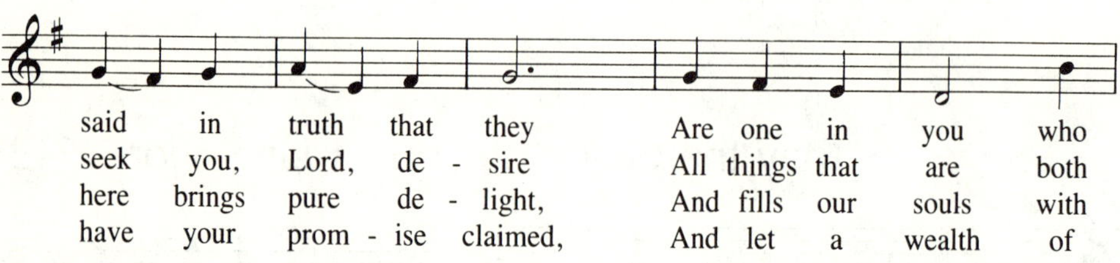
said in truth that they Are one in you who
seek you, Lord, de - sire All things that are both
here brings pure de - light, And fills our souls with
have your prom - ise claimed, And let a wealth of

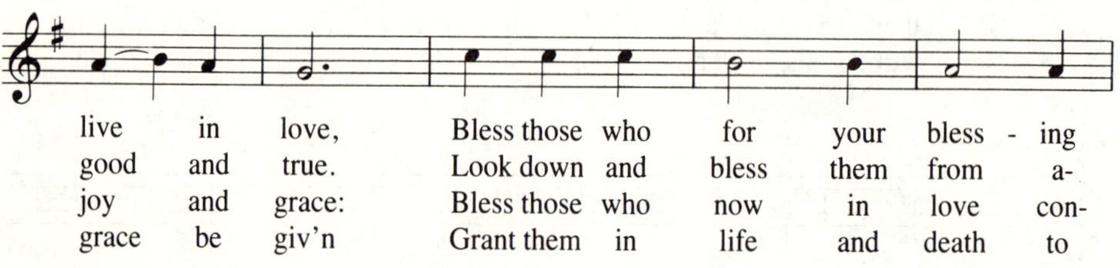
live in love, Bless those who for your bless - ing
good and true. Look down and bless them from a-
joy and grace: Bless those who now in love con-
grace be giv'n Grant them in life and death to

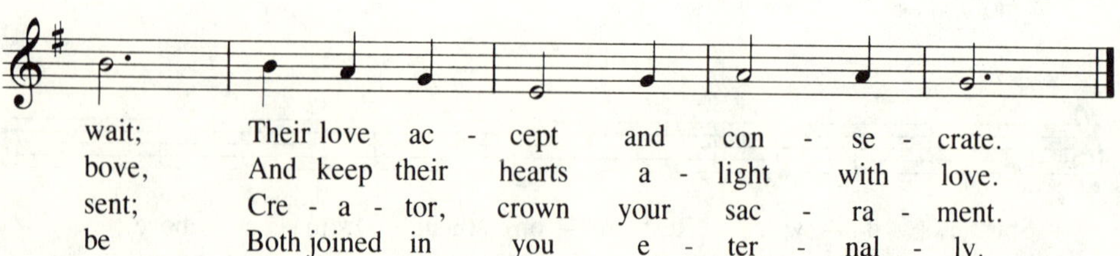
wait; Their love ac - cept and con - se - crate.
bove, And keep their hearts a - light with love.
sent; Cre - a - tor, crown your sac - ra - ment.
be Both joined in you e - ter - nal - ly.

Text: Robert H. Benson, 1871-1914, alt.
Tune: ST. CATHERINE, 8 8 8 8 88; Henry F. Hemy, 1818-1888; Adapt. by James G. Walton, 1821-1905

O Father, All-creating 744

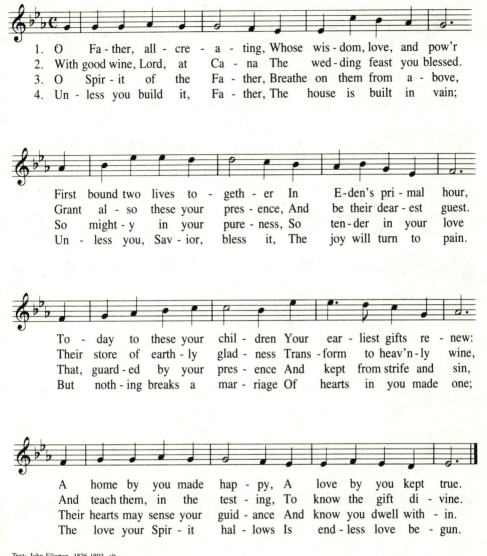

1. O Fa - ther, all - cre - a - ting, Whose wis - dom, love, and pow'r
2. With good wine, Lord, at Ca - na The wed - ding feast you blessed.
3. O Spir - it of the Fa - ther, Breathe on them from a - bove,
4. Un - less you build it, Fa - ther, The house is built in vain;

First bound two lives to - geth - er In E - den's pri - mal hour,
Grant al - so these your pres - ence, And be their dear - est guest.
So might - y in your pure - ness, So ten - der in your love
Un - less you, Sav - ior, bless it, The joy will turn to pain.

To - day to these your chil - dren Your ear - liest gifts re - new:
Their store of earth - ly glad - ness Trans - form to heav'n - ly wine,
That, guard - ed by your pres - ence And kept from strife and sin,
But noth - ing breaks a mar - riage Of hearts in you made one;

A home by you made hap - py, A love by you kept true.
And teach them, in the test - ing, To know the gift di - vine.
Their hearts may sense your guid - ance And know you dwell with - in.
The love your Spir - it hal - lows Is end - less love be - gun.

Text: John Ellerton, 1826-1893, alt.
Tune: AURELIA, 7 6 7 6 D; Samuel S. Wesley, 1810-1876

745 When Love Is Found

1. When love is found and hope comes home, Sing and be glad that two are one. When love ex - plodes and fills the sky, Praise God and share our Mak - er's joy.
2. When love has flow'red in trust and care, Build both each day that love may dare To reach be - yond home's warmth and light, To serve and strive for truth and right.
3. When love is tried as loved - ones change, Hold still to hope though all seems strange, Till ease re - turns and love grows wise Through list - 'ning ears and o - pened eyes.
4. When love is torn and trust be - trayed, Pray strength to love till tor - ments fade, Till lov - ers keep no score of wrong But hear through pain love's East - er song.
5. Praise God for love, praise God for life, In age or youth, in hus - band, wife. Lift up your hearts let love be fed Through death and life in bro - ken bread.

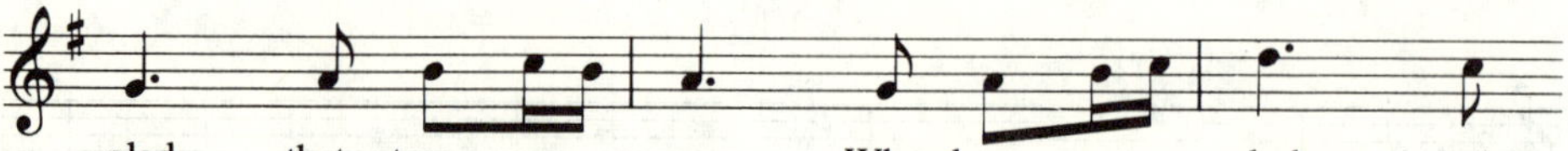

Text: Brian Wren, b.1936, © 1983, Hope Publishing Co.
Tune: O WALY WALY, LM; English; Harm. by Martin West, b.1929, © 1983, Hope Publishing Co.

746 Great God of Mercy

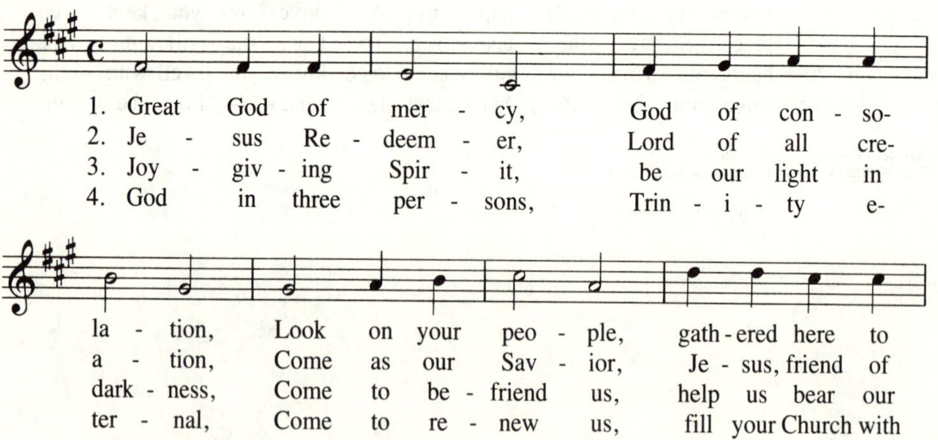
1. Great God of mer - cy, God of con - so- la - tion, Look on your peo - ple, gath - ered here to
2. Je - sus Re - deem - er, Lord of all cre- a - tion, Come as our Sav - ior, Je - sus, friend of
3. Joy - giv - ing Spir - it, be our light in dark - ness, Come to be - friend us, help us bear our
4. God in three per - sons, Trin - i - ty e- ter - nal, Come to re - new us, fill your Church with

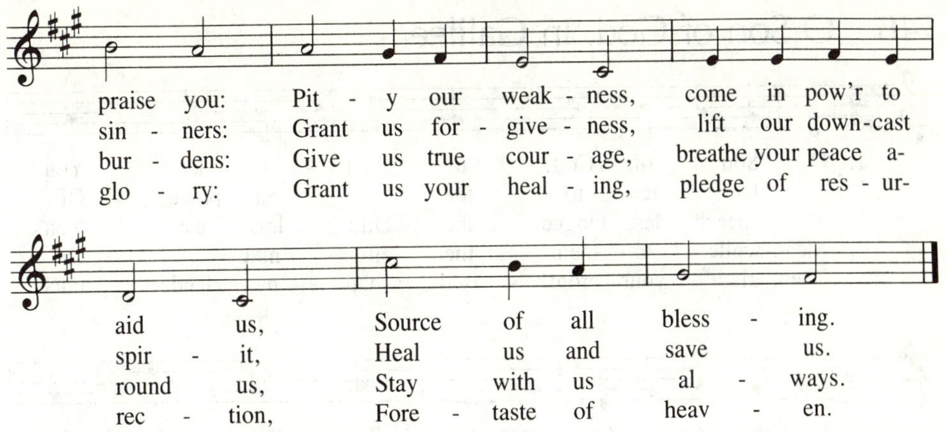
praise you: Pit - y our weak - ness, come in pow'r to aid us, Source of all bless - ing.
sin - ners: Grant us for - give - ness, lift our down-cast spir - it, Heal us and save us.
bur - dens: Give us true cour - age, breathe your peace a- round us, Stay with us al - ways.
glo - ry: Grant us your heal - ing, pledge of res - ur- rec - tion, Fore - taste of heav - en.

Text: James Quinn, SJ, b.1919, © 1980, ICEL
Tune: HERZLIEBSTER JESU, 11 11 11 5; Johann Crüger, 1598-1662

O Christ, the Healer 747

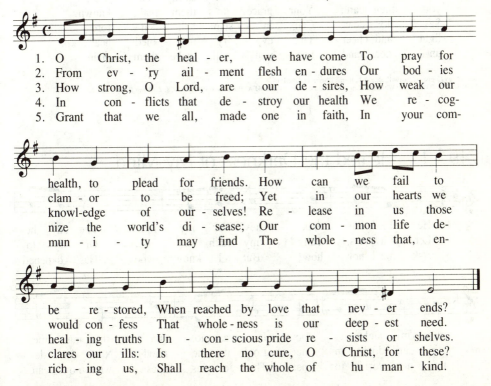

1. O Christ, the heal - er, we have come To pray for health, to plead for friends. How can we fail to be re - stored, When reached by love that nev - er ends?
2. From ev - 'ry ail - ment flesh en - dures Our bod - ies clam - or to be freed; Yet in our hearts we would con - fess That whole - ness is our deep - est need.
3. How strong, O Lord, are our de - sires, How weak our knowl-edge of our - selves! Re - lease in us those heal - ing truths Un - con - scious pride re - sists or shelves.
4. In con - flicts that de - stroy our health We re - cog- nize the world's di - sease; Our com - mon life de- clares our ills: Is there no cure, O Christ, for these?
5. Grant that we all, made one in faith, In your com- mun - i - ty may find The whole - ness that, en- rich - ing us, Shall reach the whole of hu - man - kind.

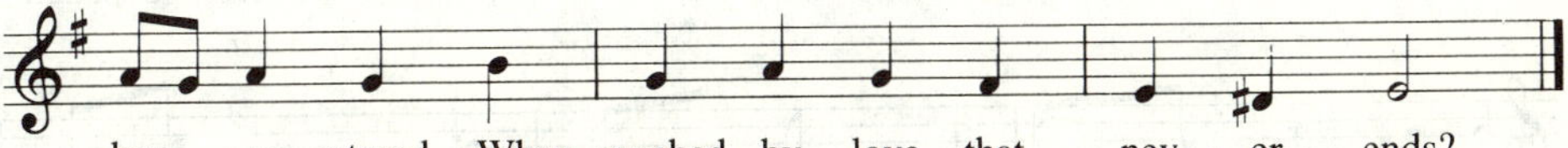

Text: Fred Pratt Green, b.1903, © 1969, Hope Publishing Co.
Tune: ERHALT UNS HERR, LM; Klug's *Geistliche Lieder,* 1543; Harm. by J.S. Bach, 1685-1750

748 O Son of God, In Galilee

1. O Son of God, in Galilee You made the deaf to hear, The mute to speak, the blind to see; O blessed Lord, be near.
2. O listen to the silent prayer Of your afflicted ones. O bid them cast on you their care; Your grace to them make known.
3. The speechless tongue, the lifeless ear You can restore, O Lord; Your "Ephphetha," O Savior dear, Can instant help afford.
4. Meanwhile to them the lis'tning ear Of steadfast faith impart, And let your word bring light and cheer To ev'ry troubled heart.
5. Then in your promised happy land Each loss will prove a gain; All myst'ries we shall understand, For you will make them plain.

Text: Anna Hoppe, 1889-1941, alt., © Lutheran Church in America
Tune: LEWIS-TOWN, CM; William Billings, 1746-1800; Harm. by Donald A. Busarow, b.1934, © 1978, *Lutheran Book of Worship*

749 He Healed the Darkness of My Mind

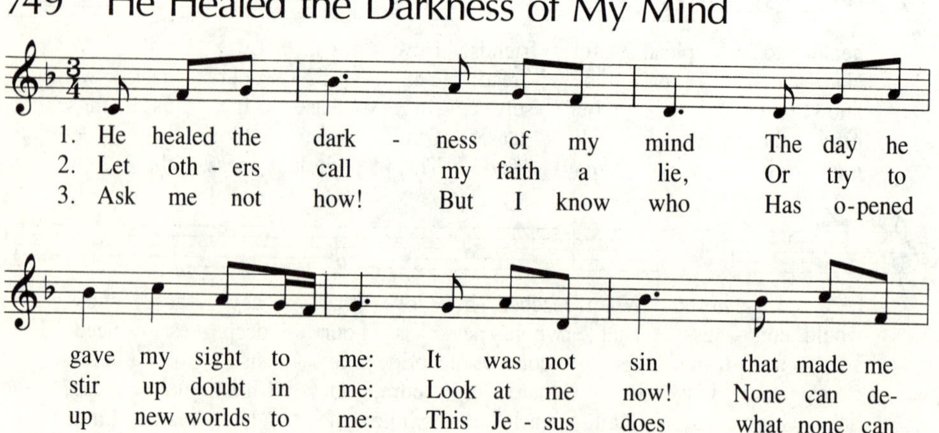
1. He healed the darkness of my mind The day he gave my sight to me: It was not sin that made me
2. Let others call my faith a lie, Or try to stir up doubt in me: Look at me now! None can de-
3. Ask me not how! But I know who Has opened up new worlds to me: This Jesus does what none can

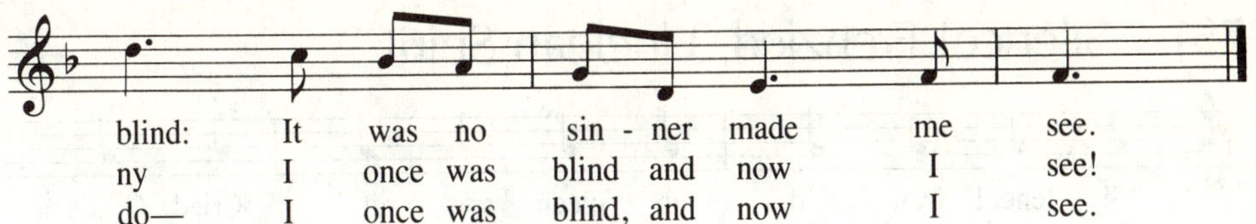

blind: It was no sin - ner made me see.
ny I once was blind and now I see!
do— I once was blind, and now I see.

Text: John 9; Fred Pratt Green, b.1903, © 1982, Hope Publishing Co.
Tune: DUNEDIN, LM; Vernon Griffiths, 1894-1985, ©

Your Hands, O Lord, in Days of Old 750

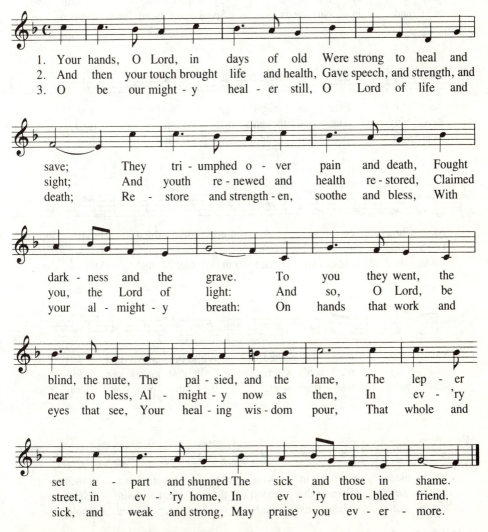

1. Your hands, O Lord, in days of old Were strong to heal and
2. And then your touch brought life and health, Gave speech, and strength, and
3. O be our might - y heal - er still, O Lord of life and

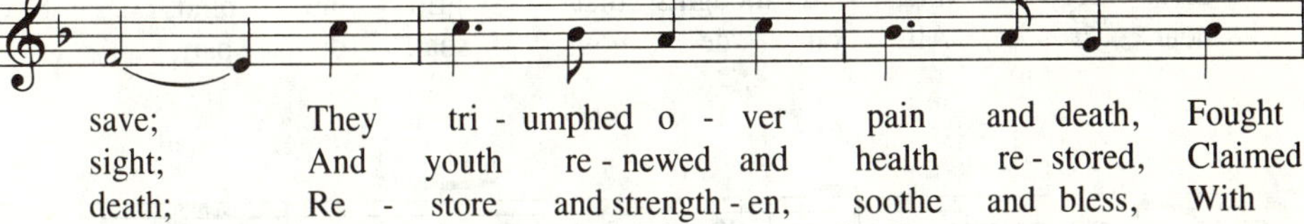

save; They tri - umphed o - ver pain and death, Fought
sight; And youth re - newed and health re - stored, Claimed
death; Re - store and strength - en, soothe and bless, With

dark - ness and the grave. To you they went, the
you, the Lord of light: And so, O Lord, be
your al - might - y breath: On hands that work and

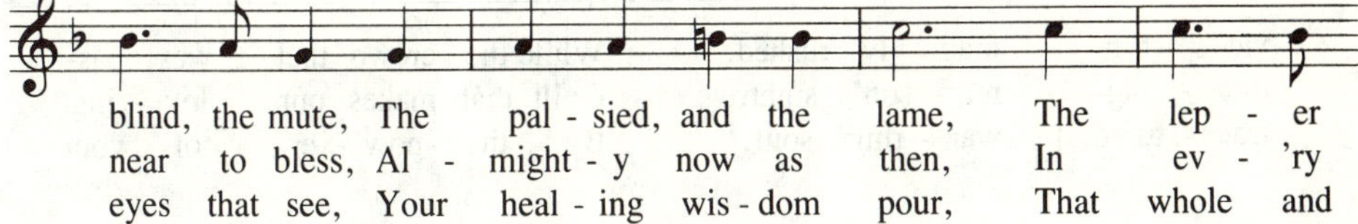

blind, the mute, The pal - sied, and the lame, The lep - er
near to bless, Al - might - y now as then, In ev - 'ry
eyes that see, Your heal - ing wis - dom pour, That whole and

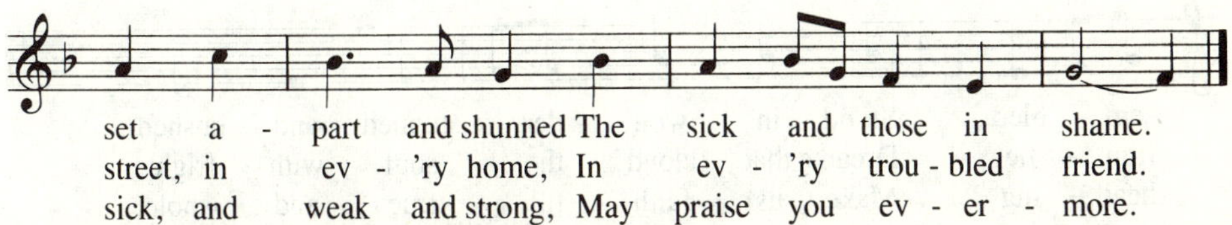

set a - part and shunned The sick and those in shame.
street, in ev - 'ry home, In ev - 'ry trou - bled friend.
sick, and weak and strong, May praise you ev - er - more.

Text: Mt. 145:35-36; Edward H. Plumtre, 1821-1891, alt., © 1986, GIA Publicaions, Inc.
Tune: MOZART, CMD; Adapt. from Wolfgang A. Mozart, 1756-1791

751 Silence! Frenzied, Unclean Spirit

1. "Si - lence! fren - zied, un - clean spir - it," Cried God's
2. Lord, the de - mons still are thriv - ing In the
3. Si - lence, Lord, the un - clean spir - it In our

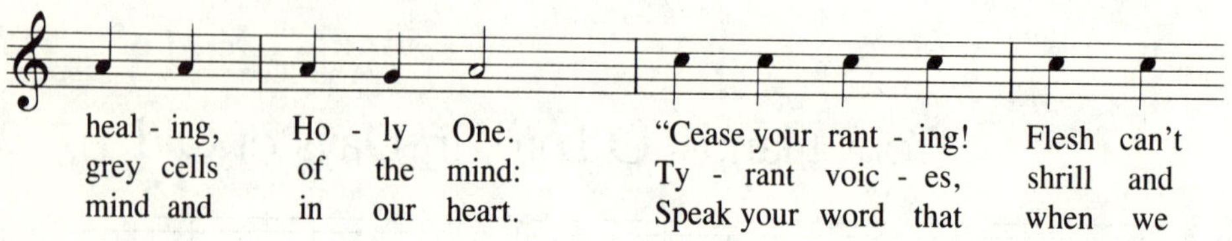
heal - ing, Ho - ly One. "Cease your rant - ing! Flesh can't
grey cells of the mind: Ty - rant voic - es, shrill and
mind and in our heart. Speak your word that when we

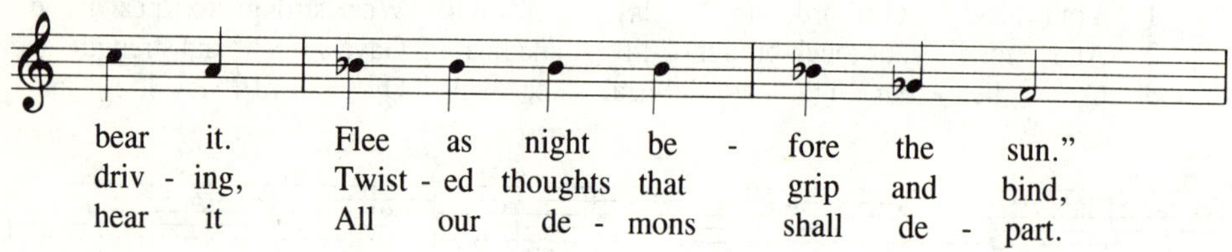
bear it. Flee as night be - fore the sun."
driv - ing, Twist - ed thoughts that grip and bind,
hear it All our de - mons shall de - part.

At Christ's voice the de - mon trem - bled, From its
Doubts that stir the heart to pan - ic, Fears dis-
Clear our thought and calm our feel - ing. Still the

vic - tim mad - ly rushed, While the crowd that was as-
tort - ing rea - son's sight, Guilt that makes our lov - ing
frac - tured, war - ring soul. By the pow - er of your

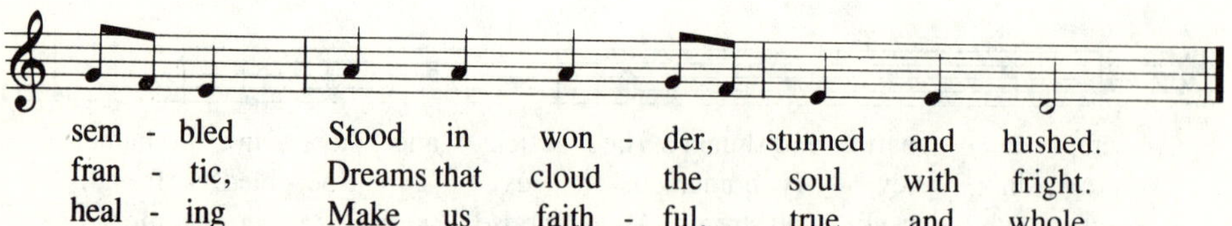
sem - bled Stood in won - der, stunned and hushed.
fran - tic, Dreams that cloud the soul with fright.
heal - ing Make us faith - ful, true and whole.

Text: Mk. 1:23-28; Thomas Troeger, b.1945
Tune: AUTHORITY, 8 7 8 7 D; Carol Doran, b.1936; (Suggested alternate tune: GENEVA)

The Master Came to Bring Good News 752

1. The Mas - ter came to bring good news,
2. The Law's ful - filled through Je - sus Christ,
3. To seek the sin - ners Je - sus came,
4. For - give us, Lord, as we for - give

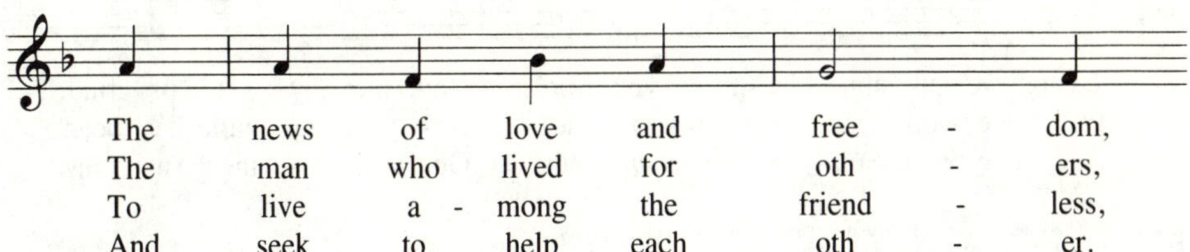
The news of love and free - dom,
The man who lived for oth - ers,
To live a - mong the friend - less,
And seek to help each oth - er.

To heal the sick and seek the poor,
The law of Christ is: Serve in love
To show them love that they might share
For - give us, Lord, and we shall live

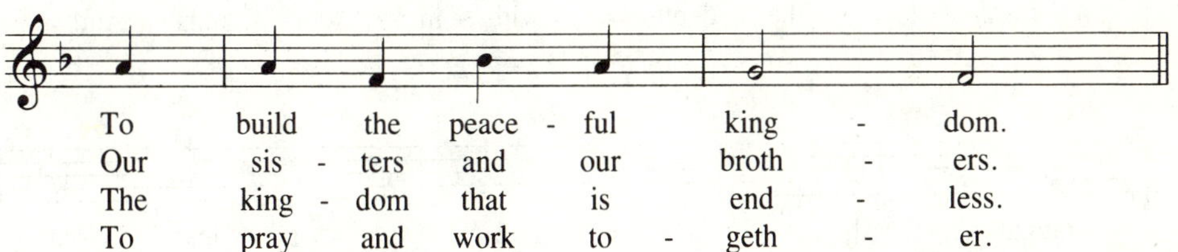
To build the peace - ful king - dom.
Our sis - ters and our broth - ers.
The king - dom that is end - less.
To pray and work to - geth - er.

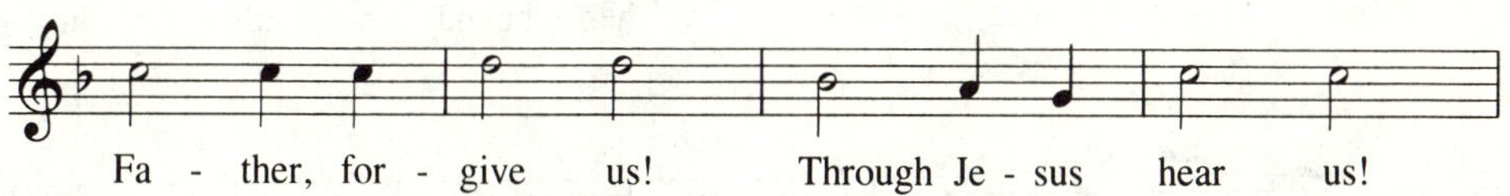
Fa - ther, for - give us! Through Je - sus hear us!

As we for - give one an - oth - er!

Text: Ralph Finn, b.1941, © 1965, GIA Publications, Inc.
Tune: ICH GLAUB AN GOTT, 8 7 8 7 with refrain; *Mainz Gesanbuch*, 1870; Harm. by Richard Proulx, b.1937, © 1986, GIA Publications, Inc.

753 Have Mercy, Lord, on Us

1. Have mer - cy, Lord, on us, For you are ev - er kind;
2. Lord, wash a - way our guilt, And cleanse us from our sin;
3. The joy your grace can give, Let us a - gain ob - tain,

Though we have sinned be - fore you, Lord, Your mer - cy let us find.
For we con - fess our wrongs, and see How great our guilt has been.
And may your Spir - it's firm sup - port Our spir - its then sus - tain.

Text: Psalm 51; Nahum Tate, 1652-1715, and Nicholas Brady, 1659-1726, alt.
Tune: SOUTHWELL, SM; Damon's *Psalmes,* 1579

754 Forgive Our Sins

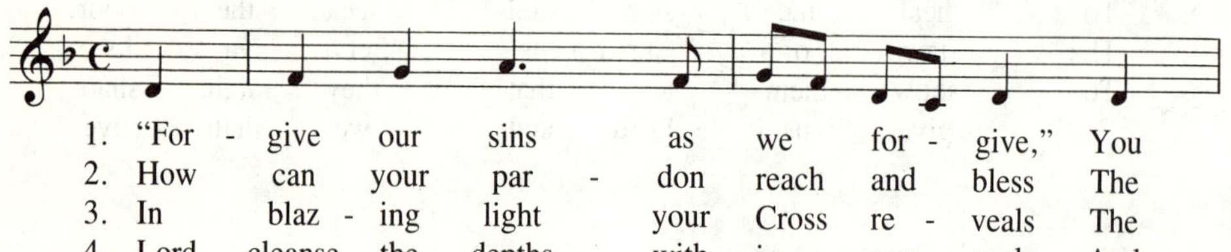

1. "For - give our sins as we for - give," You
2. How can your par - don reach and bless The
3. In blaz - ing light your Cross re - veals The
4. Lord, cleanse the depths with - in our souls And

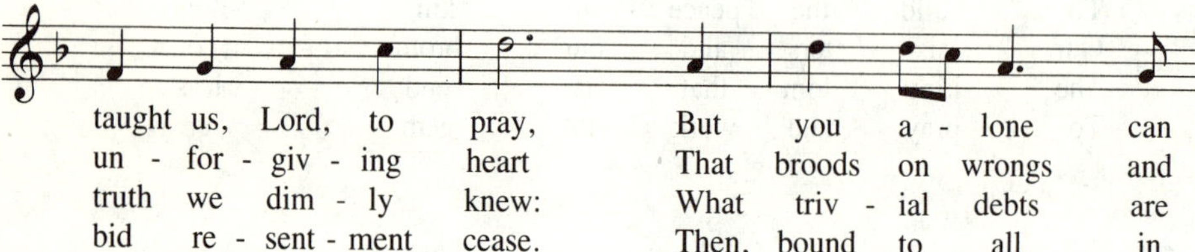

taught us, Lord, to pray, But you a - lone can
un - for - giv - ing heart That broods on wrongs and
truth we dim - ly knew: What triv - ial debts are
bid re - sent - ment cease. Then, bound to all in

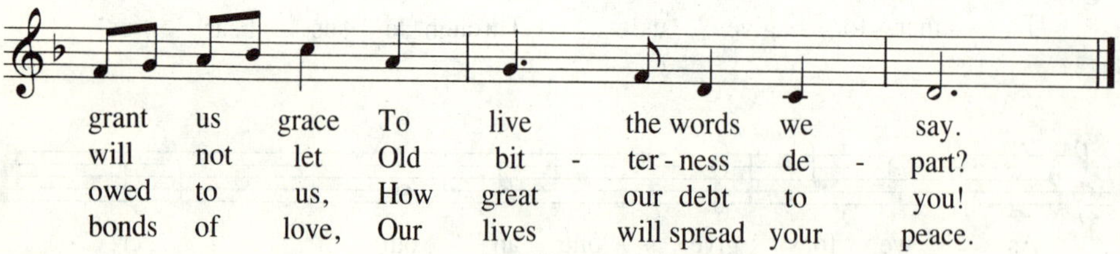

grant us grace To live the words we say.
will not let Old bit - ter - ness de - part?
owed to us, How great our debt to you!
bonds of love, Our lives will spread your peace.

Text: Rosamund Herklots, b.1905, © Oxford University Press
Tune: DETROIT, CM; Supplement to *Kentucky Harmony,* 1820; Harm. by Gerald H. Knight, 1908-1979, © The Royal School of Church Music

Our Father, We Have Wandered 755

1. Our Fa - ther, we have wan - dered And hid - den from your face; In fool - ish- ness have squan - dered Your leg - a - cy of grace. But now, in ex - ile dwell - ing, We rise with fear and shame, As dis - tant but com - pell - ing, We hear you call our name.
2. And now at length dis - cern - ing The e - vil that we do, Be - hold us Lord, re - turn - ing With hope and trust to you. In haste you come to meet us And home re - joic - ing bring, In glad - ness there to greet us With calf and robe and ring.
3. O Lord of all the liv - ing, Both ban - ished and re - stored, Com - pas - sion- ate, for - giv - ing And ev - er car - ing Lord, Grant now that our trans - gress - ing, Our faith - less - ness may cease. Stretch out your hand in bless - ing, In par - don and in peace.

Text: Kevin Nichols, b.1929, © 1980, ICEL
Tune: PASSION CHORALE, 7 6 7 6 D; Hans Leo Hassler, 1564-1612; Harm. by J.S. Bach, 1685-1750

756 Come, You Sinners, Poor and Needy

1. Come, you sin - ners, poor and need - y, Weak and wound-ed, sick and sore, Je - sus, Son of God, will save you, Full of pit - y, love, and pow'r.
2. Come, you thirst - y, come, and wel - come, God's free boun - ty glo - ri - fy; True be - lief and true re - pent - ance, Ev - 'ry grace that brings you nigh.
3. Come, you wea - ry, heav - y lad - en, Lost and ru - ined by the fall; If you tar - ry till you're bet - ter, You will nev - er come at all.

I will a - rise and go to Je - sus, He will em - brace me in his arms; In the arms of my dear Sav - ior; O there are ten thou - sand charms.

Text: Joseph Hart, 1712-1768, alt.
Tune: RESTORATION, 8 7 8 7 with refrain; American; Harm. by George Mims, b.1938, © 1979, Church of the Redeemer, Houston

757 O Saving Victim/O Salutaris

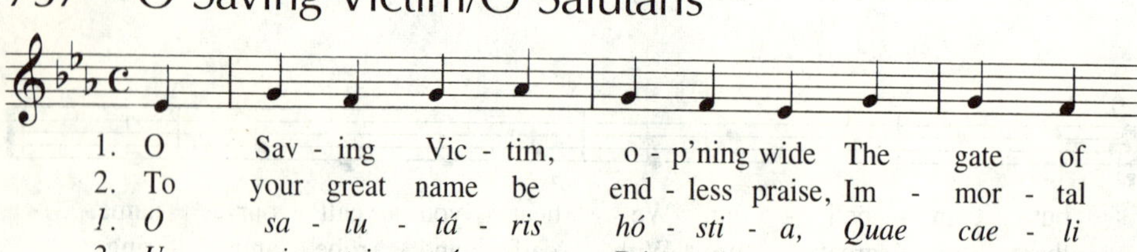
1. O Sav - ing Vic - tim, o - p'ning wide The gate of
2. To your great name be end - less praise, Im - mor - tal
1. O sa - lu - tá - ris hó - sti - a, Quae cae - li
2. U - ni tri - nó - que Dó - mi - no Sit sem - pi-

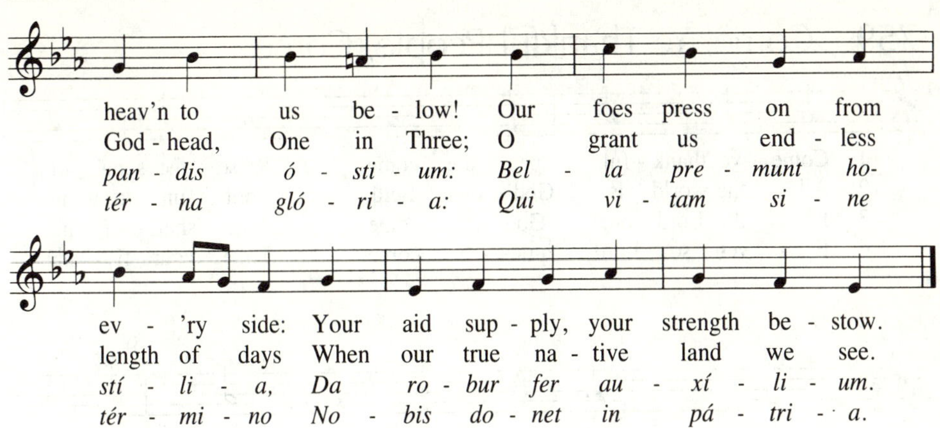
heav'n to us be - low! Our foes press on from
God - head, One in Three; O grant us end - less
pan - dis ó - sti - um: Bel - la pre - munt ho-
tér - na gló - ri - a: Qui vi - tam si - ne
ev - 'ry side: Your aid sup - ply, your strength be - stow.
length of days When our true na - tive land we see.
stí - li - a, Da ro - bur fer au - xí - li - um.
tér - mi - no No - bis do - net in pá - tri - a.

Text: Thomas Aquinas, 1227-1275; Tr. by Edward Caswall, 1814-1878, alt.
Tune: DUGUET, LM; Dieu donne Duguet, d.1767

Come Adore/Tantum Ergo 758

1. Come a - dore this won - drous pres - ence, Bow to Christ the
2. Glo - ry be to God the Fa - ther, Praise to his co-
1. Tan - tum er - go Sa - cra - mén - tum Ve - ne - ré - mur
2. Ge - ni - tó - ri, Ge - ni - tó - que Laus et ju - bi-

source of grace. Here is kept the an - cient prom - ise
e - qual Son, Ad - o - ra - tion to the Spir - it,
cér - nu - i: Et an - tí - quum do - cu - mén - tum
lá - ti - o, Sa - lus, ho - nor, vir - tus quo - que

Of God's earth - ly dwell - ing - place. Sight is blind be-
Bond of love, in God - head one. Blest be God by
No - vo ce - dat rí - tu - i: Prae - stet fi - des
Sit et be - ne - dí - cti - o: Pro - ce - dén - ti

fore God's glo - ry, Faith a - lone may see his face.
all cre - a - tion Joy - ous - ly while a - ges run.
sup - ple - mén - tum Sén - su - um de - fé - ctu - i.
ab u - tró - que Com - par sit lau - dá - ti - o.

Text: Thomas Aquinas, 1227-1274; Tr. by James Quinn, SJ, b.1919, © 1969
Tune: ST. THOMAS, 8 7 8 7 8 7; John F. Wade, 1711-1786

759 Come, Ye Thankful People, Come

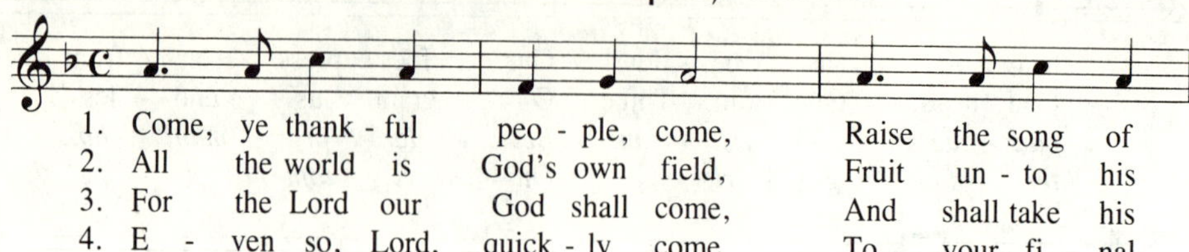
1. Come, ye thank - ful peo - ple, come, Raise the song of
2. All the world is God's own field, Fruit un - to his
3. For the Lord our God shall come, And shall take his
4. E - ven so, Lord, quick - ly come To your fi - nal

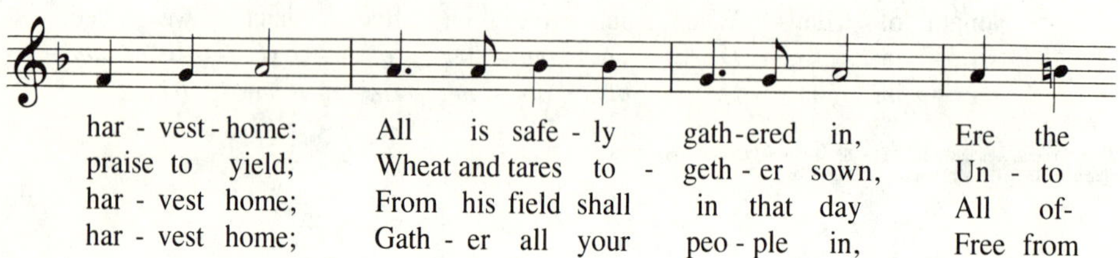
har - vest - home: All is safe - ly gath-ered in, Ere the
praise to yield; Wheat and tares to - geth - er sown, Un - to
har - vest home; From his field shall in that day All of-
har - vest home; Gath - er all your peo - ple in, Free from

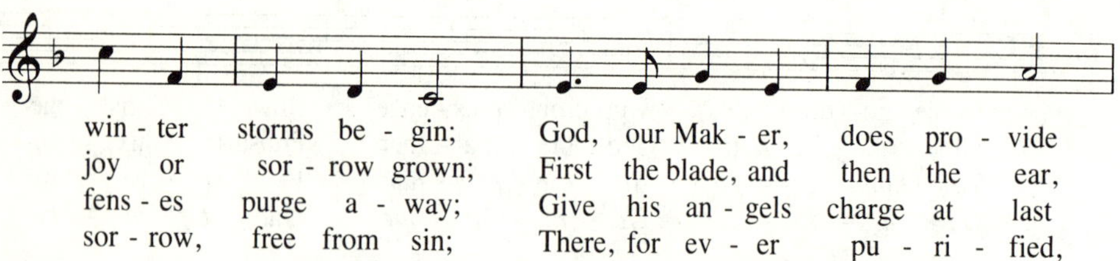
win - ter storms be - gin; God, our Mak - er, does pro - vide
joy or sor - row grown; First the blade, and then the ear,
fens - es purge a - way; Give his an - gels charge at last
sor - row, free from sin; There, for ev - er pu - ri - fied,

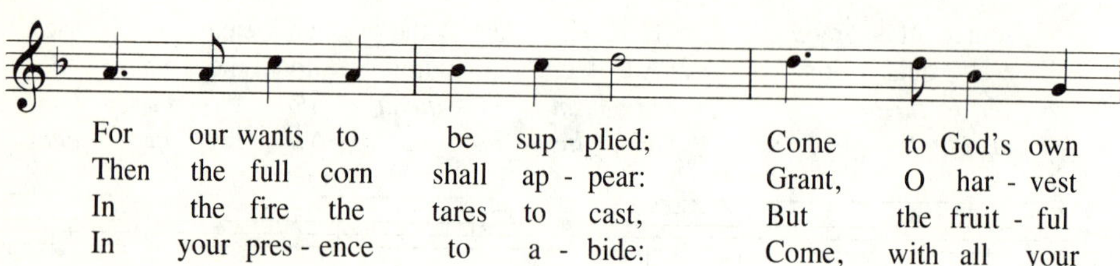
For our wants to be sup - plied; Come to God's own
Then the full corn shall ap - pear: Grant, O har - vest
In the fire the tares to cast, But the fruit - ful
In your pres - ence to a - bide: Come, with all your

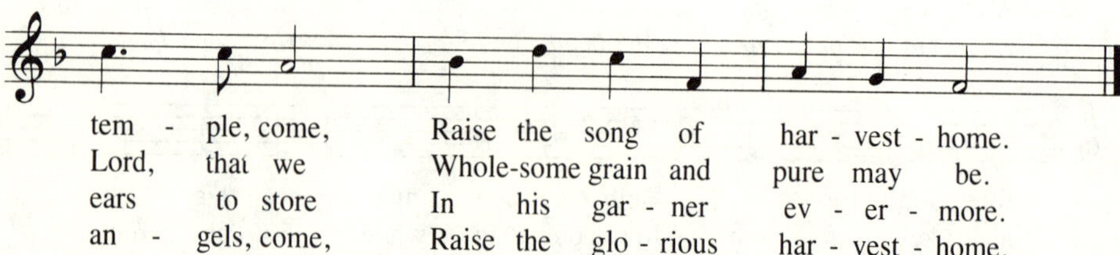
tem - ple, come, Raise the song of har - vest - home.
Lord, that we Whole-some grain and pure may be.
ears to store In his gar - ner ev - er - more.
an - gels, come, Raise the glo - rious har - vest - home.

Text: Henry Alford, 1810-1871, alt.
Tune: ST. GEORGE'S WINDSOR, 77 77 D; George J. Elvey, 1816-1893; Harm. by Richard Proulx, b.1937,

We Gather Together 760

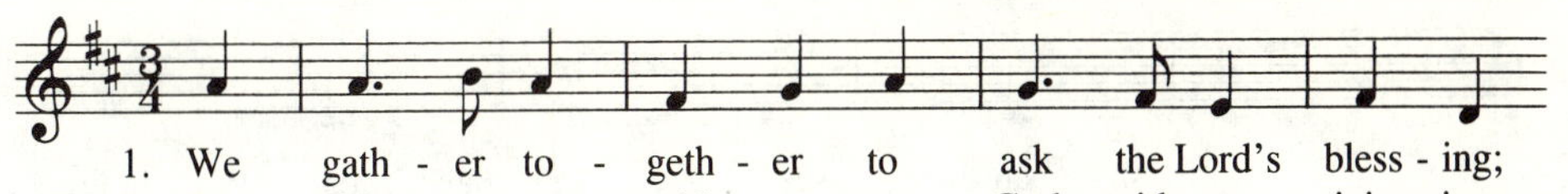

1. We gath - er to - geth - er to ask the Lord's bless - ing;
2. Be - side us to guide us, our God with us join - ing,
3. We all do ex - tol you our lead - er tri - um - phant,

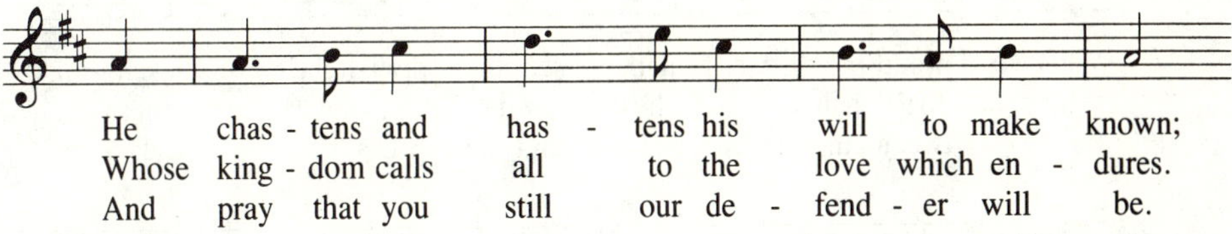

He chas - tens and has - tens his will to make known;
Whose king - dom calls all to the love which en - dures.
And pray that you still our de - fend - er will be.

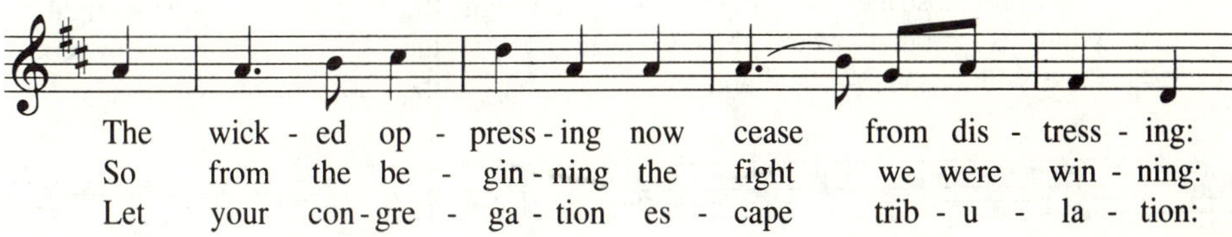

The wick - ed op - press - ing now cease from dis - tress - ing:
So from the be - gin - ning the fight we were win - ning:
Let your con - gre - ga - tion es - cape trib - u - la - tion:

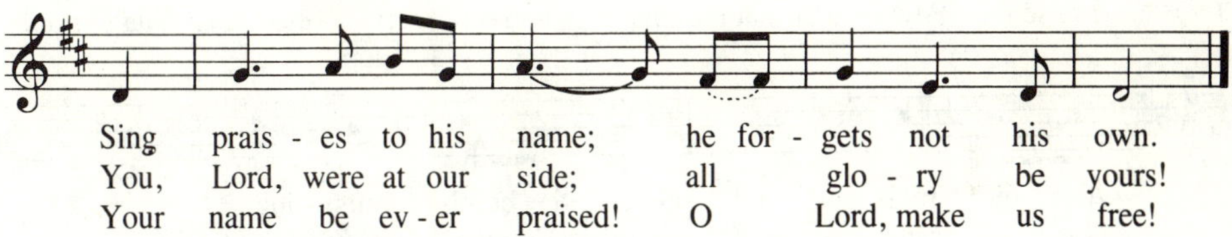

Sing prais - es to his name; he for - gets not his own.
You, Lord, were at our side; all glo - ry be yours!
Your name be ev - er praised! O Lord, make us free!

Text: *Wilt heden nu treden;* Tr. by Theodore Baker, 1851-1934, alt., © J. Curwen and Sons
Tune: KREMSER, 12 11 12 11; *Neder-landtsch Gedenckclanck,* 1626; Harm. by Edward Kremser, 1838-1914

761 Star-Spangled Banner

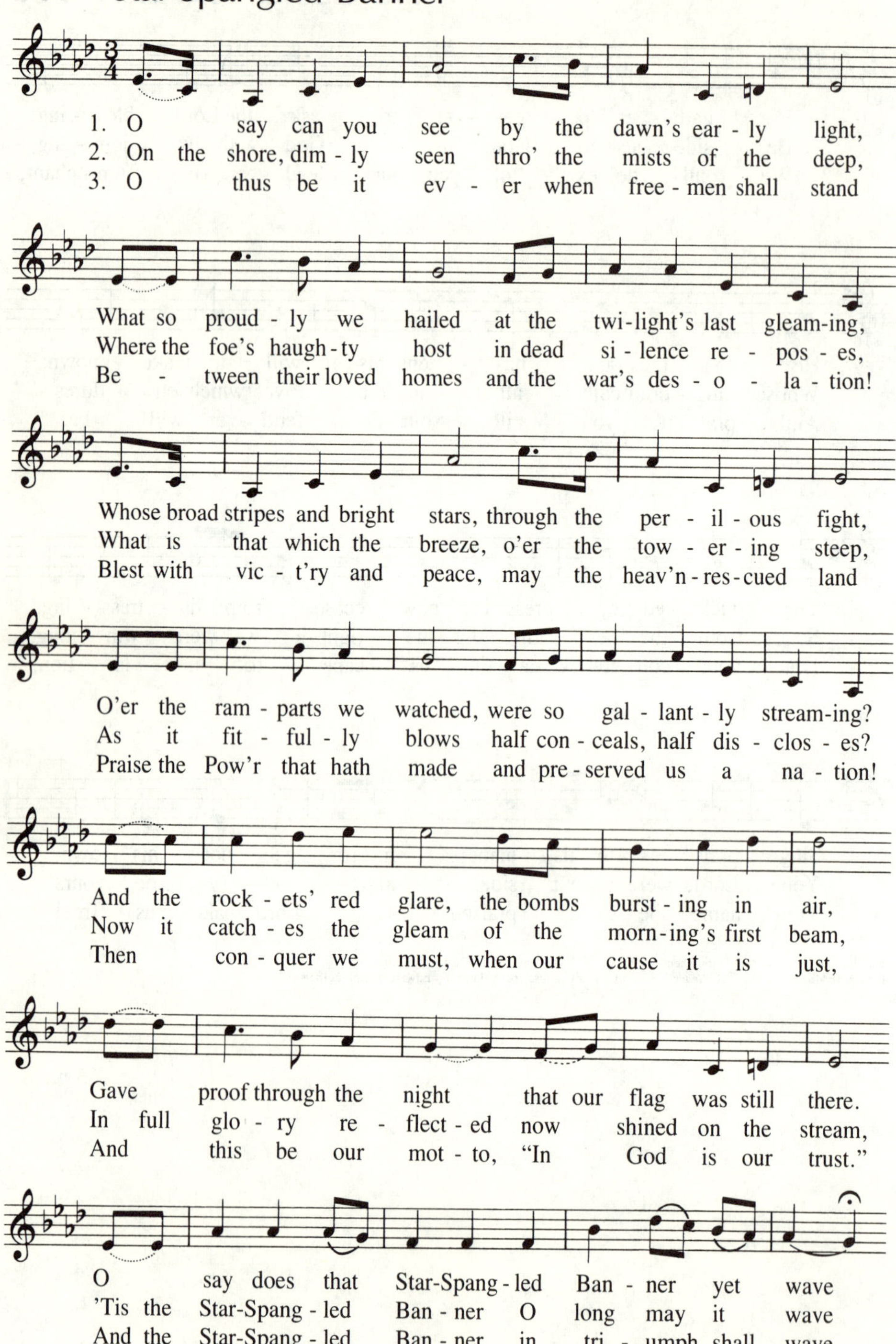
1. O say can you see by the dawn's ear - ly light,
2. On the shore, dim - ly seen thro' the mists of the deep,
3. O thus be it ev - er when free - men shall stand
What so proud - ly we hailed at the twi-light's last gleam-ing,
Where the foe's haugh-ty host in dead si - lence re - pos - es,
Be - tween their loved homes and the war's des - o - la - tion!
Whose broad stripes and bright stars, through the per - il - ous fight,
What is that which the breeze, o'er the tow - er - ing steep,
Blest with vic - t'ry and peace, may the heav'n - res - cued land
O'er the ram - parts we watched, were so gal - lant - ly stream-ing?
As it fit - ful - ly blows half con - ceals, half dis - clos - es?
Praise the Pow'r that hath made and pre - served us a na - tion!
And the rock - ets' red glare, the bombs burst - ing in air,
Now it catch - es the gleam of the morn-ing's first beam,
Then con - quer we must, when our cause it is just,
Gave proof through the night that our flag was still there.
In full glo - ry re - flect - ed now shined on the stream,
And this be our mot - to, "In God is our trust."
O say does that Star-Spang - led Ban - ner yet wave
'Tis the Star-Spang - led Ban - ner O long may it wave
And the Star-Spang - led Ban - ner in tri - umph shall wave

O'er the land of the free and the home of the brave?
O'er the land of the free and the home of the brave!
O'er the land of the free and the home of the brave!

Text: Francis S. Key, 1779-1843
Tune: STAR SPANGLED BANNER, Irregular; John S. Smith, 1750-1836

My Country, 'Tis of Thee 762

1. My coun - try, 'tis of thee, Sweet land of
2. My na - tive coun - try, thee, Land of the
3. Let mu - sic swell the breeze, And ring from
4. Our fa - thers' God, to thee, Au - thor of

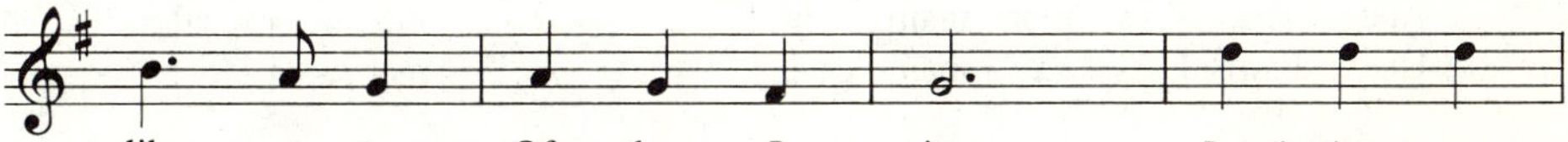

lib - er - ty, Of thee I sing; Land where my
no - ble, free; Thy name I love; I love thy
all the trees Sweet free - dom's song; Let mor - tal
lib - er - ty, To thee we sing; Long may our

fa - thers died, Land of the pil - grim's pride,
rocks and rills, Thy woods and tem - pled hills;
tongues a - wake; Let all that breathe par - take;
land be bright With free - dom's ho - ly light;

From ev - 'ry moun - tain - side Let free - dom ring!
My heart with rap - ture thrills, Like that a - bove.
Let rocks their si - lence break, The sound pro - long.
Pro - tect us by thy might, Great God, our King.

Text: Samuel F. Smith, 1808-1895
Tune: AMERICA, 66 4 666 4; *Thesaurus Musicus*, 1744

763 America the Beautiful

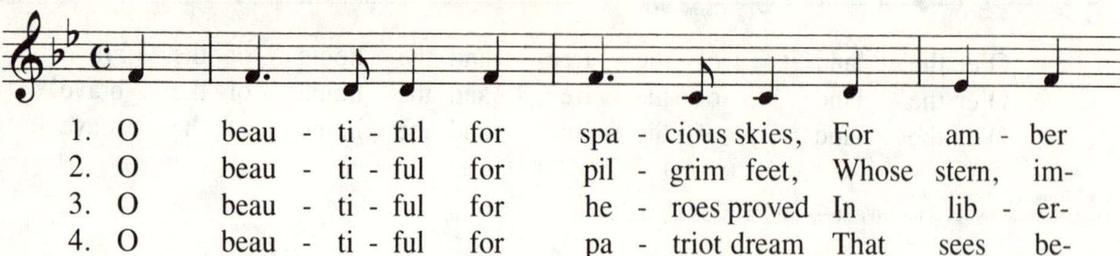
1. O beau - ti - ful for spa - cious skies, For am - ber
2. O beau - ti - ful for pil - grim feet, Whose stern, im-
3. O beau - ti - ful for he - roes proved In lib - er-
4. O beau - ti - ful for pa - triot dream That sees be-

waves of grain, For pur - ple moun-tain maj - es - ties
pas - sioned stress A thor - ough-fare for free - dom beat
at - ing strife, Who more than self their coun - try loved,
yond the years Thine al - a - bas - ter cit - ies gleam,

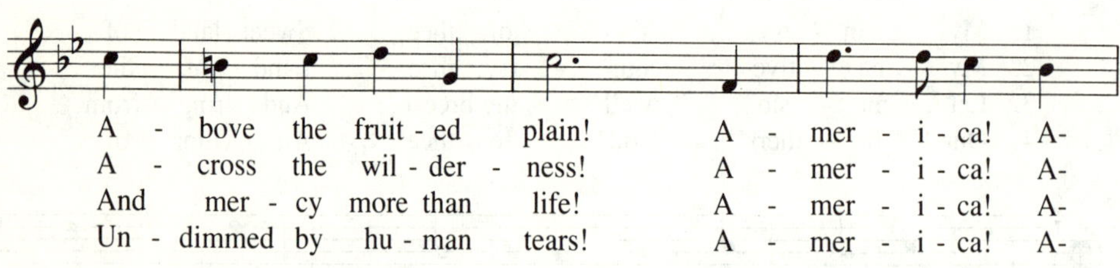
A - bove the fruit - ed plain! A - mer - i - ca! A-
A - cross the wil - der - ness! A - mer - i - ca! A-
And mer - cy more than life! A - mer - i - ca! A-
Un - dimmed by hu - man tears! A - mer - i - ca! A-

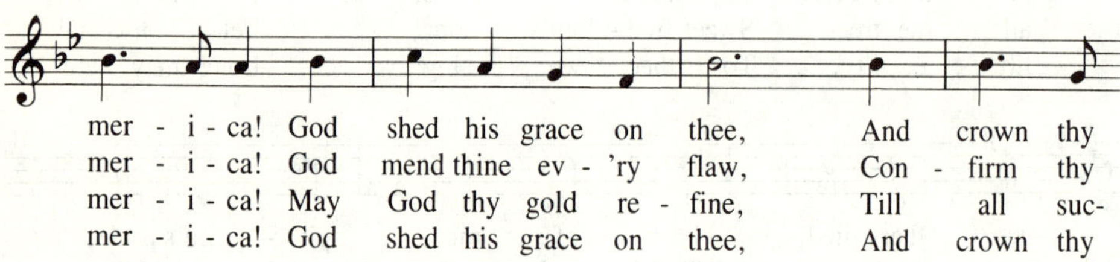
mer - i - ca! God shed his grace on thee, And crown thy
mer - i - ca! God mend thine ev - 'ry flaw, Con - firm thy
mer - i - ca! May God thy gold re - fine, Till all suc-
mer - i - ca! God shed his grace on thee, And crown thy

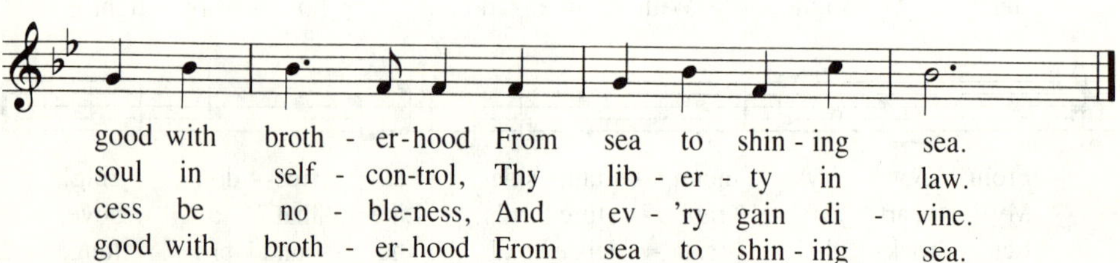
good with broth - er-hood From sea to shin - ing sea.
soul in self - con-trol, Thy lib - er - ty in law.
cess be no - ble-ness, And ev - 'ry gain di - vine.
good with broth - er-hood From sea to shin - ing sea.

Text: Katherine L. Bates, 1859-1929
Tune: MATERNA, CMD; Samuel A. Ward, 1848-1903

God of Our Fathers 764

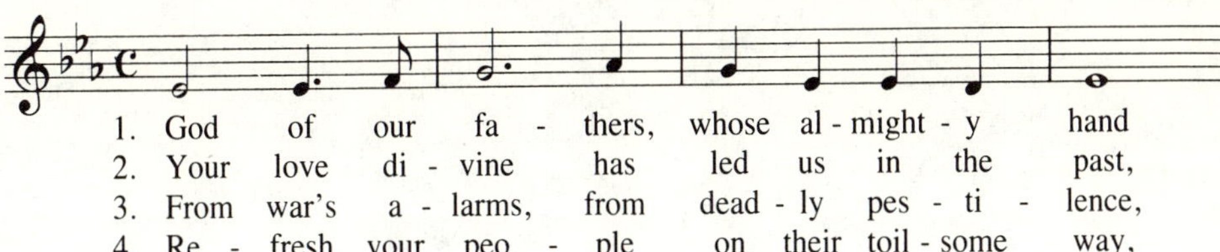
1. God of our fa - thers, whose al - might - y hand
2. Your love di - vine has led us in the past,
3. From war's a - larms, from dead - ly pes - ti - lence,
4. Re - fresh your peo - ple on their toil - some way,

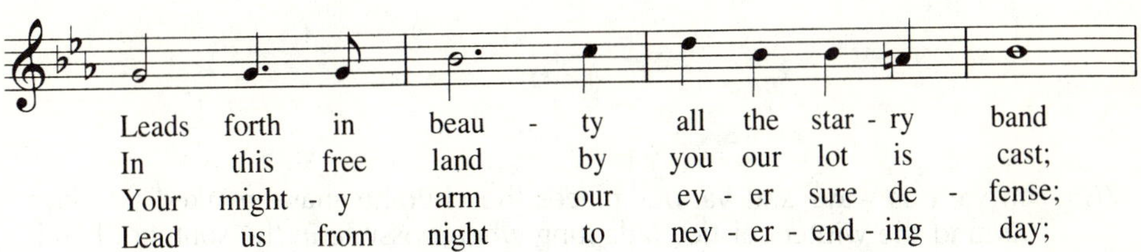
Leads forth in beau - ty all the star - ry band
In this free land by you our lot is cast;
Your might - y arm our ev - er sure de - fense;
Lead us from night to nev - er - end - ing day;

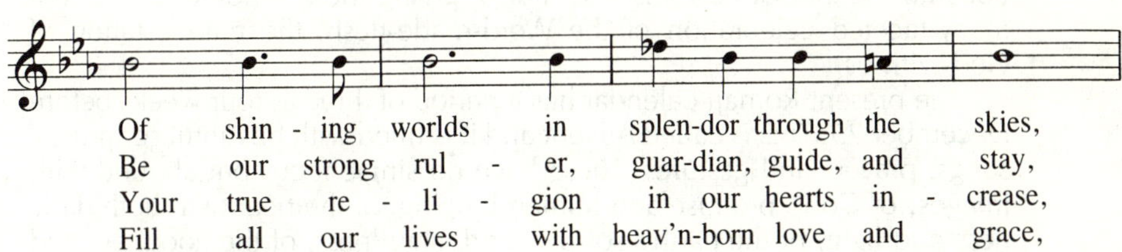
Of shin - ing worlds in splen-dor through the skies,
Be our strong rul - er, guar-dian, guide, and stay,
Your true re - li - gion in our hearts in - crease,
Fill all our lives with heav'n-born love and grace,

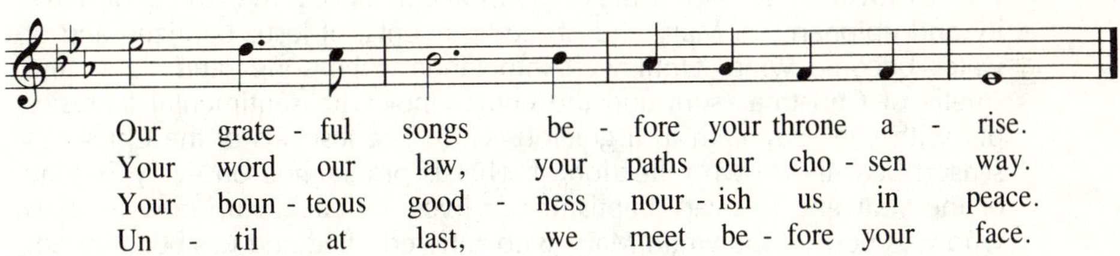
Our grate - ful songs be - fore your throne a - rise.
Your word our law, your paths our cho - sen way.
Your boun - teous good - ness nour - ish us in peace.
Un - til at last, we meet be - fore your face.

Text: Daniel C. Roberts, 1841-1907
Tune: NATIONAL HYMN, 10 10 10 10; George W. Warren, 1828-1902

Advent/Christmas

765 In various ways and various places the churches have marked the days around the winter solstice (adapting when possible in the southern hemisphere when December and January surround the summer solstice). Christians have quite naturally kept from their former religions and traditions all manner of customs and rituals, giving these a home around the many-faceted celebration of the Word-made-flesh, the manifestation of God-with-us.

The present Roman calendar has a period of three to four weeks before December 25. This is called Advent and it is filled with beautiful scriptures, songs, prayers and gestures. These have no single focus but abound with images: of God's promise and human longing, of the beauty in both darkness and light, of the earth's sorrows and its fullness, of the goodness and mystery of time. The spirit of the church's Advent is in the silence and song that arise from constant attention to the human condition.

At Christmas this spirit blossoms in acclamation: the stories of nativity and epiphany, of Mary and of the Innocents, of Jesus baptized and of water become wine. Until well into January the songs and sights and smells of Christmas surround the church not with sentimental fantasies but with everyday faith in a gracious God. The festivals of the Christmas season bear their own reflection of what is proclaimed on every Sunday of the year and in every baptism: our lives are caught up now in Jesus who was born of the virgin Mary, who suffered, died and has been raised.

The lectionary of Advent/Christmas is the foundation of these winter days. These scriptures, read and pondered year after year, turn the Christian and the church toward that peace and glory we name but do not yet know.

766 FIRST SUNDAY OF ADVENT / A

READING I *Isaiah 2, 1-5 / 1*

This is what Isaiah, son of Amoz, saw
concerning Judah and Jerusalem.
In days to come,
The mountain of the Lord's house
shall be established as the highest
mountain
and raised above the hills.
All nations shall stream toward it;

many peoples shall come and say:
"Come, let us climb the Lord's
mountain,
to the house of the God of Jacob,
That he may instruct us in his ways,
and we way walk in his paths."
For from Zion shall go forth
instruction,
and the word of the Lord from
Jerusalem.
He shall judge between the nations,
and impose terms on many peoples.
They shall beat their swords into
plowshares
and their spears into pruning hooks;
One nation shall not raise the sword
against another,
nor shall they train for war again.
O house of Jacob, come,
let us walk in the light of the Lord!

RESPONSORIAL PSALM *Psalm (121)122, 1-2.3-4.4-5.6-7.8-9 / 1*

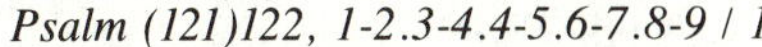

RJB
I re-joiced when I heard them say: let us go to the house of the Lord.

I rejoiced when I heard them say:
"Let us go to God's house."
And now our feet are standing
within your gates, O Jerusalem. ℟.

Jerusalem is built as a city
strongly compact.
It is there that the tribes go up,
the tribes of the Lord. ℟.

For Israel's law it is,
there to praise the Lord's name.
There were set the thrones of judgment
of the house of David. ℟.

For the peace of Jerusalem pray:
"Peace be to your homes!
May peace reign in your walls,
in your palaces, peace!" ℟.

For love of my brethren and friends
I say: "Peace upon you!"
For love of the house of the Lord
I will ask for your good. ℟.

READING II *Romans 13, 11-14 / 1*

You know the time in which we are living. It is now the hour for you to wake from sleep, for our salvation is closer than when we first accepted the faith. The night is far spent; the day draws near. Let us cast off deeds of darkness and put on the armor of light. Let us live honorably as in daylight; not in carousing and drunkenness, not in sexual excess and lust, not in quarreling and jealousy. Rather, put on the Lord Jesus Christ and make no provision for the desires of the flesh.

GOSPEL *Matthew 24, 37-44 / 1*

Jesus said to his disciples: "The coming of the Son of Man will repeat what happened in Noah's time. In the days before the flood people were eating and drinking, marrying and being married, right up to the day Noah entered the ark. They were totally unconcerned until the flood came and destroyed them. So will it be at the coming of the Son of Man. Two men will be out in the field; one will be taken and one will be left. Two women will be grinding meal; one will be taken and one will be left. Stay awake, therefore! You cannot know the day your Lord is coming.

"Be sure of this: if the owner of the house knew when the thief was coming he would keep a watchful eye and not allow his house to be broken into. You must be prepared in the same way. The Son of Man is coming at the time you least expect."

767 FIRST SUNDAY OF ADVENT / B

READING I *Isaiah 63, 16-17.19; 64, 2-7 / 2*

You, Lord, are our father,
our redeemer you are named forever.
Why do you let us wander, O Lord,
from your ways,
and harden our hearts so that we fear
you not?
Return for the sake of your servants,
the tribes of your heritage.
Oh, that you would rend the heavens
and come down,
with the mountains quaking before
you,
While you wrought awesome deeds we
could not hope for,
such as they had not heard of from of
old.
No ear has ever heard, no eye ever seen,
any God but you
doing such deeds for those who wait
for him.
Would that you might meet us doing
right,
that we were mindful of you in our
ways!
Behold, you are angry, and we are
sinful;
all of us have become like unclean
men,
all our good deeds are like polluted
rags;
We have all withered like leaves,
and our guilt carries us away like the
wind.
There is none who calls upon your
name,
who rouses himself to cling to you;
For you have hidden your face from us
and have delivered us up to our guilt.
Yet, O Lord, you are our father;
we are the clay and you are the
potter:
we are all the work of your hands.

RESPONSORIAL PSALM *Psalm (79)80, 2-3.15-16.18-19 / 2*

HH, adapt.

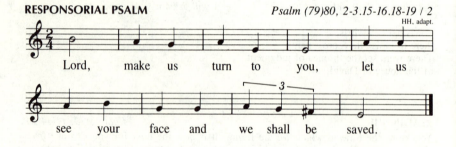

Lord, make us turn to you, let us see your face and we shall be saved.

O shepherd of Israel, hear us,
shine forth from your cherubim throne.
O Lord, rouse up your might,
O Lord, come to our help. ℟.

God of hosts, turn again, we implore,
look down from heaven and see.
Visit this vine and protect it,
the vine your right hand has planted. ℟.

May your hand be on the man you have
chosen,
the man you have given your strength.
And we shall never forsake you again;
give us life that we may call upon your
name. ℟.

READING II *1 Corinthians 1, 3-9 / 2*

Grace and peace from God our Father and the Lord Jesus Christ.

I continually thank my God for you because of the favor he has bestowed on you in Christ Jesus, in whom you have been richly endowed with every gift of speech and knowledge. Likewise, the witness I bore to Christ has been so confirmed among you that you lack no spiritual gift as you wait for the revelation of our Lord Jesus [Christ.]

He will strengthen you to the end, so that you will be blameless on the day of our Lord Jesus Christ. God is faithful, and it was he who called you to fellowship with his Son, Jesus Christ our Lord.

GOSPEL *Mark 13, 33-37 / 2*

Jesus said to his disciples: "Be constantly on the watch! Stay awake! You do not know when the appointed time will come. It is like a man traveling abroad. He leaves home and places his servants in charge, each with his own task; and he orders the man at the gate to watch with a sharp eye. Look around you! You do not know when the master of the house is coming, whether at dusk, at midnight, when the cock crows, or at early dawn. Do not let him come suddenly and catch you asleep. What I say to you, I say to all: Be on guard!"

FIRST SUNDAY OF ADVENT / C 768

READING I *Jeremiah 33, 14-16 / 3*

The days are coming, says the Lord, when I will fulfill the promise I made to the house of Israel and Judah. In those days, in that time, I will raise up for David a just shoot; he shall do what is right and just in the land. In those days Judah shall be safe and Jerusalem shall dwell secure; this is what they shall call her: "The Lord our justice."

RESPONSORIAL PSALM *Psalm (24)25, 4-5.8-9.10.14 / 3*

RJT
To you, O Lord, I lift my soul.

Lord, make me know your ways.
Lord, teach me your paths.
Make me walk in your truth, and
teach me,
for you are God my savior.
In you I hope all day long. ℟.

The Lord is good and upright.
He shows the path to those who
stray,
he guides the humble in the right
path,
he teaches his way to the poor. ℟.

His ways are faithfulness and love
for those who keep his covenant and
will.
The Lord's friendship is for those
who revere him;
to them he reveals his covenant. ℟.

READING II *1 Thessalonians 3, 12-4, 2 / 3*

May the Lord increase you and make you overflow with love for one another and for all, even as our love does for you. May he strengthen your hearts, making them blameless and holy before our God and Father at the coming of our Lord Jesus with all his holy ones.

Now, my brothers, we beg and exhort you in the Lord Jesus that, even as you learned from us how to conduct yourselves in a way pleasing to God–which you are indeed doing–so you must learn to make still greater progress. You know the instructions we gave you in the Lord Jesus.

GOSPEL *Luke 21, 25-28, 34-36 / 3*

Jesus said to his disciples: "There will be signs in the sun, the moon and the stars. On the earth, nations will be in anguish, distraught at the roaring of the sea and the waves. Men will die of fright in anticipation of what is coming upon the earth. The powers in the heavens will be shaken. After that, men will see the Son of Man coming on a cloud with great power and glory. When these things begin to happen, stand up straight and raise your heads, for your ransom is near at hand.

"Be on guard lest your spirits become bloated with indulgence and drunkenness and worldly cares. The great day will suddenly close in on you like a trap. The day I speak of will come upon all who dwell on the face of the earth, so be on the watch. Pray constantly for the strength to escape whatever is in prospect, and to stand secure before the Son of Man."

769 SECOND SUNDAY OF ADVENT / A

READING I *Isaiah 11, 1-10 / 4*

On that day
A shoot shall sprout from the stump of Jesse,
and from his roots a bud shall blossom.
The spirit of the Lord shall rest upon him:
a spirit of wisdom and of understanding,
A spirit of counsel and of strength,
a spirit of knowledge and of fear of the Lord,
and his delight shall be the fear of the Lord.
Not by appearance shall he judge,
nor by hearsay shall he decide,
But he shall judge the poor with justice,
and decide aright for the land's afflicted.
He shall strike the ruthless with the rod of his mouth,
and with the breadth of his lips he shall slay the wicked.
Justice shall be the band around his waist,
and faithfulness a belt upon his hips.

Then the wolf shall be a guest of the lamb,
and the leopard shall lie down with the kid;
The calf and the young lion shall browse together,
with a little child to guide them.
The cow and the bear shall be neighbors,
together their young shall rest;
the lion shall eat hay like the ox.
The baby shall play by the cobra's den,
and the child lay his hand on the adder's lair.
There shall be no harm or ruin on all my holy mountain;
for the earth shall be filled with knowledge of the Lord,
as water covers the sea.

On that day
The root of Jesse,
set up as a signal for the nations,
The Gentiles shall seek out,
for his dwelling shall be glorious.

RESPONSORIAL PSALM *Psalm (71)72, 1-2.7-8.12-13.17 / 4*

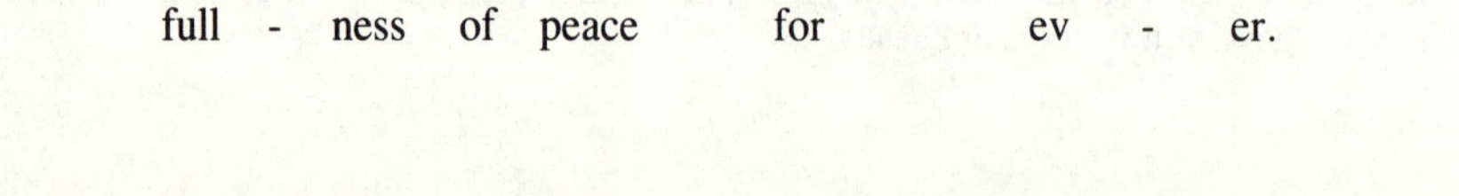

JS

Jus - tice shall flour - ish in his time, and
full - ness of peace for ev - er.

O God, give your judgment to the
king,
to a king's son your justice,
that he may judge your people in
justice
and your poor in right judgment. ℟.

In his days justice shall flourish
and peace till the moon fails.
He shall rule from sea to sea,
from the Great River to earth's
bounds. ℟.

For he shall save the
poor when they cry
and the needy who are helpless.
He will have pity on the weak
and save the lives of the poor. ℟.

May his name be blessed for ever
and endure like the sun.
Every tribe shall be blessed in him,
all nations bless his name. ℟.

READING II *Romans 15, 4-9 / 4*

Everything written before our time was written for our instruction, that we might derive hope from the lessons of patience and the words of encouragement in the Scriptures. May God, the source of all patience and encouragement, enable you to live in perfect harmony with one another according to the spirit of Christ Jesus, so that with one heart and voice you may glorify God, the Father of our Lord Jesus Christ.

Accept one another, then, as Christ accepted you, for the glory of God. Yes, I affirm that Christ became the servant of the Jews because of God's faithfulness in fulfilling the promises to the patriarchs whereas the Gentiles glorify God because of his mercy. As Scripture has it, "Therefore I will praise you among the Gentiles and I will sing to your name."

GOSPEL *Matthew 3, 1-12 / 4*

When John the Baptizer made his appearance as a preacher in the desert of Judea, this was his theme: "Reform your lives! The reign of God is at hand." It was of him that the prophet Isaiah had spoken when he said,

"A herald's voice in the desert:
'Prepare the way of the Lord,
make straight his paths.' "

John was clothed in a garment of camel's hair and wore a leather belt around his waist. Grasshoppers and wild honey were his food. At that time Jerusalem, all Judea, and the whole region around the Jordan were going out to him. They were being baptized by him in the Jordan River as they confessed their sins.

When he saw that many of the Pharisees and Sadducees were stepping forward for this bath, he said to them: "You brood of vipers! Who told you to flee from the wrath to come? Give some evidence that you mean to reform. Do not pride yourselves on the claim, 'Abraham is our father.' I tell you, God can raise up children to Abraham from these very stones. Even now the ax is laid to the root of the tree. Every tree that is not fruitful will be cut down and thrown into the fire. I baptize you in water for the sake of reform, but the one who will follow me is more powerful than I. I am not even fit to carry his sandals. He it is who will baptize you in the Holy Spirit and fire. His winnowing-fan is in his hand. He will clear his threshing floor, and gather his grain into the barn, but the chaff he will burn in unquenchable fire."

SECOND SUNDAY OF ADVENT / B 770

READING I *Isaiah 40, 1-5.9-11 / 5*

Comfort, give comfort to my people,
says your God.
Speak tenderly to Jerusalem, and
proclaim to her
that her service is at an end,
her guilt has been expiated;
Indeed, she has received from the hand
of the Lord
double for all her sins.
A voice cries out:

In the desert prepare the way of the
Lord!
Make straight in the wasteland a
highway for our God!
Every valley shall be filled in,
every mountain and hill shall be
made low;
The rugged land shall be made a plain,
the rough country, a broad valley.
Then the glory of the Lord shall be
revealed,
and all mankind shall see it together;
for the mouth of the Lord has
spoken.
Go up onto a high mountain,
Zion, herald of glad tidings;
Cry out at the top of your voice,
Jerusalem, herald of good news!
Fear not to cry out
and say to the cities of Judah:
Here is your God!
Here comes with power
the Lord God,
who rules by his strong arm;
Here is his reward with him,
his recompense before him.
Like a shepherd he feeds his flock;
in his arms he gathers the lambs,
Carrying them in his bosom,
and leading the ewes with care.

RESPONSORIAL PSALM

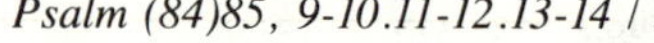

Psalm (84)85, 9-10.11-12.13-14 / 5

JRC

Lord, let us see your kind-ness, and grant us your sal - va-tion.

I will hear what the Lord God has to
say,
a voice that speaks of peace,
peace for his people and his friends
and those who turn to him in their
hearts.
His help is near for those who fear him
and his glory will dwell in our land. ℟.

Mercy and faithfulness have met;
justice and peace have embraced.
Faithfulness shall spring from the earth
and justice look down from heaven. ℟.

The Lord will make us prosper
and our earth shall yield its fruit.
Justice shall march before him
and peace shall follow his steps. ℟.

READING II *2 Peter 3, 8-14 / 5*

This point must not be overlooked, dear friends. In the Lord's eyes, one day is as a thousand years and a thousand years are as a day. The Lord does not delay in keeping his promise–though some consider it "delay." Rather, he shows you generous patience, since he wants none to perish but all to come to repentance. The day of the Lord will come like a thief, and on that day the heavens will vanish with a roar; the elements will be destroyed by fire, and the earth and all its deeds will be made manifest.

Since everything is to be destroyed in this way, what sort of men must you not be! How holy in your conduct and devotion, looking for the coming of the day of God and trying to hasten it! Because of it, the heavens will be destroyed in flames and the elements will melt away in a blaze. What we await are new heavens and a new earth where, according to his promise, the justice of God will reside. So, beloved, while waiting for this, make every effort to be found without stain of defilement, and at peace in his sight.

GOSPEL *Mark 1, 1-8 / 5*

Here begins the gospel of Jesus Christ, the Son of God. In Isaiah the prophet, it is written:

"I send my messenger before you
to prepare your way:
a herald's voice in the desert, crying,
'Make ready the way of the Lord,
clear him a straight path.' "

Thus it was that John the Baptizer appeared in the desert proclaiming a baptism of repentance which led to the forgiveness of sins. All the Judean countryside and the people of Jerusalem went out to him in great numbers. They were being baptized by him in the Jordan River as they confessed their sins. John was clothed in camel's hair, and wore a leather belt around his waist. His food was grasshoppers and wild honey. The theme of his preaching was: "One more powerful than I is to come after me. I am not fit to stoop and untie his sandal straps. I have baptized you in water; he will baptize you in the Holy Spirit."

SECOND SUNDAY OF ADVENT / C 771

READING I *Baruch 5, 1-9 / 6*

Jerusalem, take off your robe of mourning and misery;
put on the splendor of glory from God forever:
Wrapped in the cloak of justice from God,
bear on your head the mitre
that displays the glory of the eternal name.
For God will show all the earth your splendor:
you will be named by God forever
the peace of justice, the glory of God's worship.

Up, Jerusalem! stand upon the heights;
look to the east and see your children
Gathered from the east and the west
at the word of the Holy One,
rejoicing that they are remembered by God.
Led away on foot by their enemies they left you:
but God will bring them back to you
borne aloft in glory as on royal thrones.
For God has commanded
that every lofty mountain be made low,
And that the age-old depths and gorges
be filled to level ground,
that Israel may advance secure in the glory of God.
The forests and every fragrant kind of tree
have overshadowed Israel at God's command;
For God is leading Israel in joy
by the light of his glory,
with his mercy and justice for company.

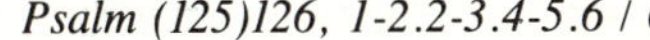

RESPONSORIAL PSALM *Psalm (125)126, 1-2.2-3.4-5.6 / 6*

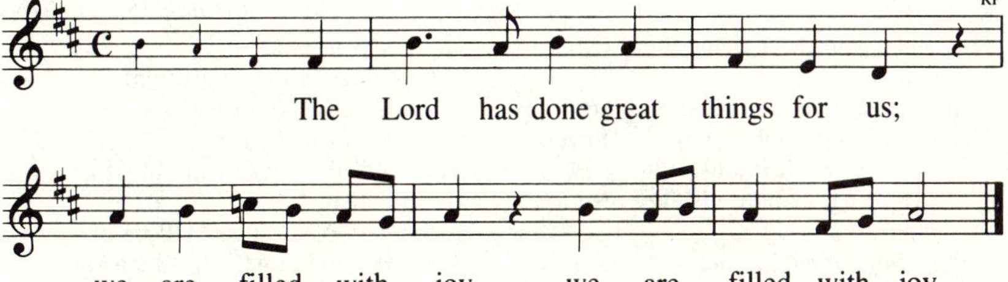
RP
The Lord has done great things for us;
we are filled with joy, we are filled with joy.

When the Lord delivered Zion from bondage,
it seemed like a dream.
Then was our mouth filled with laughter,
on our lips there were songs. ℟.

The heathens themselves said: "What marvels
the Lord worked for them!"
What marvels the Lord worked for us!
Indeed we were glad. ℟.

Deliver us, O Lord, from our bondage
as streams in dry land.
Those who are sowing in tears
will sing when they reap. ℟.

They go out, they go out, full of tears,
carrying seed for the sowing;
they come back, they come back, full
of song,
carrying their sheaves. ℟.

READING II *Philippians 1, 4-6.8-11 / 6*

In every prayer I utter, I rejoice as I plead on your behalf, at the way you have all continually helped promote the gospel from the very first day.

I am sure of this much: that he who has begun the good work in you will carry it through to completion, right up to the day of Christ Jesus. God himself can testify how much I long for each of you with the affection of Christ Jesus! My prayer is that your love may more and more abound, both in understanding and wealth of experience, so that with a clear conscience and blameless conduct you may learn to value the things that really matter, up to the very day of Christ. It is my wish that you may be found rich in the harvest of justice which Jesus Christ has ripened in you, to the glory and praise of God.

GOSPEL *Luke 3, 1-6 / 6*

In the fifteenth year of the rule of Tiberius Caesar, when Pontius Pilate was procurator of Judea, Herod tetrarch of Galilee, Philip his brother tetrarch of the region of Ituraea and Trachonitis, and Lysanias tetrarch of Abilene, during the high-priesthood of Annas and Caiaphas, the word of God was spoken to John son of Zechariah in the desert. He went about the entire region of the Jordan proclaiming a baptism of repentance which led to the forgiveness of sins, as is written in the book of the words of Isaiah the prophet:

"A herald's voice in the desert, crying,
'Make ready the way of the Lord,
clear him a straight path.
Every valley shall be filled
and every mountain and hill shall be leveled.
The windings shall be made straight
and the rough ways smooth,
and all mankind shall see the salvation of God.' "

772 THIRD SUNDAY OF ADVENT / A

READING I *Isaiah 35, 1-6.10 / 7*

The desert and the parched land will
exult;
the steppe will rejoice and bloom.
They will bloom with abundant flowers,
and rejoice with joyful song.
The glory of Lebanon will be given to
them,
the splendor of Carmel and Sharon;
They will see the glory of the Lord,
the splendor of our God.

Strengthen the hands that are feeble,
make firm the knees that are weak,
Say to those whose hearts are
frightened:
Be strong, fear not!

Here is your God,
he comes with vindication;
With divine recompense
he comes to save you.
Then will the eyes of the blind be
opened,
the ears of the deaf will be cleared;
Then will the lame leap like a stag,
then the tongue of the dumb will sing.

Those whom the Lord has ransomed
will return
and enter Zion singing,
crowned with everlasting joy;
They will meet with joy and gladness,
sorrow and mourning will flee.

RESPONSORIAL PSALM *Psalm (145)146, 6-7.8-9.9-10 / 7*

RL
O Lord, come and save us.

It is he who keeps faith for ever,
who is just to those who are oppressed.
It is he who gives bread to the
  hungry,
the Lord, who sets prisoners free. ℟.

The Lord who gives sight to the blind,
who raises up those who are bowed
  down,
the Lord, who protects the stranger,
and upholds the widow and orphan. ℟.

It is the Lord who loves the just
but thwarts the path of the wicked.
The Lord will reign for ever,
Zion's God, from age to age. ℟.

READING II *James 5, 7-10 / 7*

Be patient, my brothers, until the coming of the Lord. See how the farmer awaits the precious yield of the soil. He looks forward to it patiently while the soil receives the winter and the spring rains. You too, must be patient. Steady your hearts, because the coming of the Lord is at hand. Do not grumble against one another, my brothers, lest you be condemned. See! The judge stands at the gate. As your models in suffering hardships and in patience, brothers, take the prophets who spoke in the name of the Lord.

GOSPEL *Matthew 11, 2-11 / 7*

John in prison heard about the works Christ performed, and sent a message through his disciples to ask him, "Are you 'He who is to come' or do we look for another?" In reply, Jesus said to them: "Go back and report to John what you hear and see: the blind recover their sight, cripples walk, lepers are cured, the deaf hear, dead men are raised to life, and the poor have the good news preached to them. Blest is the man who finds no stumbling block in me."

As the messengers set off, Jesus began to speak to the crowds about John: "What did you go out to the wasteland to see–a reed swaying in the wind? Tell me, what did you go out to see–someone luxuriously dressed? Remember, those who dress luxuriously are to be found in royal palaces. Why then did you go out–to see a prophet? A prophet indeed, and something more! It is about this man that Scripture says,

'I send my messenger ahead of you
to prepare your way before you.'

"I solemnly assure you, history has not known a man born of woman greater than John the Baptizer. Yet the least born into the kingdom of God is greater than he."

THIRD SUNDAY OF ADVENT / B 773

READING I *Isaiah 61, 1-2.10-11 / 8*

The spirit of the Lord God is upon me,
  because the Lord has anointed me;
He has sent me to bring tidings to the
  lowly,
  to heal the brokenhearted,
To proclaim liberty to the captives
  and release to the prisoners,
To announce a year of favor from the
  Lord
  and a day of vindication by our God.

I rejoice heartily in the Lord,
in my God is the joy of my soul;
For he has clothed me with a robe of salvation,
and wrapped me in a mantle of justice,
Like a bridegroom adorned with a diadem,
like a bride bedecked with her jewels.
As the earth brings forth its plants,
and a garden makes its growth spring up,
So will the Lord God make justice and praise
spring up before all the nations.

RESPONSORIAL PSALM *Luke 1, 46-48.49-50.53-54 / 8*

RJB
My soul re-joic-es, my soul re-joic-es in my God.

My soul glorifies the Lord,
my spirit rejoices in God, my savior.
He looks on his servant in her nothingness;
henceforth all ages will call me blessed. ℟.

The Almighty works marvels for me.
Holy his name!
His mercy is from age to age,
on those who fear him. ℟.

He fills the starving with good things,
sends the rich away empty.
He protects Israel his servant,
remembering his mercy. ℟.

READING II *1 Thessalonians 5, 16-24 / 8*

Rejoice always, never cease praying, render constant thanks; such is God's will for you in Christ Jesus.

Do not stifle the spirit. Do not despise prophecies. Test everything; retain what is good. Avoid any semblance of evil.

May the God of peace make you perfect in holiness. May you be preserved whole and entire, spirit, soul, and body, irreproachable at the coming of our Lord Jesus Christ. He who calls us is trustworthy, therefore he will do it.

GOSPEL *John 1, 6-8.19-28 / 8*

There was a man named John sent by God, who came as a witness to testify to the light, so that through him all men might believe–but only to testify to the light, for he himself was not the light.

The testimony John gave when the Jews sent priests and Levites from Jerusalem to ask "Who are you?" was the absolute statement, "I am not the Messiah." They questioned him further, "Who, then? Elijah?" "I am not Elijah," he answered. "Are you the prophet?" "No," he replied.

Finally they said to him: "Tell us who you are, so that we can give some answer to those who sent us. What do you have to say for yourself?" He said, quoting the prophet Isaiah, "I am

'a voice in the desert, crying out:
Make straight the way of the Lord!' "

Those whom the Pharisees had sent proceeded to question him further: "If you are not the Messiah, nor Elijah, nor the prophet, why do you baptize?" John answered them: "I baptize with water. There is one among you whom you do not recognize–the one who is to come after me–the strap of whose sandal I am not worthy to unfasten." This happened in Bethany, across the Jordan, where John was baptizing.

THIRD SUNDAY OF ADVENT / C

READING I

Zephaniah 3, 14-18 / 9

Shout for joy, O daughter Zion!
sing joyfully, O Israel!
Be glad and exult with all your heart,
O daughter Jerusalem!
The Lord has removed the judgment against you,
he has turned away your enemies;
The King of Israel, the Lord, is in your midst,
you have no further misfortune to fear.
On that day, it shall be said to Jerusalem:
Fear not, O Zion, be not discouraged!
The Lord, your God, is in your midst,
a mighty savior;
He will rejoice over you with gladness,
and renew you in his love.
He will sing joyfully because of you,
as one sings at festivals.

RESPONSORIAL PSALM

Isaiah 12, 2-3.4.5-6 / 9

RJB

Cry out with joy and glad - ness: for a- mong you is the great and Ho-ly One of Is - ra - el.

Truly, God is my salvation,
I trust, I shall not fear.
For the Lord is my strength, my song,
he became my savior.
With joy you will draw water
from the wells of salvation. ℟.

Give thanks to the Lord, give praise to his name!
Make his mighty deeds known to the peoples! ℟.

Declare the greatness of his name,
sing a psalm to the Lord!
For he has done glorious deeds,
make them known to all the earth!
People of Zion, sing and shout for joy
for great in your midst is the Holy One of Israel. ℟.

READING II

Philippians 4, 4-7 / 9

Rejoice in the Lord always! I say it again. Rejoice! Everyone should see how unselfish you are. The Lord himself is near. Dismiss all anxiety from your minds. Present your needs to God in every form of prayer and in petitions full of gratitude. Then God's own peace, which is beyond all understanding, will stand guard over your hearts and minds, in Christ Jesus.

GOSPEL

Luke 3, 10-18 / 9

The crowds asked John, "What ought we to do?" In reply he said, "Let the man with two coats give to him who has none. The man who has food should do the same."

Tax collectors also came to be baptized, and they said to him, "Teacher, what are we to do?" He answered them, "Exact nothing over and above your fixed amount."

Soldiers also asked him, "What about us?" He told them, "Do not bully anyone. Denounce no one falsely. Be content with your pay."

The people were full of anticipation, wondering in their hearts whether John might be the Messiah. John answered them all by saying: "I am baptizing you in water, but there is one to come who is mightier than I. I am not fit to loosen his sandal strap. He will baptize you in the Holy Spirit and in fire. His winnowing-fan is in his hand to clear his threshing floor and gather the wheat into his granary, but the chaff he will burn in unquenchable fire." Using exhortations of this sort, he preached the good news to the people.

775 FOURTH SUNDAY OF ADVENT / A

READING I *Isaiah 7, 10-14 / 10*

The Lord spoke to Ahaz: Ask for a sign from the Lord, your God; let it be deep as the nether world, or high as the sky! But Ahaz answered, "I will not ask! I will not tempt the Lord!" Then he said: Listen, O house of David! Is it not enough for you to weary men, must you also weary my God? Therefore the Lord himself will give you this sign: the virgin shall be with child, and bear a son, and shall name him Immanuel.

RESPONSORIAL PSALM *Psalm (23)24, 1-2.3-4.5-6 / 10*

RP
Let the Lord en-ter; he is king of glo-ry.

The Lord's is the earth and its fullness,
the world and all its peoples.
It is he who set it on the seas;
on the waters he made it firm. ℟.

Who shall climb the mountain of the Lord?
Who shall stand in his holy place?
The man with clean hands and pure heart,
who desires not worthless things. ℟.

He shall receive blessings from the Lord
and reward from the God who saves him.
Such are the men who seek him,
seek the face of the God of Jacob. ℟.

READING II *Romans 1, 1-7 / 10*

Greetings from Paul, a servant of Christ Jesus, called to be an apostle and set apart to proclaim the gospel of God which he promised long ago through his prophets, as the holy Scriptures record–the gospel concerning his Son, who was descended from David according to the flesh but was made Son of God in power, according to the spirit of holiness, by his resurrection from the dead: Jesus Christ our Lord. Through him we have been favored with apostleship, that we may spread his name and bring to obedient faith all the Gentiles, among whom are you who have been called to belong to Jesus Christ.

To all in Rome, beloved of God and called to holiness, grace and peace from God our Father and the Lord Jesus Christ.

GOSPEL *Matthew 1, 18-24 / 10*

This is how the birth of Jesus Christ came about. When his mother Mary was engaged to Joseph, but before they lived together, she was found with child through the power of the Holy Spirit. Joseph her husband, an upright man unwilling to expose her to the law, decided to divorce her quietly. Such was his intention when suddenly the angel of the Lord appeared in a dream and said to him: "Joseph, son of David, have no fear about taking Mary as your wife. It is by the Holy Spirit that she has conceived this child. She is to have a son and you are to name him Jesus because he will save his people from their sins." All this happened to fulfill what the Lord had said through

the prophet:
"The virgin shall be with child
and give birth to a son,
and they shall call him Emmanuel,"
a name which means "God is with us." When Joseph awoke he did as the angel of the Lord had directed him and received her into his home as his wife.

FOURTH SUNDAY OF ADVENT / B

776

READING I *2 Samuel 7, 1-5.8-11.16 / 11*

When King David was settled in his palace, and the Lord had given him rest from his enemies on every side, he said to Nathan the prophet, "Here I am living in a house of cedar, while the ark of God dwells in a tent!" Nathan answered the king, "Go, do whatever you have in mind, for the Lord is with you." But that night the Lord spoke to Nathan and said: "Go, tell my servant David, 'Thus says the Lord: Should you build me a house to dwell in?'

" 'It was I who took you from the pasture and from the care of the flock to be commander of my people Israel. I have been with you wherever you went, and I have destroyed all your enemies before you. And I will make you famous like the great ones of the earth. I will fix a place for my people Israel; I will plant them so that they may dwell in their place without further disturbance. Neither shall the wicked continue to afflict them as they did of old, since the time I first appointed judges over my people Israel. I will give you rest from all your enemies. The Lord also reveals to you that he will establish a house for you. Your house and your kingdom shall endure forever before me; your throne shall stand firm forever.' "

RESPONSORIAL PSALM *Psalm (88)89, 2-3.4-5.27.29 / 11*

JRC
For ev - er I will sing the good-ness of the Lord.

I will sing for ever of your love, O Lord;
through all ages my mouth will proclaim your truth.
Of this I am sure, that your love lasts for ever,
that your truth is firmly established as the heavens. R.

"With my chosen one I have made a covenant;
I have sworn to David my servant:
I will establish your dynasty for ever
and set up your throne through all ages." R.

He will say to me: "You are my father,
my God, the rock who saves me."
I will keep my love for him always;
with him my covenant shall last. R.

READING II *Romans 16, 25-27 / 11*

To him who is able to strengthen you in the gospel which I proclaim when I preach Jesus Christ, the gospel which reveals the mystery hidden for many ages but now manifested through the writings of the prophets, and, at the command of the eternal God, made known to all the Gentiles that they may believe and obey–to him, the God who alone is wise, may glory be given through Jesus Christ unto endless ages. Amen.

GOSPEL *Luke 1, 26-38 / 11*

The angel Gabriel was sent from God to a town of Galilee named Nazareth, to a virgin betrothed to a man named Joseph, of the house of David. The virgin's name was Mary. Upon arriving, the angel said to her: "Rejoice, O highly favored daughter! The Lord is with you. Blessed are you among women." She was deeply troubled by his words, and wondered what his greeting meant. The angel went on to say to her: "Do not fear, Mary. You have found favor with God. You shall conceive and bear a son and give him the name Jesus. Great will be his dignity and he will be called Son of the Most High. The Lord God will give him the throne of David his father. He will rule over the house of Jacob forever and his reign will be without end."

Mary said to the angel, "How can this be since I do not know man?" The angel answered her: "The Holy Spirit will come upon you and the power of the Most High will overshadow you; hence, the holy offspring to be born will be called Son of God. Know that Elizabeth your kinswoman has conceived a son in her old age; she who was thought to be sterile is now in her sixth month, for nothing is impossible with God."

Mary said: "I am the maidservant of the Lord. Let it be done to me as you say." With that the angel left her.

777
FOURTH SUNDAY OF ADVENT / C

READING I *Micah 5, 1-4 / 12*

Thus says the Lord:
You, Bethlehem-Ephrathah
too small to be among the clans of Judah,
From you shall come forth for me
one who is to be ruler in Israel;
Whose origin is from old,
from ancient times.
(Therefore the Lord will give them up,
until the time
when she who is to give birth has borne,
And the rest of his brethren shall return
to the children of Israel.)
He shall stand firm and shepherd his flock
by the strength of the Lord,
in the majestic name of the Lord,
his God;
And they shall remain, for now his greatness
shall reach to the ends of the earth;
he shall be peace.

RESPONSORIAL PSALM *Psalm (79)80, 2-3.15-16.18-19 / 12*

HH, adapt.

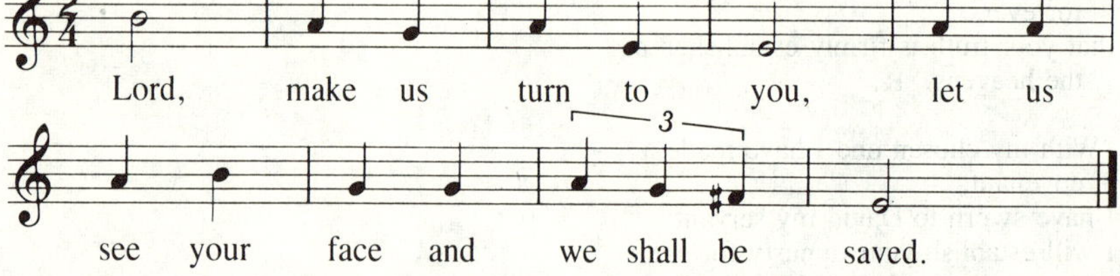

Lord, make us turn to you, let us see your face and we shall be saved.

O shepherd of Israel, hear us,
shine forth from your cherubim throne.
O Lord, rouse up your might,
O Lord, come to our help. ℟.

God of hosts, turn again, we implore,
look down from heaven and see.
Visit this vine and protect it,
the vine your right hand has planted. ℟.

May your hand be on the man you have chosen,
the man you have given your strength.
And we shall never forsake you again;
give us life that we may call upon your name. ℟.

READING II *Hebrews 10, 5-10 / 12*

On coming into the world Jesus said:
"Sacrifice and offering you did not desire, but a body you have prepared for me;
Holocausts and sin offerings you took no delight in.
Then I said, 'As is written of me in the book,
I have come to do your will, O God.' "
First he says,
"Sacrifices and offerings, holocausts and sin offerings
you neither desired nor delighted in."
(These are offered according to the prescriptions of the law.) Then he says,
"I have come to do your will."
In other words, he takes away the first covenant to establish the second.

By this "will," we have been sanctified through the offering of the body of Jesus Christ once for all.

GOSPEL *Luke 1, 39-45 / 12*

Mary set out, proceeding in haste into the hill country to a town of Judah, where she entered Zechariah's house and greeted Elizabeth. When Elizabeth heard Mary's greeting, the baby stirred in her womb. Elizabeth was filled with the Holy Spirit, and cried out in a loud voice: "Blessed are you among women and blessed is the fruit of your womb. But who am I that the mother of my Lord should come to me? The moment your greeting sounded in my ears, the baby stirred in my womb for joy. Blessed is she who trusted that the Lord's words to her would be fulfilled."

DECEMBER 25: CHRISTMAS–VIGIL 778

READING I *Isaiah 62, 1-5 / 13*

For Zion's sake I will not be silent,
for Jerusalem's sake I will not be quiet,
Until her vindication shines forth like the dawn
and her victory like a burning torch.

Nations shall behold your vindication,
and all kings your glory;
You shall be called by a new name
pronounced by the mouth of the Lord.
You shall be a glorious crown in the hand of the Lord,
a royal diadem held by your God.
No more shall men call you "Forsaken,"
or your land "Desolate,"
But you shall be called "My Delight,"
and your land "Espoused."
For the Lord delights in you,
and makes your land his spouse.

As a young man marries a virgin,
your Builder shall marry you;
And as a bridegroom rejoices in his bride
so shall your God rejoice in you.

RESPONSORIAL PSALM *Psalm (88)89, 4-5.16-17.27.29 / 13*

JRC
For ev - er I will sing the good-ness of the Lord.

"With my chosen one I have made a covenant;
I have sworn to David my servant:
I will establish your dynasty for ever
and set up your throne through all ages." ℟.

Happy the people who acclaim such a
king,
who walk, O Lord, in the light of your
face,
who find their joy every day in your
name,
who make your justice the source of
their bliss. ℟.

He will say to me: "You are my father,
my God, the rock who saves me."
I will keep my love for him always;
with him my covenant shall last. ℟.

READING II *Acts 13, 16-17.22-25 / 13*

[When Paul came to Antioch Pisidia, he entered the synagogue there] and motioning to them for silence, he began: "Fellow Israelites and you others who reverence our God, listen to what I have to say! The God of the people Israel once chose our fathers. He made this people great during their sojourn in the land of Egypt, and 'with an outstretched arm' he led them out of it. God raised up David as their king; on his behalf he testified, 'I have found David son of Jesse to be a man after my own heart who will fulfill my every wish.'

"According to his promise, God has brought forth from this man's descendants Jesus, a savior for Israel. John heralded the coming of Jesus by proclaiming a baptism of repentance to all the people of Israel. As John's career was coming to an end, he would say, 'What you suppose me to be I am not. Rather, look for the one who comes after me. I am not worthy to unfasten the sandals on his feet.' "

GOSPEL *Matthew 1, 1-25 or 1, 18-25 / 13*

For short form read only the part in brackets.

A family record of Jesus Christ,
son of David, son of Abraham.
Abraham was the father of Isaac, Isaac
the father of Jacob, Jacob the father of
Judah and his brothers.
Judah was the father of Perez and
Zerah, whose mother was Tamar.
Perez was the father of Hezron,
Hezron the father of Ram.
Ram was the father of Amminadab,
Amminadab the father of Nahshon,
Nahshon the father of Salmon.
Salmon was the father of Boaz, whose
mother was Rahab,
Boaz was the father of Obed, whose
mother was Ruth.
Obed was the father of Jesse,
Jesse the father of King David.
David was the father of Solomon,
whose mother had been the wife of
Uriah.
Solomon was the father of Rehoboam,
Rehoboam the father of Abijah,
Abijah the father of Asa.
Asa was the father of Jehoshaphat,
Jehoshaphat the father of Joram,
Joram the father of Uzziah.
Uzziah was the father of Jotham,
Jotham the father of Ahaz,
Ahaz the father of Hezekiah.
Hezekiah was the father of Manassah,
Manasseh the father of Amos,
Amos the father of Josiah.
Josiah became the father of Jechoniah
and his brothers at the time of the
Babylonian exile.
After the Babylonian exile
Jechoniah was the father of Shealtiel,
Shealtiel the father of Zerubbabel.
Zerubbabel was the father of Abiud,
Abiud the father of Eliakim,
Eliakim the father of Azor.
Azor was the father of Zadok,
Zadok the father of Achim,
Achim the father of Eliud.
Eliud was the father of Eleazar,
Eleazar the father of Matthan,
Matthan the father of Jacob.
Jacob was the father of Joseph the
husband of Mary.
It was of her that Jesus who is called
the Messiah was born.
Thus the total number of generations
is:
from Abraham to David, fourteen
generations;
from David to the Babylonian
captivity, fourteen generations;
from the Babylonian captivity to the
Messiah, fourteen generations.

[Now this is how the birth of Jesus Christ came about. When his mother Mary was engaged to Joseph, but before they lived together, she was found with child through the power of the Holy Spirit. Joseph her husband, an upright man unwilling to expose her to the law, decided to divorce her quietly. Such was his intention when suddenly the angel of the Lord appeared in a dream and said to him: "Joseph, son of David, have no fear about taking Mary as your wife. It is by the Holy Spirit that she has conceived this child. She is to have a son and you are to name him Jesus because he will save his people from their sins." All this happened to fulfill what the Lord had said through the prophet:

"The virgin shall be with child
and give birth to a son,
and they shall call him Emmanuel,"

a name which means "God with us." When Joseph awoke he did as the angel of the Lord had directed him and received her into his home as his wife. He had no relations with her at any time before she bore a son, whom he named Jesus.]

DECEMBER 25: CHRISTMAS–MASS AT MIDNIGHT 779

READING I *Isaiah 9, 1-6 / 14*

The people who walked in darkness
have seen a great light;
Upon those who dwelt in the land of gloom
a light has shown.
You have brought them abundant joy
and great rejoicing,
As they rejoice before you as at the harvest,
as men make merry when dividing spoils.
For the yoke that burdened them,
the pole on their shoulder,
And the rod of their taskmaster
you have smashed, as on the day of Midian.
For every boot that tramped in battle,
every cloak rolled in blood,
will be burned as fuel for flames.
For a child is born to us, a son is given us;
upon his shoulder dominion rests.
They name him Wonder-Counselor,
God-Hero,
Father-Forever, Prince of Peace.
His dominion is vast
and forever peaceful,
From David's throne, and over his kingdom,
which he confirms and sustains
By judgment and justice,
both now and forever.
The zeal of the Lord of hosts will do this!

RESPONSORIAL PSALM *Psalm (95)96, 1-2.2-3.11-12.13 / 14*

RP
To - day is born our Sav - ior, Christ the Lord.

O sing a new song to the Lord,
sing to the Lord all the earth.
O sing to the Lord, bless his name. ℟.

Proclaim his help day by day,
tell among the nations his glory
and his wonders among all the peoples. ℟.

Let the heavens rejoice and earth be glad,
let the sea and all within it thunder praise,
let the land and all it bears rejoice,
all the trees of the wood shout for joy. ℟.

At the presence of the Lord for he comes,
he comes to rule the earth.
With justice he will rule the world,
he will judge the peoples with his truth. ℟.

READING II *Titus 2, 11-14 / 14*

The grace of God has appeared, offering salvation to all men. It trains us to reject godless ways and worldly desires, and live temperately, justly, and devoutly in this age as we await our blessed hope, the appearing of the glory of the great God and of our Savior Christ Jesus. It was he who sacrificed himself for us, to redeem us from all unrighteousness and to cleanse for himself a people of his own, eager to do what is right.

GOSPEL *Luke 2, 1-14 / 14*

In those days Caesar Augustus published a decree ordering a census of the whole world. This first census took place while Quirinius was governor of Syria. Everyone went to register, each to his own town. And so Joseph went from the town of Nazareth in Galilee to Judea, to David's town of Bethlehem–because he was of the house and lineage of David–to register with Mary, his espoused wife, who was with child.

While they were there the days of her confinement were completed. She gave birth to her first-born son and wrapped him in swaddling clothes and laid him in a manger, because there was no room for them in the place where travelers lodged.

There were shepherds in the locality, living in the fields and keeping night watch by turns over their flock. The angel of the Lord appeared to them, as the glory of the Lord shone around them, and they were very much afraid. The angel said to them: "You have nothing to fear! I come to proclaim good news to you–tidings of great joy to be shared by the whole people. This day in David's city a savior has been born to you, the Messiah and Lord. Let this be a sign to you: in a manger you will find an infant wrapped in swaddling clothes." Suddenly, there was with the angel a multitude of the heavenly host, praising God and saying,

"Glory to God in high heaven,
peace on earth to those on whom his favor rests."

780 DECEMBER 25: CHRISTMAS–MASS AT DAWN

READING I *Isaiah 62, 11-12 / 15*

See, the Lord proclaims
to the ends of the earth:
Say to daughter Zion,
your savior comes!
Here is his reward with him,
his recompense before him.
They shall be called the holy people,
the redeemed of the Lord,
and you shall be called "Frequented,"
a city that is not forsaken.

RESPONSORIAL PSALM *Psalm (96)97, 1.6.11-12 / 15*

JRC
A light will shine on us this day: the Lord is born for us.

The Lord is king, let earth rejoice,
let all the coastlands be glad.
The skies proclaim his justice;
all peoples see his glory. ℟.

Light shines forth for the just
and joy for the upright of heart.
Rejoice, you just, in the Lord;
give glory to his holy name. ℟.

READING II *Titus 3, 4-7 / 15*

When the kindness and love of God our Savior appeared, he saved us, not because of any righteous deeds we had done, but because of his mercy. He saved us through the baptism of new birth and renewal by the Holy Spirit. This Spirit he lavished on us through Jesus Christ our Savior, that we might be justified by his grace and become heirs, in hope, of eternal life.

GOSPEL *Luke 2, 15-20*

When the angels had returned to heaven, the shepherds said to one another: "Let us go over to Bethlehem and see this event which the Lord has made known to us." They went in haste and found Mary and Joseph, and the baby lying in the manger; once they saw, they understood what had been told them concerning this child. All who heard of it were astonished at the report given them by the shepherds.

Mary treasured all these things and reflected on them in her heart. The shepherds returned, glorifying and praising God for all they had heard and seen, in accord with what had been told them.

DECEMBER 25: CHRISTMAS–MASS DURING THE DAY 781

READING I *Isaiah 52, 7-10 / 16*

How beautiful upon the mountains
are the feet of him who brings glad tidings,
Announcing peace, bearing good news,
announcing salvation, and saying to Zion, "Your God is King!"

Hark! Your watchmen raise a cry,
together they shout for joy,
For they see directly, before their eyes,
the Lord restoring Zion.
Break out together in song,
O ruins of Jerusalem!
For the Lord comforts his people,
he redeems Jerusalem.
The Lord has bared his holy arm
in the sight of all the nations;
All the ends of the earth will behold
the salvation of our God.

RESPONSORIAL PSALM *Psalm (97)98, 1.2-3.3-4.5-6 / 16*

RP
All the ends of the earth have
seen the sav - ing pow - er of God.

Sing a new song to the Lord
for he has worked wonders.
His right hand and his holy arm
have brought salvation. ℟.

The Lord has made known his salvation;
has shown his justice to the nations.
He has remembered his truth and love
for the house of Israel. ℟.

All the ends of the earth have seen
the salvation of our God.
Shout to the Lord all the earth,
ring out your joy. ℟.

Sing psalms to the Lord with the harp
with the sound of music.
With trumpets and the sound of the horn
acclaim the King, the Lord. ℟.

READING II *Hebrews 1, 1-6 / 16*

In times past, God spoke in fragmentary and varied ways to our fathers through the prophets; in this, the final age, he has spoken to us through his Son, whom he has made heir of all things and through whom he first created the universe. This Son is the reflection of the Father's glory, the exact representation of the Father's being, and he sustains all things by his powerful word. When the Son had cleansed us from our sins, he took his seat at the right hand of the Majesty in heaven, as far superior to the angels as the name he has inherited is superior to theirs.

To which of the angels did God ever say,
"You are my son; today I have begotten you"?
Or again,
"I will be his father, and he shall be my son"?
And again when he leads his first-born into the world, he says,
"Let all the angels of God worship him."

GOSPEL *John, 1-18 or 1, 1-5.9-14 / 16*

For short form read only the part in brackets.

[In the beginning was the Word;
the Word was in God's presence,
and the Word was God.
He was present to God in the beginning.
Through him all things came into being,
and apart from him nothing came to be.
Whatever came to be in him, found life,
life for the light of men.
The light shines on in darkness,
a darkness that did not overcome it.]

There was a man named John sent by God, who came as a witness to testify to the light, so that through him all men might believe–but only to testify to the light, for he himself was not the light. [The real light which gives light to every man was coming into the world.

He was in the world,
and through him the world was made,
yet the world did not know who he was.
To his own he came,
yet his own did not accept him.
Any who did accept him
he empowered to become children of God.

These are they who believe in his name–who were begotten not by blood, nor by carnal desire, nor by man's willing it, but by God.

The Word became flesh
and made his dwelling among us,
and we have seen his glory:
the glory of an only son coming from the Father,
filled with enduring love.]

John testified to him by proclaiming, "This is he of whom I said, 'The one who comes after me ranks ahead of me, for he was before me.' "

Of his fullness
we have all had a share–
love following upon love.

For while the law was a gift through Moses, this enduring love came through Jesus Christ. No one has ever seen God. It is God the only Son, ever at the Father's side, who has revealed him.

782 SUNDAY IN THE OCTAVE OF CHRISTMAS–HOLY FAMILY

READING I *Sirach 3, 2-6.12-14 / 17*

The Lord sets a father in honor over his children;
a mother's authority he confirms over her sons.
He who honors his father atones for sins;
he stores up riches who reveres his mother.
He who honors his father is gladdened by children,
and when he prays he is heard.
He who reveres his father will live a long life;
he obeys the Lord who brings comfort to his mother.
My son, take care of your father when he is old; grieve him not as long as he lives.
Even if his mind fail, be considerate with him;
revile him not in the fullness of your strength.
For kindness to a father will not be forgotten,
it will serve as a sin offering–it will take lasting root.

RESPONSORIAL PSALM *Psalm (127)128, 1-2.3.4-5 / 17*

JG

O hap-py are those who fear the Lord and walk in his ways.

O blessed are those who fear the Lord
and walk in his ways!
By the labor of your hands you shall eat.
You will be happy and prosper. ℞.

Your wife like a fruitful vine
in the heart of your house;
your children like shoots of the olive,
around your table. ℞.

Indeed thus shall be blessed
the man who fears the Lord.
May the Lord bless you from Zion
all the days of your life!
May you see your children's children
in a happy Jerusalem! ℞.

READING II *Colossians 3, 12-21 / 17*

Because you are God's chosen ones, holy and beloved, clothe yourselves with heartfelt mercy, with kindness, humility, meekness, and patience. Bear with one another; forgive whatever grievances you have against one another. Forgive as the Lord has forgiven you. Over all these virtues put on love, which binds the rest together and makes them perfect. Christ's peace must reign in your hearts, since as members of the one body you have been called to that peace. Dedicate yourselves to thankfulness. Let the word of Christ, rich as it is, dwell in you. In wisdom made perfect, instruct and admonish one another. Sing gratefully to God from your hearts in psalms, hymns, and inspired songs. Whatever you do, whether in speech or in action, do it in the name of the Lord Jesus. Give thanks to God the Father through him.

You who are wives, be submissive to your husbands. This is your duty in the Lord. Husbands, love your wives. Avoid any bitterness toward them. You children, obey your parents in everything as the acceptable way in the Lord. And fathers, do not nag your children lest they lose heart.

GOSPEL/A *Matthew 2, 13-15.19-23 / 17*

After the astrologers had left, the angel of the Lord suddenly appeared in a dream to Joseph with the command: "Get up, take the child and his mother, and flee to Egypt. Stay there until I tell you otherwise. Herod is searching for the child to destroy him." Joseph got up and took the child and his mother and left that night for Egypt. He stayed there until the death of Herod, to fulfill what the Lord had said through the prophet:

"Out of Egypt I have called my son."

But after Herod's death, the angel of the Lord appeared in a dream to Joseph in Egypt with the command: "Get up, take the child and his mother, and set out for the land of Israel. Those who had designs on the life of the child are dead." He got up, took the child and his mother, and returned to the land of Israel. He heard, however, that Archelaus had succeeded his father Herod as king of Judea, and he was afraid to go back there. Instead, because of a warning received in a dream, Joseph went to the region of Galilee. There he settled in a town called Nazareth. In this way what was said through the prophets was fulfilled:

"He shall be called a Nazorean."

GOSPEL/B *Luke 2, 22-40 or 2, 22.39-40 / 17*

For short form read only the part in brackets.

[When the day came to purify them according to the law of Moses, Mary and Joseph brought Jesus up to Jerusalem so that he could be presented to the Lord.], for it is written in the law of the Lord, "Every first-born male shall be consecrated to the Lord." They came to offer in sacrifice "a pair of turtledoves or two young pigeons," in accord with the dictate in the law of the Lord.

There lived in Jerusalem at the time a certain man named Simeon. He was just and pious, and awaited the consolation of Israel, and the Holy Spirit was upon him. It was revealed to him by the Holy Spirit that he would not experience death until he had seen the Anointed of the Lord. He came to the temple now, inspired by the Spirit; and when the parents brought in the child Jesus to perform for him the customary ritual of the law, he took him in his arms and blessed God in these words:

"Now, Master, you can dismiss your servant in peace;
you have fulfilled your word.
For my eyes have witnessed your saving deed
displayed for all the peoples to see:
A revealing light to the Gentiles,
the glory of your people Israel."

The child's father and mother were marveling at what was being said about him. Simeon blessed them and said to Mary his mother: "This child is destined to be the downfall and the rise of many in Israel, a sign that will be opposed–and you yourself shall be pierced with a sword–so that the thoughts of many hearts may be laid bare."

There was also a certain prophetess, Anna by name, daughter of Phanuel of the tribe of Asher. She had seen many days, having lived seven years with her husband after her marriage and then as a widow until she was eighty-four. She was constantly in the temple, worshiping day and night in fasting and prayer. Coming on the scene at this moment, she gave thanks to God and talked about the child to all who looked forward to the deliverance of Jerusalem.

[When the pair had fulfilled all the prescriptions of the law of the Lord, they returned to Galilee and their own town of Nazareth. The child grew in size and strength, filled with wisdom, and the grace of God was upon him.]

GOSPEL/C *Luke,2, 41-52 / 17*

The parents of Jesus used to go every year to Jerusalem for the feast of the Passover, and when he was twelve they went up for the celebration as was their custom. As they were returning at the end of the feast, the child Jesus remained behind unknown to his parents. Thinking he was in the party, they continued their journey for a day, looking for him among their relatives and acquaintances.

Not finding him, they returned to Jerusalem in search of him. On the third day they came upon him in the temple sitting in the midst of the teachers, listening to them and asking them questions. All who heard him were amazed at his intelligence and his answers.

When his parents saw him they were astonished, and his mother said to him: "Son, why have you done this to us? You see that your father and I have been searching for you in sorrow." He said to them: "Why did you search for me? Did you not know I had to be in my Father's house?" But they did not grasp what he said to them.

He went down with them then, and came to Nazareth, and was obedient to them. His mother meanwhile kept all these things in memory. Jesus, for his part, progressed steadily in wisdom and age and grace before God and men.

783 JANUARY 1: SOLEMNITY OF MARY, MOTHER OF GOD

READING I *Numbers 6, 22-27 / 18*

The Lord said to Moses: "Speak to Aaron and his sons and tell them: This is how you shall bless the Israelites. Say to them:
The Lord bless you and keep you!
The Lord let his face shine upon you,
and be gracious to you!
The Lord look upon you kindly and
give you peace!
So shall they invoke my name upon the Israelites, and I will bless them."

RESPONSORIAL PSALM *Psalm (66)67, 2-3.5.6.8 / 18*

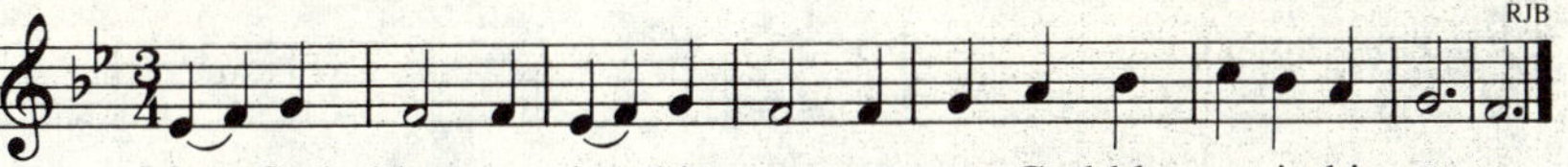
RJB
May God bless us in his mer-cy, may God bless us in his mer-cy.

O God, be gracious and bless us
and let your face shed its light upon us.
So will your ways be known upon earth
and all nations learn your saving
help. ℟.

Let the nations be glad and exult
for you rule the world with justice.
With fairness you rule the peoples,
you guide the nations on earth. ℟.

Let the peoples praise you, O God;
let all the peoples praise you.
May God still give us his blessing
till the ends of the earth revere him. ℟.

READING II *Galatians 4,4-7 / 18*

When the designated time had come, God sent forth his Son born of a woman, born under the law, to deliver from the law those who were subjected to it, so that we might receive our status as adopted sons. The proof that you are sons is the fact that God has sent forth into our hearts the spirit of his Son which cries out "Abba!" ("Father!"). You are no longer a slave but a son! And the fact that you are a son makes you an heir, by God's design.

GOSPEL *Luke 2, 16-21 / 18*

The shepherds went in haste to Bethlehem and found Mary and Joseph, and the baby lying in the manger; once they saw, they understood what had been told them concerning this child. All who heard of it were astonished at the report given them by the shepherds.

Mary treasured all these things and reflected on them in her heart. The shepherds returned, glorifying and praising God for all they had heard and seen, in accord with what had been told them.

When the eighth day arrived for his circumcision, the name Jesus was given the child, the name the angel had given him before he was conceived.

EPIPHANY 784

READING I *Isaiah 60, 1-6 / 20*

Rise up in splendor, Jerusalem! your
light has come,
the glory of the Lord shines upon
you.
See, darkness covers the earth,
and thick clouds cover the peoples;
But upon you the Lord shines,
and over you appears his glory.
Nations shall walk by your light,
and kings by your shining radiance.
Raise your eyes and look about;
they all gather and come to you:
Your sons come from afar,
and your daughters in the arms of
their nurses.

Then you shall be radiant at what you
see,
your heart shall throb and overflow,
For the riches of the sea shall be
emptied out before you,
the wealth of nations shall be
brought to you.
Caravans of camels shall fill you,
dromedaries from Midian and
Ephah;
All from Sheba shall come
bearing gold and frankincense,
and proclaiming the praises of the
Lord.

RESPONSORIAL PSALM

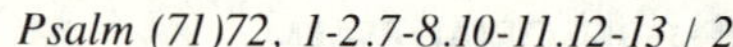
Psalm (71)72, 1-2.7-8.10-11.12-13 / 20

RP
Lord, ev'-ry na-tion on earth will a-dore you.

O God, give your judgment to the king,
to a king's son your justice,
that he may judge your people in justice
and your poor in right judgment. ℟.

In his days justice shall flourish
and peace till the moon fails.
He shall rule from sea to sea,
from the Great River to earth's
bounds. ℟.

The kings of Tarshish and the sea coasts
shall pay him tribute.
The kings of Sheba and Seba
shall bring him gifts.
Before him all kings shall fall prostrate,
all nations shall serve him. ℟.

For he shall save the poor when they
cry
and the needy who are helpless.
He will have pity on the weak
and save the lives of the poor. ℟.

READING II

Ephesians 3, 2-3.5-6 / 20

I am sure you have heard of the ministry which God in his goodness gave me in your regard. God's secret plan, as I have briefly described it, was revealed to me, unknown to men in former ages but now revealed by the Spirit to the holy apostles and prophets. It is no less than this: in Christ Jesus the Gentiles are now co-heirs with the Jews, members of the same body and sharers of the promise through the preaching of the gospel.

GOSPEL

Matthew 2, 1-12 / 20

After Jesus' birth in Bethlehem of Judea during the reign of King Herod, astrologers from the east arrived one day in Jerusalem inquiring, "Where is the newborn king of the Jews? We observed his star at its rising and have come to pay him homage." At this news King Herod became greatly disturbed, and with him all Jerusalem. Summoning all of the chief priests and scribes of the people, he inquired of them where the Messiah was to be born. "In Bethlehem of Judea," they informed him. "Here is what the prophet has written:

> 'And you, Bethlehem, land of Judah,
> are by no means least among the princes of Judah,
> since from you shall come a ruler
> who is to shepherd my people Israel.' "

Herod called the astrologers aside and found out from them the exact time of the star's appearance. Then he sent them to Bethlehem, after having instructed them: "Go and get detailed information about the child. When you have discovered something, report your findings to me so that I may go and offer him homage too."

After their audience with the king, they set out. The star which they had observed at its rising went ahead of them until it came to a standstill over the place where the child was. They were overjoyed at seeing the star, and on entering the house, found the child with Mary his mother. They prostrated themselves and did him homage. Then they opened their coffers and presented him with gifts of gold, frankincense, and myrrh.

They received a message in a dream not to return to Herod, so they went back to their own country by another route.

BAPTISM OF THE LORD

785

READING I *Isaiah 42, 1-4.6-7 / 21*

Here is my servant whom I uphold,
my chosen one with whom I am pleased,
Upon whom I have put my spirit;
he shall bring forth justice to the nations,
Not crying out, not shouting,
not making his voice heard in the street.
A bruised reed he shall not break,
and a smouldering wick he shall not quench,
Until he establishes justice on the earth;
the coastlands will wait for his teaching.

I, the Lord, have called you for the victory of justice,
I have grasped you by the hand;
I formed you, and set you
as a covenant of the people,
a light for the nations,
To open the eyes of the blind,
to bring out prisoners from confinement,
and from the dungeon, those who live in darkness.

RESPONSORIAL PSALM *Psalm (28)29, 1-2.3-4.3.9-10 / 21*

RP
The Lord will bless his peo - ple with peace.

O give the Lord you sons of God,
give the Lord glory and power;
give the Lord the glory of his name.
Adore the Lord in his holy court. ℟.

The Lord's voice resounding on the waters,
the Lord on the immensity of waters;
the voice of the Lord, full of power,
the voice of the Lord, full of splendor. ℟.

The God of glory thunders.
In his temple they all cry: "Glory!"
The Lord sat enthroned over the flood;
the Lord sits as king for ever. ℟.

READING II *Acts 10, 34-38 / 21*

Peter addressed Cornelius and the people assembled at his house in these words: "I begin to see how true it is that God shows no partiality. Rather, the man of any nation who fears God and acts uprightly is acceptable to him. This is the message he has sent to the sons of Israel, 'the good news of peace' proclaimed through Jesus Christ who is Lord of all. I take it you know what has been reported all over Judea about Jesus of Nazareth, beginning in Galilee with the baptism John preached; of the way God anointed him with the Holy Spirit and power. He went about doing good works and healing all who were in the grip of the devil, and God was with him.

GOSPEL/A *Matthew 3, 13-17 / 21*

Jesus, coming from Galilee, appeared before John at the Jordan to be baptized by him. John tried to refuse him with the protest, "I should be baptized by you, yet you come to me!" Jesus answered, "Give in for now. We must do this if we would fulfill all of God's demands." So John gave in. After Jesus was baptized, he came directly out of the water. Suddenly the sky opened and he saw the Spirit of God descend like a dove and hover over him. With that, a voice from the heavens said, "This is my beloved Son. My favor rests on him."

GOSPEL/B *Mark 1, 7-11 / 21*

The theme of John's preaching was: "One more powerful than I is to come after me. I am not fit to stoop and untie his sandal straps. I have baptized you in water; he will baptize you in the Holy Spirit."

During that time, Jesus came from Nazareth in Galilee and was baptized in the Jordan by John. Immediately on coming up out of the water he saw the sky rent in two and the Spirit descending on him like a dove. Then a voice came from the heavens: "You are my beloved Son. On you my favor rests."

GOSPEL/C *Luke 3, 15-16.21-22 / 22*

The people were full of anticipation, wondering in their hearts whether John might be the Messiah. John answered them all by saying: "I am baptizing you in water, but there is one to come who is mightier than I. I am not fit to loosen his sandal strap. He will baptize you in the Holy Spirit and in fire.

When all the people were baptized, and Jesus was at prayer after likewise being baptized, the skies opened and the Holy Spirit descended on him in visible form like a dove. A voice from heaven was heard to say, "You are my beloved Son. On you my favor rests."

Lent/Easter

On a Wednesday in February or early March the church enters into prayer and fasting and almsgiving, attending with great seriousness to its calling. Forty days later on a Thursday evening, that season of Lent ends. From Holy Thursday night until Easter Sunday afternoon, the church keeps the Paschal Triduum, the "Easter Three Days." Good Friday and Holy Saturday find Christians fasting, keeping vigil, remembering the passion, death and resurrection of the Lord until, at the great Vigil liturgy, the church celebrates this paschal mystery in baptism, confirmation and eucharist. Then, for the fifty days of Eastertime the church again sings the alleluia and rejoices to bring God's peace to the world. 786

The origins of Lent are bound up with the final stages in the initiation of those seeking to be baptized. After months or years of learning gradually the Christian way of life, the catechumens were called to spend the last weeks before baptism in fasting and prayer. The whole church stayed by the catechumens in these days. The lenten season was also kept intensely by those doing penance for their sins. Today both catechumens and penitents keep Lent with the whole church. Lent's scriptures, prayers and rites give clarity and strength to the life-long struggle against evil. That struggle is waged with many forms of prayer and fasting and practices of charity.

The origins of the fifty days of Eastertime are even more ancient. This is the springtime rejoicing of people who know their dependence on fields and flocks. It is the rejoicing of Israel remembering the exodus from slavery to freedom. It became the rejoicing of the church in the resurrection of Jesus and the presence of that risen life in the newly baptized. The Eastertime lectionary is filled with a lively peace and the quiet exuberance of those who believe that evil is not finally triumphant. When the fifty days conclude at Pentecost the church knows again how disturbing, how restless, how strong is the Spirit given by Christ.

787 FIRST SUNDAY OF LENT/A

READING I *Genesis 2, 7-9; 3, 1-7 / 22*

The Lord God formed man out of the clay of the ground and blew into his nostrils the breath of life, and so man became a living being.

Then the Lord God planted a garden in Eden, in the east, and he placed there the man whom he had formed. Out of the ground the Lord God made various trees grow that were delightful to look at and good for food, with the tree of life in the middle of the garden and the tree of the knowledge of good and bad.

Now the serpent was the most cunning of all the animals that the Lord God had made. The serpent asked the woman, "Did God really tell you not to eat from any of the trees in the garden?" The woman answered the serpent: "We may eat of the fruit of the trees in the garden; it is only about the fruit of the tree in the middle of the garden that God said, 'You shall not eat it or even touch it, lest you die.' " But the serpent said to the woman: "You certainly will not die! No, God knows well that the moment you eat of it you will be like gods who know what is good and what is bad." The woman saw that the tree was good for food, pleasing to the eyes, and desirable for gaining wisdom. So she took some of its fruit and ate it; and she also gave some to her husband, who was with her, and he ate it. Then the eyes of both of them were opened, and they realized that they were naked; so they sewed fig leaves together and made loincloths for themselves.

RESPONSORIAL PSALM *Psalm (50)51, 3-4.5-6.12-13.14.17 / 22*

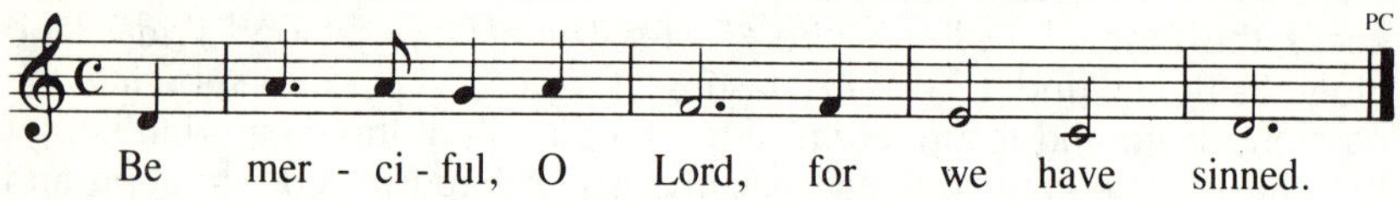
PC
Be mer - ci - ful, O Lord, for we have sinned.

Have mercy on me, God, in your
  kindness.
In your compassion blot out my
  offense.
O wash me more and more from my
  guilt
and cleanse me from my sin. ℟.

My offenses truly I know them;
my sin is always before me.
Against you, you alone, have I sinned;
what is evil in your sight I have
  done. ℟.

A pure heart create for me, O God,
put a steadfast spirit within me.
Do not cast me away from your
  presence,
nor deprive me of your holy
  spirit. ℟.

Give me again the joy of your help;
with a spirit of fervor sustain me.
O Lord, open my lips
and my mouth shall declare your
  praise. ℟.

READING II *Romans 5, 12-19 or 5, 12.17-19 / 22*

For short form read only the part in brackets.

[Through one man sin entered the world and with sin death, death thus coming to all men inasmuch as all sinned.]–before the law there was sin in the world, even though sin is not imputed when there is no law–I say, from Adam to Moses death reigned, even over those who had not sinned by breaking a precept as did Adam, that type of the Man to come.

But the gift is not like the offense. For if by the offense of the one man all died, much more did the grace of God and the gracious gift of the one man, Jesus Christ, abound for all. The gift is entirely different from the sin committed by the one man. In the first case, sentence followed upon one offense and brought condemnation, but in the second, the gift came after many offenses and brought acquittal. [If death began its reign through one man because of his offense, much more shall those who receive the overflowing grace and gift of justice live and reign through the one man, Jesus Christ.

To sum up, then: just as a single offense brought condemnation to all men, a single righteous act brought all men acquittal and life. Just as through one man's disobedience all became sinners, so through one man's obedience all shall become just.]

GOSPEL *Matthew 4, 1-11 / 22*

Jesus was led into the desert by the Spirit to be tempted by the devil. He fasted forty days and forty nights, and afterward was hungry. The tempter approached and said to him, "If you are the Son of God, command these stones to turn into bread." Jesus replied, "Scripture has it:

'Not on bread alone is man to live
but on every utterance that comes from
the mouth of God.' "

Next the devil took him to the holy city, set him on the parapet of the temple, and said, "If you are the Son of God, throw yourself down. Scripture has it:

'He will bid his angels take care of you;
with their hands they will support you
that you may never stumble on a stone.' "

Jesus answered him, "Scripture also has it:

'You shall not put the Lord your God to the test.' "

The devil then took him to a lofty mountain peak and displayed before him all the kingdoms of the world in their magnificence, promising, "All these will I bestow on you if you prostrate yourself in homage before me." At this, Jesus said to him, "Away with you, Satan! Scripture says:

'You shall do homage to the Lord your God;
him alone shall you adore.' "

At that the devil left him, and angels came and waited on him.

RITE OF ELECTION

At the beginning of Lent, is the responsibility of the bishop to call those who are judged ready to prepare for the sacraments of initiation at Easter. The bishop is to consult first with the pastors, catechists and others. The rite may take place at the cathedral. If the rite takes place in the parish church, the bishop may designate the pastor to act in his place.

This rite is also called the "Enrollment of Names." Each candidate now gives his/her name, or writes it down. When all have been enrolled, the bishop says: "You have been chosen to be initiated into the sacred mysteries at the Easter Vigil." He then speaks to them and to their sponsors about their lenten preparation for baptism.

The faithful join in prayers of intercession for the elect, as the catechumens are now called. If the eucharist is to be celebrated, the elect are first dismissed.

FIRST SUNDAY OF LENT/B 788

READING I *Genesis 9, 8-15 / 23*

God said to Noah and to his sons with him: "See, I am now establishing my covenant with you and your descendants after you and with every living creature that was with you: all the birds, and the various tame and wild animals that were with you and came out of the ark. I will establish my covenant with you, that never again shall all bodily creatures be destroyed by the waters of a flood; there shall not be another flood to devastate the earth." God added: "This is the sign that I am giving for all ages to come, of the covenant between me and you and every living creature with you: I set my bow in the clouds to serve as a sign of the covenant between me and the earth. When I bring clouds over the earth, and the bow appears in the clouds, I will recall the covenant I have made between me and you and all living beings, so that the waters shall never again become a flood to destroy all mortal beings."

RESPONSORIAL PSALM *Psalm (24)25, 4-5.6-7.8-9 / 23*

JRC
Your ways, O Lord, are love and truth,
to those who keep your cov - e - nant.

Lord, make me know your ways.
Lord, teach me your paths.
Make me walk in your truth, and teach me,
for you are God my savior. ℟.

Remember your mercy, Lord,
and the love you have shown from of old.
In your love remember me,
because of your goodness, O Lord. ℟.

The Lord is good and upright.
He shows the path to those who stray,
he guides the humble in the right path,
he teaches his way to the poor. ℟.

READING II *1 Peter 3, 18-22 / 23*

This is why Christ died for sins once for all, a just man for the sake of the unjust: so that he could lead you to God. He was put to death insofar as fleshly existence goes, but was given life in the realm of the spirit. It was in the spirit also that he went to preach to the spirits in prison. They had disobeyed as long ago as Noah's day, while God patiently waited until the ark was built. At that time, a few persons, eight in all, escaped in the ark through the water. You are now saved by a baptismal bath which corresponds to this exactly. This baptism is no removal of physical stain, but the pledge to God of an irreproachable conscience through the resurrection of Jesus Christ. He went to heaven and is at God's right hand, with angelic rulers and powers subjected to him.

GOSPEL *Mark 1, 12-15 / 23*

The Spirit sent Jesus out toward the desert. He stayed in the wasteland forty days, put to the test there by Satan. He was with the wild beasts, and angels waited on him.

After John's arrest, Jesus appeared in Galilee proclaiming God's good news: "This is the time of fulfillment. The reign of God is at hand! Reform your lives and believe in the good news!"

RITE OF ELECTION

See no. 787

FIRST SUNDAY OF LENT/C

789

READING I *Deuteronomy 26, 4-10 / 24*

Moses told the people: "The priest shall then receive the basket from you and shall set it in front of the altar of the Lord, your God. Then you shall declare before the Lord, your God, 'My father was a wandering Aramean who went down to Egypt with a small household and lived there as an alien. But there he became a nation great, strong, and numerous. When the Egyptians maltreated and oppressed us, imposing hard labor upon us, we cried to the Lord, the God of our fathers, and he heard our cry and saw our affliction, and outstretched arm, with terrifying power, with signs and wonders; and bringing us into this country, he gave us this land flowing with milk and honey. Therefore, I have now brought you the first fruits of the products of the soil which you, O Lord, have given me.' And having set them before the Lord, your God, you shall bow down in his presence. Then you and your family, together with the Levite and the aliens who live among you, shall make merry over all these good things which the Lord, your God, has given you.

RESPONSORIAL PSALM *Psalm (90)91, 1-2.10-11.12-13.14-15 / 24*

CAP

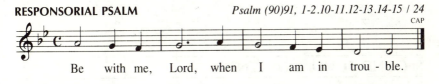

Be with me, Lord, when I am in trou - ble.

He who dwells in the shelter of the
Most High
and abides in the shade of the Almighty
says to the Lord: "My refuge,
my stronghold, my God in whom I
trust!" ℟.

Upon you no evil shall fall,
no plague approach where you dwell.
For you has he commanded his angels
to keep you in all your ways. ℟.

They shall bear you upon their hands
lest you strike your foot against a stone.
On the lion and the viper you will tread
and trample the young lion and the
dragon. ℟.

Since he clings to me in love,
I will free him,
protect him for he knows my name.
When he calls I shall answer: "I am
with you."
I will save him in distress and give him
glory.

READING II *Romans 10,8-13 / 24*

What does Scripture say? "The word is near you, on your lips and in your heart (that is, the word of faith which we preach)." For if you confess with your lips that Jesus is Lord, and believe in your heart that God raised him from the dead, you will be saved. Faith in the heart leads to justification, confession on the lips to salvation. Scripture says, "No one who believes in him will be put to shame." Here there is no difference between Jew and Greek; all have the same Lord, rich in mercy toward all who call upon him. "Everyone who calls on the name of the Lord will be saved."

GOSPEL *Luke 4, 1-13 / 24*

Jesus, full of the Holy Spirit, returned from the Jordan and was led by the Spirit into the desert for forty days, where he was tempted by the devil. During that time he ate nothing, and at the end of it he was hungry. The devil said to him, "If you are the Son of God, command this stone to turn into bread." Jesus answered him, "Scripture has it, 'Not on bread alone shall man live.' "

Then the devil took him up higher and showed him all the kingdoms of the world in a single instant. He said to him, "I will give you all this power and the glory of these kingdoms; the power has been given to me and I give it to whomever I wish. Prostrate yourself in homage before me, and it shall all be yours." In reply, Jesus said to him, "Scripture has it,

'You shall do homage to the Lord your God;
him alone shall you adore.' "

Then the devil led him to Jerusalem, set him on the parapet of the temple, and said to him, "If you are the Son of God, throw yourself down from here, for Scripture has it,

'He will bid his angels watch over you';

and again,

'With their hands they will support you,
that you may never stumble on a stone.' "

Jesus said to him in reply, "It also says, 'You shall not put the Lord your God to the test.' "

When the devil had finished all this tempting he left him, to await another opportunity.

RITE OF ELECTION

See no. 787

790 SECOND SUNDAY OF LENT/A

READING I *Genesis 12, 1-4 / 25*

The Lord said to Abram: "Go forth from the land of your kinsfolk and from your father's house to a land that I will show you.

"I will make of you a great nation,
and I will bless you;
I will make your name great,
so that you will be a blessing.
I will bless those who bless you
and curse those who curse you.
All the communities of the earth
shall find blessing in you."

Abram went as the Lord directed him, and Lot went with him. Abram was seventy-five years old when he left Haran.

RESPONSORIAL PSALM *Psalm (32)33, 4-5.18-19.20.22 / 25*

RP
Lord, let your mer - cy be on us,
as we place our trust in you.

For the word of the Lord is faithful
and all his works to be trusted.
The Lord loves justice and right
and fills the earth with his love. ℟.

The Lord looks on those who revere him,
on those who hope in his love,
to rescue their souls from death,
to keep them alive in famine. ℟.

Our soul is waiting for the Lord.
The Lord is our help and our shield.
May your love be upon us, O Lord,
as we place all our hope in you. ℟.

READING II *2 Timothy 1, 8-10 / 25*

Bear your share of the hardship which the gospel entails.

God has saved us and has called us to a holy life, not because of any merit of ours but according to his own design–the grace held out to us in Christ Jesus before the world began but now made manifest through the appearance of our Savior. He has robbed death of its power and has brought life and immortality into clear light through the gospel.

GOSPEL *Matthew 17, 1-9 / 25*

Jesus took Peter, James, and his brother John and led them up on a high mountain by themselves. He was transfigured before their eyes. His face became as dazzling as the sun, his clothes as radiant as light. Suddenly Moses and Elijah appeared to them conversing with him. Upon this, Peter said to Jesus, "Lord, how good it is for us to be here! With your permission I will erect three booths here, one for you, one for Moses, and one for Elijah." He was still speaking when suddenly a bright cloud overshadowed them. Out of the cloud came a voice which said, "This is my beloved Son on whom my favor rests. Listen to him." When they heard this the disciples fell forward on the ground, overcome with fear. Jesus came toward them and laying his hand on them, said, "Get up! Do not be afraid." When they looked up they did not see anyone but Jesus.

As they were coming down the mountainside Jesus commanded them, "Do not tell anyone of the vision until the Son of Man rises from the dead."

SECOND SUNDAY OF LENT/B 791

READING I *Genesis 22, 1-2.9.10-13.15-18 / 26*

God put Abraham to the test. He called to him, "Abraham!" "Ready!" he replied. Then God said: "Take your son Isaac, your only one, whom you love, and go to the land of Moriah. There you shall offer him up as a holocaust on a height that I will point out to you."

When they came to the place of which God had told him, Abraham built an altar there and arranged the wood on it. Then he reached out and took the knife to slaughter his son. But the Lord's messenger called to him from heaven, "Abraham, Abraham!" "Yes, Lord," he answered. "Do not lay your hand on the boy," said the messenger. "Do not do the least thing to him. I know now how devoted you are to God, since you did not withhold from me your own beloved son." As Abraham looked about, he spied a ram caught by its horns in the thicket. So he went and took the ram and offered it up as a holocaust in place of his son.

Again the Lord's messenger called to Abraham from heaven and said: "I swear by myself, declares the Lord, that because you acted as you did in not withholding from me your beloved son, I will bless you abundantly and make your descendants as countless as the stars of the sky and the sands of the seashore; your descendants shall take possession of the gates of their enemies, and in your descendants all the nations of the earth shall find blessing–all this because you obeyed my command."

RESPONSORIAL PSALM *Psalm (115)116, 10.15.16-17.18-19 / 26*

RP

I will walk in the pres-ence of the Lord, in the land of the liv-ing.

I trusted, even when I said:
"I am sorely afflicted,"

O precious in the eyes of the Lord
is the death of his faithful. ℟.

Your servant, Lord, your servant am I;
you have loosened my bonds.
A thanksgiving sacrifice I make;
I will call on the Lord's name. ℟.

My vows to the Lord I will fulfill
before all his people,
in the courts of the house of the Lord,
in your midst, O Jerusalem. ℟.

READING II *Romans 8, 31-34 / 26*

If God is for us, who can be against us? Is it possible that he who did not spare his own Son but handed him over for the sake of us all will not grant us all things besides? Who shall bring a charge against God's chosen ones? God, who justifies? Who shall condemn them? Christ Jesus, who died or rather was raised up, who is at the right hand of God and who intercedes for us?

GOSPEL *Mark 9, 2-10 / 26*

Jesus took Peter, James and John off by themselves with him and led them up a high mountain. He was transfigured before their eyes and his clothes became dazzlingly white–whiter than the work of any bleacher could make them. Elijah appeared to them along with Moses; the two were in conversation with Jesus. Then Peter spoke to Jesus: "Rabbi, how good it is for us to be here. Let us erect three booths on this site, one for you, one for Moses, and one for Elijah." He hardly knew what to say, for they were all overcome with awe. A cloud came, overshadowing them, and out of the cloud a voice: "This is my Son, my beloved. Listen to him." Suddenly looking around they no longer saw anyone with them–only Jesus.

As they were coming down the mountain, he strictly enjoined them not to tell anyone what they had seen before the Son of Man had risen from the dead. They kept this word of his to themselves, though they continued to discuss what "to rise from the dead" meant.

792

SECOND SUNDAY OF LENT/C

READING I *Genesis 15, 5-12.17-18 / 27*

God took Abram outside and said: "Look up at the sky and count the stars, if you can. Just so," he added, "shall your descendants be." Abram put his faith in the Lord, who credited it to him as an act of righteousness.

He then said to him, "I am the Lord who brought you from Ur of the Chaldeans to give you this land as a possession." "O Lord God," he asked, "how am I to know that I shall possess it?" He answered him, "Bring me a three-year-old heifer, a three-year-old she-goat, a three-year-old ram, a turtledove, and a young pigeon." He brought him all these, split them in two, and placed each half opposite the other; but the birds he did not cut up. Birds of prey swooped down on the carcasses, but Abram stayed with them. As the sun was about to set, a trance fell upon Abram, and a deep, terrifying darkness enveloped him.

When the sun had set and it was dark, there appeared a smoking brazier and a flaming torch, which passed between those pieces. It was on that occasion that the Lord made a covenant with Abram, saying: "To your descendants I give this land from the Wadi of Egypt to the Great River [the Euphrates]."

RESPONSORIAL PSALM *Psalm (26)27, 1.7-8.8-9.13-14 / 27*

RP
The Lord is my light and my sal - va - tion.

The Lord is my light and my help;
whom shall I fear?
The Lord is the stronghold of my life;
before whom shall I shrink? ℟.

O Lord, hear my voice when I call;
have mercy and answer.
Of you my heart has spoken:
"Seek his face." ℟.

It is your face, O Lord, that I seek;
hide not your face.
Dismiss not your servant in anger;
you have been my help.
Do not abandon or forsake me,
O God my help! ℟.

I am sure I shall see the Lord's
goodness
in the land of the living.
Hope in him, hold firm and take
heart.
Hope in the Lord! ℟.

READING II *Philippians 3, 17-4,1 or 3, 20-4,1 / 27*

For short form read only the part in brackets.

Be imitators of me, my brothers. Take as your guide those who follow the example that we set. Unfortunately, many go about in a way which shows them to be enemies of the cross of Christ. I have often said this to you before; this time I say it with tears. Such as these will end in disaster! Their god is their belly and their glory is in their shame. I am talking about those who are set upon the things of this world. [As you well know, we have our citizenship in heaven; it is from there that we eagerly await the coming of our savior, the Lord Jesus Christ. He will give a new form to this lowly body of ours and remake it according to the pattern of his glorified body, by his power to subject everything to himself.]

For these reasons, my brothers, you whom I so love and long for, you who are my joy and my crown, continue, my dear ones, to stand firm in the Lord.

GOSPEL *Luke 9, 28-36 / 27*

Jesus took Peter, John and James, and went up onto a mountain to pray. While he was praying, his face changed in appearance and his clothes became dazzlingly white. Suddenly two men were talking with him–Moses and Elijah. They appeared in glory and spoke of his passage which he was about to fulfill in Jerusalem. Peter and those with him had fallen into a deep sleep; but awakening, they saw his glory and likewise saw the two men who were standing with him. When these were leaving, Peter said to Jesus, "Master, how good it is for us to be here. Let us set up three booths, one for you, one for Moses, and one for Elijah." (He did not really know what he was saying.) While he was speaking, a cloud came and overshadowed them, and the disciples grew fearful as the others entered it. Then from the cloud came a voice which said, "This is my Son, my Chosen One. Listen to him." When the voice fell silent, Jesus was there alone. The disciples kept quiet, telling nothing of what they had seen at that time to anyone.

THIRD SUNDAY OF LENT/A 793

READING I *Exodus 17, 3-7 / 28*

In their thirst for water, the people grumbled against Moses, saying, "Why did you ever make us leave Egypt? Was it just to have us die here of thirst with our children and our livestock?" So Moses cried out to the Lord, "What shall I do with this people? A little more and they will stone me!" The Lord answered Moses, "Go over there in front of the people, along with some of the elders of Israel, holding in your hand, as you go, the staff with which you struck the river. I will be standing there in front of you on the rock in Horeb. Strike the rock, and the water will flow from it for the people to drink." This Moses did, in the presence of the elders of Israel. The place was called Massah and Meribah, because the Israelites quarreled there and tested the Lord, saying, "Is the Lord in our midst or not?"

RESPONSORIAL PSALM *Psalm (94)95, 1-2.6-7.8-9 / 28*

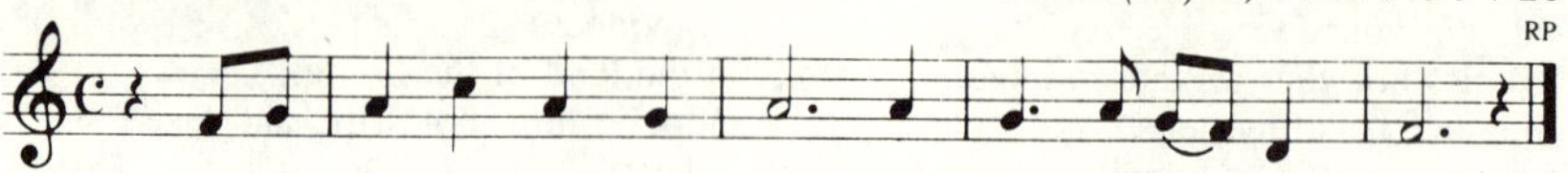
RP
If to - day you hear his voice, O hard - en not your hearts.

Come, ring out our joy to the Lord;
hail the rock who saves us.
Let us come before him, giving thanks,
with songs let us hail the Lord. ℟.

Come in; let us bow and bend low;
let us kneel before the God who made us
for he is our God and we
the people who belong to his pasture,
the flock that is led by his hand. ℟.

O that today you would listen to his voice!
"Harden not your hearts as at Meribah,
as on that day at Massah in the desert
when your fathers put me to the test;
when they tried me, though they saw my work." ℟.

READING II *Romans 5, 1-2.5-8 / 28*

Now that we have been justified by faith, we are at peace with God through our Lord Jesus Christ. Through him we have gained access by faith to the grace in which we now stand, and we boast of our hope for the glory of God. And this hope will not leave us disappointed, because the love of God has been poured out in our hearts through the Holy Spirit who has been given to us. At the appointed time, when we were still powerless, Christ died for us godless men. It is rare that anyone would lay down his life for a just man, though it is barely possible that for a good man someone may have the courage to die. It is precisely in this that God proves his love for us: that while we were still sinners, Christ died for us.

GOSPEL *John 4, 5-42 or 4, 5-15.19-26.39.40-42 / 28*

For short form read only the part in brackets.

[Jesus had to pass through Samaria, and his journey brought him to a Samaritan town named Shechem near the plot of land which Jacob had given to his son Joseph. This was the site of Jacob's well. Jesus, tired from his journey, sat down at the well.

The hour was about noon. When a Samaritan woman came to draw water, Jesus said to her, "Give me a drink." (His disciples had gone off to the town to buy provisions.) The Samaritan woman said to him, "You are a Jew. How can you ask me, a Samaritan and a woman, for a drink?" (Recall that Jews have nothing to do with Samaritans.) Jesus replied:

"If only you recognized God's gift,
and who it is that is asking you for a drink,
you would have asked him instead,
and he would have given you living water."

"Sir," she challenged him, "you don't have a bucket and this well is deep. Where do you expect to get this flowing water? Surely you don't pretend to be greater than our ancestor Jacob, who gave us this well and drank from it with his sons and his flocks?" Jesus replied:

"Everyone who drinks this water
will be thirsty again.
But whoever drinks the water I give him
will never be thirsty;
no, the water I give
shall become a fountain within him,
leaping up to provide eternal life."

The woman said to him, "Give me this water, sir, so that I won't grow thirsty and have to keep coming here to draw water."]

He told her, "Go, call your husband, and then come back here." "I have no husband," replied the woman. "You are right in saying you have no husband!" Jesus exclaimed. "The fact is, you have had five, and the man you are living with now is not your husband. What you said is true enough."

"Sir," answered the woman, ["I can see you are a prophet. Our ancestors worshiped on this mountain, but you people claim that Jerusalem is the place where men ought to worship God." Jesus told her:

> "Believe me, woman,
> an hour is coming
> when you will worship the Father
> neither on this mountain
> nor in Jerusalem.
> You people worship what you do not understand,
> while we understand what we worship;
> after all, salvation is from the Jews.
> Yet an hour is coming, and is already here,
> when authentic worshipers
> will worship the Father in Spirit and truth.
> Indeed, it is just such worshipers
> the Father seeks.
> God is Spirit,
> and those who worship him
> must worship in Spirit and truth."

The woman said to him: "I know there is a Messiah coming. (This term means Annointed.) When he comes, he will tell us everything." Jesus replied, "I who speak to you am he."]

His disciples, returning at this point, were surprised that Jesus was speaking with a woman. No one put a question, however, such as "What do you want of him?" or "Why are you talking with her?" The woman then left her water jar and went off into the town. She said to the people: "Come and see someone who told me everything I ever did! Could this not be the Messiah?" With that they set out from the town to meet him.

Meanwhile the disciples were urging him, "Rabbi, eat something." But he told them:

> "I have food to eat
> of which you do not know."

At this the disciples said to one another, "You do not suppose anyone has brought him something to eat?" Jesus explained to them:

> "Doing the will of him who sent me
> and bringing his work to completion
> is my food.
> Do you not have a saying:
> 'Four months more
> and it will be harvest!'?
> Listen to what I say:
> Open your eyes and see!
> The fields are shining for harvest!
> The reaper already collects his wages
> and gathers a yield for eternal life,
> that sower and reaper may rejoice together.
> Here we have the saying verified:
> 'One man sows; another reaps.'
> I sent you to reap
> what you had not worked for.
> Others have done the labor,
> and you have come into their gain."

[Many Samaritans from that town believed in him on the strength of the woman's word of testimony: "He told me everything I ever did." The result was that, when these Samaritans came to him, they begged him to stay with them awhile. So he stayed there two days, and through his own spoken word many more came to faith. As they told the woman: "No longer does our faith depend on your story. We have heard for ourselves, and we know that this really is the Savior of the world."]

FIRST SCRUTINY

During Lent, the elect (those catechumens who have been called to prepare for baptism at Easter) are called to come before the community for exorcisms and prayers. This takes place after the liturgy of the word on the Third, Fourth and Fifth Sundays of Lent. These rites are intended to purify the hearts and minds of the elect, to strengthen them against temptation, to help them progress in the love of God.

The presider asks the assembly to pray in silence for the elect, then to join in intercessions for them. The presider lays hands on each of the elect and prays that the elect be delivered from the power of evil and become witnesses to the gospel. A song or psalm may be sung, then the elect are dismissed as usual and the faithful continue with the liturgy of the eucharist.

794 THIRD SUNDAY OF LENT/B

READING I

Exodus 20, 1-17 or 20, 1-3.7-8.12-17 / 29

For short form read only the part in brackets.

[God delivered all these commandments:

"I, the Lord, am your God, who brought you out of the land of Egypt, that place of slavery. You shall not have other gods besides me.] You shall not carve idols for yourselves in the shape of anything in the sky above or on the earth below or in the waters beneath the earth; you shall not bow down before them or worship them. For I, the Lord, your God, am a jealous God, inflicting punishment for their fathers' wickedness on the children of those who hate me, down to the third and fourth generation; but bestowing mercy down to the thousandth generation, on the children of those who love me and keep my commandments.

["You shall not take the name of the Lord, your God, in vain. For the Lord will not leave unpunished him who takes his name in vain.

"Remember to keep holy the sabbath day.] Six days you may labor and do all your work, but the seventh day is the sabbath of the Lord, your God. No work may be done then either by you, or your son or daughter, or your male or female slave, or your beast, or by the alien who lives with you. In six days the Lord made the heavens and the earth, the sea and all that is in them; but on the seventh day he rested. That is why the Lord has blessed the sabbath day and made it holy.

["Honor your father and your mother, that you may have a long life in the land which the Lord, your God, is giving you.

"You shall not kill.

"You shall not commit adultery.

"You shall not steal.

"You shall not bear false witness against your neighbor.

"You shall not covet your neighbor's house. You shall not covet your neighbor's wife, nor his male or female slave, nor his ox or ass, nor anything else that belongs to him."]

RESPONSORIAL PSALM *Psalm (18)19, 8.9.10.11 / 29*

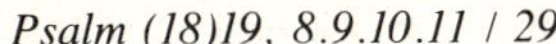

RP
Lord, you have the words of ev - er - last - ing life.

The law of the Lord is perfect,
it revives the soul.
The rule of the Lord is to be trusted,
it gives wisdom to the simple. ℟.

The precepts of the Lord are right,
they gladden the heart.
The command of the Lord is clear,
it gives light to the eyes. ℟.

The fear of the Lord is holy,
abiding for ever.
The decrees of the Lord are truth
and all of them just. ℟.

They are more to be desired than gold,
than the purest of gold
and sweeter are they than honey,
than honey from the comb. ℟.

READING II *1 Corinthians 1, 22-25 / 29*

Jews demand "signs" and Greeks look for "wisdom," but we preach Christ crucified, a stumbling block to Jews, and an absurdity to Gentiles; but to those who are called, Jews and Greeks alike, Christ is the power of God and the wisdom of God. For God's folly is wiser than men, and his weakness more powerful than men.

GOSPEL *John 2, 13-25 / 29*

As the Jewish Passover was near, Jesus went up to Jerusalem. In the temple precincts he came upon people engaged in selling oxen, sheep and doves, and others seated changing coins. He made a [kind of] whip of cords and drove them all out of the temple area, sheep and oxen alike, and knocked over the moneychangers' tables, spilling their coins. He told those who were selling doves: "Get them out of here! Stop turning my Father's house into a marketplace!" His disciples recalled the words of Scripture: "Zeal for your house consumes me."

At this the Jews responded, "What sign can you show us authorizing you to do these things? "Destroy this temple," was Jesus' answer, "and in three days I will raise it up." They retorted, "This temple took forty-six years to build, and you are going to 'raise it up in three days'!" Actually he was talking about the temple of his body. Only after Jesus had been raised from the dead did his disciples recall that he had said this, and come to believe the Scripture and the word he had spoken.

While he was in Jerusalem during the Passover festival, many believed in his name, for they could see the sign he was performing. For his part, Jesus would not trust himself to them because he knew them all. He needed no one to give him testimony about human nature. He was well aware of what was in man's heart.

FIRST SCRUTINY

See no.793

THIRD SUNDAY OF LENT/C 795

READING I *Exodus 3, 1-8.13-15 / 30*

Moses was tending the flock of his father-in-law Jethro, the priest of Midian. Leading the flock across the desert, he came to Horeb, the mountain of God. There an angel of the Lord appeared to him in fire flaming out of a bush. As he looked on, he was surprised to see that the bush, though on fire, was not consumed. So Moses decided, "I must go over to look at this remarkable sight, and see why the bush is not burned."

When the Lord saw him coming over to look at it more closely, God called out to him from the bush, "Moses! Moses!" He answered, "Here I am." God said, "Come no nearer! Remove the sandals from your feet, for the place where you stand is holy ground. I am the God of your father," he continued, "the God of Abraham, the God of Isaac, the God of Jacob." Moses hid his face, for he was afraid to look at God. But the Lord said, "I have witnessed the affliction of my people in Egypt and have heard their cry of complaint against their slave drivers, so I know well what they are suffering. Therefore I have come down to rescue them from the hands of the Egyptians and lead them out of that land into a good and spacious land, a land flowing with milk and honey."

"But," said Moses to God, "when I go to the Israelites and say to them, 'The God of your fathers has sent me to you,' if they ask me, 'What is his name?' what am I to tell them?" God replied, "I am who I am." Then he added, "This is what you shall tell the Israelites: I AM sent me to you."

God spoke further to Moses, "Thus shall you say to the Israelites: The Lord, the God of your fathers, the God of Abraham, the God of Isaac, the God of Jacob, has sent me to you.

"This is my name forever;
this is my title for all generations."

RESPONSORIAL PSALM *Psalm (102)103, 1-2.3-4.6-7.8.11 / 30*

DRH
The Lord is kind and mer - ci - ful.

My soul, give thanks to the Lord,
all my being, bless his holy name.
My soul, give thanks to the Lord
and never forget all his blessings. ℟.

It is he who forgives all your guilt,
who heals every one of your ills,
who redeems your life from the grave,
who crowns you with love and
compassion. ℟.

The Lord does deeds of justice,
gives judgment for all who are
oppressed.
He made known his ways to Moses
and his deeds to Israel's sons. ℟.

The Lord is compassion and love,
slow to anger and rich in mercy.
For as the heavens are high above the
earth
so strong is his love for those who fear
him. ℟.

READING II *1 Corinthians 10, 1-6.10-12 / 30*

I want you to remember this: our fathers were all under the cloud and all passed through the sea; by the cloud and the sea all of them were baptized into Moses. All ate the same spiritual food. All drank the same spiritual drink (they drank from the spiritual rock that was following them, and the rock was Christ), yet we know that God was not pleased with most of them, for "they were struck down in the desert."

These things happened as an example to keep us from wicked desires such as theirs. Nor are you to grumble as some of them did, to be killed by the destroying angel. The things that happened to them serve as an example. They have been written as a warning to us, upon whom the end of the ages has come. For all these reasons, let anyone who thinks he is standing upright watch out lest he fall!

GOSPEL *Luke 13, 1-9 / 30*

At that time some were present who told Jesus about the Galileans whose blood Pilate had mixed with their sacrifices. He said in reply: "Do you think that these Galileans were the greatest sinners in Galilee just because they suffered this? By no means! But I tell you, you will all come to the same end unless you reform. Or take those eighteen who were killed by a falling tower in Siloam. Do you think they were more guilty than anyone else who lived in Jerusalem? Certainly not! But I tell you, you will all come to the same end unless you begin to reform."

Jesus spoke this parable: "A man had a fig tree growing in his vineyard, and he came out looking for fruit on it but did not find any. He said to the vinedresser, 'Look here! For three years now I have come in search of fruit on this fig tree and found none. Cut it down. Why should it clutter up the ground?' In answer, the man said, 'Sir, leave it another year while I hoe around it and manure it; then perhaps it will bear fruit. If not, it shall be cut down.' "

FIRST SCRUTINY

See no. 793

FOURTH SUNDAY OF LENT/A 796

READING I *1 Samuel 16, 1.6-7.10-13 / 31*

The Lord said to Samuel: "I am sending you to Jesse of Bethlehem, for I have chosen my king from among his sons.

As Jesse and his sons came to the sacrifice, Samuel looked at Eliab and thought, "Surely the Lord's anointed is here before him." But the Lord said to Samuel: "Do not judge from his appearance or from his lofty stature, because I have rejected him. Not as man sees does God see, because man sees the appearance but the Lord looks into the heart." In the same way Jesse presented seven sons before Samuel, but Samuel said to Jesse, "The Lord has not chosen any one of these." Then Samuel asked Jesse, "Are these all the sons you have?" Jesse replied, "There is still the youngest, who is tending the sheep." Samuel said to Jesse, "Send for him; we will not begin the sacrificial banquet until he arrives here." Jesse sent and had the young man brought to them. He was ruddy, a youth handsome to behold and making a splendid appearance. The Lord said, "There–anoint him, for this is he!" Then Samuel, with the horn of oil in hand, anointed him in the midst of his brothers; and from that day on, the spirit of the Lord rushed upon David.

RESPONSORIAL PSALM *Psalm (22)23, 1-3.3-4.5.6 / 31*

RP
The Lord is my shep-herd; there is noth-ing I shall want.

The Lord is my shepherd;
there is nothing I shall want.
Fresh and green are the pastures
where he gives me repose.
Near restful waters he leads me,
to revive my drooping spirit. ℞.

He guides me along the right path;
he is true to his name.
If I should walk in the valley of
darkness
no evil would I fear.
You are there with your crook and
your staff; with these you give me
comfort. ℞.

You have prepared a banquet for me
in the sight of my foes.
My head you have anointed with oil;
my cup is overflowing. ℞.

Surely goodness and kindness shall
follow me
all the days of my life.
In the Lord's own house shall I dwell
for ever and ever. ℞.

READING II *Ephesians 5, 8-14 / 31*

There was a time when you were darkness, but now you are light in the Lord. Well, then, live as children of light. Light produces every kind of goodness and justice and truth. Be correct in your judgment of what pleases the Lord. Take no part in vain deeds done in darkness; rather, condemn them. It is shameful even to mention the things these people do in secret; but when such deeds are condemned, they are seen in the light of day, and all that then appears is light. That is why we read:

"Awake, O sleeper,
arise from the dead,
and Christ will give you light."

GOSPEL *John 9, 1-41 or 9, 1.6-9.13-17.34-38 / 31*

For short form read only the part in brackets.

[As Jesus walked along, he saw a man who had been blind from birth.] His disciples asked him, "Rabbi, was it his sin or his parents' that caused him to be born blind?" "Neither," answered Jesus:

"It was no sin, either of this man or of his parents.
Rather, it was to let God's works show forth in him.
We must do the deeds of him who sent me while it is day.
The night comes on
when no one can work.
While I am in the world I am the light of the world."

With that [Jesus spat on the ground, made mud with his saliva, and smeared the man's eyes with the mud. Then he told him, "Go, wash in the pool of Siloam." (This name means "One who has been sent.") So the man went off and washed, and came back able to see.

His neighbors and the people who had been accustomed to see him begging began to ask, "Isn't this the fellow who used to sit and beg?" Some were claiming it was he; others maintained it was not but someone who looked like him. The man himself said, "I'm the one, all right."] They said to him then, "How were your eyes opened?" He answered: "That man they call Jesus made mud and smeared it on my eyes, telling me to go to Siloam and wash. When I did go and wash, I was able to see." "Where is he?" they asked. He replied, "I have no idea."

[Next, they took the man who had been born blind to the Pharisees. (Note that it was on a sabbath that Jesus had made the mud paste and opened his eyes.) The Pharisees, in turn, began to inquire how he had recovered his sight. He told them, "He put mud on my eyes. I washed it off, and now I can see." This prompted some of the Pharisees to assert, "This man cannot be from God because he does not keep the sabbath." Others objected, "If a man is a sinner, how can he perform signs like these?" They were sharply divided over him. Then they addressed the blind man again: "Since it was your eyes he opened, what do you have to say about him?" "He is a prophet," he replied.]

The Jews refused to believe that he had really been born blind and had begun to see, until they summoned the parents of this man who now could see. "Is this your son?" they asked, "and if so, do you attest that he was blind at birth? How do you account for the fact that he now can see?" His parents answered, "We know this is our son, and we know he was blind at birth. But how he can see now, or who opened his eyes, we have no idea. Ask him. He is old enough to speak for himself." (His parents answered in this fashion because they were afraid of the Jews, who had already agreed among themselves that anyone who acknowledged Jesus as the Messiah would be put out of the synagogue. That was why his parents said, "He is of age–ask him.")

A second time they summoned the man who had been born blind and said to him, "Give glory to God! First of all, we know this man is a sinner." "I would not know whether he is a sinner or not," he answered. "I know this much: I was blind before; now I can see." They persisted: "Just what did he do to you? How did he open your eyes?" "I have told you once, but you would not listen to me," he answered them.

"Why do you want to hear it all over again? Do not tell me you want to become his disciples too?" They retorted scornfully, "You are the one who is that man's disciple. We are disciples of Moses. We know that God spoke to Moses, but we have no idea where this man comes from." He came back at them: "Well, this is news! You do not know where he comes from, yet he opened my eyes. We know that God does not hear sinners, but that if someone is devout and obeys his will, he listens to him. It is unheard of that anyone ever gave sight to a person blind from birth. If this man were not from God, he could never have done such a thing." ["What!" they exclaimed, "You are steeped in sin from your birth, and you are giving us lectures?" With that they threw him out bodily.

When Jesus heard of his expulsion, he sought him out and asked him, "Do you believe in the Son of Man?" He answered, "Who is he, sir, that I may believe in him?" "You have seen him," Jesus replied. "He is speaking to you now." ["I do believe, Lord," he said, and bowed down to worship him.] Then Jesus said:]

"I came into this world to divide it,
to make the sightless see
and the seeing blind."

Some of the Pharisees around him picked this up, saying, "You are not counting us in with the blind, are you?" To which Jesus replied:

"If you were blind
there would be no sin in that.
'But we see,' you say,
and your sin remains."

SECOND SCRUTINY

During Lent, the elect (those catechumens who have been called to prepare for baptism at Easter) are called to come before the community for exorcisms and prayers. This takes place after the liturgy of the word on the Third, Fourth and Fifth Sundays of Lent. These rites are intended to purify the hearts and minds of the elect, to strengthen them against temptation, to help them progress in the love of God.

The presider asks the assembly to pray in silence for the elect, then to join in intercessions for them. The presider lays hands on each of the elect and prays that the elect be delivered from the power of evil and become witnesses to the gospel. A song or psalm may be sung, then the elect are dismissed as usual and the faithful continue with the liturgy of the eucharist.

FOURTH SUNDAY OF LENT/B 797

READING I *2 Chronicles 36, 14-17.19-23 / 32*

All the princes of Judah, the priests and the people added infidelity to infidelity, practicing all the abominations of the nations and polluting the Lord's temple which he had consecrated in Jerusalem.

Early and often did the Lord, the God of their fathers, send his messengers to them, for he had compassion on his people and his dwelling place. But they mocked the messengers of God, despised his warnings, and scoffed at his prophets, until the anger of the Lord against his people was so inflamed that there was no remedy. Then he brought up against them the king of the Chaldeans, who slew their young men in their own sanctuary building, sparing neither young man or maiden, neither the aged nor the decrepit; he delivered all of them over into his grip. Finally, their enemies burnt the house of God, tore down the walls of Jerusalem, set all its palaces afire, and destroyed all its precious objects. Those who escaped the sword he carried captive to Babylon, where they became his and his sons' servants until the kingdom of the Persians came to power. All this was to fulfill the word of the Lord spoken by Jeremiah: "Until the land has retrieved its lost sabbaths, during all the time it lies waste it shall have rest while seventy years are fulfilled."

In the first year of Cyrus, king of Persia, in order to fulfill the word of the Lord spoken by Jeremiah, the Lord inspired King Cyrus of Persia to issue this proclamation throughout his kingdom, both by word of mouth and in writing: "Thus says Cyrus, king of Persia: 'All the kingdoms of the earth the Lord, the God of heaven, has given to me, and he has also charged me to build him a house in Jerusalem, which is in Judah. Whoever, therefore, among you belongs to any part of his people, let him go up, and may his God be with him!' "

RESPONSORIAL PSALM *Psalm (136)137, 1-2.3.4-5.6 / 32*

FS
Let my tongue be si - lenced, if I ev - er for - get you!

By the rivers of Babylon
there we sat and wept,
remembering Zion;
on the poplars that grew there
we hung up our harps. ℟.

For it was there that they asked us,
our captors, for songs,
our oppressors, for joy.
"Sing to us," they said,
"one of Zion's songs." ℟.

O how could we sing
the song of the Lord
on alien soil?
If I forget you, Jerusalem,
let my right hand wither! ℟.

O let my tongue
cleave to my mouth
if I remember you not,
if I prize not Jerusalem
above all my joys! ℟.

READING II *Ephesians 2, 4-10 / 32*

God is rich in mercy; because of his great love for us he brought us to life with Christ when we were dead in sin. By this favor you were saved. Both with and in Christ Jesus he raised us up and gave us a place in the heavens, that in the ages to come he might display the great wealth of his favor, manifested by his kindness to us in Christ Jesus. I repeat, it is owing to his favor that salvation is yours through faith. This is not your own doing, it is God's gift; neither is it a reward for anything you have accomplished, so let no one pride himself on it. We are truly his handiwork, created in Christ Jesus to lead the life of good deeds which God prepared for us in advance.

GOSPEL *John 3, 14-21 / 32*

Jesus said to Nicodemus:
"Just as Moses lifted up the serpent
in the desert,
so must the Son of Man be lifted up,
that all who believe
may have eternal life in him.
Yes, God so loved the world
that he gave his only Son,
that whoever believes in him may not
die
but may have eternal life.
God did not send the Son into the
world
to condemn the world,
but that the world might be saved
through him.
Whoever believes in him avoids
condemnation,
but whoever does not believe is
already condemned
for not believing in the name of
God's only Son.
The judgment in question is this:
the light came into the world,
but men loved darkness rather than
light
because their deeds were wicked.
Everyone who practices evil
hates the light;
he does not come near it
for fear his deeds will be exposed.
But he who acts in truth
comes into the light,
to make clear
that his deeds are done in God."

SECOND SCRUTINY
See no. 796

FOURTH SUNDAY OF LENT/C 798

READING I *Joshua 5, 9.10-12 / 33*

The Lord said to Joshua, "Today I have removed the reproach of Egypt from you."

While the Israelites were encamped at Gilgal on the plains of Jericho, they celebrated the Passover on the evening of the fourteenth of the month. On the day after the Passover they ate of the produce of the land in the form of unleavened cakes and parched grain. On that same day after the Passover on which they ate of the produce of the land, the manna ceased. No longer was there manna for the Israelites, who that year ate of the yield of the land of Canaan.

RESPONSORIAL PSALM *Psalm (33)34, 2-3.4-5.6-7 / 33*

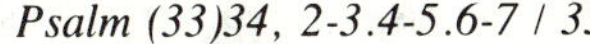

RP
Taste and see the good - ness of the Lord.

I will bless the Lord at all times,
his praise always on my lips;
in the Lord my soul shall make its boast.
The humble shall hear and be glad. ℟.

Glorify the Lord with me.
Together let us praise his name.
I sought the Lord and he answered me;
from all my terrors he set me free. ℟.

Look towards him and be radiant;
let your faces not be abashed.
This poor man called; the Lord heard him
and rescued him from all his distress. ℟.

READING II *2 Corinthians 5, 17-21 / 33*

If anyone is in Christ, he is a new creation. The old order has passed away; now all is new! All this has been done by God, who has reconciled us to himself through Christ and has given us the ministry of reconciliation. I mean that God, in Christ, was reconciling the world to himself, not counting men's transgressions against them, and that he has entrusted the message of reconciliation to us. This makes us ambassadors for Christ, God as it were appealing through us. We implored you, in Christ's name: be reconciled to God! For our sakes God made him who did not know sin to be sin, so that in him we might become the very holiness of God.

GOSPEL *Luke 15,1-3.11-32 / 33*

The tax collectors and the sinners were all gathering around Jesus to hear him, at which the Pharisees and the scribes murmured, "This man welcomes sinners and eats with them." Then he addressed this parable to them: "A man had two sons. The younger of them said to his father, 'Father, give me the share of the estate that is coming to me.' So the father divided up the property. Some days later this younger son collected all his belongings and went off to a distant land, where he squandered his money on dissolute living. After he had spent everything, a great famine broke out in that country and he was in dire need. So he attached himself to one of the propertied class of the place, who sent him to his farm to take care of the pigs. He longed to fill his belly with the husks that were fodder for the pigs, but no one made a move to give him anything. Coming to his senses at last, he said: 'How many hired hands at my father's place have more than enough to eat, while here I am starving! I will break away and return to my father, and say to him, "Father, I have sinned against God and against you; I no longer deserve to be called your son. Treat me like one of your hired hands." ' With that he set off for his father's house. While he was still a long way off, his father caught sight of him and was deeply moved. He ran out to meet him, threw his arms around his neck, and kissed him. The son said to him, 'Father, I have sinned against God and against you; I no longer deserve to be called your son.' The father said to his servants: 'Quick! Bring out the finest robe and put it on him; put a ring on his finger and shoes on his feet. Take the fatted calf and kill it. Let us eat and celebrate because this son of mine was dead and has come back to life. He was lost and is found.' Then the celebration began.

"Meanwhile the elder son was out on the land. As he neared the house on his way home, he heard the sound of music and dancing. He called one of the servants and asked him the reason for the dancing and the music. The servant answered, 'Your brother is home, and your father has killed the fatted calf because he has him back in good health.' The son grew angry at this and would not go in; but his father came out and began to plead with him.

"He said in reply to his father: 'For years now I have slaved for you. I never disobeyed one of your orders, yet you never gave me so much as a kid goat to celebrate with my friends. Then, when this son of yours returns after having gone through your property with loose women, you kill the fatted calf for him.'

" 'My son,' replied the father, 'you are with me always, and everything I have is yours. But we had to celebrate and rejoice! This brother of yours was dead and has come back to life. He was lost and is found.' "

SECOND SCRUTINY

See no. 796

799 FIFTH SUNDAY OF LENT/A

READING I *Ezekiel 37, 12-14 / 34*

Thus says the Lord God: O my people, I will open your graves and have you rise from them, and bring you back to the land of Israel. Then you shall know that I am the Lord, when I open your graves and have you rise from them, O my people! I will put my spirit in you that you may live, and I will settle you upon your land; thus you shall know that I am the Lord. I have promised, and I will do it, says the Lord.

RESPONSORIAL PSALM *Psalm (129)130, 1-2.3-4.5-6.7-8. / 34*

JRC

With the Lord there is mer-cy, and full-ness of re-demp-tion.

Out of the depths I cry to you, O Lord,
Lord, hear my voice!
O let your ears be attentive
to the voice of my pleading. ℟.

If you, O Lord, should mark our guilt,
Lord, who would survive?
But with you is found forgiveness:
for this we revere you. ℟.

My soul is waiting for the Lord,
I count on his word.
My soul is longing for the Lord
more than watchman for daybreak.
(Let the watchman count on daybreak
and Israel on the Lord.) ℟.

Because with the Lord there is mercy
and fullness of redemption,
Israel indeed he will redeem
for all its iniquity. ℟.

READING II *Romans 8, 8-11 / 34*

Those who are in the flesh cannot please God. But you are not in the flesh; you are in the spirit, since the Spirit of God dwells in you. If anyone does not have the Spirit of Christ, he does not belong to Christ. If Christ is in you, the body is indeed dead because of sin, while the spirit lives because of justice. If the Spirit of him who raised Jesus from the dead dwells in you, then he who raised Christ from the dead will bring your mortal bodies to life also through his Spirit dwelling in you.

GOSPEL *John 11, 1-45 or 11,3-7.17.20-27.33-45 / 34*

For short form read only the part in brackets.

There was a certain man named Lazarus who was sick. He was from Bethany, the village of Mary and her sister Martha. (This Mary whose brother Lazarus was sick was the one who anointed the Lord with perfume and dried his feet with her hair.) [The sisters of Lazarus sent word to Jesus to inform him, "Lord, the one you love is sick." Upon hearing this, Jesus said:

"This sickness is not to end in death;
rather it is for God's glory,
that through it the Son of God may be glorified."

Jesus loved Martha and her sister and Lazarus very much. Yet, after hearing that Lazarus was sick, he stayed on where he was for two days more. Finally he said to his disciples, "Let us go back to Judea."] "Rabbi," protested the disciples, "with the Jews only recently trying to stone you, you are going back up there again?" Jesus answered:

"Are there not twelve hours of daylight?
If a man goes walking by day he does not stumble
because he sees the world bathed in light.
But if he goes walking at night he will stumble
since there is no light in him."

After uttering these words, he added, "Our beloved Lazarus has fallen asleep, but I am going there to wake him." At this the disciples objected, "Lord, if he is asleep his life will be saved." Jesus had been speaking about his death, but they thought he meant sleep in the sense of slumber. Finally Jesus said plainly, "Lazarus is dead. For your sakes I am glad I was not there, that you may come to believe. In any event, let us go to him." Then Thomas (the name means "Twin") said to his fellow desciples, "Let us go along, to die with him."

[When Jesus arrived at Bethany, he found that Lazarus had already been in the tomb four days.] The village was not far from Jerusalem–just under two miles–and many Jewish people had come out to console Martha and Mary over their brother. [When Martha heard that Jesus was coming she went to meet him, while Mary sat at home. Martha said to Jesus, "Lord, if you had been here, my brother would never have died. Even now, I am sure that God will give you whatever you ask of him." "Your brother will rise again," Jesus assured her. "I know he will rise again," Martha replied, "in the resurrection on the last day." Jesus told her:

"I am the resurrection and the life:
whoever believes in me,
though he should die, will come to life;
and whoever is alive and believes in me will never die.

Do you believe this?" "Yes, Lord," she replied. "I have come to believe that you are the Messiah, the Son of God: he who is to come into the world."]

When she had said this she went back and called her sister Mary. "The Teacher is here, asking for you," she whispered. As soon as Mary heard this, she got up and started out in his direction. (Actually Jesus had not yet come into the village but was still at the spot where Martha had met him.) The Jews who were in the house with Mary consoling her saw her get up quickly and go out, so they followed her, thinking she was going to the tomb to weep there. When Mary came to the place where Jesus was, seeing him, she fell at his feet and said to him, "Lord, if you had been here my brother would never have died." When Jesus saw her weeping, and the Jewish folk who had accompanied her also weeping, he [(Jesus) was troubled in spirit, moved by the deepest emotions. "Where have you laid him?" he asked. "Lord, come and see," they said. Jesus began to weep, which caused the Jews to remark, "See how much he loved him!" But someone said, "He opened the eyes of that blind man. Why could he not have done something to stop this man from dying?" Once again troubled in spirit, Jesus approached the tomb.

It was a cave with a stone laid across it. "Take away the stone," Jesus directed. Martha, the dead man's sister, said to him, "Lord, it has been four days now; surely there will be a stench!" Jesus replied, "Did I not assure you that if you believed you would see the glory of God?" They then took away the stone and Jesus looked upward and said:

"Father, I thank you for having heard me.
I know that you always hear me
but I have said this for the sake of the crowd,
that they may believe that you sent me."

Having said this, he called loudly, "Lazarus, come out!" The dead man came out, bound hand and foot with linen strips, his face wrapped in a cloth. "Untie him," Jesus told them, "and let him go free."

This caused many of the Jews who had come to visit Mary, and had seen what Jesus did, to put their faith in him.]

THIRD SCRUTINY

During Lent, the elect (those catechumens who have been called to prepare for baptism at Easter) are called to come before the community for exorcisms and prayers. This takes place after the liturgy of the word on the Third, Fourth and Fifth Sundays of Lent. These rites are intended to purify the hearts and minds of the elect, to strengthen them against temptation, to help them progress in the love of God.

The presider asks the assembly to pray in silence for the elect, then to join in intercessions for them. The presider lays hands on each of the elect and prays that the elect be delivered from the power of evil and become witnesses to the gospel. A song or psalm may be sung, then the elect are dismissed as usual and the faithful continue with the liturgy of the eucharist.

800 FIFTH SUNDAY OF LENT/B

READING I

Jeremiah 31, 31-34 / 35

The days are coming, says the Lord, when I will make a new covenant with the house of Israel and the house of Judah. It will not be like the covenant I made with their fathers the day I took them by the hand to lead them forth from the land of Egypt; for they broke my covenant, and I had to show myself their master, says the Lord. But this is the covenant which I will make with the house of Israel after those days, says the Lord. I will place my law within them, and write it upon their hearts; I will be their God, and they shall be my people. No longer will they have need to teach their friends and kinsmen how to know the Lord. All, from least to greatest, shall know me, says the Lord, for I will forgive their evil-doing and remember their sin no more.

RESPONSORIAL PSALM

Psalm (50)51, 3-4.12-13.14-15 / 35

FS
Cre - ate a clean heart, a clean heart in me, O God.

Have mercy on me, God, in your
kindness.
In your compassion blot out my
offense.
O wash me more and more from my
guilt
and cleanse me from my sin. ℟.

A pure heart create for me, O God,
put a steadfast spirit within me.
Do not cast me away from your
presence,
nor deprive me of your holy spirit. ℟.

Give me again the joy of your help;
with a spirit of fervor sustain me,
that I may teach transgressors your
ways
and sinners may return to you. ℟.

READING II *Hebrews 5, 7-9 / 35*

In the days when Christ was in the flesh, he offered prayers and supplications with loud cries and tears to God, who was able to save him from death, and he was heard because of his reverence. Son though he was, he learned obedience from what he suffered; and when perfected, he became the source of eternal salvation for all who obey him.

GOSPEL *John 12, 20-33 / 35*

Among those who had come up to worship at the feast of Passover were some Greeks. They approached Philip, who was from Bethsaida in Galilee, and put this request to him: "Sir, we should like to see Jesus." Philip went to tell Andrew; Philip and Andrew in turn came to inform Jesus. Jesus answered them:

"The hour has come
for the Son of Man to be glorified.
I solemnly assure you,
unless the grain of wheat falls to the
earth and dies,
it remains just a grain of wheat.
But if it dies,
it produces much fruit.
The man who loves his life
loses it,
while the man who hates his life in
this world
preserves it to life eternal.
If anyone would serve me,
let him follow me;
where I am,
there will my servant be.
Anyone who serves me,
the Father will honor.
My soul is troubled now,
yet what should I say–
Father, save me from this hour?
But it was for this that I came to this
hour.
Father, glorify your name!"

Then a voice came from the sky:

"I have glorified it,
and will glorify it again."

When the crowd of bystanders heard the voice, they said it was thunder. Others maintained, "An angel was speaking to him." Jesus answered, "That voice did not come for my sake, but for yours.

"Now has judgment come upon this
world,
now will this world's prince be driven
out,
and I–once I am lifted up from earth–
will draw all men to myself."

(This statement of his indicated the sort of death he was going to die.)

THIRD SCRUTINY

See no. 799

FIFTH SUNDAY OF LENT/C 801

READING I *Isaiah 43, 16-21 / 36*

Thus says the Lord,
who opens a way in the sea
and a path in the mighty waters,
Who leads out chariots and horsemen,

a powerful army,
Till they lie prostrate together, never to rise,
snuffed out and quenched like a wick.
Remember not the events of the past,
the things of long ago consider not;
See, I am doing something new!
Now it springs forth, do you not perceive it?

In the desert I make a way,
in the wasteland, rivers.
Wild beasts honor me,
jackals and ostriches,
For I put water in the desert
and rivers in the wasteland
for my chosen people to drink,
The people I formed for myself,
that they might announce my praise.

RESPONSORIAL PSALM *Psalm (125)126, 1-2.2-3.4-5.6 / 36*

RP
The Lord has done great things for us;
we are filled with joy, we are filled with joy.

When the Lord delivered Zion from bondage,
it seemed like a dream.
Then was our mouth filled with laughter,
on our lips there were songs. ℟.

The heathens themselves said: "What marvels
the Lord worked for them!"
What marvels the Lord worked for us!
Indeed we were glad. ℟.

Deliver us, O Lord, from our bondage
as streams in dry land.
Those who are sowing in tears
will sing when they reap. ℟.

They go out, they go out, full of tears,
carrying seed for the sowing;
they come back, they come back, full of song,
carrying their sheaves. ℟.

READING II *Philippians 3, 8-14 / 36*

I have come to rate all as loss in the light of the surpassing knowledge of my Lord Jesus Christ. For his sake I have forfeited everything; I have accounted all else rubbish so that Christ may be my wealth and I may be in him, not having any justice of my own based on observance of the law. The justice I possess is that which comes through faith in Christ. It has its origin in God and is based on faith. I wish to know Christ and the power flowing from his resurrection; likewise to know how to share in his sufferings by being formed into the pattern of his death. Thus do I hope that I may arrive at resurrection from the dead.

It is not that I have reached it yet, or have already finished my course; but I am racing to grasp the prize if possible, since I have been grasped by Christ [Jesus]. Brothers, I do not think of myself as having reached the finish line. I give no thought to what lies behind but push on to what is ahead. My entire attention is on the finish line as I run toward the prize to which God calls me–life on high in Christ Jesus.

GOSPEL *John 8, 1-11 / 36*

Jesus went out to the Mount of Olives. At daybreak he reappeared in the temple area; and when the people started coming to him, he sat down and began to teach them. The scribes and the Pharisees led a woman forward who had been caught in adultery. They made her stand there in front of everyone. "Teacher," they said to him, "this woman has been caught in the act of adultery. In the law, Moses ordered such women to be stoned. What do you have to say about the case?" (They were posing this question to trap him, so that they could have something to accuse him of.) Jesus simply bent down and started tracing on the ground with his finger. When they persisted in their questioning, he straightened up and said to them, "Let the man among you who has no sin be the first to cast a stone at her." A second time he bent down and wrote on the ground. Then the audience drifted away one by one, beginning with the elders. This left him alone with the woman, who continued to stand there before him. Jesus finally straightened up again and said to her, "Woman, where did they all disappear to? Has no one condemned you?" "No one, sir," she answered. Jesus said, "Nor do I condemn you. You may go. But from now on, avoid this sin.

THIRD SCRUTINY

See no. 799

PASSION SUNDAY (PALM SUNDAY) 802

Passion or Palm Sunday is the last Sunday in Lent. Its closeness to the end of Lent has given this liturgy two distinct features: the procession with palms and the gospel reading of the Lord's passion. The blessing and carrying of palms celebrates Jesus' entrance into Jerusalem to accomplish his paschal mystery. The reading of the passion comes as a conclusion to all the gospel readings of the lenten Sundays: these scriptures yearly prepare catechumens and the faithful to approach the celebration of Christ's death and resurrection. That celebration takes place most especially in the sacraments of initiation at the Easter Vigil.

COMMEMORATION OF THE LORD'S ENTRANCE INTO JERUSALEM

This rite may be very simple or may involve the entire assembly in a procession with the blessing of palms and the gospel reading of Jesus' entrance into Jerusalem. Depending on the local church, then, some of the following hymns, psalms and readings will be used.

OPENING ANTIPHON 803

The following or another appropriate acclamation may be sung.

Mode VII
Adapt. Richard Proulx, 1986

Ho - san - na to the Son of Da - vid. Bless-ed is
he who comes in the name of the Lord.
O King of Is - ra - el. Ho - san - na in the high-est.

BLESSING OF BRANCHES 804

All hold branches as these are blessed. The branches may be of palm or from a tree that is native to the area. The green or flowering branches signify the victory of life.

GOSPEL/A *Matthew 21, 1-11 / 37*

As the crowd drew near Jerusalem, entering Bethphage on the Mount of Olives, Jesus sent off two disciples with the instruction: "Go into the village straight ahead of you and you will immediately find an ass tethered and her colt with her. Untie them and lead them back to me. If anyone says a word to you, say, 'The Master needs them.' Then he will let them go at once." This came about to fulfill what was said through the prophet:

"Tell the daughter of Zion,
Your king comes to you without display
riding an ass, astride a colt,
the foal of a beast of burden."

So the disciples went off and did what Jesus had ordered; they brought the ass and the colt and laid their cloaks on them, and he mounted. The huge crowd spread their cloaks on the road, while some began to cut branches from the trees and laid them along his path. The groups preceding him as well as those following kept crying out:

"God save the Son of David!
Blessed be he who comes in the name of
the Lord!
God save him from on high!

As he entered Jerusalem the whole city was stirred to its depths, demanding, "Who is this?" And the crowd kept answering, "This is the prophet Jesus from Nazareth in Galilee."

GOSPEL/B *Mark 11, 1-10 / 37*

As the crowd drew near Bethphage and Bethany on the Mount of Olives, close to Jerusalem, Jesus sent off two of his disciples with the instruction: "Go to the village straight ahead of you, and as soon as you enter it you will find tethered there a colt on which no one has ridden. Untie it and bring it back. If anyone says to you, 'Why are you doing that?' say, 'The Master needs it but he will send it back here at once.' " So they went off, and finding a colt tethered out on the street near a gate, they untied it. Some of the bystanders said to them, "What do you mean by untying that colt?" They answered as Jesus had told them to, and the men let them take it. They brought the colt to Jesus and threw their cloaks across its back, and he sat on it. Many people spread their cloaks on the road, while others spread reeds which they had cut in the fields. Those preceding him as well as those who followed cried out:

"Hosannah!
Blessed be he who comes in the name of
the Lord!
Blessed be the reign of our father David
to come!
God save him from on high!"

Or:

GOSPEL/B *John 12, 12-16 / 37*

The great crowd that had come for the feast heard that Jesus was to enter Jerusalem, so they got palm branches and came out to meet him. They kept shouting:

"Hosanna!
Blessed is he who comes in the name of
the Lord!
Blessed is the King of Israel!"

Jesus found a donkey and mounted it, in accord with Scripture:

"Fear not, O daughter of Zion!
Your king approaches you
on a donkey's colt."

(At first, the disciples did not understand all this, but after Jesus was glorified they recalled that the people had done to him precisely what had been written about him.)

GOSPEL/C *Luke 19,28-40 / 37*

Jesus went ahead with his ascent to Jerusalem. As he approached Bethphage and Bethany on the mount called Olivet, he sent two of the disciples with these instructions: "Go into the village straight ahead of you. Upon entering it you will find an ass tied there which no one has yet ridden. Untie it and lead it back. If anyone should ask you, 'Why are you untying the beast?' say, 'The Master has need of it.' "

They departed on their errand and found things just as he had said. As they untied the ass, its owners said to them, "Why are you doing that?" They explained that the Master needed it. Then they led the animal to Jesus, and laying their cloaks on it, helped him mount. They spread their cloaks on the roadway as he moved along; and on his approach to the descent from Mount Olivet, the entire crowd of disciples began to rejoice and praise God loudly for the display of power they had seen, saying:

"Blessed be he who comes as king
in the name of the Lord!
Peace in heaven
and glory in the highest!"

Some of the Pharisees in the crowd said to him, "Teacher, rebuke your disciples." He replied, "If they were to keep silence, I tell you the very stones would cry out."

PROCESSION 805

All join in the procession or at least in the song. Such a movement of people expresses the experience of Lent: the church has been called to move on, to go ever further toward the paschal mystery of death and resurrection.

Gloria, laus et honor, Mode I
Theodulph of Orleans, c.760-821
Tr. by John M. Neale, 1818-1866, alt.
Realization in proportional rhythm by Schola Antiqua, 1983
Acc. by Richard Proulx, 1983
All glo - ry, laud, and hon - or to you, Re - deem - er, King! to whom the lips of chil - dren made sweet ho - san - nas ring.
1. You are the King of Is - ra - el, and Da - vid's roy - al Son, now in the Lord's Name com - ing, our King and Bless - ed One.
2. The com - pa - ny of an - gels are prais - ing you on high; and mor - tals joined with all things cre - a - ted, make re - ply.
3. The peo - ple of the He - brews with palms be - fore you went: our praise and prayers and an - thems be - fore you we pre - sent.
4. To you be - fore your pas - sion they sang their hymns of praise: to you now high ex - al - ted, our mel - o - dy we raise.
5. Their prais - es you ac - cept - ed, ac - cept the prayers we bring, great source of love and good - ness, our Sav - ior and our King.
D.C.

The commemoration of the Lord's entrance into Jerusalem, whether this is done in a simple or solemn manner, concludes with the opening prayer of the Mass.

806 LITURGY OF THE WORD

READING I *Isaiah 50, 4-7 / 38*

The Lord God has given me
a well-trained tongue,
That I might know how to speak to the weary
a word that will rouse them.
Morning after morning
he opens my ear that I may hear;
And I have not rebelled,
have not turned back.
I gave my back to those who beat me,
my cheeks to those who plucked my beard;
My face I did not shield
from buffets and spitting.

The Lord God is my help,
therefore I am not disgraced;
I have set my face like flint,
knowing that I shall not be put to shame.

RESPONSORIAL PSALM *Psalm (21)22, 8-9.17-18.19-20.23-24 / 38*

FS
My God, my God, why have you a - ban-doned me?

All who see me deride me.
They curl their lips, they toss their heads.
"He trusted in the Lord, let him save him;
let him release him if this is his friend." ℟.

Many dogs have surrounded me,
a band of the wicked beset me.
They tear holes in my hands and my feet.
I can count every one of my bones. ℟.

They divide my clothing among them.
They cast lots for my robe.
O Lord, do not leave me alone,
my strength, make haste to help me! ℟.

I will tell of your name to my brethren
and praise you where they are assembled.
"You who fear the Lord give him praise;
all sons of Jacob, give him glory." ℟.

READING II *Philippians 2, 6-11 / 38*

Your attitude must be Christ's:
though he was in the form of God
he did not deem equality with God
something to be grasped at.
Rather, he emptied himself
and took the form of a slave,
being born in the likeness of men.
He was known to be of human estate,
and it was thus that he humbled himself,
obediently accepting even death,
death on a cross!

Because of this,
God highly exalted him
and bestowed on him the name
above every other name,
So that at Jesus' name,
every knee must bend
in the heavens, on the earth,
and under the earth,
and every tongue proclaim
to the glory of God the Father:
JESUS CHRIST IS LORD!

GOSPEL/A

Matthew 26, 14-27, 66 or 27, 11-54 / 38

The symbols of the following passion narrative represent:

N narrator;

+ Christ;

S speakers other than Christ;

P groups of speakers.

N The passion of our Lord Jesus Christ according to Matthew.

For short form read only the part in brackets.

N One of the Twelve whose name was Judas Iscariot went off to the chief priests and said,

S "What are you willing to give me if I hand Jesus over to you?"

N They paid him thirty pieces of silver, and from that time on he kept looking for an opportunity to hand him over. On the first day of the feast of Unleavened Bread, the disciples came up to Jesus and said,

P "Where do you wish us to prepare the Passover supper for you?"

\+ "Go to this man in the city and tell him, 'The Teacher says, My appointed time draws near. I am to celebrate the Passover with my disciples in your house.' "

N The disciples then did as Jesus had ordered, and prepared the Passover supper. When it grew dark he reclined at table with the Twelve. In the course of the meal he said,

\+ "I give you my word one of you is about to betray me."

N Distressed at this, they began to say to him one after another,

S "Surely it is not I, Lord?"

\+ "The man who has dipped his hand into the dish with me is the one who will hand me over. The Son of Man is departing, as Scripture says of him, but woe to that man by whom the Son of Man is betrayed. Better for him if he had never been born."

N Then Judas, his betrayer, spoke:

S "Surely it is not I, Rabbi?"

\+ "It is you who have said it."

N During the meal Jesus took bread, blessed it, broke it, and gave it to his disciples.

\+ "Take this and eat it, this is my body."

N Then he took a cup, gave thanks, and gave it to them.

\+ "All of you must drink from it, for this is my blood, the blood of the covenant, to be poured out in behalf of many for the forgiveness of sins. I tell you, I will not drink this fruit of the vine from now until the day when I drink it new with you in my Father's reign."

N Then, after singing songs of praise, they walked out to the Mount of Olives. Jesus then said to them,

\+ "Tonight your faith in me will be shaken, for Scripture has it:

'I will strike the shepherd
and the sheep of the flock will be
dispersed.'

But after I am raised up, I will go to Galilee ahead of you."

N Peter responded,

S "Though all may have their faith in you shaken, mine will never be shaken!"

\+ "I give you my word, before the cock crows tonight you will deny me three times."

S "Even though I have to die with you, I will never disown you."

N And all the other disciples said the same. Then Jesus went with them to a place called Gethsemani.

\+ "Stay here while I go over there and pray."

N He took along Peter and Zebedee's two sons. and began to experience sorrow and distress. Then he said to them,

\+ "My heart is nearly broken with sorrow. Remain here and stay awake with me."

N He advanced a little and fell prostrate in prayer.

\+ "My Father, if it is possible, let this cup pass me by. Still, let it be as you would have it, not as I.

N When he returned to his disciples, he found them asleep. He said to Peter,

\+ "So you could not stay awake with me for even an hour? Be on guard, and pray that you may not undergo trial. The spirit is willing but nature is weak."

N Withdrawing a second time, he began to pray:

+ "My Father, if this cannot pass me by without my drinking it, your will be done!"
Once more, on his return, he found them asleep; they could not keep their eyes open. He left them again, withdrew somewhat, and began to pray a third time, saying the same words as before. Finally he returned to his disciples and said to them:

+ "Sleep on now. Enjoy your rest! The hour is on us when the Son of Man is to be handed over to the power of evil men. Get up! Let us be on our way! See, my betrayer is here."

N While he was still speaking, Judas, one of the Twelve, arrived accompanied by a great crowd with swords and clubs. They had been sent by the chief priests and elders of the people. His betrayer had arranged to give them a signal, saying,

S "The man I shall embrace is the one; take hold of him."

N He immediately went over to Jesus, embraced him, and said to him,

S "Peace, Rabbi."

+ "Friend, do what you are here for!"

N At that moment they stepped forward to lay hands on Jesus, and arrested him. Suddenly one of those who accompanied Jesus put his hand to his sword, drew it, and slashed at the high priest's servant, cutting off his ear. Jesus said to him:

+ "Put back your sword where it belongs. Those who use the sword are sooner or later destroyed by it. Do you not suppose I can call on my Father to provide at a moment's notice more than twelve legions of angels? But then how would the Scriptures be fulfilled which say it must happen this way?"

N At that very time Jesus said to the crowd:

+ "Am I a brigand, that you have come armed with swords and clubs to arrest me? From day to day I sat teaching in the temple precincts, yet you never arrested me. Nonetheless, all this has happened in fulfillment of the writings of the prophets."

N Then all the disciples deserted him and fled. Those who had apprehended Jesus led him off to Caiaphas, the high priest, where the scribes and elders were convened. Peter kept following him at a distance as far as the high priest's residence. Going inside, he sat down with the guards to see the outcome. The chief priests, with the whole Sanhedrin, were busy trying to obtain false testimony against Jesus so that they might put him to death. They discovered none, despite the many false witnesses who took the stand. Finally two came forward who stated:

P "This man has declared, 'I can destroy God's sanctuary and rebuild it in three days.' "

N The high priest rose to his feet and addressed him:

S "Have you no answer to the testimony leveled against you?"

N But Jesus remained silent. The high priest then said to him:

S "I order you to tell us under oath before the living God whether you are the Messiah, the Son of God."

+ "It is you who say it. But I tell you this: Soon you will see the Son of Man seated at the right hand of the Power and coming on the clouds of heaven."

N At this the high priest tore his robes:

S "He has blasphemed! What further need have we of witnesses? Remember, you heard the blasphemy. What is your verdict?"

P "He deserves death!"

N Then they began to spit in his face and hit him. Others slapped him, saying:

P "Play the prophet for us, Messiah! Who struck you?"

N Peter was sitting in the courtyard when one of the serving girls came over to him and said,

S "You too were with Jesus the Galilean."

N He denied it in front of everyone:

S "I don't know what you are talking about!"

N When he went out to the gate another girl saw him and said to those nearby,

S "This man was with Jesus the Nazorean."

N Again he denied it with an oath:

S "I don't know the man!"

N A little while later some bystanders came over to Peter and said,

P "You are certainly one of them! Even your accent gives you away!"

N At that he began cursing and swore,

S "I don't even know the man!"

N Just then a rooster began to crow and Peter remembered the prediction Jesus had made: "Before the rooster crows you will three times disown me." He went out and began to weep bitterly.

At daybreak all the chief priests and the elders of the people took formal action against Jesus to put him to death. They bound him and led him away to be handed over to the procurator Pilate. Then Judas, who had handed him over, seeing that Jesus had been condemned, began to regret his action deeply. He took the thirty pieces of silver back to the chief priests and elders and said,

S "I did wrong to deliver up an innocent man!"

P "What is that to us? It is your affair!"

N So Judas flung the money into the temple and left. He went off and hanged himself. The chief priests picked up the silver, observing,

P "It is not right to deposit this in the temple treasury since it is blood money."

N After consultation, they used it to buy the potter's field as a cemetery for foreigners. That is why that field, even today, is called Blood Field. On that occasion, what was said through Jeremiah the prophet was fulfilled: "They took the thirty pieces of silver, the value of a man with a price on his head, a price set by the Israelites, and they paid it out for the potter's field just as the Lord had commanded me." [Jesus was arraigned before the procurator, (Pontius Pilate,) who questioned him:

S "Are you the king of the Jews?"

+ "As you say."

N Yet when he was accused by the chief priests and elders, he had made no reply. Then Pilate said to him,

S "Surely you hear how many charges they bring against you?"

N He did not answer him on a single count, much to the procurator's surprise. Now on the occasion of a festival the procurator was accustomed to release one prisoner, whom the crowd would designate. They had at the time a notorious prisoner named Barabbas. Since they were already assembled, Pilate said to them,

S "Which one do you wish me to release for you, Barabbas or Jesus the so-called Messiah?"

N He knew, of course, that it was out of jealousy that they had handed him over. While he was still presiding on the bench, his wife sent him a message:

S "Do not interfere in the case of that holy man. I had a dream about him today which has greatly upset me."

N Meanwhile, the chief priests and elders convinced the crowds that they should ask for Barabbas and have Jesus put to death. So when the procurator asked them,

S "Which one do you wish me to release for you?"

P "Barabbas,"

N Pilate said to them,

S "Then what am I to do with Jesus, the so-called Messiah?"

P "Crucify him!"

S "Why? What crime has he committed?"

N But they only shouted the louder,

P "Crucify him!"

N Pilate finally realized that he was making no impression and that a riot was breaking out instead. He called for water and washed his hands in front of the crowd, declaring as he did so,

S "I am innocent of the blood of this just man. The responsibility is yours."

N The whole people said in reply,

P "Let his blood be on us and on our children."

N At that, he released Barabbas to them. Jesus, however, he first had scourged; then he handed him over to be crucified. The procurator's soldiers took Jesus inside the praetorium and collected the whole cohort around him. They stripped off his clothes and wrapped him in a scarlet military cloak. Weaving a crown out of thorns they fixed it on his head, and stuck a reed in his right hand. Then they began to mock him by dropping to their knees before him, saying,

P "All hail, king of the Jews!"

N They also spat at him. Afterward they took hold of the reed and kept striking him on the head. Finally, when they had finished making a fool of him, they stripped him of the cloak, dressed him in his own clothes, and led him off to crucifixion. On their way out they met a Cyrenian named Simon. This man they pressed into service to carry the cross. Upon arriving at a site called Golgotha (a name which means Skull Place), they gave him a drink of wine flavored with gall, which he tasted but refused to drink. When they had crucified him, they divided his clothes among them by casting lots; then they sat down there and kept watch over him. Above his head they put the charge against him in writing: "This is Jesus, King of the Jews." Two insurgents were crucified along with him, one at his right and one at his left. People going by kept insulting him, tossing their heads and saying:

P "So you are the one who was going to destroy the temple and rebuild it in three days! Save yourself, why don't you? Come down off that cross if you are God's Son!"

N The chief priests, the scribes, and the elders also joined in the jeering:

P "He saved others but he cannot save himself! So he is the king of Israel! Let's see him come down from that cross, and then we will believe in him. He relied on God; let God rescue him now if he wants to. After all, he claimed, 'I am God's Son.' "

N The insurgents who had been crucified with him kept taunting him in the same way. From noon onward, there was darkness over whole land until midafternoon. Then toward midafternoon Jesus cried out in a loud tone,

+ "Eli, Eli, lema sabachthani?"

N That is,

+ "My God, my God, why have you forsaken me?"

N This made some of the bystanders who heard it remark,

P "He is invoking Elijah!"

N Immediately one of them ran off and got a sponge. He soaked it in cheap wine, and sticking it on a reed, tried to make him drink. Meanwhile the rest said,

P "Leave him alone. Let's see whether Elijah comes to his rescue."

N Once again Jesus cried out in a loud voice, and then gave up his spirit. Suddenly the curtain of the sanctuary was torn in two from top to bottom. The earth quaked, boulders split, tombs opened. Many bodies of saints who had fallen asleep were raised. After Jesus' resurrection they came forth from their tombs and entered the holy city and appeared to many. The centurion and his men who were keeping watch over Jesus were terror-stricken at seeing the earthquake and all that was happening, and said,

P "Clearly this was the Son of God!"]

N Many women were present looking on from a distance. They had followed Jesus from Galilee to attend to his needs. Among them were Mary Magdalene, and Mary the mother of James and Joseph, and the mother of Zebedee's sons. When evening fell, a wealthy man from Arimathea arrived, Joseph by name. He was another of Jesus' disciples, and had gone to request the body of Jesus. Thereupon Pilate issued an order for its release. Taking the body, Joseph wrapped it in fresh linen and laid it in his own new tomb which had been hewn from a formation of rock. Then he rolled a huge stone across the entrance of the tomb and went away. But Mary Magdalene and the other Mary remained sitting there, facing the tomb. The next day, the one following the Day of Preparation, the chief priests and the Pharisees called at Pilate's residence.

P "Sir, we have recalled that that impostor while he was still alive made the claim, 'After three days I will rise.' You should issue an order having the tomb kept under surveillance until the third day. Otherwise his disciples may go and steal him and tell the people, 'He has been raised from the dead!' This final imposture would be worse than the first."

S "You have a guard. Go and secure the tomb as best you can."

N So they went and kept it under surveillance of the guard, after fixing a seal to the stone.

808 **GOSPEL/B** *Mark 14, 1-15, 47 or 15, 1-39 / 38*

The symbols of the following passion narrative represent:

N narrator;

+ Christ;

S speakers other than Christ;

P groups of speakers.

N The passion of our Lord Jesus Christ according to Mark.

For short form read only the part in brackets.

N The feasts of the Passover and Unleavened Bread were to be observed in two days' time, and therefore the chief priests and scribes began to look for a way to arrest Jesus by some trick and kill him. Yet they pointed out,

P "Not during the festival, or the people may riot."

N When Jesus was in Bethany reclining at table in the house of Simon the leper, a woman entered carrying an alabaster jar of perfume made from expensive aromatic nard. Breaking the jar, she began to pour the perfume on his head. Some were saying to themselves indignantly:

P "What is the point of this extravagant waste of perfume? It could have been sold for over three hundred silver pieces and the money given to the poor."

N They were infuriated at her. But Jesus said:

\+ "Let her alone. Why do you criticize her? She has done me a kindness. The poor you will always have with you and you can be generous to them whenever you wish, but you will not always have me. She has done what she could. By perfuming my body she is anticipating its preparation for burial. I assure you, wherever the good news is proclaimed throughout the world, what she has done will be told in her memory."

N Then Judas Iscariot, one of the Twelve, went off to the chief priests to hand Jesus over to them. Hearing what he had to say, they were jubilant and promised to give him money. He for his part kept looking for an opportune way to hand him over. On the first day of Unleavened Bread, when it was customary to sacrifice the paschal lamb, his disciples said to him,

P "Where do you wish us to go to prepare the Passover supper for you?"

N He sent two of his disciples with these instructions:

\+ "Go into the city and you will come upon a man carrying a water jar. Follow him. Whatever house he enters, say to the owner, 'The Teacher asks, Where is my guest room where I may eat the Passover with my disciples?' Then he will show you an upstairs room, spacious, furnished, and all in order. That is the place you are to get ready for us."

N The disciples went off. When they reached the city they found it just as he had told them, and they prepared the Passover supper. As it grew dark he arrived with the Twelve. They reclined at table, and in the course of the meal Jesus said,

\+ "I give you my word, one of you is about to betray me, yes, one of you who is eating with me."

N They began to say to him sorrowfully, one by one,

S "Surely not I!"

\+ "It is one of the Twelve–a man who dips into the dish with me. The Son of Man is going the way the Scripture tells of him. Still, accursed be that man by whom the Son of Man is betrayed. It were better for him had he never been born."

N During the meal he took bread, blessed and broke it, and gave it to them.

\+ "Take this, this is my body."

N He likewise took a cup, gave thanks and passed it to them, and they all drank from it.

\+ "This is my blood, the blood of the covenant, to be poured out on behalf of many. I solemnly assure you, I will never again drink of the fruit of the vine until the day when I drink it in the reign of God."

N After singing songs of praise, they walked out to the Mount of Olives. Jesus then said to them:

\+ "Your faith in me shall be shaken, for Scripture has it,
'I will strike the shepherd
and the sheep will be dispersed.'
But after I am raised up, I will go to Galilee ahead of you."

N Peter said to him,

S "Even though all are shaken in faith, it will not be that way with me."

\+ "I give you my assurance, this very night before the cock crows twice, you will deny me three times."

N But Peter kept reasserting vehemently,

S "Even if I have to die with you, I will not deny you."

N They all said the same. They went then to a place named Gethsemani.

\+ "Sit down here while I pray."

N At the same time he took along with him Peter, James, and John. Then he began to be filled with fear and distress. He said to them,

\+ "My heart is filled with sorrow to the point of death. Remain here and stay awake."

N He advanced a little and fell to the ground, praying that if it were possible this hour might pass him by. He kept saying,

+ "Abba (O Father), you have the power to do all things. Take this cup away from me. But let it be as you would have it, not as I."

N When he returned he found them asleep. He said to Peter,

+ "Asleep, Simon? You could not stay awake for even an hour? Be on guard and pray that you may not be put to the test. The spirit is willing but nature is weak."

N Going back again he began to pray in the same words. Once again he found them asleep on his return. They could not keep their eyes open, nor did they know what to say to him. He returned a third time and said to them,

+ "Still sleeping? Still taking your ease? It will have to do. The hour is on us. You will see that the Son of Man is to be handed over to the clutches of evil men. Rouse yourselves and come along. See! My betrayer is near."

N Even while he was still speaking, Judas, one of the Twelve, made his appearance accompanied by a crowd with swords and clubs; these people had been sent by the chief priests, the scribes, and the elders. The betrayer had arranged a signal for them, saying,

S "The man I shall embrace is the one; arrest him and lead him away, taking every precaution."

N He then went directly over to him and said, embracing him,

S "Rabbi!"

N At this, they laid hands on him and arrested him. One of the bystanders drew his sword and struck the high priest's slave, cutting off his ear. Addressing himself to them, Jesus said,

+ "You have come out to arrest me armed with swords and clubs as if against a brigand. I was within your reach daily, teaching in the temple precincts, yet you never arrested me. But now, so that the Scriptures may be fulfilled..."

N With that, all deserted him and fled. There was a young man following him who was covered by nothing but a linen cloth. As they seized him he left the cloth behind and ran off naked. Then they led Jesus off to the high priest, and all the chief priests, the elders, and the scribes came together. Peter followed him at a distance right into the high priest's courtyard, where he found a seat with the temple guard and began to warm himself at the fire. The chief priests with the whole Sanhedrin were busy soliciting testimony against Jesus that would lead to his death, but they could not find any. Many spoke against him falsely under oath but their testimony did not agree. Some, for instance, on taking the stand, testified falsely by alleging,

P "We heard him declare, 'I will destroy this temple made by human hands.' and 'In three days I will construct another not made by human hands.'

N Even so, their testimony did not agree. The high priest rose to his feet before the court and began to interrogate Jesus:

S "Have you no answer to what these men testify against you?"

N But Jesus remained silent; he made no reply. Once again the high priest interrogated him:

S "Are you the Messiah, the Son of the Blessed One?"

+ "I am; and you will see the Son of Man seated at the right hand of the Power and coming with the clouds of heaven."

N At that the high priest tore his robes and said:

S "What further need do we have of witnesses? You have heard the blasphemy. What is your verdict?"

N They all concurred in the verdict "guilty," with its sentence of death. Some of them began to spit on him. They blindfolded him and hit him while the officers manhandled him, saying,

P "Play the prophet!"

N While Peter was down in the courtyard, one of the servant girls of the high priest came along. When she noticed Peter warming himself, she looked more closely at him and said,

S "You too were with Jesus of Nazareth."

N But he denied it:

S "I don't know what you are talking about! What are you getting at?"

N Then he went out into the gateway. At that moment a cock crowed. The servant girl, keeping an eye on him, started again to tell the bystanders,

S "This man is one of them."

N Once again he denied it. A little later

the bystanders said to Peter once more,

P "You are certainly one of them! You're a Galilean, are you not?"

N He began to curse, and to swear,

S "I do not even know the man you are talking about!"

N Just then a second cockcrow was heard and Peter recalled the prediction Jesus had made to him, "Before the cock crows twice you will disown me three times." He broke down and began to cry. [As soon as it was daybreak the chief priests, with the elders and scribes (that is, the whole Sanhedrin), reached a decision. They bound Jesus, led him away, and handed him over to Pilate. Pilate interrogated him:

S "Are you the king of the Jews?"

+ "You are the one who is saying it."

N The chief priests, meanwhile, brought many accusations against him. Pilate interrogated him again:

S "Surely you have some answer? See how many accusations they are leveling against you."

N But greatly to Pilate's surprise, Jesus made no further response. Now on the occasion of a festival he would release for them one prisoner–any man they asked for. There was a prisoner named Barabbas jailed along with rebels who had committed murder in the uprising. When the crowd came up to press their demand that he honor the custom, Pilate rejoined,

S "Do you want me to release the king of the Jews for you?"

N He was aware, of course, that it was out of jealousy that the chief priests had handed him over. Meanwhile, the chief priests incited the crowd to have him release Barabbas instead. Pilate again asked them,

S "What am I to do with the man you call the king of the Jews?"

P "Crucify him!"

N Pilate protested,

S "Why? What crime has he committed?

N They only shouted the louder,

P "Crucify him!"

N So Pilate, who wished to satisfy the crowd, released Barabbas to them, and after he had had Jesus scourged, he handed him over to be crucified. The soldiers now led Jesus away into the hall known as the praetorium; at the same time they assembled the whole cohort. They dressed him in royal purple, then wove a crown of thorns and put it on him, and began to salute him,

P "All hail!" King of the Jews!"

N Continually striking Jesus on the head with a reed and spitting at him, they genuflected before him and pretended to pay him homage. When they had finished mocking him, they stripped him of the purple, dressed him in his own clothes, and led him out to crucify him. A man named Simon of Cyrene, the father of Alexander and Rufus, was coming in from the fields, and they pressed him into service to carry the cross. When they brought Jesus to the site of Golgotha (which means "Skull Place"), they tried to give him wine drugged with myrrh, but he would not take it. Then they crucified him and divided up his garments by rolling dice for them to see what each should take. It was about nine in the morning when they crucified him. The inscription proclaiming his offense read, "The King of the Jews." With him they crucified two insurgents, one at his right and one at his left. People going by kept insulting him, tossing their heads and saying,

P "Ha, ha! So you were going to destroy the temple and rebuild it in three days! Save yourself now by coming down from the cross!"

N The chief priests and the scribes also joined in and jeered:

P "He saved others but he cannot save himself! Let the 'Messiah,' the 'king of Israel,' come down from that cross here and now, so that we can see it and believe in him!"

N The men who had been crucified with him likewise kept taunting him. When noon came, darkness fell on the whole countryside and lasted until midafternoon. At that time Jesus cried in a loud voice,

+ "Eloi, Eloi, lama sabachthani?"

N Which means,

+ "My God, my God, why have you forsaken me?"

N A few of the bystanders who heard it remarked,

P "Listen! He is calling on Elijah!"

N Someone ran off and, soaking a sponge in sour wine, stuck it on a reed to try to make him drink. The man said,

S "Now let's see whether Elijah comes to take him down."

N Then Jesus, uttering a loud cry,

breathed his last. At that moment the curtain in the sanctuary was torn in two from top to bottom. The centurion who stood guard over him, on seeing the manner of his death, declared,

S "Clearly this man was the Son of God!"]

N There were also women looking on from a distance. Among them were Mary Magdalene, Mary the mother of James the younger of Joses, and Salome. These women had followed Jesus when he was in Galilee and attended to his needs. There were also many others who had come up with him to Jerusalem. As it grew dark (it was Preparation Day, that is the eve of the sabbath), Joseph of Arimathea arrived–a distinguished member of the Sanhedrin. He was another who looked forward to the reign of God. He was bold enough to seek an audience with Pilate, and urgently requested the body of Jesus. Pilate was surprised that Jesus should have died so soon. He summoned the centurion and inquired whether Jesus was already dead. Learning from him that he was dead, Pilate released the corpse to Joseph. Then, having bought a linen shroud, Joseph took him down, wrapped him in the linen, and laid him in a tomb which had been cut out of rock. Finally he rolled a stone across the entrance of the tomb. Meanwhile, Mary Magdalene and Mary the mother of Joses observed where he had been laid.

809 **GOSPEL/C** *Luke 22, 14-23, 56 or 23, 1-49 / 38*

The symbols of the following passion narrative represent:

N narrator;

+ *Christ;*

S speakers other than Christ;

P groups of speakers.

N The Passion of our Lord Jesus Christ according to Luke.

For short form read only the part in brackets.

N When the hour arrived, Jesus took his place at table, and the apostles with him. He said to them:

+ "I have greatly desired to eat this Passover with you before I suffer. I tell you, I will not eat again until it is fulfilled in the kingdom of God."

N Then taking a cup he offered a blessing in thanks and said:

+ "Take this and divide it among you; I tell you, from now on I will not drink of the fruit of the vine until the coming of the reign of God."

N Then taking bread and giving thanks, he broke it and gave it to them, saying:

+ "This is my body to be given for you. Do this as a remembrance of me."

N He did the same with the cup after eating, saying as he did so:

+ "This cup is the new covenant in my blood, which will be shed for you."

"And yet the hand of my betrayer is with me at this table. The Son of Man is following out his appointed course, but woe to that man by whom he is betrayed."

N Then they began to dispute among themselves as to which of them would do such a deed.

A dispute arose among them about who would be regarded as the greatest.

+ "Earthly kings lord it over their people. Those who exercise authority over them are called their benefactors. Yet it cannot be that way with you. Let the greater among you be as the junior, the leader as the servant. Who, in fact, is the greater–he who reclines at table or he who serves the meal? Is it not the one who reclines at table? Yet I am in your midst as the one who serves you. You are the ones who have stood loyally by me in my temptations. I for my part assign to you the dominion my Father has assigned to me. In my kingdom, you will eat and drink at my table, and you will sit on thrones judging the twelve tribes of Israel.

"Simon, Simon! Remember that Satan has asked for you to sift you all like wheat. But I have prayed for you that your faith may never fail. You in turn must strengthen your brothers."

S "Lord, at your side I am prepared to face imprisonment and death itself."

+ "I tell you, Peter, the rooster will not crow today until you have three times denied that you know me."

N He asked them,

+ "When I sent you on mission without purse or traveling bag or sandals, were you in need of anything?"

P "Not a thing,"

+ "Now, however, the man who has a purse must carry it; the same with the traveling bag. And the man without a sword must sell his coat and buy one. It is written in Scripture,

'He was counted among the
wicked,'

and this, I tell you, must come to be fulfilled in me. All that has to do with me approaches its climax."

P "Lord, here are two swords!"

+ "Enough."

N Then he went out and made his way, as was his custom, to the Mount of Olives; his disciples accompanied him. On reaching the place he said to them,

+ "Pray that you may not be put to the test."

N He withdrew from them about a stone's throw, then went down on his knees and prayed in these words:

+ "Father, if it is your will, take this cup from me; yet not my will but yours be done."

N An angel then appeared to him from heaven to strengthen him. In his anguish he prayed with all the greater intensity, and his sweat became like drops of blood falling to the ground. Then he rose from prayer and came to his disciples, only to find them asleep, exhausted with grief.

+ "Why are you sleeping? Wake up, and pray that you may not be subjected to the trial."

N While he was still speaking a crowd came, led by the man named Judas, one of the Twelve. He approached Jesus to embrace him. Jesus said to him,

+ "Judas, would you betray the Son of Man with a kiss?"

N When the companions of Jesus saw what was going to happen, they said,

P "Lord, shall we use the sword?"

N One of them went so far as to strike the high priest's servant and cut off his right ear. Jesus said in answer to their question,

+ "Enough!"

N Then he touched the ear and healed the man.

But to those who had come out against him–the chief priests, the chiefs of the temple guard, and the ancients–Jesus said,

+ "Am I a criminal that you come out after me armed with swords and clubs? When I was with you day after day in the temple you never raised a hand against me. But this is your hour–the triumph of darkness!"

N They led him away under arrest and brought him to the house of the high priest, while Peter followed at a distance. Later they lighted a fire in the middle of the courtyard and were sitting beside it, and Peter sat among them. A servant girl saw him sitting in the light of the fire. She gazed at him intently, then said,

S "This man was with him."

N He denied the fact, saying,

S "Woman, I do not know him."

N A little while later someone else saw him and said,

S "You are one of them too."

S "No, sir, not I!"

N About an hour after that another spoke more insistently:

S "This man was certainly with him, for he is a Galilean."

S "My friend, I do not know what you are talking about."

N At the very moment he was saying this, a rooster crowed. The Lord turned around and looked at Peter, and Peter remembered the word that the Lord had spoken to him, "Before the rooster crows today you will deny me three times." He went out and wept bitterly.

Meanwhile the men guarding Jesus amused themselves at his expense. They blindfolded him first, slapped him, and then taunted him:

P "Play the prophet; which one struck you?"

N And they directed many other insulting words at him. At daybreak the council, which was made up of the elders of the people, the chief priests, and the scribes, assembled again. Once they had brought him before their council, they said,

P "Tell us, are you the Messiah?"

+ "If I tell you, you will not believe me, and if I question you, you will not answer. This much only will I say: 'From now on, the Son of Man will have his seat at the right hand of the Power of God.' "

P "So you are the Son of God?"

+ "It is you who say I am."

P "What need have we of witnesses? We have heard it from his own mouth."

N [Then the entire assembly rose up and led him (Jesus) before Pilate. They started his prosecution by saying,

P "We found this man subverting our nation, opposing the payment of taxes to Caesar, and calling himself the Messiah, a king."

N Pilate asked him,

S "Are you the king of the Jews?"

+ "That is your term."

N Pilate reported to the chief priests and the crowds,

S "I do not find a case against this man."

N But they insisted,

P "He stirs up the people by his teaching throughout the whole of Judea, from Galilee, where he began, to this very place."

N On hearing this Pilate asked if the man was a Galilean; and when he learned that he was under Herod's jurisdiction, he sent him to Herod, who also happened to be in Jerusalem at the time. Herod was extremely pleased to see Jesus. From the reports about him he had wanted for a long time to see him, and he was hoping to see him work some miracle. He questioned Jesus at considerable length, but Jesus made no answer. The chief priests and scribes were at hand to accuse him vehemently. Herod and his guards then treated him with contempt and insult, after which they put a magnificent robe on him and sent him back to Pilate. Herod and Pilate, who had previously been set against each other, became friends from that day. Pilate then called together the chief priests, the ruling class, and the people, and said to them:

S "You have brought this man before me as one who subverts the people. I have examined him in your presence and have no charge against him arising from your allegations. Neither has Herod, who therefore has sent him back to us; obviously this man has done nothing to deserve death. Therefore I mean to release him, once I have taught him a lesson."

N The whole crowd cried out,

P "Away with this man; release Barabbas for us!"

N This Barabbas had been thrown in prison for causing an uprising in the city, and for murder. Pilate addressed them again, for he wanted Jesus to be the one he released. But they shouted back,

P "Crucify him, crucify him!"

N He said to them for the third time,

S "What wrong is this man guilty of? I have not discovered anything about him deserving the death penalty. I will therefore chastise him and release him."

N But they demanded with loud cries that he be crucified, and their shouts increased in violence. Pilate then decreed that what they demanded should be done. He released the one they asked for, who had been thrown in prison for insurrection and murder, and delivered Jesus up to their wishes. As they led him away, they laid hold of one Simon the Cyrenean who was coming in from the fields. They put a crossbeam on Simon's shoulder for him to carry along behind Jesus. A great crowd of people followed him, including women who beat their breasts and lamented over him. Jesus turned to them and said:

+ "Daughters of Jerusalem, do not weep for me. Weep for yourselves and for your children. The days are coming when they will say, 'Happy are the sterile, the wombs that never bore and the breasts that never nursed,' Then they will begin saying to the mountains, 'Fall on us,' and to the hills, 'Cover us.' If they do these things in the green wood, what will happen in the dry?"

N Two others who were criminals were led along with him to be crucified. When they came to Skull Place, as it was called, they crucified him there and the criminals as well, one on his right and the other on his left. Jesus said,

+ ["Father, forgive them; they do not know what they are doing."]

N They divided his garments, rolling dice for them. The people stood there watching, and the leaders kept jeering at him, saying,

P "He saved others; let him save himself if he is the Messiah of God, the chosen one."

N The soldiers also made fun of him, coming forward to offer him their sour wine and saying,

S "If you are the king of the Jews, save yourself."

N There was an inscription over his head: "THIS IS THE KING OF THE JEWS."
One of the criminals hanging in crucifixion blasphemed him,

S "Aren't you the Messiah? Then save yourself and us.

N But the other rebuked him:

S "Have you no fear of God, seeing you are under the same sentence? We deserve it, after all. We are only paying the price for what we've done, but this man has done nothing wrong. Jesus, remember me when you enter upon your reign."

\+ "I assure you: this day you will be with me in paradise."

N It was now around midday, and darkness came over the whole land until midafternoon with an eclipse of the sun. The curtain in the sanctuary was torn in two. Jesus uttered a loud cry and said,

\+ "Father, into your hands I commend my spirit."

N After he said this, he expired. The centurion, upon seeing what had happened, gave glory to God by saying,

S "Surely this was an innocent man."

N After the crowd assembled for this spectacle witnessed what had happened, they returned beating their breasts. All his friends and the women who had accompanied him from Galilee were standing at a distance watching everything.] There was a man named Joseph, an upright and holy member of the Sanhedrin, who had not been associated with their plan or their action. He was from Arimathea, a Jewish town, and he looked expectantly for the reign of God. This man approached Pilate with a request for Jesus' body. He took it down, wrapped it in fine linen, and laid it in a tomb hewn out of the rock, in which no one had yet been buried. That was the day of Preparation, and the sabbath was about to begin. The women who had come with him from Galilee followed along behind. They saw the tomb and how his body was buried. Then they went back home to prepare spices and perfumes. They observed the sabbath as a day of rest, in accordance with the law.

Easter Triduum

810 "The Easter Triduum of the passion and resurrection of Christ is...the culmination of the entire liturgical year. What Sunday is to the week, the solemnity of Easter is to the liturgical year." (General Norms for the Liturgical Year, #18)

Lent ends quietly on Thursday afternoon. The church enters the Triduum ("three days"). On Thursday night the church begins a time of prayer and fasting, a time of keeping watch, that lasts into the great Vigil between Saturday and Sunday. The church emphasizes that the fasting of Good Friday and, if possible, of Holy Saturday are integral to the keeping of these days and the preparation for the sacraments of initiation celebrated at the Vigil. On Thursday night and on Friday afternoon or evening the church gathers to pray and to remember the many facets of the single mystery.

811 HOLY THURSDAY: EVENING MASS OF THE LORD'S SUPPER

On Thursday night Lent has ended and the church, at this Mass of the Lord's Supper, enters into the Easter Triduum. From the very first moment the all-embracing experience of these three days is proclaimed: "We should glory in the cross of our Lord Jesus Christ. For he is our salvation, our life, and our resurrection. Through him we are saved and made free." This is the whole of the great Triduum. On Thursday night, the liturgy draws us toward this through the scriptures, through the mandatum or washing of the feet which is the direct expression of our service to one another and the world, through the eucharistic banquet itself.

LITURGY OF THE WORD

READING I *Exodus 12, 1-8, 11-14 / 40*

The Lord said to Moses and Aaron in the land of Egypt, "This month shall stand at the head of your calendar; you shall reckon it the first month of the year. Tell the whole community of Israel: On the tenth of this month every one of your families must procure for itself a lamb, one apiece for each household. If a family is too small for a whole lamb, it shall join the nearest household in procuring one and shall share in the lamb in proportion to the number of persons who partake of it. The lamb must be a year-old male and without blemish. You may take it from either the sheep or the goats. You shall keep it until the fourteenth day of this month, and then, with the whole assembly of Israel present, it shall be slaughtered during the evening twilight. They shall take some of its blood and apply it to the two doorposts and the lintel of every house in which they partake of the lamb. That same night they shall eat its roasted flesh with unleavened bread and bitter herbs.

"This is how you are to eat it: with your loins girt, sandals on your feet and your staff in hand, you shall eat like those who are in flight. It is the Passover of the Lord. For on this same night I will go through Egypt, striking down every first-born of the land, both man and beast, and executing judgment on all the gods of Egypt–I, the Lord! But the blood will mark the houses where you are. Seeing the blood, I will pass over you; thus, when I strike the land of Egypt, no destructive blow will come upon you.

"This day shall be a memorial feast for you, which all your generations shall celebrate with pilgrimage to the Lord, as a perpetual institution."

RESPONSORIAL PSALM *Psalm (115)116B, 12-13.15-16.17-18 / 40*

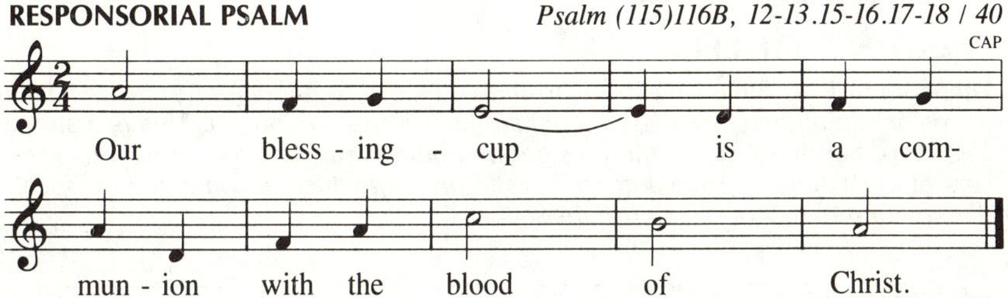
CAP
Our bless - ing - cup is a com-
mun - ion with the blood of Christ.

How can I repay the Lord
for his goodness to me?
The cup of salvation I will raise;
I will call on the Lord's name. ℟.

O precious in the eyes of the Lord
is the death of his faithful.
Your servant, Lord, your servant am I;
you have loosened my bonds. ℟.

A thanksgiving sacrifice I make:
I will call on the Lord's name.
My vows to the Lord I will fulfill
before all his people. ℟.

READING II *1 Corinthians 11.23-26 / 40*

I received from the Lord what I handed on to you, namely, that the Lord Jesus on the night in which he was betrayed took bread, and after he had given thanks, broke it and said, "This is my body, which is for you. Do this in remembrance of me." In the same way, after the supper, he took the cup, saying, "This cup is the new covenant in my blood. Do this, whenever you drink it, in remembrance of me." Every time, then, you eat this bread and drink this cup, you proclaim the death of the Lord until he comes!

GOSPEL *John 13, 1-15 / 40*

Before the feast of Passover, Jesus realized that the hour had come for him to pass from this world to the Father. He had loved his own in this world, and would show his love for them to the end. The devil had already induced Judas, son of Simon Iscariot, to hand Jesus over; and so, during the supper, Jesus–fully aware that he had come from God and was going to God, the Father who had handed everything over to him–rose from the meal and took off his cloak. He picked up a towel and tied it around himself. Then he poured water into a basin and began to wash his disciples' feet and dry them with the towel he had around him. Thus he came to Simon Peter, who said to him, "Lord are you going to wash my feet?" Jesus answered, "You may not realize now what I am doing but later you will understand." Peter replied, "You shall never wash my feet!" "If I do not wash you," Jesus answered, "you will have no share in my heritage." "Lord," Simon Peter said to him, "then not only my feet, but my hands and head as well." Jesus told him, "The man who has bathed has no need to wash [except for his feet]; he is entirely cleansed, just as you are; though not all." (The reason he said, "Not all are washed clean," was that he knew his betrayer.)

After he had washed their feet, he put his cloak back on and reclined at table once more. He said to them:

"Do you understand what I just did for you?
You address me as 'Teacher' and 'Lord,'
and fittingly enough,
for that is what I am.
But if I washed your feet–
I who am Teacher and Lord–
then you must wash each other's feet.
What I just did was to give you an example:
as I have done, so you must do."

812 WASHING OF FEET

The homily is followed by the washing of feet, the mandatum (from the Latin word for "command": "A new commandment I give to you..."). This is a simple gesture of humble service: the presider and others wash the feet of various members of the assembly. Such a gesture, with the song which accompanies it, speaks directly of the way of life Christians seek.

I give you a new commandment
Taizé Community, 1979
Jacques Berthier, b.1923

Man - da - tum no - vum do vo - bis,
di - cit Do - mi - nus, di - cit Do - mi - nus.

Other appropriate songs are: Ubi Caritas, no. 598 or 604, and Jesus Took a Towel, no. 432.

The Mass continues with the general intercessions.

813 TRANSFER OF THE HOLY EUCHARIST

When the communion rite is concluded, the eucharistic bread that remains is solemnly carried from the altar. The following hymn accompanies the procession.

Thomas Aquinas, 1227-1274
Tr. by James Quinn, SJ, b.1919

Mode III
Acc. by Gerard Farrell, OSB, b.1919

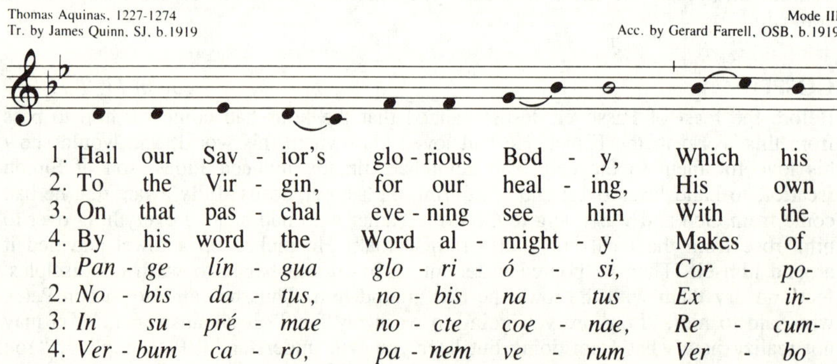
1. Hail our Sav - ior's glo - rious Bod - y, Which his
2. To the Vir - gin, for our heal - ing, His own
3. On that pas - chal eve - ning see him With the
4. By his word the Word al - might - y Makes of
1. Pan - ge lín - gua glo - ri - ó - si, Cor - po-
2. No - bis da - tus, no - bis na - tus Ex in-
3. In su - pré - mae no - cte coe - nae, Re - cum-
4. Ver - bum ca - ro, pa - nem ve - rum Ver - bo

Vir - gin Moth - er bore; Hail the Blood which, shed for sin - ners, Did a bro - ken world re - store; Hail the sac - ra - ment most ho - ly, Flesh and Blood of Christ a - dore!
Son the Fa - ther sends; From the Fa - ther's love pro - ceed - ing Sow - er, seed and word de - scends; Won - drous life of Word in - car - nate With his great - est won - der ends.
cho - sen twelve re - cline, To the old law still o - be - dient In its feast of love di - vine; Love di - vine, the new law giv - ing, Gives him - self as Bread and Wine.
bread his flesh in - deed; Wine be - comes his ver - y life-blood; Faith God's liv - ing Word must heed! Faith a - lone may safe - ly guide us Where the sens - es can - not lead! A - men.
ris my - sté - ri - um San - gui - nís - que pre - ti - ó - si, Quem in mún - di pré - ti - um Fru - ctus ven - tris ge - ne - ró - si Rex ef - fú - dit gén - ti - um.
tá - cta Vír - gi - ne, Et in mún - do con - ver - sá - tus, Spar - so vér - bi sé - mi - ne, Su - i mo - ras in - co - lá - tus Mi - ro clau - sit ór - di - ne.
bens cum frá - tri - bus, Ob - ser - vá - ta le - ge ple - ne Ci - bis in le - gá - li - bus, Ci - bum tur - bae du - o - dé - nae Se dat su - is má - ni - bus.
car - nem éf - fi - cit: Fit - que san - guis Chri - sti me - rum, Et si sen - sus dé - fi - cit, Ad fir - mán - dum cor sin - cé - rum So - la fi - des súf - fi - cit. A - men.

5. Come, adore this wondrous presence;
 Bow to Christ, the source of grace!
Here is kept the ancient promise
 Of God's earthly dwelling place!
Sight is blind before God's glory,
 Faith alone may see his face!

6. Glory be to God the Father,
 Praise to his coequal Son,
Adoration to the Spirit,
 Bond of love, in Godhead one!
Blest be God by all creation
 Joyously while ages run! Amen.

5. *Tantum ergo Sacraméntum*
 Venerémur cérnui:
Et antíquum documéntum
 Novo cedat rítui;
Praestet fides suppleméntum
 Sénsuum deféctui.

6. *Genitóri, Genitóque*
 Laus et jubilátio,
Salus, honor, virtus quoque
 Sit et benedíctio:
Procedénti ab utróque
 Compar sit laudátio. Amen.

The liturgy has no concluding rite, no dismissal. Rather, the church continues to watch and pray throughout the Triduum.

814 GOOD FRIDAY

In Good Friday's liturgy of the word and veneration of the cross there is great solemnity: a pondering of the "mystery of our faith," the passion, death and resurrection of our Lord Jesus Christ. Fasting and praying during these days, the catechumens and the baptized assemble on Good Friday in the afternoon or evening for a time of prayer together. This begins a time of silence.

LITURGY OF THE WORD

READING I

Isaiah 52, 13-53.12 / 41

See, my servant shall prosper,
he shall be raised high and greatly exalted.
Even as many were amazed at him–
so marred was his look beyond that of man,
and his appearance beyond that of mortals–
So shall he startle many nations,
because of him kings shall stand speechless;
For those who have not been told shall see,
those who have not heard shall ponder it.

Who would believe what we have heard?
To whom has the arm of the Lord been revealed?
He grew up like a sapling before him,
like a shoot from the parched earth;
There was in him no stately bearing to make us look at him,
nor appearance that would attract us to him.
He was spurned and avoided by men,
a man of suffering, accustomed to infirmity.
One of those from whom men hide their faces,
spurned, and we held him in no esteem.

Yet it was our infirmities that he bore,
our sufferings that he endured,
While we thought of him as stricken,
as one smitten by God and afflicted.
But he was pierced for our offenses,
crushed for our sins;
Upon him was the chastisement that makes us whole,
by his stripes we were healed.
We had all gone astray like sheep,
each following his own way;
But the Lord laid upon him
the guilt of us all.

Though he was harshly treated, he submitted
and opened not his mouth;
Like a lamb led to the slaughter
or a sheep before the shearers,
he was silent and opened not his mouth.
Oppressed and condemned, he was taken away,
and who would have thought any more of his destiny?
When he was cut off from the land of the living,
and smitten for the sin of his people,
A grave was assigned him among the wicked
and a burial place with evildoers,
Though he had done no wrong
nor spoken any falsehood.
[But the Lord was pleased
to crush him in infirmity.]

If he gives his life as an offering for sin,
he shall see his descendants in a long life,
and the will of the Lord shall be accomplished through him.
Because of his affliction
he shall see the light in fullness of days;
Through his suffering, my servant shall justify many,
and their guilt he shall bear.
Therefore I will give him his portion among the great,
and he shall divide the spoils with the the mighty,

Because he surrendered himself to
death
and was counted among the wicked;
And he shall take away the sins of the
many,
and win pardon for their offenses.

RESPONSORIAL PSALM *Psalm (30)31, 2.6.12-13.15-16.17.25 / 41*

DLSM
Fa - ther, I put my life in your hands.

In you, O Lord, I take refuge.
Let me never be put to shame.
In your justice, set me free,
Into your hands I commend my spirit.
It is you who will redeem me,
Lord. ℟.

In the face of all my foes
I am a reproach,
an object of scorn to my neighbors
and of fear to my friends. ℟.

Those who see me in the street
run far away from me.
I am like a dead man, forgotten,
like a thing thrown away. ℟.

But as for me, I trust in you, Lord;
I say: "You are my God."
My life is in your hands, deliver me
from the hands of those who hate
me. ℟.

"Let your face shine on your servant.
Save me in your love."
Be strong, let your heart take courage,
all who hope in the Lord. ℟.

READING II *Hebrews 4, 14-16; 5, 7-9 / 41*

We have a great high priest who has passed through the heavens, Jesus, the Son of God; let us hold fast to our profession of faith. For we do not have a high priest who is unable to sympathize with our weakness, but one who was tempted in every way that we are, yet never sinned. So let us confidently approach the throne of grace to receive mercy and favor and to find help in time of need.

In the days when he was in the flesh, Christ offered prayers and supplications with loud cries and tears to God, who was able to save him from death, and he was heard because of his reverence. Son though he was, he learned obedience from what he suffered; and when perfected, he became the source of eternal salvation for all who obey him.

GOSPEL *John 18, 1-19, 42 / 41*

The symbols of the following passion narrative represent:

N narrator;

+ Christ;

S speakers other than Christ;

P groups of speakers.

N The Passion of our Lord Jesus Christ according to John.

For short form read only the part in brackets.

N Jesus went out with his disciples across the Kidron valley. There was a garden there, and he and his disciples entered it. The place was known to Judas as well (the one who was to hand him over) because Jesus had often met there with his disciples. Judas took the cohort as well as police supplied by the chief priests and the Pharisees, and came there with lanterns, torches and weapons. Jesus, aware of all that would happen to him, stepped forward and said to them,

\+ "Who is it you want?"

P "Jesus the Nazorean."

\+ "I am he."

N (Now Judas, the one who was to hand him over, was right there with them.) As Jesus said to them, "I am he, " they retreated slightly and fell to the ground. Jesus put the question to them again,

\+ "Who is it you want?"

P "Jesus the Nazorean."

\+ "I have told you, I am he. If I am the one you want, let these men go."

N (This was to fulfill what he had said, "I have not lost one of those you gave me.") Then Simon Peter, who had a sword, drew it and struck the slave of the high priest, severing his right ear. (The slave's name was Malchus.) At that Jesus said to Peter,

\+ "Put your sword back in its sheath. Am I not to drink the cup the Father has given me?"

N Then the soldiers of the cohort, their tribune, and the Jewish police arrested Jesus and bound him. They led him first to Annas, the father-in-law of Caiaphas who was high priest that year. (It was Caiaphas who had proposed to the Jews the advantage of having one man die for the people.) Simon Peter, in company with another disciple, kept following Jesus closely. This disciple, who was known to the high priest, stayed with Jesus as far as the high priest's courtyard, while Peter was left standing at the gate. The disciple known to the high priest came out and spoke to the woman at the gate, and then brought Peter in. This servant girl who kept the gate said to Peter,

S "Aren't you one of this man's followers?"

S "Not I."

N Now the night was cold, and the servants and the guards who were standing around had made a charcoal fire to warm themselves by. Peter joined them and stood there warming himself.

N The high priest questioned Jesus, first about his disciples, then about his teaching. Jesus answered by saying:

\+ "I have spoken publicly to any who would listen.
I always taught in a synagogue or in the temple area where all the Jews come together.
There was nothing secret about anything I said.
Why do you question me? Question those who heard me when I spoke. It should be obvious they will know what I said."

N At this reply, one of the guards who was standing nearby gave Jesus a sharp blow on the face.

S "Is that any way to answer the high priest?"

\+ "If I said anything wrong produce the evidence, but if I spoke the truth why hit me?"

N Annas next sent him, bound, to the high priest Caiaphas. All through this, Simon Peter had been standing there warming himself. They said to him,

P "Are you not a disciple of his?"

S "I am not!"

P "But did I not see you with him in the garden?"

N One of the high priest's slaves insisted–as it happened, a relative of the man whose ear Peter had severed. Peter denied it again. At that moment a cock began to crow.
At daybreak they brought Jesus from Caiaphas to the praetorium. They did not enter the praetorium themselves, for they had to avoid ritual impurity if they were to eat the Passover supper. Pilate came out to them.

S "What accusation do you bring against this man?"

P "If he were not a criminal, we would certainly not have handed him over to you."

S "Why do you not take him and pass judgment on him according to your law?"

P "We may not put anyone to death."

N (This was to fulfill what Jesus had said, indicating the sort of death he would die.) Pilate went back into the praetorium and summoned Jesus.

S "Are you the King of the Jews?"

\+ "Are you saying this on your own, or have others been telling you about me?"

S "I am no Jew! It is your own people and the chief priests who have handed you over to me. What have you done?"

+ "My kingdom does not belong to this world.
If my kingdom were of this world,
my subjects would be fighting
to save me from being handed over to the Jews.
As it is, my kingdom is not here."

S "So, then, you are a king?"

+ "It is you who say I am a king.
The reason I was born,
the reason why I came into the world,
is to testify to the truth.
Anyone committed to the truth hears my voice."

S "Truth! What does that mean?"

N After this remark, Pilate went out again to the Jews and told them:

S "Speaking for myself, I find no case against this man. Recall your custom whereby I release to you someone at Passover time. Do you want me to release to you the king of the Jews?"

P "We want Barabbas, not this one!"

N (Barabbas was an insurrectionist.) Pilate's next move was to take Jesus and have him scourged. The soldiers then wove a crown of thorns and fixed it on his head, throwing around his shoulders a cloak of royal purple. Repeatedly they came up to him and said,

P "All hail, King of the Jews!"

N slapping his face as they did so. Pilate went out a second time and said to the crowd:

S "Observe what I do. I am going to bring him out to you to make you realize that I find no case against him."

N When Jesus came out wearing the crown of thorns and the purple cloak, Pilate said to them,

S "Look at the man!"

N As soon as the chief priests and the temple police saw him they shouted,

P "Crucify him! Crucify him!"

S "Take him and crucify him yourselves; I find no case against him."

P "We have our law, and according to that law he must die because he made himself God's Son."

N When Pilate heard this kind of talk, he was more afraid than ever. Going back into the praetorium, he said to Jesus,

S "Where do you come from?"

N Jesus would not give him any answer.

S "Do you refuse to speak to me? Do you not know that I have the power to release you and the power to crucify you?"

+ "You would have no power over me whatever
unless it were given to you from above.
That is why he who handed me over to you
is guilty of the greater sin."

N After this, Pilate was eager to release him, but the Jews shouted,

P "If you free this man, you are no 'Friend of Caesar.' Anyone who makes himself a king becomes Caesar's rival."

N Pilate heard what they were saying, then brought Jesus outside and took a seat on a judge's bench at the place called the Stone Pavement–Gabbatha in Hebrew. (It was the Preparation Day for Passover, and the hour was about noon.) He said to the Jews,

S "Look at your king!"

P "Away with him! Away with him! Crucify him!"

S "What! Shall I crucify your king?"

P "We have no king but Caesar."

N In the end, Pilate handed Jesus over to be crucified. Jesus was led away, and carrying the cross by himself, went out to what is called the Place of the Skull (in Hebrew, Golgotha). There they crucified him, and two others with him: one on either side, Jesus in the middle. Pilate had an inscription placed on the cross which read,

JESUS THE NAZOREAN
THE KING OF THE JEWS

This inscription, in Hebrew, Latin and Greek, was read by many of the Jews, since the place where Jesus was crucified was near the city. The chief priests of the Jews tried to tell Pilate,

P "You should not have written, 'The King of the Jews.' Write instead, 'This man claimed to be the king of the Jews.' "

S "What I have written, I have written."

N After the soldiers had crucified Jesus they took his garments and divided them four ways, one for each soldier. There was also his tunic, but this tunic was woven in one piece from top to bottom and had no seam. They said to each other,

P "We shouldn't tear it. Let's throw dice to see who gets it."

N (The purpose of this was to have the Scripture fulfilled:
"They divided my garments among them;
for my clothing they cast lots.")
And this was what the soldiers did.
Near the cross of Jesus there stood his mother, his mother's sister, Mary the wife of Clopas, and Mary Magdalene. Seeing his mother there with the disciple whom he loved, Jesus said to his mother,

\+ "Woman, this is your son."

N In turn he said to the disciple,

\+ "There is your mother."

N From that hour onward, the disciple took her into his care. After that, Jesus, realizing that everything was now finished, to bring the Scripture to fulfillment said,

\+ "I am thirsty."

N There was a jar there, full of common wine. They stuck a sponge soaked in this wine on some hyssop and raised it to his lips. When Jesus took the wine, he said,

\+ "Now it is finished."

N Then he bowed his head, and delivered over his spirit.
Since it was the Preparation Day, the Jews did not want to have the bodies left on the cross during the sabbath, for that sabbath was a solemn feast day. They asked Pilate that the legs be broken and the bodies be taken away. Accordingly, the soldiers came and broke the legs of the men crucified with Jesus, first of one, then of the other. When they came to Jesus and saw that he was already dead, they did not break his legs. One of the soldiers ran a lance into his side, and immediately blood and water flowed out. (This testimony has been given by an eyewitness, and his testimony is true. He tells what he knows is true, so that you may believe.) These events took place for the fulfillment of Scripture:
"Break none of his bones."
There is still another Scripture passage which says:
"They shall look on him whom they have pierced."
Afterward, Joseph of Arimathea, a disciple of Jesus (although a secret one for fear of the Jews), asked Pilate's permission to remove Jesus' body. Pilate granted it, so they came and took the body away. Nicodemus (the man who had first come to Jesus at night) likewise came, bringing a mixture of myrrh and aloes which weighed about a hundred pounds. They took Jesus' body, and in accordance with Jewish burial custom bound it up in wrappings of cloth with perfumed oils. In the place where he had been crucified there was a garden, and in the garden a new tomb in which no one had ever been laid. Because of the Jewish Preparation Day they laid Jesus there, for the tomb was close at hand.

GENERAL INTERCESSIONS

As at Sunday liturgy, the word service concludes with prayers of intercession. Today these prayers take a more solemn form as the church lifts up to God its own needs and those of the world.

815 VENERATION OF THE CROSS

An ancient liturgical text reads: "See here the true and most revered Tree. Hasten to kiss it and to cry out with faith: You are our help, most revered Cross." For many centuries the church has solemnly venerated the relic or image of the cross on Good Friday. It is not present as a picture of suffering only but as a symbol of Christ's passover, where "dying he destroyed our death and rising restored our life." It is the glorious, the life-giving cross that the faithful venerate with song, prayer, kneeling and a kiss.

As the cross is shown to the assembly, the following is sung.

HH
This is the wood of the cross, on which hung the

Cantor:
Sav - ior of the world. Come, let us wor - ship.
All:
Ho - ly is God, ho - ly and strong,
ho - ly and liv - ing for ev - er.

As the assembly comes forward to venerate the cross, the following or other chants and hymns may be sung.

We adore you, Lord
Taizé Community, 1979
Jacques Berthier, b.1923

A - do - ra-mus te, A - do - ra-mus te, Do-mi - ne. (hum)

HOLY COMMUNION 816

This liturgy concludes with a simple communion rite. All recite the Lord's Prayer and receive holy communion. There is no concluding rite or dismissal for the church continues to be at prayer throughout the Triduum.

HOLY SATURDAY 817

The church continues to fast and pray and to make ready for this night's great Vigil. Saturday is a day of great quiet and reflection. Catechumens, sponsors and some of the faithful may assemble during the day for prayer, the recitation of the Creed, and for the rite of Ephpheta (opening of ears and mouth).

EASTER VIGIL 818

The long preparation of the catechumens, the lenten disciplines and fast of the faithful, the vigiling and fasting and prayer that have gone on since Thursday night—all culminate in the great liturgy of this night. On this night the church assembles to spend much time listening to scriptures, praying psalms, acclaiming the death and resurrection of the Lord. Only then are the catechumens called forward and prayed over, challenged to renounce evil and affirm their faith in God, led to the font and baptized in the blessed water. The newly baptized are then anointed with chrism and the entire assembly joins in intercession and finally in the eucharist.

INTRODUCTORY RITE

BLESSING OF THE FIRE AND LIGHTING OF THE PASCHAL CANDLE

The night vigil begins with the kindling of new fire and the lighting of the assembly's paschal candle.

PROCESSION

The ministers and assembly go in procession to the place where the scriptures will be read. The following is sung during the procession.

Deacon or Priest:
All:
Christ our light.
Thanks be to God.

EASTER PROCLAMATION: THE EXSULTET

In this ancient text the church gives thanks and praise to God for all that is recalled this night: Adam's fall, the deliverance from Egypt, the passover of Christ, the wedding of earth and heaven, our reconciliation.

LITURGY OF THE WORD

At the Vigil, the liturgy of the word is an extended time of readings, silence and the chanting of psalms. On this night when the faithful know the death and resurrection of the Lord in baptism and eucharist, the church needs first to hear these scriptures which are the foundation of our life together: the creation story, Abraham and Isaac, the dividing of the sea, the poetry of Isaiah and Baruch and Ezekiel, the proclamation of Paul to the Romans and the gospel account of Jesus' resurrection.

819 **READING I** *Genesis 1, 1 - 2, 2 or 1, 1.26-31 / 42*

For short form read only the part in brackets.

[In the beginning, when God created the heavens and the earth,] the earth was a formless wasteland, and darkness covered the abyss, while a mighty wind swept over the waters.

Then God said, "Let there be light," and there was light. God saw how good the light was. God then separated the light from the darkness. God called the light "day," and the darkness he called "night." Thus evening came, and morning followed–the first day.

Then God said, "Let there be a dome in the middle of the waters to separate one body of water from the other." And so it happened: God made the dome, and it separated the water above the dome from the water below it. God called the dome "the sky." Evening came, and morning followed–the second day.

Then God said, "Let the water under the sky be gathered into a single basin, so that the dry land may appear." And so it happened: the water under the sky was gathered into its basin, and the dry land appeared. God called the dry land "the earth," and the basin of the water he called "the sea." God saw how good it was. Then God said, "Let the earth bring forth vegetation: every kind of plant that bears seed and every kind of fruit tree on earth that bears fruit with its seed in it." And so it happened: the earth brought forth every kind of plant that bears seed and every kind of fruit tree on earth that bears fruit with its seed in it. God saw how good it was. Evening came, and morning followed–the third day.

Then God said: "Let there be lights in the dome of the sky, to separate day from night. Let them mark the fixed times, the days and the years, and serve as luminaries in the dome of the sky, to shed light upon the earth." And so it happened: God made the two great lights, the greater one to govern the day, and the lesser one to govern the night; and he made the stars. God set them in the dome of the sky, to shed light upon the earth, to govern the day and the night, and to separate the light from the darkness. God saw how good it was. Evening came, and morning followed–the fourth day.

Then God said, "Let the water teem with an abundance of living creatures, and on the earth let birds fly beneath the dome of the sky." And so it happened: God created the great sea monsters and all kinds of swimming creatures with which the water teems, and all kinds of winged birds. God saw how good it was, and God blessed them, saying, "Be fertile, multiply, and fill the water of the seas; and let the birds multiply on the earth." Evening came and morning followed–the fifth day.

Then God said, "Let the earth bring forth all kinds of living creatures: cattle, creeping things, and wild animals of all kinds." And so it happened: God made all kinds of wild animals, all kinds of cattle, and all kinds of creeping things of the earth. God saw how good it was. [Then God said: "Let us make man in our image, after our likeness. Let them have dominion over the fish of the sea, the birds of the air, and the cattle, and over all the wild animals and all the creatures that crawl on the ground."

God created man in his image:
in the divine image he created him;
male and female he created them.

God blessed them, saying: "Be fertile and multiply; fill the earth and subdue it. Have dominion over the fish of the sea, the birds of the air, and all the living things that move on the earth." God also said: "See I give you every seed-bearing plant all over the earth and every tree that has seed-bearing fruit on it to be your food; and to all the animals of the land, all the birds of the air, and all the living creatures that crawl on the ground, I give all the green plants for food." And so it happened. God looked at everything he had made, and he found it very good.] Evening came, and morning followed–the sixth day.

Thus the heavens and the earth and all their array were completed. Since on the seventh day God was finished with the work he had been doing, he rested on the seventh day from all the work he had undertaken.

RESPONSORIAL PSALM *Psalm (103)104, 1-2.5-6.10.12.13-14.24.35 / 42*

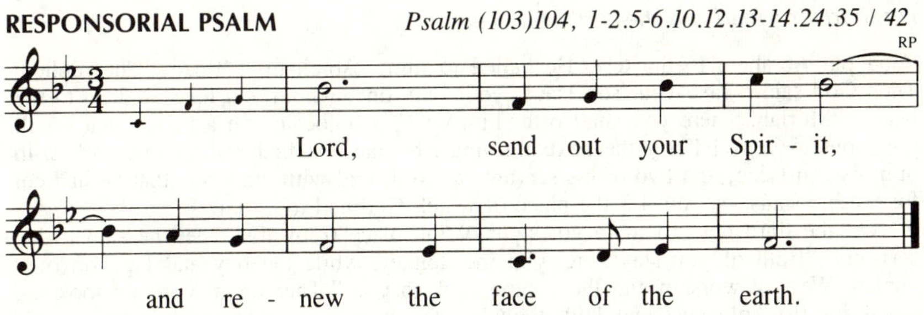
RP
Lord, send out your Spir - it,
and re - new the face of the earth.

Bless the Lord, my soul!
Lord God, how great you are,
clothed in majesty and glory,
wrapped in light as in a robe! ℟.

You founded the earth on its base,
to stand firm from age to age.
You wrapped it with the ocean like a cloak:
the waters stood higher than the mountains. ℟.

You make springs gush forth in the valleys;
they flow in between the hills.
On their banks dwell the birds of heaven;
from the branches they sing their song. ℟.

From your dwelling you water the hills;
earth drinks its fill of your gift.
You make the grass grow for the cattle
and the plants to serve man's needs,
that he may bring forth bread from the
earth. ℟.

How many are your works, O Lord!
In wisdom you have made them all.
The earth is full of your riches.
Bless the Lord, my soul. ℟.

Or:

RESPONSORIAL PSALM *Psalm (32)33, 4-5.6-7.12-13.20-22 / 42*

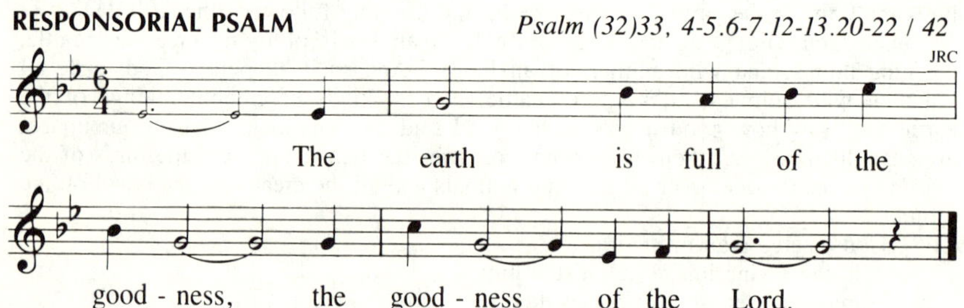
JRC
The earth is full of the
good - ness, the good - ness of the Lord.

For the word of the Lord is faithful
and all his works to be trusted.
The Lord loves justice and right
and fills the earth with his love. ℟.

By his word the heavens were made,
by the breath of his mouth all the stars.
He collects the waves of the ocean;
he stores up the depths of the sea. ℟.

They are happy, whose God is the Lord,
the people he has chosen as his own.
From the heavens the Lord looks forth,
he sees all the children of men. ℟.

Our soul is waiting for the Lord.
The Lord is our help and our shield.
May your love be upon us, O Lord,
as we place all our hope in you. ℟.

820 **READING II** *Genesis 22, 1-18 or 22, 1-2.9.10-13.15-18 / 42*

For short form read only the part in brackets.

[God put Abraham to the test. He called to him, "Abraham!" "Ready!" he replied. Then God said: "Take your son Isaac, your only one, whom you love, and go to the land of Moriah. There you shall offer him up as a holocaust on a height that I will point out to you."] Early the next morning Abraham saddled his donkey, took with him his son Isaac, and two of his servants as well, and with the wood that he had cut for the holocaust, set out for the place of which God had told him.

On the third day Abraham got sight of the place from afar. Then he said to his servants: "Both of you stay here with the donkey, while the boy and I go on over yonder. We will worship and then come back to you." Thereupon Abraham took the wood for the holocaust and laid it on his son Isaac's shoulders, while he himself carried the fire and the knife. As the two walked on together, Isaac spoke to his father Abraham. "Father!" he said. "Yes, son," he replied. Isaac continued, "Here are the fire and the wood, but where is the sheep for the holocaust?" "Son," Abraham answered, "God himself will provide the sheep for the holocaust." Then the two continued going forward.

[When they came to the place of which God had told him, Abraham built an altar there and arranged the wood on it.] Next he tied up his son Isaac, and put him on top of the wood on the altar. [Then he reached out and took the knife to slaughter his son. But the Lord's messenger called to him from heaven, "Abraham, Abraham!" "Yes, Lord," he answered. "Do not lay your hand on the boy," said the messenger. "Do not do the least thing to him. I know now how devoted you are to God, since you did not withhold from me your own beloved son." As Abraham looked about, he spied a ram caught by its horns in the thicket. So he went and took the ram and offered it up as a holocaust in place of his son.] Abraham named the site Yahweh-yireh; hence people now say, "On the mountain the Lord will see."

[Again the Lord's messenger called to Abraham from heaven and said: "I swear by myself, declares the Lord, that because you acted as you did in not withholding from me your beloved son, I will bless you abundantly and make your descendants as countless as the stars of the sky and the sands of the seashore; your descendants shall take possession of the gates of their enemies, and in your descendants all the nations of the earth shall find blessing–all this because you obeyed my command."]

RESPONSORIAL PSALM *Psalm (15)16, 5.8.9-10.11 / 42*

RP
Keep me safe, O God; you are my hope.

O Lord, it is you who are my portion
and cup;
it is you yourself who are my prize.
I keep the Lord ever in my sight;
since he is at my right hand, I shall
stand firm. ℟.

And so my heart rejoices, my soul is
glad;
even my body shall rest in safety.
For you wil not leave my soul among
the dead,
nor let your beloved know decay. ℟.

You will show me the path of life,
the fullness of joy in your presence,
at your right hand happiness for
ever. ℟.

READING III *Exodus 14.15 - 15,1 / 42* 821

The Lord said to Moses, "Why are you crying out to me? Tell the Israelites to go forward. And you, lift up your staff and, with hand outstretched over the sea, split the sea in two, that the Israelites may pass through it on dry land. But I will make the Egyptians so obstinate that they will go in after them. Then I will receive glory through Pharoah and all his army, his chariots and charioteers. The Egyptians shall know that I am the Lord, when I receive glory through Pharaoh and his chariots and charioteers."

The angel of God, who had been leading Israel's camp, now moved and went around behind them. The column of cloud also, leaving the front, took up its place behind them, so that it came between the camp of the Egyptians and that of Israel. But the cloud now became dark, and thus the night passed without the rival camps coming any closer together all night long. Then Moses stretched out his hand over the sea, and the Lord swept the sea with a strong east wind throughout the night and so turned it into dry land. When the water was thus divided, the Israelites marched into the midst of the sea on dry land, with the water like a wall to their right and to their left.

The Egyptians followed in pursuit; all Pharoah's horses and chariots and charioteers went after them right into the midst of the sea. In the night watch just before dawn the Lord cast through the column of the fiery cloud upon the Egyptian force a glance that threw it into a panic; and he so clogged their chariot wheels that they could hardly drive. With that, the Egyptians sounded the retreat before Israel because the Lord was fighting for them against the Egyptians.

Then the Lord told Moses, "Stretch out your hand over the sea, that the water may flow back upon the Egyptians, upon their chariots and their charioteers." So Moses stretched out his hand over the sea, and at dawn the sea flowed back to its normal depth. The Egyptians were fleeing head on toward the sea when the Lord hurled them into its midst. As the water flowed back, it covered the chariots and the charioteers of Pharaoh's whole army which had followed the Israelites into the sea. Not a single one of them escaped. But the Israelites had marched on dry land through the midst of the sea, with the water like a wall to their right and to their left. Thus the Lord saved Israel on that day from the power of the Egyptians. When Israel saw the Egyptians lying dead on the seashore and beheld the great power that the Lord had shown against the Egyptians, they feared the Lord and believed in him and in his servant Moses."

Then Moses and the Israelites sang this song to the Lord:
I will sing to the Lord, for he is gloriously triumphant;
horse and chariot he has cast into the sea.

RESPONSORIAL PSALM *Exodus 15, 1-2.3-4.5-6.17-18 / 42*

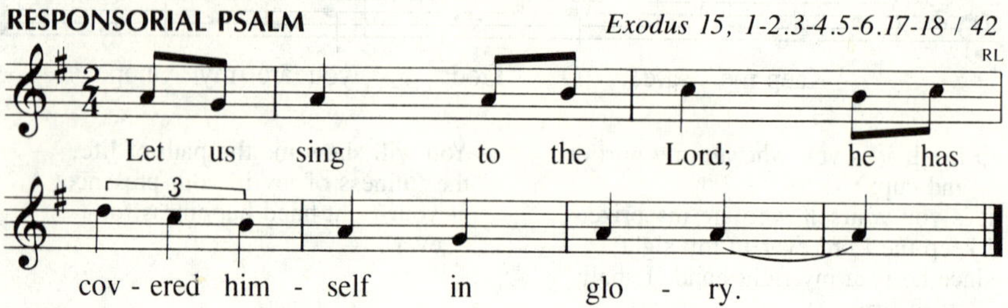
RL
Let us sing to the Lord; he has
cov - ered him - self in glo - ry.

I will sing to the Lord; glorious his triumph!
Horse and rider he has thrown into the sea!
The Lord is my strength, my song, my salvation.
This is my God and I extol him, my
father's God and I give him praise. ℟.

The Lord is a warrior! The Lord is his name.
The chariots of Pharaoh he hurled into the sea, the flower of his army is
drowned in the sea. ℟.

The deeps hide them; they sank like a stone.
Your right hand, Lord glorious in its power,
shattered the enemy. ℟.

The people you have redeemed pass
You will lead them and plant them on your mountain,
the place, O Lord, where you have
made your home, the sanctuary, Lord which your hands have made.
The Lord will reign for ever and ever! ℟.

822 **READING IV** *Isaiah 54, 5-14 / 42*

He who has become your husband is your Maker;
his name is the Lord of hosts;
Your redeemer is the Holy One of Israel,
called God of all the earth.
The Lord calls you back,
like a wife forsaken and grieved in spirit,
A wife married in youth and then cast off,
says your God.
For a brief moment I abandoned you,
but with great tenderness I will take you back.
In an outburst of wrath, for a moment
I hid my face from you;

But with enduring love I take pity on you,
says the Lord, your redeemer.
This is for me like the days of Noah,
when I swore that the waters of Noah should never again deluge the earth;
So I have sworn not to be angry with you, or to rebuke you.
Though the mountains leave their place
and the hills be shaken,
My love shall never leave you
nor my covenant of peace be shaken,
says the Lord, who has mercy on you.
O afflicted one, storm-battered and unconsoled,

I lay your pavements in carnelians,
and your foundations in sapphires;
I will make your battlements of rubies
your gates of carbuncles,
and all your walls of precious stones.
All your sons shall be taught by the Lord,
and great shall be the peace of your children.
In justice shall you be established,
far from the fear of oppression,
where destruction cannot come near you.

RESPONSORIAL PSALM

Psalm (29)30, 2.4.5-6.11-12.13 / 42

JRC
I will praise you, Lord, for you have res-cued me.

I will praise you, Lord, you have rescued me
and have not let my enemies rejoice over me.
O Lord, you have raised my soul from the dead,
restored me to life from those who sink into the grave. ℟.

Sing psalms to the Lord, you who love him,
give thanks to his holy name.
His anger lasts a moment; his favor all through life.
At night there are tears, but joy comes with dawn. ℟.

The Lord listened and had pity.
The Lord came to my help.
For me you have changed my mourning into dancing.
O Lord my God, I will thank you for ever. ℟.

READING V

Isaiah 55,1-11 / 45 823

Thus says the Lord:
All you who are thirsty,
come to the water!
You who have no money,
come, receive grain and eat;
Come, without paying and without cost;
drink wine and milk!
Why spend your money for what is not bread;
your wages for what fails to satisfy?
Heed me, and you shall eat well,
you shall delight in rich fare.
Come to me heedfully,
listen, that you may have life.
I will renew with you the everlasting covenant,
the benefits assured to David.
As I made him a witness to the peoples,
a leader and commander of nations,
So shall you summon a nation you knew not,
and nations that knew you not shall run to you,
Because of the Lord, your God,
the Holy One of Israel, who has glorified you.

Seek the Lord while he may be found,
call him while he is near.
Let the scoundrel forsake his way,
and the wicked man his thoughts;
Let him turn to the Lord for mercy;
to our God, who is generous in forgiving.
For my thoughts are not your thoughts,
nor are your ways my ways, says the Lord.
As high as the heavens are above the earth,
so high are my ways above your ways
and my thoughts above your thoughts.
For just as from the heavens
the rain and the snow come down
And do not return there
till they have watered the earth,
making it fertile and fruitful,
Giving seed to him who sows
and bread to him who eats,
So shall my word be
that goes forth from my mouth;

It shall not return to me void,
but shall do my will,
achieving the end for which I sent it.

RESPONSORIAL PSALM *Isaiah 12, 2-3.4.5-6 / 42*

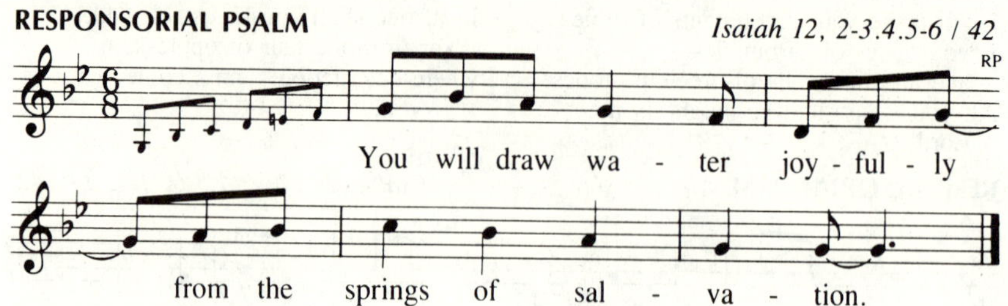
RP
You will draw wa - ter joy - ful - ly
from the springs of sal - va - tion.

Truly, God is my salvation, I trust, I
shall not fear.
For the Lord is my strength, my song,
he became my savior.
With joy you will draw water from the
wells of salvation. ℟.

Give thanks to the Lord, give praise to
his name!
Make his mighty deeds known to the
peoples!
Declare the greatness of his name. ℟.

Sing a psalm to the Lord!
For he has done glorious deeds,
make them known to all the earth!
People of Zion, sing and shout for joy,
for great in your midst is the Holy One
of Israel. ℟.

824 **READING VI** *Baruch 3, 9-15.32-4, 4 / 42*

Hear, O Israel, the commandments of
life:
listen, and know prudence!
How is it, Israel,
that you are in the land of your foes,
grown old in a foreign land,
Defiled with the dead,
accounted with those destined for the
nether world?
You have forsaken the fountain of
wisdom!
Had you walked in the way of God,
you would have dwelt in enduring
peace.
Learn where prudence is,
where strength, where understanding;
That you may know also
where are length of days, and life,
where light of the eyes, and peace.

Who has found the place of wisdom,
who has entered into her treasuries?
He who knows all things knows her;
he has probed her by his knowledge–
He who established the earth for all
time,
and filled it with four-footed beasts;
He who dismisses the light, and it
departs,
calls it, and it obeys him trembling;
Before whom the stars at their posts
shine and rejoice;
When he calls them, they answer,
"Here we are!"
shining with joy for their Maker.
Such is our God;
no other is to be compared to him:
He has traced out all the way of
understanding,
and has given her to Jacob, his
servant,
to Israel, his beloved son.

Since then she has appeared on earth,
and moved among men.
She is the book of the precepts of God,
the law that endures forever;
All who cling to her will live,
but those will die who forsake her.
Turn, O Jacob, and receive her:
walk by her light toward splendor.
Give not your glory to another,
your privileges to an alien race.
Blessed are we, O Israel;
for what pleases God is known to us!

RESPONSORIAL PSALM

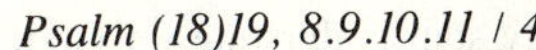

Psalm (18)19, 8.9.10.11 / 42

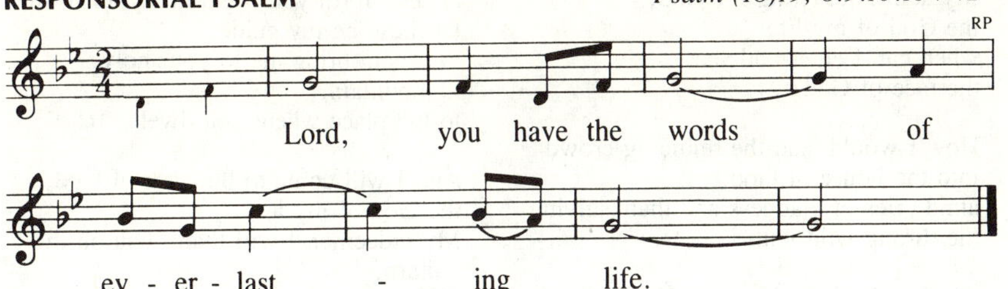
RP
Lord, you have the words of
ev - er - last - ing life.

The law of the Lord is perfect,
it revives the soul.
The rule of the Lord is to be trusted,
it gives wisdom to the simple. ℟.

The precepts of the Lord are right,
They gladden the heart.
The command of the Lord is clear,
it gives light to the eyes. ℟.

The fear of the Lord is holy,
abiding for ever.
The decrees of the Lord are truth
and all of them just. ℟.

They are more to be desired than gold,
than the purest of gold,
and sweeter are they than honey,
than honey from the comb.

READING VII

Ezekiel 36, 16-28 / 42 825

Thus the word of the Lord came to me: Son of man, when the house of Israel lived in their land, they defiled it by their conduct and deeds. In my sight their conduct was like the defilement of a menstruous woman. Therefore I poured out my fury upon them [because of the blood which they poured out on the ground, and because they defiled it with idols]. I scattered them among the nations, dispersing them over foreign lands; according to their conduct and deeds I judged them. But when they came among the nations [wherever they came], they served to profane my holy name, because it was said of them: "These are the people of the Lord, yet they had to leave their land." So I have relented because of my holy name which the house of Israel profaned among the nations where they came. Therefore say to the house of Israel: Thus says the Lord God: Not for your sakes do I act, house of Israel, but for the sake of my holy name, which you profaned among the nations, in whose midst you have profaned it. Thus the nations shall know that I am the Lord, says the Lord God, when in their sight I prove my holiness to you. For I will take you away among the nations, gather you from all foreign lands, and bring you back to your own land. I will sprinkle clean water upon you to cleanse you from all your impurities, and from all your idols I will cleanse you. I will give you a new heart and place a new spirit within you, taking from your bodies your stony hearts and giving you natural hearts. I will put my spirit within you and make you live by my statutes, careful to observe my decrees. You shall live in the land I gave your fathers; you shall be my people, and I will be your God.

RESPONSORIAL PSALM

Psalm (41)42, 3.5; (42)43, 3.4 / 42

RP

Like a deer that longs for run - ning streams, so my soul longs for you, my God.

My soul is thirsting for God,
the God of my life;
when can I enter and see
the face of God? ℟.

How I would lead the rejoicing crowd
into the house of God,
amid cries of gladness and thanksgiving,
the throng wild with joy. ℟.

O send forth your light and your truth;
let these be my guide.
Let them bring me to your holy
mountain,
to the place where you dwell. ℟.

And I will come to the altar of God,
the God of my joy.
My redeemer, I will thank you on the
harp,
O God, my God. ℟.

Or:

RESPONSORIAL PSALM *Psalm (50)51, 12-13.14-15.18-19 / 42*

FS
Cre - ate a clean heart, a clean heart in me, O God.

A pure heart create for me, O God,
put a steadfast spirit within me.
Do not cast me away from your
presence,
nor deprive me of your holy
spirit. ℟.

Give me again the joy of your help;
with a spirit of fervor sustain me,
that I may teach transgressors your
ways
and sinners may return to you. ℟.

For in sacrifice you take no delight,
burnt offering from me you would
refuse;
my sacrifice, a contrite spirit;
a humbled, contrite heart you will
not spurn. ℟.

GLORIA

PRAYER

826 **EPISTLE** *Romans 6, 3-11 / 42*

Are you not aware that we who baptize into Christ Jesus were baptized into his death? Through baptism into his death we were buried with him, so that, just as Christ was raised from the dead by the glory of the Father, we too might live a new life. If we have been united with him through likeness to his death, so shall we be through a like resurrection. This we know: our old self was crucified with him so that the sinful body might be destroyed and we might be slaves to sin no longer. A man who is dead has been freed from sin. If we have died with Christ, we believe that we are also to live with him. We know that Christ, once raised from the dead, will never die again; death has no more power over him. His death was death to sin, once for all; his life is life for God. In the same way, you must consider yourselves dead to sin but alive for God in Christ Jesus.

RESPONSORIAL PSALM

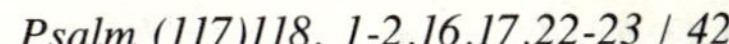

Psalm (117)118, 1-2.16.17.22-23 / 42

Chant Mode VIII
Al - le - lu - ia.

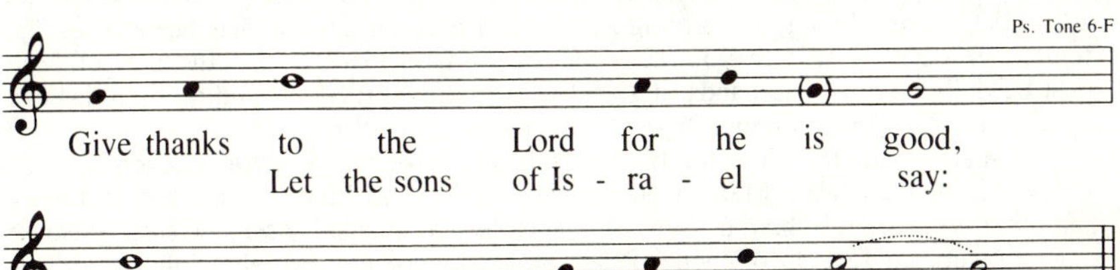
Ps. Tone 6-F
Give thanks to the Lord for he is good,
Let the sons of Is - ra - el say:

for his love en - dures for ev - er.
"His love en - dures for ev - er." ℟.

The Lord's right hand has triumphed;
his right hand raised me.
The Lord's right hand has triumphed;
I shall not die, I shall live and recount
his deeds. ℟.

The stone which the builders rejected
has become the cornerstone.
This is the work of the Lord,
a marvel in our eyes. ℟.

GOSPEL/A

Matthew 28, 1-10 / 42

After the sabbath, as the first day of the week was dawning, Mary Magdalene came with the other Mary to inspect the tomb. Suddenly there was a mighty earthquake, as the angel of the Lord descended from heaven. He came to the stone, rolled it back, and sat on it. In appearance he resembled a flash of lightning while his garments were as dazzling as snow. The guards grew paralyzed with fear of him and fell down like dead men. Then the angel spoke, addressing the women: "Do not be frightened. I know you are looking for Jesus the crucified, but he is not here. He has been raised, exactly as he promised. Come and see the spot where he was laid. Then go quickly and tell his desciples: 'He has been raised from the dead and now goes ahead of you to Galilee, where you will see him.' That is the message I have for you."

They hurried away from the tomb half-overjoyed, half-fearful, and ran to carry the good news to his disciples. Suddenly, without warning, Jesus stood before them and said "Peace!" The women came up and embraced his feet and did him homage. At this Jesus said to them, "Do not be afraid! Go and carry the news to my brothers that they are to go to Galilee, where they will see me."

GOSPEL/B

Mark 16, 1-8 / 42

When the sabbath was over, Mary Magdalene, Mary the mother of James, and Salome bought perfumed oils with which they intended to go and anoint Jesus. Very early, just after sunrise, on the first day of the week they came to the tomb. They were saying one to another, "Who will roll back the stone for us from the entrance to the tomb?" When they looked, they found that the stone had been rolled back. (It was a huge one.) On entering the tomb they saw a young man sitting at the right, dressed in a white robe. This frightened them thoroughly, but he reassured them: "You need not be amazed! You are looking for Jesus of Nazareth, the one who was crucified. He has been raised up; he is not here. See the place where they laid him. Go now and tell his disciples and Peter, 'He is going ahead of you to Galilee, where you will see him just as he told you.' " They made their way out and fled from the tomb bewildered and trembling; and because of their great fear, they said nothing to anyone.

GOSPEL/C *Luke 24, 1-12 / 42*

On the first day of the week, at dawn, the women came to the tomb bringing the spices they had prepared. They found the stone rolled back from the tomb; but when they entered the tomb, they did not find the body of the Lord Jesus. While they were still at a loss what to think of this, two men in dazzling garments appeared beside them. Terrified, the women bowed to the ground. The men said to them: "Why do you search for the living One among the dead? He is not here; he has been raised up. Remember what he said to you while he was still in Galilee–that the Son of Man must be delivered into the hands of sinful men, and be crucified, and on the third day rise again." With this reminder, his words came back to them.

On their return from the tomb, they told all these things to the Eleven and the others. The women were Mary of Magdala, Joanna, and Mary the mother of James. The other women with them also told the apostles, but the story seemed like nonsense and they refused to believe them. Peter, however, got up and ran to the tomb. He stooped down but could see nothing but the wrappings. So he went away full of amazement at what had occurred.

827 LITURGY OF BAPTISM

After the homily the catechumens are called forward. The assembly chants the litany of the saints, invoking the holy women and men of all centuries. Patron saints of the church and of the catechumens and the faithful may be included in the litany.

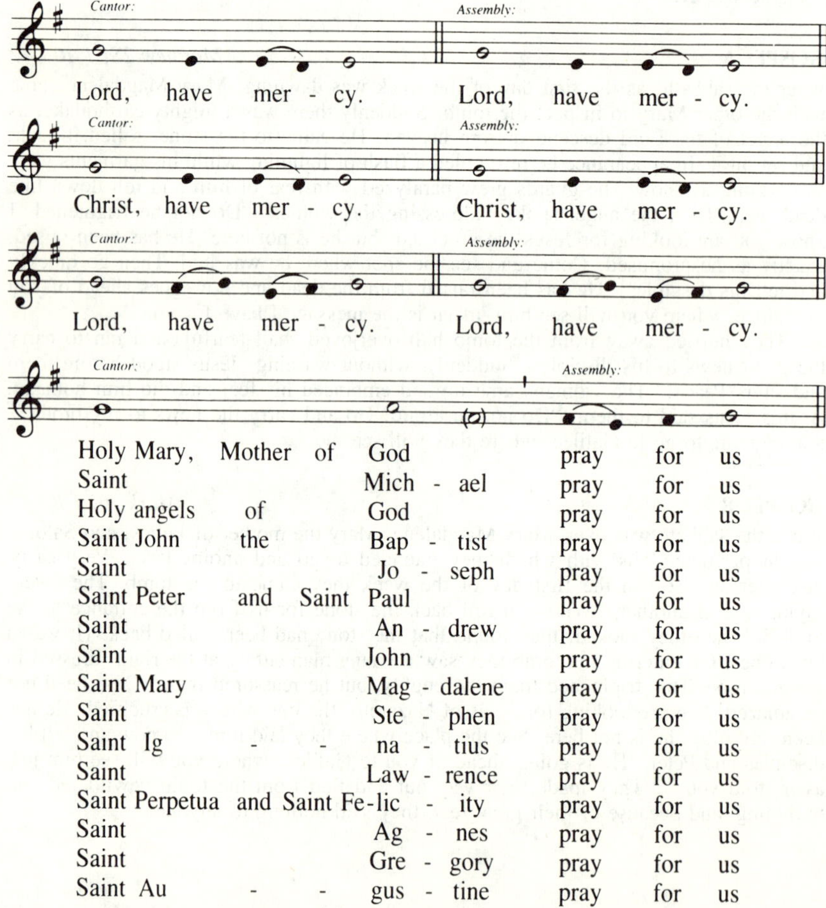
Cantor:
Lord, have mer - cy.
Assembly:
Lord, have mer - cy.
Cantor:
Christ, have mer - cy.
Assembly:
Christ, have mer - cy.
Cantor:
Lord, have mer - cy.
Assembly:
Lord, have mer - cy.
Cantor:
Assembly:
Holy Mary, Mother of God pray for us
Saint Mich - ael pray for us
Holy angels of God pray for us
Saint John the Bap - tist pray for us
Saint Jo - seph pray for us
Saint Peter and Saint Paul pray for us
Saint An - drew pray for us
Saint John pray for us
Saint Mary Mag - dalene pray for us
Saint Ste - phen pray for us
Saint Ig - - na - tius pray for us
Saint Law - rence pray for us
Saint Perpetua and Saint Fe-lic - ity pray for us
Saint Ag - nes pray for us
Saint Gre - gory pray for us
Saint Au - - gus - tine pray for us

Saint Atha - - na - sius pray for us
Saint Ba - sil pray for us
Saint Mar - tin pray for us
Saint Ben - edict pray for us
Saint Francis and Saint Dom - inic pray for us
Saint Francis Xa - vier pray for us
Saint John Vi - an - ney pray for us
Saint Cath - erine pray for us
Saint Te - - re - sa pray for us
All holy men and wo - men pray for us

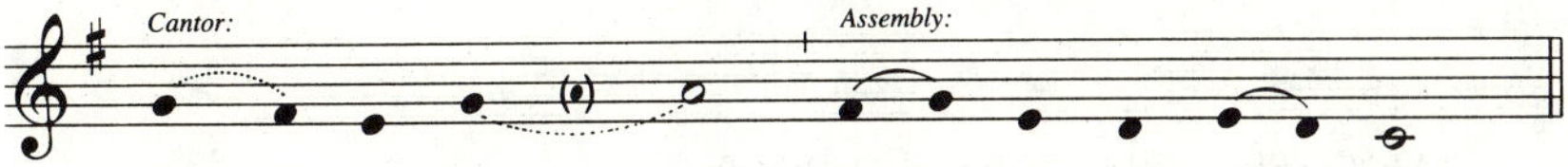

Cantor: *Assembly:*

Lord, be mer - ci - ful, Lord, save your peo - ple.
From all e - vil, Lord, save your peo - ple.
From ev - 'ry sin, Lord, save your peo - ple.
From ev - er - last - ing death, Lord, save your peo - ple.

Cantor: *Assembly:*

By your com - ing as man, Lord, save your peo - ple.
By your death and ris-ing to new life, Lord, save you peo - ple.
By your gift of the Ho - ly Spir - it, Lord, save your peo - ple.

Cantor: *Assembly:*

Be merciful to us sin - ners. Lord, hear our prayer.
Give new life to these
chosen ones by the grace of bap - tism. Lord, hear our prayer.
Jesus, Son of the liv-ing God. Lord, hear our prayer.

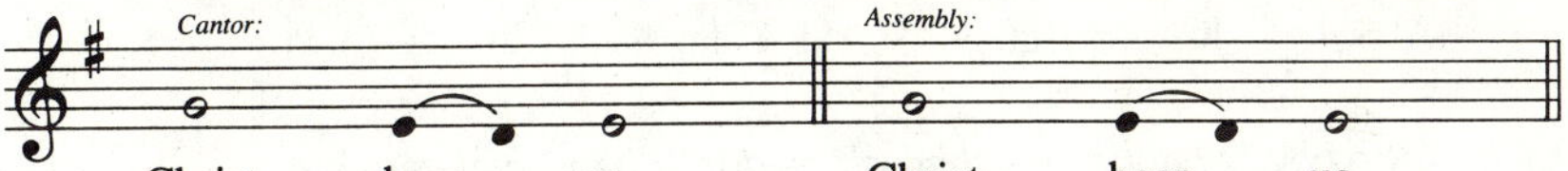

Cantor: *Assembly:*

Christ, hear us. Christ, hear us.

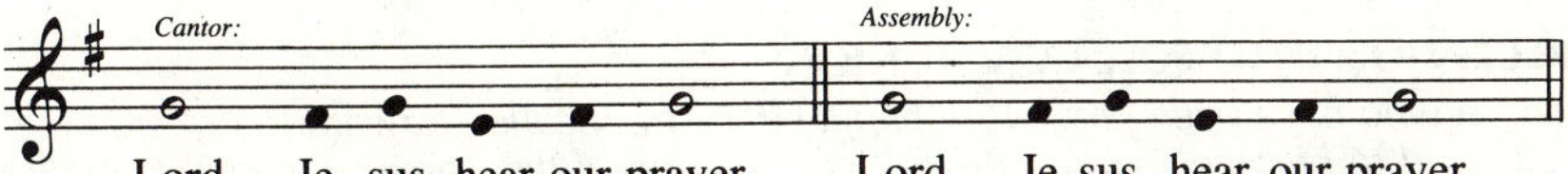

Cantor: *Assembly:*

Lord Je - sus, hear our prayer. Lord Je-sus, hear our prayer.

BLESSING OF WATER 828

The presider gives thanks and praise to God over the waters of baptism. This acclamation is sung by all.

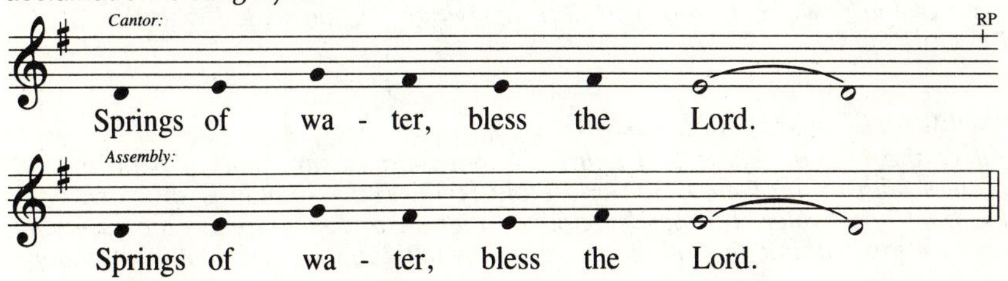
Cantor:
RP
Springs of wa - ter, bless the Lord.
Assembly:
Springs of wa - ter, bless the Lord.

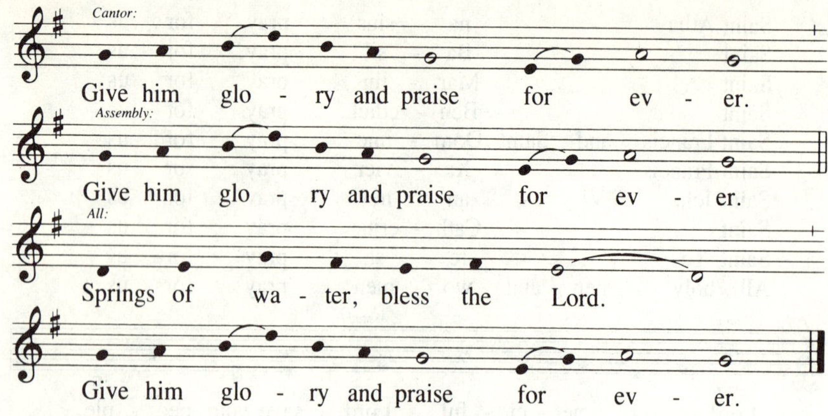
Cantor:
Give him glo - ry and praise for ev - er.
Assembly:
Give him glo - ry and praise for ev - er.
All:
Springs of wa - ter, bless the Lord.
Give him glo - ry and praise for ev - er.

829 **RENUNCIATION OF SIN AND PROFESSION OF FAITH**

Each candidate for baptism is asked to reject sin and the ways of evil and to testify to faith in Father, Son and Holy Spirit. All join to affirm this faith.

830 **THE BAPTISMS**

One by one the candidates are led into the waters, or they bend over the font, and water is poured over them as the presider says: "N., I baptize you in the name of the Father, and of the Son, and of the Holy Spirit." After each baptism, the assembly sings an acclamation.

HH
You have put on Christ, in him you have been bap-tized.
Al - le - lu - ia, al - le - lu - ia.

Each of the newly baptized is then clothed in a baptismal garment.

831 **RECEPTION INTO FULL COMMUNION**

Those who have been previously baptized are now called forward to profess their faith and to be received into the full communion of the Roman Catholic Church.

832 **CONFIRMATION**

Infants who have been baptized are anointed with chrism. Children and adults are usually confirmed: the presider prays and lays hands on them, then anoints each of the newly baptized with chrism saying: "N., be sealed with the Gift of the Holy Spirit."

833 **RENEWAL OF BAPTISMAL PROMISES**

All of the faithful repeat and affirm the rejection of sin made at baptism and profess faith in the Father, Son and Holy Spirit. The assembly is sprinkled with the baptismal water. The newly baptized then take their places in the assembly and, for the first time, join in the prayer of the faithful, the prayers of intercession.

LITURGY OF THE EUCHARIST 834

The gifts and table are prepared and the eucharist is celebrated in the usual way.

CONCLUDING RITE 835

The dismissal is sung with "alleluia", and all respond.

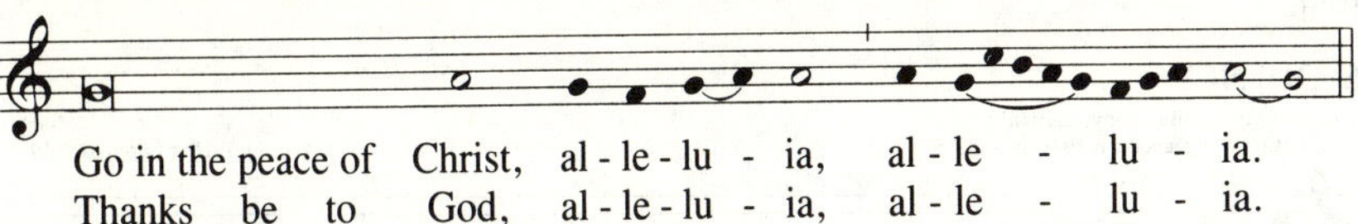
Go in the peace of Christ, al - le - lu - ia, al - le - lu - ia.
Thanks be to God, al - le - lu - ia, al - le - lu - ia.

EASTER SUNDAY 836

READING I *Acts 10, 34.37-43 / 43*

Peter addressed the people in these words: "I take it you know what has been reported all over Judea about Jesus of Nazareth, beginning in Galilee with the baptism John preached; of the way God anointed him with the Holy Spirit and power. He went about doing good works and healing all who were in the grip of the devil, and God was with him. We are witnesses to all that he did in the land of the Jews and in Jerusalem. They killed him finally, 'hanging him on a tree,' only to have God raise him up on the third day and grant that he be seen, not by all, but only by such witnesses as had been chosen beforehand by God–by us who ate and drank with him after he rose from the dead. He commissioned us to preach to the people and to bear witness that he is the one set apart by God as judge of the living and the dead. To him all the prophets testify, saying that everyone who believes in him has forgiveness of sins through his name."

RESPONSORIAL PSALM *Psalm (117)118, 1-2.16-17.22-23 / 43*

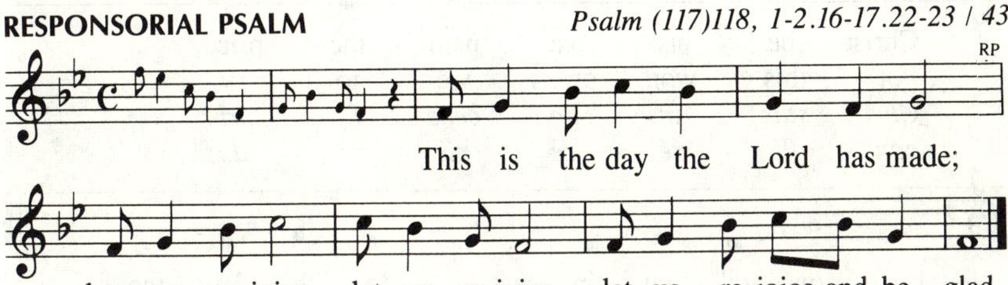
RP
This is the day the Lord has made;
let us re-joice, let us re-joice, let us re-joice and be glad.

Give thanks to the Lord for he is good,
for his love endures for ever.
Let the sons of Israel say:
"His love endures for ever." ℟.

The Lord's right hand has triumphed;
his right hand raised me.
The Lord's right hand has triumphed;
I shall not die, I shall live
and recount his deeds. ℟.

The stone which the builders rejected
has become the cornerstone.
This is the work of the Lord,
a marvel in our eyes. ℟.

READING II *Colossians 3, 1-4 / 43*

Since you have been raised up in company with Christ, set your heart on what pertains to higher realms where Christ is seated at God's right hand. Be intent on things above rather than on things on earth. After all, you have died! Your life is hidden now with Christ in God. When Christ our life appears, then you shall appear with him in glory.

Or:

READING II *1 Corinthians 5, 6-8 / 43*

Do you not know that a little yeast has its effect all through the dough? Get rid of the old yeast to make of yourselves fresh dough, unleavened loaves, as it were; Christ our Passover has been sacrificed. Let us celebrate the feast not with the old yeast, that of corruption and wickedness, but with the unleavened bread of sincerity and truth.

837 **SEQUENCE**

Ascr. to Wipo of Burgundy, d.1048
Tr. by Peter J. Scagnelli, b.1949

Mode I
Acc. by Richard Proulx, b.1937

1. Chris - tians, praise the pas - chal vic - tim!
1. *Ví - cti - mae Pa - schá - li lau - des*

Of - fer thank - ful sac - ri - fice!
im - mó - lent Chri - sti - á - ni.

2. Christ the Lamb has saved the sheep,
3. Death and life fought bit - ter - ly
2. *A - gnus ré - de - mit ó - ves:*
3. *Mors et vi - ta du - él - lo*

Christ the just one paid the price,
For this won - drous vic - to - ry;
Chri - stus ín - no - cens Pá - tri
con - fli - xé - re mi - rán - do:

Re - con - cil - ing sin - ners to the Fa - ther.
The Lord of life who died reigns glo - ri - fied!
re - con - ci - li - á - vit pec - ca - tó - res.
dux vi - tae mór - tu - us re - gnat vi - vus.

4. O Mar - y, come and say what you
6. Bright an - gels tes - ti - fied, Shroud and
4. *Dic no - bis Ma - rí - a, quid vi-*
6. *An - gé - li - cos te - stes, su - dá-*

saw at break of day. 5. "The emp - ty tomb
grave clothes side by side! 7. "Yes, Christ my hope
dí - sti in vi - a? 5. Se - púl - crum Chri-
ri - um, et ve - stes. 7. Sur - re - xit Chri-

of my liv - ing Lord! I saw Christ Je-
rose glo - ri - ous - ly. He goes be - fore
sti vi - vén - tis, et gló - ri - am
stus spes me - a: prae - cé - det su-
sus ri - sen and a - dored!
you in - to Ga - li - lee."
vi - di re - sur - gén - tis.
os in Ga - li - láe - am.
8. Share the good news, sing joy - ful-
8. Scí - mus Chrí - stum sur - re - xís-
ly: His death is vic - to - ry!
se a mór - tu - is ve - re:
Lord Je - sus, Vic - tor King, Show us mer - cy.
tu no - bis vi - ctor Rex, mi - se - ré - re.

GOSPEL *John 20, 1-9 / 43*

Early in the morning on the first day of the week, while it was still dark, Mary Magdalene came to the tomb. She saw that the stone had been moved away, so she ran off to Simon Peter and the other disciple (the one Jesus loved) and told them, "The Lord has been taken from the tomb! We don't know where they have put him!" At that, Peter and the other disciple started out on their way toward the tomb. They were running side by side, but then the other disciple outran Peter and reached the tomb first. He did not enter but bent down to peer in, and saw the wrappings lying on the ground. Presently, Simon Peter came along behind him and entered the tomb. He observed the wrappings on the ground and saw the piece of cloth which had covered the head not lying with the wrappings, but rolled up in a place by itself. Then the disciple who had arrived first at the tomb went in. He saw and believed. (Remember, as yet they did not understand the Scripture that Jesus had to rise from the dead.)

SECOND SUNDAY OF EASTER 838

READING I/A *Acts 2, 42-47 / 44*

The brethren devoted themselves to the apostles' instruction and the communal life, to the breaking of bread and the prayers. A reverent fear overtook them all, for many wonders and signs were performed by the apostles. Those who believed shared all things in common; they would sell their property and goods, dividing everything on the basis of each one's need. They went to the temple area together every day, while in their homes they broke bread. With exultant and sincere hearts they took their meals in common, praising God and winning the approval of all the people. Day by day the Lord added to their number those who were being saved.

READING I/B *Acts 4, 32-35 / 45*

The community of believers were of one heart and one mind. None of them ever claimed anything as his own; rather everything was held in common. With power the apostles bore witness to the resurrection of the Lord Jesus, and great respect was paid to them all; nor was there anyone needy among them, for all who owned property or houses sold them and donated the proceeds. They used to lay them at the feet of the apostles to be distributed to everyone according to his need.

READING I/C *Acts 5, 12-16 / 46*

Through the hands of the apostles, many signs and wonders occurred among the people. By mutual agreement, they used to meet in Solomon's Portico. No one else dared to join them, despite the fact that the people held them in great esteem. Nevertheless more and more believers, men and women in great numbers, were continually added to the Lord. The people carried the sick into the streets and laid them on cots and mattresses, so that when Peter passed by at least his shadow might fall on one or another of them. Crowds from the towns around Jerusalem would gather, too, bringing their sick and those who were troubled by unclean spirits, all of whom were cured.

RESPONSORIAL PSALM *Psalm (117)118, 2-4.13-15.22-24 / 44,45,46*

CW
Give thanks to the Lord for he is
good, his love is ev - er - last - ing.

Let the sons of Israel say:
"His love endures for ever."
Let the sons of Aaron say:
"His love endures for ever."
Let those who fear the Lord say:
"His love endures for ever." ℟.

I was thrust down, thrust down and
falling
but the Lord was my helper.
The Lord is my strength and my song;
he was my savior.
There are shouts of joy and victory
in the tents of the just. ℟.

The stone which the builders rejected
has become the cornerstone.
This is the work of the Lord,
a marvel in our eyes.
This day was made by the Lord;
we rejoice and are glad. ℟.

READING II/A *1 Peter 1, 3-9 / 44*

Praised be the God and Father of our
Lord Jesus Christ,
he who in his great mercy gave us new
birth;
a birth unto hope which draws its life
from the resurrection of Jesus Christ
from the dead;
a birth to an imperishable inheritance
incapable of fading or defilement,
which is kept in heaven for you
who are guarded with God's power
through faith;
a birth to a salvation which stands ready
to be revealed in the last days.

There is cause for rejoicing here. You may for a time have to suffer the distress of many trials; but this is so that your faith, which is more precious than the passing splendor of fire-tried gold, may by its genuineness lead to praise, glory, and honor when Jesus Christ appears. Although you have never seen him, you love him, and without seeing, you believe in him, and rejoice with inexpressible joy touched with glory because you are achieving faith's goal, your salvation.

READING II/B *1 John 5, 1-6 / 45*

Everyone who believes that Jesus is the Christ
has been begotten by God.
Now, everyone who loves the father
loves the child he has begotten.
We can be sure that we love God's children
when we love God
and do what he has commanded.
The love of God consists in this:
that we keep his commandments–
and his commandments are not burdensome.
Everyone begotten of God conquers the world,
and the power that has conquered the world
is this faith of ours.
Who, then, is conqueror of the world?
The one who believes that Jesus is the Son of God.
Jesus Christ it is who came through water and blood–
not in water only,
but in water and in blood.
It is the Spirit who testifies to this,
and the Spirit is truth.

READING II/C *Revelation 1, 9-11.12-13.17-19 / 46*

I John, your brother, who share with you the distress and the kingly reign and the endurance we have in Jesus, found myself on the island called Patmos because I proclaimed God's word and bore witness to Jesus. On the Lord's day I was caught up in ecstacy, and I heard behind me a piercing voice like the sound of a trumpet, which said, "Write on a scroll what you now see." I turned around to see whose voice it was that spoke to me. When I did so I saw seven lampstands of gold, and among the lampstands One like a Son of Man wearing an ankle-length robe, with a sash of gold about his breast.

When I caught sight of him I fell down at his feet as though dead. He touched me with his right hand and said: "There is nothing to fear. I am the First and the Last and the One who lives. Once I was dead but now I live–forever and ever. I hold the keys of death and the nether world. Write down, therefore, whatever you see in visions–what you see now and will see in time to come."

GOSPEL *John 20, 19-31 / 44,45,46*

On the evening of that first day of the week, even though the disciples had locked the doors of the place where they were for fear of the Jews, Jesus came and stood before them. "Peace be with you," he said. When he had said this, he showed them his hands and his side. At the sight of the Lord the disciples rejoiced. "Peace be with you," he said again.

"As the Father has sent me,
so I send you."

Then he breathed on them and said:

"Receive the Holy Spirit.
If you forgive men's sins,
they are forgiven them;
if you hold them bound,
they are held bound."

It happened that one of the Twelve, Thomas (the name means "Twin"), was absent when Jesus came. The other disciples kept telling him: "We have seen the Lord!" His answer was, "I'll never believe it without probing the nail- prints in his hands, without putting my finger in the nail-marks and my hand into his side."

A week later, the disciples were once more in the room, and this time Thomas was with them. Despite the locked doors, Jesus came and stood before them. "Peace be with you," he said; then, to Thomas: "Take your finger and examine my hands. Put your hand into my side. Do not persist in your unbelief, but believe!" Thomas said in response, "My Lord and my God!" Jesus then said to him:

"You became a believer because you saw me.
Blest are they who have not seen and have believed."

Jesus performed many other signs as well–signs not recorded here–in the presence of his disciples. But these have been recorded to help you believe that Jesus is the Messiah, the Son of God, so that through this faith you may have life in his name.

839 THIRD SUNDAY OF EASTER/A

READING I *Acts 2, 14.22-28 / 47*

[On the day of Pentecost] Peter stood up with the Eleven, raised his voice, and addressed them: "You who are Jews, indeed all of you staying in Jerusalem! Listen to what I have to say: Men of Israel, listen to me! Jesus the Nazorean was a man whom God sent to you with miracles, wonders and signs as his credentials. These God worked through him in your midst, as you well know. He was delivered up by the set purpose and plan of God; you even used pagans to crucify and kill him. God freed him from death's bitter pangs, however, and raised him up again, for it was impossible that death should keep its hold on him. David says of him:

'I have set the Lord ever before me,
with him at my right hand I shall not be disturbed.
My heart has been glad and my tongue has rejoiced,
my body will live on in hope,
For you will not abandon my soul to the nether world,
nor will you suffer your faithful one to undergo corruption.
You have shown me the paths of life;
you will fill me with joy in your presence.' "

RESPONSORIAL PSALM *Psalm (15)16, 1-2.5.7-8.9-10.11 / 47*

MJ
Lord, you will show us the path of life.

Preserve me, God, I take refuge in you.
I say to the Lord: "You are my God.
My happiness lies in you alone."
O Lord, it is you who are my portion and cup,
it is you yourself who are my prize. ℟.

I will bless the Lord who gives me counsel,
who even at night directs my heart.
I keep the Lord ever in my sight;
since he is at my right hand, I shall stand firm. ℟.

And so my heart rejoices, my soul is glad;
even my body shall rest in safety.
For you will not leave my soul among the dead,
nor let your beloved know decay. ℟.

You will show me the path of life,
the fullness of joy in your presence,
at your right hand happiness for ever. ℟.

READING II *1 Peter 1, 17-21 / 47*

In prayer you call upon a Father who judges each one justly, on the basis of his actions. Since this is so, conduct yourselves reverently during your sojourn in a strange land. Realize that you were delivered from the futile way of life your fathers handed on to you, not by any diminishable sum of silver or gold, but by Christ's blood beyond all price: the blood of a spotless, unblemished lamb chosen before the world's foundation and revealed for your sake in these last days. It is through him you are believers in God, the God who raised him from the dead and gave him glory. Your faith and hope, then, are centered in God.

GOSPEL *Luke 24.13-35 / 47*

Two disciples of Jesus that same day [the first day of the sabbath] were making their way to a village named Emmaus seven miles distant from Jerusalem, discussing as they went all that had happened. In the course of their lively exchange, Jesus approached and began to walk along with them. However, they were restrained from recogninzing him. He said to them, "What are you discussing as you go your way?" They halted in distress, and one of them, Cleopas by name, asked him, "Are you the only resident of Jerusalem who does not know the things that went on there these past few days?" He said to them, "What things?" They said: "All those that had to do with Jesus of Nazareth, a prophet powerful in word and deed in the eyes of God and all the people; how our chief priests and leaders delivered him up to be condemned to death, and crucified him. We were hoping that he was the one who would set Israel free. Besides all this, today, the third day since these things happened, some women of our group have just brought us some astonishing news. They were at the tomb before dawn and failed to find his body, but returned with the tale that they had seen a vision of angels who declared he was alive. Some of our number went to the tomb and found it to be just as the women said; but him they did not see."

Then he said to them, "What little sense you have! How slow you are to believe all that the prophets have announced! Did not the Messiah have to undergo all this so as to enter into his glory?" Beginning, then, with Moses and all the prophets, he interpreted for them every passage of Scripture which referred to him. By now they were near the village to which they were going, and he acted as if he were going farther. But they pressed him: "Stay with us. It is nearly evening–the day is practically over." So he went in to stay with them.

When he had seated himself with them to eat, he took bread, pronounced the blessing, then broke the bread and began to distribute it to them. With that their eyes were opened and they recognized him; whereupon he vanished from their sight. They said to one another, "Were not our hearts burning inside us as he talked to us on the road and explained the Scriptures to us?" They got up immediately and returned to Jerusalem, where they found the Eleven and the rest of the company assembled. They were greeted with "The Lord has been raised! It is true! He has appeared to Simon." Then they recounted what had happened on the road and how they had come to know him in the breaking of bread.

THIRD SUNDAY OF EASTER/B 840

READING I *Acts 3, 13-15.17-19 / 48*

Peter said to the people: "The 'God of Abraham, of Isaac, and of Jacob, the God of our fathers,' has glorified his Servant Jesus, whom you handed over and disowned in Pilate's presence when Pilate was ready to release him. You disowned the Holy and Just One and preferred instead to be granted the release of a murderer. You put to death the Author of life. But God raised him from the dead, and we are his witnesses.

"Yet I know, my brothers, that you acted out of ignorance, just as your leaders did. God has brought to fulfillment by this means what he announced long ago through all the prophets: that his Messiah would suffer. Therefore, reform your lives! Turn to God, that your sins may be wiped away!"

RESPONSORIAL PSALM *Psalm 4, 2.4.7-8.9 / 48*

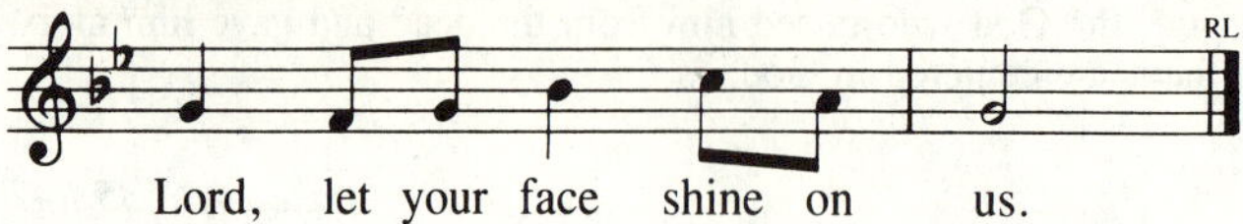
RL
Lord, let your face shine on us.

When I call, answer me, O God of justice;
from anguish you released me, have mercy and hear me! ℞.

It is the Lord who grants favors to those whom he loves;
the Lord hears me whenever I call him. ℞.

Lift up the light of your face on us, O Lord.
You have put into my heart a greater joy
than they have from abundance of corn and new wine. ℞.

I will lie down in peace and sleep comes at once
for you alone, Lord, make me dwell in safety. ℞.

READING II *1 John 2, 1-5 / 48*

My littles ones,
I am writing this to keep you from sin.
But if anyone should sin,
we have, in the presence of the Father,
Jesus Christ, an intercessor who is just.
He is an offering for our sins,
and not for our sins only,
but for those of the whole world.
The way we can be sure of our knowledge of him
is to keep his commandments.
The man who claims, "I have known him,"
without keeping his commandments,
is a liar; in such a one there is no truth.
But whoever keeps his word,
truly has the love of God made perfect in him.

GOSPEL *Luke 24, 35-48 / 48*

The disciples recounted what had happened on the road to Emmaus and how they had come to know Jesus in the breaking of bread.

While they were still speaking about all this, he himself stood in their midst [and said to them, "Peace to you."] In their panic and fright they thought they were seeing a ghost. He said to them, "Why are you disturbed? Why do such ideas cross your mind? Look at my hands and my feet; it is really I. Touch me, and see that a ghost does not have flesh and bones as I do." [As he said this he showed them his hands and feet.] They were still incredulous for sheer joy and wonder, so he said to them, "Have you anything here to eat?" They gave him a piece of cooked fish, which he took and ate in their presence. Then he said to them, "Recall those words I spoke to you when I was still with you: everything written about me in the law of Moses and the prophets and psalms had to be fulfilled." Then he opened their minds to the understanding of the Scriptures.

He said to them:"Thus it is likewise written that the Messiah must suffer and rise from the dead on the third day. In his name, penance for the remission of sins is to be preached to all the nations, beginning at Jerusalem. You are witnesses of this."

841 THIRD SUNDAY OF EASTER/C

READING I *Acts 5, 27-32.40-41 / 49*

The high priest began the interrogation of the apostles in this way:"We gave you strict orders not to teach about that name, yet you have filled Jerusalem with your teaching and are determined to make us responsible for that man's blood." To this, Peter and the apostles replied: "Better for us to obey God than men! The God of our fathers has raised up Jesus whom you put to death, 'hanging him on a tree.' He whom God has exalted at his right hand as ruler and savior is to bring repentance to Israel and forgiveness of sins. We testify to this. So too does the Holy Spirit, whom God has given to those that obey him." The Sanhedrin ordered the apostles not to speak again about the name of Jesus, and afterward dismissed them. The apostles for their part left the Sanhedrin full of joy that they had been judged worthy of ill-treatment for the sake of the Name.

RESPONSORIAL PSALM *Psalm (29)30, 2.4.5-6.11-12.13 / 49*

JRC

I will praise you, Lord, for you have res-cued me.

I will praise you, Lord, you have
rescued me
and have not let my enemies rejoice
over me.
O Lord, you have raised my soul from
the dead,
restored me to life from those who sink
into the grave. ℟.

Sing psalms to the Lord, you who love
him,
give thanks to his holy name.
His anger lasts a moment; his favor all
through life.
At night there are tears, but joy comes
with dawn. ℟.

The Lord listened and had pity.
The Lord came to my help.
For me you have changed my mourning
into dancing.
O Lord my God, I will thank you for
ever. ℟.

READING II *Revelations 5, 11-14 / 49*

I, John, had a vision, and I heard the voices of many angels who surrounded the throne and the living creatures and the elders. They were countless in number, thousands and tens of thousands, and they all cried out:
"Worthy is the lamb that was slain
to receive power and riches, wisdom
and strength,
honor and glory and praise!"

Then I heard the voices of every creature in heaven and on earth and under the earth and in the sea; everything in the universe cried aloud:
"To the One seated on the throne, and
to the Lamb,
be praise and honor, glory and might,
forever and ever!"

The four living creatures answered, "Amen," and the elders fell down and worshiped.

GOSPEL *John 21, 1-19 or 21,1-14 / 49*

For short form read only the part in brackets.

[At the Sea of Tiberias Jesus showed himself to the disciples once again. This is how the appearance took place. Assembled were Simon Peter, Thomas ("the Twin"), Nathanael (from Cana in Galilee), Zebedee's sons, and two other disciples. Simon Peter said to them, "I'm going out to fish." "We'll join you," they replied, and went off to get into their boat. All through the night they caught nothing. Just after daybreak Jesus was standing on the shore, though none of the disciples knew it was Jesus. He said to them, "Children, have you caught anything to eat?" "Not a thing," they answered. "Cast your net off to the starboard side," he suggested, "and you will find something." So they made a cast, and took so many fish they could not haul the net in. Then the disciple Jesus loved cried out to Peter, "It is the Lord!" On hearing it was the Lord, Simon Peter threw on some clothes–he was stripped–and jumped into the water.

Meanwhile the other disciples came in the boat, towing the net full of fish. Actually they were not far from land–no more than a hundred yards.

When they landed, they saw a charcoal fire there with a fish laid on it and some bread. "Bring some of the fish you just caught," Jesus told them. Simon Peter went aboard and hauled ashore the net loaded with sizable fish–one hundred and fifty-three of them! In spite of the great number, the net was not torn.

"Come and eat your meal," Jesus told them. Not one of the disciples presumed to inquire "Who are you?" for they knew it was the Lord. Jesus came over, took the bread and gave it to them, and did the same with the fish. This marked the third time that Jesus appeared to the disciples after being raised from the dead.]

When they had eaten their meal, Jesus said to Simon Peter, "Simon, son of John, do you love me more than these?" "Yes, Lord," Peter said, "you know that I love you." At which Jesus said, "Feed my lambs."

A second time he put his question, "Simon, son of John, do you love me?" "Yes, Lord," Peter said, "you know that I love you." Jesus replied, "Tend my sheep."

A third time Jesus asked him, "Simon, son of John, do you love me?" Peter was hurt because he had asked a third time, "Do you love me?" So he said to him: "Lord, you know everything. You know well that I love you." Jesus told him, "Feed my sheep."

"I tell you solemnly:
as a young man
you fastened your belt
and went about as you pleased;
but when you are older
you will stretch out your hands,
and another will tie you fast
and carry you off against your will."

(What he said indicated the sort of death by which Peter was to glorify God.) When Jesus had finished speaking he said to him, "Follow me."

842 FOURTH SUNDAY OF EASTER / A

READING I *Acts 2, 14.36-41 / 50*

[On the day of Pentecost] Peter stood up with the Eleven, raised his voice, and addressed them:"Let the whole house of Israel know beyond any doubt that God has made both Lord and Messiah this Jesus whom you crucified."

When they heard this, they were deeply shaken. They asked Peter and the other apostles, "What are we to do, brothers?" Peter answered: "You must reform and be baptized, each one of you, in the name of Jesus Christ, that your sins may be forgiven; then you will receive the gift of the Holy Spirit. It was to you and your children that the promise was made, and to all those still far off whom the Lord our God calls."

In support of his testimony he used many other arguments, and kept urging, "Save yourselves from this generation which has gone astray." Those who accepted his message were baptized; some three thousand were added that day.

RESPONSORIAL PSALM *Psalm (22)23, 1-3.3-4.5.6 / 50*

RP
The Lord is my shep - herd;
there is noth - ing I shall want.

The Lord is my shepherd;
there is nothing I shall want.
Fresh and green are the pastures
where he gives me repose.
Near restful water he leads me,
to revive my drooping spirit. ℟.

He guides me along the right path;
he is true to his name.
If I should walk in the valley of
darkness
no evil would I fear.
You are there with your crook and your
staff;
with these you give me comfort. ℟.

You have prepared a banquet for me
in the sight of my foes.
My head you have anointed with oil;
my cup is overflowing. ℟.

Surely goodness and kindness shall
follow me
all the days of my life.
In the Lord's own house shall I dwell
for ever and ever. ℟.

READING II *1 Peter 2, 20-25 / 50*

If you put up with suffering for doing what is right, this is acceptable in God's eyes. It was for this you were called, since Christ suffered for you in just this way and left you an example, to have you follow in his footsteps. He did no wrong; no deceit was found in his mouth. When he was insulted he returned no insult. When he was made to suffer, he did not counter with threats. Instead, he delivered himself up to the One who judges justly. In his own body he brought your sins to the cross, so that all of us, dead to sin, could live in accord with God's will. By his wounds you were healed. At one time you were straying like sheep, but now you have returned to the shepherd, the guardian of your souls.

GOSPEL *John 10,1-10 / 50*

Jesus said:
"Truly I assure you:
Whoever does not enter the sheepfold
through the gate
but climbs through some other way
is a thief and a marauder.
The one who enters through the gate
is a shepherd of the sheep;
the keeper opens the gate for him.
The sheep hear his voice
as he calls them by name
and leads them out.
When he has brought out [all] those
that are his,
he walks in front of them,
and the sheep follow him
because they recognize his voice.
They will not follow a stranger;
such a one they will flee,
because they do not recognize a
stranger's voice."

Even though Jesus used this figure with them, they did not grasp what he was trying to tell them. He therefore said [to them again]:

"My solemn word is this:
I am the sheepgate.
All who came before me
were thieves and marauders
whom the sheep did not heed.
"I am the gate.
Whovever enters through me
will be safe.
He will go in and out,
and find pasture.
The thief comes
only to steal and slaughter and
destroy.
I came
that they might have life
and have it to the full."

FOURTH SUNDAY OF EASTER/B 843

READING I *Acts 4, 8-12 / 51*

Peter, filled with the Holy Spirit, spoke up: "Leaders of the people! Elders! If we must answer today for a good deed done to a cripple and explain how he was restored to health, then you and all the people of Israel must realize that it was done in the name of Jesus Christ the Nazorean whom you crucified and whom God raised from the dead. In the power of that name this man stands before you perfectly sound. This Jesus is 'the stone rejected by you the builders which has become the cornerstone.' There is no salvation in anyone else, for there is no other name in the whole world given to men by which we are to be saved."

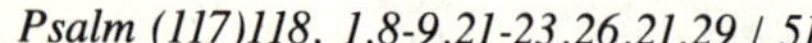

RESPONSORIAL PSALM *Psalm (117)118, 1.8-9.21-23.26.21.29 / 51*

RP
The stone re - ject - ed by the build - ers
has be - come the cor - ner - stone.

Give thanks to the Lord for he is good,
for his love endures for ever.
It is better to take refuge in the Lord
than to trust in men;
It is better to take refuge in the Lord
than to trust in the princes. ℟.

I will thank you for you have answered
and you are my savior.
The stone which the builders rejected
has become the cornerstone.
This is the work of the Lord,
a marvel in our eyes. ℟.

Blessed in the name of the Lord is he
who comes.
We bless you from the house of the
Lord;
I will thank you for you have answered
and you are my savior.
Give thanks to the Lord for he is good;
for his love endures for ever. ℟.

READING II *1 John 3, 1-2 / 51*

See what love the Father has bestowed
on us
in letting us be called children of
God!
Yet that is what we are.
The reason the world does not
recognize us
is that it never recognized the Son.

Dearly beloved,
we are God's children now;
what we shall later be has not yet
come to light.
We know that when it comes to light
we shall be like him,
for we shall see him as he is.

GOSPEL *John 10, 11-18 / 51*

Jesus said:
"I am the good shepherd;
the good shepherd lays down his life
for the sheep.
The hired hand, who is no shepherd
nor owner of the sheep,
catches sight of the wolf coming
and runs away, leaving the sheep
to be snatched and scattered by the
wolf.
That is because he works for pay;
he has no concern for the sheep.

"I am the good shepherd.
I know my sheep
and my sheep know me
in the same way that the Father
knows me
and I know the Father;
for these sheep I will give my life.
I have other sheep
that do not belong to this fold.
I must lead them, too,
and they shall hear my voice.
There shall be one flock then, one
shepherd.
The Father loves me for this:
that I lay down my life
to take it up again.
No one takes it from me;

I lay it down freely.
I have power to lay it down,
and I have power to take it up again.
This command I received from my Father."

FOURTH SUNDAY OF EASTER/C 844

READING I *Acts 13, 14.43-52 / 52*

Paul and Barnabas travelled on from Perga and came to Antioch in Pisidia. On the sabbath day they entered the synagogue and sat down. Many Jews and devout Jewish converts became their followers and they spoke to them and urged them to hold fast to the grace of God.

The following sabbath, almost the entire city gathered to hear the word of God. When the Jews saw the crowds, they became very jealous and countered with violent abuse whatever Paul said. Paul and Barnabas spoke out fearlessly, nonetheless: "The word of God has to be declared to you first of all; but since you reject it and thus convict yourselves as unworthy of everlasting life, we now turn to the Gentiles. For thus were we instructed by the Lord: 'I have made you a light to the nations, a means of salvation to the ends of the earth.' " The Gentiles were delighted when they heard this and responded to the word of the Lord with praise. All who were destined for life everlasting believed in it. Thus the word of the Lord was carried throughout that area.

But some of the Jews stirred up their influential women sympathizers and the leading men of the town, and in that way got a persecution started against Paul and Barnabas. The Jews finally expelled them from their territory. So the two shook the dust from their feet in protest and went on to Iconium. Their disciples knew only how to be filled with joy and the Holy Spirit.

RESPONSORIAL PSALM *Psalm (99)100, 1-2.3.5 / 52*

MK
We are his peo-ple: the sheep of his flock.

Cry out with joy to the Lord, all the earth.
Serve the Lord with gladness.
Come before him, singing for joy. ℟.

Know that he, the Lord, is God.
He made us, we belong to him,
we are his people, the sheep of his flock. ℟.

Indeed, how good is the Lord,
eternal his merciful love.
He is faithful from age to age. ℟.

READING II *Revelation 7, 9.14-17 / 52*

I, John, saw before me a huge crowd which no one could count from every nation and race, people and tongue. They stood before the throne and the Lamb, dressed in long white robes and holding palm branches in their hands.

Then one of the elders said to me: "These are the ones who have survived the great period of trial; they have washed their robes and made them white in the blood of the Lamb.

"It was this that brought them before God's throne:
day and night they minister to him in his temple;
he who sits on the throne will give them shelter.
Never again shall they know hunger or thirst,
nor shall the sun or its heat beat down on them, for the Lamb
on the throne will shepherd them.

He will lead them to springs of life-giving water,
and God will wipe every tear from their eyes."

GOSPEL *John 10, 27-30 / 52*

Jesus said:
"My sheep hear my voice.
I know them,
and they follow me.
I give them eternal life,
and they shall never perish.
No one shall snatch them out of my hand.
My Father is greater than all, in what he has given me,
and there is no snatching out of his hand.
The Father and I are one."

845 **FIFTH SUNDAY OF EASTER/A**

READING I *Acts 6, 1-7 / 53*

In those days, as the number of disciples grew, the ones who spoke Greek complained that their widows were being neglected in the daily distribution of food, as compared with the widows of those who spoke Hebrew. The Twelve assembled the community of the disciples and said, "It is not right for us to neglect the word of God in order to wait on the tables. Look around among your own number, brothers, for seven men acknowledged to be deeply spiritual and prudent, and we shall appoint them to this task. This will permit us to concentrate on prayer and the ministry of the word." The proposal was unanimously accepted by the community. Following this they selected Stephen, a man filled with faith and the Holy Spirit; Philip, Prochorus, Nicanor, Timon, Parmenas and Nicolaus of Antioch, who had been a convert to Judaism. They presented these men to the apostles, who first prayed over them and then imposed hands on them.

The word of God continued to spread, while at the same time the number of the disciples in Jerusalem enormously increased. There were many priests among those who embraced the faith.

RESPONSORIAL PSALM *Psalm (32)33, 1-2.4-5.18-19 / 53*

RP
Lord, let your mer - cy be on us,
as we place our trust in you.

Ring out your joy to the Lord, O you just;
for praise is fitting for loyal hearts.
Give thanks to the Lord upon the harp,
with a ten-stringed lute sing him songs. ℟.

For the word of the Lord is faithful
and all his works to be trusted.
The Lord loves justice and right
and fills the earth with his love. ℟.

The Lord looks on those who revere him,
on those who hope in his love,
to rescue their souls from death,
to keep them alive in famine. ℟.

READING II *1 Peter 2, 4-9 / 53*

Come to the Lord, a living stone, rejected by men but approved, nonetheless, and precious in God's eyes. You too are living stones, built as an edifice of spirit, into a holy priesthood, offering spiritual sacrifices acceptable to God through Jesus Christ. For Scripture has it:

"See I am laying a cornerstone in Zion,
an approved stone, and precious.
He who puts his faith in it shall not be shaken."

The stone is of value for you who have faith. For those without faith, it is rather,

"A stone which the builders rejected
that became a cornerstone."

It is likewise "an obstacle and a stumbling stone." Those who stumble and fall are the disbelievers in God's word; it belongs to their destiny to do so.

You, however are "a chosen race, a royal priesthood, a consecrated nation, a people he claims for his own to proclaim the glorious works" of the One who called you from darkness into his marvelous light.

GOSPEL *John 14, 1-12 / 53*

Jesus said to his disciples:

"Do not let you hearts be troubled.
Have faith in God
and faith in me.
In my Father's house there are many dwelling places;
otherwise, how could I have told you
that I was going to prepare a place for you?
I am indeed going to prepare a place for you,
and then I shall come back to take you with me,
that where I am you also may be.
You know the way that leads where I go."

"Lord," said Thomas, "we do not know where you are going. How can we know the way?" Jesus told him:

"I am the way, and the truth, and the life;
no one comes to the Father but through me.
If you really knew me, you would know my Father also.
From this point on you know him;
you have seen him."

"Lord," Philip said to him, "show us the Father and that will be enough for us." "Philip," Jesus replied, "after I have been with you all this time, you still do not know me?

"Whoever has seen me has seen the Father.
How can you say, 'Show us the Father?'
Do you not believe that I am in the Father
and the Father is in me?
The words I speak are not spoken of myself;
it is the Father who lives in me
accomplishing his works.
Believe me that I am in the Father
and the Father is in me,
or else, believe because of the works I do.
I solemnly assure you,
the man who has faith in me
will do the works I do, and greater far than these.
Why? Because I go to the Father."

FIFTH SUNDAY OF EASTER/B 846

READING I *Acts 9, 26-31 / 54*

When Saul arrived back in Jerusalem he tried to join the disciples there; but it turned out that they were all afraid of him. They even refused to believe that he was a disciple. Then Barnabas took him in charge and introduced him to the apostles, He explained to them how on his journey Saul had seen the Lord, who had conversed with him, and how Saul had been speaking out fearlessly in the name of Jesus at Damascus. Saul stayed on with them, moving freely about Jerusalem and expressing himself quite openly in the name of the Lord. He even addressed the Greek-speaking

Jews and debated with them. They, for their part, responded by trying to kill him. When the brothers learned of this, some of them took him down to Caesarea and sent him off to Tarsus.

Meanwhile throughout all Judea, Galilee and Samaria the church was at peace. It was being built up and was making steady progress in the fear of the Lord; at the same time it enjoyed the increased consolation of the Holy Spirit.

RESPONSORIAL PSALM *Psalm (21)22, 26-27.28.30.31-32 / 54*

DJR
I will praise you, Lord, in the as - sem-bly of your peo-ple.

My vows I will pay before those who
fear him.
The poor shall eat and shall have their
fill.
They shall praise the Lord, those who
seek him.
May their hearts live for ever and
ever! ℟.

All the earth shall remember and return
to the Lord,
all families of the nations worship
before him.
They shall worship him, all the mighty
of the earth;
before him shall bow all who go down
to the dust. ℟.

And my soul shall live for him, my
children serve him.
They shall tell of the Lord to
generations yet to come,
declare his faithfulness to peoples yet
unborn:
"These things the Lord has done." ℟.

READING II *1 John 3, 18-24 / 54*

Little children,
let us love in deed and in truth
and not merely talk about it.
This is our way of knowing we are
committed to the truth
and are at peace before him
no matter what our consciences may
charge us with;
for God is greater than our hearts
and all is known to him.

Beloved,
if our consciences have nothing to
charge us with,
we can be sure that God is with us
and that we will receive at his hands
whatever we ask.
Why? Because we are keeping his
commandments
and doing what is pleasing in his
sight.
His commandment is this:
we are to believe in the name of his
Son, Jesus Christ,
and are to love one another as he
commanded us.
Those who keep his commandments
remain in him
and he in them.
And this is how we know that he
remains in us:
from the Spirit that he gave us.

GOSPEL *John 15,1-8 / 54*

Jesus said to his disciples:
"I am the true vine
and my Father is the vinegrower.
He prunes away

every barren branch,
but the fruitful ones
he trims clean
to increase their yield.
You are clean already,
thanks to the word I have spoken to you.
Live on in me, as I do in you.
No more than a branch can bear fruit of itself
apart from the vine,
can you bear fruit
apart from me.
I am the vine, you are the branches.
He who lives in me and I in him,
will produce abundantly,
for apart from me you can do nothing.
A man who does not live in me
is like a withered, rejected branch,
picked up to be thrown in the fire and burnt.
If you live in me,
and my words stay part of you,
you may ask what you will–
it will be done for you.
My Father has been glorified
in your bearing much fruit
and becoming my disciples."

FIFTH SUNDAY OF EASTER/C 847

READING I

Acts 14, 21-27 / 55

After Paul and Barnabas had proclaimed the good news in Derbe and made numerous disciples, they retraced their steps to Lystra and Iconium first, then to Antioch. They gave their disciples reassurances, and encouraged them to persevere in the faith with this instruction: "We must undergo many trials if we are to enter into the reign of God." In each church they installed elders and, with prayer and fasting, commended them to the Lord in whom they had put their faith.

Then they passsed through Pisidia and came to Pamphylia. After preaching the message in Perga, they went down to Attalia. From there they sailed back to Antioch, where they had first been commended to the favor of God for the task they had now completed. On their arrival, they called the congregation together and related all that God had helped them accomplish, and how he had opened the door of faith to the Gentiles.

RESPONSORIAL PSALM

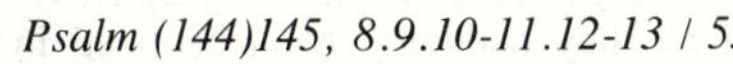
Psalm (144)145, 8.9.10-11.12-13 / 55

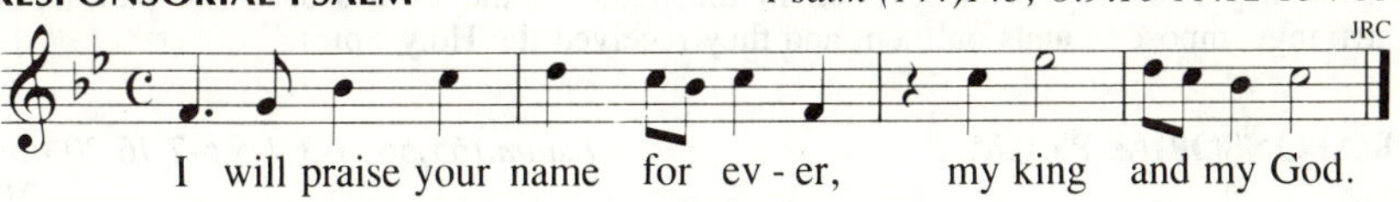
JRC
I will praise your name for ev - er, my king and my God.

The Lord is kind and full of compassion,
slow to anger, abounding in love.
How good is the Lord to all,
compassionate to all his creatures. ℟.

All your creatures shall thank you, O Lord,
and your friends shall repeat their blessing.
They shall speak of the glory of your reign
and declare your might, O God. ℟.

To make known to men your mighty deeds
and the glorious splendor of your reign.
Yours is an everlasting kingdom;
your rule lasts from age to age. ℟.

READING II

Revelation 21, 1-5 / 55

I, John, saw new heavens and a new earth. The former heavens and the former earth had passed away, and the sea was no longer. I also saw a new Jerusalem, the holy city, coming down out of heaven from God, beautiful as a bride prepared to meet her husband. I heard a loud voice from the throne cry out: "This is God's dwelling among men. He shall dwell with them and they shall be his people, and he shall be their God who is always with them. He shall wipe every tear from their eyes, and there shall be no more death or mourning, crying out or pain, for the former world has passed away."

The One who sat on the throne said to me, "See, I make all things new!"

GOSPEL *John 13, 31-33.34-35 / 55*

Once Judas had left (the cenacle), Jesus said:
"Now is the Son of Man glorified
and God is glorified in him.
[If God has been glorified in him,]
God will, in turn, glorify him in himself,
and will glorify him soon.
My children, I am not to be with you much longer.
I give you a new commandment:
Love one another.
Such as my love has been for you,
so must your love be for each other.
This is how all will know you for my disciples:
your love for one another."

848 SIXTH SUNDAY OF EASTER/A

READING *Acts 8, 5-8. 14-17 / 56*

Philip went down to the town of Samaria and there proclaimed the Messiah. Without exception, the crowds that heard Philip and saw the miracles he performed attended closely to what he had to say. There were many who had unclean spirits, which came out shrieking loudly. Many others were paralytics or cripples, and these were cured. The rejoicing in that town rose to fever pitch.

When the apostles in Jerusalem heard that Samaria had accepted the work of God, they sent Peter and John to them. The two went down to these people and prayed that they might receive the Holy Spirit. It had not as yet come down upon any of them since they had only been baptized in the name of the Lord Jesus. The pair, upon arriving, imposed hands on them and they received the Holy Spirit.

RESPONSORIAL PSALM *Psalm (65)66, 1-3.4-5.6-7.16.20 / 56*

RMH
Let all the earth cry out, cry out to God with joy.

Cry out with joy to God all the earth,
O sing to the glory of his name.
O render him glorious praise.
Say to God: "How tremendous your deeds! ℟.

Before you all the earth shall bow,
shall sing to you, sing to your name!"
Come and see the works of God,
tremendous his deeds among men. ℟.

He turned the sea into dry land,
they passed through the river dry-shod.
Let our joy then be in him;
he rules for ever by his might. ℟.

Come and hear, all who fear God.
I will tell what he did for my soul;
Blessed be God who did not reject my prayer
nor withold his love from me. ℟.

READING II *1 Peter 3, 15-18 / 56*

Venerate the Lord, that is, Christ, in your hearts. Should anyone ask you the reason for this hope of yours be ever ready to reply, but speak gently and respectfully. Keep your conscience clear so that, whenever you are defamed, those who libel your way of life in Christ may be disappointed. If it should be God's will that you suffer, it is better to do so for good deeds than for evil ones.

This is why Christ died for sins once for all, a just man for the sake of the unjust: so that he could lead you to God. He was put to death insofar as fleshly existence goes, but was given life in the realm of the spirit.

GOSPEL *John 14, 15-21 / 56*

Jesus said to his disciples:
"If you love me
and obey the commands I give you,
I will ask the Father
and he will give you another Paraclete–
to be with you always:
the Spirit of truth,
whom the world cannot accept,
since it neither sees him nor recognizes him;
but you can recognize him
because he remains with you
and will be within you.
I will not leave you orphaned;
I will come back to you.
A little while now and the world will see me no more;
but you see me
as one who has life, and you will have life.
On that day you will know
that I am in my Father,
and you in me, and I in you.
He who obeys the commandments he has from me
is the man who loves me;
and he who loves will be loved by my Father.
I too will love him
and reveal myself to him."

SIXTH SUNDAY OF EASTER/B 849

READING I *Acts 10, 25-26. 34-35. 44-48 / 57*

Peter entered the house of Cornelius who met him, dropped to his knees before Peter, and bowed low. Peter said as he helped him to his feet, "Get up! I am only a man myself."

Peter proceeded to address [the relatives and friends of Cornelius] in these words: "I begin to see how true it is that God shows no partiality. Rather, the man of any nation who fears God and acts uprightly is acceptable to him."

Peter had not finished these words when the Holy Spirit descended upon all who were listening to Peter's message. The circumcised believers who had accompanied Peter were surprised that the gift of the Holy Spirit should have been poured out on the Gentiles also, whom they could hear speaking in tongues and glorifying God. Peter put the question at that point: "What can stop these people who have received the Holy Spirit, even as we have, from being baptized with water?" So he gave orders that they be baptized in the name of Jesus Christ. After this was done, they asked him to stay with them for a few days.

RESPONSORIAL PSALM *Psalm (97)98, 1.2-3.3-4 / 57*

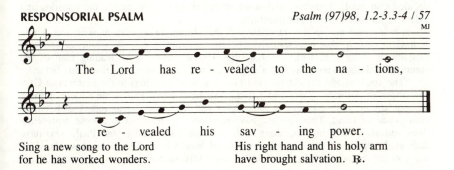

MJ
The Lord has re - vealed to the na - tions,
re - vealed his sav - ing power.

Sing a new song to the Lord
for he has worked wonders.
His right hand and his holy arm
have brought salvation. ℟.

The Lord has made known his salvation;
has shown his justice to the nations.
He has remembered his truth and love
for the house of Israel. ℟.

All the ends of the earth have seen
the salvation of our God.
Shout to the Lord all the earth,
ring out your joy. ℟.

READING II *1 John 4, 7-10 / 57*

Beloved,
let us love one another
because love is of God;
everyone who loves is begotten of God
and has knowledge of God.
The man without love has known nothing of God,
for God is love.
God's love was revealed in our midst in this way:
he sent his only Son to the world
that we might have life through him.
Love, then, consists in this:
not that we have loved God,
but that he has loved us
and has sent his Son as an offering for our sins.

GOSPEL *John 15, 9-17 / 57*

Jesus said to his disciples:
"As the Father has loved me,
so I have loved you.
Live on in my love.
You will live in my love
if you keep my commandments,
even as I have kept my Father's commandments,
and live in his love.
All this I tell you
that my joy may be yours
and your joy may be complete.
This is my commandment:
love one another
as I have loved you.
There is no greater love than this:
to lay down one's life for one's friends.
You are my friends
if you do what I command you.
I no longer speak of you as slaves,
for a slave does not know what his master is about.
Instead, I call you friends
since I have made known to you all that I heard from my Father.
It was not you who chose me,
it was I who chose you
to go forth and bear fruit.
Your fruit must endure,
so that all you ask the Father in my name
he will give you.
The command I give you is this:
that you love one another."

850 **SIXTH SUNDAY OF EASTER/C**

READING I *Acts 15, 1-2. 22-29 / 58*

Some men came down to Antioch from Judea and began to teach the brothers: "Unless you are circumcised according to Mosaic practice, you cannot be saved." This created dissension and much controversy between them and Paul and Barnabas. Finally it was decided that Paul, Barnabas, and some others should go up to see the apostles and elders in Jerusalem about this question.

It was resolved by the apostles and the elders, in agreement with the whole Jerusalem church, that representatives be chosen from among their number and sent to Antioch along with Paul and Barnabas. Those chosen were leading men of the community, Judas, known as Barsabbas, and Silas. They were to deliver this letter:

"The apostles and the elders, your brothers, send greetings to the brothers of Gentile origin in Antioch, Syria and Cilicia. We have heard that some of our number without any instructions from us have upset you with their discussions and disturbed your peace of mind. Therefore we have unanimously resolved to choose representatives and send them to you, along with our beloved Barnabas and Paul, who have dedicated themselves to the cause of our Lord Jesus Christ. Those whom we are sending you are Judas and Silas, who will convey this message by word of mouth: 'It is the decision of the Holy Spirit, and ours too, not to lay on you any burden beyond that which is strictly necessary, namely, to abstain from meat sacrificed to idols, from blood, from the meat of strangled animals, and from illicit sexual union. You will be well advised to avoid these things. Farewell.' "

RESPONSORIAL PSALM *Psalm (66)67, 2-3.5.6.8 / 58*

MK
O God, O God, let all the na - tions praise you!

O God, be gracious and bless us
and let your face shed its light upon us.
So will your ways be known upon earth
and all nations learn your saving help. ℟.

Let the nations be glad and exult
for you rule the world with justice.
With fairness you rule the peoples,
you guide the nations on earth.

Let the peoples praise you, O God;
let all the peoples praise you.
May God still give us his blessing
till the ends of the earth revere him. ℟.

READING II *Revelation 21, 10-14. 22-23 / 58*

The angel carried me away in spirit to the top of a very high mountain and showed me the holy city Jerusalem coming down out of heaven from God. It gleamed with the splendor of God. The city had the radiance of a precious jewel that sparkled like a diamond. Its wall, massive and high, had twelve gates at which twelve angels were stationed. Twelve names were written on the gates, the names of the twelve tribes of Israel. There were three gates facing east, three north, three south, and three west. The wall of the city had twelve courses of stones as its foundation, on which were written the names of the twelve apostles of the Lamb.

I saw no temple in the city. The Lord, God the Almighty, is its temple–he and the Lamb. The city had no need of sun or moon, for the glory of God gave it light, and its lamp was the Lamb.

GOSPEL *John 14, 23-29 / 58*

Jesus said to his disciples:
"Anyone who loves me
will be true to my word,
and my Father will love him;
will come to him
and make our dwelling place with him always.
He who does not love me does not keep my words.
Yet the word you hear is not mine;
it comes from the Father who sent me.
This much have I told you while I was still with you;
the Paraclete, the Holy Spirit
whom the Father will send in my name,
will instruct you in everything,
and remind you of all that I told you.
'Peace' is my farewell to you,
my peace is my gift to you;
I do not give it to you as the world gives peace.
Do not be distressed or fearful.
You have heard me say,
'I go away for a while, and I come back to you.'
If you truly loved me
you would rejoice to have me go to the Father,
for the Father is greater than I.
I tell you this now, before it takes place,
so that when it takes place you may believe."

851 ASCENSION

READING I *Acts 1, 1-11 / 59*

In my first account, Theophilus, I dealt with all that Jesus did and taught until the day he was taken up to heaven, having first instructed the apostles he had chosen through the Holy Spirit. In the time after his suffering he showed them in many convincing ways that he was alive, appearing to them over the course of forty days and speaking to them about the reign of God. On one occasion when he met with them, he told them not to leave Jerusalem: "Wait, rather, for the fullfillment of my Father's promise, of which you have heard me speak. John baptized with water, but within a few days you will be baptized with the Holy Spirit."

While they were with him they asked, "Lord are you going to restore the rule to Israel now?" His answer was: "The exact time it is not yours to know. The Father has reserved that to himself. You will recieve power when the Holy Spirit comes down on you; then you are to be my witnesses in Jerusalem, throughout Judea and Samaria, yes, even to the ends of the earth." No sooner had he said this than he was lifted up before their eyes in a cloud which took him from their sight.

They were still gazing up into the heavens when two men dressed in white stood beside them. "Men of Galilee," they said, "why do you stand here looking up at the skies? This Jesus who has been taken from you will return, just as you saw him go up into the heavens."

RESPONSORIAL PSALM

Psalm (46)47, 2-3.6-7.8-9 / 59

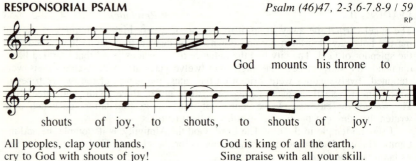

RP
God mounts his throne to
shouts of joy, to shouts, to shouts of joy.

All peoples, clap your hands,
cry to God with shouts of joy!
For the Lord, the Most High, we must
fear,
great king over all the earth. ℟.

God goes up with shouts of joy;
the Lord goes up with trumpet blast.
Sing praise for God, sing praise,
sing praise to our king, sing praise. ℟.

God is king of all the earth,
Sing praise with all your skill.
God is king over the nations;
God reigns on his holy throne. ℟.

READING II *Ephesians 1, 17-23 / 59*

May the God of our Lord Jesus Christ, the Father of glory, grant you a spirit of wisdom and insight to know him clearly. May he enlighten your innermost vision that you may know the great hope to which he has called you, the wealth of his glorious heritage to be distributed among the members of the church, and the immeasurable scope of his power in us who believe. It is like the strength he showed in raising Christ from the dead and seating him at his right hand in heaven, high above every principality, power, virtue and domination, and every name that can be given in this age or the age to come.

He has put all things under Christ's feet and has made him thus exalted, head of the church, which is his body: the fullness of him who fills the universe in all its parts.

GOSPEL/A *Matthew 28, 16-20 / 59*

The eleven disciples made their way to Galilee, to the mountain to which Jesus had summoned them. At the sight of him, those who had entertained doubts fell down in homage. Jesus came forward and addressed them in these words:

"Full authority has been given to me
both in heaven and on earth;
go, therefore, and make disciples of
all the nations.
Baptize them in the name
'of the Father
and of the Son,
and of the Holy Spirit.'
Teach them to carry out everything I
have commanded you.
And know that I am with you always,
until the end of the world!"

GOSPEL/B *Mark 16, 15-20 / 59*

[Jesus appeared to the Eleven and] said to them: "Go into the whole world and proclaim the good news to all creation. The man who believes in it and accepts baptism will be saved; the man who refuses to believe in it will be condemned. Signs like these will accompany those who have professed their faith: they will use my name to expel demons, they will speak entirely new languages, they will be able to handle serpents, they will be able to drink deadly poison without harm, and the sick upon whom they lay their hands will recover." Then, after speaking to them, the Lord Jesus was taken up into heaven and took his seat at God's right hand. The Eleven went forth and preached everywhere. The Lord continued to work with them throughout and confirm the message through the signs which accompanied them.

GOSPEL/C *Luke 24, 46-53 / 59*

Jesus said to the Eleven: "Thus it is written that the Messiah must suffer and rise from the dead on the third day. In his name, penance for the remission of sins is to be preached to the nations, beginning at Jerusalem. You are witnesses of all this. See, I send down upon you the promise of my Father. Remain here in the city until you are clothed with power from on high." He then led them out near Bethany, and with hands upraised, blessed them. As he blessed, he left them, and was taken up to heaven. They fell down to do him reverence, then returned to Jerusalem filled with joy. There they were to be found in the temple constantly, speaking the praises of God.

SEVENTH SUNDAY OF EASTER/A 852

READING I *Acts 1, 12-14 / 60*

[After Jesus was taken up into the heavens,] the apostles returned to Jerusalem from the mount called Olivet near Jerusalem, a mere sabbath's journey away. Entering the city, they went to the upstairs room where they were staying: Peter and John and James and Andrew; Philip and Thomas, Bartholomew and Matthew; James son of Alpheus; Simon, the Zealot party member, and Judas son of James. Together they devoted themselves to constant prayer. There were some women in their company and Mary the mother of Jesus, and his brothers.

RESPONSORIAL PSALM *Psalm (26)27, 1.4.7-8 / 60*

CK
I be - lieve that I shall see the good things of the
Lord in the land of the liv - ing.

The Lord is my light and my help;
whom shall I fear?
The Lord is the stronghold of my life;
before whom shall I shrink? ℟.

There is one thing I ask of the Lord,
for this I long,
to live in the house of the Lord,
all the days of my life,
to savor the sweetness of the Lord,
to behold his temple. ℟.

O Lord, hear my voice when I call;
have mercy and answer.
Of you my heart has spoken:
"Seek his face."
It is your face, O Lord, that I seek. ℟.

READING II *1 Peter 4, 13-16 / 60*

Rejoice insofar as you share Christ's sufferings. When his glory is revealed, you will rejoice exultantly. Happy are you when you are insulted for the sake of Christ, for then God's Spirit in its glory has come to rest on you. See to it that none of you suffers for being a murderer, a thief, a malefactor, or a destroyer of another's rights. If anyone suffers for being a Christian, however, he ought not be shamed. He should rather glorify God in virtue of that name.

GOSPEL *John 17,1-11 / 60*

Jesus looked up to heaven and said:
"Father, the hour has come!
Give glory to your Son
that your Son may give glory to you,
insamuch as you have given him
authority over all mankind,
that he may bestow eternal life on
those you gave him.
(Eternal life is this:
to know you, the only true God,
and him whom you have sent, Jesus
Christ.)
I have given you glory on earth
by finishing the work you gave me to
do.
Do you now, Father, give me glory at
your side,
a glory I had with you before the
world began.
I have made your name known
to those you gave me out of the
world.
These men you gave me were yours;
they have kept your word.
Now they realize
that all that you gave me comes from
you.
I entrusted to them
the message you entrusted to me,
and they received it.
They have known that in truth I came
from you,
they have believed it was you who
sent me.
"For these I pray–
not for the world
but for these you have given me,
for they are really yours.
(Just as all that belongs to me is
yours,
so all that belongs to you is mine.)
It is in them that I have been glorified.
I am in the world no more,
but these are in the world
as I come to you."

853 SEVENTH SUNDAY OF EASTER/B

READING I *Acts 1, 15-17. 20-26 / 61*

In those days Peter stood up in the midst of the brothers–there must have been a hundred and twenty gathered together. "Brothers," he said, "the saying in Scripture uttered long ago by the Holy Spirit through the mouth of David was destined to be fulfilled in Judas, the one that guided those who arrested Jesus. He was one of our number and he had been given a share in this ministry of ours.

"It is written in the Book of Psalms,
'May another take his office.'

"It is entirely fitting, therefore, that one of those who was of our company while the Lord Jesus moved among us, from the baptism of John until the day he was taken up from us, should be named as witness with us to his resurrection." At that they nominated two, Joseph (called Barsabbas, also known as Justus) and Matthias. Then they prayed: "O Lord, you read the hearts of men. Make known to us which of these two you choose for this apostolic ministry, replacing Judas, who deserted the cause and went the way he was destined to go." They then drew lots between the two men. The choice fell to Matthias, who was added to the eleven apostles.

RESPONSORIAL PSALM *Psalm (102)103, 1-2.11-12.19-20 / 61*

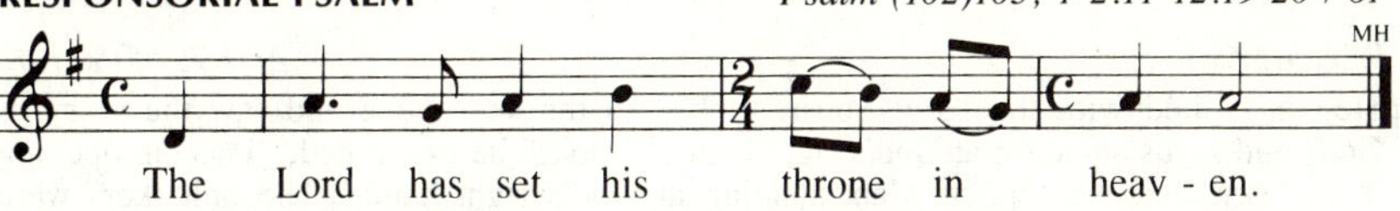
MH
The Lord has set his throne in heav - en.

My soul, give thanks to the Lord,
all my being, bless his holy name.
My soul, give thanks to the Lord
and never forget all his blessings. ℟.

For as the heavens are high above the earth
so strong is his love for those who fear him.
As far as the east is from the west
so far does he remove our sins. ℟.

The Lord has set his sway in heaven
and his kingdom is ruling over all.
Give thanks to the Lord, all his angels,
mighty in power, fulfilling his word. ℟.

READING II *1 John 4,11-16 / 61*

Beloved,
if God has loved us so,
we must have the same love for one another.
No one has ever seen God.
Yet if we love one another
God dwells in us,
and his love is brought to perfection in us.
The way we know we remain in him
and he in us
is that he has given us of his Spirit.
We have seen for ourselves, and can testify,
that the Father has sent the Son as savior of the world.
When anyone acknowledges that Jesus is the Son of God,
God dwells in him
and he in God.
We have come to know and to believe
in the love God has for us.
God is love,
and he who abides in love
abides in God,
and God in him.

GOSPEL *John 17, 11-19 / 61*

Jesus looked up to heaven and prayed:
"O Father most holy,
protect them with your name which you have given me
[that they may be one, even as we are one].
As long as I was with them,
I guarded them with your name which you gave me.
I kept careful watch,
and not one of them was lost, none
but him who was destined to be lost –
in fulfillment of Scripture.
Now, however, I come to you;
I say all this while I am still in the world
that they may share my joy completely.
I gave them your word,

and the world has hated them for it;
they do not belong to the world,
[any more than I belong to the world.]
I do not ask you to take them out of the world,
but to guard them from the evil one.
They are not of the world,
any more than I am of the world.
Consecrate them by means of truth–
'Your word is the truth.'
As you have sent me into the world,
so I have sent them into the world;
I consecrate myself for their sakes now,
that they may be consecrated in truth."

854 SEVENTH SUNDAY OF EASTER/C

READING I *Acts 7, 55-60 / 62*

Stephen, filled with the Holy Spirit, looked to the sky above and saw the glory of God, and Jesus standing at God's right hand. "Look!" he exclaimed, "I see an opening in the sky, and the Son of Man standing at God's right hand." The onlookers were shouting aloud, holding their hands over their ears as they did so. Then they rushed at him as one man, dragged him out of the city, and began to stone him. The witnesses meanwhile were piling their cloaks at the feet of a young man named Saul. As Stephen was being stoned he could be heard praying, "Lord Jesus, receive my spirit." He fell to his knees and cried out in a loud voice, "Lord, do not hold this sin against them." And with that he died.

RESPONSORIAL PSALM *Psalm (96)97, 1-2.6-7.9 / 62*

RP
The Lord is king, the most high o - ver all the earth.

The Lord is king, let earth rejoice,
let all the coastlands be glad.
His throne, justice and right. ℟.

The skies proclaim his justice;
all peoples see his glory.
All you spirits, worship him. ℟.

For you indeed are the Lord
most high above all the earth,
exalted far above all spirits. ℟.

READING II *Revelation 22, 12-14.16-17.20 / 62*

I, John, heard a voice saying to me: "Remember, I am coming soon! I bring with me the reward that will be given to each man as his conduct deserves. I am the Alpha and the Omega, the First and the Last, the Beginning and the End! Happy are they who wash their robes so as to have free access to the tree of life and enter the city through its gates!

"It is I, Jesus, who have sent my angel to give you this testimony about the churches. I am the Root and Offspring of David, the Morning Star shining bright."

The Spirit and the Bride say, "Come!" Let him who hears answer, "Come!" Let him who is thirsty come forward; let all who desire it accept the gift of life-giving water.

The One who gives this testimony says, "Yes, I am coming soon!" Amen! Come, Lord Jesus!

GOSPEL *John 17, 20-26 / 62*

Jesus looked up to heaven and said:
"I do not pray for my disciples alone.
I pray also for those who will believe in me through their word,
that all may be one
as you, Father, are in me, and I in you;
I pray that they may be [one] in us,
that the world may believe that you sent me.
I have given them the glory you gave me
that they may be one, as we are one–
I living in them, you living in me–
that their unity may be complete.
So shall the world know that you sent me,
and that you loved them as you loved me.
Father,
all those you gave me
I would have in my company
where I am,
to see this glory of mine
which is your gift to me,
because of the love you bore me before the world began.
Just Father,
the world has not known you,
but I have known you;
and these men have known that you sent me.
To them I have revealed your name,
and I will continue to reveal it
so that your love for me may live in them,
and I may live in them."

PENTECOST/VIGIL 855

READING I *Genesis 11, 1-9 / 63*

At that time the whole world spoke the same language, using the same words. While men were migrating in the east, they came upon a valley in the land of Shinar and settled down there. They said to one another, "Come, let us mold bricks and harden them with fire." They used bricks for stone, and bitumen for mortar. Then they said, "Come, let us build ourselves a city and a tower with its top in the sky, and so make a name for ourselves; otherwise we shall be scattered all over the earth." The Lord came down to see the city and the tower that the men had built. Then the Lord said: "If now, while they are one people, all speaking the same language, they have started to do this, nothing will later stop them from doing whatever they presume to do. Let us then go down and there confuse their language, so that one will not understand what another says." Thus the Lord scattered them from there all over the earth, and they stopped building the city. That is why it was called Babel, because there the Lord confused the speech of all the world. It was from that place that he scattered them all over the earth.

Or:

READING I *Exodus 19, 3-8.16-20 / 63*

Moses went up the mountain to God. Then the Lord called to him and said, "Thus shall you say to the house of Jacob; tell the Israelites: You have seen for yourselves how I treated the Egyptians and how I bore you up on my eagle wings and brought you here to myself. Therefore, if you hearken to my voice and keep my covenant, you shall be my special possession, dearer to me than all other people, though all the earth is mine. You shall be to me a kingdom of priests, a holy nation. That is what you must tell the Israelites." So Moses went and summoned the elders of the people. When he set before them all that the Lord had ordered him to tell them, the people all answered together, "Everything the Lord has said, we will do."

On the morning of the third day there were peals of thunder and lightning, and a heavy cloud over the mountain, and a very loud trumpet blast, so that all the people in the camp trembled. But Moses led the people out of the camp to meet God, and they stationed themselves at the foot of the mountain. Mount Sinai was all wrapped in smoke, for the Lord came down upon it in fire. The smoke rose from it as though from a furnace, and the whole mountain trembled violently. The trumpet blast grew louder and louder, while Moses was speaking and God answering him with thunder.

When the Lord came down to the top of Mount Sinai, he summoned Moses to the top of the mountain.

Or:

READING I *Ezekiel 37, 1-14 / 63*

The hand of the Lord came upon came upon me, and he led me out in the spirit of the Lord and set me in the center of the plain, which was now filled with bones. He made me walk among them in every direction so that I saw how many they were on the surface of the plain. How dry they were! He asked me: Son of man, can these bones come to life? "Lord God," I answered, "you alone know that." Then he said to me: Prophesy over these bones, and say to them: Dry bones, hear the word of the Lord! Thus says the Lord God to these bones: See! I will bring spirit into you, that you may come to life. I will put sinews upon you, make flesh grow over you, cover you with skin, and put spirit in you so that you may come to life and know that I am the Lord. I prophesied as I had been told, and even as I was prophesying I heard a noise; it was a rattling as the bones came together, bone joining bone. I saw the sinews and the flesh come upon them, and the skin cover them, but there was no spirit in them. Then he said to me: Prophesy to the spirit, prophesy, son of man, and say to the spirit: Thus says the Lord God: From the four winds come, O spirit, and breathe into these slain that they may come to life. I prophesied as he told me, and the spirit came to them; they came alive and stood upright, a vast army. Then he said to me: Son of man, these bones are the whole house of Israel. They have been saying, "Our bones are dried up, our hope is lost, and we are cut off." Therefore, prophesy and say to them: Thus says the Lord God: O my people, I will open your graves and have you rise from them, and bring you back to the land of Israel. Then you shall know that I am the Lord, when I open your graves and have you rise from them, O my people! I will put my spirit in you that you may live, and I will settle you upon your land; thus you shall know that I am the Lord. I have promised, and I will do it, says the Lord.

Or:

READING I *Joel 3, 1-5 / 63*

Thus says the Lord:
I will pour out
  my spirit upon all mankind.
Your sons and daughters shall prophesy,
  your old men shall dream dreams,
  your young men shall see visions;
Even upon the servants and the handmaids,
  in those days, I will pour out my spirit.
And I will work wonders in the heavens and on the earth,
  blood, fire, and columns of smoke;
The sun will be turned to darkness,
  and the moon to blood,
At the coming of the Day of the Lord,
  the great and terrible day.
  Then everyone shall be rescued
  who calls on the name of the Lord;
For on Mount Zion there shall be a remnant,
  as the Lord has said,
And in Jerusalem survivors
  whom the Lord shall call.

RESPONSORIAL PSALM *Psalm (103)104, 1-2.24.35.27-28.29.30 / 63*

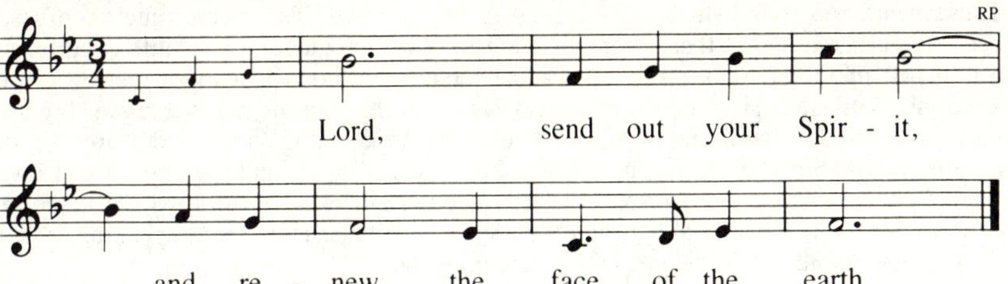
RP
Lord, send out your Spir - it,
and re - new the face of the earth.

Bless the Lord, my soul!
Lord God, how great you are,
clothed in majesty and glory,
wrapped in light as in a robe! ℟.

How many are your works, O Lord!
In wisdom you have made them all.
The earth is full of your riches.
Bless the Lord, my soul. ℟.

All of these look to you
to give them their food in due season.
You give it, they gather it up;
you open your hand, they have their
fill. ℟.

You take back your spirit, they die,
returning to the dust from which they
came.
You send forth your spirit, they are
created;
and you renew the face of the earth. ℟.

READING II *Romans 8, 22-27 / 63*

We know that all creation groans and is in agony even until now. Not only that, but we ourselves, although we have the Spirit as first fruits, groan inwardly while we await the redemption of our bodies. In hope we were saved. But hope is not hope if its object is seen; how is it possible for one to hope for what he sees? And hoping for what we cannot see means awaiting it with patient endurance.

The Spirit too helps us in our weakness, for we do not know how to pray as we ought; but the Spirit himself makes intercession for us with groanings which cannot be expressed in speech. He who searches hearts knows what the Spirit means, for the Spirit means, for the Spirit intercedes for the saints as God himself wills.

GOSPEL *John 7, 37-39 / 63*

On the last and greatest day of the festival, Jesus stood up and cried out:

"If anyone thirsts, let him come to me;
Let him drink who believes in me.
Scripture has it:
'From within him rivers of living water
shall flow.' "

(Here he was referring to the Spirit, whom those that came to believe in him were to receive. There was, of course, no Spirit as yet, since Jesus had not yet been glorified.)

PENTECOST SUNDAY 856

READING I *Acts 2, 1-11 / 64*

When the day of Pentecost came it found the brethren gathered in one place. Suddenly from up in the sky there came a noise like a strong, driving wind which was heard all through the house where they were seated. Tongues as of fire appeared which parted and came to rest on each of them. All were filled with the Holy Spirit. They began to express themselves in foreign tongues and make bold proclamation as the Spirit prompted them.

Staying in Jerusalem at the time were devout Jews of every nation under heaven. These heard the sound, and assembled in a large crowd. They were much confused because each one heard these men speaking his own language. The whole occurrence astonished them. They asked in utter amazement, "Are not all of these men who are speaking Galileans? How is it that each of us hears them in his native tongue? We are Parthians, Medes, and Elamites. We live in Mesopotamia, Judea and Cappadocia, Pontus, the province of Asia, Phrygia and Pamphylia, Egypt, and the regions of Libya around Cyrene. There are even visitors from Rome–all Jews, or those who have come over to Judaism; Cretans and Arabs too. Yet each of us hears them speaking in his own tongue about the marvels God has accomplished."

RESPONSORIAL PSALM *Psalm (103)104, 1.24.29-30.31.34 / 64*

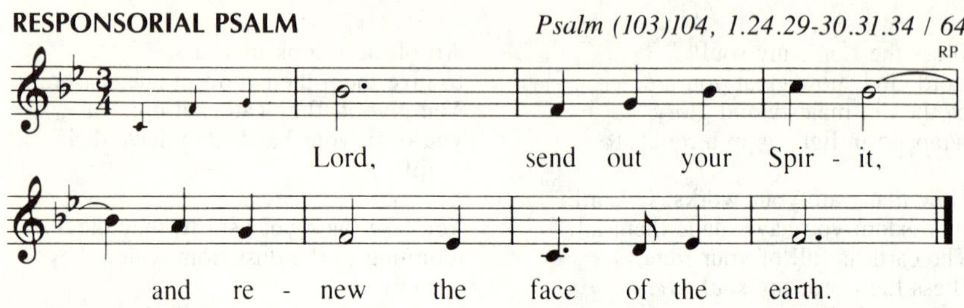
RP
Lord, send out your Spir - it,
and re - new the face of the earth.

Bless the Lord, my soul!
Lord God, how great you are.
How many are your works, O Lord!
The earth is full of your riches. ℟.

May the glory of the Lord last for ever!
May the Lord rejoice in his works!
May my thoughts be pleasing to him.
I find my joy in the Lord. ℟.

You take back your spirit, they die,
returning to the dust from which they
came.
You send forth your spirit, they are
created;
and you renew the face of the earth. ℟.

READING II *1 Corinthians 12, 3-7. 12-13 / 64*

No one can say: "Jesus is Lord," except in the Holy Spirit.

There are different gifts but the same Spirit; there are different ministries but the same Lord; there are different works but the same God who accomplishes all of them in everyone. To each person the manifestation of the Spirit is given for the common good.

The body is one and has many members, but all the members, many though they are, are one body; and so it is with Christ. It was in one Spirit that all of us, whether Jew or Greek, slave or free, were baptized into one body. All of us have been given to drink of the one Spirit.

857 **SEQUENCE**

13th C.
Tr. by Peter J. Scagnelli, b.1949

Mode I
Acc. by Adriaan Engels, b.1906

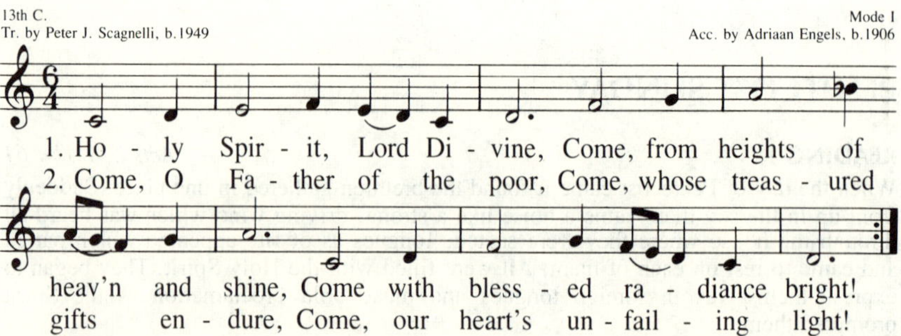
1. Ho - ly Spir - it, Lord Di - vine, Come, from heights of
2. Come, O Fa - ther of the poor, Come, whose treas - ured
heav'n and shine, Come with bless - ed ra - diance bright!
gifts en - dure, Come, our heart's un - fail - ing light!

3. Of con - so - lers, wis - est, best, And our soul's most
4. In our la - bor rest most sweet, Pleas - ant cool - ness
wel - come guest, Sweet re - fresh - ment, sweet re - pose.
in the heat, Con - so - la - tion in our woes.
5. Light most bless - ed, shine with grace In our heart's most
6. Left with - out your pres - ence here, Life it - self would
se - cret place, Fill your faith - ful through and through.
dis - ap - pear, Noth - ing thrives a - part from you!
7. Cleanse our soil - ed hearts of sin, Ar - id souls re-
8. Bend the stub - born heart and will, Melt the fro - zen,
fresh with - in, Wound - ed lives to health re - store.
warm the chill, Guide the way - ward home once more!
9. On the faith - ful who are true And pro - fess their
10. Give us vir - tue's sure re - ward, Give us your sal-
faith in you, In your sev'n - fold gift de - scend!
va - tion, Lord, Give us joys that nev - er end!

GOSPEL *John 20, 19-23 / 64*

On the evening of that first day of the week, even though the disciples had locked the doors of the place where they were for fear of the Jews, Jesus came and stood before them. "Peace be with you," he said. When he had said this, he showed them his hands and his side. At the sight of the Lord the disciples rejoiced. "Peace be with you," he said again.

"As the Father has sent me,
so I send you."

Then he breathed on them and said:

"Receive the Holy Spirit.
If you forgive men's sins,
they are forgiven them;
if you hold them bound,
they are held bound."

Ordinary Time

858 When the church assembles, there is always time to read from the scriptures. This is the book the church carries: the Law and the prophets, the books of wisdom and psalms, the letters and writings of Paul and of the other apostles, the gospels themselves. In various places and times the readings from scripture have been arranged so that the various Sundays have their assigned texts. This book of assigned scriptures is the lectionary. In the present Roman lectionary the scriptures are marked for reading through a cycle of three years.

Most of each year is called "Ordinary Time" or "Sundays of the Year." These are the weeks between the Christmas season and Lent, and the long period between Pentecost (the conclusion of the Easter season) and Advent (usually the first Sunday in December). On the Sundays of Ordinary Time, the lectionary has us read in order through the letters of the New Testament and the gospels. In the first year of the cycle, the gospel of Matthew is read from beginning to end; in the second year, Mark; in the third, Luke. Likewise, each Sunday finds the church picking up the reading of one of the letters of the New Testament roughly where the previous week's reading concluded. At present, the first reading at Sunday Mass in Ordinary Time is chosen from the Hebrew Scriptures; these texts show the richness and the continuity of faith.

Sunday by Sunday, year after year, the church reads through its book in the weeks of Ordinary Time. Each Christian, each local church, each generation listens and so finds its own life in God's word.

The Church assembles around the scriptures and around the Lord's table on Sunday. This day is called by Christians the Lord's Day. Whether the church is in Ordinary Time or in the seasons of Advent/Christmas or Lent/Easter, the Lord's Day is kept holy; it is the original feast day. The rhythm of the weekdays and the Sunday is the basic rhythm of life in Christian churches. The practices with which a church keeps the Lord's Day vary, but always and everywhere Christians assemble on this day so that the church may listen to God's word. Through the days of the week, the Sunday's scriptures are to be for reflection and nourishment as they are repeated and pondered in the households of the assembly.

SUNDAY AFTER PENTECOST–TRINITY SUNDAY/A 859

READING I *Exodus 34, 4-6. 8-9 / 165*

Early in the morning Moses went up Mount Sinai as the Lord had commanded him, taking along the two stone tablets.

Having come down in a cloud, the Lord stood with him there and proclaimed his name, "Lord." Thus the Lord passed before him and cried out, "The Lord, the Lord, a merciful and gracious God, slow to anger and rich in kindness and fidelity." Moses at once bowed down to the ground in worship. Then he said, "If I find favor with you, O Lord, do come along in our company. This is indeed a stiff-necked people; yet pardon our wickedness and sins, and receive us as your own."

RESPONSORIAL PSALM *Daniel 3, 52.53.54.55.56 / 165*

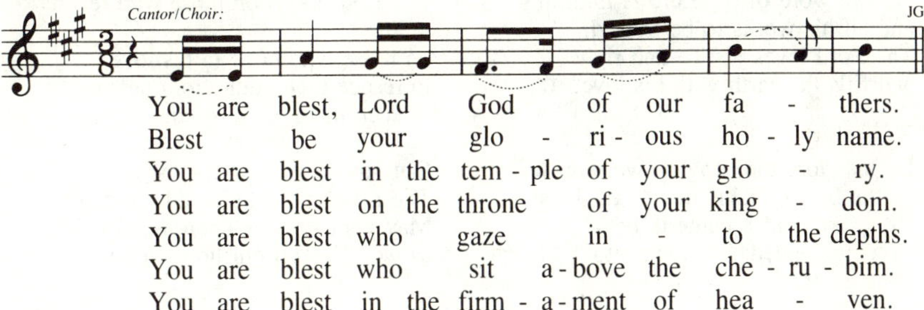
Cantor/Choir:
JG
You are blest, Lord God of our fa - thers.
Blest be your glo - ri - ous ho - ly name.
You are blest in the tem - ple of your glo - ry.
You are blest on the throne of your king - dom.
You are blest who gaze in - to the depths.
You are blest who sit a - bove the che - ru - bim.
You are blest in the firm - a - ment of hea - ven.

Assembly:
To you glo - ry and praise for ev - er - more.

READING II *2 Corinthians 13, 11-13 / 165*

Brothers, mend your ways. Encourage one another. Live in harmony and peace, and the God of love and peace will be with you. Greet one another with a holy kiss. All the holy ones send greetings to you. The grace of the Lord Jesus Christ, and the love of God, and the fellowship of the Holy Spirit be with you all!

GOSPEL *John 3, 16-18 / 165*

Jesus said to Nicodemus:
"Yes, God so loved the world
that he gave his only Son,
that whoever believes in him may not die
but may have eternal life.
God did not send the Son into the world
to condemn the world,
but that the world might be saved through him.
Whoever believes in him avoids condemnation,
but whoever does not believe is already condemned
for not believing in the name of God's only Son."

SUNDAY AFTER PENTECOST–TRINITY SUNDAY/B 860

READING I *Deuteronomy 4, 32-34.39-40 / 166*

Moses said to the people: "Ask now of the days of old, before your time, ever since God created man upon the earth; ask from one end of the sky to the other: Did anything so great ever happen before? Was it ever heard of? Did a people ever hear the voice of God speaking from the midst of fire, as you did, and live? Or did any god venture to go and take a nation for himself from the midst of another nation, by testings, by signs and wonders, by war, with his strong hand and outstretched arm, and by great terrors, all of which the Lord, your God, did for you in Egypt before your very eyes? This is why you must now know, and fix in your heart, that the Lord is God in the heavens above and on earth below, and that there is no other. You must keep his statutes and commandments which I enjoin on you today, that you and your children after you may prosper, and that you may have long life on the land which the Lord, your God, is giving you forever."

RESPONSORIAL PSALM *Psalm (32)33, 4-5.6.9.18-19.20.22 / 166*

CK

Hap-py the peo-ple the Lord has cho-sen to be his own.

For the word of the Lord is faithful
and all his works to be trusted.
The Lord loves justice and right
and fills the earth with his love. ℟.

By his word the heavens were made,
by the breath of his mouth all the stars.
He spoke; and it came to be.
He commanded; it sprang into
being. ℟.

The Lord looks on those who revere
him,
on those who hope in his love,
to rescue their souls from death,
to keep them alive in famine. ℟.

Our soul is waiting for the Lord.
The Lord is our help and our shield.
May your love be upon us, O Lord,
as we place all our hope in you. ℟.

READING II *Romans 8, 14-17 / 166*

All who are led by the Spirit of God are sons of God. You did not receive a spirit of slavery leading you back into fear, but a spirit of adoption through which we cry out, "Abba!" (that is, "Father"). The Spirit himself gives witness with our spirit that we are children of God. But if we are children, we are heirs as well: heirs of God, heirs with Christ, if only we suffer with him so as to be glorified with him.

GOSPEL *Matthew 28, 16-20 / 166*

The eleven disciples made their way to Galilee, to the mountain to which Jesus had summoned them. At the sight of him, those who had entertained doubts fell down in homage. Jesus came forward and addressed them in these words:

"Full authority has been given to me
both in heaven and on earth;
go, therefore, and make disciples of
all the nations.
Baptize them in the name
'of the Father
and of the Son,
and of the Holy Spirit.'
Teach them to carry out everything I
have commanded you.
And know that I am with you always,
until the end of the world!"

861 SUNDAY AFTER PENTECOST–TRINITY SUNDAY/C

READING I *Proverbs 8, 22-31 / 167*

Thus says the Wisdom of God:
"The Lord begot me, the first-born of
his ways,
the forerunner of his prodigies of
long ago;
From of old I was poured forth,

at the first, before the earth.
When there were no depths I was brought forth,
when there were no fountains or springs of water;
Before the mountains were settled into place,
before the hills, I was brought forth;
While as yet the earth and the fields were not made,
nor the first clods of the world.
"When he established the heavens I was there,
when he marked out the vault over the face of the deep;
When he made firm the skies above,
when he fixed fast the foundations of the earth;
When he set for the sea its limit,
so that the waters should not transgress his command;
Then was I beside him as his craftsman,
and I was his delight day by day,
Playing before him all the while,
playing on the surface of his earth;
and I found delight in the sons of men."

RESPONSORIAL PSALM *Psalm 8, 4-5.6-7.8-9 / 167*

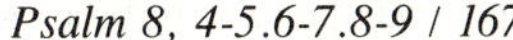

JRC
O Lord, our God, how won - der-
ful your name in all the earth!

When I see the heavens, the work of your hands,
the moon and the stars which you arranged,
what is man that you should keep him in mind,
mortal man that you care for him? ℟.

Yet you have made him little less than a god;
with glory and honor you crowned him,
gave him power over the works of your hand,
put all things under his feet. ℟.

All of them, sheep and cattle,
yes, even the savage beasts,
birds of the air, and fish
that make their way through the waters. ℟.

READING II *Romans 5, 1-5 / 167*

Now that we have been justified by faith, we are at peace with God through our Lord Jesus Christ. Through him we have gained access by faith to the grace in which we now stand, and we boast of our hope for the glory of God. But not only that—we even boast of our afflictions! We know that affliction makes for endurance, and endurance for tested virtue, and tested virtue for hope. And this hope will not leave us disappointed because the love of God has been poured out in our hearts through the Holy Spirit who been given to us.

GOSPEL *John 16, 12-15 / 167*

Jesus said to his disciples:
"I have much more to tell you,
but you cannot bear it now.
When he comes, however,
being the Spirit of truth
he will guide you to all truth.
He will not speak on his own,
but will speak only what he hears,
and will announce to you the things to come.
In doing this he will give glory to me,

because he will have received from
me
what he will announce to you.
All that the Father has belongs to me.
That is why I said that what he will
announce to you
he will have from me."

862 BODY AND BLOOD OF CHRIST/A

READING I *Deuteronomy 8, 2-3.14-16 / 168*

Moses said to the people: "Remember how for forty years now the Lord, your God, has directed all your journeying in the desert, so as to test you by affliction and find out whether or not it was your intention to keep his commandments. He therefore let you be afflicted with hunger, and then fed you with manna, a food unknown to you and your fathers, in order to show you that not by bread alone does man live, but by every word that comes forth from the mouth of the Lord.

"Remember, the Lord, your God, who brought you out of the land of Egypt, that place of slavery; who guided you through the vast and terrible desert with its saraph serpents and scorpions, its parched and waterless ground; who brought forth water for you from the flinty rock and fed you in the desert with manna, a food unknown to your fathers."

RESPONSORIAL PSALM *Psalm 147, 12-13.14-15.19-20 / 168*

CW
Praise the Lord, Je - ru - sa - lem.

O praise the Lord, Jerusalem!
Zion, praise your God!
He has strengthened the bars of your
gates,
he has blessed the children within
you. ℟.

He established peace on your borders,
he feeds you with finest wheat.
He sends out his word to the earth
and swiftly runs his command. ℟.

He makes his word known to Jacob,
to Israel his laws and decrees.
He has not dealt thus with other
nations;
he has not taught them his decrees. ℟.

READING II *1 Corinthians 10, 16-17 / 168*

Is not the cup of blessing we bless a sharing in the blood of Christ? And is not the bread we break a sharing in the body of Christ? Because the loaf of bread is one, we, many though we are, are one body for we all partake of one loaf.

GOSPEL *John 6, 51-58 / 168*

Jesus said to the crowds of Jews:
"I myself am the living bread
come down from heaven.
If anyone eats this bread
he shall live forever;
the bread I will give
is my flesh, for the life of the
world."
At this the Jews quarreled among themselves, saying, "How can he give us his

flesh to eat? Thereupon Jesus said to them:

"Let me solemnly assure you,
if you do not eat the flesh of the Son of Man
and drink his blood,
you have no life in you.
He who feeds on my flesh
and drinks my blood
has life eternal,
and I will raise him up on the last day.
For my flesh is real food
and my blood real drink.
The man who feeds on my flesh
and drinks my blood
remains in me, and I in him.
Just as the Father who has life sent me
and I have life because of the Father,
so the man who feeds on me
will have life because of me.
This is the bread that came down from heaven.
Unlike your ancestors who ate and died nonetheless,
the man who feeds on this bread shall live forever."

BODY AND BLOOD OF CHRIST/B 863

READING I *Exodus 24, 3-8 / 169*

When Moses came to the people and related all the words and ordinances of the Lord, they all answered with one voice, "We will do everything that the Lord has told us." Moses then wrote down all the words of the Lord and, rising early the next day, he erected at the foot of the mountain an altar and twelve pillars for the twelve tribes of Israel. Then, having sent certain young men of the Israelites to offer holocausts and sacrifice young bulls as peace offerings to the Lord, Moses took half of the blood and put it in large bowls; the other half he splashed on the altar. Taking the book of the covenant, he read it aloud to the people, who answered, "All that the Lord has said, we will heed and do." Then he took the blood and sprinkled it on the people, saying, "This is the blood of the covenant which the Lord has made with you in accordance with all these words of his."

RESPONSORIAL PSALM *Psalm (115)116, 12-13.15-16.17-18 / 169*

AGM
I will take the cup of sal - va - tion,
and call on the name of the Lord.

How can I repay the Lord
for his goodness to me?
The cup of salvation I will raise;
I will call on the Lord's name. ℟.

O precious in the eyes of the Lord
is the death of his faithful.
Your servant, Lord, your servant am I;
you have loosened my bonds. ℟.

A thanksgiving sacrifice I make;
I will call on the Lord's name.
My vows to the Lord I will fulfill
before all his people. ℟.

READING II *Hebrews 9, 11-15 / 169*

When Christ came as high priest of the good things which came to be, he entered once for all into the sanctuary, passing through the greater and more perfect tabernacle not made by hands, that is, not belonging to this creation. He entered not with the blood of goats and calves but with his own blood, and achieved eternal redemption. For if the blood of goats and bulls and the sprinkling of a heifer's ashes can sanctify those who are defiled so that their flesh is cleansed, how much more will the blood of Christ, who through the eternal spirit offered himself up unblemished to God, cleanse our consciences from dead works to worship the living God!

This is why he is mediator of a new covenant: since his death has taken place for deliverance from transgressions committed under the first covenant, those who are called may receive the promised eternal inheritance.

GOSPEL *Mark 14, 12-16.22-26 / 169*

On the first day of Unleavened Bread, when it was customary to sacrifice the paschal lamb, the disciples said to Jesus, "Where do you wish us to go to prepare the Passover supper for you?" He sent two of his disciples with these instructions: "Go into the city and you will come upon a man carrying a water jar. Follow him. Whatever house he enters, say to the owner, 'The Teacher asks, Where is my guestroom where I may eat the Passover with my disciples?' Then he will show you an upstairs room, spacious, furnished, and all in order. That is the place you are to get ready for us." The disciples went off. When they reached the city they found it just as he had told them, and they prepared the Passover supper.

During the meal he took bread, blessed and broke it, and gave it to them. "Take this," he said, "this is my body." He likewise took a cup, gave thanks and passed it to them, and they all drank from it. He said to them: "This is my blood, the blood of the covenant to be poured out on behalf of many. I solemnly assure you, I will never again drink of the fruit of the vine until the day when I drink it new in the reign of God."

After singing songs of praise they walked out to the Mount of Olives.

864 BODY AND BLOOD OF CHRIST/C

READING I *Genesis 14, 18-20 / 170*

Melchizedek, king of Salem, brought out bread and wine, and being a priest of God Most High, he blessed Abram with these words:
"Blessed be Abram by God Most High,
the creator of heaven and earth;
And blessed be God Most High,
who delivered your foes into your hand."

RESPONSORIAL PSALM *Psalm (109)110, 1.2.3.4 / 170*

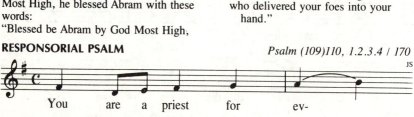

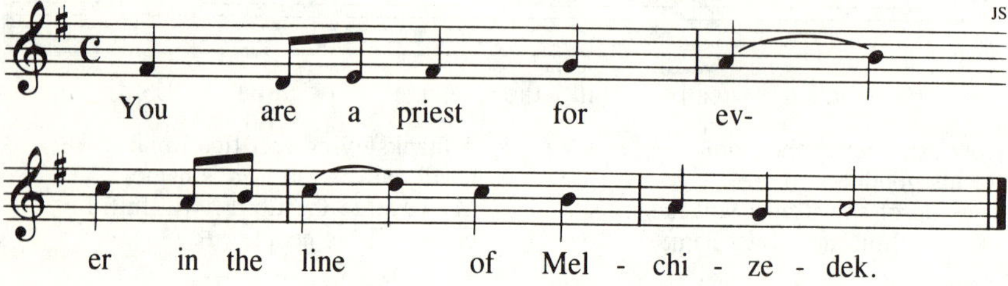
JS
You are a priest for ev-
er in the line of Mel - chi - ze - dek.

The Lord's revelation to my Master:
"Sit on my right;
your foes I will put beneath your feet." ℟.

The Lord will wield from Zion
your scepter of power;
rule in the midst of all your foes. ℟.

A prince from the day of your birth
on the holy mountains;
from the womb before the dawn I begot you. ℟.

The Lord has sworn an oath he will not change.
"You are a priest for ever,
a priest like Melchizedek of old." ℟.

READING II *1 Corinthians 11, 23-26 / 170*

I received from the Lord what I handed on to you, namely, that the Lord Jesus on the night in which he was betrayed took bread, and after he had given thanks, broke it and said, "This is my body, which is for you. Do this in remembrance of me." In the same way, after the supper, he took the cup, saying, "This cup is the new covenant in my blood. Do this, whenever you drink it, in remembrance of me." Every time, then, you eat this bread and drink this cup, you proclaim the death of the Lord until he comes!

GOSPEL *Luke 9, 11-17 / 170*

Jesus spoke to the crowds of the reign of God, and he healed all who were in need of healing.

As sunset approached, the Twelve came and said to him, "Dismiss the crowd so that they can go into the villages and farms in the neighborhood and find themselves lodging and food, for this is certainly an out-of-the-way place." He answered them, "Why do you not give them something to eat yourselves?" They replied, "We have nothing but five loaves and two fishes. Or shall we ourselves go and buy food for all these people?" (There were about five thousand men.) Jesus said to his disciples, "Have them sit down in groups of fifty or so." They followed his instructions and got them all seated. Then taking the five loaves and the two fishes, Jesus raised his eyes to heaven, pronounced a blessing over them, broke them, and gave them to his disciples for distribution to the crowd. They all ate until they had enough. What they had left, over and above, filled twelve baskets.

SACRED HEART / A 865

READING I *Deuteronomy 7, 6-11 / 171*

Moses said to the people: "You are a people sacred to the Lord, your God; he has chosen you from all the nations on the face of the earth to be a people peculiarly his own. It was not because you are the largest of all nations that the Lord set his heart on you and chose you, for you are really the smallest of all nations. It was because the Lord loved you and because of his fidelity to the oath he had sworn to your fathers, that he brought you out with his strong hand from the place of slavery, and ransomed you from the hand of Pharaoh, king of Egypt. Understand, then, that the Lord, your God, is God indeed, the faithful God who keeps his merciful covenant down to the thousandth generation toward those who love him and keep his commandments, but who repays with destruction the person who hates him; he does not dally with such a one, but makes him personally pay for it. You shall therefore carefully observe the commandments, the statutes and the decrees which I enjoin on you today."

RESPONSORIAL PSALM 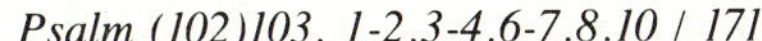
Psalm (102)103, 1-2.3-4.6-7.8.10 / 171

HH
The Lord's kind - ness is ev - er-
last - ing to those who fear him.

My soul, give thanks to the Lord,
all my being, bless his holy name.
My soul, give thanks to the Lord
and never forget all his blessings. ℟.

It is he who forgives all your guilt,
who heals every one of your ills,
who redeems your life from the grave,
who crowns you with love and
compassion. ℟.

The Lord does deeds of justice,
gives judgment for all who are
oppressed.
He made known his ways to Moses
and his deeds to Israel's sons. ℟.

The Lord is compassion and love,
slow to anger and rich in mercy.
He does not treat us according to our
sins
nor repay us according to our faults. ℟.

READING II *1 John 4, 7-16 / 171*

Beloved,
let us love one another
because love is of God;
everyone who loves is begotten of
God
and has knowledge of God.
The man without love has known
nothing of God,
for God is love.
God's love was revealed in our midst in
this way:
he sent his only Son to the world
that we might have life through him.
Love, then, consists in this:
not that we have loved God,
but that he has loved us
and has sent his Son as an offering
for our sins.
Beloved,
if God has loved us so,
we must have the same love for one
another.
No one has ever seen God.
Yet if we love one another
God dwells in us,
and his love is brought to perfection
in us.
The way we know we remain in him
and he in us
is that he has given us of his Spirit.
We have seen for ourselves, and can
testify,
that the Father has sent the Son as
savior of the world.
When anyone acknowledges that Jesus
is the Son of God,
God dwells in him
and he in God.
We have come to know and to believe
in the love God has for us.

GOSPEL *Matthew 11, 25-30 / 171*

At that time Jesus said: "Father, Lord of heaven and earth, to you I offer praise; for what you have hidden from the learned and the clever you have revealed to the merest children. Father, it is true. You have graciously willed it so. Everything has been given over to me by my Father. No one knows the Son but the Father, and no one knows the Father but the Son–and anyone to whom the Son wishes to reveal him.

"Come to me, all you who are weary and find life burdensome, and I will refresh you. Take my yoke upon your shoulders and learn from me, for I am gentle and humble of heart. Your souls will find rest, for my yoke is easy and my burden light."

866 SACRED HEART/B

READING I *Hosea 11, 1.3-4.8-9 / 172*

When Israel was a child I loved him,
out of Egypt I called my son.
Yet it was I who taught Ephraim to
walk,
who took them in my arms;
I drew them with human cords,
with bands of love;
I fostered them like one
who raises an infant to his cheeks;
Yet, though I stooped to feed my
child,
they did not know that I was their
healer.
My heart is overwhelmed,
my pity is stirred.
I will not give vent to my blazing
anger,
I will not destroy Ephraim again;
For I am God and not man,
the Holy One present among you;
I will not let the flames consume
you.

RESPONSORIAL PSALM *Isaiah 12, 2-3.4.5-6 / 172*

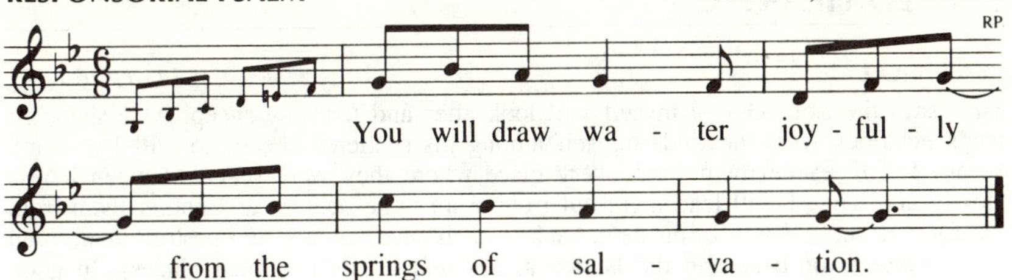
RP
You will draw wa - ter joy - ful - ly
from the springs of sal - va - tion.

Truly, God is my salvation,
I trust, I shall not fear.
For the Lord is my strength, my song,
he became my savior.
With joy you will draw water
from the wells of salvation. ℟.

Give thanks to the Lord,
give praise to his name!
Make his mighty deeds
known to the peoples!
Declare the greatness of his name.
Sing a psalm to the Lord! ℟.

For he has done glorious deeds,
make them known to all the earth!
People of Zion,
sing and shout for joy
for great in your midst
is the Holy One of Israel. ℟.

READING II *Ephesians 3, 8-12. 14-19 / 172*

To me, the least of all believers, was given the grace to preach to the Gentiles the unfathomable riches of Christ and to enlighten all men on the mysterious design which for ages was hidden in God, the Creator of all. Now, therefore, through the church, God's manifold wisdom is made known to the principalities and powers of heaven, in accord with his age-old purpose, carried out in Christ Jesus our Lord. In Christ and through faith in him we can speak freely to God, drawing near him with confidence.

That is why I kneel before the Father from whom every family in heaven and on earth takes its name; and I pray that he will bestow on you gifts in keeping with the riches of his glory. May he strengthen you inwardly through the working of his Spirit. May Christ dwell in your hearts through faith, and may charity be the root and foundation of your life. Thus you will be able to grasp fully, with all the holy ones, the breadth and length and height and depth of Christ's love, and experience this love which surpasses all knowledge, so that you may attain to the fullness of God himself.

GOSPEL *John 19, 31-37 / 172*

Since it was the Preparation Day the Jews did not want to have the bodies left on the cross during the sabbath, for that sabbath was a solemn feast day. They asked Pilate that the legs be broken and the bodies be taken away. Accordingly, the soldiers came and broke the legs of the men crucified with Jesus, first of the one, then of the other. When they came to Jesus and saw that he was already dead, they did not break his legs. One of the soldiers thrust a lance into his side, and immediately blood and water flowed out. (This testimony has been given by an eyewitness, and his testimony is true. He tells what he knows is true, so that you may believe.) These events took place for the fulfillment of Scripture:

"Break none of his bones."

There is still another Scripture passage which says:

"They shall look on him whom they have pierced."

867 SACRED HEART/C

READING I *Ezekiel 34, 11-16 / 173*

Thus says the Lord God: I myself will look after and tend my sheep. As a shepherd tends his flock when he finds himself among his scattered sheep, so will I tend my sheep. I will rescue them from every place where they were scattered when it was cloudy and dark. I will lead them out from among the peoples and gather them from the foreign lands; I will bring them back to their own country and pasture them upon the mountains of Israel [in the land's ravines and all its inhabited places]. In good pastures will I pasture them; and on the mountain heights of Israel shall be their grazing ground. There they shall lie down on good grazing ground, and in rich pastures shall they be pastured on the mountains of Israel. I myself will pasture my sheep; I myself will give them rest, says the Lord God. The lost I will seek out, the strayed I will bring back, the injured I will bind up, the sick I will heal [but the sleek and the strong I will destroy], shepherding them rightly.

RESPONSORIAL PSALM *Psalm (22)23, 1-3.3-4.5.6 / 173*

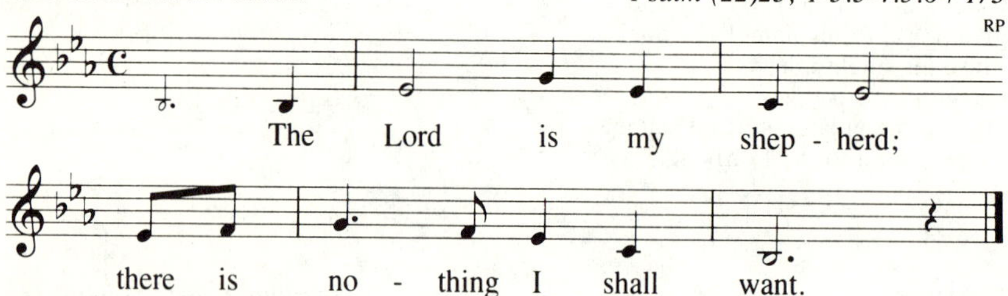
RP
The Lord is my shep - herd;
there is no - thing I shall want.

The Lord is my shepherd;
there is nothing I shall want.
Fresh and green are the pastures
where he gives me repose.
Near restful waters he leads me,
To revive my drooping spirit. ℟.

He guides me along the right path;
he is true to his name.
If I should walk in the valley of
darkness
no evil would I fear.
You are there with your crook and your
staff;
with these you give me comfort. ℟.

You have prepared a banquet for me
in the sight of my foes.
My head you have anointed with oil;
my cup is overflowing. ℟.

Surely goodness and kindness shall
follow me
all the days of my life.
In the Lord's own house shall I dwell
for ever and ever. ℟.

READING II *Romans 5, 5-11 / 173*

The love of God has been poured out in our hearts through the Holy Spirit who has been given to us. At the appointed time, when we were still powerless, Christ died for us godless men. It is rare that anyone should lay down his life for a just man, though it is barely possible that for a good man someone may have the courage to die. It is precisely in this that God proves his love for us: that while we were still sinners, Christ died for us. Now that we have been justified by his blood, it is all the more certain that we shall be saved by him from God's wrath. For if, when we were God's enemies, we were reconciled to him by the death of his Son, it is all the more certain that we who have been reconciled will be saved by his life. Not only that; we go so far as to make God our boast through our Lord Jesus Christ, through whom we have now received reconciliation.

GOSPEL *Luke 15, 3-7 / 173*

Jesus addressed this parable to the Pharisees and the scribes: "Who among you, if he has a hundred sheep and loses one of them, does not leave the ninety-nine in the wasteland and follow the lost one until he finds it? And when he finds it, he puts it on his shoulders in jubilation. Once arrived home, he invites friends and neighbors in and says to them, 'Rejoice with me because I have found my lost sheep.' I tell you, there will likewise be more joy in heaven over one repentant sinner than over ninety-nine righteous people who have no need to repent."

SECOND SUNDAY IN ORDINARY TIME/A 868

READING I *Isaiah 49,3.5-6 / 65*

The Lord said to me: you are my servant,
Israel, through whom I show my glory.

Now the Lord has spoken
who formed me as his servant from the womb,
That Jacob may be brought back to him
and Israel gathered to him;
And I am made glorious in the sight of the Lord,
and my God is now my strength!
It is too little, he says, for you to be my servant,
to raise up the tribes of Jacob,
and restore the survivors of Israel;
I will make you a light to the nations,
that my salvation may reach to the ends of the earth.

RESPONSORIAL PSALM *Psalm (39)40, 2.4.7-8.8-9.10 / 65*

RP
Here am I, Lord; I come to do your will.

I waited, I waited for the Lord
and he stooped down to me;
he heard my cry.
He put a new song into my mouth,
praise of our God. ℟.

You do not ask for sacrifice and offerings,
but an open ear.
You do not ask for holocaust and victim.
Instead, here am I. ℟.

In the scroll of the book it stands written
that I should do your will.
My God, I delight in your law
in the depth of my heart. ℟.

Your justice I have proclaimed
in the great assembly.
My lips I have not sealed;
you know it, O Lord. ℟.

READING II *1 Corinthians 1, 1-3 / 65*

Paul, called by God's will to be an apostle of Christ Jesus, and Sosthenes our brother, send greetings to the church of God which is in Corinth; to you who have been consecrated in Christ Jesus and called to be a holy people, as to all those who, wherever they may be, call on the name of our Lord Jesus Christ, their Lord and ours. Grace and peace from God our Father and the Lord Jesus Christ.

GOSPEL *John 1, 29-34 / 65*

When John caught sight of Jesus coming toward him, he exclaimed:
"Look there! The Lamb of God
who takes away the sin of the world!

It is he of whom I said:
'After me is to come a man
who ranks ahead of me,
because he was before me.'
I confess I did not recognize him, though the very reason I came baptizing with water was that he might be revealed to Israel."

John gave this testimony also:
"I saw the Spirit descend
like a dove from the sky,
and it came to rest on him.

But, as I say, I did not recognize him. The one who sent me to baptize with water told me, 'When you see the Spirit descend and rest on someone, it is he who is to baptize with the Holy Spirit,' Now I have seen for myself and have testified, 'This is God's chosen One.' "

869 SECOND SUNDAY IN ORDINARY TIME/B

READING I *1 Samuel 3, 3-10.19 / 66*

Samuel was sleeping in the temple of the Lord where the ark of God was. The Lord called to Samuel, who answered, "Here I am." He ran to Eli and said, "Here I am. You called me." "I did not call you," Eli said. "Go back to sleep." So he went back to sleep. Again the Lord called Samuel, who rose and went to Eli. "Here I am," he said. "You called me." But he answered, "I did not call you, my son. Go back to sleep." At that time Samuel was not familiar with the Lord, because the Lord had not revealed anything to him as yet. The Lord called Samuel again, for the third time. Getting up and going to Eli, he said, "Here I am. You called me." Then Eli understood that the Lord was calling the youth. So he said to Samuel, "Go to sleep, and if you are called, reply, 'Speak, Lord, for your servant is listening,' " When Samuel went to sleep in his place, the Lord came and revealed his presence, calling out as before, "Samuel, Samuel!" Samuel answered, "Speak, for your servant is listening."

Samuel grew up, and the Lord was with him, not permitting any word of his to be without effect.

RESPONSORIAL PSALM *Psalm (39)40, 2.4.7-8.8-9.10 / 66*

RP
Here am I, Lord; I come to do your will.

I waited, I waited for the Lord
and he stooped down to me;
he heard my cry.
He put a new song into my mouth,
praise of our God. ℟.

You do not ask for sacrifice and offerings,
but an open ear.
You do not ask for holocaust and victim.
Instead, here am I. ℟.

In the scroll of the book it stands written
that I should do your will.
My God, I delight in your law
in the depth of my heart. ℟.

Your justice I have proclaimed
in the great assembly.
My lips I have not sealed;
you know it, O Lord. ℟.

READING II *1 Corinthians 6, 13-15. 17-20 / 66*

The body is not for immorality; it is for the Lord, and the Lord is for the body. God who raised up the Lord, will raise us also by his power.

Do you not see that your bodies are members of Christ? Whoever is joined to the Lord becomes one spirit with him. Shun lewd conduct. Every other sin a man commits is outside his body, but the fornicator sins against his own body. You must know that your body is a temple of the Holy Spirit, who is within–the Spirit you have received from God. You are not your own. You have been purchased, and at what a price! So glorify God in your body.

GOSPEL *John 1, 35-42 / 66*

John was in Bethany across the Jordan with two of his disciples. As he watched Jesus walk by he said, "Look! There is the Lamb of God!" The two disciples heard what he said, and followed Jesus. When Jesus turned around and noticed them following him, he asked them, "What are you looking for?" They said to him, "Rabbi (which means Teacher), where do you stay?" "Come and see," he answered. So they went to see where he was lodged and stayed with him that day. (It was about four in the afternoon.)

One of the two who had followed him after hearing John was Simon Peter's brother Andrew. The first thing he did was seek out his brother Simon and tell him, "We have found the Messiah!" (which means the Anointed). He brought him to Jesus, who looked at him and said, "You are Simon, son of John; your name shall be Cephas (which is rendered Peter)."

SECOND SUNDAY IN ORDINARY TIME/C 870

READING I *Isaiah 62, 1-5 / 67*

For Zion's sake I will not be silent,
for Jerusalem's sake I will not be quiet,
Until her vindication shines forth like the dawn
and her victory like a burning torch.

Nations shall behold your vindication,
and all kings your glory;
You shall be called by a new name
pronounced by the mouth of the Lord.
You shall be a glorious crown in the hand of the Lord,
a royal diadem held by your God.
No more shall men call you "Forsaken,"
or your land "Desolate,"
But you shall be called "My Delight,"
and your land "Espoused."
For the Lord delights in you,
and makes your land his spouse.
As a young man marries a virgin,
your Builder shall marry you;
And as a bridegroom rejoices in his bride,
so shall your God rejoice in you.

RESPONSORIAL PSALM *Psalm (95)96, 1-2.2-3.7-8.9-10 / 67*

RC
Pro - claim his mar - vel-ous deeds to all the na - tions.

O sing a new song to the Lord,
sing to the Lord all the earth.
O sing to the Lord, bless his name. ℟.

Proclaim his help day by day,
tell among the nations his glory
and his wonders among all the peoples. ℟.

Give the Lord, you families of peoples,
give the Lord glory and power;
give the Lord the glory of his name. ℟.

Worship the Lord in his temple.
O earth, tremble before him.
Proclaim to the nations: "God is king."
He will judge the peoples in fairness. ℟.

READING II *1 Corinthians 12, 4-11 / 67*

There are different gifts but the same Spirit; there are different ministries but the same Lord; there are different works but the same God who accomplishes all of them in everyone. To each person the manifestation of the Spirit is given for the common good. To one the Spirit gives wisdom in discourse, to another the power to express knowledge. Through the Spirit one receives faith; by the same Spirit another is given the gift of healing, and still another miraculous powers. Prophecy is given to one; to another power to distinguish one spirit from another. One receives the gift of tongues, another that of interpreting the tongues. But it is one and the same Spirit who produces all these gifts, distributing them to each as he wills.

GOSPEL *John 2, 1-12 / 67*

There was a wedding at Cana in Galilee, and the mother of Jesus was there. Jesus and his disciples had likewise been invited to the celebration. At a certain point the wine ran out, and Jesus' mother told him, "They have no more wine." Jesus replied, "Woman, how does this concern of yours involve me? My hour has not yet come." His mother instructed those waiting on table, "Do whatever he tells you." As prescribed for Jewish ceremonial washings, there were at hand six stone water jars, each one holding fifteen to twenty-five gallons. "Fill those jars with water," Jesus ordered, at which they filled them to the brim. "Now," he said, "draw some out and take it to the waiter in charge." They did as he instructed them. The waiter in charge tasted the water made wine, without knowing where it had come from; only the waiters knew, since they had drawn the water. Then the waiter in charge called the groom over and remarked to him: "People usually serve the choice wine first; then when the guests have been drinking awhile, a lesser vintage. What you have done is keep the choice wine until now." Jesus performed this first of his signs at Cana in Galilee. Thus did he reveal his glory, and his disciples believed in him.

After this he went down to Capernaum, along with his mother and brothers [and his disciples] but they stayed there only a few days.

871 THIRD SUNDAY IN ORDINARY TIME/A

READING I *Isaiah 8, 23-9,3 / 68*

First he degraded the land of Zebulun and the land of Naphtali; but in the end he has glorified the seaward road, the land west of the Jordan, the District of the Gentiles.

Anguish has taken wing, dispelled is darkness:
for there is no gloom where but now there was distress.
The people who walked in darkness
have seen a great light;

Upon those who dwelt in the land of gloom
a light has shone.
You have brought them abundant joy
and great rejoicing,
As they rejoice before you as at the harvest,
as men make merry when dividing spoils.
For the yoke that burdened them,
the pole on their shoulder,
And the rod of their taskmaster
you have smashed, as on the day of Midian.

RESPONSORIAL PSALM *Psalm (26)27, 1.4.13-14 / 68*

RP
The Lord is my light and my sal - va - tion.

The Lord is my light and my help;
whom shall I fear?

The Lord is the stronghold of my life;
before whom shall I shrink? ℟.

There is one thing I ask of the Lord,
for this I long,
to live in the house of the Lord,
all the days of my life,
to savor the sweetness of the Lord,
to behold his temple. ℟.

I am sure I shall see the Lord's
goodness
in the land of the living.
Hope in him, hold firm and take heart.
Hope in the Lord! ℟.

READING II *1 Corinthians 1,10-13.17 / 68*

I beg you, brothers, in the name of our Lord Jesus Christ, to agree in what you say. Let there be no factions; rather, be united in mind and judgment. I have been informed, my brothers, by certain members of Chloe's household that you are quarreling among yourselves. This is what I mean: One of you will say, "I belong to Paul," another, "I belong to Apollos," still another, "Cephas has my allegiance," and the fourth, "I belong to Christ." Has Christ, then, been divided into parts? Was it Paul who was crucified for you? Was it in Paul's name that you were baptized? Christ did not send me to baptize but to preach the gospel–not with wordy "wisdom," however, lest the cross of Christ be rendered void of its meaning!

GOSPEL *Matthew 4, 12-23 or 4,12-17 / 68*

For short form read only the part in brackets.

[When Jesus heard that John had been arrested, he withdrew to Galilee. He left Nazareth and went down to live in Capernaum by the sea near the territory of Zebulun and Naphtali, to fulfill what had been said through Isaiah the prophet:

"Land of Zebulun, land of Naphtali
along the sea beyond the Jordan,
heathen, Galilee:
a people living in darkness
has seen a great light.
On those who inhabit a land overshadowed by death,
light has arisen."

From that time on Jesus began to proclaim this theme: "Reform your lives! The kingdom of heaven is at hand."]

As he was walking along the Sea of Galilee he watched two brothers, Simon now known as Peter, and his brother Andrew, casting a net into the sea. They were fishermen. He said to them, "Come after me and I will make you fishers of men." They immediately abandoned their nets and became his followers. He walked along farther and caught sight of two other brothers, James, Zebedee's son, and his brother John. They too were in their boat, getting their nets in order with their father, Zebedee. He called them, and immediately they abandoned boat and father to follow him.

Jesus toured all of Galilee. He taught in their synagogues, proclaimed the good news of the kingdom, and cured the people of every disease and illness.

THIRD SUNDAY IN ORDINARY TIME/B 872

READING I *Jonah 3, 1-5.10 / 69*

The word of the Lord came to Jonah saying: "Set out for the great city of Nineveh, and announce to it the message that I will tell you." So Jonah made ready and went to Nineveh according to the Lord's bidding. Now Nineveh was an enormously large city; it took three days to go through it. Jonah began his journey through the city, and had gone but a single day's walk announcing, "Forty days more and Nineveh shall be destroyed," when the people of Nineveh believed God; they proclaimed a fast and all of them, great and small, put on sackcloth.

When God saw by their actions how they turned from their evil way, he repented of the evil that he had threatened to do to them; he did not carry it out.

RESPONSORIAL PSALM *Psalm (24)25, 4-5.6-7.8-9 / 69*

RP
Teach me your ways, O Lord, teach me your ways.

Lord, make me know your ways.
Lord, teach me your paths.
Make me walk in your truth, and teach me,
for you are God my savior. ℟.

Remember your mercy, Lord,
and the love you have shown from of old.
In your love remember me,
because of your goodness, O Lord. ℟.

The Lord is good and upright.
He shows the path to those who stray,
he guides the humble in the right path,
he teaches his way to the poor. ℟.

READING II *1 Corinthians 7, 29-31 / 69*

I tell you, brothers, the time is short. From now on those with wives should live as though they had none; those who weep should live as though they were not weeping, and those who rejoice as though they were not rejoicing; buyers should conduct themselves as though they owned nothing, and those who make use of the world as though they were not using it, for the world as we know it is passing away.

GOSPEL *Mark 1, 14-20 / 69*

After John's arrest, Jesus appeared in Galilee proclaiming God's good news: "This is the time of fulfillment. The reign of God is at hand! Reform your lives and believe in the good news!"

As he made his way along the Sea of Galilee, he observed Simon and his brother Andrew casting their nets into the sea; they were fishermen. Jesus said to them, "Come after me; I will make you fishers of men." They immediately abandoned their nets and became his followers. Proceeding a little farther along, he caught sight of James, Zebedee's son, and his brother John. They too were in their boat putting their nets in order. He summoned them on the spot. They abandoned their father Zebedee, who was in the boat with the hired men, and went off in his company.

873 THIRD SUNDAY IN ORDINARY TIME/C

READING I *Nehemiah 8, 2-4.5-6.8-10 / 70*

Ezra the priest brought the law before the assembly, which consisted of men, women, and those children old enough to understand. Standing at one end of the open place that was before the Water Gate, he read out of the book from daybreak till midday, in the presence of the men, the women, and those children old enough to understand; and all the people listened attentively to the book of the law. Ezra the scribe stood on a wooden platform that had been made for the occasion. Ezra opened the scroll so that all the people might see it (for he was standing higher up than any of the people); and, as he opened it, all the people rose. Ezra blessed the Lord, the great God, and all the people, their hands raised high, answered, "Amen, amen!" Then they bowed down and prostrated themselves before the Lord, their faces to the ground. Ezra read plainly from the book of the law of God, interpreting it so that all could understand what was read. Then [Nehemiah, that is, His Excellency, and] Ezra the priest-scribe [and the Levites who were instructing the people] said to all the people: "Today is holy to the Lord your God. Do not be sad, and do not weep"–for all the people were weeping as they heard the words of the law. He said further: "Go, eat rich foods and drink sweet drinks, and allot portions to those who had nothing prepared; for today is holy to our Lord. Do not be saddened this day, for rejoicing in the Lord must be your strength!"

RESPONSORIAL PSALM *Psalm (18)19, 8.9.10.15 / 70*

CW
Your words, Lord, are spir - it and life.

The law of the Lord is perfect,
it revives the soul.
The rule of the Lord is to be trusted,
it gives wisdom to the simple. ℟.

The precepts of the Lord are right,
they gladden the heart.
The command of the Lord is clear,
it gives light to the eyes. ℟.

The fear of the Lord is holy,
abiding forever.
The decrees of the Lord are truth
and all of them just. ℟.

May the spoken words of my mouth,
the thoughts of my heart,
win favor in your sight, O Lord,
my rescuer, my rock! ℟.

READING II *1 Corinthians 12, 12-30 or 12, 12-14.27 / 70*

For short form read only the part in brackets.

[The body is one and has many members, but all the members, many though they are, are one body; and so it is with Christ. It was in one Spirit that all of us, whether Jew or Greek, slave or free, were baptized into one body. All of us have been given to drink of the one Spirit. Now the body is not one member, it is many.] If the foot should say, "Because I am not a hand I do not belong to the body," would it then no longer belong to the body? If the ear should say, "Because I am not an eye I do not belong to the body," would it then no longer belong to the body? If the body were all eye, what would happen to our hearing? If it were all ear, what would happen to our smelling? As it is, God has set each member of the body in the place he wanted it to be. If all the members were alike, where would the body be? There are, indeed, many different members, but one body. The eye cannot say to the hand, "I do not need you," any more than the head can say to the feet, "I do not need you." Even those members of the body which seem less important are in fact indispensable. We honor the members we consider less honorable by clothing them with greater care, thus bestowing on the less presentable a propriety which the more presentable already have. God has so constructed the body as to give greater honor to the lowly members, that there may be no dissension in the body, but that all the members may be concerned for one another. If one member suffers, all the members suffer with it; if one member is honored, all the members share its joy.

[You, then, are the body of Christ. Every one of you is a member of it.] Furthermore, God has set up in the church first apostles, second prophets, third teachers, then miracle workers, healers, assistants, administrators, and those who speak in tongues. Are all apostles? Are all prophets? Are all teachers? Do all work miracles or have the gift of healing? Do all speak in tongues, all have the gift of interpretation of tongues?

GOSPEL *Luke 1, 1-4; 4,14-21 / 70*

Many have undertaken to compile a narrative of the events which have been fulfilled in our midst, precisely as those events were transmitted to us by the original eye-witnesses and ministers of the word. I too have carefully traced the whole sequence of events from the beginning, and have decided to set it in writing for you, Theophilus, so that Your Excellency may see how reliable the instruction was that you received.

Jesus returned in the power of the Spirit to Galilee, and his reputation spread throughout the region. He was teaching in their synagogues, and all were loud in his praise.

He came to Nazareth where he had been reared, and entering the synagogue on the sabbath as he was in the habit of doing, he stood up to do the reading. When the book of the prophet Isaiah was handed him, he unrolled the scroll and found the passage where it was written:

"The spirit of the Lord is upon me;
therefore he has anointed me.
He has sent me to bring glad tidings to the poor,
to proclaim liberty to captives,
Recovery of sight to the blind
and release to prisoners,
To announce a year of favor from the Lord."

Rolling up the scroll he gave it back to the assistant and sat down. All in the synagogue had their eyes fixed on him. Then he began by saying to them, "Today this Scripture passage is fulfilled in your hearing."

874 FOURTH SUNDAY OF ORDINARY TIME / A

READING I *Zephaniah 2, 3; 3, 12-13 / 71*

Seek the Lord, all you humble of the earth,
who have observed his law;
Seek justice, seek humility;
perhaps you may be sheltered
on the day of the Lord's anger.

But I will leave as a remnant in your midst
a people humble and lowly,
Who shall take refuge in the name of the Lord:
the remnant of Israel.
They shall do no wrong
and speak no lies;
Nor shall there be found in their mouths
a deceitful tongue;
They shall pasture and couch their flocks
with none to disturb them.

RESPONSORIAL PSALM *Psalm (145)146, 6-7.8-9.9-10 / 71*

RP
Hap - py the poor in spir - it;
the king - dom of heav - en is theirs!

It is he who keeps faith for ever,
who is just to those who are oppressed.
It is he who gives bread to the hungry,
the Lord, who sets prisoners free. ℟.

The Lord who gives sight to the blind,
who raises up those who are bowed down.
It is the Lord who loves the just;
the Lord, who protects the stranger. ℟.

The Lord upholds the widow and orphan,
but thwarts the path of the wicked.
The Lord will reign for ever,
Zion's God, from age to age.
Alleluia. ℟.

READING II *1 Corinthians 1, 26-31 / 71*

Brothers, you are among those called. Consider your own situation. Not many of you are wise, as men account wisdom; not many are influential; and surely not many are well-born. God chose those whom the world considers absurd to shame the wise; he singled out the weak of this world to shame the strong. He chose the world's lowborn and despised, those who count for nothing, to reduce to nothing those who were something; so that mankind can do no boasting before God. God it is who has given you life in Christ Jesus. He has made him our wisdom and also our justice, our sanctification, and our redemption. This is just as you find it written, "Let him who would boast, boast in the Lord."

GOSPEL *Matthew 5, 1-12 / 71*

When Jesus saw the crowds, he went up on the mountainside. After he had sat down, his disciples gathered around him, and he began to teach them:

"How blest are the poor in spirit: the reign of God is theirs.
Blest too are the sorrowing; they shall be consoled.
[Blest are the lowly; they shall inherit the land.]
Blest are they who hunger and thirst for holiness; they shall have their fill.
Blest are they who show mercy; mercy shall be theirs.
Blest are the single-hearted, for they shall see God.
Blest too are the peacemakers; they shall be called sons of God.
Blest are those persecuted for holiness' sake; the reign of God is theirs.
Blest are you when they insult you and persecute you and utter every kind of slander against you because of me.
Be glad and rejoice, for your reward in heaven is great."

FOURTH SUNDAY IN ORDINARY TIME / B 875

READING I *Deuteronomy 18, 15-20 / 72*

Moses spoke to the people, saying: "A prophet like me will the Lord, your God, raise up for you from among your own kinsmen; to him you shall listen. This is exactly what you requested of the Lord, your God, at Horeb on the day of the assembly, when you said, 'Let us not again hear the voice of the Lord, our God, nor see this great fire any more, lest we die.' And the Lord said to me, 'This was well said. I will raise up for them a prophet like you from among their kinsmen, and will put my words into his mouth; he shall tell them all that I command him. If any man will not listen to my words which he speaks in my name, I myself will make him answer for it. But if a prophet presumes to speak in my name an oracle that I have not commanded him to speak, or speaks in the name of other gods, he shall die.' "

RESPONSORIAL PSALM *Psalm (94)95, 1-2.6-7.7-9 / 72*

RP
If to-day you hear his voice, O hard-en not your hearts.

Come, ring out our joy to the Lord;
hail the rock who saves us.
Let us come before him, giving thanks,
with songs let us hail the Lord. ℟.

Come in; let us bow and bend low;
let us kneel before the God who made us
for he is our God and we
the people who belong to his pasture,
the flock that is led by his hand. ℟.

O that today you would listen to his voice!
"Harden not your hearts as at Meribah,
as on that day at Massah in the desert
when your fathers put me to the test;
when they tried me, though they saw my work." ℟.

READING II *1 Corinthians 7, 32-35 / 72*

I should like you to be free of all worries. The unmarried man is busy with the Lord's affairs, concerned with pleasing the Lord; but the married man is busy with this world's demands and is occupied with pleasing his wife. This means he is divided. The virgin–indeed, any unmarried woman–is concerned with the things of the Lord, in pursuit of holiness in body and spirit. The married woman, on the other hand, has the cares of this world to absorb her and is concerned with pleasing her husband. I am going into this with you for your own good. I have no desire to place restrictions on you, but I do want to promote what is good, what will help you to devote yourselves entirely to the Lord.

GOSPEL *Mark 1.21-28 / 72*

[In the city of Capernaum,] Jesus entered the synagogue on the sabbath and began to teach. The people were spellbound by his teaching because he taught with authority and not like the scribes.

There appeared in their synagogue a man with an unclean spirit that shrieked: "What do you want of us, Jesus of Nazareth? Have you come to destroy us? I know who you are–the Holy One of God!" Jesus rebuked him sharply: "Be quiet! Come out of the man!" At that the unclean spirit convulsed the man violently and with a loud shriek came out of him. All who looked on were amazed. They began to ask one another: "What does this mean? A completely new teaching in a spirit of authority! He gives orders to unclean spirits and they obey him!" From that point on his reputation spread throughout the surrounding region of Galilee.

876 FOURTH SUNDAY IN ORDINARY TIME / C

READING I *Jeremiah 1, 4-5.17-19 / 73*

In the days of Josiah the word of the Lord came to me thus:
Before I formed you in the womb I
knew you,
before you were born I dedicated
you,
a prophet to the nations I appointed
you.

But do you gird your loins;
stand up and tell them
all that I command you.
Be not crushed on their account,
as though I would leave you crushed
before them;
For it is I this day
who have made you a fortified city,
A pillar of iron, a wall of brass,
against the whole land:
Against Judah's kings and princes,
against its priests and people.
They will fight against you, but not
prevail over you,
for I am with you to deliver you,
says the Lord.

RESPONSORIAL PSALM *Psalm (70)71, 1-2.3-4.5-6.15-17 / 73*

EE
I will sing of your sal - va - tion.

In you, O Lord, I take refuge;
let me never be put to shame.
In your justice rescue me, free me;
pay heed to me and save me. ℟.

Be a rock where I can take refuge,
a mighty stronghold to save me;
for you are my rock, my stronghold.
Free me from the hand of the
wicked. ℟.

It is you, O Lord, who are my hope,
my trust, O Lord, since my youth.
On you I have leaned from my birth,
from my mother's womb you have been
my help. ℟.

My lips will tell of your justice
and day by day of your help
O God, you have taught me from my
youth
and I proclaim your wonders still. ℟.

READING II *1 Corinthians 12, 31-13, 13 or 13, 4-13 / 73*

For short form read only the part in brackets.

Set your hearts on the greater gifts.

Now I will show you the way which surpasses all the others. If I speak with human tongues and angelic as well, but do not have love, I am a noisy gong, a clanging cymbal. If I have the gift of prophecy and, with full knowledge, comprehend all mysteries, if I have faith great enough to move mountains, but have not love, I am nothing. If I give everything I have to feed the poor and hand over my body to be burned, but have not love, I gain nothing.

[Love is patient; love is kind. Love is not jealous, it does not put on airs, it is not snobbish. Love is never rude, it is not self-seeking, it is not prone to anger; neither does it brood over injuries. Love does not rejoice in what is wrong but rejoices with the truth. There is no limit to love's forebearance, to its trust, its hope, its power to endure.

Love never fails. Prophecies will cease, tongues will be silent, knowledge will pass away. Our knowledge is imperfect and our prophesying is imperfect. When the perfect comes, the imperfect will pass away. When I was a child I used to talk like a child, think like a child, reason like a child. When I became a man I put childish ways aside. Now we see indistinctly, as in a mirror; then we shall see face to face. My knowledge is imperfect now; then I shall know even as I am known. There are in the end three things that last: faith, hope, and love, and the greatest of these is love.]

GOSPEL *Luke 4, 21-30 / 73*

Jesus began speaking in the synagogue: "Today this Scripture passage is fulfilled in your hearing." All who were present spoke favorably of him; they marveled at the appealing discourse which came from his lips. They also asked, "Is not this Joseph's son?"

He said to them, "You will doubtless quote me the proverb, 'Physician, heal yourself,' and say, 'Do here in your own country the things we have heard you have done in Capernaum.' But in fact," he went on, "no prophet gains acceptance in his native place. Indeed, let me remind you, there were many widows in Israel in the days of Elijah when the heavens remained closed for three and a half years and a great famine spread over the land. It was to none of these that Elijah was sent, but to a widow of Zarephath near Sidon. Recall, too, the many lepers in Israel in the time of Elisha the prophet; yet not one was cured except Naaman the Syrian."

At these words the whole audience in the synagogue was filled with indignation. They rose up and expelled him from the town, leading him to the brow of the hill on which it was built, and intending to hurl him over the edge. But he went straight through their midst and walked away.

FIFTH SUNDAY IN ORDINARY TIME / A 877

READING I *Isaiah 58, 7-10 / 74*

Thus says the Lord:
Share your bread with the hungry,
shelter the oppressed and the
homeless;

Clothe the naked when you see them,
and do not turn your back on your
own.

Then your light shall break forth like
the dawn,
and your wound shall quickly be
healed;
Your vindications shall go before you,
and the glory of the Lord shall be
your rear guard.
Then you shall call, and the Lord will
answer,
you shall cry for help, and he will
say: Here I am!

If you remove from your midst
oppression,
false accusation and malicious
speech;
If you bestow your bread on the hungry
and satisfy the afflicted;
Then light shall rise for you in the
darkness,
and the gloom shall become for you
like midday.

RESPONSORIAL PSALM *Psalm (111)112, 4-5.6-7.8-9 / 74*

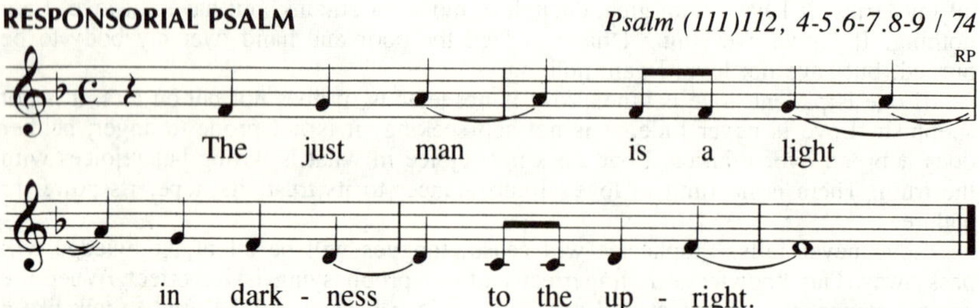
RP
The just man is a light in dark - ness to the up - right.

He is a light in the darkness for the
upright;
he is generous, merciful and just.
The good man takes pity and lends,
He conducts his affairs with
honor. ℟.

The just man will never waver;
he will be remembered for ever.
He has no fear of evil news;
with a firm heart he trusts in the
Lord. ℟.

With a steadfast heart he will not fear;
Open-handed, he gives to the poor;
His justice stands firm for ever.
His head will be raised in glory. ℟.

READING II *1 Corinthians 2, 1-5 / 74*

As for myself, brothers, when I came to you I did not come proclaiming God's testimony with any particular eloquence or "wisdom." No, I determined that while I was with you I would speak of nothing but Jesus Christ and him crucified. When I came among you it was in weakness and fear, and with much trepidation. My message and my preaching had none of the persuasive force of "wise" argumentation, but the convincing power of the Spirit. As a consequence, your faith rests not on the wisdom of men but on the power of God.

GOSPEL *Matthew 5, 13-16 / 74*

Jesus said to his disciples: "You are the salt of the earth. But what if salt goes flat? How can you restore its flavor? Then it is good for nothing but to be thrown out and trampled under foot.

"You are the light of the world. A city set on a hill cannot be hidden. Men do not light a lamp and then put it under a bushel basket. They set it on a stand where it gives light to all in the house. In the same way, your light must shine before men so that they may see goodness in your acts and give praise to your heavenly Father."

FIFTH SUNDAY IN ORDINARY TIME / B

878

READING I *Job 7, 1-4.6-7 / 75*

Job spoke, saying:
Is not man's life on earth a drudgery?
Are not his days those of a hireling?
He is a slave who longs for the shade,
a hireling who waits for his wages.
So I have been assigned months of misery,
and troubled nights have been told off for me.

If in bed I say, "When shall I arise?"
then the night drags on;
I am filled with restlessness until the dawn.

My days are swifter than a weaver's shuttle;
they come to an end without hope.
Remember that my life is like the wind;
I shall not see happiness again.

RESPONSORIAL PSALM *Psalm (146)147, 1-2.3-4.5-6 / 75*

MJ
Praise the Lord, praise the Lord, who
heals the brok - en - heart - ed.

Praise the Lord for he is good;
sing to our God for he is loving:
to him our praise is due.
The Lord builds up Jerusalem
and brings back Israel's exiles. ℟.

He heals the broken-hearted,
he binds up all their wounds.
He fixes the number of the stars;
he calls each one by its name. ℟.

Our Lord is great and almighty;
his wisdom can never be measured.
The Lord raises the lowly;
he humbles the wicked to the dust. ℟.

READING II *1 Corinthians 9, 16-19.22-23 / 75*

Preaching the gospel is not the subject of a boast; I am under compulsion and have no choice. I am ruined if I do not preach it! If I do it willingly, I have my recompense; if unwillingly, I am nonetheless entrusted with a charge. And this recompense; if unwillingly, I am nonetheless entrusted with a charge. And the recompense of mine? It is simply this, that when preaching I offer the gospel free of charge and do not make full use of the authority the gospel gives me.

Although I am not bound to anyone, I made myself the slave of all so as to win over as many as possible. To the weak I became a weak person with a view to winning the weak. I have made myself all things to all men in order to save at least some of them. In fact, I do all that I do for the sake of the gospel in the hope of having a share in its blessings.

GOSPEL *Mark 1, 29-39 / 75*

Upon leaving the synagogue, Jesus entered the house of Simon and Andrew with James and John. Simon's mother-in-law lay ill with a fever, and the first thing they did was to tell him about her. He went over to her and grasped her hand and helped her up, and the fever left her. She immediately began to wait on them.

After sunset, as evening drew on, they brought him all who were ill and those possessed by demons. Before long the whole town was gathered outside the door. Those whom he cured, who were variously afflicted, were many, and so were the demons he expelled. But he would not permit the demons to speak, because they knew him. Rising early the next morning, he went off to a lonely place in the desert; there he was absorbed in prayer. Simon and his companions managed to track him down; and when they found him, they told him, "Everybody is looking for you!" He said to them: "Let us move on to the neighboring villages so that I may proclaim the good news there also. That is what I have come to do." So he went into their synagogues preaching the good news and expelling demons throughout the whole of Galilee.

879 FIFTH SUNDAY IN ORDINARY TIME / C

READING I

Isaiah 6, 1-2.3-8 / 76

In the year King Uzziah died, I saw the Lord seated on a high and lofty throne, with the train of his garment filling the temple. Seraphim were stationed above.

"Holy, holy, holy, is the Lord of hosts!" they cried one to the other. "All the earth is filled with his glory!" At the sound of that cry, the frame of the door shook and the house was filled with smoke.

Then I said, "Woe is me, I am doomed! For I am a man of unclean lips, living among a people of unclean lips; yet my eyes have seen the King, the Lord of hosts!" Then one of the seraphim flew to me, holding an ember which he had taken with tongs from the altar.

He touched my mouth with it. "See," he said, "now that this has touched your lips, your wickedness is removed, your sin purged."

Then I heard the voice of the Lord saying, "Whom shall I send? Who will go for us?" "Here I am," I said; "send me!"

RESPONSORIAL PSALM

Psalm (137) 138, 1-2.2-3.4-5.7-8 / 76

RMH
In the sight of the an-gels I will sing your prais-es, Lord.

I thank you, Lord, with all my heart,
you have heard the words of my mouth.
In the presence of the angels I will
bless you.
I will adore before your holy
temple. ℟.

I thank you for your faithfulness and
love
which excel all we ever knew of you.
On the day I called, you answered;
you increased the strength of my
soul. ℟.

All earth's kings shall thank you
when they hear the words of your
mouth.
They shall sing of the Lord's ways:
"How great is the glory of the
Lord!" ℟.

You stretch out your hand and save me,
your hand will do all things for me.
Your love, O Lord, is eternal,
discard not the work of your hands. ℟.

READING II

1 Corinthians 15, 1-11 or 15, 3-8.11 / 76

For short form read only the part in brackets.

[Brothers,] I want to remind you of the gospel I preached to you, which you received and in which you stand firm. You are being saved by it at this very moment if you retain it as I preached it to you. Otherwise you have believed in vain. [I handed on to you first of all what I myself received, that Christ died for our sins in accord with the Scriptures; that he was buried and, in accord with the Scriptures, rose on the third day; that he was seen by Cephas, then by the Twelve. After that he was seen by five hundred brothers at once, most of whom are still alive, although some have fallen asleep. Next he was seen by James; then by all the apostles. Last of all he was seen by me, as one born out of the normal course.] I am the least of the apostles; in fact, because I persecuted the church of God, I do not even deserve the name. But by God's favor I am what I am. This favor of his to me has not proved fruitless. Indeed, I have worked harder than all the others, not on my own but through the favor of God. [In any case, whether it be I or they, this is what we preach and this is what you believed.]

GOSPEL *Luke 5, 1-11 / 76*

As the crowd pressed in on Jesus to hear the word of God, he saw two boats moored by the side of the lake; the fishermen had disembarked and were washing their nets. He got into one of the boats, the one belonging to Simon, and asked him to pull out a short distance from the shore; then, remaining seated, he continued to teach the crowds from the boat. When he had finished speaking he said to Simon, "Put out into deep water and lower your nets for a catch." Simon answered, "Master, we have been hard at it all night long and have caught nothing; but if you say so, I will lower the nets." Upon doing this they caught such a great number of fish that their nets were at the breaking point. They signaled to their mates in the other boat to come and help them. These came, and together they filled the two boats until they nearly sank.

At the sight of this, Simon Peter fell at the knees of Jesus saying, "Leave me, Lord. I am a sinful man." For indeed, amazement at the catch they had made seized him and all his shipmates, as well as James and John, Zebedee's sons, who were partners with Simon. Jesus said to Simon, "Do not be afraid. From now on you will be catching men." With that they brought their boats to land, left everything, and became his followers.

SIXTH SUNDAY IN ORDINARY TIME / A 880

READING I *Sirach 15, 15-20 / 77*

If you choose you can keep the commandments;
it is loyalty to do his will.
There are set before you fire and water;
to whichever you choose, stretch forth your hand.
Before man are life and death,
whichever he chooses shall be given him.
Immense is the wisdom of the Lord;
he is mighty in power, and all-seeing.
The eyes of God see all he has made;
he understands man's every deed.
No man does he command to sin,
to none does he give strength for lies.

RESPONSORIAL PSALM *Psalm (118)119, 1-2.4-5.17-18.33-34 / 77*

RP
Hap - py are they who fol-low the law of the Lord!

They are happy whose life is blameless,
who follow God's law!
They are happy who do his will,
seeking him with all their hearts. ℞.

You have laid down your precepts
to be obeyed with care.
May my footsteps be firm
to obey your statutes. ℞.

Bless your servant and I shall live
and obey your word.
Open my eyes that I may see
the wonders of your law. ℟.

Teach me the demands of your statutes
and I will keep them to the end.
Train me to observe your law,
to keep it with my heart. ℟.

READING II *1 Corinthians 2, 6-10 / 77*

There is, to be sure, a certain wisdom which we express among the spiritually mature. It is not a wisdom of this age, however, nor of the rulers of this age who are men headed for destruction. No, what we utter is God's wisdom: a mysterious, a hidden wisdom. God planned it before all ages for our glory. None of the rulers of this age knew the mystery; if they had known it, they would never have crucified the Lord of glory. Of this wisdom it is written:

"Eye has not seen, ear has not heard,
nor has it so much as dawned on man
what God has prepared for those who love him."

Yet God has revealed this wisdom to us through the Spirit. The Spirit scrutinizes all matters, even the deep things of God.

GOSPEL *Matthew 5, 17-37 or 5, 20-22.27-28.33-34.37 / 77*

For short form read only the part in brackets.

[Jesus said to his disciples:] "Do not think that I have come to abolish the law and the prophets. I have come, not to abolish them, but to fufill them. Of this much I assure you: until heaven and earth pass away, not the smallest letter of the law, nor the smallest part of a letter, shall be done away with until it all comes true. That is why whoever breaks the least significant of these commands and teaches others to do so shall be called least in the kingdom of God. Whoever fulfills and teaches these commands shall be great in the kingdom of God. [I tell you, unless your holiness surpasses that of the scribes and Pharisees you shall not enter the kingdom of God.

"You have heard the commandment imposed on your forefathers, 'You shall not commit murder; every murderer will be liable to judgement.' What I say to you is: everyone who grows angry with his brother will be liable to judgement;] any man who uses abusive language toward his brother shall be answerable to the Sanhedrin, and if he holds him in contempt he risks the fires of Gehenna. If you bring your gift to the altar and there recall that your brother has anything against you, leave your gift at the altar, go first to be reconciled with your brother, and then come and offer your gift. Lose no time; settle with your opponent while on your way to court with him. Otherwise your opponent may hand you over to the judge, who will hand you over to the guard, who will throw you into prison. I warn you, you will not be released until you have paid the last penny.

["You have heard the commandment, 'You shall not commit adultery.' What I say to you is anyone who looks lustfully at a woman has already committed adultery with her in his thoughts.] If your right eye is your trouble, gouge it out and throw it away! Better to lose part of your body than to have it all cast into Gehenna. Again, if your right hand is your trouble, cut it off and throw it away! Better to lose part of your body than to have it all cast into Gehenna.

"It was also said, 'Whenever a man divorces his wife, he must give her a decree of divorce.' What I say to you is: everyone who divorces his wife–lewd conduct is a separate case–forces her to commit adultery. The man who marries a divorced woman likewise commits adultery.

["You have heard the commandment imposed on your forefathers, 'Do not take a false oath; rather make good to the Lord all your pledges.' What I tell you is: do not swear at all.] Do not swear by heaven (it is God's throne), nor by the earth (it is his footstool), nor by Jerusalem (it is the city of the great King); do not swear by your head (you cannot make a single hair white or black). [Say, 'Yes' when you mean 'Yes' and 'No' when you mean 'No.' Anything beyond that is from the evil one."]

SIXTH SUNDAY IN ORDINARY TIME / B 881

READING I *Leviticus 13, 1-2.44-46 / 78*

The Lord said to Moses and Aaron, "If someone has on his skin a scab or pustule or blotch which appears to be the sore of leprosy, he shall be brought to Aaron, the priest, or to one of the priests among his descendants. If the man is leprous and unclean, the priest shall declare him unclean by reason of the sore on his head.

"The one who bears the sore of leprosy shall keep his garments rent and his head bare, and shall muffle his beard; he shall cry out, 'Unclean, unclean!' As long as the sore is on him he shall declare himself unclean, since he is in fact unclean. He shall dwell apart, making his abode outside the camp."

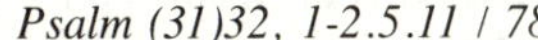

RESPONSORIAL PSALM *Psalm (31)32, 1-2.5.11 / 78*

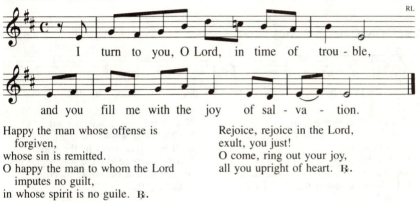

RL
I turn to you, O Lord, in time of trou - ble,
and you fill me with the joy of sal - va - tion.

Happy the man whose offense is
forgiven,
whose sin is remitted.
O happy the man to whom the Lord
imputes no guilt,
in whose spirit is no guile. ℟.

But now I have acknowledged my sins;
my guilt I did not hide.
I said: "I will confess my offense to the
Lord."
And you, Lord, have forgiven the guilt
of my sin. ℟.

Rejoice, rejoice in the Lord,
exult, you just!
O come, ring out your joy,
all you upright of heart. ℟.

READING II *1 Corinthians 10, 31-11, 1 / 78*

Whether you eat or drink–whatever you do–you should do all for the glory of God. Give no offense to Jew or Greek or to the church of God, just as I try to please all in any way I can by seeking not my own advantage, but that of the many that they may be saved. Imitate me as I imitate Christ.

GOSPEL *Mark 1, 40-45 / 78*

A leper approached Jesus with a request, kneeling down as he addressed him: "If you will to do so, you can cure me." Moved with pity, Jesus stretched out his hand, touched him, and said: "I do will it. Be cured." The leprosy left him then and there, and he was cured. Jesus gave him a stern warning and sent him on his way. "Not a word to anyone, now," he said. "Go off and present yourself to the priest and offer for your cure what Moses prescribed. That should be a proof for them." The man went off and began to proclaim the whole matter freely, making the story public. As a result of this, it was no longer possible for Jesus to enter a town openly. He stayed in desert places; yet people kept coming to him from all sides.

882 SIXTH SUNDAY IN ORDINARY TIME / C

READING I *Jeremiah 17,5-8 / 79*

Thus says the Lord:
Cursed is the man who trusts in human beings,
who seeks his strength in flesh,
whose heart turns away from the Lord.
He is like a barren bush in the desert
that enjoys no change of season,
But stands in a lava waste,
a salt and empty earth.
Blessed is the man who trusts in the Lord,
whose hope is the Lord.
He is like a tree planted beside the waters
that stretches out its roots to the stream:
It fears not the heat when it comes,
its leaves stay green;
In the year of drought it shows no distress,
but still bears fruit.

RESPONSORIAL PSALM *Psalm 1, 1-2.3.4.6 / 79*

RJT
Hap-py are they who hope, who hope in the Lord.

Happy indeed is the man
who follows not the counsel of the wicked,
nor lingers in the way of sinners
nor sits in the company of scorners,
but whose delight is the law of the Lord
and who ponders his law day and night. ℟.

He is like a tree that is planted
beside the flowing waters,
that yields its fruit in due season
and whose leaves shall never fade;
and all that he is shall prosper. ℟.

Not so are the wicked, not so!
For they like winnowed chaff
shall be driven away by the wind.
For the Lord guards the way of the just
but the way of the wicked leads to doom. ℟.

READING II *1 Corinthians 15, 12.16-20 / 79*

If Christ is preached as raised from the dead, how is it that some of you say there is no resurrectrion of the dead? If the dead are not raised, then Christ was not raised; and if Christ was not raised, your faith is worthless. You are still in your sins, and those who have fallen asleep in Christ are the deadest of the dead. If our hopes in Christ are limited to this life only, we are the most pitiable of men.

But as it is, Christ has been raised from the dead, the first fruits of those who have fallen asleep.

GOSPEL *Luke 6, 17.20-26 / 79*

When Jesus came down the mountain, he stopped at a level stretch where there were many of his disciples; a large crowd of people was with them from all Judea and Jerusalem and the coast of Tyre and Sidon. Then, raising his eyes to his disciples, he said:

"Blest are you poor; the reign of God is yours.
Blest are you who hunger; filled you shall be.

Blest are you who are weeping; you shall laugh.

"Blest shall you be when men hate you, when they ostracize you and insult you and proscribe your name as evil because of the Son of Man. On the day they do so, rejoice and exult, for your reward shall be great in heaven. Thus it was that their fathers treated the prophets.

"But woe to you rich, for your consolation is now.
Woe to you who are full; you shall go hungry.
Woe to you who laugh now; you shall weep in your grief.
"Woe to you when all speak well of you.
Their fathers treated the false prophets in just this way."

SEVENTH SUNDAY IN ORDINARY TIME / A 883

READING I *Leviticus 19, 1-2.17-18 / 80*

The Lord said to Moses, "Speak to the whole Israelite community and tell them: Be holy, for I, the Lord, your God, am holy.

"You shall not bear hatred for your brother in your heart. Though you may have to reprove your fellow man, do not incur sin because of him. Take no revenge and cherish no grudge against your fellow countrymen. You shall love your neighbor as yourself. I am the Lord."

RESPONSORIAL PSALM *Psalm (102)103, 1-2.3-4.8.10.12.12-13 / 80*

DRH
The Lord is kind and mer - ci - ful.

My soul, give thanks to the Lord,
all my being, bless his holy name.
My soul, give thanks to the Lord
and never forget all his blessings. ℟.

It is he who forgives all your guilt,
who heals every one of your ills,
who redeems your life from the grave,
who crowns you with love and compassion. ℟.

The Lord is compassion and love,
slow to anger and rich in mercy.
He does not treat us according to our sins
nor repay us according to our faults. ℟.

As far as the east is from the west
so far does he remove our sins.
As a father has compassion on his sons,
the Lord has pity on those who fear him. ℟.

READING II *1 Corinthians 3, 16-23 / 80*

Are you not aware that you are the temple of God, and that the Spirit of God dwells in you? If anyone destroys God's temple, God will destroy him. For the temple of God is holy, and you are that temple.

Let no one delude himself. If any one of you thinks he is wise in a worldly way, he had better become a fool. In that way he will really be wise, for the wisdom of this world is absurdity with God. Scripture says, "He catches the wise in their craftiness"; and again, "The Lord knows how empty are the thoughts of the wise." Let there be no boasting about men. All things are yours, whether it be Paul, or Apollos, or Cephas, or the world, or life, or death, or the present, or the future: all these are yours, and you are Christ's and Christ is God's.

GOSPEL *Matthew 5, 38-48 / 80*

Jesus said to his disciples: "You have heard the commandment, 'An eye for and eye, a tooth for a tooth.' But what I say to you is: offer no resistance to injury. When a person strikes you on the right cheek, turn and offer the other. If anyone wants to go to law over your shirt, hand him your coat as well. Should anyone press you into service for one mile, go with him two miles. Give to the man who begs from you. Do not turn your back on the borrower.

"You have heard the commandment, 'You shall love your countryman but hate your enemy.' My command to you is: Love your enemies, pray for your persecutors. This will prove that you are sons of your heavenly Father, for his sun rises on the bad and the good, he rains on the just and the unjust. If you love those who love you, what merit is there in that? Do not tax collectors do as much? And if you greet your brothers only, what is so praiseworthy about that? Do not pagans do as much? In a word, you must be perfected as your heavenly Father is perfect."

884 SEVENTH SUNDAY IN ORDINARY TIME / B

READING I *Isaiah 43, 18-19.21-22.24-25 / 81*

Thus says the Lord:
Remember not the events of the past,
  the things of long ago consider not;
See, I am doing something new!
  Now it springs forth, do you not
    perceive it?
In the desert I make a way,
  in the wasteland, rivers.
The people whom I formed for myself,
  that they might announce my praise.
Yet you did not call upon me, O Jacob,
  for you grew weary of me, O Israel.
You burdened me with your sins,
  and wearied me with your crimes.
It is I, I, who wipe out,
  for my own sake, your offenses;
  your sins I remember no more.

RESPONSORIAL PSALM *Psalm (40)41, 2-3.4-5.13-14 / 81*

JRC
Lord, heal my soul, for I have sinned a - gainst you.

Happy the man who considers the poor
  and the weak.
The Lord will save him in the day of evil,
will guard him, give him life, make
  him happy in the land
and will not give him up to the will of
  his foes. ℟.

The Lord will help him on his bed
  of pain,
he will bring him back from sickness to
  health.
As for me, I said: "Lord, have mercy
  on me,
heal my soul for I have sinned against
  you." ℟.

If you uphold me I shall be unharmed
and set in your presence for evermore.
Blessed be the Lord, the God of Israel
from age to age. Amen. Amen. ℟.

READING II *2 Corinthians 1, 18-22 / 81*

As God keeps his word, I declare that my word to you is not "yes" one minute and "no" the next. Jesus Christ, whom Silvanus, Timothy, and I preached to you as Son of God, was not alternately "yes" and "no"; he was never anything but "yes." Whatever promises God has made have been fulfilled in him; therefore it is through him that we address our Amen to God when we worship together. God is the one who firmly establishes us along with you in Christ; it is he who anointed us and has sealed us, thereby depositing the first payment, the Spirit in our hearts.

GOSPEL *Mark 2, 1-12 / 81*

After a lapse of several days Jesus came back to Capernaum and word got around that he was at home. At that they began to gather in great numbers. There was no longer any room for them, even around the door. While he was delivering God's word to them, some people arrived bringing a paralyzed man to him. The four who carried him were unable to bring him to Jesus because of the crowd, so they began to open up the roof over the spot where Jesus was. When they had made a hole, they let down the mat on which the paralytic was lying. When Jesus saw their faith, he said to the paralyzed man, "My son, your sins are forgiven." Now some of the scribes were sitting there asking themselves: "Why does the man talk in that way? He commits blasphemy! Who can forgive sins except God alone?" Jesus was immediately aware of their reasoning though they kept it to themselves, and he said to them: "Why do you harbor these thoughts? Which is easier, to say to the paralytic, 'Your sins are forgiven,' or to say, 'Stand up, pick up your mat, and walk again'? That you may know that the Son of Man has authority on earth to forgive sins" (he said to the paralyzed man), "I command you: Stand up! Pick up your mat and go home." The man stood and picked up his mat and went outside in the sight of everyone. They were awestruck; all gave praise to God, saying, "We have never seen anything like this!"

SEVENTH SUNDAY IN ORDINARY TIME/C 885

READING I *1 Samuel 26, 2.7-9.12-13.22-23 / 82*

Saul went off down to the desert of Ziph with three thousand picked men of Israel, to search for David in the desert of Ziph. So David and Abishai went among Saul's soldiers by night and found Saul lying asleep within the barricade, with his spear thrust into the ground at his head and Abner and his men sleeping around him.

Abishai whispered to David: "God has delivered your enemy into your grasp this day. Let me nail him to the ground with one thrust of the spear; I will not need a second thrust!" But David said to Abishai, "Do not harm him, for who can lay hands on the Lord's anointed and remain unpunished? So David took the spear and the water jug from their place at Saul's head, and they got away without anyone's seeing or knowing or awakening. All remained asleep, because the Lord had put them into a deep slumber.

Going across to an opposite slope, David stood on a remote hilltop at a great distance from Abner, Son of Ner, and the troops. He said: "Here is the king's spear. Let an attendant come over to get it. The Lord will reward each man for his justice and faithfulness. Today, though the Lord delivered you into my grasp, I would not harm the Lord's anointed."

RESPONSORIAL PSALM *Psalm (102)103, 1-2.3-4.8.10.12-13 / 82*

DRH
The Lord is kind and mer - ci - ful.

My soul, give thanks to the Lord,
all my being, bless his holy name.
My soul, give thanks to the Lord
and never forget all his blessings. ℟.

It is he who forgives all your guilt,
who heals every one of your ills,
who redeems your life from the grave,
who crowns you with love and
compassion. ℟.

The Lord is compassion and love,
slow to anger and rich in mercy.
He does not treat us according to our sins
nor repay us according to our faults. ℟.

As far as the east is from the west
so far does he remove our sins.
As a father has compassion on his sons,
the Lord has pity on those who fear him. ℟.

READING II *1 Corinthians 15, 45-49 / 82*

Scripture has it that Adam, the first man, became a living soul; the last Adam has become a life-giving spirit. Notice the spiritual was not first; first came the natural and after that the spiritual. The first man was of earth, formed from dust, the second is from heaven. Earthly men are like the man of earth, heavenly men are like the man of heaven. Just as we resemble the man from earth, so shall we bear the likeness of the man from heaven.

GOSPEL *Luke 6, 27-38 / 82*

Jesus said to his disciples: "To you who hear me, I say: Love your enemies, do good to those who hate you; bless those who curse you and pray for those who maltreat you. When someone slaps you on one cheek, turn and give him the other; when someone takes your coat, let him have your shirt as well. Give to all who beg from you. When a man takes what is yours, do not demand it back. Do to others what you would have them do to you. If you love those who love you, what credit is that to you? Even sinners love those who love them. If you do good to those who do good to you, how can you claim any credit? Sinners do as much. If you lend to those from whom you expect repayment, what merit is there in it for you? Even sinners lend to sinners, expecting to be repaid in full.

"Love your enemy and do good; lend without expecting repayment. Then will your recompense be great. You will rightly be called sons of the Most High, since he himself is good to the ungrateful and the wicked.

"Be compassionate, as your Father is compassionate. Do not judge, and you will not be judged. Do not condemn, and you will not be condemned. Pardon, and you shall be pardoned. Give, and it shall be given to you. Good measure pressed down, shaken together, running over, will they pour into the fold of your garment. For the measure you measure will be measured back to you."

886 EIGHTH SUNDAY IN ORDINARY TIME / A

READING I *Isaiah 49, 14-15 / 83*

Zion said, "The Lord has forsaken me;
my Lord has forgotten me."
Can a mother forget her infant,
be without tenderness for the child of her womb?

Even should she forget,
I will never forget you.

RESPONSORIAL PSALM *Psalm (61)62, 2-3.6-7.8-9 / 83*

RJB
Rest in God a - lone, rest in God a - lone, my soul, my soul.

In God alone is my soul at rest;
my help comes from him.

He alone is my rock, my stronghold,
my fortress; I stand firm. ℟.

In God alone be at rest, my soul,
for my hope comes from him.
He alone is my rock, my stronghold,
my fortress; I stand firm. ℟.

In God is my safety and glory,
the rock of my strength.
Take refuge in God, all you people.
Trust him at all times.
Pour out your hearts before him. ℟.

READING II *1 Corinthians 4, 1-5 / 83*

Men should regard us as servants of Christ and administrators of the mysteries of God. The first requirement of an administrator is that he prove trustworthy. It matters little to me whether you or any human court pass judgment on me. I do not even pass judgment on myself. Mind you, I have nothing on my conscience. But that does not mean that I am declaring myself innocent. The Lord is the one to judge me, so stop passing judgment before the time of his return. He will bring to light what is hidden in darkness and manifest the intentions of hearts. At that time, everyone will receive his praise from God.

GOSPEL *Matthew 6, 24-34 / 83*

Jesus said to his disciples: "No man can serve two masters. He will either hate one and love the other or be attentive to one and despise the other. You cannot give yourself to God and money. I warn you, then: do not worry about your livelihood, what you are to eat or drink or use for clothing. Is not life more than food? Is not the body more valuable than clothes?

"Look at the birds in the sky. They do not sow or reap, they gather nothing into barns; yet your heavenly Father feeds them. Are not you more important then they? Which of you by worrying can add a moment to his lifespan? As for clothes, why be concerned? Learn a lesson from the way the wild flowers grow. They do not work; they do not spin. Yet I assure you, not even Solomon in all his splendor was arrayed like one of these. If God can clothe in such splendor the grass of the field, which blooms today and is thrown on the fire tomorrow, will he not provide much more for you, O weak in faith! Stop worrying, then, over questions like, 'What are we to eat, or what are we to drink, or what are we to wear?' The unbelievers are always running after these things. Your heavenly Father knows all that you need. Seek first his kingship over you, his way of holiness, and all these things will be given you besides. Enough, then, of worrying about tomorrow. Let tomorrow take care of itself. Today has enough troubles of its own."

EIGHTH SUNDAY IN ORDINARY TIME/B 887

READING I *Hosea 2, 16-17.21-22 / 84*

Thus says the Lord:
I will lead her into the desert
and speak to her heart.
She shall respond there as in the days of
her youth,
when she came up from the land of
Egypt.

I will espouse you to me forever:
I will espouse you in right and in
justice,
in love and in mercy;
I will espouse you in fidelity,
and you shall know the Lord.

RESPONSORIAL PSALM *Psalm (102)103, 1-2.3-4.8.10.12-13 / 84*

DRH
The Lord is kind and mer - ci - ful.

My soul, give thanks to the Lord,
all my being, bless his holy name.

My soul, give thanks to the Lord
and never forget all his blessings. ℟.

It is he who forgives all your guilt,
who heals every one of your ills,
who redeems your life from the grave,
who crowns you with love and
compassion. ℟.

As far as the east is from the west
so far does he remove our sins.
As a father has compassion on his
sons,
the Lord has pity on those who fear
him. ℟.

The Lord is compassion and love,
slow to anger and rich in mercy.
He does not treat us according to our
sins
nor repay us according to our faults. ℟.

READING II *2 Corinthians 3, 1-6 / 84*

Do I need letters of recommendation to you or from you as others might? You are my letter, known and read by all men, written on your hearts. Clearly you are a letter of Christ which I have delivered, a letter written not with ink but by the Spirit of the living God, not on tablets of stone but on tablets of flesh in the heart.

This great confidence in God is ours, through Christ. It is not that we are entitled of ourselves to take credit for anything. Our sole credit is from God, who has made us qualified ministers of a new covenant, a covenant, not of a written law but of spirit. The written law kills, but the Spirit gives life.

GOSPEL *Mark 2, 18-22 / 84*

John's disciples and the Pharisees were accustomed to fast. People came to Jesus with the objection, "Why do John's disciples and those of the Pharisees fast while yours do not?" Jesus replied: "How can the guests at a wedding fast as long as the groom is still among them? So long as the groom stays with them, they cannot fast. The day will come, however, when the groom will be taken away from them; on that day they will fast. No one sews a patch of unshrunken cloth on an old cloak. If he should do so, the very thing he used to cover the hole would pull away–the new from the old–and the tear would get worse. Similarly, no man pours new wine into the old wine-skins. If he does so, the wine will burst the skins and both wine and skins will be lost. No, new wine is poured into new skins."

888 EIGHTH SUNDAY IN ORDINARY TIME / C

READING I *Sirach 27, 4-7 / 85*

When a sieve is shaken, the husks
appear;
so do a man's faults when he speaks.
As the test of what the potter molds is
in the furnace,
so in his conversation is the test of a
man.

The fruit of a tree shows the care it has
had;
so too does a man's speech disclose
the bent of his mind.
Praise no man before he speaks,
for it is then that men are tested.

RESPONSORIAL PSALM *Psalm (91)92, 2-3.13-14.15-16 / 85*

RP
Lord, it is good to give thanks to you.

It is good to give thanks to the Lord,
to make music to your name, O Most
High,

to proclaim your love in the morning
and your truth in the watches of the
night. ℟.

The just will flourish like the palm tree
and grow like a Lebanon cedar.
Planted in the house of the Lord
they will flourish in the courts of our
God. ℟.

Still bearing fruit when they are old,
still full of sap, still green,
to proclaim that the Lord is just.
In him, my rock, there is no wrong. ℟.

READING II *1 Corinthians 15, 54-58 / 85*

When the corruptible frame takes on incorruptibility and the mortal immortality, then will the saying of Scripture be fulfilled: "Death is swallowed up in victory." "O death, where is your victory? O death, where is your sting?" The sting of death is sin, and sin gets its power from the law. But thanks be to God who has given us the victory through our Lord Jesus Christ. Be steadfast and persevering, my beloved brothers, fully engaged in the work of the Lord. You know that your toil is not in vain when it is done in the Lord.

GOSPEL *Luke 6, 39-45 / 85*

Jesus used images in speaking to the disciples: "Can a blind man act as guide to a blind man? Will they not both fall into a ditch? A student is not above his teacher; but every student when he has finished his studies will be on a par with his teacher.

"Why look at the speck in your brother's eye when you miss the plank in your own? How can you say to your brother, 'Brother let me remove the speck from your eye' yet fail yourself to see the plank lodged in your own? Hypocrite, remove the plank from your own eye first; then you will see clearly enough to remove the speck from your brother's eye.

"A good tree does not produce decayed fruit any more then a decayed tree produces good fruit. Each tree is known by its yield. Figs are not taken from thornbushes, nor grapes picked from brambles. A good man produces goodness from the good in his heart; an evil man produces evil out of his store of evil. Each man speaks from his heart's abundance."

NINTH SUNDAY IN ORDINARY TIME / A 889

READING I *Deuteronomy 11, 18.26-28 / 86*

Moses told the people, "Take these words of mine into your heart and soul. Bind them at your wrist as a sign, and let them be a pendant on your forehead.

"I set before you here, this day, a blessing and a curse: a blessing for obeying the commandments of the Lord, your God, which I enjoin on you today; a curse if you do not obey the commandments of the Lord, your God, but turn aside from the way I ordain for you today, to follow other gods, whom you have not known."

RESPONSORIAL PSALM *Psalm (30)31, 2-3.3-4.17.25 / 86*

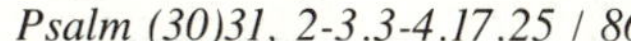

MK
Lord, Lord, be my rock of safe - ty.

In you, O Lord, I take refuge.
Let me never be put to shame.
In your justice, set me free,
hear me and speedily rescue me. ℟.

Be a rock of refuge for me,
a mighty stronghold to save me,
for you are my rock, my stronghold.
For your name's sake, lead me and
guide me. ℟.

Let your face shine on your servant.
Save me in your love.
Be strong, let your heart take courage,
all who hope in the Lord. ℟.

READING II *Romans 3, 21-25.28 / 86*

Now the justice of God has been manifested apart from the law, even though both law and prophets bear witness to it–that justice of God which works through faith in Jesus Christ for all who believe. All men have sinned and hence are deprived of the glory of God. All men are now undeservedly justified by the gift of God, through the redemption wrought in Christ Jesus. Through his blood, God made him the means of expiation for all who believe.

For we hold that a man is justified by faith apart from observance of the law.

GOSPEL *Matthew 7, 21-27 / 86*

Jesus said to his disciples: "None of those who cry out, 'Lord, Lord' will enter the kingdom of God but only the one who does the will of my Father in heaven. When that day comes, many will plead with me, 'Lord, Lord, have we not prophesied in your name? Have we not exorcised demons by its power? Did we not do many miracles in your name as well?' Then I will declare to them solemnly, 'I never knew you. Out of my sight, you evildoers!'

"Anyone who hears my words and puts them into practice is like the wise man who built his house on rock. When the rainy season set in, the torrents came and the winds blew and buffeted his house. It did not collapse; it had been solidly set on rock. Anyone who hears my words but does not put them into practice is like the foolish man who built his house on sandy ground. The rains fell, the torrents came, the winds blew and lashed against his house. It collapsed under all this and was completely ruined."

890 NINTH SUNDAY IN ORDINARY TIME / B

READING I *Deuteronomy 5, 12-15 / 87*

"Take care to keep holy the sabbath day as the Lord, your God, commanded you. Six days you may labor and do all your work; but the seventh day is the sabbath of the Lord, your God. No work may be done then, whether by you, or your son or daughter, or your male or female slave, or your ox or ass or any of your beasts, or the alien who lives with you. Your male and female slave should rest as you do. For remember that you too were once slaves in Egypt, and the Lord, your God, brought you from there with his strong hand and outstretched arm. That is why the Lord, your God, has commanded you to observe the sabbath day."

RESPONSORIAL PSALM *Psalm (80)81, 3-4.5-6.6-8.10-11 / 87*

RC
Sing with joy to God! Sing to God our help!

Raise a song and sound the timbrel,
the sweet-sounding harp and the lute;
blow the trumpet at the new moon,
when the moon is full, on our feast. ℟.

For this is Israel's law,
a command of the God of Jacob.
He imposed it as a rule on Joseph,
when he went out against the land of
Egypt. ℟.

A voice I did not know said to me:
"I freed your shoulder from the burden;
your hands were freed from the load.
You called in distress and I saved
you. ℟.

Let there be no foreign god among you,
no worship of an alien god.
I am the Lord your God,
who brought you from the land of
Egypt." ℟.

READING II *2 Corinthians 4, 6-11 / 87*

God, who said, "Let light shine out of darkness," has shone in our hearts, that we in turn might make known the glory of God shining on the face of Christ. This treasure we possess in earthen vessels to make it clear that its surpassing power comes from God and not from us. We are afflicted in every way possible, but we are not crushed; full of doubts, we never despair. We are persecuted but never abandoned; we are struck down but never destroyed. Continually we carry about in our bodies the dying of Jesus so that in our bodies the life of Jesus may also be revealed. While we live, we are constantly being delivered to death for Jesus' sake, so that the life of Jesus may be revealed in our mortal flesh.

GOSPEL *Mark 2, 23-3, 6 or 2, 23-28 / 87*

For short form read only the part in brackets.

[It happened that Jesus was walking through standing grain on the sabbath, and his disciples began to pull off heads of grain as they went along. At this the Pharisees protested: "Look! Why do they do a thing not permitted on the sabbath?" He said to them: "Have you never read what David did when he was in need and he and his men were hungry? How he entered God's house in the days of Abiathar the high priest and ate the holy bread which only the priests were permitted to eat? He even gave it to his men." Then he said to them: "The sabbath was made for man, not man for the sabbath. That is why the Son of Man is lord even of the sabbath."]

He returned to the synagogue where there was a man whose hand was shriveled up. They kept an eye on Jesus to see whether he would heal him on the sabbath, hoping to be able to bring an accusation against him. He addressed the man with the shriveled hand: "Stand up here in front!" Then he said to them: "Is it permitted to do a good deed on the sabbath or an evil one? To preserve life–or to destroy it?" At this they remained silent. He looked around at them angrily, for he was deeply grieved that they had closed their minds against him. Then he said to the man, "Stretch out your hand." The man did so and his hand was perfectly restored. When the Pharisees went outside, they immediately began to plot with the Herodians on how they might destroy him.

NINTH SUNDAY IN ORDINARY TIME / C 891

READING I *1 Kings 8, 41-43 / 88*

Solomon prayed in the temple, saying, "To the foreigner, likewise, who is not of your people Israel, but comes from a distant land to honor you (since men will learn of your great name and your mighty hand and your outstretched arm), when he comes and prays toward this temple, listen from your heavenly dwelling. Do all that the foreigner asks of you, that all the peoples of earth may know your name, may fear you as do your people Israel, and may acknowledge that this temple which I have built is dedicated to your honor.

RESPONSORIAL PSALM *Psalm(116)117, 1.2 / 88*

CAP
Go out to all the world, and tell the Good News.

O praise the Lord, all you nations,
acclaim him all you peoples! ℟.

Strong is his love for us;
he is faithful for ever. ℟.

READING II *Galatians 1, 1-2. 6-10 / 88*

Paul, an apostle sent not by or men or by any man, but by Jesus Christ and God his Father who raised him from the dead–I and my brothers who are with me, send greetings to the churches in Galatia. I am amazed that you are so soon deserting him who called you in accord with his gracious design in Christ and are going over to another gospel. But there is no other. Some who wish to alter the gospel of Christ must have confused you. For if even we or an angel from heaven should preach to you a gospel not in accord with the one we delivered to you, let a curse be upon him! I repeat what I have just said: if anyone preaches a gospel to you other then the one you received, let a curse be upon him!

Whom would you say I am trying to please at this point–men or God? Is this how I seek to ingratiate myself with men? If I were trying to win man's approval, I would surely not be serving Christ!

GOSPEL *Luke 7, 1-10 / 88*

When Jesus had finished his discourse in the hearing of the people, he entered Capernaum. A centurion had a servant he held in high regard, who was at that moment sick to the point of death. When he heard about Jesus he sent some Jewish elders to him, asking him to come and save the life of his servant. Upon approaching Jesus they petitioned him earnestly. "He deserves this favor from you," they said, "because he loves our people, and even built our synagogue for us." Jesus set out with them. When he was only a short distance from the house, the centurion sent friends to tell him: "Sir, do not trouble yourself, for I am not worthy to have you enter my house. That is why I did not presume to come to you myself. Just give the order and my servant will be cured. I too am a man who knows the meaning of an order, having soldiers under my command. I say to one, 'On your way,' and off he goes; to another, 'Come here,' and he comes; to my slave, 'Do this,' and he does it." Jesus showed amazement on hearing this, and turned to the crowd which was following him to say, "I tell you, I have never found so much faith among the Israelites." When the deputation returned to the house, they found the servant in perfect health.

892 TENTH SUNDAY IN ORDINARY TIME / A

READING I *Hosea 6, 3-6 / 89*

"Let us know, let us strive to know the Lord;
as certain as the dawn is his coming,
and his judgment shines forth like the light of day!
He will come to us like the rain,
like spring rain that waters the earth."

What can I do with you, Ephraim?
What can I do with you, Judah?
Your piety is like a morning cloud,
like the dew that early passes away.
For this reason I smote them through the prophets,
I slew them by the words of my mouth;
For it is love that I desire, not sacrifice,
and knowledge of God rather than holocausts.

RESPONSORIAL PSALM *Psalm (49)50, 1.8.12-13.14-15 / 89*

RJB

To the up-right I will show the sav-ing pow'r of God.

The God of gods, the Lord,
has spoken and summoned the earth,
from the rising of the sun to its setting.

"I find no fault with your sacrifices,
your offerings are always before me. ℟.

Were I hungry, I would not tell you,
for I own the world and all it holds.
Do you think I eat the flesh of bulls,
or drink the blood of goats? ℟.

Pay your sacrifice of thanksgiving to
God
and render him your votive offerings.
Call on me in the day of distress.
I will free you and you shall honor
me." ℟.

READING II *Romans 4, 18-25 / 89*

Abraham believed hoping against hope, and so became the father of many nations, just as it was once told him, "Numerous as this shall your descendants be." Without growing weak in faith he thought of his own body, which was as good as dead (for he was nearly a hundred years old), and of the dead womb of Sarah. Yet he never questioned or doubted God's promise; rather, he was strengthened in faith and gave glory to God, fully persuaded that God could do whatever he had promised. Thus his faith was credited to him as justice.

The words, "It was credited to him," were not written with him alone in view; they were intended for us too. For our faith will be credited to us also if we believe in him who raised Jesus our Lord from the dead, the Jesus who was handed over to death for our sins and raised up for our justification.

GOSPEL *Matthew 9, 9-13 / 89*

As Jesus moved about, he saw a man named Matthew at his post where taxes were collected. He said to him, "Follow me." Matthew got up and followed him. Now it happened that, while Jesus was at table in Matthew's home, many tax collectors and those known as sinners came to join Jesus and his disciples at dinner. The Pharisees saw this and complained to his disciples, "What reason can the Teacher have for eating with tax collectors and those who disregard the law?" Overhearing the remark, he said: "People who are in good health do not need a doctor; sick people do. Go and learn the meaning of the words, 'It is mercy I desire and not sacrifice.' I have come to call not the self-righteous, but sinners."

TENTH SUNDAY IN ORDINARY TIME / B 893

READING I *Genesis 3, 9-15 / 90*

[After Adam had eaten of the tree] the Lord God called him and asked him "Where are you?" He answered, "I heard you in the garden; but I was afraid because I was naked, so I hid myself." Then he asked, "Who told you that you were naked? You have eaten, then, from the tree of which I had forbidden you to eat!" The man replied, "The woman whom you put here with me–she gave me fruit from the tree, and so I ate it." The Lord God then asked the woman, "Why did you do such a thing?" The woman answered "The serpent tricked me into it, so I ate it."

Then the Lord God said to the serpent:

"Because you have done this, you shall be banned
from all the animals
and from all the wild creatures;
On your belly shall you crawl,
and dirt shall you eat
all the days of your life.
I will put enmity between you and the woman,
and between your offspring and hers;
He will strike at your head,
while you strike at his heel."

RESPONSORIAL PSALM *Psalm (129)130, 1-2.3-4.5-6.7-8 / 90*

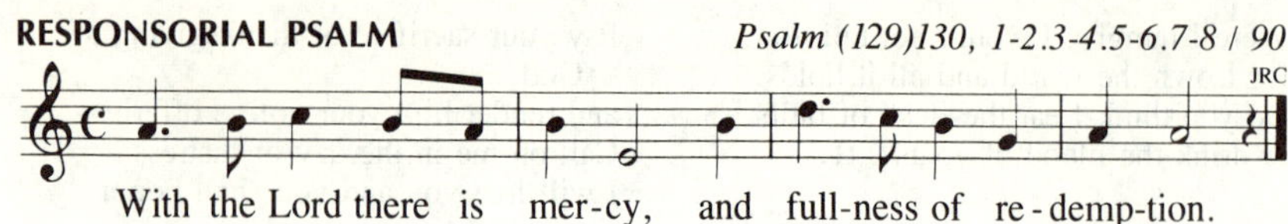
JRC
With the Lord there is mer-cy, and full-ness of re-demp-tion.

Out of the depths I cry to you, O Lord,
Lord, hear my voice!
O let your ears be attentive
to the voice of my pleading. ℟.

If you, O Lord, should mark our guilt,
Lord, who would survive?
But with you is found forgiveness:
for this we revere you. ℟.

My soul is waiting for the Lord,
I count on his word.
My soul is longing for the Lord
more than watchman for daybreak.
(Let the watchman count on daybreak
and Israel on the Lord.) ℟.

Because with the Lord there is mercy
and fullness of redemption,
Israel indeed he will redeem
from all its iniquity. ℟.

READING II *2 Corinthians 4, 13-5, 1 / 90*

We have that spirit of faith of which the Scripture says, "Because I believed, I spoke out." We believe and so we speak, knowing that he who raised up the Lord Jesus will raise us up along with Jesus and place both us and you in his presence. Indeed, everything is ordered to your benefit, so that the grace bestowed in abundance may bring greater glory to God because they who give thanks are many.

We do not lose heart because our inner being is renewed each day, even though our body is being destroyed at the same time. The present burden of our trial is light enough and earns for us an eternal weight of glory beyond all comparison. We do not fix our gaze on what is seen but on what is unseen. What is seen is transitory; what is not seen lasts forever.

Indeed, we know that when the earthly tent in which we dwell is destroyed we have a dwelling provided for us by God, a dwelling in the heavens, not made by hands, but to last forever.

GOSPEL *Mark 3, 20-35 / 90*

Jesus came to the house with his disciples and again the crowd assembled, making it impossible for them to get any food whatever. When his family heard of this, they came to take charge of him, saying, "He is out of his mind;" while the scribes who arrived from Jerusalam asserted, "He is possessed by Beelzebul," and "He expels demons with the help of the prince of demons." Summoning them, he then began to speak to them by way of examples: "How can Satan expel Satan? If a kingdom is torn by civil strife, that kingdom cannot last. If a household is divided according to loyalties, that household will not survive. Similarly, if Satan has suffered mutiny in his ranks and is torn by dissension, he cannot endure; he is finished. No one can enter a strong man's house and despoil his property unless he has first put him under restraint. Only then can he plunder his house.

"I give you my word, every sin will be forgiven mankind and all the blasphemies men utter, but whoever blasphemes against the Holy Spirit will never be forgiven. He carries the guilt of his sin without end." He spoke thus because they had said, "He is possessed by an unclean spirit."

His mother and his brothers arrived, and as they stood outside they sent word to him to come out. The crowd seated around him told him, "Your mother and your brothers and sisters are outside asking for you." He said in reply, "Who are my mother and my brothers?" And gazing around him at those seated in the circle he continued, "These are my mother and my brothers. Whoever does the will of God is brother and sister and mother to me."

TENTH SUNDAY IN ORDINARY TIME / C 894

READING I *1 Kings 17, 17-24 / 91*

The son of the mistress of the house fell sick, and his sickness grew more severe until he stopped breathing. So she said to Elijah, "Why have you done this to me, O man of God? Have you come to me to call attention to my guilt and to kill my son?" "Give me your son," Elijah said to her. Taking him from her lap, he carried him to the upper room where he was staying, and laid him on his own bed. He called out to the Lord: "O Lord my God, will you afflict even the widow with whom I am staying by killing her son?" Then he stretched himself out upon the child three times and called out to the Lord: "O Lord, my God, let the life breath return to the body of this child." The Lord heard the prayer of Elijah; the life breath returned to the child's body and he revived. Taking the child, Elijah brought him down into the house from the upper room and gave him to his mother. "See!" Elijah said to her "your son is alive." "Now indeed I know that you are a man of God," the woman replied to Elijah. "The word of the Lord comes truly from your mouth."

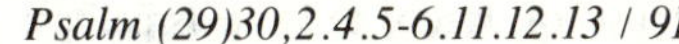

RESPONSORIAL PSALM *Psalm (29)30,2.4.5-6.11.12.13 / 91*

JRC
I will praise you, Lord, for you have res-cued me.

I will praise you, Lord, you have rescued me
and have not let my enemies rejoice over me.
O Lord, you have raised my soul from the dead,
restored me to life from those who sink into the grave. ℟.

Sing psalms to the Lord, you who love him,
give thanks to his holy name.
His anger lasts a moment; his favor all through life.
At night there are tears, but joy comes with dawn. ℟.

The Lord listened and had pity.
The Lord came to my help.
For me you have changed my mourning into dancing,
O Lord my God, I will thank you for ever. ℟.

READING II *Galatians 1, 11-19 / 91*

I assure you, brothers, the gospel I proclaimed to you is no mere human invention. I did not receive it from any man, nor was I schooled in it. It came by revelation from Jesus Christ. You have heard, I know, the story of my former way of life in Judaism. You know that I went to extremes in persecuting the Church of God and tried to destroy it; I made progress in Jewish observances far beyond most of my contemporaries, in my excess of zeal to live out all the traditions of my ancestors.

But the time came when he who had set me apart before I was born and called me by his favor chose to reveal his Son through me, that I might spread among the Gentiles the good tidings concerning him. Immediately, without seeking human advisers or even going to Jerusalem to see those who were apostles before me, I went off to Arabia; later I returned to Damascus. Three years after that I went up to Jerusalem to get to know Cephas, with whom I stayed fifteen days. I did not meet any other apostles except James, the brother of the Lord.

GOSPEL *Luke 7, 11-17 / 91*

Jesus went to a town called Naim, and his disciples and a large crowd accompanied him. As he approached the gate of the town a dead man was being carried out, the only son of a widowed mother. A considerable crowd of townsfolk were with her. The Lord was moved with pity upon seeing her and said to her, "Do not cry." Then he stepped forward and touched the litter; at this the bearers halted. He said, "Young man, I bid you get up." The dead man sat up and began to speak. Then Jesus gave him back to his mother. Fear seized them all and they began to praise God. "A great prophet has risen among us," they said; and, "God has visited his people." This was the report that spread about him throughout Judea and the surrounding country.

895 ELEVENTH SUNDAY IN ORDINARY TIME / A

READING I *Exodus 19, 2-6 / 92*

The Israelites came to the desert of Sinai [and] pitched camp.

While Israel was encamped here in front of the mountain, Moses went up the mountain to God. Then the Lord called to him and said, "Thus shall you say to the house of Jacob; tell the Israelites: You have seen for yourselves how I treated the Egyptians and how I bore you up on eagle wings, and brought you here to myself. Therefore, if you hearken to my voice and keep my covenant, you shall be my special possession, dearer to me than all other people, though all the earth is mine. You shall be to me a kingdom of priests, a holy nation."

RESPONSORIAL PSALM *Psalm (99)100, 1-2.3.5 / 92*

MK
We are his peo - ple: the sheep of his flock.

Cry out with joy to the Lord, all the
earth.
Serve the Lord with gladness.
Come before him singing for joy. ℟.

Know that he, the Lord, is God.
He made us, we belong to him,
we are his people, the sheep of his
flock. ℟.

Indeed, how good is the Lord,
eternal his merciful love.
He is faithful from age to age. ℟.

READING II *Romans 5, 6-11 / 92*

At the appointed time, when we were still powerless, Christ died for us godless men. It is rare that anyone should lay down his life for a just man, though it is barely possible that for a good man someone may have the courage to die. It is precisely in this that God proves his love for us: that while we were still sinners, Christ died for us. Now that we have been justified by his blood, it is all the more certain that we shall be saved by him from God's wrath. For if, when we were God's enemies, we were reconciled to him by the death of his Son, it is all the more certain that we who have been reconciled will be saved by his life. Not only that; we go so far as to make God our boast through our Lord Jesus Christ, through whom we have now received reconciliation.

GOSPEL *Matthew 9, 36-10, 8 / 92*

At the sight of the crowds, the heart of Jesus was moved with pity. They were lying prostrate from exhaustion, like sheep without a shepherd. He said to his disciples:

"The harvest is good but laborers are scarce. Beg the harvest master to send out laborers to gather his harvest."

Then he summoned his twelve disciples and gave them authority to expel unclean spirits and cure sickness and disease of every kind.

The names of the twelve apostles are these: first Simon, now known as Peter, and his brother Andrew; James, Zebedee's son, and his brother John; Philip and Bartholomew, Thomas and Matthew the tax collector; James, son of Alphaeus, and Thaddaeus; Simon the Zealot party member, and Judas Iscariot, who betrayed him. Jesus sent these men on mission as the Twelve, after giving them the following instructions:

"Do not visit pagan territiory and do not enter a Samaritan town. Go instead after the lost sheep of the house of Israel. As you go, make this announcement: 'The reign of God is at hand!' Cure the sick, raise the dead, heal the leprous, expel demons. The gift you have received, give as a gift."

ELEVENTH SUNDAY IN ORDINARY TIME / B 896

READING I

Ezekiel 17, 22-24 / 93

Thus says the Lord God:
I, too, will take from the crest of the cedar,
from its topmost branches tear off a tender shoot,
And plant it on a high and lofty mountain;
on the mountain heights of Israel I will plant it.
It shall put forth branches and bear fruit,
and become a majestic cedar.
Birds of every kind shall dwell beneath it,
every winged thing in the shade of its boughs.
And all the trees of the field shall know
that I, the Lord,
Bring low the high tree,
lift high the lowly tree,
Wither up the green tree,
and make the withered tree bloom.
As I, the Lord, have spoken, so will I do.

RESPONSORIAL PSALM

Psalm (91)92, 2-3.13-14.15-16 / 93

RP
Lord, it is good to give thanks to you.

It is good to give thanks to the Lord,
to make music to your name, O Most High,
to proclaim your love in the morning
and your truth in the watches of the night. ℟.

The just will flourish like the palm tree
and grow like a Lebanon cedar.
Planted in the house of the Lord
they will flourish in the courts of our God. ℟.

Still bearing fruit when they are old,
still full of sap, still green,
to proclaim that the Lord is just.
In him, my rock, there is no wrong. ℟.

READING II

2 Corinthians 5, 6-10 / 93

We continue to be confident. We know that while we dwell in the body we are away from the Lord. We walk by faith, not by sight. I repeat, we are full of confidence, and would much rather be away from the body and at home with the Lord. This being so, we make it our aim to please him whether we are with him or away from him.

The lives of all of us are to be revealed before the tribunal of Christ so that each one may receive his recompense, good or bad, according to his life in the body.

GOSPEL *Mark 4, 26-34 / 93*

Jesus said to the crowd: "This is how it is with the reign of God. A man scatters seed on the ground. He goes to bed and gets up day after day. Through it all the seed sprouts and grows without his knowing how it happens. The soil produces of itself first the blade, then the ear, finally the ripe wheat in the ear. When the crop is ready he 'wields the sickle, for the time is ripe for harvest.' "

"He went on to say: "What comparison shall we use for the reign of God? What image will help to present it? It is like mustard seed which, when planted in the soil, is the smallest of all the earth's seeds, yet once it is sown, springs up to become the largest of shrubs, with branches big enough for the birds of the sky to build nests in its shade." By means of many such parables he taught them the message in a way they could understand. To them he spoke only by way of parable, while he kept explaining things privately to his disciples.

897

ELEVENTH SUNDAY IN ORDINARY TIME / C

READING I *2 Samuel 12, 7-10.13 / 94*

Nathan said to David: "Thus says the Lord God of Israel: 'I anointed you king of Israel. I rescued you from the hand of Saul. I gave you your lord's house and your lord's wives for your own. I gave you the house of Israel and of Judah. And if this were not enough, I could count up for you still more. Why have you spurned the Lord and done evil in his sight? You have cut down Uriah the Hittite with the sword; you took his wife as your own, and him you killed with the sword of the Ammonites. Now therefore, the sword shall never depart from your house, because you have despised me and have taken the wife of Uriah to be your wife.' " Then David said to Nathan, "I have sinned against the Lord." Nathan answered David: "The Lord on his part has forgiven your sin: you shall not die."

RESPONSORIAL PSALM *Psalm (31)32, 1-2.5.7.11 / 94*

JRC
Lord, for - give the wrong I have done.

Happy the man whose offense is
forgiven, whose sin is remitted.
O happy the man to whom the
Lord imputes no guilt,
in whose spirit is no guile. ℟.

But now I have acknowledged my sins;
my guilt I did not hide.
I said: "I will confess my offense to the
Lord."
And you, Lord, have forgiven the guilt
of my sin. ℟.

You are my hiding place, O Lord;
you save me from distress.
(You surround me with cries of
deliverance.) ℟.

Rejoice, rejoice in the Lord,
exult, you just!
O come, ring out your joy,
all you upright of heart. ℟.

READING II *Galatians 2, 16.19-21 / 94*

Knowing that a man is not justified by legal observance but by faith in Jesus Christ, we too have believed in him in order to be justified by faith in Christ, not by observance of the law; for by works of the law no one will be justified. It was through the law that I died to the law, to live for God. I have been crucified with Christ, and the life I live now is not my own; Christ is living in me. I still live my human life, but it is a life of faith in the Son of God, who loved me and gave himself for me. I will not treat God's gracious gift as pointless. If justice is available through the law, then Christ died to no purpose!

GOSPEL

Luke 7, 36-8, 3 or 7, 36-50 / 94

For short form read only the part in brackets.

[There was a certain Pharisee who invited Jesus to dine with him. Jesus went to the Pharisee's home and reclined to eat. A woman known in the town to be a sinner learned that he was dining in the Pharisee's home. She brought in a vase of perfumed oil and stood behind him at his feet, weeping so that her tears fell upon his feet. Then she wiped them with her hair, kissing them and perfuming them with the oil. When his host, the Pharisee, saw this, he said to himself, "If this man were a prophet, he would know who and what sort of woman this is that touches him–that she is a sinner." In answer to his thoughts, Jesus said to him, "Simon, I have something to propose to you." "Teacher," he said, "speak."

"Two men owed money to a certain moneylender: one owed a total of five hundred coins, the other fifty. Since neither was able to repay, he wrote off both debts. Which of them was more grateful to him?" Simon answered, "He, I presume, to whom he remitted the larger sum." Jesus said to him, "You are right."

Turning to the woman he said to Simon: "You see this woman? I came to your home and you provided me no water for my feet. She has washed my feet with her tears and wiped them with her hair. You gave me no kiss, but she has not ceased kissing my feet since I entered. You did not anoint my head with oil, but she has anointed my feet with perfume. I tell you that is why her many sins are forgiven–because of her great love. Little is forgiven the one whose love is small."

He said to her then, "Your sins are forgiven," at which his fellow guests began to ask among themselves, "Who is this that he even forgives sins?" Meanwhile he said to the woman, "Your faith has been your salvation. Go now in peace."]

After this he journeyed through towns and villages preaching and proclaiming the good news of the kingdom of God. The Twelve accompanied him, and also some women who had been cured of evil spirits and maladies: Mary called the Magdalene, from whom seven devils had gone out, Joanna, the wife of Herod's steward Chuza, Susanna, and many others who were assisting them out of their means.

TWELFTH SUNDAY IN ORDINARY TIME / A 898

READING I

Jeremiah 20, 10-13 / 95

Jeremiah said:
"Yes, I hear the whisperings of many:
'Terror on every side!
Denounce! let us denounce him!'
All those who were my friends
are on the watch for any misstep of mine.
'Perhaps he will be trapped; then we can prevail,
and take our vengeance on him.'
But the Lord is with me, like a mighty champion:
my persecutors will stumble, they will not triumph
In their failure they will be put to utter shame,
to lasting, unforgettable confusion.
O Lord of hosts, you who test the just,
who probe mind and heart,
Let me witness the vengeance you take on them,
for to you I have entrusted my cause.
Sing to the Lord,
praise the Lord,
For he has rescued the life of the poor
from the power of the wicked!"

RESPONSORIAL PSALM *Psalm (68)69, 8-10.14.17.33-35 / 95*

CAP
Lord, in your great love, an - swer me.

It is for you that I suffer taunts,
that shame covers my face,
that I have become a stranger to my
brothers,
an alien to my own mother's sons.
I burn with zeal for your house
and taunts against you fall on me. ℟.

This is my prayer to you,
my prayer for your favor.
In your great love, answer me, O God,
with your help that never fails;
Lord, answer, for your love is kind;
in your compassion, turn towards
me. ℟.

The poor when they see it will be glad
and God-seeking hearts will revive;
for the Lord listens to the needy
and does not spurn his servants in their
chains.
Let the heavens and the earth give him
praise,
the sea and all its living creatures. ℟.

READING II *Romans 5, 12-15 / 95*

Just as through one man sin entered the world and with sin death, death thus coming to all men inasmuch as all sinned–before the law there was sin in the world, even though sin is not imputed when there is no law–I say, from Adam to Moses death reigned, even over those who had not sinned by breaking a precept as did Adam, that type of the man to come.

But the gift is not like the offense. For if by the offense of the one man all died, much more did the grace of God and the gracious gift of the one man, Jesus Christ, abound for all.

GOSPEL *Matthew 10, 26-33 / 95*

Jesus said to his apostles: "Do not let men intimidate you. Nothing is concealed that will not be revealed, and nothing hidden that will not become known. What I tell you in darkness, speak in the light. What you hear in private, proclaim from the housetops.

"Do not fear those who deprive the body of life but cannot destroy the soul. Rather fear him who can destroy both body and soul in Gehenna. Are not two sparrows sold for next to nothing? Yet not a single sparrow falls to the ground without your Father's consent. As for you, every hair of your head has been counted; so do not be afraid of anything. You are worth more than an entire flock of sparrows. Whoever acknowledges me before men I will acknowledge before my Father in heaven. Whoever disowns me before men I will disown before my Father in heaven."

899 TWELFTH SUNDAY IN ORDINARY TIME / B

READING I *Job 38, 1.8-11 / 96*

The Lord addressed Job out of the
storm and said:
Who shut within doors the sea,
when it burst forth from the womb;
When I made the clouds its garment
and thick darkness its swaddling
bands?
When I set limits for it
and fastened the bar of its door,
And said: Thus far shall you come but
no farther,
and here shall your proud waves be
stilled!

RESPONSORIAL PSALM *Psalm (106)107, 23-24.25-26.28-29.30-31 / 96*

JRC
Give thanks to the Lord, his love is ev - er - last-ing.

Some sailed to the sea in ships
to trade on the mighty waters.
These men have seen the Lord's deeds,
the wonders he does in the deep. ℟.

For he spoke; he summoned the gale,
tossing the waves of the sea
up to heaven and back into the deep;
their soul melted away in their
distress. ℟.

Then they cried to the Lord in their
need
and he rescued them from their distress.
He stilled the storm to a whisper;
all the waves of the sea were
hushed. ℟.

They rejoiced because of the calm
and he led them to the haven they
desired.
Let them thank the Lord for his love,
the wonders he does for men. ℟.

READING II *2 Corinthians 5, 14-17 / 96*

The love of Christ impels us who have reached the conviction that since one died for all, all died. He died for all so that those who live might live no longer for themselves, but for him who for their sakes died and was raised up.

Because of this we no longer look on anyone in terms of mere human judgment. If at one time we so regarded Christ, we no longer know him by this standard. This means that if anyone is in Christ, he is a new creation. The old order has passed away; now all is new!

GOSPEL *Mark 4, 35-41 / 96*

One day as evening drew on, Jesus said to his disciples, "Let us cross over to the farther shore." Leaving the crowd, they took him away in the boat in which he was sitting, while the other boats accompanied him. It happened that a bad squall blew up. The waves were breaking over the boat and it began to ship water badly. Jesus was in the stern through it all, sound asleep on a cushion. They finally woke him and said to him, "Teacher, doesn't it matter to you that we are going to drown?" He awoke and rebuked the wind and said to the sea: "Quiet! Be still!" The wind fell off and everything grew calm. Then he said to them, "Why are you so terrified? Why are you lacking in faith?" A great awe overcame them at this. They kept saying to one another, "Who can this be that the wind and the sea obey him?"

TWELFTH SUNDAY IN ORDINARY TIME / C 900

READING I *Zechariah 12, 10-11 / 97*

I will pour out on the house of David and on the inhabitants of Jerusalem a spirit of grace and petition; and they shall look on him whom they have thrust through, and they shall mourn for him as one mourns for an only son, and they shall grieve over him as one grieves over a first-born.

On that day the mourning in Jerusalem shall be as great as the mourning of Hadadrimmon of the plain of Megiddo.

RESPONSORIAL PSALM

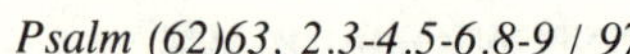
Psalm (62)63, 2.3-4.5-6.8-9 / 97

RP
My soul is thirst-ing for you, O
Lord, thirst - ing for you my God.

O God, you are my God, for you I long;
for you my soul is thirsting.
My body pines for you
like a dry, weary land without water. ℟.

So I gaze on you in the sanctuary
to see your strength and your glory.
For your love is better than life,
my lips will speak your praise. ℟.

So I will bless you all my life,
in your name I will lift up my hands.
My soul shall be filled as with a banquet,
my mouth shall praise you with joy. ℟.

For you have been my help;
in the shadow of your wings I rejoice.
My soul clings to you;
your right hand holds me fast. ℟.

READING II *Galatians 3, 26-29 / 97*

Each one of you is a son of God because of your faith in Christ Jesus. All of you who have been baptized into Christ have clothed yourselves with him. There does not exist among you Jew or Greek, slave or freeman, male or female. All are one in Christ Jesus. Furthermore, if you belong to Christ, you are the descendants of Abraham, which means you inherit all that was promised.

GOSPEL *Luke 9, 18-24 / 97*

One day when Jesus was praying in seclusion and his disciples were with him, he put the question to them, "Who do the crowds say that I am?" "John the Baptizer," they replied, "and some say Elijah, while others claim that one of the prophets of old has returned from the dead." "But you–who do you say that I am?" he asked them. Peter said in reply, "The Messiah of God." He strictly forbade them to tell this to anyone. "The Son of Man," he said, "must first endure many sufferings, be rejected by the elders, the high priests and the scribes, and be put to death, and then be raised up on the third day."

Jesus said to all: "Whoever wishes to be my follower must deny his very self, take up his cross each day, and follow in my steps. Whoever would save his life will lose it, and whoever loses his life for my sake will save it."

901 THIRTEENTH SUNDAY IN ORDINARY TIME / A

READING I *2 Kings 4, 8-11.14-16 / 98*

One day Elisha came to Shunem, where there was a woman of influence, who urged him to dine with her. Afterward, whenever he passed by, he used to stop there to dine. So she said to her husband, "I know that he is a holy man of God. Since he visits us often, let us arrange a little room on the roof and furnish it for him with a bed, table, chair, and lamp, so that when he comes to us he can stay there." Sometime later Elisha arrived and stayed in the room overnight.

Later Elisha asked, "Can something be done for her?" "Yes!" Gehazi answered. "She has no son, and her husband is getting on in years." "Call her," said Elisha. When she had been called, and stood at the door, Elisha promised, "This time next year you will be fondling a baby son."

RESPONSORIAL PSALM *Psalm (88)89, 2-3.16-17.18-19 / 98*

JRC
For ev - er I will sing the good-ness of the Lord.

I will sing for ever of your love, O
  Lord;
through all ages my mouth will proclaim
  your truth.
Of this I am sure, that your love lasts
  for ever,
that your truth is firmly established as
  the heavens. ℟.

Happy the people who acclaim such a
  king,
who walk, O Lord, in the light of your
  face,
who find their joy every day in your
  name,
who make your justice the source of
  their bliss. ℟.

For you, O Lord, are the glory of their
  strength;
by your favor it is that our might is
  exalted;
for our ruler is in the keeping of the
  Lord;
our king in the keeping of the Holy One
  of Israel. ℟.

READING II *Romans 6, 3-4.8-11 / 98*

Are you not aware that we who were baptized into Christ Jesus were baptized into his death? Through baptism into his death we were buried with him, so that, just as Christ was raised from the dead by the glory of the Father, we too might live a new life. If we have died with Christ, we believe that we are also to live with him. We know that Christ, once raised from the dead, will never die again; death has no more power over him. His death was death to sin, once for all; his life is life for God. In the same way, you must consider yourselves dead to sin but alive for God in Christ Jesus.

GOSPEL *Matthew 10, 37-42 / 98*

Jesus said to his apostles: "Whoever loves father or mother, son or daughter, more than me is not worthy of me. He who will not take up his cross and come after me is not worthy of me. He who seeks only himself brings himself to ruin, whereas he who brings himself to nought for me discovers who he is.

"He who welcomes you welcomes me, and he who welcomes me welcomes him who sent me. He who welcomes a prophet because he bears the name of prophet receives a prophet's reward; he who welcomes a holy man because he is known as holy receives a holy man's reward. And I promise you that whoever gives a cup of cold water to one of these lowly ones because he is a disciple will not want for his reward."

THIRTEENTH SUNDAY IN ORDINARY TIME / B 902

READING I *Wisdom 1, 13-15; 2, 23-24 / 99*

God did not make death,
  nor does he rejoice in the destruction
    of the living.
For he fashioned all things that they
    might have being;
  and the creatures of the world are
    wholesome,

And there is not a destructive drug
    among them
  nor any domain of the nether world
    on earth,
For justice is undying.

For God formed man to be
imperishable;
the image of his own nature he made
him.

But by the envy of the devil, death
entered the world,
and they who are in his possession
experience it.

RESPONSORIAL PSALM *Psalm (29)30, 2.4.5-6.11.12.13 / 99*

JRC
I will praise you, Lord, for you have res-cued me.

I will praise you, Lord, you have
rescued me
and have not let my enemies rejoice
over me.
O Lord, you have raised my soul from
the dead,
restored me to life from those who sink
into the grave. ℟.

Sing psalms to the Lord, you who love
him,
give thanks to his holy name.
His anger lasts a moment; his favor all
through life.
At night there are tears, but joy comes
with dawn. ℟.

The Lord listened and had pity.
The Lord came to my help.
For me you have changed my mourning
into dancing.
O Lord my God, I will thank you for
ever. ℟.

READING II *2 Corinthians 8.7.9.13-15 / 99*

Just as you are rich in every respect, in faith and discourse, in knowledge, in total concern, and in our love for you, you may also abound in your work of charity.

You are well acquainted with the favor shown you by our Lord Jesus Christ: how for your sake he made himself poor though he was rich, so that you might become rich by his poverty. The relief of others ought not to impoverish you; there should be a certain equality. Your plenty at the present time should supply their need so that their surplus may in turn one day supply your need, with equality as the result. It is written, "He who gathered much had no excess and he who gathered little had no lack."

GOSPEL *Mark 5, 21-43 or 5, 21-24.35-43 / 99*

For short form read only the part in brackets.

[When Jesus had crossed back to the other side of the Sea of Galilee in the boat, a large crowd gathered around him and he stayed close to the lake. One of the officials of the synagogue, a man named Jairus, came near. Seeing Jesus, he fell at his feet and made this earnest appeal: "My little daughter is critically ill. Please come and lay your hands on her so that she may get well and live." The two went off together and a large crowd followed, pushing against Jesus.]

There was a woman in the area who had been afflicted with a hemorrhage for a dozen years. She had received treatment at the hands of doctors of every sort and exhausted her savings in the process, yet she got no relief; on the contrary, she only grew worse. She had heard about Jesus and came up behind him in the crowd and put her hand to his cloak. "If I just touch his clothing," she thought, "I shall get well." Immediately her flow of blood dried up and the feeling that she was cured of her affliction ran through her whole body. Jesus was immediately conscious that healing power had gone out from him. Wheeling about in the crowd, he began to ask, "Who touched my clothing?" His disciples said to him, "You can see how this crowd hems you in, yet you ask, 'Who touched me?' " Despite this he kept looking around to see the woman who had done it. Fearful and beginning to tremble now as she realized what had happened, the woman came and fell in front of him and told him the whole truth. He said to her, "Daughter, it is your faith that has cured you. Go in peace and be free of this illness."

He had not finished speaking when [people from the official's house arrived saying, "Your daughter is dead. Why bother the Teacher further?" Jesus disregarded the report that had been brought and said to the offical: "Fear is useless. What is needed is trust." He would not permit anyone to follow him except Peter, James, and James's brother John. As they approached the house of the synagogue leader, Jesus was struck by the noise of people wailing and crying loudly on all sides. He entered and said to them: "Why do you make this din with your wailing? The child is not dead. She is asleep." At this they began to ridicule him. Then he put them all out.

Jesus took the child's father and mother and his own companions and entered the room where the child lay. Taking her hand he said to her, "Talitha, koum," which means, "Little girl, get up." The girl, a child of twelve, stood up immediately and began to walk around. At this the family's astonishment was complete. He enjoined them strictly not to let anyone know about it, and told them to give her something to eat.]

THIRTEENTH SUNDAY IN ORDINARY TIME / C 903

READING I *1 Kings 19, 16.19-21 / 100*

The Lord said to Elijah: "You shall anoint Elisha, son of Shaphat of Abel-meholah, as prophet to succeed you."

Elijah set out, and came upon Elisha, son of Shaphat, as he was plowing with twelve yoke of oxen; he was following the twelfth. Elijah went over to him and threw his cloak over him. Elisha left the oxen, ran after Elijah, and said, "Please, let me kiss my father and mother goodbye, and I will follow you." "Go back!" Elijah answered. "Have I done anything to you?" Elisha left him and taking the yoke of oxen, slaughtered them; he used the plowing equipment for fuel to boil their flesh, and gave it to his people to eat. Then he left and followed Elijah as his attendant.

RESPONSORIAL PSALM *Psalm (15)16, 1-2.5.7-8.9-10.11 / 100*

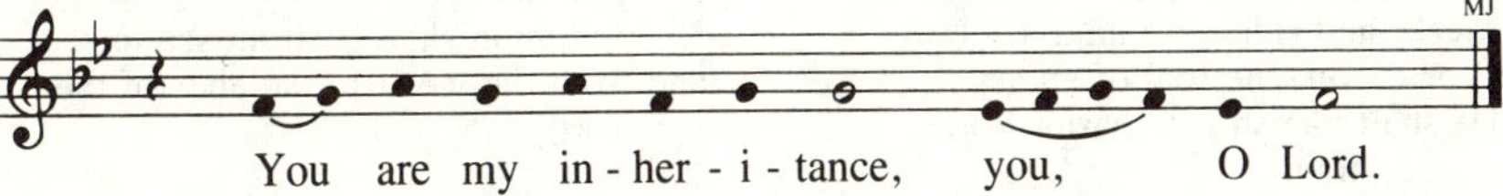
MJ
You are my in - her - i - tance, you, O Lord.

Preserve me, God, I take refuge in you.
I say to the Lord: "You are my God."
O Lord, it is you who are my portion
and cup,
it is you yourself who are my prize. ℟.

I will bless the Lord who gives me
counsel,
who even at night directs my heart.
I keep ther Lord ever in my sight;
since he is at my right hand, I shall
stand firm. ℟.

And so my heart rejoices, my soul is
glad;
even my body shall rest in safety.
For you will not leave my soul among
the dead,
nor let your beloved know decay. ℟.

You will show me the path of life,
the fullness of joy in your presence,
at your right hand happiness for
ever. ℟.

READING II *Galatians 5, 1.13-18 / 100*

It was for liberty that Christ freed us. So stand firm, and do not take on yourselves the yoke of slavery a second time!

My brothers, remember that you have been called to live in freedom–but not a freedom that gives free rein to the flesh. Out of love, place yourselves at one another's service. The whole law has found its fulfillment in this one saying: "You shall love your neighbor as yourself." If you go on biting and tearing one another to pieces, take care! You will end up in mutual destruction!

My point is that you should live in accord with the spirit and you will not yield to the cravings of the flesh. The flesh lusts against the spirit and the spirit against the flesh; the two are directly opposed. This is why you do not do what your will intends. If you are guided by the spirit, you are not under the law.

GOSPEL *Luke 9, 51-62 / 100*

As the time approached when Jesus was to be taken from this world, he firmly resolved to proceed toward Jerusalem, and sent messengers on ahead of him. These entered a Samaritan town to prepare for his passing through, but the Samaritans would not welcome him because he was on his way to Jerusalem. When his disciples James and John saw this, they said, "Lord, would you not have us call down fire from heaven to destroy them?" He turned toward them only to reprimand them. Then they set off for another town.

As they were making their way along, someone said to him, "I will be your follower wherever you go." Jesus said to him, "The foxes have lairs, the birds of the sky have nests, but the Son of Man has nowhere to lay his head." To another he said, "Come after me." The man replied, "Let me bury my father first." Jesus said to him, "Let the dead bury their dead; come away and proclaim the kingdom of God." Yet another said to him, "I will be your follower, Lord, but first let me take leave of my people at home." Jesus answered him, "Whoever puts his hand to the plow but keeps looking back is unfit for the reign of God."

904 FOURTEENTH SUNDAY IN ORDINARY TIME / A

READING I *Zechariah 9, 9-10 / 101*

Rejoice heartily, O daughter Zion,
  shout for joy, O daughter Jerusalem!
See, your king shall come to you;
  a just savior is he,
Meek, and riding on an ass,
  on a colt, the foal of an ass.
He shall banish the chariot from
    Ephraim,
  and the horse from Jerusalem;
The warrior's bow shall be banished,
  and he shall proclaim peace to the
    nations.
His dominion shall be from sea to sea,
and from the River to the ends of the
    earth.

RESPONSORIAL PSALM *Psalm (144)145, 1-2.8-9.10-11.13-14 / 101*

JRC
I will praise your name for ev - er,
my king and my God.

I will give you glory, O God my King,
I will bless your name for ever.

I will bless you day after day
and praise your name for ever. ℟.

The Lord is kind and full of compassion,
slow to anger, abounding in love.
How good is the Lord to all,
compassionate to all his
creatures. ℟.

All your creatures shall thank you, O
Lord,
and your friends shall repeat their
blessing.
They shall speak of the glory of your
reign
and declare your might, O God. ℟.

The Lord is faithful in all his words
and loving in all his deeds.
The Lord supports all who fall
and raises all who are bowed
down. ℟.

READING II *Romans 8, 9.11-13 / 101*

You are not in the flesh; you are in the spirit, since the Spirit of God dwells in you. If anyone does not have the Spirit of Christ, he does not belong to Christ. If the Spirit of him who raised Jesus from the dead dwells in you, then he who raised Christ from the dead will bring your mortal bodies to life also through his Spirit dwelling in you.

We are debtors, then, my brothers–but not to the flesh, so that we should live according to the flesh. If you live according to the flesh, you will die; but if by the spirit you put to death the evil deeds of the body, you will live.

GOSPEL *Matthew 11, 25-30 / 101*

On one occasion Jesus spoke thus: "Father, Lord of heaven and earth, to you I offer praise; for what you have hidden from the learned and the clever you have revealed to the merest children. Father, it is true. You have graciously willed it so. Everything has been given over to me by my Father. No one knows the Son but the Father, and no one knows the Father but the Son–and anyone to whom the Son wishes to reveal him.

"Come to me, all you who are weary and find life burdensome, and I will refresh you. Take my yoke upon your shoulders and learn from me, for I am gentle and humble of heart. Your souls will find rest, for my yoke is easy and my burden light."

FOURTEENTH SUNDAY IN ORDINARY TIME / B 905

READING I *Ezekiel 2, 2-5 / 102*

Spirit entered into me and set me on my feet, and I heard the one who was speaking say to me: Son of man, I am sending you to the Israelites, rebels who have rebelled against me; they and their fathers have revolted against me to this very day. Hard of face and obstinate of heart are they to whom I am sending you. But you shall say to them: Thus says the Lord God! And whether they heed or resist–for they are a rebellious house–they shall know that a prophet has been among them.

RESPONSORIAL PSALM *Psalm (122)123, 1-2.3-4 / 102*

ST
Our eyes are fixed on the Lord, plead-ing for his mer-cy.

To you have I lifted up my eyes,
you who dwell in the heavens;
my eyes like the eyes of slaves
on the hand of their lords. ℟.

Like the eyes of a servant
on the hand of her mistress,
so our eyes are on the Lord our God
till he show us his mercy. ℞.

Have mercy on us, Lord, have mercy.
We are filled with contempt.
Indeed all too full is our soul
with the scorn of the rich,
(with the proud man's disdain). ℞.

READING II *2 Corinthians 12, 7-10 / 102*

As to the extraordinary revelations, in order that I might not become conceited I was given a thorn in the flesh, an angel of Satan to beat me and keep me from getting proud. Three times I begged the Lord that this might leave me. He said to me, "My grace is enough for you, for in weakness power reaches perfection." And so I willingly boast of my weaknesses instead, that the power of Christ may rest upon me.

Therefore I am content with weakness, with mistreatment, with distress, with persecutions and difficulties for the sake of Christ; for when I am powerless it is then that I am strong.

GOSPEL *Mark 6, 1-6 / 102*

Jesus went to his own part of the country followed by his disciples. When the sabbath came he began to teach in the synagogue in a way that kept his large audience amazed. They said: "Where did he get all this? What kind of wisdom is he endowed with? How is it such miraculous deeds are accomplished by his hands? Isn't this the carpenter, the son of Mary, a brother of James and Joses and Judas and Simon? Aren't his sisters our neighbors here?" They found him too much for them. Jesus' response to all this was: "No prophet is without honor except in his native place, among his own kindred, and in his own house." He could work no miracle there, apart from curing a few who were sick by laying hands on them, so much did their lack of faith distress him. He made the rounds of the neighboring villages instead, and spent his time teaching.

906 FOURTEENTH SUNDAY IN ORDINARY TIME / C

READING I *Isaiah 66, 10-14 / 103*

Rejoice with Jerusalem and be glad
because of her,
all you who love her;
Exult, exult with her,
all you who were mourning over her!
Oh, that you may suck fully
of the milk of her comfort,
That you may nurse with delight
at her abundant breasts!
For thus says the Lord:
Lo, I will spread prosperity over her
like a river,
and the wealth of the nations like an
overflowing torrent.
As nurslings, you shall be carried in her
arms,
and fondled in her lap;
As a mother comforts her son,
so will I comfort you;
in Jerusalem you shall find your
comfort.
When you see this, your heart shall
rejoice,
and your bodies flourish like the
grass;
the Lord's power shall be known to his
servants.

RESPONSORIAL PSALM *Psalm (65)66, 1-3.4-5.6-7.16.20 / 103*

RMH
Let all the earth cry out, cry out to God with joy.

Cry out with joy to God all the earth,
O sing to the glory of his name.
O render him glorious praise.
Say to God: "How tremendous your
deeds! ℞.

Before you all the earth shall bow,
shall sing to you, sing to your name!"
Come and see the works of God,
tremendous his deeds among
men. ℟.

He turned the sea into dry land,
they passed through the river dry-shod.
Let joy then be in him;
he rules for ever by his might. ℟.

Come and hear, all who fear God.
I will tell what he did for my soul;
Blessed be God who did not reject my
prayer
nor withhold his love from me. ℟.

READING II *Galatians 6, 14-18 / 103*

May I never boast of anything but the cross of the Lord Jesus Christ! Through it, the world has been crucified to me and I to the world. It means nothing whether one is circumcised or not. All that matters is that one is created anew. Peace and mercy on all who follow this rule of life, and on the Israel of God.

Henceforth, let no man trouble me, for I bear the brand marks of Jesus in my body.

Brothers, may the favor of our Lord Jesus Christ be with your spirit. Amen.

GOSPEL *Luke 10, 1-12.17-20 or 10, 1-9 / 103*

For short form read only the part in brackets.

[The Lord appointed a further seventy-two and sent them in pairs before him to every town and place he intended to visit. He said to them: "The harvest is rich but the workers are few; therefore ask the harvest-master to send workers to his harvest. Be on your way, and remember: I am sending you as lambs in the midst of wolves. Do not carry a walking staff or traveling bag; wear no sandals and greet no one along the way. On entering any house, first say, 'Peace to this house.' If there is a peaceable man there, your peace will rest on him; if not, it will come back to you. Stay in the one house eating and drinking what they have, for the laborer is worth his wage. Do not move from house to house.

"Into whatever city you go, after they welcome you, eat what they set before you, and cure the sick there. Say to them, 'The reign of God is at hand.'] If the people of any town you enter do not welcome you, go into its streets and say, 'We shake the dust of this town from our feet as testimony against you. But know that the reign of God is near.' I assure you, on that day the fate of Sodom will be less severe than that of such a town."

The seventy-two returned in jubilation saying, "Master, even the demons are subject to us in your name." He said in reply: "I watched Satan fall from the sky like lightning. See what I have done; I have given you power to tread on snakes and scorpions and all the forces of the enemy, and nothing shall ever injure you. Nevertheless, do not rejoice so much in the fact that the devils are subject to you as that your names are inscribed in heaven."

FIFTEENTH SUNDAY IN ORDINARY TIME / A 907

READING I *Isaiah 55,10-11/104*

Just as from the heavens
the rain and snow come down
And do not return there
till they have watered the earth,
making it fertile and fruitful,
Giving seed to him who sows
and bread to him who eats,

So shall my word be
that goes forth from my mouth;
It shall not return to me void,
but shall do my will,
achieving the end for which I sent
it.

RESPONSORIAL PSALM *Psalm (64)65, 10.11.12-13.14 / 104*

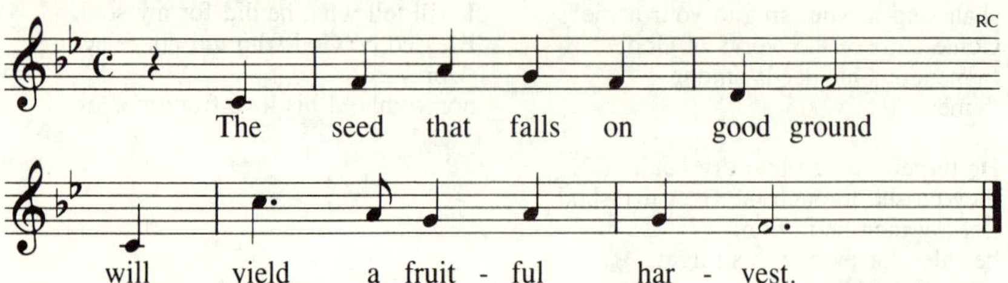
RC
The seed that falls on good ground
will yield a fruit - ful har - vest.

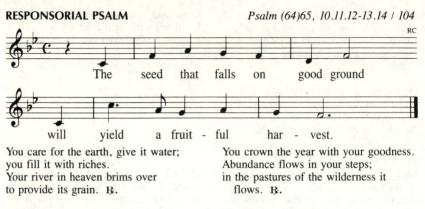

You care for the earth, give it water;
you fill it with riches.
Your river in heaven brims over
to provide its grain. ℟.

And thus you provide for the earth;
you drench its furrows;
you level it, soften it with showers;
you bless its growth. ℟.

You crown the year with your goodness.
Abundance flows in your steps;
in the pastures of the wilderness it
flows. ℟.

The hills are girded with joy,
the meadows covered with flocks,
the valleys are decked with wheat.
They shout for joy, yes, they sing. ℟.

READING II *Romans 8, 18-23 / 104*

I consider the sufferings of the present to be as nothing compared with the glory to be revealed in us. Indeed the whole created world eagerly awaits the revelation of the sons of God. Creation was made subject to futility, not of its own accord but by him who once subjected it; yet not without hope, because the world itself will be freed from its slavery to corruption and share in the glorious freedom of the children of God. Yes, we know that all creation groans and is in agony even until now. Not only that, but we ourselves, although we have the Spirit as first fruits, groan inwardly while we await the redemption of our bodies.

GOSPEL *Matthew 13, 1-23 or 13, 1-9 / 104*

For short form read only the part in brackets.

[Jesus, on leaving the house on a certain day, sat down by the lakeshore. Such great crowds gathered around him that he went and took his seat in a boat while the crowd stood along the shore. He addressed them at length in parables, speaking in this fashion:

"One day a farmer went out sowing. Part of what he sowed landed on a footpath, where birds came and ate it up. Part of it fell on rocky ground where it had little soil. It sprouted at once since the soil had no depth, but when the sun rose and scorched it, it began to wither for lack of roots. Again part of the seed fell among thorns, which grew up and choked it. Part of it, finally, landed on good soil and yielded grain at a hundred- or sixty- or thirty-fold. Let everyone heed what he hears!"]

When the disciples got near him, they asked him, "Why do you speak to them in parables?" He answered: "To you has been given a knowledge of the mysteries of the reign of God, but it has not been given to the others. To the man who has, more will be given until he grows rich; the man who has not, will lose what little he has.

"I use parables when I speak to them because they look but do not see, they listen but do not hear or understand. Isaiah's prophecy is fulfilled in them which says:

'Listen as you will, you shall not understand,
look intently as you will, you shall not see.
Sluggish indeed is this peoples's heart.
They have scarcely heard with their ears,
they have firmly closed their eyes;
otherwise they might see with their eyes,
and hear with their ears,

and understand with their hearts,
and turn back to me,
and I should heal them.'

"But blest are your eyes because they see and blest are your ears because they hear. I assure you, many a prophet and many a saint longed to see what you see but did not see it, to hear what you hear but did not hear it.

"Mark well, then, the parable of the sower. The seed along the path is the man who hears the message about God's reign without understanding it. The evil one approaches him to steal away what was sown in his mind. The seed that fell on patches of rock is the man who hears the message and at first receives it with joy. But he has no roots, so he lasts only for a time. When some setback or persecution involving the message occurs, he soon falters. What was sown among briers is the man who hears the message, but then worldly anxiety and the lure of money choke it off. Such a one produces no yield. But what was sown on good soil is the man who hears the message and takes it in. He it is who bears a yield of a hundred- or sixty- or thiry-fold."

FIFTEENTH SUNDAY IN ORDINARY TIME / B 908

READING I *Amos 7, 12-15 / 105*

Amaziah (priest of Bethel) said to Amos, "Off with you, visionary, flee to the land of Judah! There earn your bread by prophesying, but never again prophesy in Bethel; for it is the king's sanctuary and a royal temple." Amos answered Amaziah, "I was no prophet, nor have I belonged to a company of prophets; I was a shepherd and a dresser of sycamores. The Lord took me from following the flock, and said to me, Go, prophesy to my people Israel."

RESPONSORIAL PSALM *Psalm (84)85, 9-10.11-12.13-14 / 105*

JRC
Lord, let us see your kind-ness, and grant us your sal - va-tion.

I will hear what the Lord God has to say,
a voice that speaks of peace.
His help is near for those who fear him
and his glory will dwell in our land. ℟.

Mercy and faithfulness have met;
justice and peace have embraced.
Faithfulness shall spring from the earth
and justice look down from heaven. ℟.

The Lord will make us prosper
and our earth shall yield its fruit.
Justice shall march before him
and peace shall follow his steps. ℟.

READING II *Ephesians 1, 3-14 or 1, 3-10 / 105*

For short form read only the part in brackets.

[Praised be the God and Father of our Lord Jesus Christ, who has bestowed on us in Christ every spiritual blessing in the heavens! God chose us in him before the world began, to be holy and blameless in his sight, to be full of love; he likewise predestined us through Christ Jesus to be his adopted sons–such was his will and pleasure–that all might praise the divine favor he has bestowed on us in his beloved.

It is in Christ and through his blood that we have been redeemed and our sins forgiven, so immeasurably generous is God's favor to us. God has given us the wisdom to understand fully the mystery, the plan he was pleased to decree in Christ, to be carried out in the fullness of time: namely, to bring all things in the heavens and on earth into one under Christ's headship.]

In him we were chosen; for in the decree of God, who administers everything according to his will and counsel, we were predestined to praise his glory by being the first to hope in Christ. In him you too were chosen; when you heard the glad tidings of salvation, the word of truth, and believed in it, you were sealed with the Holy Spirit who had been promised. He is the pledge of our inheritance, the first payment against the full redemption of a people God has made his own to praise his glory.

GOSPEL *Mark 6, 7-13 / 105*

Jesus summoned the Twelve and began to send them out two by two, giving them authority over unclean spirits. He instructed them to take nothing on the journey but a walking stick–no food, no traveling bag, not a coin in the purses in their belts. They were however, to wear sandals. "Do not bring a second tunic," he said and added: "Whatever house you find yourself in, stay there until you leave the locality. If any place will not receive you or hear you, shake its dust from your feet in testimony against them as you leave." With that they went off, preaching the need of repentance. They expelled many demons, anointed the sick with oil, and worked many cures.

909 FIFTEENTH SUNDAY IN ORDINARY TIME / C

READING I *Deuteronomy 30, 10-14 / 106*

Moses said to the people: "If only you heed the voice of the Lord, your God, and keep his commandments and statutes that are written in this book of the law, when you return to the Lord, your God, with all your heart and all your soul.

"For this command which I enjoin on you today is not too mysterious and remote for you. It is not up in the sky, that you should say, 'Who will go up in the sky to get it for us and tell us of it, that we may carry it out?' Nor is it across the sea, that you should say, 'Who will cross the sea to get it for us and tell us of it, that we may carry it out?' No, it is something very near to you, already in your mouths and in your hearts; you have only to carry it out."

RESPONSORIAL PSALM *Psalm (68)69, 14.17.30-31.33-34.36.37 / 106*

JRC/RJB
Turn to the Lord in your need, and you will live.

This is my prayer to you,
my prayer for your favor.
In your great love, answer me, O God,
with your help that never fails.
Lord, answer, for your love is kind;
in your compassion, turn towards me. ℟.

As for me in my poverty and pain,
let your help, O God, lift me up.
I will praise God's name with a song;
I will glorify him with thanksgiving. ℟.

The poor when they see it will be glad
and God-seeking hearts will revive;
for the Lord listens to the needy
and does not spurn his servants in their chains. ℟.

For God will bring help to Zion
and rebuild the cities of Judah.
The sons of his servants shall inherit it;
those who love his name shall dwell there. ℟.

READING II *Colossians, 1, 15-20 / 106*

Christ Jesus is the image of the invisible God, the first-born of all creatures. In him everything in heaven and on earth was created, things visible and invisible, whether thrones or dominations, principalities or powers; all were created through him and for him. He is before all else that is. In him everything continues in being. It is he who is head of the body, the church; he who is the beginning, the firstborn of the dead, so that primacy may be his in everything. It pleased God to make absolute fullness reside in him and, by means of him, to reconcile everything in his person, everything, I say, both on earth and in the heavens, making peace through the blood of his cross.

GOSPEL *Luke 10, 25-37 / 106*

On one occasion a lawyer stood up to pose this problem to Jesus: "Teacher, what must I do to inherit everlasting life?" Jesus answered him: "What is written in the law? Have you read it?" He replied:

"You shall love the Lord your God
with all your heart,
with all your soul,
with all your strength,
and with all your mind;
and your neighbor as yourself."

Jesus said, "You have answered correctly. Do this and you shall live." But because he wished to justify himself he said to Jesus, "And who is my neighbor?" Jesus replied: "There was a man going down from Jerusalem to Jericho who fell in with robbers. They stripped him, beat him, and then went off leaving him half-dead. A priest happened to be going down the same road; he saw him but continued on. Likewise there was a Levite who came the same way; he saw him and went on. But a Samaritan who was journeying along came on him and was moved to pity at the sight. He approached him and dressed his wounds, pouring in oil and wine as a means to heal. He then hoisted him on his own beast and brought him to an inn, where he cared for him. The next day he took out two silver pieces and gave them to the innkeeper with the request: 'Look after him, and if there is any further expense I will repay you on my way back.'

"Which of these three, in your opinion, was neighbor to the man who fell in with the robbers?" The answer came, "The one who treated him with compassion." Jesus said to him, "Then go and do the same."

SIXTEENTH SUNDAY IN ORDINARY TIME / A 910

READING I *Wisdom 12, 13.16-19 / 107*

There is no god besides you who have
the care of all,
that you need show you have not
unjustly condemned.
For your might is the source of justice;
your mastery over all things makes
you lenient to all.
For you show your might when the
perfection of your power is
disbelieved;
and in those who know you, you
rebuke temerity.
But though you are master of might,
you judge with clemency,
and with much lenience you govern
us;
for power, whenever you will,
attends you.
And you taught your people, by these
deeds,
that those who are just must be kind;
And you gave your sons good ground
for hope
that you would permit repentance for
their sins.

RESPONSORIAL PSALM *Psalm (85)86, 5-6.9-10.15-17 / 107*

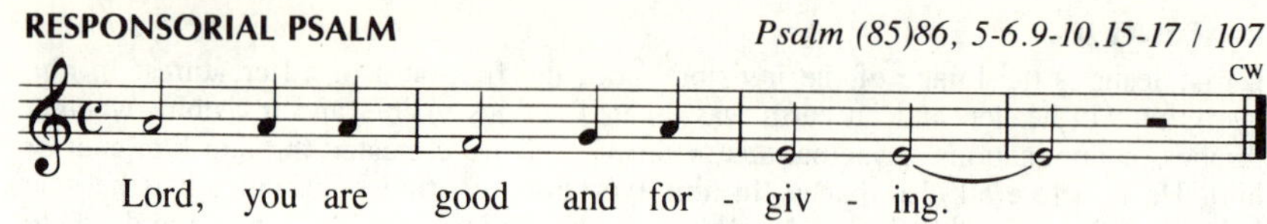
CW
Lord, you are good and for - giv - ing.

O Lord, you are good and forgiving,
full of love to all who call.
Give heed, O Lord, to my prayer
and attend to the sound of my
voice. ℟.

All the nations shall come to adore you
and glorify your name, O Lord,
for you are great and do marvelous
deeds,
you who alone are God. ℟.

But you, God of mercy and compassion,
slow to anger, O Lord,
abounding in love and truth,
turn and take pity on me.
O give your strength to your
servant. ℟.

READING II *Romans 8, 26-27 / 107*

The Spirit too helps us in our weakness, for we do not know how to pray as we ought; but the Spirit himself makes intercession for us with groanings which cannot be expressed in speech. He who searches hearts knows what the Spirit means, for the Spirit intercedes for the saints as God himself wills.

GOSPEL *Matthew 13, 24-43 or 13,24-30 / 107*

For short form read only the part in brackets.

[Jesus proposed to the crowd another parable: "The reign of God may be likened to a man who sowed good seed in his field. While everyone was asleep, his enemy came and sowed weeds through his wheat, and then made off. When the crop began to mature and yield grain, the weeds made their appearance as well. The owner's slaves came to him and said, 'Sir, did you not sow good seed in your field? Where are the weeds coming from?' He answered, 'I see an enemy's hand in this.' His slaves said to him, 'Do you want us to go out and pull them up?' 'No,' he replied, 'pull up the weeds and you might take the wheat along with them. Let them grow together until harvest; then at harvest time I will order the harvesters, first collect the weeds and bundle them up to burn, then gather the wheat into my barn.' "]

He proposed still another parable: "The reign of God is like a mustard seed which someone took and sowed in his field. It is the smallest seed of all, yet when full-grown it is the largest of plants. It becomes so big a shrub that the birds of the sky come and build their nests in its branches."

He offered them still another image: "The reign of God is like yeast which a woman took and kneaded into three measures of flour. Eventually the whole mass of dough began to rise." All these lessons Jesus taught the crowds in the form of parables. He spoke to them in parables only, to fulfill what had been said through the prophet:

"I will open my mouth in parables,
I will announce what has lain hidden since
the creation of the world."

Then, dismissing the crowds, he went home. His disciples came to him with the request, "Explain to us the parable of the weeds in the field." He said in answer: "The farmer sowing good seed is the Son of Man; the field is the world, the good seed the citizens of the kingdom. The weeds are the followers of the evil one and the enemy who sowed them is the devil. The harvest is the end of the world, while the harvesters are the angels. Just as weeds are collected and burned, so it will be at the end of the world. The Son of Man will dispatch his angels to collect from his kingdom all who draw others to apostasy, and all evildoers. The angels will hurl them into the fiery furnace where they will wail and grind their teeth. Then the saints will shine like the sun in their Father's kingdom. Let everyone heed what he hears!"

SIXTEENTH SUNDAY IN ORDINARY TIME / B

911

READING I *Jeremiah 23,1-6 / 108*

Woe to the shepherds who mislead and scatter the flock of my pasture, says the Lord. Therefore, thus says the Lord, the God of Israel, against the shepherds who shepherd my people: You have scattered my sheep and driven them away. You have not cared for them, but I will take care to punish your evil deeds. I myself will gather the remnant of my flock from all the lands to which I have driven them and bring them back to their meadow; there they shall increase and multiply. I will appoint shepherds for them who will shepherd them so that they need no longer fear and tremble; and none shall be missing, says the Lord.

Behold, the days are coming, says the Lord,
when I shall raise up a righteous shoot to David;
As king he shall reign and govern wisely,
he shall do what is just and right in the land.
In his days Judah shall be saved,
Israel shall dwell in security.
This is the name they give him:
"The Lord our justice."

RESPONSORIAL PSALM *Psalm (22)23, 1-3.3-4.5.6 / 108*

RP
The Lord is my shep - herd;
there is noth - ing I shall want.

The Lord is my shepherd;
there is nothing I shall want.
Fresh and green are the pastures
where he gives me repose.
Near restful waters he leads me,
to revive my drooping spirit. ℟.

He guides me along the right path;
he is true to his name.
If I should walk in the valley of darkness
no evil would I fear.
You are there with your crook and your staff;
with these you give me comfort. ℟.

You have prepared a banquet for me
in the sight of my foes.
My head you have anointed with oil;
my cup is overflowing. ℟.

Surely goodness and kindness shall follow me
all the days of my life.
In the Lord's own house shall I dwell
for ever and ever. ℟.

READING II *Ephesians 2, 13-18 / 108*

In Christ Jesus you who once were far off have been brought near through the blood of Christ. It is he who is our peace, and who made the two of us one by breaking down the barrier of hostility that kept us apart. In his own flesh he abolished the law with its commands and precepts, to create in himself one new man from us who had been two, and to make peace, reconciling both of us to God in one body through his cross which put that enmity to death. He came and "announced the good news of peace to you who were far off, and to those who were near"; through him we both have access in one Spirit to the Father.

GOSPEL *Mark 6, 30-34 / 108*

The apostles returned to Jesus and reported to him all that they had done and what they had taught. He said to them, "Come by yourselves to an out-of-the-way place and rest a little." People were coming and going in great numbers, making it impossible for them to so much as eat. So Jesus and the apostles went off in the boat by themselves to a deserted place. People saw them leaving, and many got to know about it. People from all the towns hastened on foot to the place, arriving ahead of them.

Upon disembarking Jesus saw a vast crowd. He pitied them, for they were like sheep without a shepherd; and he began to teach them at great length.

912 SIXTEENTH SUNDAY IN ORDINARY TIME / C

READING I *Genesis 18, 1-10 / 109*

The Lord appeared to Abraham by the terebinth of Mamre, as he sat in the entrance of his tent, while the day was growing hot. Looking up, he saw three men standing nearby. When he saw them, he ran from the entrance of the tent to greet them; and bowing to the ground, he said: "Sir, if I may ask you this favor, please do not go on past your servant. Let some water be brought, that you may bathe your feet, and then rest yourselves under the tree. Now that you have come this close to your servant, let me bring you a little food, that you may refresh yourselves; and afterward you may go on your way." "Very well," they replied, "do as you have said."

Abraham hastened into the tent and told Sarah, "Quick, three seahs of fine flour! Knead it and make rolls." He ran to the herd, picked out a tender, choice steer, and gave it to a servant, who quickly prepared it. Then he got some curds and milk, as well as the steer that had been prepared, and set these before them; and he waited on them under the tree while they ate.

"Where is your wife Sarah?" they asked him, "There in the tent," he replied. One of them said, "I will surely return to you about this time next year, and Sarah will then have a son."

RESPONSORIAL PSALM *Psalm (14)15, 2-3.3-4.5 / 109*

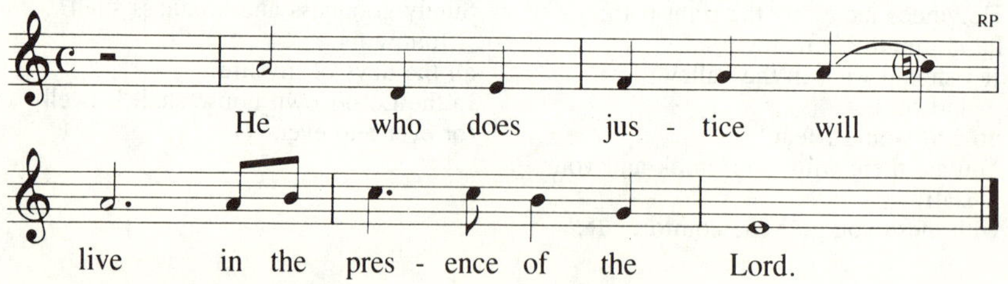
RP
He who does jus - tice will
live in the pres - ence of the Lord.

He who walks without fault,
he who acts with justice
and speaks the truth from his heart,
he who does not slander with his
tongue. ℟.

He who does no wrong to his
brother,
who casts no slur on his neighbor,
who holds the godless in disdain,
but honors those who fear the Lord; ℟.

Who takes no interest on a loan
and accepts no bribes against the
innocent.
Such a man will stand firm for
ever. ℟.

READING II *Colossians 1, 24-28 / 109*

Even now I find my joy in the suffering I endure for you. In my own flesh I fill up what is lacking in the sufferings of Christ for the sake of his body, the church. I became a minister of this church through the commission God gave me to preach among you his word in its fullness, that mystery hidden from ages and generations past but now revealed to his holy ones. God has willed to make known to them the glory beyond price which this mystery brings to the Gentiles–the mystery of Christ in you, your hope of glory. This is the Christ we proclaim while we admonish all men and teach them in the full measure of wisdom, hoping to make every man complete in Christ.

GOSPEL *Luke 10, 38-42 / 109*

Jesus entered a village where a woman named Martha welcomed him to her home. She had a sister named Mary, who seated herself at the Lord's feet and listened to his words. Martha, who was busy with all the details of hospitality, came to him and said, "Lord, are you not concerned that my sister has left me alone to do the household tasks? Tell her to help me."

The Lord in reply said to her: "Martha, Martha, you are anxious and upset about many things; one thing only is required. Mary has chosen the better portion and she shall not be deprived of it."

SEVENTEENTH SUNDAY IN ORDINARY TIME / A 913

READING I *1 Kings 3, 5.7-12 / 110*

The Lord appeared to Solomon in a dream at night. God said, "Ask something of me and I will give it to you." Solomon answered: "O Lord, my God, you have made me, your servant, king to succeed my father David; but I am a mere youth, not knowing at all how to act. I serve you in the midst of the people whom you have chosen, a people so vast that it cannot be numbered or counted. Give your servant, therefore, an understanding heart to judge your people and to distinguish right from wrong. For who is able to govern this vast people of yours?"

The Lord was pleased that Solomon made this request. So God said to him: "Because you have asked for this–not for a long life for yourself, nor for riches, nor for the life of your enemies, but for understanding so that you may know what is right–I do as you requested. I give you a heart so wise and understanding that there has never been anyone like you up to now, and after you there will come no one to equal you."

RESPONSORIAL PSALM *Psalm (118)119, 57.72.76-77.127-128.129-130 / 110*

RJB
Lord, I love your com - mands.

My part, I have resolved, O Lord,
is to obey your word.
The law from your mouth means more
to me
than silver and gold. ℟.

Let your love be ready to console me
by your promise to your servant.
Let your love come and I shall live
for your law is my delight. ℟.

That is why I love your commands
more than finest gold,
why I rule my life by your precepts,
and hate false ways. ℟.

Your will is wonderful indeed;
therefore I obey it.
The unfolding of your word gives light
and teaches the simple. ℟.

READING II *Romans 8, 28-30 / 110*

We know that God makes all things work together for the good of those who love him, who have been called according to his decree. Those whom he foreknew he predestined to share the image of his Son, that the Son might be the first-born of many brothers. Those he predestined he likewise called; those he called he also justified; and those he justified he in turn glorified.

GOSPEL *Matthew 13, 44-52 or 13, 44-46 / 110*

For short form read only the part in brackets.

[Jesus said to the crowd: "The reign of God is like a buried treasure which a man found in a field. He hid it again, and rejoicing at his find went and sold all he had and bought that field. Or again, the kingdom of heaven is like a merchant's search for fine pearls. When he found one really valuable pearl, he went back and put up for sale all that he had and bought it.]

"The reign of God is also like a dragnet thrown into the lake, which collected all sorts of things. When it was full they hauled it ashore and sat down to put what was worthwhile into containers. What was useless they threw away. That is how it will be at the end of the world. Angels will go out and separate the wicked from the just and hurl the wicked into the fiery furnace, where they will wail and grind their teeth.

"Have you understood all this?" "Yes," they answered; to which he replied, "Every scribe who is learned in the reign of God is like the head of a household who can bring from his store the new and the old."

914 SEVENTEENTH SUNDAY IN ORDINARY TIME / B

READING I *2 Kings 4, 42-44 / 111*

A man came from Baal-shalishah bringing to Elisha, the man of God, twenty barley loaves made from the firstfruits, and fresh grain in the ear. "Give it to the people to eat," Elisha said. But his servant objected, "How can I set this before a hundred men?" "Give it to the people to eat," Elisha insisted. "For thus says the Lord, 'They shall eat and there shall be some left over.' " And when they had eaten, there was some left over, as the Lord had said.

RESPONSORIAL PSALM *Psalm (144)145, 10-11.15-16.17-18 / 111*

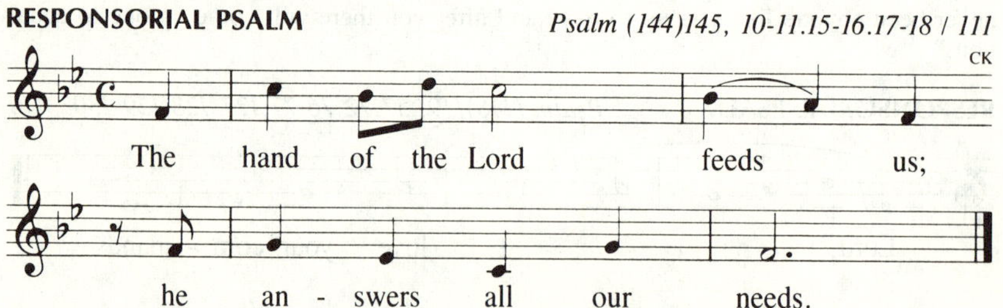
CK
The hand of the Lord feeds us;
he an - swers all our needs.

All your creatures shall thank you, O Lord,
and your friends shall repeat their blessing.

They shall speak of the glory of your reign
and declare your might, O God. ℟.

The eyes of all creatures look to you
and you give them their food in due
time.
You open wide your hand,
grant the desires of all who live. ℞.

The Lord is just in all his ways
and loving in all his deeds.
He is close to all who call him,
who call on him from their hearts. ℞.

READING II *Ephesians 4, 1-6 / 111*

I plead with you as a prisoner for the Lord, to live a life worthy of the calling you have received, with perfect humility, meekness, and patience, bearing with one another lovingly. Make every effort to preserve unity which has the Spirit as its origin and peace as its binding force. There is but one body and one Spirit, just as there is but one hope given all of you by your call. There is one Lord, one faith, one baptism; one God and Father of all, who is over all, and works through all, and is in all.

GOSPEL *John 6, 1-15 / 111*

Jesus crossed the Sea of Galilee [to the shore] of Tiberias; a vast crowd kept following him because they saw the signs he was performing for the sick. Jesus then went up the mountain and sat down there with his disciples. The Jewish feast of Passover was near; when Jesus looked up and caught sight of a vast crowd coming toward him, he said to Philip, "Where shall we buy bread for these people to eat?" (He knew well what he intended to do but he asked this to test Philip's response.) Philip replied, "Not even with two hundred days' wages could we buy loaves enough to give each of them a mouthful!"

One of Jesus' disciples, Andrew, Simon Peter's brother, remarked to him, "There is a lad here who has five barley loaves and a couple of dried fish, but what good is that for so many?" Jesus said, "Get the people to recline." Even though the men numbered about five thousand, there was plenty of grass for them to find a place on the ground. Jesus then took the loaves of bread, gave thanks, and passed them around to those reclining there; he did the same with the dried fish, as much as they wanted. When they had had enough, he told his disciples, "Gather up the crusts that are left over so that nothing will go to waste." At this, they gathered twelve baskets full of pieces left over by those who had been fed with the five barley loaves.

When the people saw the sign he had performed they began to say, "This is undoubtedly the Prophet who is to come into the world." At that, Jesus realized that they would come and carry him off to make him king, so he fled back to the mountain alone.

SEVENTEENTH SUNDAY IN ORDINARY TIME / C 915

READING I *Genesis 18, 20-32 / 112*

The Lord said: "The outcry against Sodom and Gomorrah is so great, and their sin so grave, that I must go down and see whether or not their actions fully correspond to the cry against them that comes to me. I mean to find out."

While the two men walked on farther toward Sodom, the Lord remained standing before Abraham. Then Abraham drew nearer to him and said: "Will you sweep away the innocent with the guilty? Suppose there were fifty innocent people in the city; would you wipe out the place, rather than spare it for the sake of the fifty innocent people within it? Far be it from you to do such a thing, to make the innocent die with the guilty, so that the innocent and the guilty would be treated alike! Should not the judge of all the world act with justice?" The Lord replied, "If I find fifty innocent people in the city of Sodom, I will spare the whole place for their sake." Abraham spoke up again: "See how I am presuming to speak to my Lord, though I am but dust and ashes! What if there are five less than fifty innocent people? Will you destroy the whole city because of those five?" "I will not destroy it," he answered, "if I find forty-five there." But Abraham persisted, saying, "What if only forty are found there?" He replied, "I will forbear doing it for the sake of the forty." Then he said, "Let not my Lord grow impatient if I go on. What if only thirty are found there?" He replied, "I will forbear doing it if I can find but thirty there." Still he went on, "Since I have thus dared to speak to my Lord, what if there are no more than twenty?" "I will not destroy it," he answered, "For the sake of the twenty." But he still persisted: "Please, let not my Lord grow angry if I speak up this last time. What if there are at least ten there?" "For the sake of those ten," he replied, "I will not destroy it."

RESPONSORIAL PSALM

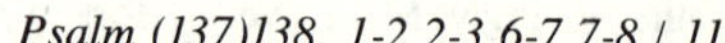

Psalm (137)138, 1-2.2-3.6-7.7-8 / 112

RCV
Lord, on the day I called for help, you an-swered me.

I thank you, Lord, with all my heart,
you have heard the words of my mouth.
In the presence of the angels I will
bless you.
I will adore before your holy
temple. ℟.

I thank you for your faithfulness and
love
which excel all we ever knew of you.
On the day I called, you answered;
you increased the strength of my
soul. ℟.

The Lord is high yet he looks on the
lowly
and the haughty he knows from afar.
Though I walk in the midst of affliction
you give me life and frustrate my
foes. ℟.

You stretch out your hand and save me,
your hand will do all things for me.
Your love, O Lord, is eternal,
discard not the work of your hands. ℟.

READING II *Colossians 2, 12-14 / 112*

In baptism you were not only buried with him but also raised to life with him because you believed in the power of God who raised him from the dead. Even when you were dead in sin and your flesh was uncircumcised, God gave you new life in company with Christ. He pardoned all our sins. He canceled the bond that stood against us with all its claims, snatching it up and nailing it to the cross.

GOSPEL *Luke 11, 1-13 / 112*

One day Jesus was praying in a certain place. When he had finished, one of his disciples asked him, "Lord, teach us to pray as John taught his disciples." He said to them, "When you pray, say:

"Father,
hallowed be your name,
your kingdom come.
Give us each day our daily bread.
Forgive us our sins
for we too forgive all who do us wrong;
and subject us not to the trial."

Jesus said to them: "If one of you knows someone who comes to him in the middle of the night and says to him, 'Friend, lend me three loaves, for a friend of mine has come in from a journey and I have nothing to offer him'; and he from inside should reply, 'Leave me alone. The door is shut now and my children and I are in bed. I can't get up to look after your needs'–I tell you, even though he does not get up and take care of the man because of friendship, he will find himself doing so because of his persistence and give him such as he needs.

"So I say to you, 'Ask and you shall receive; seek and you shall find; knock and it shall be opened to you,'

"For whoever asks, receives; whoever seeks, finds; whoever knocks, is admitted. What father among you will give his son a snake if he asks for fish, or hand him a scorpion if he asks for an egg? If you, with all your sins, know how to give your children good things, how much more will the heavenly Father give the Holy Spirit to those who ask him."

EIGHTEENTH SUNDAY IN ORDINARY TIME / A 916

READING I *Isaiah 55, 1-3 / 113*

All you who are thirsty,
come to the water!
You who have no money,
come, receive grain and eat;
Come, without paying and without cost,
drink wine and milk!
Why spend your money for what is not bread;
your wages for what fails to satisfy?
Heed me, and you shall eat well,
you shall delight in rich fare.
Come to me heedfully,
listen, that you may have life.
I will renew with you the everlasting covenant,
the benefits assured to David.

RESPONSORIAL PSALM *Psalm (144)145, 8-9.15-16.17-18 / 113*

CK
The hand of the Lord feeds us;
he an - swers all our needs.

The Lord is kind and full of compassion,
slow to anger, abounding in love.
How good is the Lord to all,
compassionate to all his creatures. ℟.

The eyes of all creatures look to you
and you give them their food in due time.
You open wide your hand,
grant the desires of all who live. ℟.

The Lord is just in all his ways
and loving in all his deeds.
He is close to all who call him,
who call on him from their hearts. ℟.

READING II *Romans 8, 35.37-39 / 113*

Who will separate us from the love of Christ? Trial, or distress, or persecution, or hunger, or nakedness, or danger, or the sword? Yet in all this we are more than conquerors because of him who has loved us. For I am certain that neither death nor life, neither angels or principalities, neither the present nor the future, nor powers, neither height nor depth nor any other creature, will be able to separate us from the love of God that comes to us in Christ Jesus, our Lord.

GOSPEL *Matthew 14, 13-21 / 113*

When Jesus heard [of the death of John the Baptizer], he withdrew by boat to a deserted place by himself. The crowds heard of it and followed him on foot from the towns. When he disembarked and saw the vast throng, his heart was moved with pity, and he cured their sick. As evening drew on, his disciples came to him with the suggestion: "This is a deserted place and it is already late. Dismiss the crowds so that they may go to the villages and buy some food for themselves." Jesus said to them: "There is no need for them to disperse. Give them something to eat yourselves." "We have nothing here," they replied, "but five loaves and a couple of fish." "Bring them here," he said. Then he ordered the crowds to sit down on the grass. He took the five loaves and two fish, looked up to heaven, blessed and broke them and gave the loaves to the disciples, who in turn gave them to the people. All those present ate their fill. The fragments which remained, when gathered up, filled twelve baskets. Those who ate were about five thousand, not counting women and children.

917 EIGHTEENTH SUNDAY IN ORDINARY TIME / B

READING I *Exodus 16, 2-4.12-15 / 114*

The whole Israelite community grumbled against Moses and Aaron. The Israelites said to them, "Would that we had died at the Lord's hand in the land of Egypt, as we sat by our fleshpots and ate our fill of bread! But you had to lead us into this desert to make the whole community die of famine!"

Then the Lord said to Moses, "I will now rain down bread from heaven for you. Each day the people are to go out and gather their daily portion; thus will I test them, to see whether they follow my instructions or not.

"I have heard the grumbling of the Israelites. Tell them: In the evening twilight you shall eat flesh, and in the morning you shall have your fill of bread, so that you may know that I, the Lord, am your God."

In the evening quail came up and covered the camp. In the morning a dew lay all about the camp, and when the dew evaporated, there on the surface of the desert were fine flakes like hoarfrost on the ground. On seeing it, the Israelites asked one another, "What is this?" for they did not know what it was. But Moses told them, "This is the bread which the Lord has given you to eat."

RESPONSORIAL PSALM *Psalm (77)78, 3-4.23-24.25.54 / 114*

RC
The Lord gave them bread, gave them bread from heav-en.

The things we have heard and understood,
the things our fathers have told us
these we will not hide from their children
but will tell them to the next generation:
the glories of the Lord and his might
and the marvelous deeds he has done. ℟.

Yet he commanded the clouds above
and opened the gates of heaven.
He rained down manna for their food,
and gave them bread from heaven. ℟.

Mere men ate the bread of angels.
He sent them abundance of food.
So he brought them to his holy land,
to the mountain which his right hand had won. ℟.

READING II *Ephesians 4, 17.20-24 / 114*

I declare and solemnly attest in the Lord that you must no longer live as the pagans do–their minds empty. That is not what you learned when you learned Christ! I am supposing, of course, that he has been preached and taught to you in accord with the truth that is in Jesus: namely, that you must lay aside your former way of life and the old self which deteriorates through illusion and desire, and acquire a fresh, spiritual way of thinking. You must put on that new man created in God's image, whose justice and holiness are born of truth.

GOSPEL *John 6, 24-35 / 114*

When the crowds saw that neither Jesus nor his disciples were at the place where Jesus had eaten the bread, they too embarked in the boats and went to Capernaum looking for Jesus.

When they found him on the other side of the lake, they said to him, "Rabbi, when did you come here?" Jesus answered them:

"I assure you,
you are not looking for me because
you have seen signs
but because you have eaten your fill
of the loaves.
You should not be working for
perishable food
but for food that remains unto life
eternal,
food which the Son of Man will give
you;
it is on him that God the Father has
set his seal."

At this they said to him, "What must we do to perform the works of God?" Jesus replied:

"This is the work of God:
have faith in the One he sent."

"So that we can put faith in you," they asked him, "what sign are you going to perform for us to see? What is the 'work' you do? Our ancestors had manna to eat in the desert; according to Scripture, 'He gave them bread from the heavens to eat.' " Jesus said to them:

"I solemnly assure you,
it was not Moses who gave you bread
from the heavens;
it is my Father who gives you the
real heavenly bread.
God's bread comes down from
heaven and gives life to the
world."

"Sir, give us this bread always," they besought him.

Jesus explained to them:

"I myself am the bread of life.
No one who comes to me shall ever
be hungry,
no one who believes in me shall
thirst again."

EIGHTEENTH SUNDAY IN ORDINARY TIME / C 918

READING I *Ecclesiates 1, 2; 2, 21-23 / 115*

Vanity of vanities, says Qoheleth, vanity of vanities! All things are vanity!

Here is a man who has labored with wisdom and knowledge and skill, and to another, who has not labored over it, he must leave his property. This also is vanity and a great misfortune. For what profit comes to a man from all the toil and anxiety of heart with which he has labored under the sun? All his days sorrow and grief are his occupation; even at night his mind is not at rest. This also is vanity.

RESPONSORIAL PSALM *Psalm (94)95, 1-2.6-7.8-9 / 115*

RP
If to - day you hear his voice, O hard - en not your hearts.

Come, ring out our joy to the Lord;
hail the rock who saves us.

Let us come before him, giving thanks,
with songs let us hail the Lord. ℟.

Come in; let us bow and bend low;
let us kneel before the God who made us
for he is our God and we
the people who belong to his pasture,
the flock that is led by his hand. ℟.

O that today you would listen to his voice!
"Harden not your hearts as at Meribah,
as on that day at Massah in the desert
when your fathers put me to the test;
when they tried me, though they saw my work." ℟.

READING II *Colossians 3, 1-5.9-11 / 115*

Since you have been raised up in company with Christ, set your heart on what pertains to higher realms where Christ is seated at God's right hand. Be intent on things above rather than on things of earth. After all, you have died! Your life is hidden now with Christ in God. When Christ our life appears, then you shall appear with him in glory.

Put to death whatever in your nature is rooted in earth: fornication, uncleanness, passion, evil desires, and that lust which is idolatry. Stop lying to one another. What you have done is put aside your old self with its past deeds and put on a new man, one who grows in knowledge as he is formed anew in the image of his Creator. There is no Greek or Jew here, circumcised or uncircumcised, foreigner, Scythian, slave, or freeman. Rather, Christ is everything in all of you.

GOSPEL *Luke 12, 13-21 / 115*

Someone in the crowd said to Jesus, "Teacher, tell my brother to give me my share of our inheritance." He replied, "Friend, who has set me up as your judge or arbiter?" Then he said to the crowd, "Avoid greed in all its forms. A man may be wealthy, but his possessions do not guarantee him life."

He told them a parable in these words: "There was a rich man who had a good harvest. 'What shall I do?' he asked himself. 'I have no place to store my harvest. I know!' he said, 'I will pull down my grain bins and build larger ones. All my grain and my goods will go there. Then I will say to myself: You have blessings in reserve for years to come. Relax! Eat heartily, drink well. Enjoy yourself.' But God said to him, 'You fool! This very night your life shall be required of you. To whom will all this piled-up wealth of yours go?' That is the way it works with the man who grows rich for himself instead of growing rich in the sight of God."

919 NINETEENTH SUNDAY IN ORDINARY TIME / A

READING I *1 Kings 19, 9.11-13 / 116*

Elijah came to a cave [from the mountain of God, Horeb], where he took shelter. Then the Lord said, "Go outside and stand on the mountain before the Lord; the Lord will be passing by." A strong and heavy wind was rending the mountains and crushing rocks before the Lord–but the Lord was not in the wind. After the wind there was an earthquake–but the Lord was not in the earthquake. After the earthquake there was a fire–but the Lord was not in the fire. After the fire there was a tiny whispering sound. When he heard this, Elijah hid his face in his cloak and went and stood at the entrance of the cave.

RESPONSORIAL PSALM *Psalm (84)85, 9.10.11-12.13-14 / 116*

JRC

Lord, let us see your kind-ness, and grant us your sal - va-tion.

I will hear what the Lord God has to say,
a voice that speaks of peace.

His help is near for those who fear him
and his glory will dwell in our land. ℟.

Mercy and faithfulness have met;
justice and peace have embraced.
Faithfulness shall spring from the earth
and justice look down from heaven. ℟.

The Lord will make us prosper
and our earth shall yield its fruit.
Justice shall march before him
and peace shall follow his steps. ℟.

READING II *Romans 9, 1-5 / 116*

I speak the truth in Christ: I do not lie. My conscience bears me witness in the Holy Spirit that there is great grief and constant pain in my heart. Indeed, I could even wish to be separated from Christ for the sake of my brothers, my kinsmen the Israelites. Theirs were the adoption, the glory, the covenants, the lawgiving, the worship, and the promises; theirs were the patriarchs, and from them came the Messiah (I speak of his human origins). Blessed forever be God who is over all! Amen.

GOSPEL *Matthew 14, 22-33 / 116*

[After the crowds had their fill] Jesus insisted that his disciples get into the boat and precede him to the other side. When he had sent them away, he went up on the mountain by himself to pray, remaining there alone as evening drew on. Meanwhile the boat, already several hundred yards out from shore, was being tossed about in the waves raised by strong head winds. At about three in the morning, he came walking toward them on the lake. When the disciples saw him walking on the water, they were terrified. "It is a ghost!" they said, and in their fear they began to cry out. Jesus hastened to reassure them: "Get hold of yourselves! It is I. Do not be afraid!" Peter spoke up and said, "Lord if it is really you, tell me to come to you across the water." "Come!" he said. So Peter got out of the boat and began to walk on the water moving toward Jesus. But when he perceived how strong the wind was, becoming frightened he began to sink, and cried out, "Lord, save me!" Jesus at once stretched out his hand and caught him. "How little faith you have!" he exclaimed. "Why did you falter?" Once they had climbed into the boat, the wind died down. Those who were in the boat showed him reverence, declaring, "Beyond doubt you are the Son of God!"

NINETEENTH SUNDAY IN ORDINARY TIME / B 920

READING I *1 Kings 19, 4-8 / 117*

Elijah went a day's journey into the desert, until he came to a broom tree and sat beneath it. He prayed for death: "This is enough, O Lord! Take my life, for I am no better than my fathers." He lay down and fell asleep under the broom tree, but then an angel touched him and ordered him to get up and eat. He looked and there at his head was a hearth cake and jug of water. After he ate and drank, he lay down again, but the angel of the Lord came back a second time, touched him, and ordered, "Get up and eat, else the journey will be too long for you!" He got up, ate and drank; then strengthened by that food, he walked forty days and forty nights to the mountain of God, Horeb.

RESPONSORIAL PSALM *Psalm (33)34, 2-3.4-5.6-7.8-9 / 117*

RP
Taste and see the good - ness of the Lord.

I will bless the Lord at all times,
his praise always on my lips;
in the Lord my soul shall make its
boast.
The humble shall hear and be glad. ℟.

Glorify the Lord with me.
Together let us praise him name.
I sought the Lord and he answered me;
from all my terrors he set me free. ℟.

Look towards him and be radiant;
let your faces not be abashed.
This poor man called; the Lord heard him
and rescued him from all his distress. ℟.

The angel of the Lord is encamped
around those who revere him, to rescue them.
Taste and see that the Lord is good.
He is happy who seeks refuge in him. ℟.

READING II *Ephesians 4, 30-5, 2 / 117*

Do nothing to sadden the Holy Spirit with whom you were sealed against the day of redemption. Get rid of all bitterness, all passion and anger, harsh words, slander, and malice of every kind. In place of these, be kind to one another, compassionate, and mutually forgiving, just as God has forgiven you in Christ.

Be imitators of God as his dear children. Follow the way of love, even as Christ loved you. He gave himself for us as an offering to God, a gift of pleasing fragrance.

GOSPEL *John 6, 41-51 / 117*

The Jews started to murmur in protest because Jesus claimed, "I am the bread that came down from heaven." They kept saying: "Is this not Jesus, the son of Joseph? Do we not know his father and mother? How can he claim to have come down from heaven?" "Stop your murmuring," Jesus told them.

"No one can come to me
unless the Father who sent me draws him;
I will raise him up on the last day.
It is written in the prophets:
'They shall all be taught by God.'
Everyone who has heard the Father
and learned from him
comes to me.
Not that anyone has seen the Father–
only the one who is from God
has seen the Father.
Let me firmly assure you,
he who believes has eternal life.
I am the bread of life.
Your ancestors ate manna in the desert, but they died.
This is the bread that comes down from heaven,
for a man to eat and never die.
I myself am the living bread
come down from heaven.
If anyone eats this bread
he shall live forever;
the bread I will give
is my flesh, for the life of the world."

921 NINETEENTH SUNDAY IN ORDINARY TIME / C

READING I *Wisdom 18, 6-9 / 118*

That night was known beforehand to our fathers,
that, with sure knowledge of the oaths in which they put their faith,
they might have courage.
Your people awaited
the salvation of the just and the destruction of their foes.
For when you punished our adversaries,
in this you glorified us whom you had summoned.
For in secret the holy children of the good were offering sacrifice
and putting into effect with one accord the divine institution.

RESPONSORIAL PSALM *Psalm (32)33, 1.12.18-19.20-22 / 118*

CK

Hap-py the peo-ple the Lord has cho-sen to be his own.

Ring out your joy to the Lord, O you just;
for praise is fitting for loyal hearts.
They are happy, whose God is the Lord,
the people he has chosen as his own. ℟.

The Lord looks on those who revere
him,
on those who hope in his love,
to rescue their souls from death,
to keep them alive in famine. ℟.

Our soul is waiting for the Lord.
The Lord is our help and our shield.
May your love be upon us, O Lord,
as we place all our hope in you. ℟.

READING II *Hebrews 11.1-2.8-19 or 11, 1-2.8-12 / 118*

For short form read only the part in brackets.

[Faith is confident assurance concerning what we hope for, and conviction about things we do not see. Because of faith the men of old were approved by God. By faith Abraham obeyed when he was called, and went forth to the place he was to receive as a heritage; he went forth, moreover, not knowing where he was going. By faith he sojourned in the promised land as in a foreign country, dwelling in tents with Isaac and Jacob, heirs of the same promise; for he was looking forward to the city with foundations, whose designer and maker is God. By faith Sarah received power to conceive though she was past the age, for she thought that the One who had made the promise was worthy of trust. As a result of this faith, there came forth from one man, who was himself as good as dead, descendants as numerous as the stars in the sky and the sands of the seashore.]

All of these died in faith. They did not obtain what had been promised but saw and saluted it from afar. By acknowledging themselves to be strangers and foreigners on the earth, they showed that they were seeking a homeland. If they had been thinking back to the place from which they had come, they would have had the opportunity of returning there. But they were searching for a better, a heavenly home. Wherefore God is not ashamed to be called their God, for he has prepared a city for them. By faith Abraham, when put to the test, offered up Isaac; he who had received the promises was ready to sacrifice his only son, of whom it was said, "Through Isaac shall your descendants be called." He reasoned that God was able to raise from the dead, and so he received Isaac back as a symbol.

GOSPEL *Luke 12, 32-48 or 12, 35-40 / 118*

[Jesus said to his disciples:] "Do not live in fear, little flock. It has pleased your Father to give you the kingdom. Sell what you have and give alms. Get purses for yourselves that do not wear out, a never-failing treasure with the Lord which no thief comes near nor any moth destroys. Wherever your treasure lies, there your heart will be.

["Let your belts be fastened around your waists and your lamps be burning ready. Be like men awaiting their master's return from a wedding, so that when he arrives and knocks, you will open for him without delay. It will go well with those servants whom the master finds wide-awake on his return. I tell you, he will put on an apron, seat them at tables, and proceed to wait on them. Should he happen to come at midnight or before sunrise and find them prepared, it will go well with them. You know as well as I that if the head of the house knew when the thief was coming he would not let him break into his house. Be on guard, therefore. The Son of Man will come when you least expect him."]

Peter said, "Do you intend this parable for us, Lord, or do you mean it for the whole world?" The Lord said, "Who in your opinion is that faithful, farsighted steward whom the master will set over his servants to dispense their ration of grain in season? That servant is fortunate whom his master finds busy when he returns. Assuredly, his master will put him in charge of all his property. But if the servant says to himself, 'My master is taking his time about coming' and begins to abuse the housemen and servant girls, to eat and drink and get drunk, that servant's master will come back on a day when he does not expect him, at a time he does not know. He will punish him severely and rank him among those undeserving of trust. The slave who knew his master's wishes but did not prepare to fulfill them will get a severe beating, whereas the one who did not know them and who nonetheless deserved to be flogged will get off with fewer stripes. When much has been given a man, much will be required of him. More will be asked of a man to whom more has been entrusted.

922 TWENTIETH SUNDAY IN ORDINARY TIME / A

READING I *Isaiah 56, 1.6-7 / 119*

Thus says the Lord:
Observe what is right, do what is just;
  for my salvation is about to come,
  my justice, about to be revealed.

The foreigners who join themselves
  to the Lord,
  ministering to him,
Loving the name of the Lord,
  and becoming his servants–
All who keep the sabbath free from
  profanation
  and hold to my covenant,
Them I will bring to my holy
  mountain
  and make joyful in my house of
  prayer;
Their holocausts and sacrifices
  will be acceptable on my altar,
For my house shall be called
  a house of prayer for all peoples.

RESPONSORIAL PSALM *Psalm (66)67, 2-3.5.6.8 / 119*

MK
O God, O God, let all the na - tions praise you!

O God, be gracious and bless us
and let your face shed its light upon us.
So will your ways be known upon earth
and all nations learn your saving
  help. ℟.

Let the nations be glad and exult
for you rule the world with justice.
With fairness you rule the peoples,
you guide the nations on earth. ℟.

Let the peoples praise you, O God;
let all the peoples praise you.
May God still give us his blessing
till the ends of the earth revere him. ℟.

READING II *Romans 11, 13-15.29-32 / 119*

I say this now to you Gentiles: Inasmuch as I am the apostle of the Gentiles, I glory in my ministry, trying to rouse my fellow Jews to envy and save some of them. For is their rejection has meant reconciliation for the world, what will their acceptance mean? Nothing less athan life from the dead!

God's gifts and his call are irrevocable. Just as you were once disobedient to God and now have received mercy through their disobedience, so they have become disobedient-since God wished to show you mercy-that they too may receive mercy. God had imprisoned all in disobedience that he might have mercy on all.

GOSPEL *Matthew 15, 21-28 / 119*

Jesus withdrew to the district of Tyre and Sidon. It happened that a Canaanite woman living in that locality presented herself, crying out to him, "Lord, Son of David, have pity on me! My daughter is terribly troubled by a demon." He gave her no word of response. His disciples came up and began to entreat him, "Get rid of her. She keeps shouting after us." "My mission is only to the lost sheep of the house of Israel." Jesus replied. She came forward then and did him homage with the plea, "Help me,

Lord!" But he answered, "It is not right to take the food of sons and daughters and throw it to the dogs." "Please, Lord, " she insisted, "even the dogs eat the leavings that fall from their masters' tables." Jesus then said in reply, "Woman, you have great faith! Your wish will come to pass." That very moment her daughter got better.

TWENTIETH SUNDAY IN ORDINARY TIME / B 923

READING I

Proverbs 9, 1-6 / 120

Wisdom has built her house,
she has set up her seven columns;
She has dressed her meat, mixed her wine,
yes, she has spread her table.
She has sent out her maidens; she calls from the heights out over the city:
"Let whoever is simple turn in here;
to him who lacks understanding, I say,
Come, eat of my food, and drink of the wine I have mixed!
Forsake foolishness that you may live;
advance in the way of understanding.

RESPONSORIAL PSALM

Psalm (33)34, 2-3.10-11.12-13.14-15 / 120

RP
Taste and see the good - ness of the Lord.

I will bless the Lord at all times,
his praise always on my lips;
in the Lord my soul shall make its boast.
The humble shall hear and be glad. ℟.

Come, children, and hear me
that I may teach you the fear of the Lord.
Who is he who longs for life
and many days, to enjoy his prosperity? ℟.

Revere the Lord, you his saints.
They lack nothing, those who revere him.
Strong lions suffer want and go hungry
but those who seek the Lord lack no blessing. ℟.

Then keep your tongue from evil
and your lips from speaking deceit.
Turn aside from evil and do good;
seek and strive after peace. ℟.

READING II

Ephesians 5, 15-20 / 120

Keep careful watch over your conduct. Do not act like fools, but like thoughtful men. Make the most of the present opportunity, for these are evil days. Do not continue in ignorance, but try to discern the will of the Lord. Avoid getting drunk on wine that leads to debauchery. Be filled with the Spirit, addressing one another in psalms and hymns and inspired songs. Sing praise to the Lord with all your hearts. Give thanks to God the Father always and for everything in the name of our Lord Jesus Christ.

GOSPEL

John 6, 51-58 / 120

Jesus said to the crowds:
"I myself am the living bread
come down from heaven.
If anyone eats this bread
he shall live forever;
the bread I will give
is my flesh, for the life of the world."

At this the Jews quarreled among themselves, saying, "How can he give us his flesh to eat?" Thereupon Jesus said to them:

"Let me solemnly assure you,
if you do not eat the flesh of the Son of Man
and drink his blood,
you have no life in you.
He who feeds on my flesh

and drinks my blood
has life eternal,
and I will raise him up on the last day.
For my flesh is real food
and my blood real drink.
The man who feeds on my flesh
and drinks my blood
remains in me, and I in him.
Just as the Father who has life sent me
and I have life because of the Father,
so the man who feeds on me
will have life because of me.
This is the bread that came down
from heaven.
Unlike your ancestors who ate and
died nonetheless,
The man who feeds on this bread
shall live forever."

924 TWENTIETH SUNDAY IN ORDINARY TIME / C

READING I

Jeremiah 38, 4-6.8-10 / 121

The princes said to the king: "Jeremiah ought to be put to death; he demoralizes the soldiers who are left in this city, and all the people, by speaking of such things to them; he is not interested in the welfare of our people, but in their ruin." King Zedekiah answered: "He is in your power to;" for the king could do nothing with them. And so they took Jeremaih and threw him into the cistern of Prince Malchiah, which was in the quarters of the guard, letting him down with ropes. There was no water in the cistern, only mud, and Jeremiah sank into the mud.

Ebed-melech went to the Gate of Benjamin from the palace and said to the king: "My lord king, these men have been at fault in all they have done to the prophet Jeremiah, casting him into the cistern. He will die of famine on the spot, for there is no more food in the city." Then the king ordered Ebed-melech the Cushite to take three men along with him, and draw the prophet Jeremiah out of the cistern before he should die.

RESPONSORIAL PSALM

Psalm (39)40, 2.3.4.18 / 121

RJB/RP
Lord, come to my aid!

I waited, I waited for the Lord
and he stooped down to me. ℟.

He heard my cry.
He drew me from the deadly pit,
from the miry clay.
He set my feet upon a rock
and made my footsteps firm. ℟.

He put a new song into my mouth,
praise of our God.
Many shall see and fear
and shall trust in the Lord. ℟.

As for me, wretched and poor,
the Lord thinks of me.
You are my rescuer, my help,
O God, do not delay. ℟.

READING II

Hebrews 12, 1-4 / 121

Since we for our part are surrounded by a cloud of witnesses; let us lay aside every encumbrance of sin which clings to us and persevere in running the race which lies ahead; let us keep our eyes fixed on Jesus, who inspires and perfects our faith. For the sake of the joy which lay before him he endured the cross, heedless of its shame. He has taken his seat at the right of the throne of God. Remember how he endured the opposition of sinners; hence do not grow despondent or abandon the struggle.

GOSPEL

Luke 12, 49-53 / 121

Jesus said to his disciples: "I have come to light a fire on the earth. How I wish the blaze were ignited! I have a baptism to receive. What anguish I feel till it is over! Do you think I have come to establish peace on the earth? I assure you, the contrary is true; I have come for division. From now on, a household of five will be divided three against two and two against three; father will be split against son and son against father, mother against daughter and daughter against mother, mother-in-law against daughter-in-law, daughter-in-law against mother-in-law."

TWENTY-FIRST SUNDAY IN ORDINARY TIME / A 925

READING I *Isaiah 22, 15.19-23 / 122*

Thus says the Lord, the God of hosts:
Up, go to that official,
Shebna, master of the palace:
"I will thrust you from your office
and pull you down from your station.

On that day I will summon my servant
Eliakim, son of Hilkiah;
I will clothe him with your robe,
and gird him with your sash,
and give over to him your authority.
He shall be a father to the inhabitants
of Jerusalem,
and to the house of Judah.
I will place the key of the House of
David on his shoulder;
when he opens, no one shall shut,
when he shuts, no one shall open.
I will fix him like a peg in a sure spot,
to be a place of honor for his
family."

RESPONSORIAL PSALM *Psalm (137)138, 1-2.2-3.6.8 / 122*

RP
Lord, your love is e - ter - nal;
do not for - sake the work of your hands.

I thank you, Lord, with all my heart,
you have heard the words of my mouth.
In the presence of the angels I will
bless you.
I will adore before your holy
temple. ℟.

I thank you for your faithfulness and
love
which excel all we ever knew of you.
On the day I called, you answered;
you increased the strength of my
soul. ℟.

The Lord is high yet he looks on the
lowly
and the haughty he knows from afar.
Your love, O Lord, is eternal,
discard not the work of your hands. ℟.

READING II *Romans 11, 33-36 / 122*

How deep are the riches and the wisdom and the knowledge of God! How inscrutable his judgments, how unsearchable his ways! For "who has known the mind of the Lord? Or who has been his counselor? Who has given him anything so as to deserve return?" For from him and through him and for him all things are. To him be glory forever. Amen.

GOSPEL *Matthew 16, 13-20 / 122*

When Jesus came to the neighborhood of Caesarea Philippi, he asked his disciples this question: "Who do people say that the Son of Man is?" They replied, "Some say

John the Baptizer, others Elijah, still others Jeremiah or one of the prophets." "And you," he said to them, "who do you say that I am?" "You are the Messiah," Simon Peter answered, "the Son of the living God!" Jesus replied, "Blest are you, Simon son of John! No mere man has revealed this to you, but my heavenly Father. I for my part declare to you, you are 'Rock,' and on this rock I will build my church, and the jaws of death shall not prevail against it. I will entrust to you the keys of the kingdom of heaven. Whatever you declare bound on earth shall be bound in heaven; whatever you declare loosed on earth shall be loosed in heaven." Then he strictly ordered his disciples not to tell anyone that he was the Messiah.

926 TWENTY-FIRST SUNDAY IN ORDINARY TIME / B

READING I *Joshua 24, 1-2.15-17.18 / 123*

Joshua gathered together all the tribes of Israel at Shechem, summoning their elders, their leaders, their judges and their officers. When they stood in ranks before God, Joshua addressed all the people: "If it does not please you to serve the Lord, decide today whom you will serve, the gods your fathers served beyond the River or the Gods of the Amorites in whose country you are dwelling. As for me and my household, we will serve the Lord."

But the people answered, "Far be it from us to forsake the Lord for the service of other gods. For it was the Lord, our God, who brought us and our fathers up out of the land of Egypt, out of a state of slavery. He performed those great miracles before our very eyes and protected us along our entire journey and among all the peoples through whom we passed. Therefore we also will serve the Lord, for he is our God."

RESPONSORIAL PSALM *Psalm (33)34, 2-3.16-17.18-19.20-21.22-23 / 123*

RP
Taste and see the good - ness of the Lord.

I will bless the Lord at all times,
his praise always on my lips;
in the Lord my soul shall make its boast.
The humble shall hear and be glad. ℟.

The Lord turns his face against the wicked
to destroy their remembrance from the earth.
The Lord turns his eyes to the just
and his ears to their appeal. ℟.

They call and the Lord hears
and rescues them in all their distress.
The Lord is close to the broken-hearted;
those whose spirit is crushed he will save. ℟.

Many are the trials of the just man but
from them all the Lord will rescue him.
He will keep guard over all his bones,
not one of his bones shall be broken. ℟.

Evil brings death to the wicked;
those who hate the good are doomed.
The Lord ransoms the souls of his servants.
Those who hide in him shall not be condemned. ℟.

READING II *Ephesians 5, 21-32 / 123*

Defer to one another out of reverence for Christ.

Wives should be submissive to their husbands as if to the Lord because the husband is head of his wife just as Christ is head of his body, the church, as well as its savior. As the church submits to Christ, so wives should submit to their husbands in everything.

Husbands, love your your wives, as Christ loved the church. He gave himself up for her to make her holy, purifying her in the bath of water by the power of the word, to present to himself a glorious church, holy and immaculate, without stain or wrinkle or anything of that sort. Husbands should love their wives as they do their own bodies. He who loves his wife loves himself. Observe that no one ever hates his own flesh; no, he nourishes it and takes care of it as Christ cares for the church-for we are members of his body.

"For this reason a man shall leave his father
and mother,
and shall cling to his wife,
and the two shall be made into one."

This is a great foreshadowing; I mean that it refers to Christ and the church.

GOSPEL *John 6, 60-69 / 123*

Many of the disciples of Jesus remarked, "This sort of talk is hard to endure! How can anyone take it seriously?" Jesus was fully aware that his disciples were murmuring in protest at what he had said. "Does it shake your faith?" he asked them.

"What, then, if you were to see the Son
of man
ascend to where he was before...?
It is the spirit that gives life;
the flesh is useless.
The words I spoke to you
are spirit and life.
Yet among you there are some who do
not believe."

(Jesus knew from the start, of course, the ones who refused to believe, and the one who would hand him over.) He went on to say:

"This is why I have told you
that no one can come to me
unless it is granted him by the Father."

From this time on, many of his disciples broke away and would not remain in his company any longer. Jesus then said to the Twelve, "Do you want to leave me too?" Simon Peter answered him, "Lord, to whom shall we go? You have the words of eternal life. We have come to believe; we are convinced that you are God's holy one."

TWENTY-FIRST SUNDAY IN ORDINARY TIME / C 927

READING I *Isaiah 66, 18-21 / 124*

I come to gather nations of every language; they shall come and see my glory. I will set a sign among them; from them I will send fugitives to the nations: to Tarshish, Put and Lud, Mosoch, Tubal and Javan, to the distant coastlands that have never heard of my fame, or seen my glory; and they shall proclaim my glory among the nations. They shall bring all your brethren from all the nations as an offering to the Lord, on horses and in chariots, in carts, upon mules and dromedaries, to Jerusalem, my holy mountain, says the Lórd, just as the Israelites bring their offering to the house of the Lord in clean vessels. Some of these I will take as priests and Levites, says the Lord.

RESPONSORIAL PSALM *Psalm (116)117, 1.2 / 124*

CAP
Go out to all the world and tell the Good News.

O praise the Lord, all you nations,
acclaim him all you peoples! ℟.

Strong is his love for us;
he is faithful for ever. ℟.

READING II *Hebrews 12, 5-7.11-13 / 124*

You have forgotten the encouraging words addressed to you as sons:

"My sons, do not disdain the discipline of the Lord
nor lose heart when he reproves you;
For, whom the Lord loves, he disciplines;
he scourges every son he receives."

Endure your trials as the discipline of God, who deals with you as sons. For what son is there whom his father does not discipline? At the time it is administered, all discipline seems a cause for grief and not for joy, but later it brings forth the fruit of peace and justice to those who are trained in its school. So strengthen your drooping hands and your weak knees. Make straight the paths you walk on, that your halting limbs may not be dislocated but healed.

GOSPEL *Luke 13, 22-30 / 124*

Jesus went through cities and towns teaching–all the while making his way toward Jerusalem. Someone asked him, "Lord, are they few in number who are to be saved?" He replied: "Try to come in through the narrow door. Many, I tell you, will try to enter and be unable. When once the master of the house has risen to lock the door and you stand outside knocking and saying, 'Sir, open for us,' he will say in reply, 'I do not know where you come from.' Then you will begin to say, 'We ate and drank in your company. You taught in our streets.' But he will answer, 'I tell you, I do not know where you come from. Away from me, you evildoers!'

"There will be wailing and grinding of teeth when you see Abraham, Isaac, Jacob, and all the prophets safe in the kingdom of God, and you yourselves rejected. People will come from the east and the west, from the north and the south, and will take their place at the feast in the kingdom of God. Some who are last will be first and some who are first will be last."

928 TWENTY-SECOND SUNDAY IN ORDINARY TIME / A

READING I *Jeremiah 20, 7-9 / 125*

You duped me, O Lord, and I let
myself be duped;
you were too strong for me, and you
triumphed.
All the day I am an object of laughter;
everyone mocks me.
Whenever I speak, I must cry out,
violence and outrage is my message;
The word of the Lord has brought me
derision and reproach all the day.
I say to myself, I will not mention him,
I will speak in his name no more.
But then it becomes like fire burning in
my heart,
imprisoned in my bones;
I grow weary holding it in,
I cannot endure it.

RESPONSORIAL PSALM *Psalm (62)63, 2.3-4.5-6.8-9 / 125*

RP
My soul is thirst-ing for you, O
Lord, thirst - ing for you my God.

O God, you are my God, for you I long;
for you my soul is thirsting.
My body pines for you
like a dry, weary land without water. ℟.

So I gaze on you in the sanctuary
to see your strength and your glory.
For your love is better than life,
my lips will speak your praise. ℟.

So, I will bless you all my life,
in your name I will lift up my hands.
My soul shall be filled as with a
banquet,
my mouth shall praise you with joy. ℟.

For you have been my help;
in the shadow of your wings I rejoice.
My soul clings to you;
your right hand holds me fast. ℟.

READING II *Romans 12, 1-2 / 125*

Brothers, I beg you through the mercy of God to offer your bodies as a living sacrifice holy and acceptable to God, your spiritual worship. Do not conform yourselves to this age, but be transformed by the renewal of your mind, so that you may judge what is God's will, what is good, pleasing and perfect.

GOSPEL *Matthew 16, 21-27 / 125*

From then on Jesus [the Messiah] started to indicate to his disciples that he must go to Jerusalem to suffer greatly there at the hands of the elders, the chief priests, and the scribes, and to be put to death, and raised up on the third day. At this, Peter took him aside and began to remonstrate with him. "May you be spared, Master! God forbid that any such thing ever happen to you!" Jesus turned on Peter and said, "Get out of my sight, you satan! You are trying to make me trip and fall. You are not judging by God's standards but by man's."

Jesus then said to his disciples: "If a man wishes to come after me, he must deny his very self, take up his cross, and begin to follow in my footsteps. Whoever would save his life will lose it, but whoever loses his life for my sake will find it. What profit would a man show if he were to gain the whole world and ruin himself in the process? What can a man offer in exchange for his very self? The Son of Man will come with his Father's glory accompanied by his angels. When he does he will repay each man according to his conduct."

TWENTY-SECOND SUNDAY IN ORDINARY TIME / B 929

READING I *Deuteronomy 4, 1-2.6-8 / 126*

Moses told his people: "Now, Israel, hear the statutes and decrees which I am teaching you to observe, that you may live, and may enter in and take possession of the land which the Lord, the God of your fathers, is giving you. In your observance of the commandments of the Lord, your God, which I enjoin upon you, you shall not add to what I command you nor subtract from it. Observe them carefully, for thus will you give evidence of your wisdom and intelligence to the nations, who will hear of all these statutes and say, 'This great nation is truly a wise and intelligent people.' For what great nation is there that has gods so close to it as the Lord, our God, is to us whenever we call upon him? Or what great nation has statutes and decrees that are as just as this whole law which I am setting before you today?"

RESPONSORIAL PSALM *Psalm (14)15, 2-3.3-4.4-5 / 126*

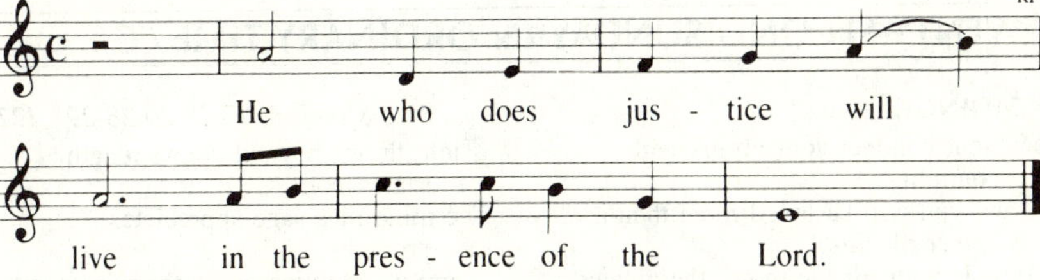
RP
He who does jus - tice will
live in the pres - ence of the Lord.

He who walks without fault,
he who acts with justice
and speaks the truth from his heart,
he who does not slander with his
tongue, ℟.

He who does no wrong to his
brother,
who casts no slur on his neighbor,
who holds the godless in disdain,
but honors those who fear the Lord. ℟.

He who keeps his pledge, come what
may,
who takes no interest on a loan
and accepts no bribes against the
innocent.
Such a man will stand firm for ever. ℟.

READING II *James 1, 17-18.21-22.27 / 126*

Every worthwhile gift, every genuine benefit comes from above, descending from the Father of the heavenly luminaries, who cannot change and who is never shadowed over. He wills to bring us to birth with a word spoken in truth so that we may be a kind of firstfruits of his creatures.

Humbly welcome the word that has taken root in you, with its power to save you. Act on this word. If all you do is listen to it, you are deceiving yourselves.

Looking after orphans and widows in their distress and keeping oneself unspotted by the world make for pure worship without stain before our God and Father.

GOSPEL *Mark 7, 1-8.14-15.21-23 / 126*

The Pharisees and some of the experts in the law who had come from Jerusalem gathered around Jesus. They had observed a few of his disciples eating meals without having purified–that is to say, washed–their hands. The Pharisees, and in fact all the Jews, cling to the custom of their ancestors and never eat without scrupulously washing their hands. Moreover, they never eat anything from the market without first sprinkling it. There are many other traditions they observe–for example, the washing of cups and jugs and kettles. So the Pharisees and the scribes questioned him: "Why do your disciples not follow the tradition of our ancestors, but instead take food without purifying their hands?" He said to them :"How accurately Isaiah prophesied about you hypocrites when he wrote,

'This people pays me lip service
but their heart is far from me.
Empty is the reverence they do me
because they teach as dogmas mere human precepts.'

You disregard God's commandment and cling to what is human tradition."

He summoned the crowd again and said to them: "Hear me, all of you, and try to understand. Nothing that enters a man from outside can make him impure; that which comes out of him, and only that, constitutes impurity. Let everyone heed what he hears!

"Wicked designs come from the deep recesses of the heart: acts of fornication, theft, murder, adulterous conduct, greed, maliciousness, deceit, sensuality, envy, blasphemy, arrogance, an obtuse spirit. All these evils come from within and render a man impure."

930 TWENTY-SECOND SUNDAY IN ORDINARY TIME / C

READING I *Sirach 3, 17-18.20.28-29 / 127*

My son, conduct your affairs with
humility,
and you will be loved more than a
giver of gifts.
Humble yourself the more, the greater
you are,
and you will find favor with God.
What is too sublime for you, seek not,
into things beyond your strength
search not.
The mind of a sage appreciates
proverbs,
and an attentive ear is the wise man's
joy.
Water quenches a flaming fire,
and alms atone for sins.

RESPONSORIAL PSALM *Psalm (67)68, 4-5.6-7.10-11 / 127*

RJB
God, in your good - ness, you have made a home for the poor.

But the just shall rejoice at the presence
of God,
they shall exult and dance for joy.
O sing to the Lord, make music to his
name.
Rejoice in the Lord, exult at his
presence. ℟.

Father of the orphan, defender
of the widow,
such is God in his holy place.
God gives the lowly a home
to live in;
he leads the prisoners forth
into freedom. ℟.

You poured down, O God, a generous
rain;
when your people were starved you
gave them new life.
It was there that your people found a
home,
prepared in your goodness, O God, for
the poor. ℟.

READING II *Hebrews 12, 18-19.22-24 / 127*

You have not drawn near to an untouchable mountain and a blazing fire, and gloomy darkness and storm and trumpet blast, and a voice speaking words, such that those who heard begged that they be not addressed to them. No, you have drawn near to Mount Zion and the city of the living God, the heavenly Jerusalem, to myriads of angels in festal gathering, to the assembly of the first-born enrolled in heaven, to God the judge of all, to the spirits of just men made perfect, to Jesus, the mediator of a new covenant.

GOSPEL *Luke 14, 1.7-14 / 127*

When Jesus came on a sabbath to eat a meal in the house of one of the leading Pharisees, they observed him closely.

He went on to address a parable to the guests, noticing how they were trying to get the places of honor at the table: "When you are invited by someone to a wedding party, do not sit in the place of honor in case some greater dignitary has been invited. Then the host might come and say to you, 'Make room for this man,' and you would have to proceed shamefacedly to the lowest place. What you should do when you have been invited is go and sit in the lowest place, so that when your host approaches you he will say, 'My friend, come up higher.' This will win you the esteem of your fellow guests. For everyone who exalts himself shall be humbled and he who humbles himself shall be exalted."

He said to the one who had invited him: "Whenever you give a lunch or dinner, do not invite your friends or brothers or relatives or wealthy neighbors. They might invite you in return and thus repay you. No, when you have a reception, invite beggars and the crippled, the lame and the blind. You should be pleased that they cannot repay you, for you will be repaid in the resurrection of the just."

TWENTY-THIRD SUNDAY IN ORDINARY TIME / A 931

READING I *Ezekiel 33, 7-9 / 128*

You, son of man, I have appointed watchman for the house of Israel; when you hear me say anything, you shall warn them for me. If I tell the wicked man that he shall die, and you do not speak out to dissuade the wicked man from his ways, he [the wicked man] shall die for his guilt, but I will hold you responsible for his death. But if you warn the wicked man, trying to turn him from his way, and he refuses to turn from his way, he shall die for his guilt, but you shall save yourself.

RESPONSORIAL PSALM *Psalm (94)95, 1-2.6-7.8-9 / 128*

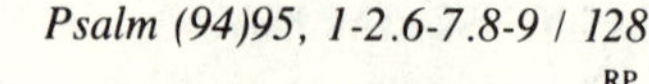

RP

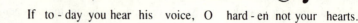

If to-day you hear his voice, O hard-en not your hearts.

Come, ring out our joy to the Lord;
hail the rock who saves us.
Let us come before him, giving thanks,
with songs let us hail the Lord. ℞.

Come in let us bow and bend low;
let us kneel before the God who
made us
for he is our God and we the
people who belong to his pasture,
the flock that is led by his hand. ℞.

O that today you would listen to his
voice!
"Harden not your hearts as at Meribah,
as on that day at Massah in the desert
when your fathers put me to the test;
when they tried me, though they saw
my work." ℞.

READING II *Romans 13, 8-10 / 128*

Owe no debt to anyone except the debt that binds us to love one another. He who loves his neighbor has fulfilled the law. The commandments, "You shall not commit adultery; you shall not murder; you shall not steal; you shall not covet," and any other commandment there may be are all summed up in this, "You shall love your neighbor as yourself." Love never does any wrong to the neighbor, hence love is the fulfillment of the law.

GOSPEL *Matthew 18, 15-20 / 128*

Jesus said to his disciples: "If your brother should commit some wrong against you, go and point out his fault, but keep it between the two of you. If he listens to you, you have won your brother over. If he does not listen, however, summon another, so that every case may stand on the word of two or three witnesses. If he ignores them, refer it to the church. If he ignores even the church, then treat him as you would a Gentile or a tax collector. I assure you, whatever you declare bound on earth shall be held bound in heaven, and whatever you declare loosed on earth shall be held loosed in heaven.

"Again I tell you, if two of you join your voices on earth to pray for anything whatever, it shall be granted you by my Father in heaven. Where two or three are gathered in my name, there am I in their midst."

932 TWENTY-THIRD SUNDAY IN ORDINARY TIME / B

READING I *Isaiah 35, 4-7 / 129*

Say to those whose hearts are
frightened:
Be strong, fear not!
Here is your God,
he comes with vindication;
With divine recompense
he comes to save you.
Then will the eyes of the blind be
opened,
the ears of the deaf be cleared;

Then will the lame leap like a stag,
then the tongue of the dumb will
sing.

Streams will burst forth in the desert,
and rivers in the steppe.
The burning sands will become pools,
and the thirsty ground, springs of
water.

RESPONSORIAL PSALM *Psalm (145)146, 7.8-9.9-10 / 129*

RP

Praise the Lord, my soul! Praise the Lord!

It is he who keeps faith for ever,
who is just to those who are oppressed.
It is he who gives bread to the
hungry,
the Lord, who sets prisoners free. ℟.

The Lord who gives sight to the blind,
who raises up those who are bowed
down,
the Lord, who protects the stranger
and upholds the widow and orphan. ℟.

It is the Lord who loves the just
but thwarts the path of the wicked.
The Lord will reign for ever,
Zion's God, from age to age. ℟.

READING II *James 2, 1-5 / 129*

My brothers, your faith in our Lord Jesus Christ glorified must not allow of favoritism. Suppose there should come into your assembly a man fashionably dressed, with gold rings on his fingers, and at the same time a poor man dressed in shabby clothes. Suppose further you were to take notice of the well-dressed man and say, "Sit right here, please;" whereas you were to say to the poor man, "You can stand!" or "Sit over there by my footrest." Have you not in a case like this discriminated in your hearts? Have you not set yourselves up as judges who hand down corrupt decisions?

Listen, dear brothers. Did not God choose those who are poor in the eyes of the world to be rich in faith and heirs of the kingdom he promised to those who love him?

GOSPEL *Mark 7, 31-37 / 129*

Jesus left Tyrian territory and returned by way of Sidon to the Sea of Galilee, into the district of the Ten Cities. Some people brought him a deaf man who had a speech impediment and begged him to lay his hand on him. Jesus took him off by himself away from the crowd. He put his fingers into the man's ears and, spitting, touched his tongue; then he looked up to heaven and emitted a groan. He said to him, "Ephphatha!" (that is, "Be opened!") At once the man's ears were opened; he was freed from the impediment, and began to speak plainly. Then he enjoined them strictly not to tell anyone; but the more he ordered them not to, the more they proclaimed it. Their amazement went beyond all bounds: "He has done everything well! He makes the deaf hear and the mute speak!"

TWENTY-THIRD SUNDAY IN ORDINARY TIME / C 933

READING I *Wisdom 9, 13-18 / 130*

For what man knows God's counsel,
or who can conceive what the Lord
intends?
For the deliberations of mortals are
timid,
and unsure are our plans.
For the corruptible body burdens the
soul
and the earthen shelter weighs down
the mind that has many concerns.
And scarce do we guess the things on
earth,
and what is within our grasp we find
with difficulty;
but when things are in heaven, who
can search them out?
Or who ever knew your counsel, except
you had given Wisdom
and sent your holy spirit from on
high?
And thus were the paths of those on
earth made straight.

RESPONSORIAL PSALM *Psalm (89)90, 3-4.5-6.12-13.14-17 / 130*

EE
In ev-'ry age, O Lord, you have been our re - fuge.

You turn men back into dust
and say: "Go back, sons of men."
To your eyes a thousand years
are like yesterday, come and gone,
no more than a watch in the night. ℟.

You sweep men away like a dream,
like grass which springs up in the morning.
In the morning it springs up and flowers;
by evening it withers and fades. ℟.

Make us know the shortness of our life
that we may gain wisdom of heart.
Lord, relent! Is your anger for ever?
Show pity to your servants. ℟.

In the morning, fill us with your love;
we shall exult and rejoice all our days.
Let the favor of the Lord be upon us:
give success to the work of our hands
(give success to the work of our hands). ℟.

READING II *Philemon 9-10.12-17 / 130*

I, Paul, ambassador of Christ and now a prisoner for him, appeal to you for my child, whom I have begotten during my imprisonment. It is he I am sending to you–and that means I am sending my heart!

I had wanted to keep him with me, that he might serve me in your place while I am in prison for the gospel; but I did not want to do anything without your consent, that kindness might not be forced on you but freely bestowed. Perhaps he was separated from you for a while for this reason: that you might possess him forever, no longer as a slave but as more than a slave, a beloved brother, especially dear to me; and how much more than a brother to you, since now you will know him both as a man and in the Lord.

If then you regard me as a partner, welcome him as you would me.

GOSPEL *Luke 14, 25-33 / 130*

On one occasion when a great crowd was with Jesus, he turned to them and said, "If anyone comes to me without turning his back on his father and mother, his wife and his children, his brothers and sisters, indeed his very self, he cannot be my follower. Anyone who does not take up his cross and follow me cannot be my disciple. If one of you decides to build a tower, will he not first sit down and calculate the outlay to see if he has enough money to complete the project? He will do that for fear of laying the foundation and then not being able to complete the work; at which all who saw it would then jeer at him, saying, 'That man began to build what he could not finish.'

"Or if a king is about to march on another king to do battle with him, will he not sit down first and consider whether, with ten thousand men, he can withstand an enemy coming against him with twenty thousand? If he cannot, he will send a delegation while the enemy is still at a distance, asking for terms of peace. In the same way, none of you can be my disciple if he does not renounce all his posssessions."

934 TWENTY-FOURTH SUNDAY IN ORDINARY TIME / A

READING I *Sirach 27, 30-28, 7 / 131*

Wrath and anger are hateful things,
yet the sinner hugs them tight.
The vengeful will suffer the Lord's vengeance,
for he remembers their sins in detail.
Forgive your neighbor's injustice;
then when you pray, your own sins will be forgiven.

Should a man nourish anger against his fellows
and expect healing from the Lord?
Should a man refuse mercy to his fellows,
yet seek pardon for his own sins?
If he who is but flesh cherishes wrath,
who will forgive his sins?

Remember your last days, set enmity aside;
remember death and decay, and cease from sin!
Think of the commandments, hate not your neighbor;
of the Most High's covenant, and overlook faults.

RESPONSORIAL PSALM

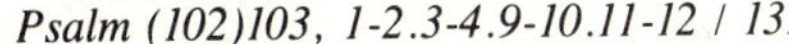

Psalm (102)103, 1-2.3-4.9-10.11-12 / 131

HH
The Lord is kind and mer - ci - ful;
slow to an - ger, and rich in com - pas - sion.

My soul, give thanks to the Lord,
all my being, bless his holy name.
My soul, give thanks to the Lord
and never forget all his blessings. ℟.

His wrath will come to an end;
he will not be angry for ever.
He does not treat us according to our sins
nor repay us according to our faults. ℟.

It is he who forgives all your guilt,
who heals every one of your ills,
who redeems your life from the grave,
who crowns you with love and compassion. ℟.

For as the heavens are high above the earth
so strong is his love for those who fear him.
As far as the east is from the west,
so far does he remove our sins. ℟.

READING II *Romans 14, 7-9 / 131*

None of us lives as his own master and none of us dies as his own master. While we live we are responsible to the Lord, and when we die we die as his servants. Both in life and in death we are the Lord's. That is why Christ died and came to life again, that he might be Lord of both the dead and the living.

GOSPEL *Matthew 18, 21-35 / 131*

Peter came up and asked Jesus, "Lord, when my brother wrongs me, how often must I forgive him? Seven times?" "No," Jesus replied, "not seven times; I say, seventy times seven times. That is why the reign of God may be said to be like a king who decided to settle accounts with his officials. When he began his auditing, one was brought in who owed him a huge amount. As he had no way of paying it, his master ordered him to be sold, along with his wife, his children, and all his property, in payment of the debt. At that the official prostrated himself in homage and said, 'My lord, be patient with me and I will pay you back in full.' Moved with pity, the master let the official go and wrote off the debt. But when the same official went out he met a fellow servant who owed him a mere fraction of what he himself owed. He seized him and throttled him. 'Pay back what you owe,' he demanded. His fellow servant dropped to his knees and began to plead with him, 'Just give me time and I will pay you back in full.' But he would hear none of it. Instead, he had him put in jail until he paid back what he owed. When his fellow servants saw what had happened they were badly shaken, and went to their master to report the whole incident. His master sent for him and said, 'You worthless wretch! I canceled your entire debt when you pleaded with me. Should you not have dealt mercifully with your fellow servant, as I dealt with you?' Then in anger the master handed him over to torturers until he paid back all that he owed. My heavenly Father will treat you in exactly the same way unless each of you forgives his brother from his heart."

935 TWENTY-FOURTH SUNDAY IN ORDINARY TIME / B

READING I *Isaiah 50, 4-9 / 132*

The Lord God opens my ear that I may
    hear
And I have not rebelled,
  have not turned back.
I gave my back to those who beat me,
  my cheeks to those who plucked my
    beard;
My face I did not shield
  from buffets and spitting.

The Lord God is my help,
  therefore I am not disgraced;
I have set my face like flint,
  knowing that I shall not be put to
    shame.
He is near who upholds my right;
  if anyone wishes to oppose me,
  let us appear together.
Who disputes my right?
  Let him confront me.
See, the Lord God is my help;
  who will prove me wrong?

RESPONSORIAL PSALM *Psalm (114)115, 1-2.3-4.5-6.8-9 / 132*

RP

I will walk in the pres-ence of the Lord, in the land of the liv-ing.

I love the Lord for he has heard
the cry of my appeal;
for he turned his ear to me
in the day when I called him. ℟.

They surrounded me, the snares of
  death,
with the anguish of the tomb;
they caught me, sorrow and distress.
I called on the Lord's name.
O Lord, my God, deliver me! ℟.

How gracious is the Lord, and just;
our God has compassion.
The Lord protects the simple hearts;
I was helpless so he saved me. ℟.

He has kept my soul from death,
(my eyes from tears)
and my feet from stumbling.
I will walk in the presence of the Lord
in the land of the living. ℟.

READING II *James 2, 14-18 / 132*

My brothers, what good is it to profess faith without practicing it? Such faith has no power to save one, has it? If a brother or sister has nothing to wear and no food for the day, and you say to them, "Good-bye and good luck! Keep warm and well fed," but do not meet their bodily needs, what good is that? So it is with the faith that does nothing in practice. It is thoroughly lifeless.

To such a person one might say, "You have faith and I have works–is that it?" Show me your faith without works, and I will show you the faith that underlies my works!

GOSPEL *Mark 8, 27-35 / 132*

Jesus and his disciples set out for the villages around Caesarea Philippi. On the way he asked the disciples this question: "Who do people say that I am?" They replied, "Some, John the Baptizer, others, Elijah, still others, one of the prophets." "And you," he went on to ask, "who do you say that I am?" Peter answered him, "You are the Messiah!" Then he strictly ordered them not to tell anyone about him.

He then began to teach them that the Son of Man had to suffer much, be rejected by the elders, the chief priests, and the scribes, be put to death, and rise three days later. He said this quite openly. Peter then took him aside and began to remonstrate with him. At this he turned around and, eyeing the disciples, reprimanded Peter in turn: "Get out of my sight, you satan! You are not judging by God's standards but by man's!"

He summoned the crowd with his disciples and said to them: "If a man wishes to come after me, he must deny his very self, take up his cross, and follow in my steps. Whoever would save his life will lose, it, but whoever loses his life for my sake and the gospel's will save it."

TWENTY-FOURTH SUNDAY IN ORDINARY TIME / C 936

READING I *Exodus 32, 7-11.13-14 / 133*

The Lord said to Moses, "Go down at once to your people, whom you brought out of the land of Egypt, for they have become depraved. They have soon turned aside from the way I pointed out to them, making for themselves a molten calf and worshiping it, sacrificing to it and crying out, 'This is your God, O Israel, who brought you out of the land of Egypt!' I see how stiff-necked this people is," continued the Lord to Moses. "Let me alone, then, that my wrath may blaze up against them to consume them. Then I will make of you a great nation."

But Moses implored the Lord, his God, saying, "Why, O Lord, should your wrath blaze up against your own people, whom you brought out of the land of Egypt with such great power and with so strong a hand? Remember your servants Abraham, Isaac and Israel, and how you swore to them by your own self, saying, 'I will make your descendants as numerous as the stars in the sky; and all this land that I promised, I will give you descendants as their perpetual heritage.' " So the Lord relented in the punishment he had threatened to inflict on his people.

RESPONSORIAL PSALM 
Psalm (50)51, 3-4.12-13.17.19 / 133

JJC
I will rise and go to my fa - ther.

Have mercy on me, God, in your
 kindness.
In your compassion blot out my
 offense.
O wash me more and more from my
 guilt
and cleanse me from my sin. ℟.

A pure heart create for me, O God,
put a steadfast spirit within me.
Do not cast me away from your
 presence,
nor deprive me of your holy spirit. ℟.

O Lord, open my lips
and my mouth shall declare your praise.
My sacrifice, a contrite spirit,
a humbled, contrite heart you will not
 spurn. ℟.

READING II *1 Timothy 1, 12-17 / 133*

I thank Christ Jesus our Lord, who has strengthened me, that he has made me his servant and judged me faithful. I was once a blasphemer, a persecutor, a man filled with arrogance; but because I did not know what I was doing in my unbelief, I have been treated mercifully, and the grace of our Lord has been granted me in overflowing measure, along with the faith and love which are in Christ Jesus. You can depend on this as worthy of full acceptance: that Christ Jesus came into the world to save sinners. Of these I myself am the worst. But on that very account I was dealt with mercifully, so that in me, as an extreme case, Jesus Christ might display all his patience, and that I might become an example to those who would later have faith in him and gain everlasting life. To the King of ages, the immortal, the invisible, the only God, be honor and glory forever and ever! Amen.

GOSPEL

Luke 15, 1-32 or 15, 1-10 / 133

For short form read only the part in brackets.

[The tax collectors and sinners were all gathering around to hear Jesus, at which the Pharisees and the scribes murmured, "This man welcomes sinners and eats with them." Then he addressed this parable to them: "Who among you, if he has a hundred sheep and loses one of them does not leave the ninety-nine in the wasteland and follow the lost one until he finds it? And when he finds it, he puts it on his shoulders in jubilation. Once arrived home, he invites friends and neighbors in and says to them, 'Rejoice with me because I have found my lost sheep.' I tell you, there will likewise be more joy in heaven over one repentant sinner than over ninety-nine righteous people who have no heed to repent.

"What woman, if she has ten silver pieces and loses one, does not light a lamp and sweep the house in a diligent search until she has retrieved what she lost? And when she finds it, she calls in her friends and neighbors to say, 'Rejoice with me! I have found the silver piece I lost.' I tell you, there will be the same kind of joy before the angels of God over one repentant sinner."]

Jesus said to them: "A man had two sons. The younger of them said to his father, 'Father, give me the share of the estate that is coming to me.' So the father divided up the property. Some days later this younger son collected all his belongings and went off to a distant land, where he squandered his money on dissolute living. After he had spent everything, a great famine broke out in that country and he was in dire need. So he attached himself to one of the propertied class of the place, who sent him to his farm to take care of the pigs. He longed to fill his belly with the husks that were fodder for the pigs, but no one made a move to give him anything. Coming to his senses at last, he said: 'How many hired hands at my father's place have more than enough to eat, while here I am starving! I will break away and return to my father, and say to him, "Father, I have sinned against God and against you; I no longer deserve to be called your son. Treat me like one of your hired hands." ' With that he set off for his father's house. While he was still a long way off, his father caught sight of him and was deeply moved. He ran out to meet him, threw his arms around his neck, and kissed him. The son said to him, 'Father, I have sinned against God and against you; I no longer deserve to be called your son.' The father said to his servants: 'Quick! bring out the finest robe and put it on him; put a ring on his finger and shoes on his feet. Take the fatted calf and kill it. Let us eat and celebrate because this son of mine was dead and has come back to life. He was lost and is found.' Then the celebration began.

"Meanwhile the elder son was out on the land. As he neared the house on his way home, he heard the sound of music and dancing. He called one of the servants and asked him the reason for the dancing and the music. The servant answered, 'Your brother is home, and your father has killed the fatted calf because he has him back in good health.' The son grew angry at this and would not go in; but his father come out and began to plead with him.

"He said in reply to his father: 'For years now I have slaved for you. I never disobeyed one of your orders, yet you never gave me so much as a kid goat to celebrate with my friends. Then, when this son of yours returns after having gone through your property with loose women, you kill the fatted calf for him.'

" 'My son,' replied the father, 'you are with me always, and everything I have is yours. But we had to celebrate and rejoice! This brother of yours was dead, and has come back to life. He was lost, and is found.' "

TWENTY-FIFTH SUNDAY IN ORDINARY TIME / A

937

READING I

Isaiah 55, 6-9 / 134

Seek the Lord while he may be found,
call him while he is near.
Let the scoundrel forsake his way,
and the wicked man his thoughts;
Let him turn to the Lord for mercy;
to our God, who is generous in forgiving.
For my thoughts are not your thoughts,
nor are your ways my ways, says the Lord.
As high as the heavens are above the earth,
so high are my ways above your ways
and my thoughts above your thoughts.

RESPONSORIAL PSALM

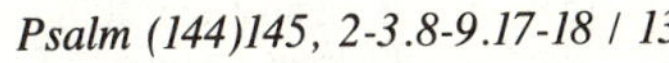
Psalm (144)145, 2-3.8-9.17-18 / 134

JS
The Lord is near to all who call on him.

I will bless you day after day
and praise your name for ever.
The Lord is great, highly to be praised,
his greatness cannot be measured. ℟.

The Lord is kind and full of compassion,
slow to anger, abounding in love.
How good is the Lord to all,
compassionate to all his creatures. ℟.

The Lord is just in all his ways
and loving in all his deeds.
He is close to all who call him,
who call on him from their hearts. ℟.

READING II

Philippians 1, 20-24.27 / 134

Christ will be exalted through me, whether I live or die. For, to me, "life" means Christ; hence dying is so much gain. If, on the other hand, I am to go on living in the flesh, that means productive toil for me–and I do not know which to prefer. I am strongly attracted by both: I long to be freed from this life and to be with Christ, for that is the far better thing; yet it is more urgent that I remain alive for your sakes. Conduct yourselves, then, in a way worthy of the gospel of Christ.

GOSPEL

Matthew 20, 1-16 / 134

Jesus told his disciples this parable: "The reign of God is like the case of the owner of an estate who went out at dawn to hire workmen for his vineyard. After reaching an agreement with them for the usual daily wage, he sent them out to his vineyard. He came out about midmorning and saw other men standing around the marketplace without work, so he said to them, 'You too go along to my vineyard and I will pay you whatever is fair.' At that they went away. He came out again around noon and midafternoon and did the same. Finally, going out in late afternoon he found still others standing around. To these he said, 'Why have you been standing here idle all day?' 'No one has hired us,' they told him. He said, 'You go to the vineyard too.' When evening came the owner of the vineyard said to his foreman, 'Call the workmen and give them their pay, but begin with the last group and end with the first.' When those hired late in the afternoon came up they received a full day's pay, and when the first group appeared they supposed they would get more; yet they received the same daily wage. Thereupon they complained to the owner, 'This last group did only an hour's work, but you have put them on the same basis as us who have worked a full day in the scorching heat.' 'My friend,' he said to one in reply, 'I do you no injustice. You agreed on the usual wage, did you not? Take your pay and go home. I intend to give this man who was hired last the same pay as you. I am free to do as I please with my money, am I not? Or are you envious because I am generous?' Thus the last shall be first and the first shall be last."

938 TWENTY-FIFTH SUNDAY IN ORDINARY TIME / B

READING I *Wisdom 2, 12.17-20 / 135*

[The wicked say:]
Let us beset the just one, because he is obnoxious to us;
he sets himself against our doings,
Reproaches us for transgressions of the law
and charges us with violations of our training.
Let us see whether his words be true;
let us find out what will happen to him.
For if the just one be the son of God, he will defend him
and deliver him from the hand of his foes.
With revilement and torture let us put him to the test
that we may have proof of his gentleness
and try his patience.
Let us condemn him to a shameful death;
for according to his own words, God will take care of him.

RESPONSORIAL PSALM *Psalm (53)54, 3-4.5.6-8 / 135*

Anon.
The Lord up-holds my life.

O God, save me by your name;
by your power, uphold my cause.
O God, hear my prayer;
listen to the words of my mouth. ℟.

For proud men have risen against me,
ruthless men seek my life.
They have no regard for God. ℟.

But I have God for my help.
The Lord upholds my life.
I will sacrifice to you with willing heart
and praise your name for it is good. ℟.

READING II *James 3, 16-4, 3 / 135*

Where there are jealousy and strife, there also are inconstancy and all kinds of vile behavior. Wisdom from above, by contrast, is first of all innocent. It is also peaceable, lenient, docile, rich in sympathy and the kindly deeds that are its fruit, impartial and sincere. The harvest of justice is sown in peace for those who cultivate peace.

Where do the conflicts and disputes among you originate? Is it not your inner cravings that make war within your members? What you desire you do not obtain, and so you resort to murder. You envy and you cannot acquire, so you quarrel and fight. You do not obtain because you do not ask. You ask and you do not receive because you ask wrongly, with a view to squandering what you receive on your pleasures.

GOSPEL *Mark 9, 30-37 / 135*

Jesus and his disciples came down the mountain and began to go through Galilee, but he did not want anyone to know about it. He was teaching his disciples in this vein:

"The Son of Man is going to be delivered into the hands of men who will put him to death; three days after his death he will rise." Though they failed to understand his words, they were afraid to question him.

They returned to Capernaum and Jesus, once inside the house, began to ask them, "What were you discussing on the way home?" At this they fell silent, for on the way they had been arguing about who was the most important. So he sat down and called the Twelve around him and said, "If anyone wishes to rank first, he must remain the last one of all and the servant of all." Then he took a little child, stood him in their midst, and putting his arms around him, said to them, "Whoever welcomes a child such as this for my sake welcomes me. And whoever welcomes me welcomes, not me, but him who sent me."

TWENTY-FIFTH SUNDAY IN ORDINARY TIME / C 939

READING I *Amos 8, 4-7 / 136*

Hear this, you who trample upon the needy
and destroy the poor of the land!
"When will the new moon be over," you ask,
"that we may sell our grain,
and the sabbath, that we may display the wheat?
We will diminish the ephah,
add to the shekel,
and fix our scales for cheating!
We will buy the lowly man for silver,
and the poor man for a pair of sandals;
even the refuse of the wheat we will sell!"
The Lord has sworn by the pride of Jacob:
Never will I forget a thing they have done!

RESPONSORIAL PSALM *Psalm (112)113, 1-2.4-6.7-8 / 136*

CAP
3
Praise the Lord who lifts up the poor.

Praise, O servants of the Lord,
praise the name of the Lord!
May the name of the Lord be blessed
both now and for evermore! ℟.

High above all nations is the Lord,
above the heavens his glory.
Who is like the Lord, our God,
who has risen on high to his throne
yet stoops from the heights to look down,
to look down upon heaven and earth? ℟.

From the dust he lifts up the lowly,
from the dungheap he raises the poor
to set him in the company of princes,
yes, with the princes of his people. ℟.

READING II *1 Timothy 2, 1-8 / 136*

First of all, I urge that petitions, prayers, intercessions, and thanksgivings be offered for all men, especially for kings and those in authority, that we may be able to lead undisturbed and tranquil lives in perfect piety and dignity. Prayer of this kind is good, and God our savior is pleased with it, for he wants all men to be saved and come to know the truth. And the truth is this:

"God is one.
One also is the mediator between God and men,

the man Christ Jesus,
who gave himself as a ransom for all."

This truth was attested at the fitting time. I have been made its herald and apostle (believe me, I am not lying but speak the truth), the teacher of the nations in the true faith.

It is my wish, then, that in every place the men shall offer prayers with blameless hands held aloft, and be free from anger and dissension.

GOSPEL *Luke 16, 1-13 or 16, 10-13 / 136*

For short form read only the part in brackets.

[Jesus said to his disciples:] "A rich man had a manager who was reported to him for dissipating his property. He summoned him and said, 'What is this I hear about you? Give me an account of your service, for it is about to come to an end.' The manager thought to himself, 'What shall I do next? My employer is sure to dismiss me. I cannot dig ditches. I am ashamed to go begging. I have it! Here is a way to make sure that people will take me into their homes when I am let go.'

"So he called in each of his master's debtors, and said to the first, 'How much do you owe my master?' The man replied, 'A hundred jars of oil.' The manager said, 'Take your invoice, sit down quickly, and make it fifty.' Then he said to a second, 'How much do you owe?' The answer came, "A hundred measures of wheat,' and the manager said, 'Take your invoice and make it eighty.'

"The owner then gave his devious employee credit for being enterprising! Why? Because the wordly take more initiative than the other worldly when it comes to dealing with their own kind.

"What I say to you is this: Make friends for yourselves through your use of this world's goods, so that when they fail you, a lasting reception will be yours. [If you can trust a man in little things, you can also trust him in greater; while anyone unjust in a slight matter is also unjust in greater. If you cannot be trusted with elusive wealth, who will trust you with lasting? And if you have not been trustworthy with someone else's money, who will give you what is your own?

"No servant can serve two masters. Either he will hate the one and love the other or be attentive to the one and despise the other. You cannot give yourself to God and money."]

940 TWENTY-SIXTH SUNDAY IN ORDINARY TIME / A

READING I *Ezekiel 18, 25-28 / 137*

You say, "The Lord's way is not fair!" Hear now, house of Israel: Is it my way that is unfair, or rather, are not your ways unfair? When a virtuous man turns away from virtue to commit iniquity, and dies, it is because of the iniquity he commited that he must die. But if a wicked man, turning from the wickedness he has committed, does what is right and just, he shall preserve his life; since he has turned away from all the sins which he committed, he shall surely live, he shall not die.

RESPONSORIAL PSALM *Psalm (24)25, 4-5.6-7.8-9 / 137*

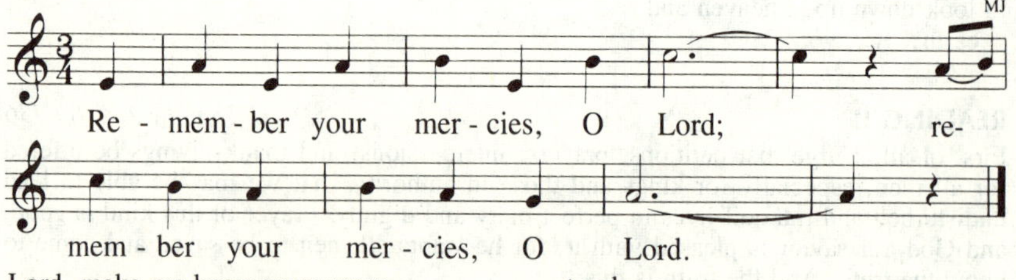
MJ
Re - mem - ber your mer - cies, O Lord; re-
mem - ber your mer - cies, O Lord.

Lord, make me know your ways.
Lord, teach me your paths.
Make me walk in your truth, and
teach me,
for you are God my savior. ℟.

Remember your mercy, Lord,
and the love you have shown from of old.
Do not remember the sins of my youth.
In your love remember me,
because of your goodness, O Lord. ℟.

The Lord is good and upright.
He shows the path to those who stray,
he guides the humble in the right path,
he teaches his way to the poor. ℟.

READING II *Philippians 2, 1-11 or 2, 1-5 / 137*

For short form read only the part in brackets.

[In the name of the encouragement you owe me in Christ, in the name of the solace that love can give, of fellowship in spirit, compassion, and pity, I beg you: make my joy complete by your unanimity, possessing the one love, united in spirit and ideals. Never act out of rivalry or conceit; rather, let all parties think humbly of others as superior to themselves, each of you looking to others' interests rather than his own. Your attitude must be Christ's:]

Though he was in the form of God,
he did not deem equality with God
something to be grasped at.
Rather, he emptied himself
and took the form of a slave,
being born in the likeness of men.
He was known to be of human estate
and it was thus that he humbled himself,
obediently accepting even death,
death on a cross!
Because of this,
God highly exalted him
and bestowed on him the name
above every other name,
So that at Jesus' name
every knee must bend
in the heavens, on the earth,
and every tongue proclaim
to the glory of God the Father:
JESUS CHRIST IS LORD!

GOSPEL *Matthew 21, 28-32 / 137*

Jesus said to the chief priests and elders of the people: "What do you think of this case? There was a man who had two sons. He approached the elder and said, 'Son, go out and work in the vineyard today.' The son replied, 'I am on my way, sir'; but he never went. Then the man came to his second son and said the same thing. This son said in reply, 'No, I will not'; but afterward he regretted it and went. Which of the two did what the father wanted?" They said, "The second." Jesus said to them, "Let me make it clear that tax collectors and prostitutes are entering the kingdom of God before you. When John came preaching a way of holiness, you put no faith in him; but the tax collectors and the prostitutes did believe in him. Yet even when you saw that, you did not repent and believe in him."

TWENTY-SIXTH SUNDAY IN ORDINARY TIME / B 941

READING I *Numbers 11, 25-29 / 138*

The Lord came down in the cloud and spoke to Moses. Taking some of the spirit that was on him, he bestowed it on the seventy elders; and as the spirit came to rest on them, they prophesied.

Now two men, one named Eldad and the other Medad, were not in the gathering but had been left in the camp. They too had been on the list, but had not gone out to the tent; yet the spirit came to rest on them also, and they prophesied in the camp. So, when a young man quickly told Moses, "Eldad and Medad are prophesying in the camp," Joshua, son of Nun, who from his youth had been Moses' aide, said, "Moses, my lord, stop them." But Moses answered him, "Are you jealous for my sake? Would that all the people of the Lord were prophets! Would that the Lord might bestow his spirit on them all!"

RESPONSORIAL PSALM *Psalm (18)19, 8.10.12-13.14 / 138*

RC
The pre-cepts of the Lord give joy to the heart.

The law of the Lord is perfect,
it revives the soul.
The rule of the Lord is to be trusted,
it gives wisdom to the simple. ℟.

The fear of the Lord is holy,
abiding for ever.
The decrees of the Lord are truth
and all of them just. ℟.

So in them your servant finds
instruction;
great reward is in their keeping.
But who can detect all his errors?
From hidden faults acquit me. ℟.

From presumption restrain your servant
and let it not rule me.
Then shall I be blameless,
clean from grave sin. ℟.

READING II *James 5, 1-6 / 138*

You rich, weep and wail over your impending miseries. Your wealth has rotted, your fine wardrobe has grown moth-eaten, your gold and silver have corroded, and their corrosion shall be a testimony against you; it will devour your flesh like a fire. See what you have stored up for yourselves against the last days. Here, crying aloud, are the wages you withheld from the farmhands who harvested your fields. The shouts of the harvesters have reached the ears of the Lord of hosts. You lived in wanton luxury on the earth; you fattened yourselves for the day of slaughter. You condemned, even killed, the just man; he does not resist you.

GOSPEL *Mark 9, 38-43.45.47-48 / 138*

John said to Jesus, "Teacher, we saw a man using your name to expel demons and we tried to stop him because he is not of our company." Jesus said in reply: "Do not try to stop him. No man who performs a miracle using my name can at once speak ill of me. Anyone who is not against us is with us. Any man who gives you a drink of water because you belong to Christ will not, I assure you, go without his reward. But it would be better if anyone who leads astray one of these simple believers were to be plunged in the sea with a great millstone fastened around his neck.

"If your hand is your difficulty, cut it off! Better for you to enter life maimed than to keep both hands and enter Gehenna, with its unquenchable fire. If your foot is your undoing, cut it off! Better for you to enter life crippled than to be thrown into Gehenna with both feet. If your eye is your downfall, tear it out! Better for you to enter the kingdom of God with one eye than to be thrown with both eyes into Gehenna, where 'the worm dies not and the fire is never extinguished.' "

942 TWENTY-SIXTH SUNDAY IN ORDINARY TIME / C

READING I *Amos 6, 1.4-7 / 139*

Woe to the complacent in Zion!
Lying upon beds of ivory,
stretched comfortably on their
couches,
They eat lambs taken from the flock,
and calves from the stall!
Improvising to the music of the harp,
like David, they devise their own
accompaniment.
They drink wine from bowls
and anoint themselves with the best
oils;
yet they are not made ill by the
collapse of Joseph!
Therefore, now they shall be the first to
go into exile,
and their wanton revelry shall be
done away with.

RESPONSORIAL PSALM *Psalm (145)146, 7.8-9 .9-10 / 139*

RP
Praise the Lord, my soul! Praise the Lord!

It is he who keeps faith for ever,
who is just to those who are oppressed.
It is he who gives bread to the
hungry,
the Lord, who sets prisoners free. ℟.

The Lord who gives sight to the blind,
who raises up those who are bowed
down,
the Lord, who protects the stranger
and upholds the widow and orphan. ℟.

It is the Lord who loves the just
but thwarts the path of the wicked.
The Lord will reign for ever,
Zion's God, from age to age. ℟.

READING II *1 Timothy 6, 11-16 / 139*

Man of God that you are, seek after integrity, piety, faith, love, steadfastness, and a gentle spirit. Fight the good fight of faith. Take firm hold on the everlasting life to which you were called when, in the presence of many witnesses, you made your noble profession of faith. Before God, who gives life to all, and before Christ Jesus, who in bearing witness made his noble profession before Pontius Pilate, I charge you to keep God's command without blame or reproach until our Lord Jesus Christ shall appear. This appearance God will bring to pass at his chosen time. He is the blessed and only ruler, the King of kings and Lord of lords who alone has immortality and who dwells in inapproachable light, whom no human being has ever seen or can see. To him be honor and everlasting rule! Amen.

GOSPEL *Luke 16, 19-31 / 139*

Jesus said to the Pharisees: "Once there was rich man who dressed in purple and linen and feasted splendidly every day. At his gate lay a begger named Lazarus who was covered with sores. Lazarus longed to eat the scraps that fell from the rich man's table. The dogs even came and licked his sores. Eventually the beggar died. He was carried by angels to the bosom of Abraham. The rich man likewise died and was buried. From the abode of the dead where he was in torment, he raised his eyes and saw Abraham afar off, and Lazarus resting in his bosom.

"He called out, 'Father Abraham, have pity on me. Send Lazarus to dip the tip of his finger in water to refresh my tongue, for I am tortured in these flames.' 'My child,' replied Abraham, 'remember that you were well off in your lifetime, while Lazarus was in misery. Now he has found consolation here, but you have found torment. And that is not all. Between you and us there is fixed a great abyss, so that those who might wish to cross from here to you cannot do so, nor can anyone cross from your side to us.'

" 'Father, I ask you, then,' the rich man said, 'send him to my father's house where I have five brothers. Let him be a warning to them so that they may not end in this place of torment.' Abraham answered, 'They have Moses and the prophets. Let them hear them.' 'No, Father Abraham,' replied the rich man. 'But if someone would only go to them from the dead, then they would repent.' Abraham said to him, 'If they do not listen to Moses and the prophets, they will not be convinced even if one should rise from the dead.' "

943 TWENTY-SEVENTH SUNDAY IN ORDINARY TIME / A

READING I *Isaiah 5, 1-7 / 140*

Let me now sing of my friend,
my friend's song concerning his vineyard.
My friend had a vineyard
on a fertile hillside;
He spaded it, cleared it of stones,
and planted the choicest vines;
Within it he built a watchtower,
and hewed out a wine press.
Then he looked for the crop of grapes,
but what it yielded was wild grapes.

Now, inhabitants of Jerusalem and men of Judah,
judge between me and my vineyard:
What more was there to do for my vineyard
that I had not done?
Why, when I looked for the crop of grapes,
did it bring forth wild grapes?
Now, I will let you know
what I mean to do to my vineyard:
Take away its hedge, give it to grazing,
break through its wall, let it be trampled!
Yes, I will make it a ruin:
it shall not be pruned or hoed,
but overgrown with thorns and briers;
I will command the clouds
not to send rain upon it.
The vineyard of the Lord of hosts is the house of Israel,
and the men of Judah are his cherished plant;
He looked for judgment, but see, bloodshed!
for justice, but hark, the outcry!

RESPONSORIAL PSALM *Psalm (79)80, 9.12.13-14.15-16.19-20 / 140*

RC
The vine-yard of the Lord is the house of Is - ra - el.

You brought a vine out of Egypt;
to plant it you drove out the nations.
It stretched out its branches to the sea,
to the Great River it stretched out its shoots. ℟.

Then, why have you broken down its walls?
It is plucked by all who pass by.
It is ravaged by the boar of the forest,
devoured by the beasts of the field. ℟.

God of hosts, turn again, we implore,
look down from heaven and see.
Visit this vine and protect it,
the vine your right hand has planted. ℟.

And we shall never forsake you again:
give us life that we may call upon your name.
God of hosts, bring us back;
let your face shine on us and we shall be saved. ℟.

READING II *Philippians 4, 6-9 / 140*

Dismiss all anxiety from your minds. Present your needs to God in every form of prayer and in petitions full of gratitude. Then God's own peace, which is beyond all understanding, will stand guard over your hearts and minds, in Christ Jesus.

Finally, my brothers, your thoughts should be wholly directed to all that is true, all that deserves respect, all that is honest, pure, admirable, decent, virtuous, or worthy of praise. Live according to what you have learned and accepted, what you have heard me say and seen me do. Then will the God of peace be with you.

GOSPEL *Matthew 21, 33-43 / 140*

Jesus said to the chief priests and elders of the people: "Listen to another parable. There was a property owner who planted a vineyard, put a hedge around it, dug out a vat, and erected a tower. Then he leased it out to tenant farmers and went on a journey. When vintage time arrived he dispatched his slaves to the tenants to obtain his share of the grapes. The tenants responded by seizing the slaves. They beat one, killed another, and stoned a third. A second time he dispatched even more slaves than before, but they treated them the same way. Finally he sent his son to them, thinking 'They will respect my son.' When they saw the son, the tenants said to one another, 'Here is the one who will inherit everything. Let us kill him and then we shall have his inheritance!' With that they seized him, dragged him outside the vineyard and killed him. What do you suppose the owner of the vineyard will do to those tenants when he comes?" They replied, "He will bring that wicked crowd to a bad end and lease his vineyard out to others who will see to it that he has grapes at vintage time." Jesus said to them, "Did you never read in the Scriptures,

'The stone which the builders rejected
has become the keystone of the structure.
It was the Lord who did this
and we find it marvelous to behold'?

For this reason, I tell you, the kingdom of God will be taken away from you and given to a people that will yield a rich harvest."

TWENTY-SEVENTH SUNDAY IN ORDINARY TIME / B 944

READING I *Genesis 2, 18-24 / 141*

The Lord God said: "It is not good for the man to be alone. I will make a suitable partner for him." So the Lord God formed out of the ground various wild animals and various birds of the air, and he brought them to the man to see what he would call them; whatever the man called each of them would be its name. The man gave names to all the cattle, all the birds of the air, and all wild animals; but none proved to be the suitable partner for the man.

So the Lord God cast a deep sleep on the man, and while he was asleep, he took out one of his ribs and closed up its place with flesh. The Lord God then built up into a woman the rib that he had taken from the man. When he brought her to the man, the man said:

"This one, at last, is bone of my bones
  and flesh of my flesh;
This one shall be called 'woman,'
  for out of 'her man ' this one has been taken."

That is why a man leaves his father and mother and clings to his wife, and the two of them become one body.

RESPONSORIAL PSALM *Psalm (127)128, 1-2.3.4-5.6 / 141*

AGM
May the Lord bless and pro-tect us all the days of our life.

O blessed are those who fear the Lord
and walk in his ways!
By the labor of your hands you shall
  eat.
You will be happy and prosper. ℟.

Your wife like a fruitful vine
in the heart of your house;
your children like shoots of the olive
around your table. ℟.

Indeed thus shall be blessed
the man who fears the Lord.
May the Lord bless you from Zion
all the days of your life! ℟.

May you see your children's children
in a happy Jerusalem!
On Israel, peace! ℟.

READING II *Hebrews 2, 9-11 / 141*

Jesus was made for a little while lower than the angels, that through God's gracious will he might taste death for the sake of all men. Indeed, it was fitting that, when bringing many sons to glory, God, for whom and through whom all things exist, should make their leader in the work of salvation perfect through suffering. He who consecrates and those who are consecrated have one and the same Father. Therefore, he is not ashamed to call them brothers.

GOSPEL *Mark 10, 2-16 or 10, 2-12 / 141*

For short form read only the part in brackets.

[Some Pharisees came up and as a test began to ask Jesus whether it was permissible for a husband to divorce his wife. In reply he said, "What command did Moses give you?" They answered, "Moses permitted divorce and the writing of a decree of divorce." But Jesus told them: "He wrote that commandment for you because of your stubbornness. At the beginning of creation God made them male and female; for this reason a man shall leave his father and mother and the two shall become as one. They are no longer two but one flesh. Therefore let no man separate what God has joined." Back in the house again, the disciples began to question him about this. He told them, "Whoever divorces his wife and marries another commits adultery against her; and the woman who divorces her husband and marries another commits adultery."]

People were bringing their little children to him to have him touch them, but the disciples were scolding them for this. Jesus became indignant when he noticed it and said to them: "Let the children come to me and do not hinder them. It is to just such as these that the kingdom of God belongs. I assure you that whoever does not accept the kingdom of God like a little child shall not enter into it." Then he embraced them and blessed them, placing his hands on them.

945 TWENTY-SEVENTH SUNDAY IN ORDINARY TIME / C

READING I *Habakkuk 1, 2-3; 2, 2-4 / 142*

How long, O Lord? I cry for help
but you do not listen!
I cry out to you, "Violence!"
but you do not intervene.
Why do you let me see ruin;
why must I look at misery?
Destruction and violence are before me;
there is strife, and clamorous discord.
Then the Lord answered me and said:
Write down the vision
Clearly upon the tablets,
so that one can read it readily.
For the vision still has its time,
presses on to fulfillment, and will not disappoint;
If it delays, wait for it,
it will surely come, it will not be late.
The rash man has no integrity;
but the just man, because of his faith, shall live.

RESPONSORIAL PSALM *Psalm (94)95, 1-2.6-7.8-9 / 142*

RP

If to - day you hear his voice, O hard - en not your hearts.

Come, ring out your joy to the Lord;
hail the rock who saves us.
Let us come before him giving thanks,
with songs let us hail the Lord. ℞.

Come in, let us bow and bend low;
let us kneel before the God who made us
for he is our God, and we
the people who belong to his pasture,
the flock that is led by his hand. ℟.

O that today you would listen to his voice!
"Harden not your hearts as at Meribah,
as on that day at Massah in the desert
when your forbears put me to the test;
when they tried me, though they saw my work." ℟.

READING II *2 Timothy 1, 6-8, 13-14 / 142*

I remind you to stir into flame the gift of God bestowed when my hands were laid on you. The Spirit God has given us is no cowardly spirit, but rather one that makes us strong, loving and wise. Therefore, never be ashamed of your testimony to our Lord, nor of me, a prisoner for his sake; but with the strength which comes from God bear your share of the hardship which the gospel entails.

Take as a model of sound teaching what you have heard me say, in faith and love in Christ Jesus. Guard the rich deposit of faith with the help of the Holy Spirit who dwells within us.

GOSPEL *Luke 17, 5-10 / 142*

The apostles said to the Lord, "Increase our faith," and he answered: "If you had faith the size of a mustard seed, you could say to this sycamore, 'Be uprooted and transplanted into the sea,' and it would obey you.

"If one of you had a servant plowing or herding sheep and he came in from the fields, would you say to him, 'Come and sit down at table'? Would you not rather say, 'Prepare my supper. Put on your apron and wait on me while I eat and drink. You can eat and drink afterward'? Would he be grateful to the servant who was only carrying out his orders? It is quite the same with you who hear me. When you have done all you have been commanded to do, say, 'We are useless servants. We have done no more than our duty.' "

TWENTY-EIGHTH SUNDAY IN ORDINARY TIME / A 946

READING I *Isaiah 25, 6-10 / 143*

On this mountain the Lord of hosts
will provide for all peoples
A feast of rich food and choice wines,
juicy, rich food and pure, choice wines.
On this mountain he will destroy
the veil that veils all peoples,
The web that is woven over all nations;
he will destroy death forever.
The Lord God will wipe away
the tears from all faces;
The reproach of his people he will remove
from the whole earth; for the Lord has spoken.

On that day it will be said:
"Behold our God, to whom we looked to save us!
This is the Lord for whom we looked;
let us rejoice and be glad that he has saved us!"
For the hand of the Lord will rest on this mountain.

RESPONSORIAL PSALM *Psalm (22)23, 1-3.3-4.5.6 / 143*

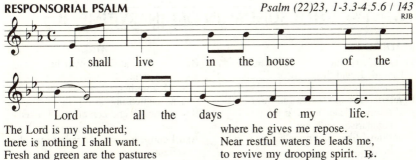

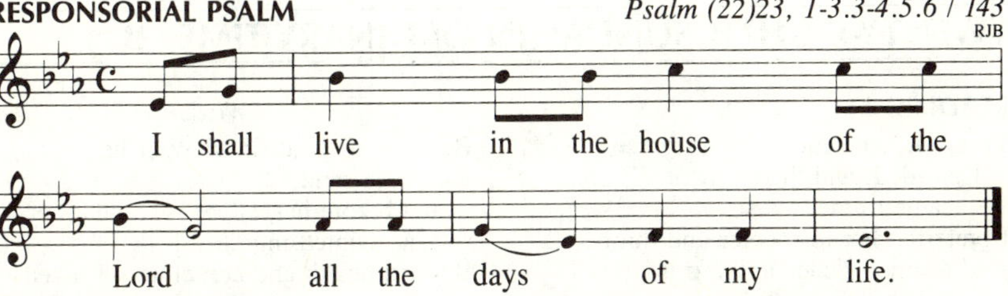
RJB
I shall live in the house of the
Lord all the days of my life.

The Lord is my shepherd;
there is nothing I shall want.
Fresh and green are the pastures
where he gives me repose.
Near restful waters he leads me,
to revive my drooping spirit. ℟.

He guides me along the right path;
he is true to his name.
If I should walk in the valley of
  darkness
no evil would I fear.
You are there with your crook and your
  staff;
with these you give me comfort. ℟.

You have prepared a banquet for me
in the sight of my foes.
My head you have anointed with oil;
my cup is overflowing. ℟.

Surely goodness and kindness shall
  follow me
all the days of my life.
In the Lord's own house shall I dwell
for ever and ever. ℟.

READING II *Philippians 4, 12-14.19-20 / 143*

I am experienced in being brought low, yet I know what it is to have an abundance. I have learned how to cope with every circumstance–how to eat well or go hungry, to be well provided for or do without. In him who is the source of my strength I have strength for everything.

Nonetheless, it was kind of you to want to share in my hardships.

My God in turn will supply your needs fully, in a way worthy of his magnificent riches in Christ Jesus. All glory to our God and Father for unending ages! Amen.

GOSPEL *Matthew 22, 1-14 or 22, 1-10 / 143*

For short form read only the part in brackets.

[Jesus began to address the chief priests and elders of the people, once more using parables. "The reign of God may be likened to to a king who gave a wedding banquet for his son. He dispatched his servants to summon the invited guests to the wedding, but they refused to come. A second time he sent other servants, saying: 'Tell those who were invited; see, I have my dinner prepared! My bullocks and corn-fed cattle are killed; everything is ready. Come to the feast.' Some ignored the invitation and went their way, one to his farm, another to his business. The rest laid hold of his servants, insulted them, and killed them. At this the king grew furious and sent his army to destroy those murderers and burn their city. Then he said to his servants: 'The banquet is ready, but those who were invited were unfit to come. That is why you must go out into the byroads and invite to the wedding anyone you come upon.' The servants then went out into the byroads and rounded up everyone they met, bad as well as good. This filled the wedding hall with banqueters.]

"When the king came in to meet the guests, however, he caught sight of a man not properly dressed for a wedding feast. 'My friend,' he said, 'how is it you came in here not properly dressed?' The man had nothing to say. The king then said to the attendants, 'Bind him hand and foot and throw him out into the night to wail and grind his teeth.' The invited are many, the elect are few."

947 TWENTY-EIGHTH SUNDAY IN ORDINARY TIME / B

READING I *Wisdom 7, 7-11 / 144*

I prayed, and prudence was given me;
  I pleaded, and the spirit of Wisdom
    came to me.
I preferred her to scepter and throne,
And deemed riches nothing in
    comparison with her,
  nor did I liken any priceless gem to
    her;
Because all gold, in view of her, is a
    little sand,
  and before her, silver is to be
    accounted mire.
Beyond health and comeliness I loved
    her,
And I chose to have her rather than the
    light,

because the splendor of her never
yields to sleep.

Yet all good things together came to me
in her company,
and countless riches at her hands.

RESPONSORIAL PSALM *Psalm (89)90, 12-13.14-15.16-17 / 144*

RJB

Fill us with your love, O Lord, and we will sing for joy!

Make us know the shortness of our life
that we may gain wisdom of heart.
Lord, relent! Is your anger for ever?
Show pity to your servants. ℟.

In the morning, fill us with your love;
we shall exult and rejoice all our days.
Give us joy to balance our affliction
for the years when we knew
misfortune. ℟.

Show forth your work to your servants;
let your glory shine on their children.
Let the favor of the Lord be upon us:
give success to the work of our hands
(give success to the work of our
hands). ℟.

READING II *Hebrews 4, 12-13 / 144*

God's word is living and effective, sharper than any two-edged sword. It penetrates and divides soul and spirit, joints and marrow; it judges the reflections and thoughts of the heart. Nothing is concealed from him; all lies bare and exposed to the eyes of him to whom we must render an account.

GOSPEL *Mark 10, 17-30 or 10, 17-27 / 144*

For short form read only the part in brackets.

[As Jesus was setting out on a journey a man came running up, knelt down before him and asked, "Good Teacher, what must I do to share in everlasting life?" Jesus answered, "Why do you call me good? No one is good but God alone. You know the commandments:

'You shall not kill;
You shall not commit adultery;
You shall not steal;
You shall not bear false witness;
You shall not defraud;
Honor your father and your mother.' "

He replied. "Teacher, I have kept all these since my childhood." Then Jesus looked at him with love and told him, "There is one thing more you must do. Go and sell what you have and give to the poor; you will then have treasure in heaven. After that come and follow me." At these words the man's face fell. He went away sad, for he had many possessions. Jesus looked around and said to his disciples, "How hard it is for the rich to enter the kingdom of God!" The disciples could only marvel at his words. So Jesus repeated what he had said: "My sons, how hard it is to enter the kingdom of God! It is easier for a camel to pass through a needle's eye than for a rich man to enter the kingdom of God."

They were completely overwhelmed at this, and exclaimed to one another, "Then who can be saved?" Jesus fixed his gaze on them and said, "For man it is impossible but not for God. With God all things are possible."]

Peter was moved to say to him: "We have put aside everything to follow you!" Jesus answered: "I give you my word, there is no one who has given up home, brothers or sisters, mother or father, children or property, for me and for the gospel who will not receive in this present age a hundred times as many homes, brothers and sisters, mothers, children and property–and persecution besides–and in the age to come, everlasting life."

948 TWENTY-EIGHTH SUNDAY IN ORDINARY TIME / C

READING I *2 Kings 5, 14-17 / 145*

Naaman went down and plunged into the Jordan seven times at the word of Elisha, the man of God. His flesh became again like the flesh of a little child, and he was clean [of his leprosy].

He returned with his whole retinue to the man of God. On his arrival he stood before him and said, "Now I know that there is no God in all the earth, except in Israel. Please accept a gift from your servant."

"As the Lord lives whom I serve, I will not take it," Elisha replied; and despite Naaman's urging he still refused. Naaman said: "If you will not accept, please let me, your servant, have two mule-loads of earth, for I will no longer offer holocaust or sacrifice to any other god except to the Lord."

RESPONSORIAL PSALM *Psalm (97)98, 1.2-3.3-4 / 145*

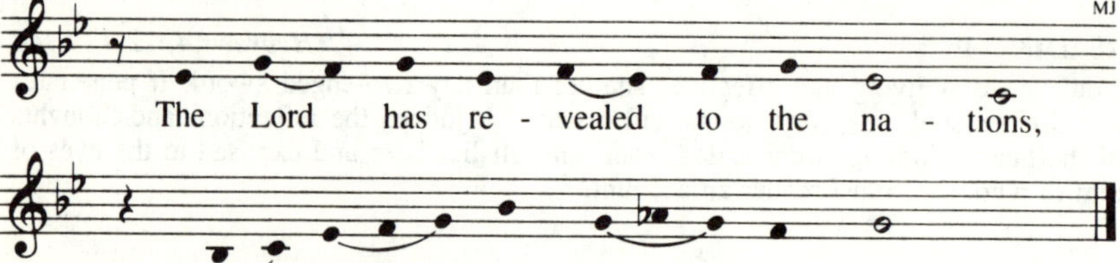
MJ
The Lord has re - vealed to the na - tions,
re - vealed his sav - ing power.

Sing a new song to the Lord
for he has worked wonders.
His right hand and his holy arm
have brought salvation. ℟.

The Lord has made known his
salvation;
has shown his justice to the nations.
He has remembered his truth and love
for the house of Israel. ℟.

All the ends of the earth have seen
the salvation of our God.
Shout to the Lord, all the earth,
ring out your joy, ℟.

READING II *2 Timothy 2, 8-13 / 145*

Remember that Jesus Christ, a descendant of David, was raised from the dead. This is the gospel I preach; in preaching it I suffer as a criminal, even to the point of being thrown into chains–but there is no chaining the word of God! Therefore I bear with all of this for the sake of those whom God has chosen, in order that they may obtain the salvation to be found in Christ Jesus and with it eternal glory.

You can depend on this:
If we have died with him
we shall also live with him;
If we hold out to the end
we shall also reign with him.

But if we deny him he will deny us. If we are unfaithful, he will still remain faithful; for he cannot deny himself.

GOSPEL *Luke 17, 11-19 / 145*

On his journey to Jerusalem Jesus passed along the borders of Samaria and Galilee. As he was entering a village, ten lepers met him. Keeping their distance, they raised their voices and said, "Jesus, Master, have pity on us!" When he saw them, he responded, "Go and show yourselves to the priests." On their way there they were cured. One of them, realizing that he had been cured, came back praising God in a loud voice. He threw himself on his face at the feet of Jesus and spoke his praises. This man was a Samaritan.

Jesus took the occasion to say, "Were not all ten made whole? Where are the other nine? Was there no one to return and give thanks to God except this foreigner?" He said to the man, "Stand up and go your way; your faith has been your salvation."

TWENTY-NINTH SUNDAY IN ORDINARY TIME / A 949

READING I *Isaiah 45, 1.4-6 / 146*

Thus says the Lord to his anointed,
Cyrus,
whose right hand I grasp,
Subduing nations before him,
and making kings run in his service,
Opening doors before him
and leaving the gates unbarred:
For the sake of Jacob, my servant,
of Israel, my chosen one,
I have called you by your name,
giving you a title, though you knew
me not.
I am the Lord and there is no other,
there is no God besides me.
It is I who arm you, though you know
me not,
so that toward the rising and the
setting of the sun,
men may know that there is none
besides me.
I am the Lord, there is no other.

RESPONSORIAL PSALM *Psalm (95)96, 1.3.4-5.7-8.9-10 / 146*

RP
Give the Lord glo - ry, glo - ry and hon - or.

O sing a new song to the Lord,
sing to the Lord all the earth.
Tell among the nations his glory
and his wonders among all the
peoples. ℟.

The Lord is great and worthy of praise,
to be feared above all gods;
the gods of the heathens are naught.
It was the Lord who made the
heavens. ℟.

Give the Lord, you families of peoples,
give the Lord glory and power;
give the Lord the glory of his name.
Bring an offering and enter his
courts. ℟.

Worship the Lord in his temple.
O earth, tremble before him.
Proclaim to the nations: "God is king."
He will judge the peoples in
fairness. ℟.

READING II *1 Thessalonians 1, 1-5 / 146*

Paul, Silvanus, and Timothy, to the church of Thessalonians who belong to God the Father and the Lord Jesus Christ. Grace and peace be yours.

We keep thanking God for all of you and we remember you in our prayers, for we constantly are mindful before our God and Father of the way you are proving your faith, and laboring in love, and showing constancy in hope in our Lord Jesus Christ. We know, too, brothers beloved of God, how you were chosen. Our preaching of the gospel proved not a mere matter of words for you but one of power; it was carried on in the Holy Spirit and out of complete conviction.

GOSPEL *Matthew 22, 15-21 / 146*

The Pharisees went off and began to plot how they might trap Jesus in speech. They sent their disciples to him, accompanied by Herodian sympathizers, who said: "Teacher, we know you are a truthful man and teach God's way sincerely. You court no one's favor and do not act out of human respect. Give us your opinion, then, in this case. Is it lawful to pay tax to the emperor or not?" Jesus recognized their bad faith and said to them, "Why are you trying to trip me up, you hypocrites? Show me the coin used for the tax." When they handed him a small Roman coin he asked them "Whose head is this, and whose inscription?" "Caesar's," they replied. At that he said to them, "Then give to Caesar what is Caesar's, but give to God what is God's."

950 TWENTY-NINTH SUNDAY IN ORDINARY TIME / B

READING I *Isaiah 53, 10-11 / 147*

[But the Lord was pleased
to crush him in infirmity.]
If he gives his life as an offering for sin,
he shall see his descendants in a long life,
and the will of the Lord shall be accomplished through him.

Because of his affliction
he shall see the light in fullness of days;
Through his suffering, my servant shall justify many,
and their guilt he shall bear.

RESPONSORIAL PSALM *Psalm (32)33, 4-5.18-19.20.22 / 147*

RP
Lord, let your mer - cy be on us,
as we place our trust in you.

For the word of the Lord is faithful
and all his works to be trusted.
The Lord loves justice and right
and fills the earth with his love. ℟.

The Lord looks on those who revere him,
on those who hope in his love,
to rescue their souls from death,
to keep them alive in famine. ℟.

Our soul is waiting for the Lord.
The Lord is our help and our shield.
May your love be upon us, O Lord,
as we place all our hope in you. ℟.

READING II *Hebrews 4, 14-16 / 147*

We have a great high priest who has passed through the heavens, Jesus, the Son of God; let us hold fast to our profession of faith. For we do not have a high priest who is unable to sympathize with our weakness, but one who was tempted in every way that we are, yet never sinned. So let us confidently approach the throne of grace to receive mercy and favor and to find help in time of need.

GOSPEL *Mark 10, 35-45 or 10, 42-45 / 147*

For short form read only the part in brackets.

Zebedee's sons, James and John, approached Jesus. "Teacher," they said, "we want you to grant our request." "What is it?" he asked. They replied, "See to it that we sit, one at your right and the other at your left, when you come into your glory." Jesus told them, "You do not know what you are asking. Can you drink the cup I shall drink or be baptized in the same bath of pain as I?" "We can," they told him. Jesus said in response, "From the cup I drink of you shall drink; the bath I am immersed in you shall share. But sitting at my right or my left is not mine to give; that is for those for whom it has been reserved." The other ten, on hearing this, became indignant at James and John. [Jesus called them (the Twelve) together and said to them: "You know how among the Gentiles those who seem to exercise authority lord it over them; their great ones make their importance felt. It cannot be like that with you. Anyone among you who aspires to greatness must serve the rest; whoever wants to rank first among you must serve the needs of all. The Son of Man has not come to be served but to serve–to give his life in ransom for the many."]

TWENTY-NINTH SUNDAY IN ORDINARY TIME / C 951

READING I *Exodus 17, 8-13 / 148*

Amalek came and waged war against Israel. Moses, therefore, said to Joshua, "Pick out certain men, and tomorrow go out and engage Amalek in battle. I will be standing on top of the hill with the staff of God in my hand." So Joshua did as Moses told him: he engaged Amalek in battle after Moses had climbed to the top of the hill with Aaron and Hur. As long as Moses kept his hands raised up, Israel had the better of the fight, but when he let his hands rest, Amalek had the better of the fight. Moses's hands, however, grew tired; so they put a rock in place for him to sit on. Meanwhile Aaron and Hur supported his hands, one on one side and one on the other, so that his hands remained steady till sunset. And Joshua mowed down Amalek and his people with the edge of the sword.

RESPONSORIAL PSALM *Psalm (120)121, 1-2.3-4.5-6.7-8 / 148*

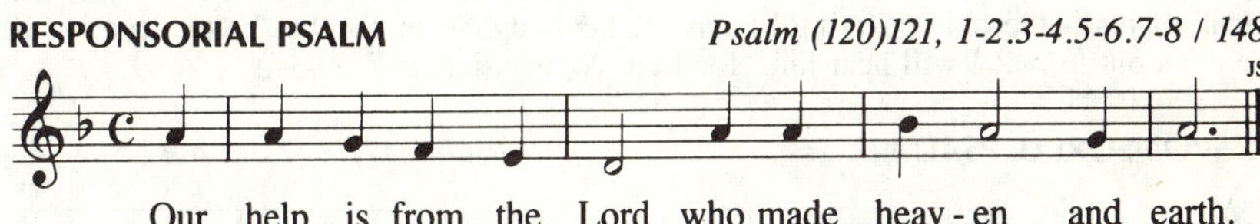
JS
Our help is from the Lord who made heav - en and earth.

I lift up my eyes to the mountains;
from where shall come my help?
My help shall come from the Lord
who made heaven and earth. ℟.

May he never allow you to stumble!
Let him sleep not, your guard.
No, he sleeps not nor slumbers,
Israel's guard. ℟.

The Lord is your guard and your shade;
at your right side he stands.
By day the sun shall not smite you
nor the moon in the night. ℟.

The Lord will guard you from evil,
he will guard your soul.
The Lord will guard your going and
coming
both now and for ever. ℟.

READING II *2 Timothy 3, 14-4, 2 / 148*

You must remain faithful to what you have learned and believed, because you know who your teachers were. Likewise from your infancy you have known the sacred Scriptures, the source of the wisdom which through faith in Jesus Christ leads to salvation. All Scripture is inspired of God and is useful for teaching–for reproof, correction, and training in holiness so that the man of God may be fully competent and equipped for every good work.

In the presence of God and of Christ Jesus, who is coming to judge the living and the dead, and by his appearing and his kingly power, I charge you to preach the word, to stay with this task whether convenient or inconvenient–correcting, reproving, appealing–constantly teaching and never losing patience.

GOSPEL *Luke 18, 1-8 / 148*

Jesus told his disciples a parable on the necessity of praying always and not losing heart: "Once there was a judge in a certain city who respected neither God nor man. A widow in that city kept coming to him saying, 'Give me my rights against my opponent.' For a time he refused, but finally he thought, 'I care little for God or man, but this widow is wearing me out. I am going to settle in her favor or she will end by doing me violence.' " The Lord said, "Listen to what the corrupt judge has to say. Will not God then do justice to his chosen who call out to him day and night? Will he delay long over them, do you suppose? I tell you, he will give them swift justice. But when the Son of Man comes, will he find any faith on the earth?"

952 **THIRTIETH SUNDAY IN ORDINARY TIME / A**

READING I *Exodus 22, 20-26 / 149*

"You shall not molest or oppress an alien, for you were once aliens yourselves in the land of Egypt. You shall not wrong any widow or orphan. If ever you wrong them and they cry out to me, I will surely hear their cry. My wrath will flare up, I will kill you with the sword; then your own wives will be widows, and your children orphans.

"If you lend money to one of your poor neighbors among my people, you shall not act like an extortioner toward him by demanding interest from him. If you take your neighbor's cloak as a pledge, you shall return it to him before sunset; for this cloak of his is the only covering he has for his body. What else has he to sleep in? If he cries out to me, I will hear him; for I am compassionate."

RESPONSORIAL PSALM *Psalm (17)18, 2-3.3-4.47.51 / 149*

RP
I love you, I love you, Lord, my strength.

I love you, Lord, my strength,
my rock, my fortress, my savior. ℟.

My God is the rock where I take refuge;
my shield, my mighty help, my
stronghold.
The Lord is worthy of all praise,
when I call I am saved from my
foes. ℟.

Long life to the Lord, my rock!
Praised be the God who saves me.
He has given great victories to his
king
and shown his love for his
anointed. ℟.

READING II *1 Thessalonians 1, 5-10 / 149*

You know as well as we do what we proved to be like when, while still among you, we acted on your behalf. You, in turn, became imitators of us and of the Lord, receiving the word despite great trials, with the joy that comes from the Holy Spirit. Thus you became a model for all the believers of Macedonia and Achaia. The word of the Lord has echoed forth from you resoundingly. This is true not only in Macedonia and Achaia; throughout every region your faith in God is celebrated, which makes it needless for us to say anything more. The people of those parts are reporting what kind of reception we had from you and how you turned to God from idols, to serve him who is the living and true God and to await from heaven the Son he raised from the dead–Jesus, who delivers us from the wrath to come.

GOSPEL *Matthew 22, 34-40 / 149*

When the Pharisees heard that Jesus had silenced the Sadducees, they assembled in a body; and one of them, a lawyer, in an attempt to trip him up, asked him, "Teacher, which commandment of the law is the greatest?"
Jesus said to him:
" 'You shall love the Lord your God
with your whole heart,
with your whole soul,
and with all your mind.'
This is the greatest and first commandment. The second is like it:
'You shall love your neighbor as yourself.' On these two commandments the whole law is based, and the prophets as well."

THIRTIETH SUNDAY IN ORDINARY TIME / B 953

READING I *Jeremiah 31, 7-9 / 150*

Thus says the Lord:
Shout with joy for Jacob,
exult at the head of the nations;
proclaim your praise and say:
The Lord has delivered his people,
the remnant of Israel.
Behold, I will bring them back
from the land of the north;
I will gather them from the ends of the world,
with the blind and the lame in their midst,
The mothers and those with child;
they shall return as an immense throng.
They departed in tears,
but I will console them and guide them;
I will lead them to brooks of water,
on a level road, so that none shall stumble.
For I am a father to Israel,
Ephraim is my first-born.

RESPONSORIAL PSALM *Psalm (125)126, 1-2.2-3.4-5.6 / 150*

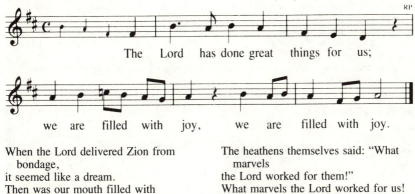

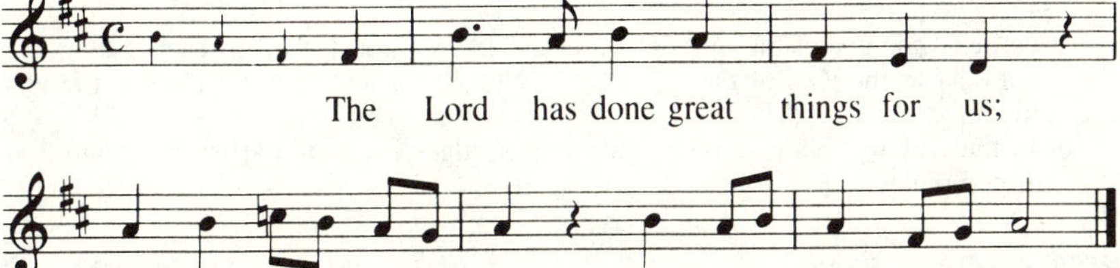
RP
The Lord has done great things for us;
we are filled with joy, we are filled with joy.

When the Lord delivered Zion from bondage,
it seemed like a dream.
Then was our mouth filled with laughter,
on our lips there were songs. ℞.

The heathens themselves said: "What marvels
the Lord worked for them!"
What marvels the Lord worked for us!
Indeed we were glad. ℞.

Deliver us, O Lord, from our bondage
as streams in dry land.
Those who are sowing in tears
will sing when they reap. ℟.

They go out, they go out, full of tears,
carrying seed for the sowing;
they come back, they come back, full
of song,
carrying their sheaves. ℟.

READING II *Hebrews 5, 1-6 / 150*

Every high priest is taken from among men and made their representative before God, to offer gifts and sacrifices for sins. He is able to deal patiently with erring sinners, for he is himself beset by weakness and so must make sin offerings for himself as well as for the people. One does not take this honor on his own initiative, but only when called by God as Aaron was. Even Christ did not glorify himself with the office of high priest; he received it from the One who said to him,

"You are my son;
today I have begotten you;"

just as he says in another place,

"You are a priest forever,
according to the order of Melchizedek."

GOSPEL *Mark 10, 46-52 / 150*

As Jesus was leaving Jericho with his disciples and a sizable crowd, there was a blind beggar Bartimaeus ("son of Timaeus") sitting by the roadside. On hearing that it was Jesus of Nazareth, he began to call out, "Jesus, Son of David, have pity on me!" Many people were scolding him to make him keep quiet, but he shouted all the louder, "Son of David, have pity on me!" Then Jesus stopped and said, "Call him over." So they called the blind man over, telling him as they did so, "You have nothing whatever to fear from him! Get up! He is calling you!" He threw aside his cloak, jumped up and came to Jesus. Jesus asked him, "What do you want me to do for you?" "Rabboni," the blind man said, "I want to see." Jesus said in reply, "Be on your way! Your faith has healed you." Immediately he received his sight and started to follow him up the road.

954 THIRTIETH SUNDAY IN ORDINARY TIME / C

READING I *Sirach 35, 12-14.16-18 / 151*

The Lord is a God of justice,
who knows no favorites.
Though not unduly partial toward the
weak,
yet he hears the cry of the oppressed.
He is not deaf to the wail of the
orphan,
nor to the widow when she pours out
her complaint.

He who serves God willingly is heard;
his petition reaches the heavens.
The prayer of the lowly pierces the
clouds;
it does not rest till it reaches its goal,
Nor will it withdraw till the Most High
responds,
judges justly and affirms the right.

RESPONSORIAL PSALM *Psalm (33)34, 2-3.17-18.19.23 / 151*

3
DRH
The Lord hears the cry of the poor.

I will bless the Lord at all times,
his praise always on my lips;
in the Lord my soul shall make its boast.
The humble shall hear and be glad. ℟.

The Lord turns his eyes to the just
and his ears to their appeal.
They call and the Lord hears
and rescues them in all their
distress. ℟.

The Lord is close to the broken-hearted;
those whose spirit is crushed he will
save.
The Lord ransoms the souls of his
servants.
Those who hide in him shall not be
condemned. ℟.

READING II *2 Timothy 4, 6-8, 16-18 / 151*

I am already being poured out like a libation. The time of my dissolution is near. I have fought the good fight, I have finished the race, I have kept the faith. From now on a merited crown awaits me; on that Day the Lord, just judge that he is, will award it to me–and not only to me but to all who have looked for his appearing with eager longing.

At the first hearing of my case in court, no one took my part. In fact, everyone abandoned me. May it not be held against them! But the Lord stood by my side and gave me strength, so that through me the preaching task might be completed and all the nations might hear the gospel. That is how I was saved from the lion's jaws. The Lord will continue to rescue me from all attempts to do me harm and will bring me safe to his heavenly kingdom. To him be glory forever and ever. Amen.

GOSPEL *Luke 18, 9-14 / 151*

Jesus spoke this parable addressed to those who believed in their own self-righteousness while holding everyone else in contempt: "Two men went up to the temple to pray; one was a Pharisee, the other a tax collector. The Pharisee with head unbowed prayed in this fashion: 'I give you thanks, O God, that I am not like the rest of men–grasping, crooked, adulterous–or even like this tax collector. I fast twice a week. I pay tithes on all I possess.' The other man, however, kept his distance, not even daring to raise his eyes to heaven. All he did was beat his breast and say, 'O God, be merciful to me, a sinner.' Believe me, this man went home from the temple justified but the other did not. For everyone who exalts himself shall be humbled while he who humbles himself shall be exalted."

THIRTY-FIRST SUNDAY IN ORDINARY TIME / A 955

READING I *Malachi 1, 14-2, 2.8-10 / 152*

A great King am I, says the Lord of
hosts,
and my name will be feared among
the nations.
If you do not lay it to heart,
to give glory to my name, says the
Lord of hosts,
I will send a curse upon you
and of your blessing I will make a
curse.
Yes, I have already cursed it,
because you do not lay it to heart.
You have turned aside from the way,
and have caused many to falter by
your instruction;
You have made void the covenant of
Levi,
says the Lord of hosts.
I, therefore, have made you
contemptible
and base before all the people,
Since you do not keep my ways,
but show partiality in your decisions.

Have we not all the one Father?
Has not the one God created us?
Why then do we break faith with each
other,
violating the covenant of our fathers?

RESPONSORIAL PSALM *Psalm (130)131, 1.2.3 / 152*

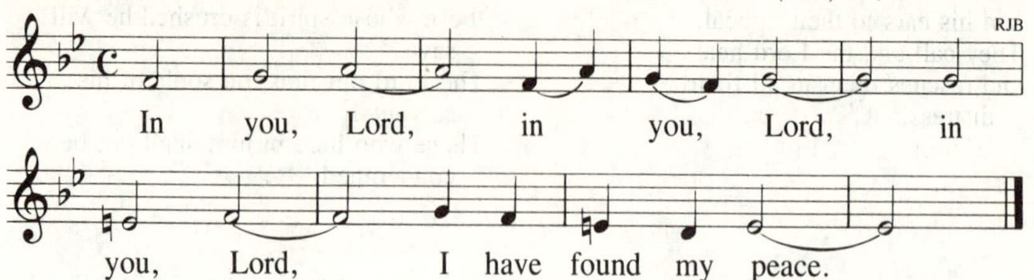
RJB
In you, Lord, in you, Lord, in
you, Lord, I have found my peace.

O Lord, my heart is not proud
nor haughty my eyes.
I have not gone after things too great
nor marvels beyond me. ℟.

Truly I have set my soul
in silence and peace.
A weaned child on its mother's breast,
even so is my soul. ℟.

O Israel, hope in the Lord
both now and for ever. ℟.

READING II *1 Thessalonians 2, 7-9.13 / 152*

While we were among you we were as gentle as any nursing mother fondling her little ones. So well disposed were we toward you, in fact, that we wanted to share with you not only God's tidings but our very lives, you had become so dear to us. You must recall, brothers, our efforts and our toil: how we worked day and night all the time we preached God's good tidings to you in order not to impose on you in any way. That is why we thank God constantly that in receiving his message from us you took it, not as the word of men, but as it truly is, the word of God at work within you who believe.

GOSPEL *Matthew 23, 1-12 / 152*

Jesus told the crowds and his disciples: "The scribes and Pharisees have succeeded Moses as teachers; therefore, do everything and observe everything they tell you. But do not follow their example. Their words are bold but their deeds are few. They bind up heavy loads, hard to carry, to lay on other men's shoulders, while they themselves will not lift a finger to budge them. All their works are performed to be seen, They widen their phylacteries and wear huge tassels. They are fond of places of honor at banquets and the front seats in synagogues, of marks of respect in public and of being called 'Rabbi.' As to you, avoid the title 'Rabbi.' One among you is your teacher, the rest are learners. Do not call anyone on earth your father. Only one is your father, the One in heaven. Avoid being called teachers. Only one is your teacher, the Messiah. The greatest among you will be the one who serves the rest. Whoever exalts himself shall be humbled, but whoever humbles himself shall be exalted."

956 THIRTY-FIRST SUNDAY IN ORDINARY TIME / B

READING I *Deuteronomy 6, 2-6 / 153*

Moses told the people: Fear the Lord, your God, and keep, throughout the days of your lives, all his statutes and commandments which I enjoin on you, and thus have long life. Hear then, Israel, and be careful to observe them, that you may grow and prosper the more, in keeping with the promise of the Lord, the God of your fathers, to give you a land flowing with milk and honey. "Hear, O Israel! The Lord is our God, the Lord alone! Therefore, you shall love the Lord, your God, with all your heart, and with all your soul, and with all your strength. Take to heart these words which I enjoin on you today."

RESPONSORIAL PSALM *Psalm (17)18, 2-3.3-4.47.51 / 153*

RP
I love you, I love you, Lord, my strength.

I love you, Lord, my strength,
my rock, my fortress, my savior. ℟.

My God is the rock where I take
refuge;
my shield, my mighty help, my
stronghold.
The Lord is worthy of all praise;
when I call I am saved from my
foes. ℟.

Long life to the Lord, my rock!
Praised be the God who saves me.
He has given great victories to his
king
and shown his love for his
anointed. ℟.

READING II *Hebrews 7, 23-28 / 153*

Under the old covenant there were many priests because they were prevented by death from remaining in office; but Jesus, because he remains forever, has a priesthood which does not pass away. Therefore he is always able to save those who approach God through him, since he forever lives to make intercession for them.

It was fitting that we should have such a high priest: holy, innocent, undefiled, separated from sinners, higher than the heavens. Unlike the other high priests, he has no need to offer sacrifice day after day, first for his own sins and then for those of the people; he did that once for all when he offered himself. For the law sets up as high priests men who are weak, but the word of the oath which came after the law appoints as priest the Son, made perfect forever.

GOSPEL *Mark 12, 28-34 / 153*

One of the scribes came up to Jesus, and asked him, "Which is the first of all the commandments?" Jesus replied: "This is the first:

'Hear, O Israel! The Lord our God is Lord alone!
Therefore you shall love the Lord your God
with all your heart,
with all your soul,
with all your mind,
and with all your strength.'

This is the second,

"You shall love your neighbor as yourself.'

There is no other commandment greater than these." The scribe said to him: "Excellent, Teacher! You are right in saying, 'He is the One, there is no other than he.' Yes, 'to love him with all our heart, with all our thoughts and with all our strength, and to love our neighbor as ourselves' is worth more than any burnt offering or sacrifice." Jesus approved the insight of this answer and told him, "You are not far from the reign of God." And no one had the courage to ask him any more questions.

THIRTY-FIRST SUNDAY IN ORDINARY TIME / C 957

READING I *Wisdom 11, 22-12, 1 / 154*

Before the Lord the whole universe is
as a grain from a balance
or a drop of morning dew come
down upon the earth.

But you have mercy on all, because
you can do all things;
and you overlook the sins of men
that they may repent.
For you love all things that are
and loathe nothing that you have
made;
for what you hated, you would not have
fashioned.

And how could a thing remain, unless
you willed it;
or be preserved, had it not been
called forth by you?
But you spare all things, because they
are yours, O Lord and lover of
souls,
for your imperishable spirit is in all
things!

RESPONSORIAL PSALM

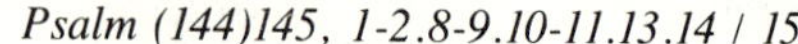

Psalm (144)145, 1-2.8-9.10-11.13.14 / 154

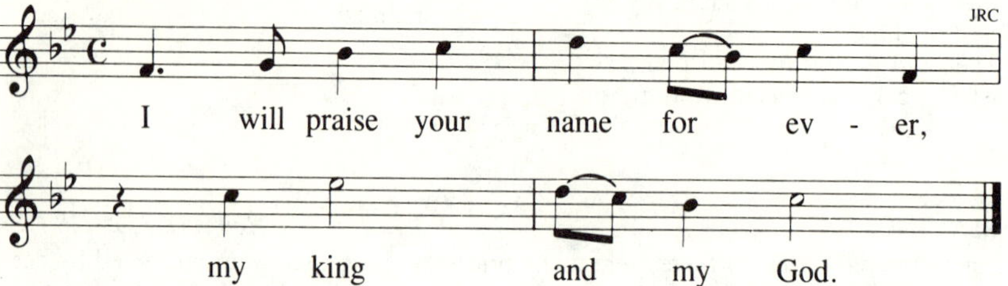
JRC
I will praise your name for ev - er,
my king and my God.

I will give you glory, O God my King,
I will bless your name for ever.
I will bless you day after day
and praise your name for ever. ℟.

All your creatures shall thank you, O
Lord,
and your friends shall repeat their
blessing.
They shall speak of the glory of your
reign
and declare your might, O God. ℟.

The Lord is kind and full of compassion,
slow to anger, abounding in love.
How good is the Lord to all,
compassionate to all his creatures. ℟.

The Lord is faithful in all his words
and loving in all his deeds.
The Lord supports all those who fall
and raises all who are bowed
down. ℟.

READING II *2 Thessalonians 1, 11-2,2 / 154*

We pray for you always that our God may make you worthy of his call, and fulfill by his power every honest intention and work of faith. In this way the name of our Lord Jesus may be glorified in you and you in him, in accord with the gracious gift of our God and of the Lord Jesus Christ.

On the question of the coming of our Lord Jesus Christ and our being gathered to him, we beg you, brothers, not to be so easily agitated or terrified, whether by an oracular utterance or rumor or a letter alleged to be ours, into believing that the day of the Lord is here.

GOSPEL *Luke 19, 1-10 / 154*

Jesus, upon entering Jericho, passed through the city. There was a man there named Zacchaeus, the chief tax collector and a wealthy man. He was trying to see what Jesus was like, but being small of stature, was unable to do so because of the crowd. He first ran on in front, then climbed a sycamore tree which was along Jesus' route, in order to see him. When Jesus came to the spot he looked up and said, "Zacchaeus, hurry down. I mean to stay at your house today." He quickly descended, and welcomed him with delight. When this was observed, everyone began to murmur, "He has gone to a sinner's house as a guest." Zacchaeus stood his ground and said to the Lord: "I give half my belongings, Lord, to the poor. If I have defrauded anyone in the least, I pay him back fourfold." Jesus said to him: "Today salvation has come to this house, for this is what it means to be a son of Abraham. The Son of Man has come to search out and save what was lost."

THIRTY-SECOND SUNDAY IN ORDINARY TIME / A 958

READING I

Wisdom 6, 12-16 / 155

Resplendent and unfading is Wisdom,
and she is readily perceived by those who love her,
and found by those who seek her.
She hastens to make herself known in anticipation of men's desire;
he who watches for her at dawn shall not be disappointed,
for he shall find her sitting by his gate.
For taking thought of her is the perfection of prudence,
and he who for her sake keeps vigil shall quickly be free from care;
Because she makes her own rounds,
seeking those worthy of her,
and graciously appears to them in the ways,
and meets them with all solicitude.

RESPONSORIAL PSALM

Psalm (62)63, 2.3-4.5-6.7-8 / 155

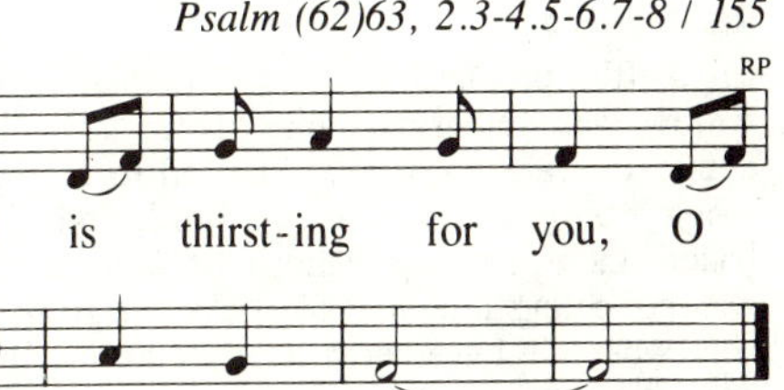

RP

My soul is thirst-ing for you, O Lord, thirst-ing for you my God.

O God, you are my God, for you I long;
for you my soul is thirsting.
My body pines for you
like a dry, weary land without water. ℟.

So I gaze on you in the sanctuary
to see your strength and your glory.
For your love is better than life,
my lips will speak your praise. ℟.

So I will bless you all my life,
in your name I will lift up my hands.
My soul shall be filled as with a banquet,
my mouth shall praise you with joy. ℟.

On my bed I remember you.
On you I muse through the night
for you have been my help;
in the shadow of your wings I rejoice. ℟.

READING II

1 Thessalonians 4, 13-18 or 4, 13-14 / 155

For short form read only the part in brackets.

[We would have you be clear about those who sleep in death, brothers; otherwise you might yield to grief like those who have no hope. For if we believe that Jesus died and rose, God will bring forth with him from the dead those also who have fallen asleep believing in him.] We say to you, as if the Lord himself had said it, that we who live, who survive until his coming, will in no way have an advantage over those who have fallen asleep. No, the Lord himself will come down from heaven at the word of command, at the sound of the archangel's voice and God's trumpet; and those who have died in Christ will rise first. Then we, the living, the survivors will be caught up with them in the clouds to meet the Lord in the air. Thenceforth we shall be with the Lord unceasingly. Console one another with this message.

GOSPEL

Matthew 25, 1-13 / 155

Jesus told this parable to his disciples: "The reign of God can be likened to ten bridesmaids who took their torches and went out to welcome the groom. Five of them were foolish, while the other five were sensible. The foolish ones, in taking their torches, brought no oil along, but the sensible ones took flasks of oil as well as their torches. The groom delayed his coming, so they all began to nod, then to fall asleep. At midnight someone shouted, 'The groom is here! Come out and greet him!' At the outcry all the virgins woke up and got their torches ready. The foolish ones said to the sensible, 'Give us some of your oil. Our torches are going out.' But the sensible ones replied, 'No, there may not be enough for you and us. You had better go to the dealers and buy yourselves some.' While they went off to buy it the groom arrived, and the ones who were ready went in to the wedding with him. Then the door was barred. Later the other bridesmaids came back. 'Master, master!' They cried. 'Open the door for us.' But he answered, 'I tell you, I do not know you.' The moral is: keep your eyes open, for you know not the day or the hour."

959 THIRTY-SECOND SUNDAY IN ORDINARY TIME / B

READING I *1 Kings 17, 10-16 / 156*

Elijah [the prophet] went to Zarephath. As he arrived at the entrance of the city, a widow was gathering sticks there; he called out to her, "Please bring me a small cupful of water to drink." She left to get it, and he called out after her, "Please bring along a bit of bread." "As the Lord, your God, lives," she answered, " I have nothing baked; there is only a handful of flour in my jar and a little oil in my jug. Just now I was collecting a couple of sticks, to go in and prepare something for myself and my son; when we have eaten it, we shall die." "Do not be afraid," Elijah said to her. "Go and do as you propose. But first make me a little cake and bring it to me. Then you can prepare something for yourself and your son. For the Lord, the God of Israel, says, 'The jar of flour shall not go empty, nor the jug of oil run dry, until the day when the Lord sends rain upon the earth.' " She left and did as Elijah had said. She was able to eat for a year, and he and her son as well; the jar of flour did not go empty, nor the jug of oil run dry, as the Lord had foretold through Elijah.

RESPONSORIAL PSALM *Psalm (145)146, 7.8-9.9-10 / 156*

RP

Praise the Lord, my soul! Praise the Lord!

It is he who keeps faith for ever,
who is just to those who are oppressed.
It is he who gives bread to the
hungry,
the Lord, who sets prisoners free. ℟.

The Lord who gives sight to the blind,
who raises up those who are bowed
down,
the Lord, who protects the stranger
and upholds the widow and orphan. ℟.

It is the Lord who loves the just
but thwarts the path of the wicked.
The Lord will reign for ever,
Zion's God, from age to age. ℟.

READING II *Hebrews 9, 24-28 / 156*

Christ did not enter into a sanctuary made by hands, a mere copy of the true one; he entered heaven itself that he might appear before God now on our behalf. Not that he might offer himself there again and again, as the high priest enters year after year into the sanctuary with blood that is not his own; were that so, he would have had to suffer death over and over from the creation of the world. But now he has appeared, at the end of the ages to take away sins once for all by his sacrifice. Just as it is appointed that men die once, and after death be judged, so Christ was offered up once to take away the sins of many; he will appear a second time not to take away sin but to bring salvation to those who eagerly await him.

GOSPEL *Mark 12, 38-44 or 12, 41-44 / 156*

For short form read only the part in brackets.

In the course of his teaching Jesus said: "Be on guard against the scribes who like to parade around in their robes and accept marks of respect in public, front seats in the synagogues, and places of honor at banquets. These men devour the savings of widows and recite long prayers for appearance' sake; it is they who will receive the severest sentence."

[Taking a seat opposite the treasury, he observed the crowd putting money into the collection box. Many of the wealthy put in sizable amounts; but one poor widow came and put in two small copper coins worth about a cent. He called his disciples over and told them: "I want you to observe that this poor widow contributed more than all the others who donated to the treasury. They gave from their surplus wealth, but she gave from her want, all that she had to live on."]

THIRTY-SECOND SUNDAY IN ORDINARY TIME / C 960

READING I *2 Maccabees 7, 1-2. 9-14 / 157*

It happened that seven brothers with their mother were arrested and tortured with whips and scourges by the king, to force them to eat pork in violation of God's law. One of the brothers, speaking for the others, said: "What do you expect to achieve by questioning us? We are ready to die rather than transgress the laws of our ancestors."

At the point of death the second brother said: "You accursed fiend, you are depriving us of this present life, but the King of the world will raise us up to live again forever. It is for his laws that we are dying."

After him the third suffered their cruel sport. He put out his tongue at once when told to do so, and bravely held out his hands, as he spoke these noble words: "It was from Heaven that I received these; for the sake of his laws I disdain them; from him I hope to receive them again." Even the king and his attendants marveled at the young man's courage, because he regarded his sufferings as nothing.

After he had died, they tortured and maltreated the fourth brother in the same way. When he was near death, he said, "It is my choice to die at the hands of men with the God-given hope of being restored to life by him; but for you, there will be no resurrection to life."

RESPONSORIAL PSALM *Psalm (16)17, 1.5-6.8.15 / 157*

HH
Lord, when your glo-ry ap-pears, my joy will be full.

Lord, hear a cause that is just,
pay heed to my cry.
Turn your ear to my prayer,
no deceit is on my lips. ℟.

I kept my feet firmly in your paths;
there was no faltering in my steps.
I am here and I call, you will hear me,
  O God.
Turn your ear to me; hear my words. ℟.

Guard me as the apple of your eye.
Hide me in the shadow of your wings.
As for me, in my justice I shall see
  your face
and be filled, when I awake, with the
  sight of your glory. ℟.

READING II *2 Thessalonians 2, 16-3, 5 / 157*

May our Lord Jesus Christ himself, may God our Father who loved us and in his mercy gave us eternal consolation and hope, console your hearts and strengthen them for every good work and word.

For the rest, brothers, pray for us that the word of the Lord may make progress and be hailed by many others, even as it has been by you. Pray that we may be delivered from confused and evil men. For not everyone has faith; the Lord, however, keeps faith; he it is who will strenghten you and guard you against the evil one. In the Lord we are confident that you are doing and will continue to do whatever we enjoin. May the Lord rule your hearts in the love of God and the constancy of Christ.

GOSPEL *Luke 20, 27-38 or 20, 27.34-38 / 157*

For short form read only the part in brackets.

[Some Sadducees came forward (the ones who claim there is no resurrection)] to pose this problem to Jesus: "Master, Moses prescribed that if a man's brother dies leaving a wife and no child, the brother should marry the widow and raise posterity to his brother. Now there were seven brothers. The first one married and died childless. Next, the second brother married the widow, then the third, and so on. All seven died without leaving her any children. Finally the widow herself died. At the resurrection, whose wife will she be? Remember, seven married her."

[Jesus said to them: "The children of this age marry and are given in marriage, but those judged worthy of a place in the age to come and of resurrection from the dead do not. They become like angels and are no longer liable to death. Sons of the resurrection, they are sons of God. Moses in the passage about the bush showed that the dead rise again when he called the Lord the God of Abraham, and the God of Isaac, and the God of Jacob. God is not the God of the dead but of the living. All are alive for him."]

961 THIRTY-THIRD SUNDAY IN ORDINARY TIME / A

READING I *Proverbs 31, 10-13.19-20.30-31 / 158*

When one finds a worthy wife,
her value is far beyond pearls.
Her husband, entrusting his heart to her,
has an unfailing prize.
She brings him good, and not evil,
all the days of her life.
She obtains wool and flax
and makes cloth with skillful hands.
She puts her hands to the distaff,
and her fingers ply the spindle.
She reaches out her hands to the poor,
and extends her arms to the needy.
Charm is deceptive and beauty fleeting;
the woman who fears the Lord is to be praised.
Give her a reward of her labors,
and let her works praise her at the city gates.

RESPONSORIAL PSALM *Psalm (127)128, 1-2.3.4-5 / 158*

JG
O hap-py are those who fear the Lord and walk in his ways.

O blessed are those who fear the Lord
and walk in his ways!
By the labor of your hands you shall eat.
You will be happy and prosper. ℞.

Your wife like a fruitful vine
in the heart of your house;
your children like shoots of the olive,
around your table. ℟.

Indeed thus shall be blessed
the man who fears the Lord.
May the Lord bless you from Zion
all the days of your life!
May you see your children's children
in a happy Jerusalem! ℟.

READING II *1 Thessalonians 5, 1-6 / 158*

As regards specific times and moments, brothers, we do not need to write you; you know very well that the day of the Lord is coming like a thief in the night. Just when people are saying, "Peace and security," ruin will fall on them with the suddenness of pains overtaking a woman in labor, and there will be no escape. You are not in the dark, brothers, that the day might catch you off guard, like a thief. No, all of you are children of light and of the day. We belong neither to darkness nor to night; therefore let us not be asleep like the rest, but awake and sober!

GOSPEL *Matthew 25, 14-30 or 25, 14-15.19-20 / 158*

For short form read only the part in brackets.

[Jesus told this parable to his disciples: "A man was going on a journey. He called in his servants and handed his funds over to them according to each man's abilities. To one he disbursed five thousand silver pieces, to a second two thousand, and to a third a thousand.] Then he went away. Immediately the man who received the five thousand went to invest it and made another five. In the same way, the man who received the two thousand doubled his figure. The man who received the thousand went off instead and dug a hole in the ground, where he buried his master's money. [After a long absence, the master of those servants came home and settled accounts with them. The man who had received the five thousand came forward bringing the additional five. 'My lord,' he said, 'you let me have five thousand. See, I have made five thousand more.'] His master said to him, 'Well done! You are an industrious and reliable servant. Since you were dependable in a small matter I will put you in charge of larger affairs. Come, share your master's joy!' The man who had received the two thousand then stepped forward. 'My lord.' he said, 'you entrusted me with two thousand and I have made two thousand more.' His master said to him, 'Cleverly done! You too are an industrious and reliable servant. Since you were dependable in a small matter I will put you in charge of larger affairs. Come, share your master's joy!'

"Finally the man who had received the thousand stepped forward, 'My lord,' he said, 'I knew you were a hard man. You reap where you did not sow and gather where you did not scatter, so out of fear I went off and buried your thousand silver pieces in the ground. Here is your money back.' His master exclaimed: 'You worthless, lazy lout! You know I reap where I did not sow and gather where I did not scatter. All the more reason to deposit my money with the bankers, so that on my return I could have had it back with interest. You there! Take the thousand away from him and give it to the man with the ten thousand. Those who have, will get more until they grow rich, while those who have not, will lose even the little they have. Throw this worthless servant into the darkness outside, where he can wail and grind his teeth.' "

THIRTY-THIRD SUNDAY IN ORDINARY TIME / B 962

READING I *Daniel 12, 1-3 / 159*

At that time there shall arise
Michael, the great prince,
guardian of your people;
It shall be a time unsurpassed in distress
since nations began until that time.
At that time your people shall escape,
everyone who is found written in the book.
Many of those who sleep
in the dust of the earth shall awake;

Some shall live forever,
others shall be an everlasting horror
and disgrace.
But the wise shall shine brightly
like the splendor of the firmament,
And those who lead the many to justice
shall be like the stars forever.

RESPONSORIAL PSALM *Psalm (15)16, 5.8.9-10,11 / 159*

RP
Keep me safe, O God; you are my hope.

O Lord, it is you who are my portion
and cup,
it is you yourself who are my prize.
I keep you, Lord, ever in my sight;
since you are at my right hand, I shall
stand firm. ℟.

And so my heart rejoices, my soul is
glad;
even my body shall rest in safety.
For you will not leave my soul among
the dead,
nor let your beloved know decay. ℟.

You will show me the path of life,
the fullness of joy in your presence,
at your right hand happiness for
ever. ℟.

READING II *Hebrews 10.11-14.18 / 159*

Every other priest stands ministering day by day, and offering again and again those same sacrifices which can never take away sins. But Jesus offered one sacrifice for sins and took his seat forever at the right hand of God; now he waits until his enemies are placed beneath his feet. By one offering he has forever perfected those who are being sanctified. Once sins have been forgiven, there is no further offering for sin.

GOSPEL *Mark 13, 24-32 / 159*

Jesus said to his disciples: "During that period after trials of every sort the sun will be darkened, the moon will not shed its light, stars will fall out of the skies, and the heavenly hosts will be shaken. Then men will see the Son of Man coming in the clouds with great power and glory. He will dispatch his messengers and assemble his chosen from the four winds, from the farthest bounds of earth and sky. Learn a lesson from the fig tree. Once the sap of its branches runs high and it begins to sprout leaves, you know that summer is near. In the same way, when you see these things happening, you will know that he is near, even at the door. I assure you, this generation will not pass away until all these things take place. The heavens and the earth will pass away, but my words will not.

"As to the exact day or hour, no one knows it, neither the angels in heaven nor even the Son, but only the Father."

963 THIRTY-THIRD SUNDAY IN ORDINARY TIME / C

READING I *Malachi 3, 19-20 / 160*

Lo, the day is coming, blazing like an
oven,
when all the proud and all evildoers
will be stubble,
And the day that is coming will set
them on fire,
leaving them neither root nor branch,
says the Lord of hosts.
But for you who fear my name, there
will arise
the sun of justice with its healing
rays.

RESPONSORIAL PSALM *Psalm (97)98, 5-6.7-8.9 / 160*

RC
The Lord comes to rule the earth, to rule with jus - tice.

Sing psalms to the Lord with the harp
with the sound of music.
With trumpets and the sound of the
horn
acclaim the King, the Lord. ℟.

Let the sea and all within it, thunder;
the world, and all its peoples.
Let the rivers clap their hands
and the hills ring out their joy. ℟.

At the presence of the Lord, for he
comes,
he comes to rule the earth.
He will rule the world with justice
and the peoples with fairness. ℟.

READING II *2 Thessalonians 3, 7-12 / 160*

You know how you ought to imitate us. We did not live lives of disorder when we were among you, nor depend on anyone for food. Rather, we worked day and night, laboring to the point of exhaustion so as not to impose on any of you. Not that we had no claim on you, but that we might present ourselves as an example for you to imitate. Indeed, when we were with you we used to lay down the rule that anyone who would not work should not eat.

We hear that some of you are unruly, not keeping busy but acting like busybodies. We enjoin all such, and we urge them strongly in the Lord Jesus Christ to earn the food they eat by working quietly.

GOSPEL *Luke 21, 5-19 / 160*

Some were speaking of how the temple was adorned with precious stones and votive offerings. Jesus said, "These things you are contemplating–the day will come when not one stone will be left on another, but it will all be torn down." They asked him, "When will this occur, Teacher? And what will be the sign it is going to happen?" He said, "Take care not to be misled. Many will come in my name, saying, 'I am he' and 'The time is at hand.' Do not follow them. Neither must you be perturbed when you you hear of wars and insurrections. These things are bound to happen first, but the end does not follow immediately."

He said to them further: "Nation will rise against nation and kingdom against kingdom. There will be great earthquakes, plagues and famines in various places–and in the sky fearful omens and great signs. But before any of this, they will manhandle and persecute you, summoning you to synagogues and prisons, bringing you to trial before kings and governors, all because of my name. You will be brought to give witness on account of it. I bid you resolve not to worry about your defense beforehand, for I will give you words and a wisdom which none of your adversaries can take exception to or contradict. You will be delivered up even by your parents, brothers, relatives and friends, and some of you will be put to death. All will hate you because of me, yet not a hair of your head will be harmed. By patient endurance you will save your lives."

LAST SUNDAY IN ORDINARY TIME–CHRIST THE KING / A 964

READING I *Ezekiel 34, 11-12.15-17 / 161*

Thus says the Lord God: I myself will look after and tend my sheep. As a shepherd tends his flock when he finds himself among his scattered sheep, so will I tend my sheep. I will rescue them from every place where they were scattered when it was cloudy and dark. I myself will pasture my sheep; I myself will give them rest, says the Lord God. The lost I will seek out, the strayed I will bring back, the injured I will bind up, the sick I will heal [but the sleek and the strong I will destroy], shepherding them rightly.

As for you, my sheep, says the Lord God, I will judge between one sheep and another, between rams and goats.

RESPONSORIAL PSALM *Psalm (22)23, 1-2.2-3.5-6 / 161*

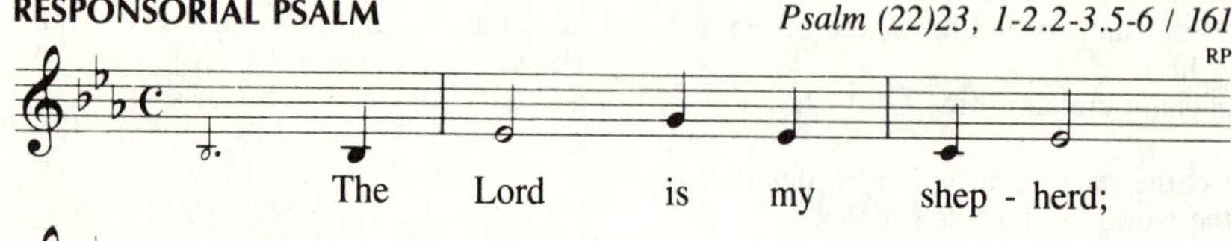
RP
The Lord is my shep - herd;

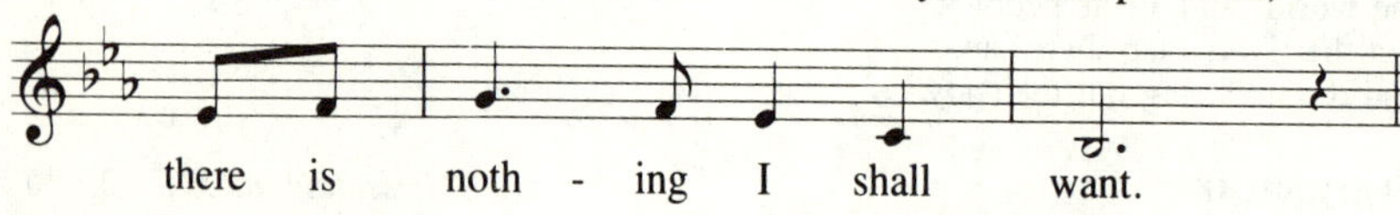
there is noth - ing I shall want.

The Lord is my shepherd;
there is nothing I shall want.
Fresh and green are the pastures
where he gives me repose. ℟.

Near restful waters he leads me,
to revive my drooping spirit.
He guides me along the right path;
he is true to his name. ℟.

You have prepared a banquet for me
in the sight of my foes.
My head you have anointed with oil;
my cup is overflowing. ℟.

Surely goodness and kindness shall
follow me
all the days of my life.
In the Lord's own house shall I dwell
for ever and ever. ℟.

READING II *1 Corinthians 15, 20-26.28 / 161*

Christ has been raised from the dead, the first fruits of those who have fallen asleep. Death came through a man; hence the resurrection of the dead comes through a man also. Just as in Adam all die, so in Christ all will come to life again, but each one in proper order: Christ the first-fruits and then, at his coming, all those who belong to him. After that will come the end, when, after having destroyed every sovereignty, authority, and power, he will hand over the kingdom to God the Father. Christ must reign until God has put all enemies under his feet, and the last enemy to be destroyed is death. When, finally, all has been subjected to the Son, he will then subject himself to the One who made all things subject to him, so that God may be all in all.

GOSPEL *Matthew 25, 31-46 / 161*

Jesus said to his disciples: "When the Son of Man comes in his glory, escorted by all the angels of heaven, he will sit upon his royal throne, and all the nations will be assembled before him. Then he will separate them into two groups, as a shepherd separates sheep from goats. The sheep he will place on his right hand, the goats on his left. The king will say to those on his right: 'Come. You have my Father's blessing! Inherit the kingdom prepared for you from the creation of the world. For I was hungry and you gave me food, I was thirsty and you gave me drink. I was a stranger and you welcomed me, naked and you clothed me. I was ill and you comforted me, in prison and you came to visit me.' Then the just will ask him: 'Lord, when did we see you hungry and feed you or see you thirsty and give you drink? When did we welcome you away from home or clothe you in your nakedness? When did we visit you when you were ill or in prison?' The king will answer them: 'I assure you, as often as you did it for one of my least brothers, you did it for me.'

"Then he will say to those on his left: 'Out of my sight, you condemned, into that everlasting fire prepared for the devil and his angels! I was hungry and you gave me no food, I was thirsty and you gave me no drink. I was away from home and you gave me no welcome, naked and you gave me no clothing. I was ill and in prison and you did not come to comfort me.' They in turn will ask: 'Lord, when did we see you hungry or thirsty or away from home or naked or ill or in prison and not attend you in your needs?' He will answer them: 'I assure you, as often as you neglected to do it to one of these least ones, you neglected to do it to me.' These will go off to eternal punishment and the just to eternal life."

LAST SUNDAY IN ORDINARY TIME–CHRIST THE KING / B 965

READING I

Daniel 7, 13-14 / 162

As the visions during the night
continued, I saw
One like a son of man coming,
on the clouds of heaven;
When he reached the Ancient One
and was presented before him,
He received dominion, glory, and
kingship;
nations and peoples of every
language serve him.
His dominion is an everlasting
dominion
that shall not be taken away,
his kingship shall not be destroyed.

RESPONSORIAL PSALM

Psalm (92)93, 1.1-2.5 / 162

RJB
The Lord is king; he is robed in maj - es - ty.

The Lord is king, with majesty
enrobed;
the Lord has robed himself with might,
he has girded himself with power. ℟.

The world you made firm, not to be
moved;
your throne has stood firm from of old.
From all eternity, O Lord, you are. ℟.

Truly your decrees are to be trusted.
Holiness is fitting to your house,
O Lord, until the end of time. ℟.

READING II

Revelation 1, 5-8 / 162

Jesus Christ is the faithful witness, the first-born from the dead and ruler of the kings of earth. To him who loves us and freed us from our sins by his own blood, who has made us a royal nation of priests in the service of his God and Father–to him be glory and power forever and ever! Amen.
See, he comes amid the clouds!
Every eye shall see him,
even of those who pierced him.
All the peoples of the earth
shall lament him bitterly.
So it is to be! Amen!

The Lord God says, "I am the Alpha and the Omega, the One who is and who was and who is to come, the Almighty!"

GOSPEL

John 18, 33-37 / 162

Pilate said to Jesus: "Are you the king of the Jews?" Jesus answered, "Are you saying this on your own, or have others been telling you about me?" "I am no Jew!" Pilate retorted. "It is your own people and the chief priests who have handed you over to me. What have you done?" Jesus answered:

"My kingdom does not belong to this world.
If my kingdom were of this world,
my subjects would be fighting
to save me from being handed over to the Jews.
As it is, my kingdom is not here."
At this Pilate said to him, "So, then, you are a king?" Jesus replied:
"It is you who say I am a king.
The reason I was born,
the reason why I came
into the world,
is to testify to the truth.
Anyone committed to the truth hears my voice."

966 LAST SUNDAY IN ORINARY TIME–CHRIST THE KING / C

READING I *2 Samuel 5, 1-3 / 163*

All the tribes of Israel came to David in Hebron and said: "Here we are, your bone and your flesh. In days past, when Saul was our king, it was you who led the Israelites out and brought them back. And the Lord said to you, 'You shall shepherd my people Israel and shall be commander of Israel.' " When all the elders of Israel came to David in Hebron, King David made an agreement with them there before the Lord, and they anointed him king of Israel.

RESPONSORIAL PSALM *Psalm (121)122, 1-2.3-4.4-5 / 163*

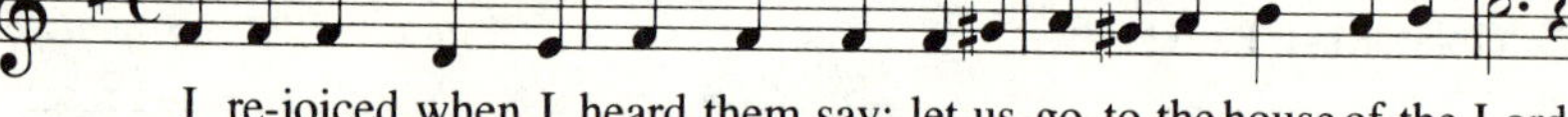
RJB
I re-joiced when I heard them say: let us go to the house of the Lord.

I rejoiced when I heard them say:
"Let us go to God's house."
And now our feet are standing
within your gates, O Jerusalem. ℟.

Jerusalem is built as a city
strongly compact.
It is there that the tribes go up,
the tribes of the Lord. ℟.

For Israel's law it is,
there to praise the Lord's name.
There were set the thrones of judgment
of the house of David. ℟.

READING II *Colossians 1, 12-20 / 163*

Give thanks to the Father for having made you worthy to share the lot of the saints in light. He rescued us from the power of darkness and brought us into the kingdom of his beloved Son. Through him we have redemption, the forgiveness of our sins.

He is the image of the invisible God, the first-born of all creatures. In him everything in heaven and on earth was created, things visible and invisible, whether thrones or dominations, principalities or powers; all were created through him, and for him. He is before all else that is. In him everything continues in being. It is he who is head of the body, the church; he who is the beginning, the first-born of the dead, so that primacy may be his in everything. It pleased God to make absolute fullness reside in him and, by means of him, to reconcile everything in his person, everything, I say, both on earth and in the heavens, making peace through the blood of his cross.

GOSPEL *Luke 23, 35-43 / 163*

The people stood there watching, and the leaders kept jeering at Jesus, saying, "He saved others; let him save himself if he is the Messiah of God, the chosen one." The soldiers also made fun of him, coming forward to offer him their sour wine and saying, "If you are the king of the Jews, save yourself." There was this inscription over his head:

"THIS IS THE KING OF THE JEWS."
One of the criminals hanging in crucifixion blasphemed him, "Aren't you the Messiah? Then save yourself and us." But the other one rebuked him: "Have you no fear of God, seeing you are under the same sentence? We deserve it, after all. We are only paying the price for what we've done, but this man has done nothing wrong." He then said, "Jesus, remember me when you enter upon your reign." And Jesus replied, "I assure you: this day you will be with me in paradise."

Seasons: Weekday Psalm Responses

967 FIRST WEEK OF ADVENT

Monday / *176*
I rejoiced when I heard them say:
let us go to the house of the Lord.

Tuesday / *177*
Justice shall flourish in his time,
and fullness of peace for ever.

Wednesday / *178*
I shall live in the house of the Lord
all the days of my life.

Thursday / *179*
Blessed is he who comes in the name of the Lord.

Or: Alleluia.

Friday / *180*
The Lord is my light and my salvation.

Or: Alleluia.

Saturday / *181*
Happy are all who long for the coming of the Lord.

Or: Alleluia.

968 SECOND WEEK OF ADVENT

Monday / *182*
Our God will come to save us!

Tuesday / *183*
The Lord our God comes in strength.

Wednesday / *184*
O bless the Lord, my soul.

Thursday / *185*
The Lord is kind and merciful;
slow to anger, and rich in compassion.

Friday / *186*
Those who follow you, Lord, will have the light of life.

Saturday / *187*
Lord, make us turn to you,
let us see your face and we shall be saved.

THIRD WEEK OF ADVENT 969

Monday / *188*
Teach me your ways, O Lord.

Tuesday / *189*
The Lord hears the cry of the poor.

Wednesday / *190*
Let the clouds rain down the Just One,
and the earth bring forth a savior.

Thursday / *191*
I will praise you, Lord,
for you have rescued me.

Friday / *192*
O God, let all the nations praise you!

LAST DAYS OF ADVENT 970

December 17 / *194*
Justice shall flourish in his time,
and fullness of peace for ever.

December 18 / *195*
Justice shall flourish in his time,
and fullness of peace for ever.

December 19 / *196*
Fill me with your praise
and I will sing your glory!

December 20 / *197*
Let the Lord enter;
he is king of glory

December 21 / *198*
Cry out with joy in the Lord, you holy ones;
sing a new song to him.

December 22 / *199*
My heart rejoices in the Lord, my Savior.

December 23 / *200*
Lift up your heads and see;
your redemption is near at hand.

December 24 / *201*
Mass in the Morning
For ever I will sing the goodness of the Lord.

SEASON OF CHRISTMAS 971

December 29 / *203*
Let heaven and earth exult in joy!

December 30 / *204*
Let heaven and earth exult in joy!

December 31 / *205*
Let heaven and earth exult in joy!

January 2 / *206*
All the ends of the earth have seen the saving power of God.

January 3 / *207*
All the ends of the earth have seen the saving power of God.

January 4 / *208*
All the ends of the earth have seen the savings power of God.

January 5 / *208*
Let all the earth cry out to God with joy.

January 6 / *209*
Praise the Lord, Jerusalem.
Or: Alleluia.

January 7 / *211*
The Lord takes delight in his people.
Or: Alleluia.

972 AFTER EPIPHANY

Monday / *213*
I will give you all the nations for your heritage.

Tuesday / *214*
Lord, every nation on earth will adore you.

Wednesday / *215*
Lord, every nation on earth will adore you.

Thursday / *216*
Lord, every nation on earth will adore you.

Friday / *217*
Praise the Lord, Jerusalem.
Or: Alleluia.

Saturday / *218*
The Lord takes delight in his people.
Or: Alleluia.

973 ASH WEDNESDAY

READING I *Joel 2, 12-18 / 220*

Even now, says the Lord,
return to me with your whole heart,
with fasting, and weeping, and mourning;
Rend your hearts, not your garments,
and return to the Lord, your God.
For gracious and merciful is he,
slow to anger, rich in kindness,
and relenting in punishment.
Perhaps he will again relent
and leave behind him a blessing,
Offerings and libations
for the Lord, your God.
Blow the trumpet in Zion!
proclaim a fast,
call an assembly;
Gather the people,
notify the congregation;
Assemble the elders,
gather the children
and the infants at the breast;
Let the bridegroom quit his room,
and the bride her chamber.
Between the porch and the altar
let the priests, the ministers of the Lord, weep,
And say, "Spare, O Lord, your people,
and make not your heritage a reproach,
with the nations ruling over them!
Why should they say among the peoples,
'Where is their God?' "
Then the Lord was stirred to concern for his
land and took pity on his people.

RESPONSORIAL PSALM *Psalm (50)51, 3-4.5-6.12-13.14.17 / 220*

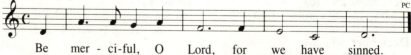

PC

Be mer - ci-ful, O Lord, for we have sinned.

Have mercy on me, God, in your kindness.
In your compassion blot out my offense.
O wash me more amd more from my guilt
and cleanse me from my sin. ℟.

My offenses truly I know them;
my sin is always before me.
Against you, you alone, have I sinned;
what is evil in your sight I have done. ℟.

A pure heart create for me, O God,
put a steadfast spirit within me.
Do not cast me away from your
presence,
nor deprive me of your holy spirit. ℟.

Give me again the joy of your help;
with a spirit of fervor sustain me,
O Lord, open my lips
and my mouth shall declare your
praise. ℟.

READING II *2 Corinthians 5,20 - 6, 2 / 220*

We are ambassadors for Christ, God as it were appealing through us. We implore you, in Christ's name: be reconciled to God! For our sakes God made him who did not know sin to be sin, so that in him we might become the very holiness of God.

As your fellow workers we beg you not to receive the grace of God in vain. For he says, "In an acceptable time I have heard you; on a day of salvation I have helped you." Now is the acceptable time! Now is the day of salvation!

GOSPEL *Matthew 6, 1-6.16-18 / 220*

Jesus said to his disciples: "Be on guard against performing religious acts for people to see. Otherwise expect no recompense from your heavenly Father. When you give alms, for example, do not blow a horn before you in synagogues and streets like hypocrites looking for applause. You can be sure of this much, they are already repaid. In giving alms you are not to let your left hand know what your right hand is doing. Keep your deeds of mercy secret, and your Father who sees in secret will repay you.

"When you are praying, do not behave like the hypocrites who love to stand and pray in synagogues or on street corners in order to be noticed. I give you my word, they are already repaid. Whenever you pray go to your room, close your door, and pray to your Father in private. Then your Father, who sees what no man sees, will repay you.

"When you fast, you are not to look glum as the hypocrites do. They change the appearance of their faces so that others may see they are fasting. I assure you, they are already repaid. When you fast, see to it that you groom your hair and wash your face. In that way no one can see you are fasting but your Father who is hidden; and your Father who sees what is hidden will repay you."

AFTER ASH WEDNESDAY 974

Thursday / *221*
Happy are they who hope in the
Lord.

Friday / *222*
A broken, humbled heart, O God,
you will not scorn.

Saturday / *223*
Teach me your way, O Lord, that I
may be faithful in your sight.

FIRST WEEK OF LENT 975

Monday / *225*
Your words, Lord, are spirit and
life.

Tuesday / *226*
From all their afflictions
God will deliver the just.

Wednesday / *227*
A broken, humbled heart,
O God, you will not scorn.

Thursday / *228*
Lord, on the day I called for help,
you answered me.

Friday / *229*
If you, O Lord, laid bare our guilt
who could endure it?

Saturday / *230*
Happy are they who follow the law
of the Lord.

976 SECOND WEEK OF LENT

Monday / *231*
Lord, do not deal with us as our sins deserve.

Tuesday / *232*
To the upright
I will show the saving power of God.

Wednesday / *233*
Save me, O Lord, in your steadfast love.

Thursday / *234*
Happy are they who hope in the Lord.

Friday / *235*
Remember the marvels the Lord has done.

Saturday / *236*
The Lord is kind and merciful.

977 THIRD WEEK OF LENT

Optional Mass / *237*
If today you hear his voice,
harden not your hearts.

Monday / *238*
My soul is thirsting for the living God:
when shall I see him face to face?

Tuesday / *239*
Remember your mercies, O Lord.

Wednesday / *240*
Praise the Lord, Jerusalem.

Thursday / *241*
If today you hear his voice,
harden not your hearts.

Friday / *242*
I am the Lord, your God:
hear my voice.

Saturday / *243*
It is steadfast love, not sacrifice,
that God desires.

978 FOURTH WEEK OF LENT

Optional Mass / *244*
The Lord is my light and my salvation.

Monday / *245*
I will praise you, Lord, for you have rescued me.

Tuesday / *246*
The mighty Lord is with us;
The God of Jacob is our refuge

Wednesday / *247*
The Lord is kind and merciful.

Thursday / *248*
Lord, remember us,
for the love you bear your people.

Friday / *249*
The Lord is near to broken hearts.

Saturday / *250*
Lord, my God, I take shelter in you.

FIFTH WEEK OF LENT 979

Optional Mass / *251*
Lord, when your glory appears,
my joy will be full.

Monday / *252*
Though I walk in the valley of darkness,
I fear no evil, for you are with me.

Tuesday / *253*
O Lord, hear my prayer,
and let my cry come to you.

Wednesday / *254*
Glory and praise for ever!

Thursday / *255*
The Lord remembers his covenant for ever.

Friday / *256*
In my distress I called upon the Lord,
and he heard my voice.

Saturday / *257*
The Lord will guard us,
like a shepherd guarding his flock.

HOLY WEEK 980

Monday / *258*
The Lord is my light and my salvation.

Tuesday / *259*
I will sing of your salvation.

Wednesday / *260*
Lord, in your great love, answer me.

OCTAVE OF EASTER 981

Monday / *261*
Keep me safe, O God;
you are my hope.
Or: Alleluia.

Tuesday / / *262*
The earth is full of the goodness of the Lord.
Or: Alleluia.

Wednesday / *263*
The earth is full of the goodness of the Lord.
Or: Alleluia.

Thursday / *264*
O Lord, our God,
how wonderful your name in all the earth!
Or: Alleluia.

Friday / *265*
The stone rejected by the builders has become the cornerstone.
Or: Alleluia.

Saturday / *266*
I praise you, Lord,
for you have answered me.
Or: Alleluia.

982 SECOND WEEK OF EASTER

Monday / *267*
Happy are all who put their trust in
Or: Alleluia.

Tuesday / *268*
The Lord is king;.
he is robed in majesty.
Or: Alleluia.

Wednesday / *269*
The Lord hears the cry of the poor.
Or: Alleluia.

Thursday / *270*
The Lord hears the cry of the poor.
Or: Alleluia.

Friday / *271*
One thing I seek: to dwell in the house of the Lord.
Or: Alleluia.

Saturday / *272*
Lord, let your mercy be on us,
as we place our trust in you.
Or: Alleluia.

983 THIRD WEEK OF EASTER

Monday / *273*
Happy are those of blameless life.
Or: Alleluia.

Tuesday / *274*
Into your hands, O Lord,
I entrust my spirit.
Or: Alleluia.

Wednesday / *275*
Let all the earth cry out to God with joy.
Or: Alleluia.

Thursday / *276*
Let all the earth cry out to God with joy.
Or: Alleluia.

Friday / *277*
Go out to all the world,
and tell the Good News.
Or: Alleluia.

Saturday / *278*
What return can I make to the Lord
for all that he gives to me?
Or: Alleluia.

984 FOURTH WEEK OF EASTER

Monday / *279*
My soul is thirsting for the living God.
Or: Alleluia.

Tuesday / *280*
All you nations, praise the Lord.
Or: Alleluia.

Wednesday / *281*
O God, let all the nations praise you!
Or: Alleluia.

Thursday / *282*
For ever I will sing the goodness of the Lord.
Or: Alleluia.

Friday / *283*
You are my Son;
this day have I begotten you.
Or: Alleluia.

Saturday / *284*
All the ends of the earth have seen the saving power of God.
Or: Alleluia.

FIFTH WEEK OF EASTER 985

Monday / *285*
Not to us, O Lord,
but to your name give the glory.
Or: Alleluia.

Tuesday / *286*
Your friends tell the glory of your kingship, Lord.
Or: Alleluia.

Wednesday / *287*
I rejoiced when I heard them say:
let us go to the house of the Lord.
Or: Alleluia.

Thursday / *288*
Proclaim his marvelous deeds
to all the nations.
Or: Alleluia.

Friday / *289*
I will praise you among the nations, O Lord.
Or: Alleluia.

Saturday / *290*
Let all the earth cry out to God with joy.
Or: Alleluia.

SIXTH WEEK OF EASTER 986

Monday / *291*
The Lord takes delight in his people.
Or: Alleluia.

Tuesday / *292*
Your right hand has saved me, O Lord.
Or: Alleluia.

Wednesday / *293*
Heaven and earth are filled with your glory.
Or: Alleluia.

Thursday / *294*
The Lord has revealed to the nations his saving power.
Or: Alleluia.

Friday / *295*
God is king of all the earth.
Or: Alleluia.

Saturday / *296*
God is king of all the earth.
Or: Alleluia.

SEVENTH WEEK OF EASTER 987

Monday / *297*
Sing to God, O kingdoms of the earth.
Or: Alleluia.

Tuesday / *298*
Sing to God, O kingdoms of the earth.
Or: Alleluia.

Wednesday / *299*
Sing to God, O kingdoms of the earth.
Or: Alleluia.

Thursday / *300*
Keep me safe, O God;
you are my hope.
Or: Alleluia.

Friday / *301*
The Lord has set his throne in heaven.
Or: Alleluia.

Saturday / *302*
The just will gaze on your face, O Lord.
Or: Alleluia.

Ordinary Time: Psalm Responses

988 **FIRST WEEK IN ORDINARY TIME**

Monday / *305*
I Let all his angels worship him.
II To you, Lord, I will offer a sacrifice of praise.
Or: Alleluia.

Tuesday / *306*
I You gave your Son authority over all creation.
II My heart rejoices in the Lord, my Savior.

Wednesday / *307*
I The Lord remembers his covenant for ever.
Or: Alleluia.
II Here am I, Lord; I come to do your will.

Thursday / *308*
I If today you hear his voice, harden not your hearts.
II Save us, Lord, in your mercy.

Friday / *309*
I Do not forget the works of the Lord!
II For ever I will sing the goodness of the Lord.

Saturday / *310*
I Your words, Lord, are spirit and life.
II Lord, your strength gives joy to the king.

989 **SECOND WEEK IN ORDINARY TIME**

Monday / *311*
I You are a priest for ever, in the line of Melchizedek.
II To the upright I will show the saving power of God.

Tuesday / *312*
I The Lord will remember his covenant for ever.
Or: Alleluia.
II I have found David, my servant.

Wednesday / *313*

I You are a priest for ever,
in the line of Melchizedek.

II Blessed be the Lord, my Rock!

Thursday / *314*

I Here am I, Lord;
I come to do your will.

II In God I trust;
I shall not fear.

Friday / *315*

I Kindness and truth shall meet.

II Have mercy on me, God, have mercy.

Saturday / *316*

I God mounts his throne to shouts of joy;
a blare of trumpets for the Lord.

II Let us see your face, Lord,
and we shall be saved.

THIRD WEEK IN ORDINARY TIME 990

Monday / *317*

I Sing to the Lord a new song,
for he has done marvelous deeds.

II My faithfulness and love shall be with him.

Tuesday / *318*

I Here am I, Lord;
I come to do your will.

II Who is this king of glory?
It is the Lord!

Wednesday / *319*

I You are a priest for ever,
in the line of Melchizedek.

II For ever I will keep my love for him.

Thursday / *320*

I Lord, this is the people that longs to see your face.

II God will give him the throne of David, his father.

Friday / *321*

I The salvation of the just comes from the Lord.

II Be merciful, O Lord, for we have sinned.

Saturday / *322*

I Blessed be the Lord God of Israel,
for he has visited his people.

II Create a clean heart in me, O God.

FOURTH WEEK IN ORDINARY TIME 991

Monday / *323*

I Let your hearts take comfort,
all who hope in the Lord.

II Lord, rise up and save me.

Tuesday / *324*

I They will praise you, Lord, who long for you.

II Listen, Lord, and answer me.

Wednesday / *325*

I The Lord's kindness is everlasting to those who fear him.

II Lord, forgive the wrong I have done.

Thursday / *326*

I God, in your temple, we ponder your love.

II Lord, you are exalted over all.

Friday / *327*

I The Lord is my light and my salvation.

II Blessed be God my salvation!

Saturday / *328*

I The Lord is my shepherd;
there is nothing I shall want.

II Lord, teach me your decrees.

992 FIFTH WEEK IN ORDINARY TIME

Monday / *329*

I May the Lord be glad in his works.

II Lord, go up to the place of your rest!

Tuesday / *330*

I O Lord, our God,
how wonderful your name in all the earth!

II How lovely is your dwelling-place,
Lord, mighty God!

Wednesday / *331*

I Oh, bless the Lord, my soul!

II The mouth of the just man murmurs wisdom.

Thursday / *332*

I Happy are those who fear the Lord.

II Lord, remember us,
for the love you bear your people.

Friday / *333*

I Happy are those whose sins are forgiven.

II I am the Lord, your God:
hear my voice.

Saturday / *334*

I In every age, O Lord, you have been our refuge.

II Lord, remember us,
for the love you bear your people.

993 SIXTH WEEK IN ORDINARY TIME

Monday / *335*

I Offer to God a sacrifice of praise.

II Be kind to me, Lord, and I shall live.

Tuesday / *336*

I The Lord will bless his people with peace.

II Happy the man you teach, O O Lord.

Wednesday / *337*

I To you, Lord, I will offer a sacrifice of praise.

Or: Alleluia.

II He who does justice shall live on the Lord's holy mountain.

Thursday / *338*

I From heaven the Lord looks down on the earth.

II The Lord hears the cry of the poor.

Friday / *339*

I Happy the people the Lord has chosen to be his own.

II Happy are those who do what the Lord commands.

Saturday / *340*

I I will praise your name for ever, Lord.

II You will protect us, Lord.

SEVENTH WEEK IN ORDINARY TIME 994

Monday / *341*
I The Lord is king; he is robed in majesty.
II The precepts of the Lord give joy to the heart.

Tuesday / *342*
I Commit your life to the Lord, and he will help you.
II Throw your cares on the Lord, and he will support you.

Wednesday / *343*
I O Lord, great peace have they who love the law.
II Happy the poor in spirit; the kingdom of heaven is theirs!

Thursday / *344*
I Happy are they who hope in the Lord.
II Happy the poor in spirit; the kingdom of heaven is theirs!

Friday / *345*
I Guide me, Lord, in the way of your commands.
II The Lord is kind and merciful.

Saturday / *346*
I The Lord's kindness is everlasting to those who fear him.
II Let my prayer come like incense before you.

EIGHTH WEEK IN ORDINARY TIME 995

Monday / *347*
I Let the just exult and rejoice in the Lord.
II The Lord will remember his covenant for ever.
Or: Alleluia.

Tuesday / *348*
I To the upright I will show the saving power of God.
II The Lord has made known his salvation.

Wednesday / *349*
I Show us, O Lord, the light of your kindness.
II Praise the Lord, Jerusalem.
Or: Alleluia.

Thursday / *350*
I By the word of the Lord the heavens were made.
II Come with joy into the presence of the Lord.

Friday / *351*
I The Lord takes delight in his people.
II The Lord comes to judge the earth.

Saturday / *352*
I The precepts of the Lord give joy to the heart.
II My soul is thirsting for you, O Lord my God.

NINTH WEEK IN ORDINARY TIME 996

Monday / *353*
I Happy the man who fears the Lord.
Or: Alleluia.
II In you, my God, I place my trust.

Tuesday / *354*
I The heart of the just man is secure, trusting in the Lord.
Or: Alleluia.
II In every age, O Lord, you have been our refuge.

Wednesday / *355*
I To you, O Lord, I lift my soul.
II To you, O Lord, I lift up my eyes.

Thursday / *356*
I Happy are those who fear the Lord.
II Teach me your ways, O Lord.

Friday / *357*
I Praise the Lord, my soul!
Or: Alleluia.
II O Lord, great peace have they who love your law.

Saturday / *358*
I Blessed be God, who lives for ever.
II I will sing of your salvation.

997 TENTH WEEK IN ORDINARY TIME

Monday / *359*
I Taste and see the goodness of the Lord.
II Our help is from the Lord
who made heaven and earth.

Tuesday / *360*
I Lord, let your face shine on me.
II Lord, let your face shine on us.

Wednesday / *361*
I Holy is the Lord our God.
II Keep me safe, O God;
you are my hope.

Thursday / *362*
I The glory of the Lord will dwell in our land.
II It is right to praise you in Zion, O God.

Friday / *363*
I To you, Lord, I will offer a sacrifice of praise.
Or: Alleluia.
II I long to see your face, O Lord.

Saturday / *364*
I The Lord is kind and merciful.
II You are my inheritance, O Lord.

998 ELEVENTH WEEK IN ORDINARY TIME

Monday / *365*
I The Lord has made known his salvation.
II Lord, listen to my groaning.

Tuesday / *366*
I Praise the Lord, my soul!
Or: Alleluia.
II Be merciful, O Lord, for we have sinned.

Wednesday / *367*
I Happy the man who fears the Lord.
Or: Alleluia.
II Let your hearts take comfort, all who hope in the Lord.

Thursday / *368*
I Your works, O Lord, are justice and truth.
Or: Alleluia.
II Let good men rejoice in the Lord.

Friday / *369*

I From all their afflictions God will deliver the just.

II The Lord has chosen Zion for his dwelling.

Saturday / *370*

Taste and see the goodness of the Lord.

II For ever I will keep my love for him.

TWELFTH WEEK IN ORDINARY TIME 999

Monday / *371*

I Happy the people the Lord has chosen to be his own.

II Help us with your right hand, O Lord, and answer us.

Tuesday / *372*

I He who does justice will live in the presence of the Lord.

II God upholds his city for ever.

Wednesday / *373*

I The Lord remembers his covenant for ever.

Or: Alleluia.

II Teach me the way of your decrees, O Lord.

Thursday / *374*

I Give thanks to the Lord for he is good.

Or: Alleluia.

II For the glory of your name, O Lord, deliver us.

Friday / *375*

I See how the Lord blesses those who fear him.

II Let my tongue be silenced, if I ever forget you!

Saturday / *376*

I The Lord has remembered his mercy.

II Lord, forget not the life of your poor ones.

THIRTEENTH WEEK IN ORDINARY TIME 1000

Monday / *377*

I The Lord is kind and merciful.

II Remember this, you who never think of God.

Tuesday / *378*

I O Lord, your kindness is before my eyes.

II Lead me in your justice, Lord.

Wednesday / *379*

I The Lord hears the cry of the poor.

II To the upright I will show the saving power of God.

Thursday / *380*

I I will walk in the presence of the Lord,
in the land of the living.

Or: Alleluia.

II The judgments of the Lord are true,
and all of them just.

Friday / *381*
I Give thanks to the Lord for he is good.
Or: Alleluia.
II Man does not live on bread alone,
but on every word that comes from the mouth of God.

Saturday / *382*
I Praise the Lord for he is good!
Or: Alleluia.
II The Lord speaks of peace to his people.

1001 **FOURTEENTH WEEK IN ORDINARY TIME**

Monday / *383*
I In you, my God, I place my trust.
II The Lord is kind and merciful.

Tuesday / *384*
I In my justice, I shall see your face, O Lord.
II The house of Israel trusts in the Lord.
Or: Alleluia.

Wednesday / *385*
I Lord, let your mercy be on us,
as we place our trust in you.
II Seek always the face of the Lord.
Or: Alleluia.

Thursday / *386*
I Remember the marvels the Lord has done.
Or: Alleluia.
II Let us see your face, Lord,
and we shall be saved.

Friday / *387*
I The salvation of the just comes from the Lord.
II My mouth will declare your praise.

Saturday / *388*
I Turn to the Lord in your need
and you will live.
II The Lord is king;
he is robed in majesty.

1002 **FIFTEENTH WEEK IN ORDINARY TIME**

Monday / *389*
I Our help is in the name of the Lord.
II To the upright I will show the saving power of God.

Tuesday / *390*
I Turn to the Lord in your need, and you will live.
II God upholds his city for ever.

Wednesday / *391*
I The Lord is kind and merciful.
II The Lord will not abandon his people.

Thursday / *392*
I The Lord remembers his covenant for ever.
Or: Alleluia.
II From heaven the Lord looks down on the earth.

Friday / *393*

I I will take the cup of salvation,
and call on the name of the Lord.

Or: Alleluia.

II You saved my life, O Lord;
I shall not die.

Saturday / *394*

I His love is everlasting.

Or: Alleluia.

II Do not forget the poor, O Lord!

SIXTEENTH WEEK IN ORDINARY TIME 1003

Monday / *395*

I Let us sing to the Lord;
he has covered himself in glory.

II To the upright I will show the saving power of God.

Tuesday / *396*

I Let us sing to the Lord;
he has covered himself in glory.

II Lord, let us see your kindness.

Wednesday / *397*

I The Lord gave them bread from heaven.

II I will sing of your salvation.

Thursday / *398*

I Glory and praise for ever!

II You are the source of life, O Lord.

Friday / *399*

I Lord, you have the words of everlasting life.

II The Lord will guard us,
like a shepherd guarding his flock.

Saturday / *400*

I Offer to God a sacrifice of praise.

II How lovely is your dwelling-place,
Lord, mighty God!

SEVENTEENTH SUNDAY IN ORDINARY TIME 1004

Monday / *401*

I Give thanks to the Lord for he is good.

Or: Alleluia.

II You have forgotten God who gave you birth.

Tuesday / *402*

I The Lord is kind and merciful.

II For the glory of your name,
O Lord, deliver us.

Wednesday / *403*

I Holy is the Lord our God.

II God is my refuge on the day of distress.

Thursday / *404*

I How lovely is your dwelling-place,
Lord, mighty God!

II Blest are they whose help is the God of Jacob.

Or: Alleluia.

Friday / *405*

I Sing with joy to God our help.

II Lord, in your great love, answer me.

Saturday / *406*

I O God, let all the nations praise you!

II Lord, in your great love, answer me.

1005 EIGHTEENTH WEEK IN ORDINARY TIME

Monday / *407*

I Sing with joy to God our help.

II Teach me your laws, O Lord.

Tuesday / *408*

I Be merciful, O Lord, for we have sinned.

II The Lord will build up Zion again,
and appear in all his glory.

Wednesday / *409*

I Lord, remember us,
for the love you bear your people.

Or: Alleluia.

II The Lord will guard us,
like a shepherd guarding his flock.

Thursday / *410*

I If today you hear his voice,
harden not your hearts.

II Create a clean heart in me, O God.

Friday / *411*

I I remember the deeds of the Lord.

II It is I who deal death and give life.

Saturday / *412*

I I love you, Lord, my strength.

II You will never abandon those who seek you, Lord.

1006 NINETEENTH WEEK IN ORDINARY TIME

Monday / *413*

I Praise the Lord, Jerusalem.

Or: Alleluia.

II Heaven and earth are filled with your glory.

Or: Alleluia.

Tuesday / *414*

I The portion of the Lord is his people.

II How sweet to my taste is your promise!

Wednesday / *415*

I Blessed be God who filled my soul with life!

II The glory of the Lord is higher than the skies.

Or: Alleluia.

Thursday / *416*

I Alleluia.

II Do not forget the works of the Lord!

Friday / *417*

I His love is everlasting.

Or: Alleluia.

II You have turned from your anger to comfort me.

Saturday / *418*

I You are my inheritance, O Lord.

II Create a clean heart in me, O God.

TWENTIETH WEEK IN ORDINARY TIME 1007

Monday / *419*
I Lord, remember us, for the love you bear your people.
II You have forgotten God who gave you birth.

Tuesday / *420*
I The Lord speaks of peace to his people.
II It is I who deal death and give life.

Wednesday / *421*
I Lord, your strength gives joy to the king.
II The Lord is my shepherd; there is nothing I shall want.

Thursday / *422*
I Here am I, Lord; I come to do your will.
II I will pour clean water on you and wash away all your sins.

Friday / *423*
I Praise the Lord, my soul!
Or: Alleluia.
II Give thanks to the Lord, his love is everlasting.
Or: Alleluia.

Saturday / *424*
I See how the Lord blesses those who fear him.
II The glory of the Lord will dwell in our land.

TWENTY-FIRST WEEK IN ORDINARY TIME 1008

Monday / *425*
I The Lord takes delight in his people.
Or: Alleluia.
II Proclaim his marvelous deeds to all the nations.

Tuesday / *426*
I You have searched me and you know me, Lord.
II The Lord comes to judge the earth.

Wednesday / *427*
I You have searched me and you know me, Lord.
II Happy are those who fear the Lord.

Thursday / *428*
I Fill us with your love, O Lord, and we will sing for joy!
II I will praise your name for ever, Lord.

Friday / *429*
I Let good men rejoice in the Lord.
II The earth is full of the goodness of the Lord.

Saturday / *430*
I The Lord comes to rule the earth with justice.
II Happy the people the Lord has chosen to be his own.

1009 TWENTY-SECOND WEEK IN ORDINARY TIME

Monday / *431*
I The Lord comes to judge the earth.

II Lord, I love your commands.

Tuesday / *432*
I I believe that I shall see the good things of the Lord in the land of the living.

II The Lord is just in all his ways.

Wednesday / *433*
I I trust in the kindness of God for ever.

II Happy the people the Lord has chosen to be his own.

Thursday / *434*
I The Lord has made known his salvation.

II To the Lord belongs the earth and all that fills it.

Friday / *435*
I Come with joy into the presence of the Lord.

II The salvation of the just comes from the Lord.

Saturday / *436*
I God himself is my help.

II The Lord is near to all who call him.

1010 TWENTY-THIRD WEEK IN ORDINARY TIME

Monday / *437*
I In God is my safety and my glory.

II Lead me in your justice, Lord.

Tuesday / *438*
I The Lord is compassionate to all his creatures.

II The Lord takes delight in his people.

Or: Alleluia.

Wednesday / *439*
I The Lord is compassionate to all his creatures.

II Listen to me, daughter;
see and bend your ear.

Thursday / *440*
I Let everything that breathes praise the Lord!

Or: Alleluia.

II Guide me, Lord, along the everlasting way.

Friday / *441*
I You are my inheritance, O Lord.

II How lovely is your dwelling-place,
Lord, mighty God!

Saturday / *442*
I Blessed be the name of the Lord for ever.

Or: Alleluia.

II To you, Lord, I will offer a sacrifice of praise.

TWENTY-FOURTH WEEK IN ORDINARY TIME 1011

Monday / *443*

I Blest be the Lord for he has herd my prayer.

II Proclaim the death of the Lord until he comes again.

Tuesday / *444*

I I will walk with blameless heart.

II We are his people:
the sheep of his flock.

Wednesday / *445*

I How great are the works of the Lord!

Or: Alleluia.

II Happy the people the Lord has chosen to be his own.

Thursday / *446*

I How great are the works of the Lord!

Or: Alleluia.

II Give thanks to the Lord, for he is good.

Or: Alleluia.

Friday / *447*

I Happy the poor in spirit;
the kingdom of heaven is theirs!

II Lord, when your glory appears,
my joy will be full.

Saturday / *448*

I Come with joy into the presence of the Lord.

II I will walk in the presence of God,
with the light of the living.

TWENTY-FIFTH WEEK IN ORDINARY TIME 1012

Monday / *449*

I The Lord has done marvels for us.

II He who does justice shall live on the Lord's holy mountain.

Tuesday / *450*

I I rejoiced when I heard them say:
let us go to the house of the Lord.

II Guide me, Lord, in the way of your commands.

Wednesday / *451*

I Blessed be God, who lives for ever.

II Your word, O Lord, is a lamp for my feet.

Thursday / *452*

I The Lord takes delight in his people.

II In every age, O Lord, you have been our refuge.

Friday / *453*

I Hope in God; I will praise him,
my savior and my God.

II Blessed be the Lord, my Rock!

Saturday / *454*

I The Lord will guard us,
like a shepherd guarding his flock.

II In every age, O Lord, you have been our refuge.

1013 TWENTY-SIXTH WEEK IN ORDINARY TIME

Monday / *455*

I The Lord will build up Zion again,
and appear in all his glory.

II Lord, bend your ear and hear my prayer.

Tuesday / *456*

I God is with us.

II Let my prayer come before you, Lord.

Wednesday / *457*

I Let my tongue be silenced, if I ever forget you!

II Let my prayer come before you, Lord.

Thursday / *458*

I The precepts of the Lord give joy to the heart.

II I believe that I shall see the good things of the Lord in the land of the living.

Friday / *459*

I For the glory of your name, O Lord, deliver us.

II Guide me, Lord, along the everlasting way.

Saturday / *460*

I The Lord listens to the poor.

II Lord, let your face shine on me.

1014 TWENTY-SEVENTH WEEK IN ORDINARY TIME

Monday / *461*

I You will rescue my life from the pit, O Lord.

II The Lord will remember his covenant for ever.

Or: Alleluia.

Tuesday / *462*

I If you, O Lord, laid bare our guilt,
who could endure it?

II Guide me, Lord, along the everlasting way.

Wednesday / *463*

I Lord, you are tender and full of love.

II Go out to all the world,
and tell the Good News.

Or: Alleluia.

Thursday / *464*

I Happy are they who hope in the Lord.

II Blessed be the Lord God of Israel,
for he has visited his people.

Friday / *465*

I The Lord will judge the world with justice.

II The Lord will remember his covenant for ever.

Or: Alleluia.

Saturday / *466*

I Let good men rejoice in the Lord.

II The Lord remembers his covenant for ever.

Or: Alleluia.

TWENTY-EIGHTH WEEK IN ORDINARY TIME 1015

Monday / *467*

I The Lord has made known his salvation.

II Blessed be the name of the Lord for ever.

Or: Alleluia.

Tuesday / *468*

I The heavens proclaim the glory of God.

II Let your loving kindness come to me, O Lord.

Wednesday / *469*

I Lord, you give back to every man,
according to his works.

II Those who follow you, Lord, will have the light of life.

Thursday / *470*

I With the Lord there is mercy,
and fullness of redemption.

II The Lord has made known his salvation.

Friday / *471*

I I turn to you, Lord, in time of trouble,
and you fill me with the joy of salvation.

II Happy the people the Lord has chosen to be his own.

Saturday / *472*

I The Lord remembers his covenant for ever.

Or: Alleluia.

II You gave your Son authority over all your creation.

TWENTY-NINTH WEEK IN ORDINARY TIME 1016

Monday / *473*

I Blessed be the Lord God of Israel,
for he has visited his people.

II The Lord made us, we belong to him.

Tuesday / *474*

I Here am I, Lord;
I come to do your will.

II The Lord speaks of peace to his people.

Wednesday / *475*

I Our help is in the name of the Lord.

II You will draw water joyfully from the springs of salvation.

Thursday / *476*

I Happy are they who hope in the Lord.

II The earth is full of the goodness of the Lord.

Friday / *477*

I Teach me your laws, O Lord.

II Lord, this is the people that long to see your face.

Saturday / *478*

I Lord, this is the people that longs to see your face.

II I rejoiced when I heard them say:
let us go to the house of the Lord.

1017 THIRTIETH WEEK IN ORDINARY TIME

Monday / *479*

I Our God is the God of salvation.

II Behave like God as his very dear children.

Tuesday / *480*

I The Lord has done marvels for us.

II Happy are those who fear the Lord.

Wednesday / *481*

I All my hope, O Lord,
is in your loving kindness.

II The Lord is faithful in all his words.

Thursday / *482*

I Save me, O Lord,
in your kindness.

II Blessed be the Lord, my Rock!

Friday / *483*

I Praise the Lord, Jerusalem.

II How great are the works of the Lord!

Or: Alleluia.

Saturday / *484*

I The Lord will not abandon his people.

II My soul is thirsting for the living God.

1018 THIRTY-FIRST WEEK IN ORDINARY TIME

Monday / *485*

I Lord, in your great love, answer me.

II In you, Lord, I have found my peace.

Tuesday / *486*

I In you, Lord, I have found my peace.

II I will praise you, Lord, in the assembly of your people.

Wednesday / *487*

I Happy the man who is merciful
and lends to those in need.

Or: Alleluia.

II The Lord is my light and my salvation.

Thursday / *488*

I I believe that I shall see the good things of the Lord in the land of the living.

II Let hearts rejoice who search for the Lord.

Or: Alleluia.

Friday / *489*

I The Lord has revealed to the nations his saving power.

II I rejoiced when I heard them say:
Let us go to the house of the Lord.

Saturday / *490*

I I will praise your name for ever, Lord.

II Happy the man who fears the Lord.

Or: Alleluia.

THIRTY-SECOND WEEK IN ORDINARY TIME 1019

Monday / *491*

I Guide me, Lord, along the everlasting way.

II Lord, this is the people that longs to see your face.

Tuesday / *492*

I I will bless the Lord at all times.

II The salvation of the just comes from the Lord.

Wednesday / *493*

I Rise up, O God, bring judgment to the earth.

II The Lord is my shepherd;
there is nothing I shall want.

Thursday / *494*

I Your word is for ever, O Lord.

II Blest are they whose help is the God of Jacob.

Or: Alleluia.

Friday / *495*

I The heavens proclaim the glory of God.

II Happy are they who follow the law of the Lord!

Saturday / *496*

I Remember the marvels the Lord has done.

Or: Alleluia.

II Happy the man who fears the Lord.

Or: Alleluia.

THIRTY-THIRD WEEK IN ORDINARY TIME 1020

Monday / *497*

I Give me life, O Lord,
and I will do your commands.

II Those who are victorious I will feed from the tree of life.

Tuesday / *498*

I The Lord upholds me.

II Him who is victorious I will sit beside me on my throne.

Wednesday / *499*

I Lord, when your glory appears,
my joy will be full.

II Holy, holy, holy Lord, mighty God!

Thursday / *500*

I To the upright I will show the saving power of God.

II The Lamb has made us a kingdom of priests to serve our God.

Or: Alleluia.

Friday / *501*

I We praise your glorious name, O mighty God.

II How sweet to my taste is your promise!

Saturday / *502*

I I will rejoice in your salvation, O Lord.

II Blessed be the Lord, my Rock!

1021 THIRTY-FOURTH WEEK IN ORDINARY TIME

Monday / *503*
I Glory and praise for ever!
II Lord, this is the people that longs to see your face.

Tuesday / *504*
I Give glory and eternal praise to him.
II The Lord comes to judge the earth.

Wednesday / *505*
I Give glory and eternal praise to him.
II Great and wonderful are all your works,
Lord, mighty God!

Thursday / *506*
I Give glory and eternal praise to him.
II Blessed are they who are called to the wedding feast of the Lamb.

Friday / *507*
I Give glory and eternal praise to him.
II Here God lives among his people.

Saturday / *508*
I Give glory and eternal praise to him.
II Maranatha! Come, Lord Jesus!

Saints: Weekday Psalm Responses

JANUARY

January 2 / *510*
BASIL THE GREAT AND GREGORY NAZIANZEN
cf. 1065 or 1066

January 4
ELIZABETH ANN SETON
cf. 1068

January 5
JOHN NEUMANN
Proclaim his marvelous deeds
to all the nations.

January 6
ANDRE BESSETTE
cf. 1068

January 7 / *511*
RAYMOND OF PENYAFORT
cf.1065

January 13 / *512*
HILARY
cf. 1065 or 1066

January 17 / *513*
ANTHONY
cf. 1068

January 20 / *514*
FABIAN
cf. 1064 or 1065

SEBASTIAN / *515*
cf. 1064

January 21 / *516*
AGNES
cf. 1064 or 1067

Jaunary 22 / *517*
VINCENT
cf. 1064

January 24 / *518*
FRANCIS DE SALES
cf. 1065 or 1066

January 25 / *519*
CONVERSION OF PAUL
Go out to all the world,
and tell the Good News.

Or: Alleluia.

January 26 / *520*
TIMOTHY AND TITUS
cf. 1065

January 27 / *521*
ANGELA MERICI
cf. 1067 or 1068

January 28 / *522*
THOMAS AQUINAS
cf. 1065 or 1066

January 31 / *523*
JOHN BOSCO
cf. 1065 or 1068

1023 FEBRUARY 2: PRESENTATION OF THE LORD

Forty days after the celebration of Christmas, this feast tells of how Mary and Joseph brought the child to the Temple. There the aged Simeon took the baby in his arms and proclaimed that Jesus would be "a light to the Gentiles, the glory of Israel." These words have been sung for centuries on February 2 as Christians have blessed and carried lighted candles in procession.

BLESSING OF CANDLES AND PROCESSION

As the candles are lighted, this antiphon (with optional verses) may be sung:

Antiphon

Chant Mode VIII
Setting by Richard Proulx, 1985
The Lord will come to us with might - y pow - er,
bring-ing light to eyes of those who serve him well.

Psalm (118)119, 105-108.111-112

1. Your word is a lamp for my steps
2. I have sworn and made up my mind
3. Lord, I am deeply af - flict - ed;
4. Accept O Lord, the homage of my lips,
5. Your will is my heritage for ev - er,
6. I set myself to carry out your will
1. and a light for my path.
2. to o - bey your de - crees. ℟.
3. by your word give me life.
4. and teach me your de - crees. ℟.
5. the joy of my heart.
6. in full - ness for ev - er. ℟.

When the candles have been blessed, the presider invites all: "Let us go forth in peace to meet the Lord." During the procession, the following may be sung: 1024

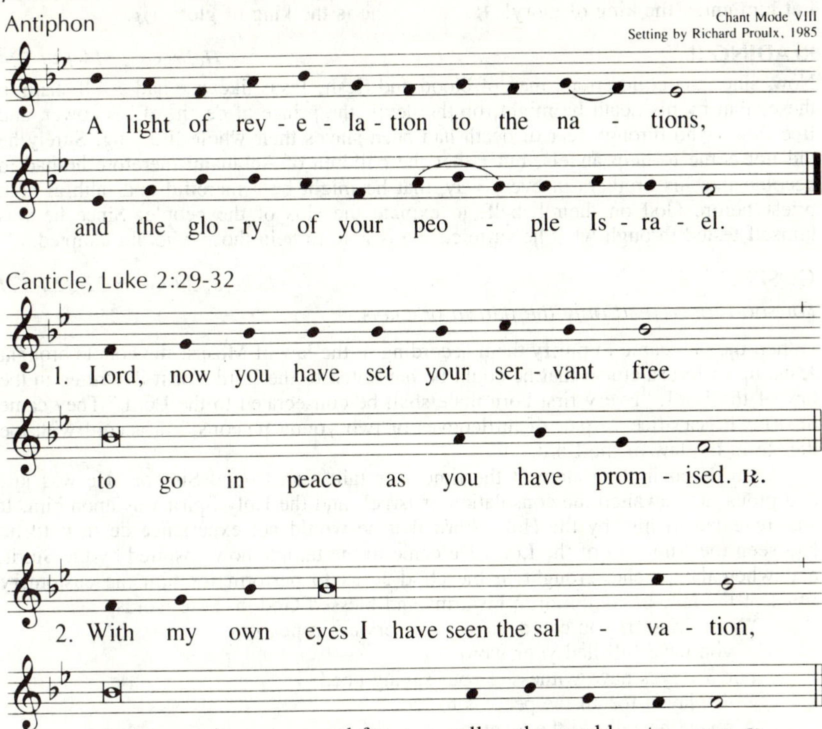
Antiphon
Chant Mode VIII
Setting by Richard Proulx, 1985
A light of rev - e - la - tion to the na - tions,
and the glo - ry of your peo - ple Is - ra - el.
Canticle, Luke 2:29-32
1. Lord, now you have set your ser - vant free
to go in peace as you have prom - ised. ℟.
2. With my own eyes I have seen the sal - va - tion,
which you have prepared for all the world to see. ℟.

READING I *Malachi 3, 1-4 / 524*

The Lord God said:
Lord, I am sending my messenger to
  prepare the way before me;
And suddenly there will come to the
  temple the Lord whom you seek,
And the messenger of the covenant
  whom you desire.
 Yes, he is coming, says the Lord of
  hosts.
But who will endure the day of his
  coming?
 And who can stand when he appears?
For he is like the refiner's fire, or like
  the fuller's lye.
He will sit refining and purifying
  [silver],
 and he will purify the sons of Levi,
Refining them like gold or like silver
  that they may offer due sacrifice to
  the Lord.
Then the sacrifice of Judah and
  Jerusalem will please the Lord,
 as in the days of old, as in years
  gone by.

RESPONSORIAL PSALM *Psalm (23)24, 7.8.9.10 / 524*

RP
Who is this king of glo - ry? It is the Lord.

O gates, lift high your heads;
grow higher, ancient doors.
Let him enter, the king of glory! ℟.

Who is the king of glory?
The Lord, the mighty, the valiant,
the Lord, the valiant in war. ℟.

O gates, lift high your heads;
grow higher, ancient doors.
Let him enter, the king of glory! ℟.

Who is he, the king of glory?
He, the Lord of armies,
he is the king of glory. ℟.

READING II *Hebrews 2, 14-18 / 524*

Now, since the children are men of blood and flesh, Jesus likewise had a full share in these, that by his death he might rob the devil, the prince of death, of his power, and free those who through fear of death had been slaves their whole life long. Surely he did not come to help angels, but rather the children of Abraham; therefore he had to become like his brothers in every way, that he might be a merciful and faithful high priest before God on their behalf, to expiate the sins of the people. Since he was himself tested through what he suffered, he is able to help those who are tempted.

GOSPEL *Luke 2, 22-40 or 22-32 / 524*

For short form, read only the part in brackets.

[When the day came to purify them according to the law of Moses, the couple brought Jesus up to Jerusalem so that he could be presented to the Lord, for it is written in the law of the Lord, "Every first-born male shall be consecrated to the Lord." They came to offer in sacrifice "a pair of turtledoves or two young pigeons," in accord with the dictate in the law of the Lord.

There lived in Jerusalem at the time a certain man named Simeon. He was just and pious, and awaited the consolation of Israel, and the Holy Spirit was upon him. It was revealed to him by the Holy Spirit that he would not experience death until he had seen the Anointed of the Lord. He came to the temple now, inspired by the Spirit; and when the parents brought in the child Jesus to perform for him the customary ritual of the law, he took him in his arms and blessed God in these words:

"Now, Master, you can dismiss your servant in peace;
you have fulfilled your word.
For my eyes have witnessed your saving deed
displayed for all the peoples to see:
A revealing light to the Gentiles,
the glory of your people Israel."]

The child's father and mother were marveling at what was being said about him. Simeon blessed them and said to Mary his mother: "This child is destined to be the downfall and the rise of many in Israel, a sign that will be opposed–and you yourself shall be pierced with a sword–so that the thoughts of many hearts may be laid bare."

There was also a certain prophetess, Anna by name, daughter of Phanuel of the tribe of Asher. She had seen many days, having lived seven years with her husband after her marriage and then as a widow until she was eighty-four. She was constantly in the temple, worshiping day and night in fasting and prayer. Coming on the scene at this moment, she gave thanks to God and talked about the child to all who looked forward to the deliverance of Jerusalem.

When the pair had fulfilled all the prescriptions of the law of the Lord, they returned to Galilee and their own town of Nazareth. The child grew in size and strength, filled with wisdom, and the grace of God was upon him.

1025 **February 3** / *525*
BLASE
cf. 1064 or 1065

ANSGAR / *526*
cf. 1065

February 5 / *527*
AGATHA
cf. 1064 or 1067

February 6 / *528*
PAUL MIKI AND COMPANIONS
cf. 1064

February 8 / *529*
JEROME EMILIANI
cf. 1068

February 10 / *530*
SCHOLASTICA
cf. 1067 or 1068

February 11 / *531*
OUR LADY OF LOURDES
cf. 1063

February 14 / *532*
CYRIL AND METHODIUS
cf. 1065 or 1068

February 17 / *533*
SEVEN FOUNDERS OF THE ORDER OF SERVITES
cf. 1068

February 21 / *534*
PETER DAMIAN
cf. 1065 or 1066 or 1068

February 22 / *535*
CHAIR OF PETER
The Lord is my shepherd;
there is nothing I shall want.

February 23 / *536*
POLYCARP
cf. 1064 or 1065

MARCH 1026

March 4 / *537*
CASIMIR
cf. 1068

March 7 / *538*
PERPETUA AND FELICITY
cf. 1064

March 8 / *539*
JOHN OF GOD
cf. 1068

March 9 / *540*
FRANCES OF ROME
cf. 1068

March 17 / *541*
PATRICK
cf. 1065

March 18 / *542*
CYRIL OF JERUSALEM
cf. 1065 or 1066

MARCH 19: JOSEPH, HUSBAND OF MARY 1027

READING I *2 Samuel 7, 4-5.12-14.16 / 543*

The Lord spoke to Nathan and said: "Go, tell my servant David, 'When your time comes and you rest with your ancestors, I will raise up your heir after you, sprung from your loins, and I will make his kingdom firm. It is he who shall build a house for my name. And I will make his royal throne firm forever. I will be a father to him, and he shall be a son to me. Your house and your kingdom shall endure forever before me; your throne shall stand firm forever.' "

RESPONSORIAL PSALM *Psalm (88)89, 2-3.4-5.27.29 / 543*

RC
The Son of Da-vid will live for ev - er.

I will sing for ever of your love, O
  Lord;
through all ages my mouth will
  proclaim your truth.

Of this I am sure, that your love lasts
  for ever,
that your truth is firmly established
  as the heavens. ℟.

'With my chosen one I have made a
covenant;
I have sworn to David my servant:
I will establish your dynasty for ever
and set up your throne through all
ages.' ℟.

He will say to me: "You are my father,
my God, the rock who saves me."
I will keep my love for him always;
with him my covenant shall last. ℟.

READING II *Romans 4, 13.16-18.22 / 543*

Certainly the promise made to Abraham and his descendants that they would inherit the world did not depend on the law; it was made in view of the justice that comes from faith. Hence, all depends on faith, everything is a grace. Thus the promise holds true for all Abraham's descendants, not only for those who have the law but for those who have his faith. He is father of us all, which is why Scripture says, "I have made you father of many nations." Yes, he is our father in the sight of God in whom he believed, the God who restores the dead to life and calls into being those things which had not been. Hoping against hope, Abraham believed and so became the father of many nations, just as it was once told him, "Numerous as this shall your descendants be." Thus his faith was credited to him as justice.

GOSPEL *Matthew 1, 16.18-21.24 / 543*

Jacob was the father of Joseph the husband of Mary. It was of her that Jesus who is called the Messiah was born. Now this is how the birth of Jesus Christ came about. When his mother Mary was engaged to Joseph, but before they lived together, she was found with child through the power of the Holy Spirit. Joseph her husband, an upright man unwilling to expose her to the law, decided to divorce her quietly. Such was his intention when suddenly an angel of the Lord appeared in a dream and said to him: "Joseph, son of David, have no fear about taking Mary as your wife. It is by the Holy Spirit that she has conceived this child. She is to have a son and you are to name him Jesus because he will save his people from their sins." When Joseph awoke he did as the angel of the Lord had directed him.

Or:

GOSPEL *Luke 2,41-51 / 543*

The parents of Jesus used to go every year to Jerusalem for the feast of the Passover, and when he was twelve they went up for the celebration as was their custom. As they were returning at the end of the feast, the child Jesus remained behind unknown to his parents. Thinking he was in the party, they continued their journey for a day, looking for him among their relatives and acquaintances.

Not finding him, they returned to Jerusalem in search of him. On the third day they came upon him in the temple sitting in the midst of the teachers, listening to them and asking them questions. All who heard him were amazed at his intelligence and his answers.

When his parents saw him they were astonished, and his mother said to him: "Son, why have you done this to us? You see that your father and I have been searching for you in sorrow." He said to them: "Why did you search for me? Did you not know I had to be in my Father's house?" But they did not grasp what he said to them.

He went down with them then and came to Nazareth, and was obedient to them.

1028 **March 23** / *544*

TURIBUS DE MOGROVEJO

cf. 1065

MARCH 25: ANNUNCIATION OF OUR LORD

READING I *Isaiah 7, 10-14 / 545*

The Lord spoke to Ahaz: Ask for a sign from the Lord, your God; let it be deep as the nether world, or high as the sky! But Ahaz answered, "I will not ask! I will not tempt the Lord!" Then he said: Listen, O house of David! Is it not enough for you to weary men, must you also weary my God? Therefore the Lord himself will give you this sign: the virgin shall be with child, and bear a son, and shall name him Immanuel.

RESPONSORIAL PSALM *Psalm (39)40, 7-8.8-9.10.11 / 545*

RP
Here am I, Lord; I come to do your will.

You do not ask for sacrifice and
offerings,
but an open ear.
You do not ask for holocaust and
victim.
Instead, here am I. ℟.

In the scroll of the book it stands
written
that I should do your will.
My God, I delight in your law
in the depth of my heart. ℟.

Your justice I have proclaimed
in the great assembly.
My lips I have not sealed;
you know it, O Lord. ℟.

I have not hidden your justice in my
heart
but declared your faithful help.
I have not hidden your love and your
truth
from the great assembly. ℟.

READING II *Hebrews 10, 4-10 / 545*

It is impossible for the blood of bulls and goats to take sins away. Wherefore, on coming into the world, Jesus said:

"Sacrifice and offering you did not desire,
but a body you have prepared for me;
Holocausts and sin offerings you took no delight in.
Then I said, 'As it is written of me in the book,
I have come to do your will, O God.' "

First he says,

"Sacrifices and offerings, holocausts and sin offerings
you neither desired nor delighted in."

(These are offered according to the prescripitons of of the law.) Then he says,

"I have come to do your will."

In other words, he takes away the first covenant to establish the second.

By this "will," we have been sanctified through the offering of the body of Jesus Christ once for all.

GOSPEL *Luke 1, 26-38 / 545*

The angel Gabriel was sent from God to a town of Galilee named Nazareth, to a virgin betrothed to a man named Joseph, of the house of David. The virgin's name was Mary. Upon arriving, the angel said to her: "Rejoice, O highly favored daughter! The Lord is with you. Blessed are you among women." She was deeply troubled by his words, and wondered what his greeting meant. The angel went on to say to her: "Do not fear, Mary. You have found favor with God. You shall conceive and bear a son and give him the name Jesus. Great will be his dignity and he will be called Son of the Most High. The Lord God will give him the throne of David his father. He will rule over the house of Jacob forever and his reign will be without end."

Mary said to the angel, "How can this be since I do not know man?" The angel answered her: "The Holy Spirit will come upon you and the power of the Most High will overshadow you; hence, the holy offspring to be born will be called Son of God. Know that Elizabeth your kinswoman has conceived a son in her old age; she who was thought to be sterile is now in her sixth month, for nothing is impossible with God."

Mary said: "I am the maidservant of the Lord. Let it be done to me as you say." With that the angel left her.

1030 **APRIL**

April 2 / *546*
FRANCIS OF PAOLA
cf. 1068

April 4 / *547*
ISIDORE
cf. 1065 or 1066

April 5 / *548*
VINCENT FERRER
cf. 1065

April 7 / *549*
JOHN BAPTIST DE LA SALLE
cf. 1065 or 1068

April 11 / *550*
STANISLAUS
cf. 1064 or 1065

April 13 / *551*
MARTIN I
cf. 1064 or 1065

April 21 / *552*
ANSELM
cf. 1065 or 1066

April 23 / *553*
GEORGE
cf. 1064

April 24 / *554*
FIDELIS OF SIGMARINGEN
cf. 1064 or 1065

April 25 / *555*
MARK
For ever I will sing the goodness of the Lord.
Or: Alleluia.

April 28 / *556*
PETER CHANEL
cf. 1064 or 1065

April 29 / *557*
CATHERINE OF SIENA
cf. 1067

April 30 / *558*
PIUS V
cf. 1065

1031 **MAY**

May 1 / *559*
JOSEPH THE WORKER
Lord, give success to the work of our hands.
Or: Alleluia.

May 2 / *560*
ATHANASIUS
cf. 1065 or 1066

May 3 / *561*
PHILIP AND JAMES
Their message goes out through all the earth.
Or: Alleluia.

May 12 / *562*
NEREUS AND ACHILLEUS
cf. 1064

PANCRAS / *563*
cf. 1064

May 14 / *564*
MATTHIAS
The Lord will give him a seat with the leaders of his people.
Or: Alleluia.

May 15
ISIDORE
cf. 1068

May 18 / *565*
JOHN I
cf. 1064 or 1065

May 20 / *566*
BERNARDINE OF SIENA
cf. 1065

May 25 / *567*
VENERABLE BEDE
cf. 1065 or 1066

GREGORY VII / *568*
cf. 1065

MARY MAGDALENE DE PAZZI / *569*
cf. 1067 or 1068

May 26 / *570*
PHILIP NERI
cf. 1065 or 1068

May 27 / *571*
AUGUSTINE OF CANTERBURY
cf. 1065

May 31 / *572*
VISITATION
Among you is the great and Holy One of Israel.

Saturday following the Second Sunday after Pentecost / *573*
IMMACULATE HEART OF MARY
cf. 1063

JUNE 1032

June 1 / *574*
JUSTIN
cf. 1064

June 2 / *575*
MARCELLINUS AND PETER
cf. 1064

June 3 / *576*
CHARLES LWANGA AND COMPANIONS
cf. 1064

June 5 / *577*
BONIFACE
cf. 1064 or 1065

June 6 / *578*
NORBERT
cf. 1065 or 1068

June 9 / *579*
EPHREM
cf. 1066

June 11 / *580*
BARNABAS
The Lord has revealed to the nations his saving power.

June 13 / *581*
ANTHONY OF PADUA
cf. 1065 or 1066 or 1068

June 19 / *582*
ROMUALD
cf. 1068

June 21 / *583*
ALOYSIUS GONZAGA
cf. 1068

June 22 / *584*
PAULINUS OF NOLA
cf. 1065

JOHN FISHER / *585*
AND THOMAS MORE
cf. 1064

1033 JUNE 24: BIRTH OF JOHN THE BAPTIST / VIGIL

READING I *Jeremiah 1, 4-10 / 586*

The word of the Lord came to me thus:
Before I formed you in the womb I
knew you,
before you were born I dedicated
you,
a prophet to the nations I appointed
you.
"Ah , Lord God!" I said,
"I know not how to speak; I am too
young."

But the Lord answered me,
Say not, "I am too young."
To whomever I send you, you shall go;
whatever I command you, you shall
speak.
Have no fear before them,
because I am with you to deliver
you, says the Lord.

Then the Lord extended his hand and
touched my mouth, saying,
See, I place my words in your mouth!
This day I set you
over nations and over kingdoms,
To root up and to tear down,
to destroy and to demolish,
to build and to plant.

RESPONSORIAL PSALM *Psalm (70)71, 1-2.3-4.5-6.15.17 / 586*

RC

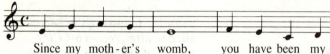

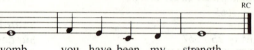

Since my moth-er's womb, you have been my strength.

In you, O Lord, I take refuge;
let me never be put to shame.
In your justice rescue me, free me;
pay heed to me and save me. ℞.

It is you, O Lord, who are my hope,
my trust, O Lord, since my youth.
On you I have leaned from my birth,
from my mother's womb you have
been my help. ℞.

Be a rock where I can take refuge,
a mighty stronghold to save me;
for you are my rock, my stronghold.
Free me from the hand of the
wicked. ℞.

My lips will tell of your justice
and day by day of your help.
O God, you have taught me from my
youth
and I proclaim your wonders still. ℞.

READING II *1 Peter 1, 8-12 / 586*

It is true you have never seen Jesus Christ, but in the present age you believe in him without seeing him, and rejoice with inexpressible joy touched with glory because you are achieving faith's goal, your salvation. This is the salvation which the prophets carefully searched out and examined. They prophesied a divine favor that was destined to be yours. They investigated the times and the circumstances which the Spirit of Christ within them was pointing to, for he predicted the sufferings destined for Christ and the glories that would follow. They knew by revelation that they were providing, not for themselves but for you, what has now been proclaimed to you by those who preach the gospel to you in the power of the Holy Spirit sent from heaven. Into these matters angels long to search.

GOSPEL *Luke 1, 5-17 / 586*

In the days of Herod, king of Judea, there was a priest named Zechariah of the priestly class of Abijah; his wife was a descendant of Aaron named Elizabeth. Both were just in the eyes of God, blamelessly following all the commandments and ordinances of the Lord. They were childless, for Elizabeth was sterile; moreover, both were advanced in years.

Once, when it was the turn of Zechariah's class and he was fulfilling his functions as a priest before God, it fell to him by lot according to priestly usage to enter the sanctuary of the Lord and offer incense. While the full assembly of people was praying outside at the incense hour, an angel of the Lord appeared to him, standing at the right of the altar of incense. Zechariah was deeply disturbed upon seeing him, and overcome by fear.

The angel said to him: "Do not be frightened, Zechariah; you prayer has been heard. Your wife Elizabeth shall bear a son whom you shall name John. Joy and gladness will be yours, and many will rejoice at his birth; for he will be great in the eyes of the Lord. He will never drink wine or strong drink, and he will be filled with the Holy Spirit from his mother's womb. Many of the sons of Israel will he bring back to the Lord their God. God himself will go before him, in the spirit and power of Elijah, to turn the hearts of fathers to their children and the rebellious to the wisdom of the just, and to prepare for the Lord a people well-disposed."

JUNE 24: BIRTH OF JOHN THE BAPTIST/DURING THE DAY 1034

READING I *Isaiah 49, 1-6 / 587*

Hear me, O coastlands,
listen, O distant peoples.
The Lord called me from birth,
from my mother's womb he gave me my name.
He made me a sharp-edged sword
and concealed me in the shadow of his arm.
He made me a polished arrow,
in his quiver he hid me.
You are my servant, he said to me,
Israel, through whom I show my glory.

Though I thought I had toiled in vain,
and for nothing, uselessly, spent my strength
Yet my reward is with the Lord,
my recompense is with my God.
For now the Lord has spoken
who formed me as his servant from the womb,
That Jacob may be brought back to him
and Israel gathered to him;
And I am made glorious in the sight of the Lord,
and my God is now my strength!
It is too little, he says, for you to be my servant,
to raise up the tribes of Jacob,
and restore the survivors of Israel;
I will make you a light to the nations.
that my salvation may reach to the ends of the earth.

RESPONSORIAL PSALM *Psalm (138)139, 1-3.13-14.14-15 / 587*

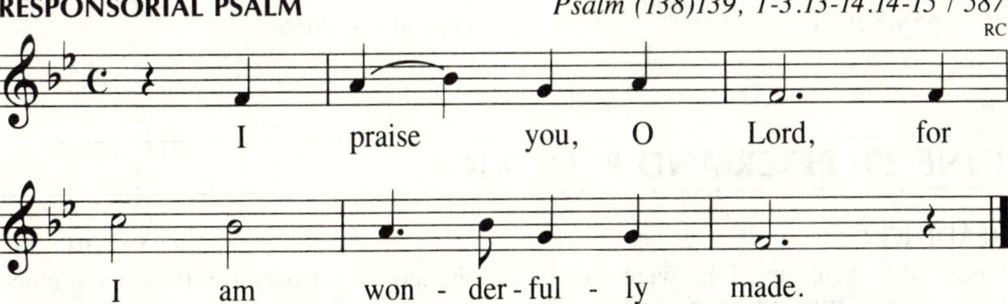
RC
I praise you, O Lord, for
I am won - der - ful - ly made.

O Lord, you search me and you know me,
you know my resting and my rising,
you discern my purpose from afar.
You mark when I walk or lie down,
all my ways lie open to you. ℟.

For it was you who created my being,
knit me together in my mother's womb.
I thank you for the wonder of my being,
for the wonders of all your creation. ℟.

Already you knew my soul,
my body held no secret from you
when I was being fashioned in secret
and moulded in the depths of the earth. ℟.

READING II *Acts 13, 22-26 / 587*

Paul said: "God raised up David as their king; on his behalf God testified, 'I have found David son of Jesse to be a man after my own heart who will fulfill my every wish.'

"According to his promise, God has brought forth from this man's descendants Jesus, a savior for Israel. John heralded the coming of Jesus by proclaiming a baptism of repentance to all the people of Israel. As John's career was coming to an end, he would say, 'What you suppose me to be I am not. Rather, look for the one who comes after me. I am not worthy to unfasten the sandals on his feet.' My brothers, children of the family of Abraham and you others who reverence our God, it was to us that this message of salvation was sent forth."

GOSPEL *Luke 1, 57-66.80 / 587*

When Elizabeth's time for delivery arrived, she gave birth to a son. Her neighbors and relatives, upon hearing that the Lord had extended his mercy to her, rejoiced with her. When they assembled for the circumcision of the child on the eighth day, they intended to name him after his father Zechariah. At this his mother intervened, saying, "No, he is to be called John."

They pointed out to her, "None of your relatives has this name." Then, using signs, they asked the father what he wished him to be called.

He signaled for a writing tablet and wrote the words, "His name is John." This astonished them all. At that moment his mouth was opened and his tongue loosed, and he began to speak in praise of God.

Fear descended on all in the neighborhood; throughout the hill country of Judea these happenings began to be recounted to the last detail. All who heard stored these things up in their hearts, saying, "What will this child be?" and, "Was not the hand of the Lord upon him?"

The child grew up and matured in spirit. He lived in the desert until the day when he made his public appearance in Israel.

1035 **June 27** / *588*
CYRIL OF ALEXANDRIA
cf. 1065 or 1066

June 28 / *589*
IRENAEUS
cf. 1064 or 1066

1036 JUNE 29: PETER AND PAUL/VIGIL

READING I *Acts 3, 1-10 / 590*

Once, when Peter and John were going up to the temple for prayer at the three o'clock hour, a man crippled from birth was being carried in. They would bring him every day and put him at the temple gate called "the Beautiful" to beg from the people as they entered. When he saw Peter and John on their way in, he begged them for an alms. Peter fixed his gaze on the man; so did John. "Look at us!" Peter said. The cripple gave them his whole attention, hoping to get something. Then Peter said: "I have neither silver nor gold, but what I have I give you! In the name of Jesus Christ the Nazorean, walk!" Then Peter took him by the right hand and pulled him up. Immediately that beggar's feet and ankles became strong; he jumped up, stood for a moment, then began to walk around. He went into the temple with them–walking, jumping about, and praising God. When the people saw him moving and giving praise to God, they recognized him as the beggar who used to sit at the Beautiful Gate of the temple. They were struck with astonishment–utterly stupefied at what had happened to him.

RESPONSORIAL PSALM *Psalm (18)19, 2-3.4-5 / 590*

JJC
Their mes - sage goes out through all the earth.

The heavens proclaim the glory of God
and the firmament shows forth the work
of his hands.
Day unto day takes up the story
and night unto night makes known the
message. ℟.

No speech, no word, no voice is heard
yet their span extends through all the
earth,
their words to the utmost bounds of the
world. ℟.

READING II *Galatians 1, 11-20 / 590*

I assure you, brothers, the gospel I proclaimed to you is no mere human invention. I did not receive it from any man, nor was I schooled in it. It came by revelation from Jesus Christ. You have heard, I know, the story of my former way of life in Judaism. You know that I went to extremes in persecuting the church of God and tried to destroy it; I made progress in Jewish observance far beyond most of my contemporaries, in my excess of zeal to live out all the traditions of my ancestors.

But the time came when he who had set me apart before I was born and called me by his favor chose to reveal his Son to me, that I might spread among the Gentiles the good tidings concerning him. Immediately, without seeking human advisers or even going to Jerusalem to see those who were apostles before me, I went off to Arabia; later I returned to Damascus. Three years after that I went up to Jerusalem to get to know Cephas, with whom I stayed fifteen days. I did not meet any other apostles except James, the brother of the Lord. I declare before God that what I have just written is true.

GOSPEL *John 21, 15-19 / 590*

When Jesus had appeared to his disciples and had eaten with them, he said to Simon Peter, "Simon, son of John, do you love me more than these?" "Yes, Lord," Peter said, "you know that I love you." At which Jesus said, "Feed my lambs."

A second time he put his question, "Simon, son of John, do you love me?" "Yes, Lord," Peter said, "you know that I love you." Jesus replied, "Tend my sheep."

A third time Jesus asked him, "Simon, son of John, do you love me?" Peter was hurt because he had asked a third time, "Do you love me?" So he said to him: "Lord you know everything. You know well that I love you." Jesus told him, "Feed my sheep.

"I tell you solemnly:
as a young man
you fastened your belt
and went about as you pleased;
but when you are older
you will stretch out your hands,
and another will tie you fast
and carry you off against your will."

(What he said indicated the sort of death by which Peter was to glorify God.) When Jesus had finished speaking he said to him, "Follow me."

JUNE 29: PETER AND PAUL/MASS DURING THE DAY 1037

READING I *Acts 12, 1-11 / 591*

King Herod started to harass some of the members of the church. He beheaded James the brother of John, and when he saw that this pleased certain of the Jews, he took

Peter into custody too. During the feast of Unleavened Bread he had him arrested and thrown into prison, with four squads of soldiers to guard him. Herod intended to bring him before the people after the Passover. Peter was thus detained in prison, while the church prayed fervently to God on his behalf. During the night before Herod was to bring him to trial, Peter was sleeping between two soldiers, fastened with double chains, while guards kept watch at the door. Suddenly an angel of the Lord stood nearby and light shone in the cell. He tapped Peter on the side and woke him. "Hurry, get up!" he said. With that, the chains dropped from Peter's wrists. The angel said, "Put on your belt and your sandals!" This he did. Then the angel told him, "Now put on your cloak and follow me."

Peter followed him out, but with no clear realization that this was taking place through the angel's help. The whole thing seemed to him a mirage. They passed the first guard, then the second, and finally came to the iron gate leading out to the city, which opened for them of itself. They emerged and made their way down a narrow alley, when suddenly the angel left him. Peter had recovered his senses by this time, and said, "Now I know for certain that the Lord has sent his angel to rescue me from Herod's clutches and from all that the Jews hoped for."

RESPONSORIAL PSALM *Psalm (33)34, 2-3.4-5.6-7.8-9 / 591*

HH
The an - gel of the Lord will res-cue those who fear him.

I will bless the Lord at all times,
his praise always on my lips;
in the Lord my soul shall make its
boast.
The humble shall hear and be glad. ℟.

Glorify the Lord with me.
Together let us praise his name.
I sought the Lord and he answered me;
from all my terrors he set me free. ℟.

Look towards him and be radiant;
let your faces not be abashed.
This poor man called; the Lord heard
him
and rescued him from all his
distress. ℟.

The angel of the Lord is encamped
around those who revere him, to rescue
them.
Taste and see that the Lord is good.
He is happy who seeks refuge in
him. ℟.

READING II *2 Timothy 4, 6-8.17-18 / 591*

I am already being poured out like a libation. The time of my dissolution is near. I have fought the good fight, I have finished the race, I have kept the faith. From now on a merited crown awaits me; on that Day the Lord, just judge that he is, will award it to me–and not only to me but to all who have looked for his appearing with eager longing. But the Lord stood by my side and gave me strength, so that through me the preaching task might be completed and all the nations might hear the gospel. That is how I was saved from the Lion's jaws. The Lord will continue to rescue me from all attempts to do me harm and will bring me safe to his heavenly kingdom. To him be glory forever and ever. Amen.

GOSPEL *Matthew 16, 13-19 / 591*

When Jesus came to the neighborhood of Caesarea Philippi, he asked his disciples this question: "Who do people say that the Son of Man is?" They replied, "Some say John the Baptizer, others Elijah, still others Jeremiah or one of the prophets." "And you,"he said to them, "who do you say that I am?" "You are the Messiah," Simon Peter answered, "the Son of the living God!" Jesus replied, "Blest are you, Simon son of John! No mere man has revealed this to you, but my heavenly Father. I for my part declare to you, you are 'Rock,' and on this rock I will build my church, and the jaws of death shall not prevail against it. I will entrust to you the keys of the kingdom of heaven. Whatever you declare bound on earth shall be bound in heaven; whatever you declare loosed on earth shall be loosed in heaven."

June 30 / *592* 1038

FIRST MARTYRS OF THE CHURCH OF ROME

cf. 1064

JULY 1039

July 3 / *593*

THOMAS

Go out to all the world,
and tell the Good News.

July 4 / *594*

ELIZABETH OF PORTUGAL

cf. 1068

JULY 4: INDEPENDENCE DAY 1040

RESPONSORIAL PSALM *Psalm (84)85, 9-10.11-12.13-14*

RP
The Lord speaks of peace to his peo - ple.

I will hear what the Lord God has to say,
a voice that speaks of peace,
peace for his people and his friends
and those who turn to him in their hearts.
His help is near for those who fear him
and his glory will dwell in our land. ℟.

Mercy and faithfulness have met;
justice and peace have embraced.
Faithfulness shall spring from the earth
and justice look down from heaven. ℟.

The Lord will make us prosper
and our earth shall yield its fruit.
Justice shall march before him
and peace shall follow his steps. ℟.

July 5 / *595* 1041

ANTHONY ZACCARIA

cf. 1065 or 1068

July 6 / *596*

MARIA GORETTI

cf. 1064 or 1067

July 11 / *597*

BENEDICT

cf. 1068

July 13 / *598*

HENRY

cf. 1068

July 14 / *599*
KATERI TEKAKWITHA /
cf. 1067

CAMILLUS DE LELLIS
cf. 1068

July 15 / *600*
BONAVENTURE
cf. 1065 or 1066

July 16 / *601*
OUR LADY OF MOUNT CARMEL
cf. 1063

July 21 / *602*
LAWRENCE OF BRINDISI
cf. 1065 or 1066

July 22 / *603*
MARY MAGDALENE
My soul is thirsting for you, O Lord, my God.

July 23 / *604*
BRIDGET
cf. 1068

July 25 / *605*
JAMES
Those who sow in tears, shall reap with shouts of joy.

July 26 / *606*
JOACHIM AND ANN
God will give him the throne of David, his father.

July 29 / *607*
MARTHA
cf. 1068

July 30 / *608*
PETER CHRYSOLOGUS
cf. 1065 or 1066

July 31 /
IGNATIUS OF LOYOLA
cf. 1065 or 1068

1042 AUGUST

August 1 / *610*
ALPHONSUS LIGUORI
cf. 1065 or 1066

August 2 / *611*
EUSEBIUS OF VERCELLI
cf. 1065

August 4 / *612*
JOHN VIANNEY
cf. 1065

August 5 / *613*
DEDICATION OF SAINT MARY MAJOR
cf. 1062

1043 AUGUST 6: TRANSFIGURATION

READING I *Daniel 7, 9-10.13-14 / 615*

As Daniel watched:
Thrones were set up and the Ancient One took his throne.
His clothing was snow bright, and the hair on his head as white as wool;
His throne was flames of fire, with wheels of burning fire.
A surging stream of fire flowed out from where he sat;
Thousands upon thousands were ministering to him,
and myriads upon myriads attended him.

The court was convened and the books were opened. As the visions during the night continued, I saw
One like a son of man coming, on the clouds of heaven;
When he reached the Ancient One and was presented before him,
He received dominion, glory, and kingship;

nations and peoples of every
language served him.
His dominion is an everlasting
dominion that shall not be taken
away,
his kingship shall not be destroyed.

RESPONSORIAL PSALM *Psalm (96)97, 1-2.5-6.9 / 615*

RP
The Lord is king, the most high o-ver all the earth.

The Lord is king, let earth rejoice,
let all the coastlands be glad.
Cloud and darkness are his raiment;
his throne, justice and right. ℟.

The mountains melt like wax
before the Lord of all the earth.
The skies proclaim his justice;
all peoples see his glory. ℟.

For you indeed are the Lord
most high above all the earth,
exalted far above all spirits. ℟.

READING II *2 Peter 1, 16-19 / 615*

It was not by way of cleverly concocted myths that we taught you about the coming in power of our Lord Jesus Christ, for we are eyewitnesses of his sovereign majesty. He received glory and praise from God the Father when that unique declaration came to him out of the majestic splendor: "This is my beloved Son on whom my favor rests." We ourselves heard this said from heaven while we were in his company on the holy mountain. Besides, we possess the prophetic message as something altogether reliable. Keep your attention closely fixed on it, as you would on a lamp shining in a dark place until the first streaks of dawn appear and the morning star rises in your hearts.

GOSPEL/A *Matthew 17, 1-9 / 615*

Jesus took Peter, James, and his brother John and led them up on a high mountain by themselves. He was transfigured before their eyes. His face became as dazzling as the sun, his clothes an radiant as light. Suddenly Moses and Elijah appeared to them conversing with him. Upon this, Peter said to Jesus, "Lord, how good it is for us to be here! With your permission I will erect three booths here, one for you, one for Moses, and one for Elijah." He was still speaking when suddenly a bright cloud overshadowed them. Out of the cloud came a voice which said, "This is my beloved Son on whom my favor rests. Listen to him." When they heard this the disciples fell forward on the ground, overcome with fear. Jesus came toward them and, laying his hand on them, said, "Get up! Do not be afraid." When they looked up they did not see anyone but Jesus.

As they were coming down the mountainside Jesus commanded them, "Do not tell anyone of the vision until the Son of Man rises from the dead."

GOSPEL/B *Mark 9, 2-10 / 615*

Jesus took Peter, James, and John off by themselves with him and led them up a high mountain. He was transfigured before their eyes and his clothes became dazzlingly white–whiter than the work of any bleacher could make them. Elijah appeared to them along with Moses; the two were in conversation with Jesus. Then Peter spoke to Jesus: "Rabbi, how good it is for us to be here. Let us erect three booths on this site, one for you, one for Moses, and one for Elijah." He hardly knew what to say, for they were all overcome with awe. A cloud came, overshadowing them, and out of the cloud a voice: "This is my Son, my beloved. Listen to him." Suddenly looking around they no longer saw anyone with them–only Jesus.

As they were coming down the mountain, he strictly enjoined them not to tell anyone what they had seen, before the Son of Man had risen from the dead. They kept this word of his to themselves, though they continued to discuss what "to rise from the dead" meant.

GOSPEL/C *Luke 9, 28-36 / 615*

Jesus took Peter, John and James, and went up onto a mountain to pray. While he was praying, his face changed in appearance and his clothes became dazzlingly white. Suddenly two men were talking with him–Moses and Elijah. They appeared in glory and spoke of his passage, which he was about to fulfill in Jerusalem. Peter and those with him had fallen into a deep sleep; but awakening, they saw his glory and likewise saw the two men who were standing with him. When these were leaving, Peter said to Jesus, "Master, how good it is for us to be here. Let us set up three booths, one for you, one for Moses, and one for Elijah." (He did not really know what he was saying.) While he was speaking, a cloud came and overshadowed them, and the disciples grew fearful as the others entered it. Then from the cloud came a voice which said, "This is my Son, my Chosen One. Listen to him." When the voice fell silent, Jesus was there alone. The disciples kept quiet, telling nothing of what they had seen at that time to anyone.

1044 **August 7** / *618*

SIXTUS II

cf. 1064

CAJETAN

cf. 1065 or 1068

August 8 / *617*

DOMINIC

cf. 1065 or 1068

August 10

LAWRENCE

Happy the man who is merciful
and lends to those in need.

August 11 / *619*

CLARE

cf. 1068

August 13 / *620*

PONTIAN AND HIPPOLYTUS

cf. 1064 or 1065

August 14 /

MAXIMILIAN MARY KOLBE

Precious in the eyes of the Lord
is the death of his faithful ones.

1045 AUGUST 15: ASSUMPTION/VIGIL

READING I *1 Chronicles 15, 3-4.15.16;16,1-2 / 621*

David assembled all Israel in Jerusalem to bring the ark of the Lord to the place which he had prepared for it. David also called together the sons of Aaron and the Levites.

The Levites bore the ark of God on their shoulders with poles, as Moses had ordained according to the word of the Lord.

David commanded the chiefs of the Levites to appoint their brethren as chanters, to play on musical instruments, harps, lyres, and cymbals, to make a loud sound of rejoicing.

They brought in the ark of God and set it within the tent which David had pitched for it. Then they offered up holocausts and peace offerings to God. When David had finished offering up the holocausts and peace offerings, he blessed the people in the name of the Lord.

RESPONSORIAL PSALM *Psalm (131)132, 6-7.9-10.13-14 / 621*

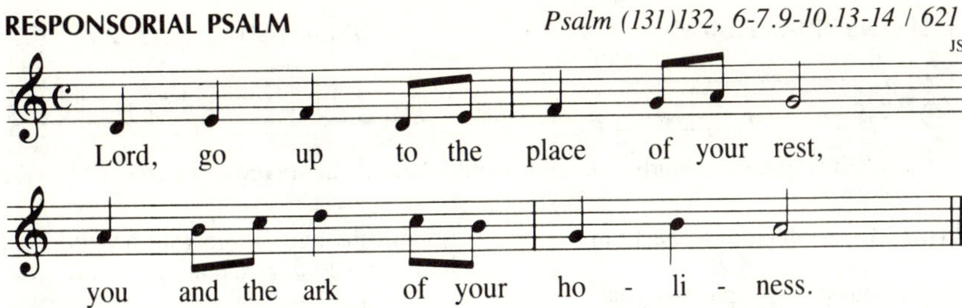
JS
Lord, go up to the place of your rest,
you and the ark of your ho - li - ness.

At Ephrata we heard of the ark;
we found it in the plains of Yearim.
"Let us go to the place of his dwelling;
let us go to kneel at his footstool." ℟.

Your priests shall be clothed with
holiness;
your faithful shall ring out their joy.
For the sake of David your servant
do not reject your anointed. ℟.

For the Lord has chosen Zion;
he has desired it for his dwelling:
"This is my resting-place for ever,
here have I chosen to live." ℟.

READING II *1 Corinthians 15, 54-57 / 621*

When the corruptible frame takes on incorruptibility and the mortal immortality, then will the saying of Scripture be fulfilled: "Death is swallowed up in victory." "O death, where is your victory? O death, where is your sting?" The sting of death is sin, and sin gets its power from the law. But thanks be to God who has given us the victory through our Lord Jesus Christ.

GOSPEL *Luke 11, 27-28 / 621*

While Jesus was speaking to the crowd, a woman called out, "Blest is the womb that bore you and the breasts that nursed you!" "Rather," he replied, "blest are they who hear the word of God and keep it."

AUGUST 15: ASSUMPTION/MASS DURING THE DAY 1046

READING I *Revelation 11, 19; 12, 1-6.10 / 622*

God's temple in heaven opened and in the temple could be seen the ark of his covenant.

A great sign appeared in the sky, a woman clothed with the sun, with the moon under her feet, and on her head a crown of twelve stars. Because she was with child, she wailed aloud in pain as she labored to give birth. Then another sign appeared in the sky: it was a huge dragon, flaming red, with seven heads and ten horns; on his head were seven diadems. His tail swept a third of the stars from the sky and hurled them down to the earth. Then the dragon stood before the woman about to give birth, ready to devour her child when it should be born. She gave birth to a son–a boy who is destined to shepherd all the nations with an iron rod. Her child was snatched up to God and to his throne. The woman herself fled into the desert, where a special place had been prepared for her by God.

Then I heard a loud voice in heaven say:
"Now have salvation aand power come,
the reign of our God and the authority of his Anointed One."

RESPONSORIAL PSALM *Psalm (44)45, 10.11.12.16 / 622*

3

HH

The queen stands at your right hand, ar-rayed in gold.

Listen, O daughter, give ear to my
words:
forget your own people and your
father's house. ℟.

So will the king desire your beauty;
he is your lord, pay homage to him. ℟.

They are escorted amid gladness and
joy;
they pass within the palace of the
king. ℟.

READING II *1 Corinthians 15, 20-26 / 622*

Christ has been raised from the dead, the first fruits of those who have fallen asleep. Death came through a man; hence the resurrection of the dead comes through a man also. Just as in Adam all die, so in Christ all will come to life again, but each one in proper order: Christ the first fruits and then, at his coming, all those who belong to him. After that will come the end, when, after having destroyed every sovereignty, authority, and power, he will hand over the kingdom to God the Father. Christ must reign until God has put all enemies under his feet.

GOSPEL *Luke 1, 39-56 / 622*

Mary set out, proceeding in haste into the hill country to a town of Judah, where she entered Zechariah's house and greeted Elizabeth. When Eizabeth heard Mary's greeting, the baby stirred in her womb. Elizabeth was filled with the Holy Spirit and cried out in a loud voice: "Blessed are you among women and blessed is the fruit of your womb. But who am I that the mother of my Lord should come to me? The moment your greeting sounded in my ears, the baby stirred in my womb for joy. Blessed is she who trusted that the Lord's words to her would be fulfilled."

Then Mary said:

"My being proclaims the greatness
of the Lord,
my spirit finds joy in God my
savior,
For he has looked upon his servant in
her lowliness;
all ages to come shall call me
blessed.
God who is mighty has done great
things for me,
holy is his name;
His mercy is from age to age
on those who fear him.
"He has shown might with his arm;
he has confused the proud in their
inmost thoughts.
He has deposed the mighty from their
thrones
and raised the lowly to high
places.
The hungry he has given every good
thing,
while the rich he has sent empty
away.
He has upheld Israel his servant,
ever mindful of his mercy;
Even as he promised our fathers,
promised Abraham and his
descendants forever."

Mary remained with Elizabeth about three months and then returned home.

1047 **August 16** / *623*
STEPHEN OF HUNGARY
cf. 1068

August 19 / *624*
JOHN EUDES
cf. 1065 or 1068

August 20 / *625*
BERNARD
cf. 1066 or 1068

August 21 / *626*
PIUS X
cf. 1065

August 22 / *627*
QUEENSHIP OF MARY
cf. 1063

August 23 / *628*
ROSE OF LIMA
cf. 1067 or 1068

August 24 / *628*
BARTHOLOMEW
Your friends tell the glory of your kingship, Lord.

August 25 / *630*
LOUIS
cf. 1068

JOSEPH CALASANZ / *631*
cf. 1065 or 1068

August 27 / *632*
MONICA
cf. 1068

August 28 / *633*
AUGUSTINE
cf. 1065 or 1066

August 29 / *634*
BEHEADING OF JOHN THE BAPTIST
I will sing of your salvation.

FIRST MONDAY IN SEPTEMBER: LABOR DAY 1048

RESPONSORIAL PSALM *Psalm (89)90, 2.3-4.12-13.14.16*

RP

Lord, give suc - cess to the work of our hands.

Before the mountains were born
or the earth or the world brought forth,
you are God, without beginning or
end. ℟.

You turn men back into dust
and say: "Go back, sons of men."
To your eyes a thousand years
are like yesterday, come and gone,
no more than a watch in the night. ℟.

Make us know the shortness of our life
that we may gain wisdom of heart.
Lord, relent! Is your anger for ever?
Show pity to your servants. ℟.

In the morning, fill us with your love;
we shall exult and rejoice all our days.
Show forth your work to your servants;
let your glory shine on their
children. ℟.

SEPTEMBER 1049

September 3 / *635*
GREGORY THE GREAT
cf. 1065 or 1066

September 8 / *636*
BIRTH OF MARY
With delight I rejoice in the Lord.

September 9
PETER CLAVER
cf. 1065

September 13 / *637*
JOHN CHRYSOSTOM
cf. 1065 or 1066

1050 SEPTEMBER 14: TRIUMPH OF THE CROSS

READING I *Numbers 21, 4-9 / 638*

With their patience worn out by the journey, the people complained against God and Moses, "Why have you brought us up from Egypt to die in this desert, where there is no food or water? We are disgusted with this wretched food!"

In punishment the Lord sent among the people saraph serpents, which bit the people so that many of them died. Then the people came to Moses and said, "We have sinned in complaining against the Lord and you. Pray the Lord to take the serpents from us." So Moses prayed for the people, and the Lord said to Moses, "Make a saraph and mount it on a pole, and if anyone who has been bitten looks at it, he will recover." Moses accordingly made a bronze serpent and mounted it on a pole, and whenever anyone who had been bitten by a serpent looked at the bronze serpent, he recovered.

RESPONSORIAL PSALM *Psalm (77)78, 1-2.34-35.36-37.38 / 638*

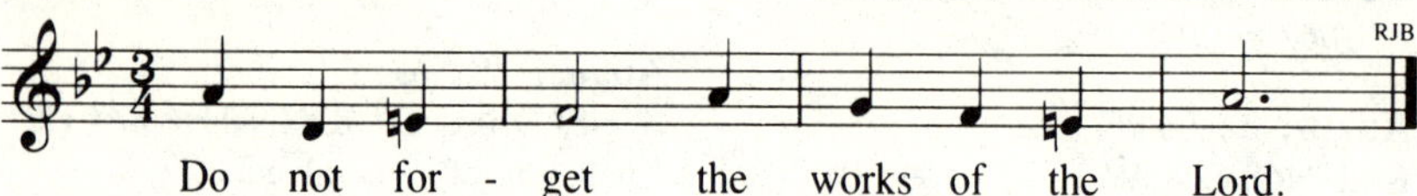
RJB
Do not for - get the works of the Lord.

Give heed, my people, to my teaching;
turn your ear to the words of my
mouth.
I will open my mouth in a parable
and reveal hidden lessons of the
past. ℟.

When he slew them then they would
seek him,
return and seek him in earnest.
They would remember that God was
their rock,
God the Most High their redeemer. ℟.

But the words they spoke were mere
flattery;
they lied to him with their lips.
For their hearts were not truly with him;
they were not faithful to his
covenant. ℟.

Yet he who is full of compassion
forgave their sin and spared them.
So often he held back his anger
when he might have stirred up his
rage. ℟.

READING II *Philippians 2, 6-11 / 638*

Christ Jesus, though he was in the form
of God,
did not deem equality with God
something to be grasped at.

Rather, he emptied himself
and took the form of a slave,
being born in the likeness of men.

He was known to be of human estate
and it was thus that he humbled
himself,
obediently accepting even death,
death on a cross!

Because of this,
God highly exalted him
and bestowed on him the name
above every other name,

So that at Jesus' name
every knee must bend
in the heavens, on the earth,
and under the earth,
and every tongue proclaim
to the glory of God the Father:
JESUS CHRIST IS LORD!

GOSPEL *John 3, 13-17 / 638*

Jesus said to Nicodemus:
"No one has gone up to heaven
except the One who came down
from there–
the Son of Man [who is in heaven].
Just as Moses lifted up the serpent in
the desert,
so must the Son of Man be lifted up,

that all who believe
may have eternal life in him.
Yes, God so loved the world
that he gave his only Son,
that whoever believes in him may not die
but may have eternal life.
God did not send the Son into the world
to comdemn the world,
but that the world might be saved through him."

1051

September 15 / *639*
OUR LADY OF SORROWS
Save me, O Lord, in your steadfast love

September 16 / *640*
CORNELIUS AND CYPRIAN
cf. 1064 or 1065

September 17 / *641*
ROBERT BELLARMINE
cf. 1065 or 1066

September 19 / *642*
JANUARIUS
cf. 1064 or 1065

September 20 /
ANDREW KIM TAEGŎN,
PAUL CHŎNG HASANG,
AND COMPANIONS
Those who sow in tears shall sing
for joy when they reap.

September 21 / *643*
MATTHEW
Their message goes out through all the earth.

September 26 / *644*
COSMAS AND DAMIAN
cf. 1064

September 27 / *645*
VINCENT DE PAUL
cf. 1065 or 1068

September 28 / *646*
WENCESLAUS
cf. 1064

September 29 / *647*
MICHAEL, GABRIEL, AND RAPHAEL
In the sight of the angels
I will sing your praise, Lord.

September 30 / *648*
JEROME
cf. 1065 or 1066

OCTOBER 1052

October 1 / *649*
THERESA OF THE CHILD JESUS
cf. 1067 or 1068

October 2 / *650*
GUARDIAN ANGELS
He has put his angels in charge of you,
to guard you in all your ways.

October 4 / *651*
FRANCIS OF ASSISI
cf. 1068

October 6 / *652*
BRUNO
cf. 1065 or 1068

MARIE ROSE DUROCHER
cf. 1067

October 7 / *653*
OUR LADY OF THE ROSARY
cf. 1063

October 9 / *654*
DENIS AND COMPANIONS
cf. 1064

JOHN LEONARDI / *655*
cf. 1065 or 1068

October 14 / *656*
CALLISTUS I
cf. 1064 or 1065

October 15 / *657*
THERESA OF JESUS
1067 or 1068

October 16 / *658*
HEDWIG
cf. 1068

MARGARET MARY ALACOQUE / *659*
cf.1067 or 1068

October 17 / *660*
IGNATIUS OF ANTIOCH
cf. 1064 or 1065

October 18 / *661*
LUKE
Your friends tell the glory of your kingship, Lord.

October 19 / *662*
ISAAC JOGUES AND COMPANIONS
cf. 1064 or 1065

PAUL OF THE CROSS / *663*
cf. 1065 or 1068

October 23 / *664*
JOHN OF CAPISTRANO
cf. 1065

October 24 / *665*
ANTHONY CLARET
cf. 1065

October 28 / *666*
SIMON AND JUDE
Their message goes out through all the earth.

1053 **NOVEMBER 1: ALL SAINTS**

READING I *Revelation 7, 2-4.9-14 / 667*

I, John, saw another angel come up from the east holding the seal of the living God. He cried out at the top of his voice to the four angels who were given power to ravage the land and the sea, "Do no harm to the land or the sea or the trees until we imprint this seal on the foreheads of the servants of our God." I heard the number of those who were so marked–one hundred and forty-four thousand from every tribe of Israel.

After this I saw before me a huge crowd which no one could count from every nation, race, people, and tongue. They stood before the throne and the Lamb, dressed in long white robes and holding palm branches in their hands. They cried out in a loud voice, "Salvation is from our God, who is seated on the throne, and from the Lamb!" All the angels who were standing around the throne and the elders and the four living creatures fell down before the throne to worship God. They said: "Amen! Praise and glory, wisdom, thanksgiving, and honor, power and might to our God forever and ever. Amen!"

Then one of the elders asked me, "Who do you think these are, all dressed in white? And where have they come from?" I said to him, "Sir, you should know better than I." He then told me, "These are the ones who have survived the great period of trial; they have washed their robes and made them white in the blood of the Lamb.

RESPONSORIAL PSALM *Psalm (23)24, 1-2.3-4.5-6 / 667*

JRC
Lord, this is the peo - ple that longs to see your face.

The Lord's is the earth and its fullness,
the world and all its peoples.
It is he who set it on the seas;
on the waters he made it firm. ℟.

Who shall climb the mountain of the Lord?
Who shall stand in his holy place?
The man with clean hands and pure heart,
who desires not worthless things. ℟.

He shall receive blessings from the Lord
and reward from the God who saves him.
Such are the men who seek him,
seek the face of the God of Jacob. ℟.

READING II *1 John 3, 1-3 / 667*

See what love the Father has bestowed on us
in letting us be called children of God!
Yet that in fact is what we are.
The reason the world does not recognize us
is that it never recognized the Son.
Dearly beloved,
we are God's children now;
what we shall later be has not yet come to light.
We know that when it comes to light
we shall be like him,
for we shall see him as he is.
Everyone who has this hope basded on him
keeps himself pure, as he is pure.

GOSPEL *Matthew 5, 1-12 / 667*

When Jesus saw the crowds he went up on the mountainside. After he had sat down his disciples gathered around him, and he began to teach them:

"How blest are the poor in spirit: the reign of God is theirs.
Blest too are the sorrowing; they shall be consoled.
[Blest are the lowly; they shall inherit the land.]
Blest are they who hunger and thirst for holiness;
they shall have their fill.
Blest are they who show mercy; mercy shall be theirs.
Blest are the single-hearted, for they shall see God.
Blest too the peacemakers; they shall be called sons of God.
Blest are those persecuted for holiness' sake; the reign of God is theirs.
Blest are you when they insult you and persecute you and utter every kind of slander against you because of me.
Be glad and rejoice, for your reward in heaven is great."

November 2 / *668*
ALL SOULS
cf. 163 or 193 to 202

November 3 / *669*
MARTIN DE PORRES
cf. 1068

November 4 / *670* 1054
CHARLES BORROMEO
cf. 1065

1055 **NOVEMBER 9: DEDICATION OF SAINT JOHN LATERAN**

RESPONSORIAL PSALM *1 Chronicles 29, 10.11.11-12 / 703*

cf. 1062 or the following:

RP
We praise your glo - ri-ous name, O might-y God.

Blessed are you, O Lord,
the God of Israel our father,
for ever, for ages unending. ℟.

Yours, Lord, are greatness and power,
and splendor, triumph and glory.
All is yours, in heaven and on
earth. ℟.

Yours, O Lord, is the kingdom,
you are supreme over all.
Both honor and riches come from
you. ℟.

You are the ruler of all,
from your hand come strength and
power,
from your hand come greatness and
might. ℟.

1056 **November 10** / *672*
LEO THE GREAT
cf. 1065 or 1066

November 11 / *673*
MARTIN OF TOURS
cf. 1068

November 12 / *674*
JOSAPHAT
cf. 1064 or 1065

November 13
FRANCES XAVIER CABRINI
cf. 1067

November 15 / *675*
ALBERT THE GREAT
cf. 1065 or 1066

November 16 / *676*
MARGARET OF SCOTLAND
cf. 1068

GERTRUDE / *677*
cf. 1067 or 1068

November 17 / *678*
ELIZABETH OF HUNGARY
cf. 1068

November 18 / *679*
DEDICATION OF THE CHURCHES OF PETER AND PAUL
The Lord has revealed to the nations his saving power.

November 21 / *680*
PRESENTATION OF MARY
cf. 1063

November 22 / *681*
CECILIA
cf. 1064 or 1067

November 23 / *682*
CLEMENT I
cf. 1064 or 1065

COLUMBAN / *683*
cf. 1065 or 1068

November 30 / *684*
ANDREW
Their message goes out through all the earth.

THANKSGIVING DAY — 1057

RESPONSORIAL PSALM *Psalm (66)67, 2-3.5.7-8*

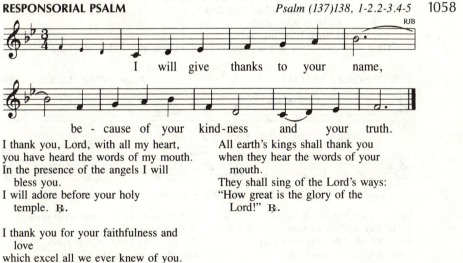

RP
The earth has yield - ed its fruits;

God, our God has blessed us.

O God, be gracious and bless us
and let your face shed its light upon us.
So will your ways be known upon earth
and all nations learn your saving
help. ℟.

Let the nations be glad and exult
for you rule the world with justice.
With fairness you rule the peoples,
you guide the nations on earth. ℟.

The earth has yielded its fruit
for God, our God, has blessed us.
May God still give us his blessing
till the ends of the earth revere him. ℟.

RESPONSORIAL PSALM *Psalm (137)138, 1-2.2-3.4-5* 1058

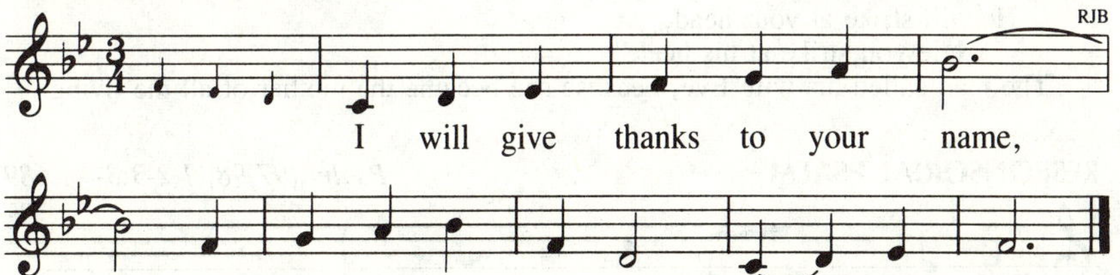
RJB
I will give thanks to your name,
be - cause of your kind-ness and your truth.

I thank you, Lord, with all my heart,
you have heard the words of my mouth.
In the presence of the angels I will
bless you.
I will adore before your holy
temple. ℟.

I thank you for your faithfulness and
love
which excel all we ever knew of you.
On the day I called, you answered;
you increased the strength of my
soul. ℟.

All earth's kings shall thank you
when they hear the words of your
mouth.
They shall sing of the Lord's ways:
"How great is the glory of the
Lord!" ℟.

DECEMBER — 1059

December 3 / *685*
FRANCIS XAVIER
cf. 1065

December 4 / *686*
JOHN DAMASCENE
cf. 1065 or 1066

December 6 / *687*
NICHOLAS
cf. 1065

December 7 / *688*
AMBROSE
cf. 1065 or 1066

1060 # DECEMBER 8: IMMACULATE CONCEPTION

READING I *Genesis 3, 9-15.20 / 689*

After Adam had eaten of the tree the Lord God called to the man and asked him, "Where are you?" He answered, "I heard you in the garden; but I was afraid, because I was naked, so I hid myself." Then he asked, "Who told you that you were naked? You have eaten, then, from the tree of which I had forbidden you to eat!" The man replied, "The woman whom you put here with me–she gave me fruit from the tree, and so I ate it." The Lord God then asked the woman, "Why did you do such a thing?" The woman answered, "The serpent tricked me into it, so I ate it."

Then the Lord God said to the serpent:
"Because you have done this, you shall be banned
from all the animals
and from all the wild creatures;
On your belly shall you crawl,
and dirt shall you eat
all the days of your life.
I will put enmity between you and the woman,
and between your offspring and hers;
He will strike at your head,
while you strike at his heel."

The man called his wife Eve, because she became the mother of all the living.

RESPONSORIAL PSALM *Psalm (97)98, 1.2-3.3-4 / 689*

JRC
Sing to the Lord a new song,
for he has done mar - vel - ous deeds.

Sing a new song to the Lord
for he has worked wonders.
His right hand and his holy arm
have brought salvation. ℟.

The Lord has made known his
salvation;
has shown his justice to the nations.
He has remembered his truth and love
for the house of Israel. ℟.

All the ends of the earth have seen
the salvation of our God.
Shout to the Lord, all the earth,
ring out your joy. ℟.

READING II *Ephesians 1, 3-6.11-12 / 689*

Praised be the God and Father of our Lord Jesus Christ, who has bestowed on us in Christ every spiritual blessing in the heavens! God chose us in him before the world began, to be holy and blameless in his sight, to be full of love; likewise he predestined us through Christ Jesus to be his adopted sons–such was his will and pleasure–that all might praise the divine favor he has bestowed on us in his beloved.

In him we were chosen; for in the decree of God, who administers everything according to his will and counsel, we were predestined to praise his glory by being the first to hope in Christ.

GOSPEL *Luke 1, 26-38 / 689*

The angel Gabriel was sent from God to a town of Galilee named Nazareth, to a virgin betrothed to a man named Joseph, of the house of David. The virgin's name was Mary. Upon arriving, the angel said to her: "Rejoice, O highly favored daughter! The Lord is with you. Blessed are you among women." She was deeply troubled by his words, and wondered what his greeting meant. The angel went on to say to her: "Do not fear, Mary. You have found favor with God. You shall conceive and bear a son and give him the name Jesus. Great will be his dignity and he will be called Son of of the Most High. The Lord God will give him the throne of David his father. He will rule over the house of Jacob forever and his reign will be without end."

Mary said to the angel, "How can this be since I do not know man?" The angel answered her: "The Holy Spirit will come upon you and the power of the Most High will overshadow you; hence, the holy offspring to be born will be called Son of God. Know that Elizabeth your kinswoman has conceived a son in her old age; she who was thought to be sterile is now in her sixth month, for nothing is impossible with God."

Mary said: "I am the maidservant of the Lord. Let it be done to me as you say." With that the angel left her.

December 11 / *690*
DAMASUS I
cf. 1065

December 12 / *691*
OUR LADY OF GUADALUPE
cf. 1063

JANE FRANCES DE CHANTAL
cf. 1068

December 13 / *692*
LUCY
cf. 1064 or 1067

December 14 / *693*
JOHN OF THE CROSS
cf. 1065 or 1066

December 21 / *694*
PETER CANISIUS
cf. 1065 or 1066

December 23 / *695*
JOHN OF KANTY
cf. 1065

December 26 / *696*
STEPHEN
Into your hands, O Lord,
I entrust my spirit.

December 27 / *697*
JOHN
Let good men rejoice in the Lord.

December 28 / *698*
HOLY INNOCENTS
Our soul has escaped like a bird
from the hunter's net.

December 29 / *699*
THOMAS BECKET
cf. 1064 or 1065

December 31 / *700*
SYLVESTER I
cf. 1065

Commons: Psalm Responses

1062 **DEDICATION OF A CHURCH** / *703*

1 We praise your glorious name, O mighty God.

2 How lovely is your dwelling-place, Lord, mighty God!

Or: Here God lives among his people.

3 Let us come before the Lord and praise him.

4 I rejoiced when I heard them say: let us go to the house of the Lord.

Or: Let us go rejoicing to the house of the Lord.

1063 **COMMON OF THE BLESSED VIRGIN MARY** / *709*

1 My heart rejoices in the Lord, my Savior.

2 You are the highest honor of our race.

3 Listen to me, daughter; see and bend your ear.

4 Blessed be the name of the Lord for ever.

Or: Alleluia.

5 The Almighty has done great things for me and holy is his name.

Or: O Blessed Virgin Mary, you carried the Son of the eternal Father.

1064 **COMMON OF MARTYRS** / *715*

1 Into your hands, O Lord, I entrust my spirit.

2 The Lord set me free from all my fears.

3 Our soul has escaped like a bird from the hunter's net.

4 Those who sow in tears, shall reap with shouts of joy.

COMMON OF PASTORS / *721* 1065

1 You are my inheritance, O Lord.

2 The Lord is my shepherd;
there is nothing I shall want.

3 For ever I will sing the goodness of the Lord.

4 Proclaim his marvelous deeds to all the nations.

5 You are a priest for ever,
in the line of Melchizedek.

6 Go out to all the world,
and tell the Good News.

Or: Alleluia.

COMMON OF DOCTORS OF THE CHURCH / *727* 1066

1 The judgments of the Lord are true,
and all of them just.

Or: Your words, Lord, are spirit and life.

2 The mouth of the just man murmurs wisdom

3 Lord, teach me your decrees.

COMMON OF VIRGINS / *733* 1067

1 Listen to me, daughter;
see and bend your ear.

Or: The bridegroom is here;
let us go out to meet Christ the Lord.

2 Alleluia.

COMMON OF SAINTS / *739* 1068

1 Happy are they who hope in the Lord.

Or: The just man will flourish like a palm tree
in the garden of the Lord.

2 He who does justice shall live on the Lord's holy mountain.

3 You are my inheritance, O Lord.

4 I will bless the Lord at all times.

Or: Taste and see the goodness of the Lord.

5 Oh, bless the Lord, my soul.

6 Happy the man who fears the Lord

Or: Alleluia.

7 Happy are those who fear the Lord.

8 In you, Lord, I have found my peace.

Seasonal Psalms

The lectionary provides that a seasonal psalm may be used in place of the appointed responsorial psalm for the day. The following is a representative selection of these seasonal psalms.

ADVENT SEASON

1069 **RESPONSORIAL PSALM** *Psalm (24)25, 4-5.8-9.10.14 / 175*

RJT
To you, O Lord, I lift my soul.

Lord, make me know your ways.
Lord, teach me your paths.
Make me walk in your truth, and
teach me,
for you are God my savior.
In you I hope all day long. ℟.

The Lord is good and upright.
He shows the path to those who stray,
he guides the humble in the right path,
he teaches his way to the poor. ℟.

His ways are faithfulness and love
for those who keep his covenant and
will.
The Lord's friendship is for those who
revere him;
to them he reveals his covenant. ℟.

CHRISTMAS

Use the psalm for Christmas Mass During the Day, no. 781

LENT

RESPONSORIAL PSALM *Psalm (50)51, 3-4.5-6.12-13.14.17 / 175* 1070

PC
Be mer - ci-ful, O Lord, for we have sinned.

Have mercy on me, God, in your kindness.
In your compassion blot out my offense.
O wash me more and more from my guilt. ℟.

My offenses truly I know them;
my sin is always before me.
Against you, you alone, have I sinned;
what is evil in your sight I have done. ℟.

A pure heart create for me, O God,
put a steadfast spirit within me.
Do not cast me away from your presence,
nor deprive me of your holy spirit. ℟.

Give me again the joy of your help;
with a spirit of fervor sustain me.
O Lord, open my lips
and my mouth shall declare your praise. ℟.

EASTER

RESPONSORIAL PSALM *Psalm (117)118, 1-2.16-17.22-23 / 175* 1071

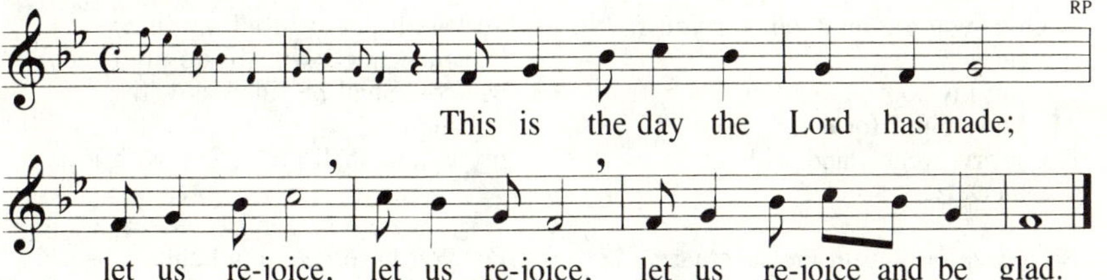
RP
This is the day the Lord has made;
let us re-joice, let us re-joice, let us re-joice and be glad.

Give thanks to the Lord for he is good,
for his love endures for ever.
Let the sons of Israel say:
'His love endures for ever.' ℟.

The Lord's right hand has triumphed;
his right hand raised me.
The Lord's right hand has triumphed;
I shall not die, I shall live
and recount his deeds. ℟.

The stone which the builders rejected
has become the cornerstone.
This is the work of the Lord,
a marvel in our eyes. ℟.

ORDINARY TIME

1072 **RESPONSORIAL PSALM** *Psalm (18)19, 8.9.10.11 / 175*

DRH
The Lord is kind and mer - ci - ful.

The law of the Lord is perfect,
it revives the soul.
The rule of the Lord is to be trusted,
it gives wisdom to the simple. ℟.

The precepts of the Lord are right,
they gladden the heart.
The command of the Lord is clear,
it gives light to the eyes. ℟.

The fear of the Lord is holy,
abiding for ever.
The decrees of the Lord are truth
and all of them just. ℟.

They are more to be desired than gold,
than the purest of gold
and sweeter are they than honey,
than honey from the comb. ℟.

1073 **RESPONSORIAL PSALM** *Psalm (62)63,2.3-4.5-6.8-9 / 175*

RP
My soul is thirst-ing for you, O
Lord, thirst - ing for you my God.

O God, you are my God, for you I long;
for you my soul is thirsting.
My body pines for you
like a dry, weary land without water. ℟.

So I gaze on you in the sanctuary
to see your strength and your glory.
For your love is better than life,
my lips will speak your praise. ℟.

So I will bless you all my life,
in your name I will lift up my hands.
My soul shall be filled as with a banquet,
my mouth shall praise you with joy. ℟.

For you have been my help;
in the shadow of your wings I rejoice.
My soul clings to you;
your right hand holds me fast. ℟.

1074 **RESPONSORIAL PSALM** *Psalm (99)100,1-2.3.5 / 175*

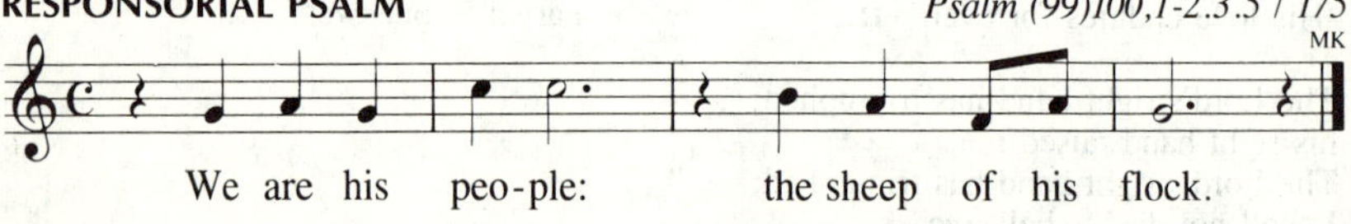
MK
We are his peo-ple: the sheep of his flock.

Cry out with joy to the Lord, all the earth.
Serve the Lord with gladness.
Come before him, singing for joy. ℟.

Know that he, the Lord, is God.
He made us, we belong to him,
we are his people, the sheep of his flock. ℟.

Indeed, how good is the Lord,
eternal his merciful love.
He is faithful from age to age. ℟.

RESPONSORIAL PSALM 1075

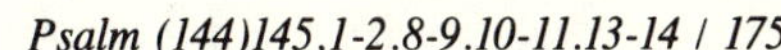

Psalm (144)145,1-2.8-9.10-11.13-14 / 175

JRC

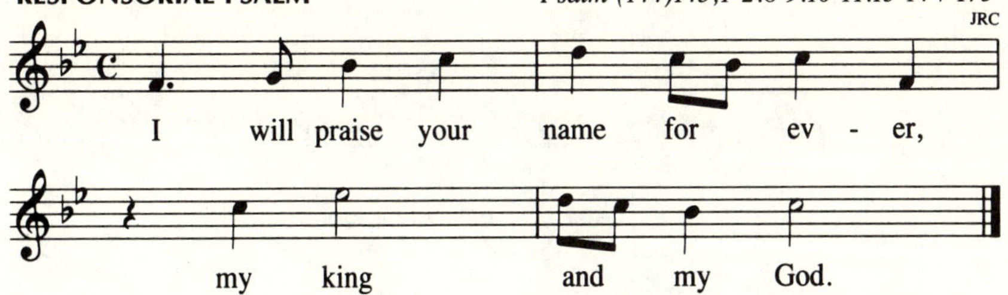
I will praise your name for ev - er,
my king and my God.

I will give you glory, O God my King,
I will bless your name for ever.
I will bless you day after day
and praise your name for ever. ℟.

The Lord is kind and full of compassion
slow to anger, abounding in love.
How good is the Lord to all,
compassionate to all his creatures. ℟.

All your creatures shall thank you, O Lord,
and your friends shall repeat their blessing.
They shall speak of the glory of your reign
and declare your might, O God. ℟.

The Lord is faithful in all his words
and loving in all his deeds.
The Lord supports all who fall
and raises all who are bowed down. ℟.

Seasonal Responses

The following psalm responses are drawn from five previously published psalm collections in wide use throughout the church. They are: "Songs of Israel" Vols. I and II (Peloquin), "Seasonal Responsorial Psalms" (Roff), "Psalms for the Church Year" (Isele), and "Psalms for the Church Year" (Haugen/Haas).

ADVENT SEASON

1076
Psalm (24)25
JR
To you, O Lord, I lift up my soul.
1077
Psalm (24)25
CAP
To you, O Lord, I lift up my soul.
1078
Psalm (24)25
DCI
To you, O Lord, I lift up my soul.
1079
Psalm (24)25
MH
To you, O Lord, I lift my
soul, to you, I lift my soul.

Psalm (84)85
CAP
1080
Lord, let us see your kind - ness,
and grant us your sal - va - tion.
Psalm (84)85
MH
1081
Lord, let us see your kind - ness;
Lord, let us see your kind - ness.
CHRISTMAS SEASON
Psalm (97)98
JR
1082
All the ends of the earth have
seen the sav - ing pow'r of God.
Psalm (97)98
CAP
1083
All the ends of the earth have seen the sav - ing
pow - er of God. All the ends of the
earth have seen the sav - ing pow - er of God.
Psalm (97)98
DCI
1084
All the ends of the earth have
seen the sav - ing pow'r of God.

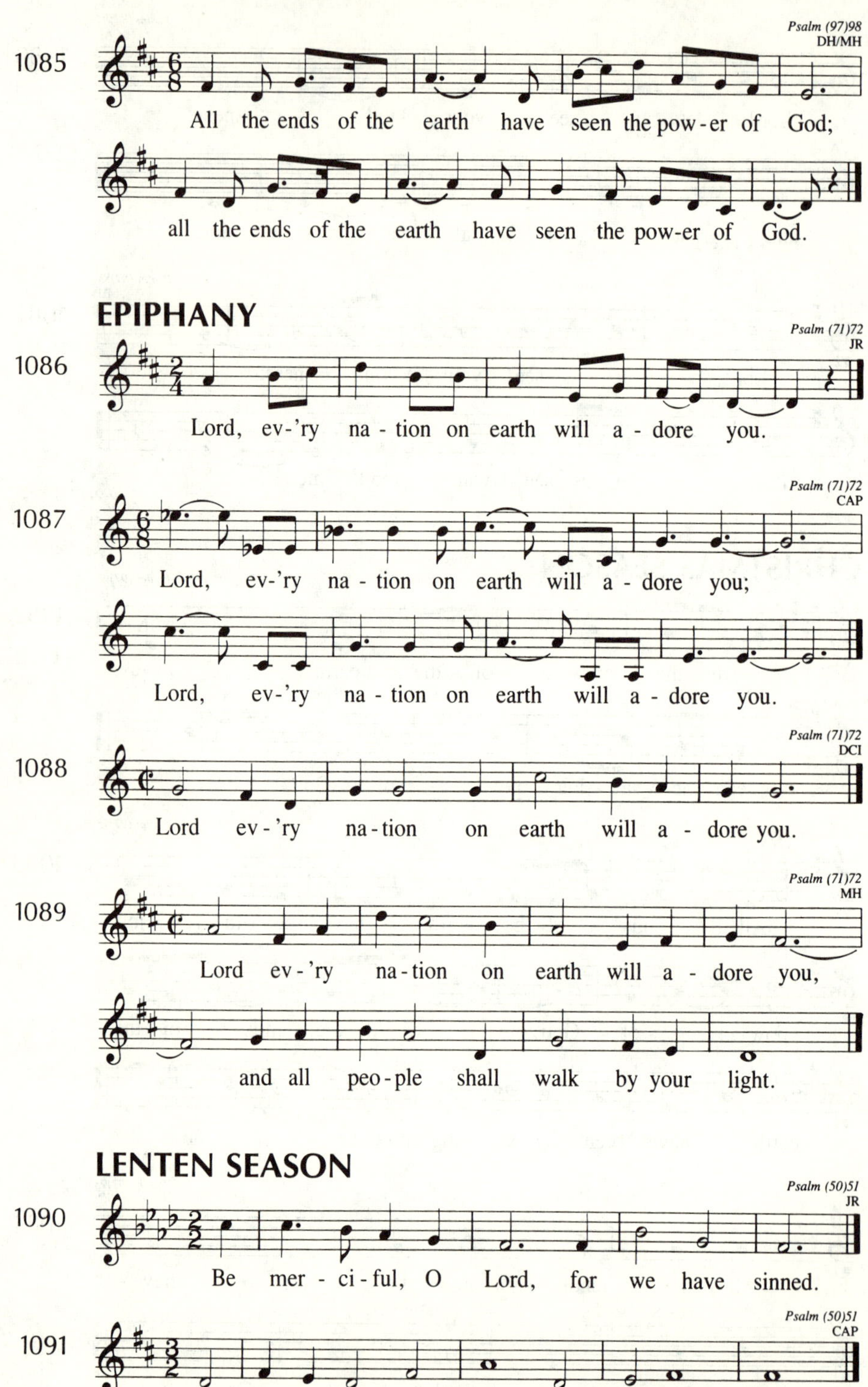
1085
Psalm (97)98
DH/MH
All the ends of the earth have seen the pow-er of God;
all the ends of the earth have seen the pow-er of God.
EPIPHANY
1086
Psalm (71)72
JR
Lord, ev-'ry na - tion on earth will a - dore you.
1087
Psalm (71)72
CAP
Lord, ev-'ry na - tion on earth will a - dore you;
Lord, ev-'ry na - tion on earth will a - dore you.
1088
Psalm (71)72
DCI
Lord ev - 'ry na - tion on earth will a - dore you.
1089
Psalm (71)72
MH
Lord ev - 'ry na - tion on earth will a - dore you,
and all peo - ple shall walk by your light.
LENTEN SEASON
1090
Psalm (50)51
JR
Be mer - ci - ful, O Lord, for we have sinned.
1091
Psalm (50)51
CAP
Be mer - ci - ful, O Lord, for we have sinned.

1092

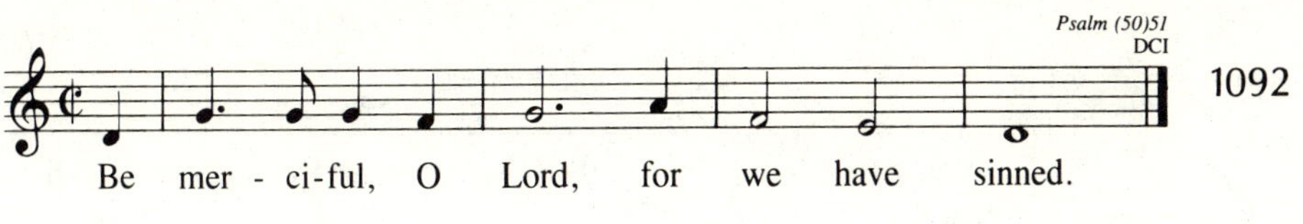
Psalm (50)51
DCI
Be mer - ci-ful, O Lord, for we have sinned.

1093

Psalm (50)51
MH
Be mer-ci - ful, O Lord, for we have sinned; be
mer-ci - ful, O Lord, for we have sinned.

1094

Psalm (90)91
CAP
Be with me, Lord, when I am in trou - ble.

1095

Psalm (90)91
MH
Be with me, Lord, when I am in
trou-ble, be with me, Lord, I pray.

1096

Psalm (129)130
CAP
With the Lord there is mer - cy,
and full - ness of re - demp - tion.

1097

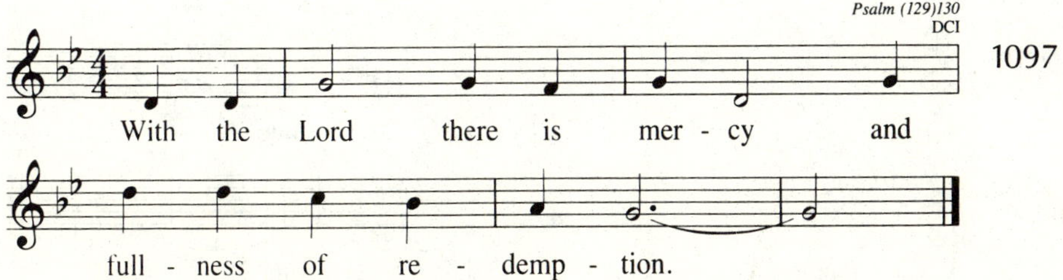
Psalm (129)130
DCI
With the Lord there is mer - cy and
full - ness of re - demp - tion.

Psalm (129)130
MH
1098
With the Lord there is mer - cy, and
full - ness of re - demp - tion.
HOLY WEEK
Psalm (21)22
JR
1099
My God, my God, why have you a - ban-doned me?
Psalm (21)22
CAP
1100
My God, my God, why have you a - ban - doned me?
Psalm (21)22
DCI
1101
My God, my God, why have you a-
ban - doned me, a - ban - doned me?
Psalm (21)22
MH
1102
My God, my God, O why have
you a - ban - doned me?
EASTER VIGIL
Psalm (135)136
JR
1103
His love is ev - er - last - ing.
Psalm (135)136
CAP
1104
His love is ev - er - last - ing, his
love is ev - er - last - ing.

Psalm (135)136
DH/MH

1105

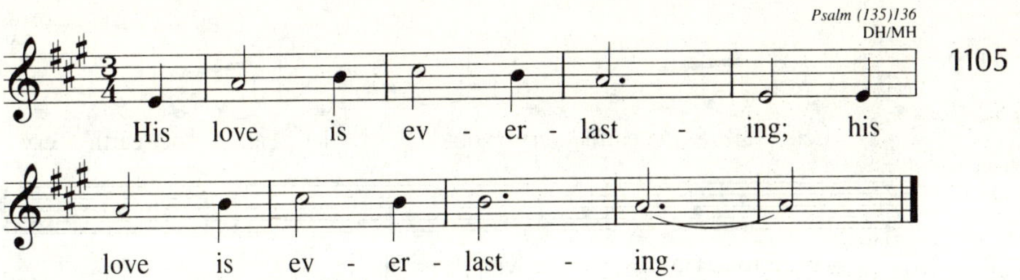
His love is ev - er - last - ing; his
love is ev - er - last - ing.

EASTER SEASON

Psalm (117)118
CAP

1106

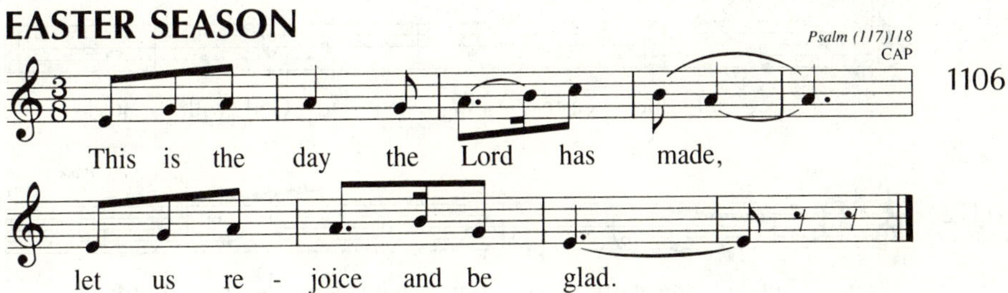
This is the day the Lord has made,
let us re - joice and be glad.

Psalm (117)118
DCI

1107

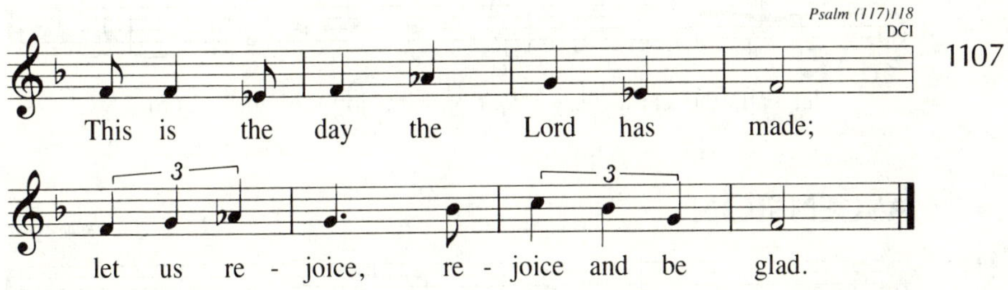
This is the day the Lord has made;
let us re - joice, re - joice and be glad.

Psalm (117)118
MH

1108

Psalm (65)66
JR

1109

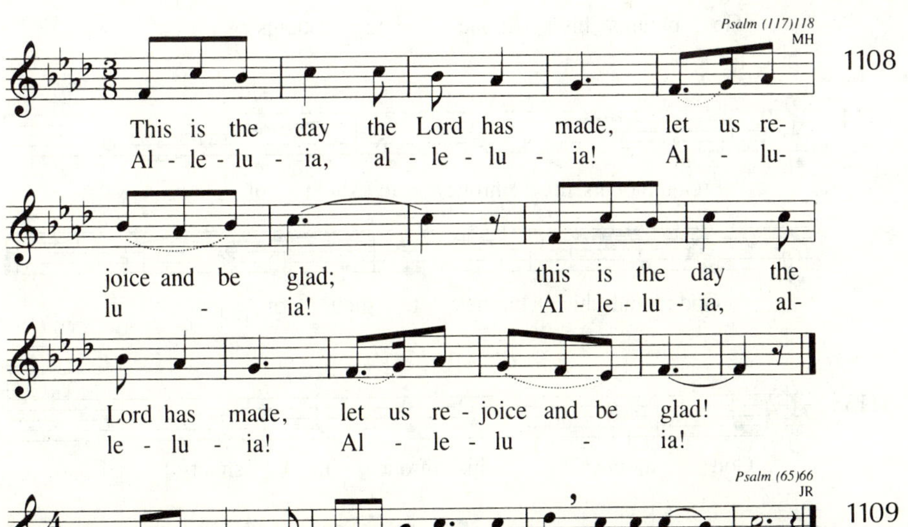
This is the day the Lord has made, let us re-
Al - le - lu - ia, al - le - lu - ia! Al - lu-
joice and be glad; this is the day the
lu - ia! Al - le - lu - ia, al-
Lord has made, let us re - joice and be glad!
le - lu - ia! Al - le - lu - ia!
Let all the earth cry out to God with joy. Al - le - lu - ia.

Psalm (65)66
CAP
1110
Let all the earth cry out, let all the earth cry out to God with joy.
Psalm (65)66
DCI
1111
Let all the earth cry out to God with joy!
Psalm (65)66
MH
1112
Let all the earth cry out with joy to the Lord; let all the earth cry out with joy to the Lord!
ASCENSION
Psalm (46)47
JR
1113
God mounts his throne to shouts of joy.
Psalm (46)47
CAP
1114
God mounts his throne to shouts of joy; God mounts his throne to shouts of joy.
Psalm (46)47
DCI
1115
God mounts his throne to shouts of joy, to shout, shout, shouts, of joy.

Psalm (46)47
MH

1116

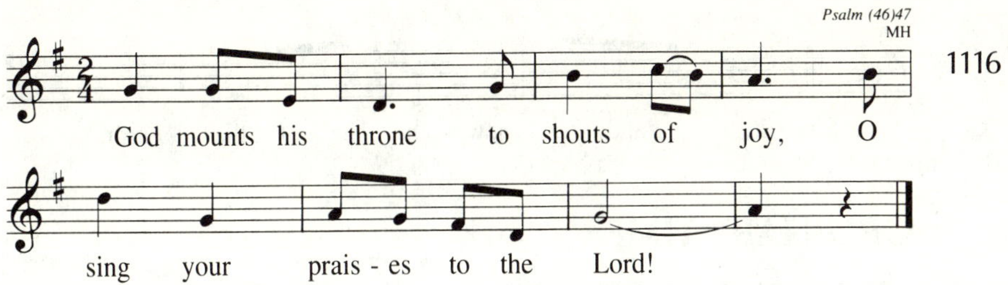
God mounts his throne to shouts of joy, O
sing your prais - es to the Lord!

PENTECOST

Psalm (103)104
JR

1117

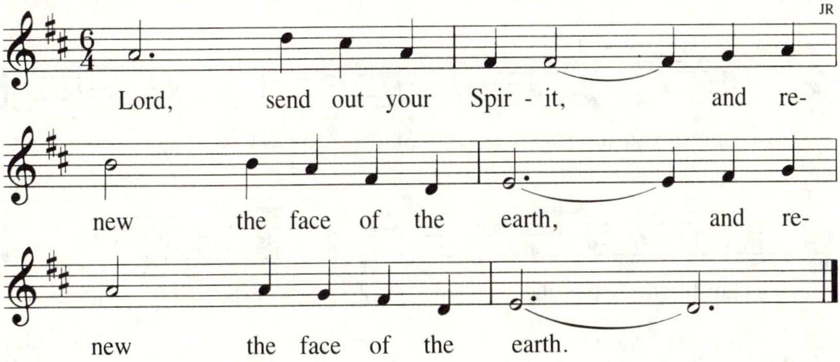

Lord, send out your Spir - it, and renew the face of the earth, and renew the face of the earth.

Psalm (103)104
CAP

1118

Lord, send out your Spir-it and re - new the face of the earth.
Lord, send out your Spir - it and re - new the face of the
earth, and re - new the face of the earth.

Psalm (103)104
DCI

1119

Lord, send out your Spir - it and re - new the face of the earth.

Psalm (103)104
DH

1120

Lord, send out your Spir - it, and renew the face of the earth; Lord, send out your

Spir - it, and re - new the face of the earth.

ORDINARY TIME

1121 *Psalm (18)19* CAP

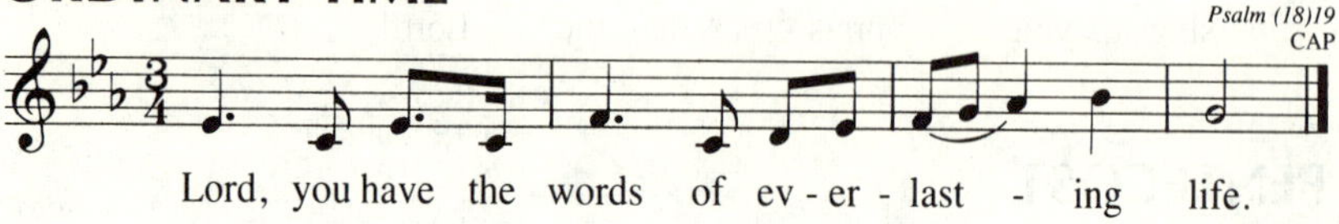

Lord, you have the words of ev - er - last - ing life.

1122 *Psalm (18)19* DCI

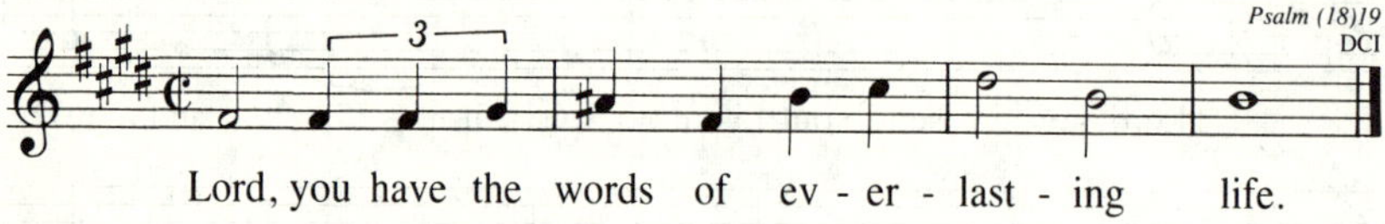

3

Lord, you have the words of ev - er - last - ing life.

1123 *Psalm (18)19* DH

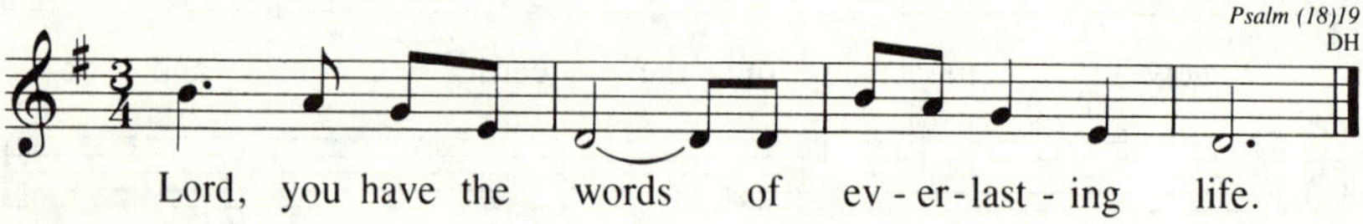

Lord, you have the words of ev - er - last - ing life.

1124 *Psalm (26)27* JR

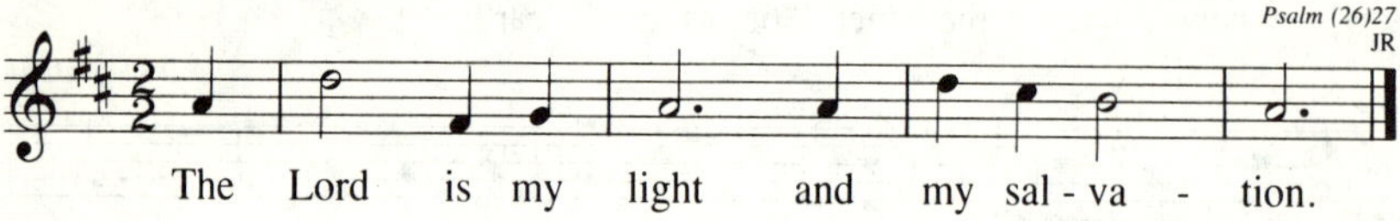

The Lord is my light and my sal - va - tion.

1125 *Psalm (26)27* CAP

The Lord is my light and my sal- va - tion.

1126 *Psalm (26)27* DH

The Lord is my light and my sal - va - tion, of whom should I be a - fraid, of whom should I be a - fraid?

1127 *Psalm (33)34* JR

I will bless the Lord, I will bless the Lord at all times.

Psalm (33)34
CAP
1128
Taste and see the good - ness of the Lord.
Psalm (33)34
DCI
1129
O taste and see the good-ness of the Lord. O
taste and see the good-ness of the Lord.
Psalm (33)34
MH
1130
Taste and see the good-ness of the Lord, the
good - ness of the Lord.
Psalm (62)63
CAP
1131
My soul is thirst-ing for you, O Lord, my God.
Psalm (62)63
MH
1132
O God, I seek you, my soul thirsts for
you, your love is fin-er than life.
Psalm (94)95
CAP
1133
If to - day you hear his voice,
hard - en not your hearts.

1134 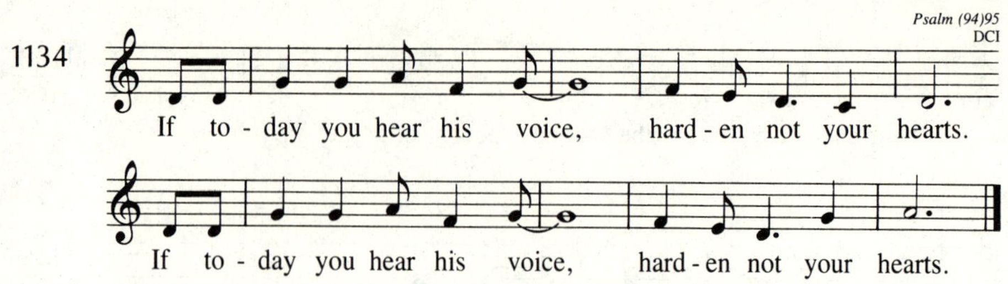
Psalm (94)95
DCI
If to - day you hear his voice, hard - en not your hearts.
If to - day you hear his voice, hard - en not your hearts.

1135 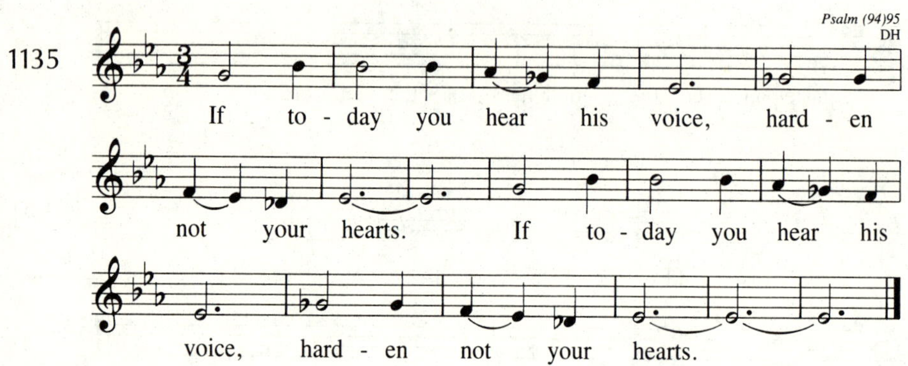
Psalm (94)95
DH
If to - day you hear his voice, hard - en
not your hearts. If to - day you hear his
voice, hard - en not your hearts.

1136 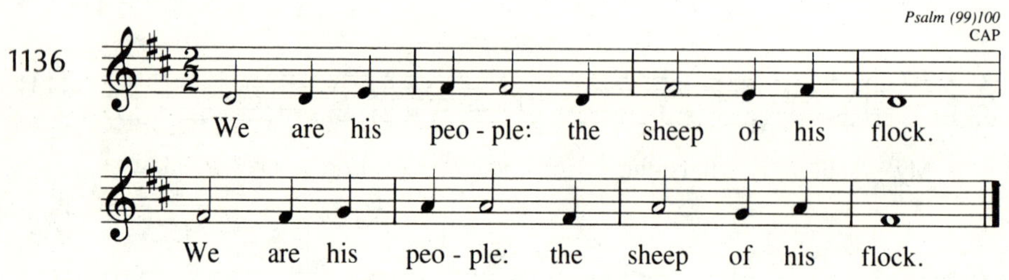
Psalm (99)100
CAP
We are his peo - ple: the sheep of his flock.
We are his peo - ple: the sheep of his flock.

1137 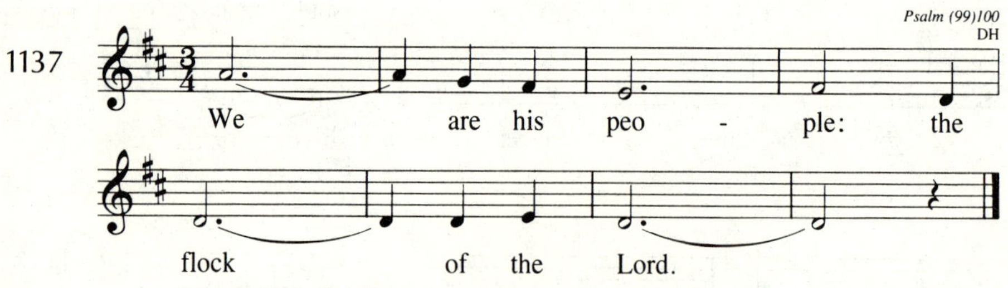
Psalm (99)100
DH
We are his peo - ple: the
flock of the Lord.

1138 
Psalm (102)103
JR
The Lord is kind and mer - ci - ful.

Psalm (102)103
CAP
1139
The Lord is kind and mer - ci - ful. The Lord is
kind and mer - ci - ful.
Psalm (102)103
DCI
1140
The Lord is kind and mer - ci - ful. The
Lord is kind and mer - ci - ful.
Psalm (102)103
MH
1141
The Lord is kind and mer - ci - ful,
the Lord is kind and mer-ci - ful.
Psalm (144)145
CAP
1142
I will praise your name for ev - er, my king and my God.
Psalm (144)145
DH
1143
I will praise your name, my king and my God.
I will praise your name, my king and my God.

LAST WEEKS IN ORDINARY TIME

Psalm (121)122
JR

1144

Let us go re - joic - ing to the house of the Lord.

1145

Psalm (121)122
CAP

Let us go re - joic - ing to the
house of the Lord. Let us go re-
joic - ing to the house of the Lord.

1146

Psalm (121)122
DCI

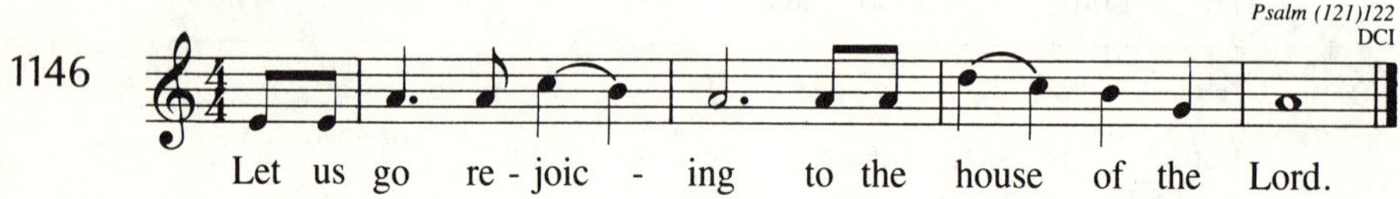
Let us go re - joic - ing to the house of the Lord.

1147

Psalm (121)122
MH

Come, let us go re - joic - ing to the
house of the Lord; Come, let us go re-
joic - ing to the house of the Lord.

MISCELLANEOUS

1148

Psalm (22)23
DCI

I shall live in the house of the
Lord all the days of my life.

1149

Psalm (22)23
DCI

The Lord is my shep-herd; there is noth-ing I shall want.

1150

Psalm (30)31
MH
Fa - ther, I put my life in your hands.

1151

Psalm (115)116
MH
Our bless - ing cup is a com - mun - ion with the
blood of the Lord.

Prayers of the Individual and Household

1152 This book contains the texts and music which are used when the church assembles for the liturgy. With these pages members of the assembly may join fully in the Sunday eucharist, the liturgy of the hours, the celebration of the sacraments. All of these liturgies are, in fact, the work of the assembly, the work of Christians who gather to do those deeds–in word, in song, in gesture–which are the foundation and the strength of our lives. Over the years, the book itself becomes less and less necessary for we gradually learn many things by heart, making these words and tunes fully our own.

The texts in this section are not those of the assembly but those of the individual or household. They are included here because the daily prayer of Christians, prayers alone or in small groups, are part of our tradition, part of what we need for the daily expression of our faith. Many of the texts which follow have been the strength and sustenance of those who have walked the way of Jesus. Some of these prayers we already know by heart. Others will be learned with repetition. That is the intention, for most of these prayers are not meant to be read. They are words to be in the heart and on the lips at various times: by morning, by night, at table. Others are for special circumstances: when someone is ill, at the time of death, at times of thanksgiving.

Some of the prayers found in the liturgy itself are included or suggested here. When these become the regular prayer of an individual, the liturgy itself is the source of the Christian's spirit and life. This happens also when the scriptures read in the Sunday assembly are read and pondered again through the week. It happens when the verses of the psalm sung on Sunday become part of morning and evening prayer all week long. Such habits mean that we begin to come to the Sunday liturgy not as spectators but as celebrants, as the ones responsible for the liturgy.

The task of these prayers is to be with us day by day, over the years, to shape our lives. The prayers known by heart are a daily remembering and affirming of what became of us by baptism. Such prayers, coming day after day, in season and out, whatever the mood and circumstances, have us pray as the church. The individual becomes the voice of creation's praise, becomes the lament of the oppressed and suffering, becomes the whole world's giving of thanks.

MORNING PRAYERS

THE SIGN OF THE CROSS 1153

This prayer is not the words but the sign itself. The cross is made on the whole upper part of the body, or simply on the forehead, or the lips, or the heart. By this gesture the Christian renews that baptism which plunged us into the death of the Lord so that we live now in Christ. The common words of the sign of the cross recall our baptism.

In the name of the Father,
and of the Son,
and of the Holy Spirit.

Or, when signing the lips:

Lord, open my lips and my mouth will proclaim your praise.

GLORY TO GOD 1154

The strongest note of morning prayer is the praise of God who has kept us through the night and given us this new day. There are two common forms of the Gloria.

Glory to the Father, and to the Son, and to the Holy Spirit:
as it was in the beginning, is now, and will be forever. Amen.

Or:

Glory to God in the highest,
  and peace to his people on earth.

Lord God, heavenly King,
almighty God and Father,
  we worship you, we give you thanks,
  we praise you for your glory.

Lord Jesus Christ, only Son of the Father,
Lord God, Lamb of God,
you take away the sin of the world:
have mercy on us;
you are seated at the right hand of the Father:
  receive our prayer.

For you alone are the Holy One,
you alone are the Lord,
you alone are the Most High,
  Jesus Christ,
  with the Holy Spirit,
  in the glory of God the Father. Amen.

1155 **THE LORD'S PRAYER**

This prayer is used by many to mark not only the morning but several times of the day. The first translation is the one to which most Catholics are accustomed, the second is a translation used more and more by Christians of many churches.

Our Father, who art in heaven,
hallowed be thy name.
Thy kingdom come.
Thy will be done on earth
as it is in heaven.
Give us this day our daily bread,
and forgive us our trespasses
as we forgive those who trespass against us;
and lead us not into temptation
but deliver us from evil. Amen.

Or:

1156 Our Father in heaven,
hallowed be your Name,
your kingdom come,
your will be done,
on earth as in heaven.
Give us today our daily bread.
Forgive us our sins
as we forgive those who sin against us.
Save us from the time of trial
and deliver us from evil.
For the kingdom, the power
and the glory are yours,
now and for ever. Amen.

1157 **ANCIENT PRAYERS FOR MORNING**

The first of these is the beginning of the "Hear, O Israel" prayer; this is the cornerstone of Jewish prayer and would have been the daily prayer of Jesus, his family and his disciples. The blessings which follow accompany some of the actions of early morning. The final text is from Psalm 95, long used at morning prayer.

Hear, O Israel: the Lord is our God, the Lord is One!
Blessed is his glorious kingdom for ever and ever!

Blessed are you, Lord our God, ruler of the universe,
opening the eyes of the blind.

Blessed are you, Lord our God, ruler of the universe,
clothing the naked.

Blessed are you, Lord our God, ruler of the universe,
setting captives free.

Blessed are you, Lord our God, ruler of the universe,
guiding our footsteps.

Blessed are you, Lord our God, ruler of the universe,
taking the sleep from my eyes and the slumber from my eyelids.

Come, let us sing to the Lord; 1158
and shout with joy to the Rock who saves us.
Let us approach him with praise and thanksgiving
and sing joyful songs to the Lord.

Come, then, let us bow down and worship,
bending the knee before the Lord, our maker.
For he is our God and we are his people,
the flock he shepherds.

MORNING PSALMS 1159

In addition to Psalm 95, above, the psalms of morning are the psalms of praise, especially Psalms 148, 149 and 150 (nos. 79, 80 and 81). Other morning prayers are Psalm 51 (no. 41) and Psalm 63 (no.42).

MORNING HYMNS 1160

Morning hymns will be found at nos. 4, and 671 through 675.

THE BENEDICTUS 1161

The Benedictus or Song of Zachary from Luke 1:68-79 is a morning prayer for the day when God's compassion like "the dawn from on high shall break upon us, to shine on those who dwell in darkness and the shadow of death, and to guide our feet into the way of peace." It is found at no. 89, with a metrical setting at no. 6.

MORNING PRAYER OF SAINT PATRICK 1162

The Lorica *or "Breastplate" is an ancient Celtic prayer attributed to Saint Patrick. A metrical setting is found at no. 671.*

I arise today
through the strength of heaven,
light of the sun,
radiance of the moon,
splendor of fire,
speed of lightning,
swiftness of the wind,
depth of the sea,
stability of the earth,
firmness of the rock.

I arise today
through God's strength to pilot me,
God's might to uphold me,
God's wisdom to guide me,
God's eye to look before me,
God's ear to hear me,
God's word to speak for me,
God's hand to guard me,
God's way to lie before me,
God's shield to protect me,
God's hosts to save me
from the snares of the devil,

from everyone who desires me ill,
afar and near,
alone or in a multitude.
Christ with me, Christ before me, Christ behind me,
Christ in me, Christ beneath me, Christ above me,
Christ on my right, Christ on my left,
Christ when I lie down, Christ when I sit down, Christ when I arise,
Christ in the heart of everyone who thinks of me,
Christ in mouth of everyone who speaks of me,
Christ in the eye that sees me,
Christ in the ear that hears me.

DAYTIME PRAYERS

1163 **THE JESUS PRAYER**

This is one of the most widely used of those prayers which are meant to be repeated over and over again so that the one praying becomes completely caught up in prayer. Often prayers like this one are intended to be in rhythm with one's breathing.

Lord Jesus Christ,
Son of the living God,
have mercy on me, a sinner.

1164 **THE ROSARY**

The rosary is another prayer which in its repetition draws us into contemplation of the mysteries of our salvation. The rosary begins with the Apostle's Creed (no. 239) and consists of groups of ten Hail Marys, each group preceded by the Lord's Prayer and followed by the Glory to the Father. Each decade has traditionally been given to pondering one aspect of the paschal mystery:

The Joyful Mysteries

1. The Annunciation (Luke 1:30-33)
2. The Visitation (Luke 1:50-53)
3. The Nativity (Luke 2:10-11)
4. The Presentantion (Luke 2:29-32)
5. The Finding of Jesus in the Temple (Luke 2:48-52)

The Sorrowful Mysteries

1. The Agony in the Garden (Matthew 26:38-39)
2. The Scourging (John 19:1)
3. The Crowning with Thorns (Mark 15:16-17)
4. Jesus Carries His Cross (John 19:17)
5. The Crucifixion (John 19:28-30)

The Glorious Mysteries

1. The Resurrection (Mark 16:6-8)
2. The Ascension (Acts 1:10-11)
3. The Coming of the Holy Spirit (Acts 2:1-4)
4. The Assumption (Song of Songs 2:3-6)
5. The Coronation of Mary (Luke 1:51-54)

The prayer which makes up the rosary is the Hail Mary. Its words are drawn from the scriptures and the intercession of the church.

Hail Mary, full of grace, 1165
the Lord is with you!
Blessed are you among women
and blessed is the fruit of your womb, Jesus.
Holy Mary, mother of God,
pray for us sinners,
now and at the hour of our death. Amen.

THE ANGELUS 1166

This is the prayer prayed in early morning, at noon, and at the end of the work day. Through this constant presence in the midst of everyday, the Christian proclaims that all of our time and all of our human space is transformed by the incarnation, the presence of God with us.

The angel spoke God's message to Mary
and she conceived of the Holy Spirit.
Hail Mary...

"I am the lowly servant of the Lord:
let it be done to me according to your word."
Hail Mary...

And the Word became flesh
and lived among us.
Hail Mary...

Pray for us, holy Mother of God,
that we may become worthy of the promises of Christ.

Lord,
fill our hearts with your grace:
once, through the message of an angel
you revealed to us the incarnation of your Son:
now, through his suffering and death
lead us to the glory of his resurrection.

DIVINE PRAISES 1167

These prayers may be used together, or each short line can be repeated over and over (as with the Jesus Prayer).

Blessed be God.
Blessed be his holy name.
Blessed be Jesus Christ, true God and true man.
Blessed be the name of Jesus.
Blessed be his most sacred heart.
Blessed be his most precious blood.
Blessed be Jesus in the most holy sacrament of the altar.
Blessed be the Holy Spirit, the Paraclete.
Blessed be the great mother of God, Mary most holy.
Blessed be her holy and immaculate conception.
Blessed be her glorious assumption.

Blessed be the name of Mary, virgin and mother.
Blessed be Joseph, her most chaste spouse.
Blessed be God in his angels and in his saints.

EVENING PRAYERS

1168 **PRAISE OF GOD FOR CHRIST, OUR LIGHT**

The prayer as day ends has often begun with a verse or hymn in praise of God who has given us in Christ our true light. The ancient hymn Phos Hilaron, *"O Radiant Light," is a beautiful expression of this (nos. 12 and 679). This praise is also contained in the simple invocation:*

Jesus Christ is the light of the world,
a light no darkness can overpower.

1169 **EVENING PSALMS**

Psalm 141 prays:

Let my prayer arise before you like incense,
the raising of my hands like an evening oblation.

This is the primary psalm of evening prayer (no. 74) as it prays for God's protection. Other appropriate psalms of the evening are Psalm 23 (no. 32), Psalm 121 (no. 66) and Psalm 123 (no. 68).

1170 **EVENING HYMNS**

Evening hymns will be found at nos. 676 through 681.

1171 **INTERCESSIONS**

At baptism the Christian receives the responsibility to intercede at all times, to be the voice of all creation and of all people before God. Each day we bring the needs and sufferings of our world. Such prayers are often made in the evening: our work is finished and we place all the world in God's care. The following prayers show how broad is the church's intercession. They may serve as an example for an individual's prayer.

For peace from on high and for our salvation, let us pray to the Lord. Lord, hear our prayer.
For the welfare of all churches and for the unity of the human family, let us pray...
For (name), our pope, (name), our bishop, and (name), our pastor, and for all ministers of the gospel, let us pray...
For nations and governments and for all who serve them, let us pray...
For this city and for every city and community and for all who live in them, let us pray...
For the good earth which God has given us and for the wisdom and will to conserve it, let us pray...
For the safety of travelers, the recovery of the sick, the care of the destitute and the release of prisoners, let us pray...
For an angel of peace to guide and protect us, let us pray...
For a peaceful evening and a night free from sin, let us pray...

THE MAGNIFICAT 1172

The Song of Mary from Luke 1:46-55 has long been a part of evening prayer of Christians. It is strong in its praise and in its vision of justice brought by God. It is found at nos. 87 and 88, with metrical versions at nos. 15 and 534.

NIGHT PRAYERS

CONFESSION 1173

Before sleep, the Christian recalls with sorrow the failures of the day and gives thanks to God for the love which surrounds us. Another prayer, The Act of Contrition, is found at no. 1194.

I confess to almighty God,
and to you, my brothers and sisters,
that I have sinned through my own fault
in my thoughts and in my words,
in what I have done,
and in what I have failed to do;
and I ask blessed Mary, ever virgin,
all the angels and saints,
and you, my brothers and sisters,
to pray for me to the Lord our God.

SHORT PRAYERS 1174

May the almighty Lord give us a restful night
and a peaceful death.

Keep us, Lord, as the apple of your eye
and shelter us in the shadow of you wing.

Protect us, Lord, as we stay awake;
watch over us as we sleep,
that awake, we may keep watch with Christ,
and asleep, rest in his peace.

Into your hands, Lord, I commend my spirit.
O Lord our God, make us lie down in peace
and raise us up to life.

Visit this house,
we beg you, Lord,
and banish from it
the deadly power of the evil one.
May your holy angels dwell here
to keep us in peace,
and may your blessing be always upon us.

Hear us, Lord,
and send your angel from heaven
to visit and protect,
to comfort and defend
all who live in this house.

1175 **NIGHT PSALMS**

The traditional psalms of night are Psalm 4 (no. 25), Psalm 91 (no. 49) and Psalm 134 (no. 72).

1176 **NIGHT HYMNS**

Night hymns are found at nos. 20 and 676 through 681.

1177 **CANTICLE OF SIMEON**

The words spoken by Simeon in the Temple (Luke 2:29-32) are often used as a night prayer for the church. It is found at nos. 22 and 90, with metrical versions at nos. 676 and 691.

1178 **ANTHEMS OF MARY**

The last prayer of night is addressed to our mother. The Salve Regina *(no. 703) is used throughtout the year; during Eastertime it is replaced by the* Regina Caeli *(no. 443). Another appropriate prayer is the* Memorare.

Remember, most loving virgin Mary,
never was it heard
that anyone who turned to you for help
was left unaided.
Inspired by this confidence,
though burdened by my sins,
I run to your protection
for you are my mother.
Mother of the Word of God,
do not despise my words of pleading
but be merciful and hear my prayer.

MEAL PRAYERS

At table we learn to give God thanks and praise for all the fruit of the earth and work of human hands.

1179 **BEFORE MEALS**

Bless us, O Lord, and these thy gifts
which we are about to receive
from thy bounty;
through Christ our Lord. Amen.

Or:

The eyes of all hope in you, Lord,
and you give them food in due season.
You open your hand,
and every creature is filled with your blessing.

Or:

Blessed are you, Lord our God, ruler of the universe,
for you bring forth bread from the earth.

AFTER MEALS 1180

We give you thanks
for all your gifts,
almighty God,
living and reigning
now and for ever.

Or:

Blessed be the Lord
of whose bounty we have received
and by whose goodness we live.

SUNDAY PRAYERS 1181

Sunday is called by Christians "The Lord's Day." On this day Christians assemble, listen to the scriptures, gather at the holy table and share in communion. Sunday is the highest day in our calendar. It is appropriate to prepare for the eucharistic assembly by reading and reflecting on the Sunday's scriptures. Week by week these scriptures are read at the liturgy as a foundation for all our worship and all our lives. In the eucharistic prayer and the holy communion, we "proclaim the death of the Lord until he comes" (1 Corinthians 11:26). Thus each Sunday we gather as the church "to praise and thank God, to remember and make present God's great deeds, to offer common prayer, to realize and celebrate the kingdom of peace and justice" (United States Bishops' Committee on the Liturgy, Environment and Art in Catholic Worship*). Some traditional prayers of preparation for Mass and thanksgiving after Mass are found below. Among the hymns which are especially appropriate for Sunday are nos. 661 through 663. The eucharistic hymns of Thomas Aquinas are fitting prayers both before and after communion: nos. 489, 758, 759 and 813. Among the psalms which have been used as communion prayers are Psalm 23 (no. 32), Psalm 34 (no. 36) and Psalm 147 (no. 78).*

HOW HOLY THIS FEAST 1182

How holy this feast
in which Christ is our food:
his passion is recalled,
grace fills our hearts,
and we receive a pledge of the glory to come.

You gave them bread from heaven to be their food.
And this bread contained all goodness.

Lord Jesus Christ,
you gave us the eucharist
as the memorial of your suffering and death.
May our worship of this sacrament of your body and blood
help us to experience the salvation you won for us
and the peace of the kingdom
where you live with the Father and the Holy Spirit,
one God, for ever and ever. Amen.

1183 **ANIMA CHRISTI**

Soul of Christ, sanctify me.
Body of Christ, heal me.
Blood of Christ, drench me.
Water from the side of Christ, wash me.
Passion of Christ, strengthen me.
Good Jesus, hear me.
In your wounds shelter me.
From turning away keep me.
From the evil one protect me.
At the hour of my death call me.
Into your presence lead me,
to praise you with all your saints
for ever and ever. Amen.

1184 **PRAYER TO THE VIRGIN MARY**

Mary, holy virgin mother,
I have received your Son, Jesus Christ.
With love you became his mother,
gave birth to him, nursed him,
and helped him grow to manhood.
With love I return him to you,
to hold once more,
to love with all your heart,
and to offer him to the Holy Trinity
as our supreme act of worship
for your honor and for the good
of all your children.
Mother, ask God to forgive my sins
and to help me serve him more faithfully.
Keep me true to Christ until death,
and let me come to praise him with you
for ever and ever. Amen.

1185 PRAYER FOR FRIDAYS

In their 1983 letter, The Challenge of Peace, *the bishops of the United States called on Catholics to join them in fasting, prayer and charity on Fridays: "As a tangible sign of our need and desire to do penance we, for the cause of peace, commit ourselves to fast and abstinence on each Friday of the year... Every Friday should be a day significantly devoted to prayer, penance, and almsgiving for peace."*

All praise be yours, God our Creator,
as we wait in joyful hope
for the flowering of justice and the fullness of peace.
All praise for this day, this Friday.
By our weekly fasting and prayer
cast out the spirit of war, of fear and mistrust,
and make us grow hungry for human kindness,
thirsty for solidarity

with all the people of your dear earth.
May all our prayer, our fasting and our deeds
be done in the name of Jesus. Amen.

TIMES OF NEED

There are many scriptures, hymns and psalms in this book which give voice to our prayers for our own needs, for the needs of others and of the world. A familiarity with the psalms especially will lead the Christian to many prayers in troubled times.

IN TIMES OF SICKNESS 1186

All-powerful and ever-living God,
the lasting health of all who believe in you,
hear us as we ask your loving help for the sick;
restore their health,
that they may again offer joyful thanks in your Church.

Or:

God of love,
ever caring,
ever strong,
stand by us in our time of need.
Watch over your child who is sick,
Look after him/her in every danger,
and grant him/her your healing and peace.

IN TIME OF SUFFERING 1187

Lord Jesus Christ, by your patience in suffering you hallowed earthly pain
and gave us the example of obedience to your Father's will:
Be near me in my time of weakness and pain;
sustain me by your grace, that my strength and courage may not fail;
heal me, if it be your will;
and help me always to believe that what happens to me here
is of little account if you hold me in eternal life,
my Lord and my God.

WHEN DEATH IS NEAR 1188

Go forth, Christian soul, from this world
in the name of God the almighty Father, who created you,
in the name of Jesus Christ, Son of the living God, who suffered for you,
in the name of the Holy Spirit, who has poured out upon you,
go forth, faithful Christian.
May you live in peace this day,
may your home be with God in Zion,
with Mary, the virgin mother of God,
with Joseph, and all the angels and saints.

Or:

Saints of God, come to his/her aid!
Come to meet him/her, angels of the Lord!

1189 **WHEN SOMEONE HAS DIED**

Eternal rest grant to him/her/them, O Lord,
and let perpetual light shine upon him/her/them.

Or:

Loving and merciful God,
we entrust our brother/sister to your mercy.
You loved him/her greatly in this life:
now that he/she is freed from all its cares,
give him/her happiness and peace for ever.
The old order has passed away;
welcome him/her now into paradise
where there will be no more sorrow,
no more weeping or pain,
but only peace and joy
with Jesus, your Son,
and the Holy Spirit
for ever and ever. Amen.

Or:

1190 God of all consolation,
in your unending love and mercy for us
you turn the darkness of death
into the dawn of new life.
Show compassion to your people in their sorrow.
Be our refuge and our strength
to lift us from the darkness of this grief
to the peace and light of your presence.
Your Son, our Lord Jesus Christ,
by dying for us, conquered death
and by rising again, restored life.
May we then go forward eagerly to meet him,
and after our life on earth
be reunited with our brothers and sisters
where every tear will be wiped away.
We ask this through Christ our Lord. Amen.

1191 **PSALMS IN TIME OF NEED**

Among the psalms which are prayed in times of sickness and sorrow are the following: Psalm 6 (no. 26), Psalm 25 (no. 33), Psalm 42 (no. 37), Psalm 63 (no. 42) and Psalm 103 (no. 55).

1192 **PRAYER TO MARY**

We turn to you for protection,
holy Mother of God.
Listen to our prayers
and help us in our needs.
Save us from every danger,
glorious and blessed Virgin.

PRAYER FOR PEACE 1193

Lord, make me an instrument of your peace:
where there is hatred, let me sow love;
where there is injury, pardon;
where there is doubt, faith;
where there is despair, hope;
where there is darkness, light;
where there is sadness, joy.
O divine Master, grant that I may not so much seek
to be consoled as to console,
to be understood as to understand,
to be loved as to love.
For it is in giving that we receive,
it is in pardoning that we are pardoned,
it is in dying that we are born to eternal life.

PENANCE AND RECONCILIATION 1194

The rite of reconciliation for several penitents is at no. 125. When a person alone comes to celebrate the sacrament with a priest, the priest greets the penitent. Then the penitent makes the sign of the cross and the priest invites the penitent to have trust in God. A reading from scripture follows. After this, the penitent may say a prayer of confession (for example, "I confess to almighty God" no. 1173). The penitent then makes a confession of sin and receives counsel from the priest. The penitent may then recite one of the following prayers or use some other way to express sorrow.

My God,
I am sorry for my sins with all my heart.
In choosing to do wrong
and failing to do good,
I have sinned against you
whom I should love above all things.
I firmly intend, with your help,
to do penance,
to sin no more,
and to avoid whatever leads me to sin.

Or:

Our Savior Jesus Christ
suffered and died for us.
In his name, my God, have mercy.

Or:

Lord Jesus, Son of God,
have mercy on me, a sinner.

The priest then extends hands over the penitent's head and speaks the absolution. The priest may then say: "Give thanks to the Lord, for he is good" and the penitent responds: "His mercy endures for ever." Then the priest dismisses the penitent in peace.

1195 **VARIOUS PRAYERS OF PENANCE AND RECONCILIATION**

Lord,
turn to us in mercy,
and forgive all our sins
that we may serve you in true freedom.

1196 Father of mercies
and God of consolation,
you do not wish the sinner to die
but to be converted and live.
Come to the aid of your people,
that they may turn from their sins
and live for you alone.
May we be attentive to your word,
confess our sins, receive your forgiveness,
and be always grateful for your loving kindness.
Help us to live the truth in love
and grow into the fullness of Christ, your Son,
who lives and reigns for ever and ever. Amen.

1197 Father, all-powerful and ever-living God,
we do well always and everywhere to give you thanks.
When you punish us, you show your justice;
when you pardon us, you show your kindness;
yet always your mercy enfolds us.
When you chastise us, you do not wish to condemn us;
when you spare us, you give us time to amend for ours sins
through Christ our Lord. Amen.

1198 God and Father of us all,
you have forgiven our sins
and sent us your peace.
Help us to forgive each other
and to work together to establish peace in the world.

1199 **PSALMS OF PENANCE AND RECONCILIATION**

Among the psalms which speak of sin, of sorrow and of forgiveness are the following: Psalm 51 (no. 41), Psalm 90 (no. 48), Psalm 123 (no. 68), Psalm 130 (no. 71) and Psalm 139 (no. 73).

VARIOUS PRAYERS

1200 **COME, HOLY SPIRIT**

Come, Holy Spirit, fill the hearts of your faithful,
and kindle in them the fire of your love.
Send forth your Spirit and they shall be created,
and you will renew the face of the earth.

Lord, by the light of the Holy Spirit
you have taught the hearts of your faithful.
In the same Spirit
help us to relish what is right
and always rejoice in your consolation.

LITANY OF THE HOLY NAME 1201

Lord, have mercy	Lord, have mercy
Christ, have mercy	Christ, have mercy
Lord, have mercy	Lord, have mercy
God our Father in heaven	have mercy on us
God the Son, Redeemer of the world	have mercy on us
God the Holy Spirit	have mercy on us
Holy Trinity, one God	have mercy on us
Jesus, Son of the living God	have mercy on us
Jesus, splendor of the Father	have mercy on us
Jesus, brightness of the everlasting light	have mercy on us
Jesus, king of glory	have mercy on us
Jesus, dawn of justice	have mercy on us
Jesus, Son of the Virgin Mary	have mercy on us
Jesus, worthy of our love	have mercy on us
Jesus, mighty God	have mercy on us
Jesus, father of the world to come	have mercy on us
Jesus, prince of peace	have mercy on us
Jesus, all-powerful	have mercy on us
Jesus, pattern of patience	have mercy on us
Jesus, model of obedience	have mercy on us
Jesus, gentle and humble of heart	have mercy on us
Jesus, lover of chastity	have mercy on us
Jesus, lover of us all	have mercy on us
Jesus, God of peace	have mercy on us
Jesus, author of life	have mercy on us
Jesus, model of goodness	have mercy on us
Jesus, seeker of souls	have mercy on us
Jesus, our God	have mercy on us
Jesus, our refuge	have mercy on us
Jesus, father of the poor	have mercy on us
Jesus, treasure of the faithful	have mercy on us
Jesus, Good Shepherd	have mercy on us
Jesus, the true light	have mercy on us
Jesus, eternal wisdom	have mercy on us
Jesus, infinite goodness	have mercy on us
Jesus, our way and our life	have mercy on us
Jesus, joy of angels	have mercy on us
Jesus, king of patriarchs	have mercy on us
Jesus, teacher of apostles	have mercy on us
Jesus, master of evangelists	have mercy on us
Jesus, courage of martyrs	have mercy on us
Jesus, light of confessors	have mercy on us
Jesus, purity of virgins	have mercy on us
Jesus, crown of saints	have mercy on us
Lord, be merciful	Jesus, save your people
From all evil	Jesus, save your people
From every sin	Jesus, save your people

From the snares of the devil | Jesus, save your people
From your anger | Jesus, save your people
From the spirit of infidelity | Jesus, save your people
From everlasting death | Jesus, save your people
From the neglect of your Holy Spirit | Jesus, save your people

By the mystery of your incarnation | Jesus, save your people
By your birth | Jesus, save your people
By your childhood | Jesus, save your people
By your hidden life | Jesus, save your people
By your public ministry | Jesus, save your people
By your agony and crucifixion | Jesus, save your people
By your abandonment | Jesus, save your people
By your grief and sorrow | Jesus, save your people
By your death and burial | Jesus, save your people
By your rising to new life | Jesus, save your people
By your return to the Father | Jesus, save your people
By your gift of the holy eucharist | Jesus, save your people
By your joy and glory | Jesus, save your people

1202 **LITANY OF LORETTO**

Lord, have mercy | Lord, have mercy
Christ, have mercy | Christ, have mercy
Lord, have mercy | Lord, have mercy

God our Father in heaven | have mercy on us
God the Son, Redeemer of the world | have mercy on us*
God the Holy Spirit | have mercy on us
Holy Trinity, one God | have mercy on us

Holy Mary | pray for us
Holy Mother of God | pray for us
Most honored of virgins | pray for us
Mother of Christ | pray for us
Mother of the Church | pray for us
Mother of divine grace | pray for us
Mother most pure | pray for us
Mother of chaste love | pray for us
Mother and virgin | pray for us
Sinless Mother | pray for us
Dearest of Mothers | pray for us
Model of motherhood | pray for us
Mother of good counsel | pray for us
Mother of our Creator | pray for us
Mother of our Savior | pray for us
Virgin most wise | pray for us
Virgin rightly praised | pray for us
Virgin rightly renowned | pray for us
Virgin most powerful | pray for us
Virgin gentle in mercy | pray for us
Faithful Virgin | pray for us

Mirror of justice	pray for us
Throne of wisdom	pray for us
Cause of our joy	pray for us
Shrine of the Spirit	pray for us
Glory of Israel	pray for us
Vessel of selfless devotion	pray for us
Mystical Rose	pray for us
Tower of David	pray for us
Tower of ivory	pray for us
House of gold	pray for us
Ark of the covenant	pray for us
Gate of heaven	pray for us
Morning star	pray for us
Health of the sick	pray for us
Refuge of sinners	pray for us
Comfort of the troubled	pray for us
Help of Christians	pray for us
Queen of angels	pray for us
Queen of patriarchs and prophets	pray for us
Queen of apostles and martyrs	pray for us
Queen of confessors and virgins	pray for us
Queen of all saints	pray for us
Queen conceived without sin	pray for us
Queen assumed into heaven	pray for us
Queen of the rosary	pray for us
Queen of peace	pray for us

1203 Acknowledgements

The publisher gratefully acknowledges the following holders of copyright whose permission has been granted for the inclusion of material in this book. Every effort has been made to determine the ownership of all tunes, texts and harmonizations used in this edition and to make proper arrangements for their use. The publisher regrets any error or oversight which may have occurred and will readily make proper acknowledgement in future editions if such omission is made known. Acknowledgements are stated in accordance with the requirements of the individual copyright holder.

PSALM TONES

The Gelineau Psalm Tones are © 1963, The Grail, England, GIA Publications, Inc., agent. The ownership of the remaining psalm tones is as follows (each tone is only listed the first time it appears): Laurence Bevenot, nos. 28, 34, 43, 60 and 66, ©, Ampleforth Abbey Trustees. The Chrysogonus Waddell, OCSO, tone, no. 29, © Gethsemani Abbey. The tones from *Lutheran Worship,* nos. 26 and 87, © 1982, Concordia Publishing House. The tones by A. Gregory Murray, OSB, nos. 25, 35, 797 and 881, © L.J. Carey and Co. Ltd. (Ascherberg, Hopwood & Crew, Ltd.). The tones by Robert Kreutz, no. 76, and Douglas Mews, no. 37, © International Committee on English in the Liturgy, Inc. The tone at no. 24, © 1979, Robert Knox Kennedy. The tone at no. 40, © 1973, David Hurd. All remaining psalm tones are the copyright of GIA Publications, Inc.

SERVICE MUSIC AND HYMNS

Other than the psalm tones, all music found from nos. 1 to 354, and nos. 765 to 1151, is copyright by GIA Publications, Inc., with the exception of those items specified below.

2 Text: © 1969, James Quinn, SJ. By permission of Geoffrey Chapman, a division of Cassell Ltd. Music: © 1980, GIA Publications, Inc.

4 Text: © Oxford University Press

6 Text: © 1969, James Quinn, SJ. By permission of Geoffrey Chapman, a division of Cassell Ltd.

12 Text: © William G. Storey

92 Music: © 1979, ICEL

112 Music: © 1977, ICEL

176 © 1970, 1977, ICEL

177 Text: © 1985, ICEL

276 Music from *1972 Communion Service* © 1972, Oxford University Press

284 Music: © 1980, ICEL

287 © 1984, Les Presses de Taizé, GIA Publications, Inc., agent.

288 Music: © 1971, Manna Music. Arr.: © 1971,1975, Celebration, P.O. Box 309, Aliquippa, PA 15001 All rights reserved.

292 Music: © 1980, David M. Young

294 Music: © 1980, ICEL

295 © 1980, Les Presses de Taizé, GIA Publications, Inc., agent.

297 © 1984, Les Presses de Taizé, GIA Publications, Inc., agent.

298 © 1979, Les Presses de Taizé, GIA Publications, Inc., agent.

299 © 1977, GIA Publications, Inc.

305 © Studio SM, Paris

309 Adaptation: © 1980, Church Pension Fund. Harm: © 1986, GIA Publications, Inc.

323 Music from *1972 Communion Service* © 1972, Oxford University Press

327 Music: © Huguenin Schola Cantorum

329 © 1980, Les Presses de Taizé, GIA Publications, Inc., agent.

336 © 1984, Les Presses de Taizé, GIA Publications, Inc., agent.

337 © 1980, Les Presses de Taizé, GIA Publications, Inc., agent.

355 Text: © 1982, Hope Publishing Co., Carol Stream, IL 60188

357 Harm: © 1975, GIA Publications, Inc.

358 Text: © 1970, Mayhew McCrimmon Ltd.

359 Text: © David Higham Assoc. Ltd.

360 © 1983, GIA Publications, Inc.

361 © 1980 ICEL.

362 Text: © 1982, Hope Publishing Co., Carol Stream, IL 60188. Music: From *Enlarged Songs of Praise* © Oxford University Press

364 Harm: © National Christian Education Council

365 Text: From *English Praise* © 1975, Oxford University Press. Music: © J. Curwen and Sons

367 Harm: © 1958, Basilian Fathers, assigned to Ralph Jusko Publications, Inc.

368 Text: © 1985, The Church Pension Fund. Harm: © 1986, GIA Publications, Inc.

369 © 1984, Les Presses de Taizé, GIA Publications, Inc., agent.

371 Text: © 1982, Hope Publishing Co., Carol Stream, IL 60188

378 Harm: © Oxford University Press

380 Text: © Fredrick Harris Music Co. Ltd., Oakville, Ontario, Canada. Setting: © 1978, *Lutheran Book of Worship.* Used by permission of Augsburg Publishing House.

381 Text: © Oxford University Press. Harm: © A. R. Mowbray and Co. Ltd., Oxford, England

384 Text: © 1964; Harm: © 1986, GIA Publications, Inc.

385 Text: "A Christmas Hymn" from *Advice to A Prophet and Other Poems* © 1961, Richard Wilbur. Reprinted by permission of Harcourt Brace Jovanovich, Inc. Music: © 1984, GIA Publications, Inc.

387 Descant with accompaniment: From *Carols for Choirs,* © 1961, Oxford University Press

388 Translation © 1978, *Lutheran Book of Worship*

389 Text: © 1978, *Lutheran Book of Worship.* Used by permission of Augsburg Publishing House.

390 Text: © 1978, *Lutheran Book of Worship.* Used by permission of Augsburg Publishing House.

392 Descant with accompaniment: From *Carols for Choirs,* © 1961, Oxford University Press

393 Harm: © Rosalind Rusbridge, 44 Archfield Rd., Bristol, BS6 6BQ, England

394 Text: © 1927. Renewed 1955 by Eleanor Farjeon. Reprinted by permission of Harold Ober Assoc. Inc. Music: © The Estate of Leo Sowerby

Acknowledgements/*continued*

395 Text: © 1969, James Quinn, SJ. Printed by permission of Geoffrey Chapman a division of Cassell Ltd.
396 Harm: From the *English Hymnal* © Oxford University Press
397 Text: By permission of Mrs. John W. Work III. Harm: © 1971, Walton Music Corp.
398 Harm: © 1985, GIA Publications, Inc.
401 © 1979, Les Presses de Taizé, GIA Publications, Inc., agent.
402 Harm: © 1957, Novello and Co. Ltd.
404 Harm: © 1986, GIA Publications, Inc.
408 Harm: © Oxford University Press
412 Text: © 1984, Hope Publishing Co., Carol Stream, IL 60188
414 Text: © 1980, International Committee on English in the Liturgy, Inc. All rights reserved. Harm: © 1975, GIA Publications, Inc.
415 Harm: © 1986, GIA Publications, Inc.
416 Psalm Text: © 1963, The Grail. Harm: © 1986, GIA Publications, Inc.
418 © 1985, Oxford University Press, Inc.
420 Text: © Peter J. Scagnelli
421 Text: © 1971, Faber Music Ltd., London. Reprinted from *New Catholic Hymnal* by permission of the publishers. Harm: © 1986, GIA Publications, Inc.
423 © 1981, Les Presses de Taizé, GIA Publications, Inc., agent.
424 Text: © Peter J. Scagnelli. Harm: © 1975, GIA Publications, Inc.
425 © 1980, Les Presses de Taizé, GIA Publications, Inc., agent.
426 Text: © Author. Harm: © 1971, Faber Music Lit., London. Reprinted from *New Catholic Hymnal* by permission of the publishers.
427 Harm: © 1975, GIA Publications, Inc.
429 © 1979, Les Presses de Taizé, GIA Publications, Inc., agent.
430 © 1979, Les Presses de Taizé, GIA Publications, Inc., agent.
431 Text and tune: © 1969, and arr: © 1982, Hope Publishing Co., Carol Stream, IL 60188
432 © Gethsemani Abbey
435 Rhythmic reconstruction: © 1983, Schola Antiqua Inc. Harm: © 1986, GIA Publications, Inc.
436 Harm: From *The Hymnal,* 1940 © 1940, 1943, 1961, Church Pension Fund
437 Harm: © 1986, GIA Publications, Inc.
439 Music: © John Ireland Trust, 35 St. Mary's Mansions, London W2 1SQ, England
440 © 1984, Les Presses de Taizé, GIA Publications, Inc., agent.
441 Text and Tune: © 1973, The Word of God Music, P.O. Box 8617, Ann Arbor, MI 48107. All rights reserved. Harm. and Desc: © 1979, Celebration, P.O. Box 309, Aliquippa, PA 15001 All rights reserved.
443 Harm: © 1986, GIA Publications, Inc.
444 Text: © Oxford University Press. Music: From *English Hymnal* © Oxford University Press
446 © 1983, GIA Publications, Inc.
447 Harm: © 1975, GIA Publications, Inc.
448 Text: © Peter J. Scagnelli. Harm: © 1975, GIA Publications, Inc.
449 Harm: From *Lutheran Worship* © 1969, Concordia Publishing House
452 Harm: © 1980, GIA Publications, Inc.
453 Text: © Oxford University Press. Harm: © 1986, GIA Publications, Inc.
454 © 1979, Les Presses de Taizé, GIA Publications, Inc., agent.
455 Text: © 1978, *Lutheran Book of Worship.* Used by permission of Augsburg Publishing House.
458 Melody: © 1975, Richard Hillert from Setting One of Holy Communion in the *Lutheran Book of Worship* © 1978. Permission to use the melody in additional arrangements must be obtained from the copyright holder.
465 © 1984, Les Presses de Taizé, GIA Publications, Inc., agent.
466 Text: © 1975, Hope Publishing Co., Carol Stream, IL 60188
469 Harm: From the *English Hymnal* © Oxford University Press
470 Text: © 1978, Jeffery W. Rowthorn. Music: ©1942. Renewal 1970, Hope Publishing Co., Carol Stream, IL 60188
472 Music: From the *English Hymnal* © Oxford University Press
473 © 1979, Les Presses de Taizé, GIA Publications, Inc., agent.
474 Text: © Oxford University Press
475 Text: © 1971, John Webster Grant. Harm: © 1975, GIA Publications, Inc.
477 Text: From *English Praise* © 1975, Oxford University Press. Music: © 1983, GIA Publications, Inc.
478 © 1969, Hope Publishing Co., Carol Stream, IL 60188.
479 Harm: © 1975, GIA Publications, Inc.
480 Music: © 1986, GIA Publications, Inc. Text: © 1968, Hope Publishing Co., Carol Stream, IL 60188
481 Text: © 1984, Hope Publishing Co., Carol Stream, IL 60188. Music: © 1974, 1986, Harold Flammer, Inc., Delaware Water Gap, PA 18327, International copyright secured. All rights reserved. Used with permission.
482 Harm: © 1986, GIA Publications, Inc.
483 Text: *A Monastic Breviary* © Order of the Holy Cross, West Park, New York. Music: © 1983, Hank Beebe. All rights reserved.
484 Text: © 1959, 1965, 1966, 1977, Order of St. Benedict, Inc. Published by Liturgical Press, Collegeville, MN 56321. Harm: © 1958, Basilian Fathers, assigned to Ralph Jusko Publications, Inc.
489 Trans: © 1971, Faber Music Ltd., London. Reprinted from *New Catholic Hymnal* by permission of the publishers. Harm. © 1986, GIA Publications, Inc.
490 Harm: From the *English Hymnal* © Oxford University Press
495 Harm: © 1975, GIA Publications, Inc.
497 Text: © 1941, Irene C. Mueller. Harm: © 1986, GIA Publications, Inc.
499 Music: From *Enlarged Songs of Praise* © Oxford University Press
500 Text: From *Enlarged Songs of Praise* © Oxford University Press
501 Text: © 1966,1984, Willard F. Jabusch. Harm: © 1986, GIA Publications, Inc.
503 Text: © 1971, Walton Music Corp. Harm: © 1986, GIA Publications, Inc.
504 Text: © 1982, Hope Publishing Co., Carol Stream, IL 60188
506 Text: © 1981, Hope Publishing Co., Carol Stream, IL 60188. Music: © 1986, GIA Publications, Inc.
507 Music: From *Enlarged Songs of Praise* © Oxford University Press
508 Harm: From *English Praise* © 1975, Oxford University Press
509 Text: © 1982, Hope Publishing Co., Carol Stream, IL 60188
510 © 1970,1975, Celebration, P.O. Box 309, Aliquippa, PA 15001 All rights reserved.
511 Text: © 1969, Concordia Publishing House
513 Text: © 1969, James Quinn, SJ. Printed by permission of Geoffrey Chapman, a division of Cassell Ltd.
514 Text: © 1954, Renewal 1982, and music: Music: © 1966, Hope Publishing Co., Carol Stream, IL 60188
515 Text: © 1970, Mayhew McCrimmon Ltd. Music: © 1979, Carl Schalk
516 Text: © 1953, Renewal 1981, Hymn Society of America, Texas Christian University, Fort Worth, TX 76129
517 © 1968, Augsburg Publishing House. Used by permission.
518 Text: © 1982, Hope Publishing Co., Carol Stream, IL 60188. Music: © 1971, Walton Music Corp.
519 © 1980, Les Presses de Taizé, GIA Publications, Inc., agent.
520 Text: © J. Curwen and Sons. Harm: From the *English Hymnal* © Oxford University Press
522 Text: © 1975 and Music © 1973, Hope Publishing Co., Carol Stream, IL 60188.
525 Text: Courtesy of Charles Scribner's Sons
526 Text: © 1972, GIA Publications, Inc.
527 Trans: © 1978, Church Pension Fund
529 Music: © 1973, Hope Publishing Co., Carol Stream, IL 60188.
531 © 1979, Hope Publishing Co., Carol Stream, IL 60188

Acknowledgements/*continued*

532 Music: © Oxford University Press
533 Text: © 1974, and harm: © 1977, Hope Publishing Co., Carol Stream, IL 60188
534 Text: © 1962, Hope Publishing Co., Carol Stream, IL 60188. Music: © Oxford University Press
535 Text: © 1982, Hope Publishing Co., Carol Stream, IL 60188
536 Music: © 1975, The Church Pension Fund
538 Text: © Canon John E. Bowers. Music From *English Hymnal* © Oxford University Press
540 Text: © Hope Publishing Co., Carol Stream, IL 60188. Harm: © 1978, GIA Publications, Inc.
541 Text: © 1982, Hope Publishing Co., Carol Stream, IL 60188
542 Text: © 1980, Hope Publishing Co., Carol Stream, IL 60188. Music: © 1980, GIA Publications, Inc.
543 Text: © 1969, Hope Publishing Co., Carol Stream, IL 60188
544 Text: © 1970, Mayhew McCrimmon Ltd. Tune: © Composer
545 © 1973, Hope Publishing Co., Carol Stream, IL 60188.
547 Descant: © 1953, Novello and Co. Ltd.
548 © 1979, Les Presses de Taizé, GIA Publications, Inc., agent.
549 Text: © 1972, Hope Publishing Co., Carol Stream, IL 60188
550 © 1973, Hope Publishing Co., Carol Stream, IL 60188.
552 Music: 1974, 1986 Harold Flammer, Inc., Delaware Water Gap, PA 18327. International copyright secured. All rights reserved. Used with permission.
553 © 1979, Les Presses de Taizé, GIA Publications, Inc., agent.
554 Text: © 1972, GIA Publications, Inc.
555 © 1979, Les Presses de Taizé, GIA Publications, Inc., agent.
556 Text: © Hope Publishing Co., Carol Stream, IL 60188. Music: © J. Curwen and Sons.
558 Text: © 1940, The Church Pension Fund
559 Harm: Executors of G.H. Knight
561 © 1982, Les Presses de Taizé, GIA Publications, Inc., agent.
562 Text: © 1970, Hope Publishing Co., Carol Stream, IL 60188. Music: © Francis Jackson
563 Text: © 1979, Hope Publishing Co., Carol Stream, IL 60188
564 Text: © 1982, Hope Publishing Co., Carol Stream, IL 60188. Music: © 1986, GIA Publications, Inc.
565 Text: © 1954. Renewal 1982, Hymn Society of America, Texas Christian University, Fort Worth, TX 76129
566 Text: © 1979, Stainer and Bell, Ltd. Used by permission of Galaxy Music Corp., New York, NY, sole US agent. Music: © 1986, GIA Publications, Inc.
568 Text: From *Enlarged Songs of Praise* © Oxford University Press. Harm: © 1985, Hope Publishing Co., Carol Stream, IL 60188
569 Music: © 1911, Stainer and Bell, Ltd. Used by permission of Galaxy Music Corp., New York, NY, sole US agent.
570 Text: © 1941, The Church Pension Fund
572 Harm: © 1986, GIA Publications, Inc.
573 Text: © 1984, Hope Publishing Co., Carol Stream, IL 60188
574 © 1985, Oxford University Press, Inc.
575 Text: © 1982, Hope Publishing Co., Carol Stream, IL 60188
576 Text: © 1982, Hope Publishing Co., Carol Stream, IL 60188
577 Text: © 1974, Hope Publishing Co., Carol Stream, IL 60188 Music: © SEFIM, Secretariat des Editeurs, 13 Avenue Savornin, 94240, L'hay-les-roses, France
578 Text: © 1970, Mayhew McCrimmon Ltd., 10-12 High Street, Great Wakering, Essex, England. All rights reserved. Music: © 1986, GIA Publications, Inc.
580 © 1972, Maranatha! Music
581 Text: © 1984, Hope Publishing Co., Carol Stream, IL 60188
582 Text: © 1971, Faber Music Ltd., London. Reprinted from *New Catholic Hymnal* by permission of the publishers. Music: © Mrs. Alfred M. Smith
583 Harm: © Hope Publishing Co., Carol Stream, IL 60188.
584 Text: © 1982, Carl P. Daw, Jr. Tune: © Skinner Chavez-Melo. Used by permission.
585 Harm: © 1975, GIA Publications, Inc.
586 Text: By permission of Augsburg Publishing House
587 Text: © J.W. Shore. Tune: © Composer
589 Text: © 1985, and music: © 1969, Hope Publishing Co., Carol Stream, IL 60188
590 Text: © 1969, James Quinn, SJ. By permission of Geoffrey Chapman, a division of Cassell Ltd. Harm: © Estate of T.H. Weaving
591 Music: Reprinted from "Six Wesley Songs for the Young" ©, 1971 Josef Weinberger Ltd.
592 Text: © 1968, Hope Publishing Co., Carol Stream, IL 60188. Music: © J. Curwen and Sons
593 Music: © 1969, Faith and Life Press
594 Text: © in this version, 1982 Hope Publishing Co., Carol Stream, IL 60188.
596 Music: © 1977, GIA Publications, Inc.
597 © 1983, Thomas H. Troeger and Carol Doran
598 Trans: © 1975, 1986, GIA Publications, Inc. Harm: © 1986, GIA Publications, Inc.
599 Text: © 1970, Mayhew McCrimmon Ltd. Music: © 1986, GIA Publications, Inc.
600 Harm: From *Cantate Domino* © 1980, Oxford University Press
602 Text and harm: © 1969, Concordia Publishing House
603 Texts from *Revised Standard Version* © Division of Christian Education of the National Council of the Churches of Christ in the USA. Music: © 1974, Novello and Co. Ltd.
604 © 1979, Les Presses de Taizé, GIA Publications, Inc., agent.
606 Harm: © 1975, GIA Publications, Inc.
607 Harm: From the *English Hymnal* © Oxford University Press
608 Harm: © 1986, GIA Publications, Inc.
609 Harm: © A. Gregory Murray, Downside Abbey, Stratton on the Fosse, Bath BA3 4RH
612 Tune: © The Jesuit Fathers, London. Reprinted by permission of Peter Janson-Smith, Ltd., London. Harm: © 1934, Oxford University Press
613 Harm: © 1986, GIA Publications, Inc.
614 Text: © 1974, Hope Publishing Co., Carol Stream, IL 60188. Harm: © 1986, GIA Publications, Inc.
615 Text: © Mrs. M. Rees
616 Text: © 1982, Hope Publishing Co., Carol Stream, IL 60188
618 Text: © Christian Conference of Asia
619 © 1972, GIA Publications, Inc.
620 Harm: © 1985, GIA Publications, Inc.
621 Text: © 1969, Galliard Ltd. Used by permission of Galaxy Music Corp., New York, NY, sole US agent. Music: © 1969, Hope Publishing Co., Carol Stream, IL 60188
622 Text: © 1982, Hope Publishing Co., Carol Stream, IL 60188. Music: Reprinted from "Six Wesley Songs for the Young" © 1971, Josef Weinberger Ltd.
623 Text: © 1975, and music: © 1980, Hope Publishing Co., Carol Stream, IL 60188
624 Text: © Oxford University Press. Music: © 1969, Hope Publishing Co., Carol Stream, IL 60188
625 Text: © 1968, Hope Publishing Co., Carol Stream, IL 60188. Harm: © Executors of the late Dr. Basil Harwood
626 Text: © 1971, Hope Publishing Co., Carol Stream, IL 60188. Music: © Thomas V. Griffiths
627 Text: © 1969, James Quinn, SJ. By permission of Geoffrey Chapman, a division of Cassell Ltd.
628 Text: © 1955, 1964, Abingdon Press
629 Text: © 1980, Hope Publishing Co., Carol Stream, IL 60188
630 Text: © Oxford University Press
631 Text: © 1961, Hymn Society of America, Texas Christian University, Fort Worth, TX 76129
632 Text: From *Songs of Praise* © Oxford University Press. Harm: © 1975, GIA Publications, Inc.
633 Text: © 1986, and music: © 1970, GIA Publications, Inc.
635 Text and Tune: © 1972, Chantry Music Press, Inc. Harm: © 1975, GIA Publications, Inc.
636 Text and Harm: © 1963, Galliard Ltd. Used by permission of Galaxy Music Corp., New York, NY, sole US agent.
637 Text: © 1982, Hope Publishing Co., Carol Stream, IL 60188. Tune: © 1986, GIA Publications, Inc.

Acknowledgements/*continued*

638 Text: © Oxford University Press. Music: From the *Clarendon Hymnbook* © Oxford University Press
639 Text: © 1983, Hope Publishing Co., Carol Stream, IL 60188. Tune: © 1986, GIA Publications, Inc.
640 Text: "Baptism By Fire" from *Incendiary Fellowship* © 1967, David Elton Trueblood. Reprinted by permission of Harper & Row, Publishers, Inc. Harm: © 1975, Broadman Press. All rights reserved. International Copyright Secured. Used by Permission.
641 © 1927, Edward B. Marks. By permission of Hal Leonard Corporation, Milwaukee, WI 53213
642 Text: © Lee M. Baldwin
643 Text: © 1968, Hope Publishing Co., Carol Stream, IL 60188
644 © 1963, Galliard Ltd. Used by permission of Galaxy Music Corp., New York, NY, sole US agent.
645 Text: From *Enlarged Songs of Praise* © Oxford University Press. Harm: © 1975, GIA Publications, Inc.
646 Text: © 1954. Renewal 1982, Hymn Society of America, Texas Christian University, Fort Worth, TX 76129. Music: From the *Revised Church Hymnary* © 1927, Oxford University Press
647 Text: © 1968, Hope Publishing Co., Carol Stream, IL 60188. Music: © 1971, Faber Music Ltd., London. Reprinted from *New Catholic Hymnal* by permission of the publishers.
648 Text: © 1967, Hope Publishing Co., Carol Stream, IL 60188. Setting: © 1969, *Contemporary Worship I: Hymns*. Used by permission of Augsburg Publishing House.
649 Text: © 1968, Hope Publishing Co., Carol Stream, IL 60188. Tune: © 1975, GIA Publications, Inc.
650 Text: © 1958, Hymn Society of America, Texas Christian University, Fort Worth, TX 76129. Music: © 1975, GIA Publications, Inc.
651 Text: © George Utech. Music: © 1986, GIA Publications, Inc.
653 Text: © American Peace Society. Reprinted with permission of the Helen Dwight Reid Educational Foundation, 400 Albemarle St., NW, Washington, DC 20016. Tune: © 1985, GIA Publications, Inc.
654 Text: © 1982, Carl P. Daw, Jr. Tune: © 1916. 1944, Roberton Publications. Reproduced by permission of the publisher: Theodore Presser Co., sole representative. Harm: © 1986, GIA Publications, Inc.
655 Text: © Stewart Cross. Tune: © 1942, The Church Pension Fund
656 Text: © 1975, Hope Publishing Co., Carol Stream, IL 60188. Harm: From the *English Hymnal* © Oxford University Press
657 © 1984, Les Presses de Taizé, GIA Publications, Inc., agent.
658 © 1968, Hope Publishing Co., Carol Stream, IL 60188
659 Text: © American Tract Society, Garland, Texas
660 Text: © 1969, James Quinn, SJ. By permission of Geoffrey Chapman, a division of Cassell Ltd.
661 Text: © 1983 and Music © 1982, Hope Publishing Co., Carol Stream, IL 60188
663 Text: © 1968, Hope Publishing Co., Carol Stream, IL 60188. Music: From the *Clarendon Hymnbook* © Oxford University Press
664 © 1973, Hope Publishing Co., Carol Stream, IL 60188
665 © 1982, GIA Publications, Inc.
666 Harm: © 1969, Concordia Publishing House
667 Text: © 1979, and music: © 1942. Renewal 1970, Hope Publishing Co., Carol Stream, IL 60188
668 © 1969, Hope Publishing Co., Carol Stream, IL 60188
670 Music: © 1973, Concordia Publishing House
671 Music: © 1983, GIA Publications, Inc.
672 © 1975, Celebration, P.O. Box 309, Aliquippa, PA 15001 All rights reserved.
673 Text: © 1969, James Quinn, SJ. By permission of Geoffrey Chapman, a division of Cassell Ltd. Harm: © A. Gregory Murray, Downside Abbey, Stratton on the Fosse, Bath BA3 4RH
674 Text: From "The Children's Bells", pub. Oxford University Press © David Higham Assoc. Ltd.
676 © 1980, Les Presses de Taizé, GIA Publications, Inc., agent.
677 Text: © 1969, James Quinn, SJ. By permission of Geoffrey Chapman, a division of Cassel Ltd.
680 Text: © Benedictine Nuns, St. Mary's Abbey, West Malling
681 Text: © Anne LeCroy. Music: © 1985, GIA Publications, Inc.
682 Text: © Oxford University Press. Harm: © A. Gregory Murray, Downside Abbey, Stratton on the Fosse, Bath BA3 4RH
683 Text: © John Arlott. Harm: © National Christian Education Council
684 Text: © 1973, Hope Publishing Co., Carol Stream, IL 60188. Music: © 1986, GIA Publications, Inc.
685 Text: © Harper and Row. Harm: © 1940, The Church Pension Fund
687 Harm: © 1986, GIA Publications, Inc.
688 Music: © 1986, GIA Publications, Inc.
689 Harm: © 1986, GIA Publications, Inc.
690 Harm: © 1975, GIA Publications, Inc.
691 Text: © 1969, James Quinn, SJ. By permission of Geoffrey Chapman, a division of Cassell Ltd. Harm: © 1975, GIA Publications, Inc.
692 Music: © 1986, GIA Publications, Inc.
693 © 1972, Canadian Catholic Conference, Ottowa, Canada. Reproduced with permission.
694 Text: © 1979, Hymn Society of America, Texas Christian University, Fort Worth, TX 76129. Harm: © 1975, GIA Publications, Inc.
695 © 1961, H. Freeman and Co., London WC2H 0LD
697 Text: © 1980, Hope Publishing Co., Carol Stream, IL 60188. Music: © Boekencentrum, Gravenhage, Netherlands
699 Text: © Anne LeCroy. Music: © Boekencentrum, Gravenhage, Netherlands
700 Text: © Esme. D. E. Bird
701 Text: © 1977, and music: © 1985, Hope Publishing Co., Carol Stream, IL 60188
702 Harm: © Willis Music Company
703 Trans: © 1954 and harm: © 1986, GIA Publications, Inc.
704 © Hymns Ancient and Modern, Ltd.
705 Music: From the *English Hymnal* © Oxford University ress
706 Text: © 1985, The Church Pension Fund
707 Text and Harm: From the *English Hymnal* © Oxford University Press.
708 Text: © 1971, Faber Music Ltd., London. Reprinted from *New Catholic Hymnal* by permission of the publishers.
709 Text: © 1967, Gooi en Sticht bv. Hilversum, The Netherlands. International copyright secured. Revised translation © 1984, TEAM Publications
710 Stanzas 1-3: © Board of Publication, Lutheran Church in America. Stanza 4: © 1958, *Service Book and Hymnal*. Used by permission of Augsburg Publishing House. Harm: © 1983, Hope Publishing Co., Carol Stream, IL 60188
711 © 1971, Faber Music Ltd., London. Reprinted from *New Catholic Hymnal* by permission of the publishers.
713 Harm: © 1986, GIA Publications, Inc.
714 Text: From *English Praise* © 1975, Oxford University Press
715 The text "Let us with joy our voices raise", has been reprinted with permission of the copyright owner, F.E.L Publications, Ltd., 2545 Chandler Ave., Suite 5, Las Vegas, NV 89120, Phone: (702)736-9420. Further reproduction (even words only or one time usage) is not permitted without F.E.L.'s written permission.
717 Text: © Peter J. Scagnelli. Harm: © 1969, Condordia Publishing House
719 Harm: © 1975, GIA Publications, Inc.
720 Text: © 1982, Hope Publishing Co., Carol Stream, IL 60188. Harm: © A. Gregory Murray, Downside Abbey, Stratton on the Fosse, Bath BA3 4RH
721 Text: © John B. Geyer
722 Text: © 1978, Thomas E. Herbranson, from *Lutheran Book of Worship*. Music: © 1964, Abingdon Press
723 Text: © 1971, Faber Music Ltd., London. Reprinted from *New Catholic Hymnal* by permission of the publishers.
724 © 1969, Hope Publishing Co., Carol Stream, IL 60188
725 Harm: © A. Gregory Murray, Downside Abbey, Stratton on the Fosse, Bath BA3 4RH
726 Text: © 1971, Hope Publishing Co., Carol Stream, IL 60188. Harm: © 1938, J. Fisher and Bro.
727 Harm: © 1983, GIA Publications, Inc.
728 Harm: © 1986, GIA Publications, Inc.
730 Harm: © 1986, GIA Publications, Inc.

Acknowledgements/*continued*

731 Text: From *Enlarged Songs of Praise* © Oxford University Press. Tune: © 1957, H.W. Gray Co., Inc., a division of Belwin-Mills Publishing Corporation. Copyright renewed. Used with permission. All rights reserved. Harm: © Christian Board of Education, Christian Church (Disciples of Christ)
734 © 1984, Les Presses de Taizé, GIA Publications, Inc., agent.
735 Harm: © 1986, GIA Publications, Inc.
736 © 1977, Archdiocese of Philadelphia
738 © 1970, GIA Publications, Inc.
739 Text: © 1968, Hope Publishing Co., Carol Stream, IL 60188
742 Text: © 1971, GIA Publications, Inc. Harm: © National Christian Education Council
745 Text and Harm: © 1983, Hope Publishing Co., Carol Stream, IL 60188
746 Text: © 1980, ICEL
747 Text: © 1969, Hope Publishing Co., Carol Stream, IL 60188
748 Text: © Board of Publication, Lutheran Church in America. Setting: © 1978, *Lutheran Book of Worship.* Used by permission of Augsburg Publishing House.
749 Text: © 1982, Hope Publishing Co., Carol Stream, IL 60188. Music: © Thomas V. Griffiths
750 Text: © 1986, GIA Publications, Inc.
751 © 1984, Oxford University Press, Inc.
752 Text: © 1965, GIA Publications, Inc. Harm: © 1986, GIA Publications, Inc.
754 Text: © Oxford University Press. Harm: Executors of G.H. Knight
755 Text: © 1980, International Committee on English in the Liturgy, Inc.
756 Harm: © 1979, Church of the Redeemer Episcopal, Houston, TX
758 Trans: © 1969, James Quinn, SJ. By permission of Geoffrey Chapman, a division of Cassell Ltd.
759 Harm: © 1986, GIA Publications, Inc.
760 Text: © J. Curwen and Sons
805 Rhythmic Reconstruction: © 1984, Schola Antiqua Inc. Harm: © 1985, GIA Publications, Inc.
813 Text: © 1969, James Quinn, SJ. By permission of Geoffrey Chapman, a division of Cassell Ltd.
830 Music: © 1977, International Committee on English in the Liturgy, Inc.
837 Trans: © 1983, Peter J. Scagnelli
857 Trans: © 1986, Peter J. Scagnelli; Acc: © Boekencentrum, Gravenhage, Netherlands

PRAYERS

1158, 1174 (Protect us, Lord) from *Liturgy of the Hours* © 1970, International Committee on English in the Liturgy, Inc. All rights reserved.
1166, 1173, 1174 (Visit this house, and Hear us, Lord), 1178, 1180, 1182, 1183, 1184, 1192, 1200-1202 from *A Book of Prayers*, © 1982, International Committee on English in the Liturgy, Inc. All rights reserved.
1185 © Archdiocese of Chicago
1186, 1188-1190, from *Pastoral Care of the Sick* © 1982, International Committee on English in the Liturgy, Inc. All rights reserved.
1187 From *The Book of Common Prayer*, 1979
1194-1198 From *Rite of Penance* © 1974, International Committee on English in the Liturgy, Inc. All rights reserved.

Scripture Passages Related to Hymns 1204

GENESIS

1:	God, Who Stretched the Spangled Heavens 648
	Many and Great, O God, Are Your Works 503
	Over the Chaos of the Empty Waters 483
	Praise the Spirit in Creation 477
	Thy Strong Word Didst Cleave the Darkness 511
	This Is the Day When Light Was First Created 663
1:1-5	God, Whose Almighty Word 486
1:2-3	On This Day, the First of Days 662
1:3	God, Omnipotent, Eternal 563
	Let There Be Light 653
1:3-5	Morning Has Broken 674
	This Is the Day When Light Was First Created 663
1:12	I Sing the Mighty Power of God 502
1:26-27	On This Day, the First of Days 662
1:31	All Things Bright and Beautiful 505
2:2-3	On This Day, the First of Days 662
8:22	Now Join We to Praise the Creator 647
12:1	The God of Abraham Praise 537
14:18	The God of Abraham Praise 537
22:1-18	God Spoke to Our Father Abraham 578
22:16-17	The God of Abraham Praise 537

EXODUS

3:6	The God of Abraham Praise 537
3:14	The God of Abraham Praise 537
14:29	Come, Ye Faithful, Raise the Strain 456
15:	At the Lamb's High Feast We Sing 459, 460
	Come, Ye Faithful, Raise the Strain 456
	When Israel Was in Egypt's Land 508
	Who Can Measure Heaven and Earth 509
15:2	The God of Abraham Praise 537
16 & 17	Shepherd of Souls 728
19.4	The God of Abraham Praise 537
19:20	The Glory of These Forty Days 422
20:	O Come, O Come, Emmanuel 357
33:14	The God of Abraham Praise 537
33:18-23	Holy, Holy, Holy! Lord God Almighty 485

NUMBERS

24:17	What Star Is This 407

DEUTERONOMY

6:2-6	God Be in My Head 567
8:3	Shepherd of Souls 728
30:19-20	Come, Let Us Love the Unborn Generations 639
32:3	Sing Praise to God Who Reigns Above 528

JOSHUA

3:14-17	Let Saints on Earth in Concert Sing 741

I SAMUEL

15:29	All Hail the Power of Jesus' Name 494, 495

I KINGS

8:30,36,39	Only Begotten, Word of God Eternal 666
19:	He Comes to Us as One Unknown 573

II KINGS

2:11	The Glory of These Forty Days 422

Scripture Passages Related to Hymns/*continued*

I CHRONICLES

14:15	He Comes to Us as One Unknown 573
16:	When in Our Music God Is Glorified 549
17:16-17	Amazing Grace 583

II CHRONICLES

6:21,39	Only Begotten, Word of God Eternal 666

JUDITH

15:9-10	Let Us with Joy Our Voices Raise 715

JOB

3:17-18	Jesus Shall Reign 492
19:25	I Know That My Redeemer Lives 445

PSALMS

8:	The Works of the Lord Are Created in Wisdom 504
9:12	Come, We That Love the Lord 552
16:11	The God of Abraham Praise 537
18:1-2	Christ's Church Shall Glory in His Power 616
19:	The Stars Declare His Glory 506
19:2-3,4-5	Let All on Earth Their Voices Raise 716
19:4-6	Jesus Shall Reign 492
23:	Jesus, Shepherd of Our Souls 649
	My Shepherd Will Supply My Need 606
	O Lord, You Died That All Might Live 740
	The King of Love My Shepherd Is 609
	The Living God My Shepherd Is 612
	The Lord, the Lord, the Lord Is My Shepherd 613
24:	Hail the Day That Sees Him Rise 471
	The King of Glory 501
24:1	Reap Me the Earth 544
24:7-10	All Glory, Laud, and Honor 428
	Lift Up Your Heads, O Mighty Gates 363
24:10	The Royal Banners Forward Go 435
29:	All Glory, Laud, and Honor 428, 805
29:10	O God of Love, O King of Peace 652
33:	There's a Wideness in God's Mercy 595, 596
36:6-7	Immortal, Invisible, God Only Wise 512
36:10	O Jesus, Joy of Loving Hearts 605
44:1-4,8-9	God of Our Fathers 764
45:3-4	Come, Now Almighty King 487
46:	Christ's Church Shall Glory in His Power 616
	God Is Our Fortress and Our Rock 575, 576
	How Firm a Foundation 585
46:8	O God of Love, O King of Peace 652
46:9	Crown Him with Many Crowns 496
50:2	The God of Abraham Praise 537
51:	Have Mercy, Lord, on Us 753
	O for a Heart to Praise My God 591
	Parce Domine 416
51:12-13	Come, Now Almighty King 487
63:	God Is My Great Desire 581
63:2	O Jesus, Joy of Loving Hearts 605
65:5-13,9-13	I Sing the Mighty Power of God 502
	America the Beautiful 763
66:	From All That Dwell below the Skies 521
67:6-7	Come, Ye Thankful People, Come 759
72:	Jesus Shall Reign 492
	The King Shall Come When Morning Dawns 373

Scripture Passages Related to Hymns/*continued*

	To Jesus Christ, Our Sovereign King 497
72:5-17	Crown Him with Many Crowns 496
	From All That Dwell below the Skies 521
72:12-13	The Church of Christ in Every Age 626
78:25	Alleluia! Sing to Jesus 737
90:1-5	O God, Our Help in Ages Past 579
95:	Rejoice, the Lord Is King 493
95:1-2,6-7,8-9	O for a Heart to Praise My God 591
96:	Let All on Earth Their Voices Raise 716
	Sing a New Song to the Lord 550
	The King Shall Come When Morning Dawns 373
	The Royal Banners Forward Go 435
98:	Earth and All Stars 517
	New Songs of Celebration 533
	Sing to the Lord a Joyful Song 532
	Sing a New Song to the Lord 550
98:	The King Shall Come When Morning Dawns 373
98:49	Joy to the World 399
100:	All People That On Earth Do Dwell 669, 670
	Come, Rejoice before Your Maker 664
	Christians, Lift Up Your Hearts 538
	Jubilate Deo 555
	Let All the World in Every Corner Sing 536
	Praise to the Lord, the Almighty 547
102:1-7	Great God of Mercy 746
	O Christ, the Healer 747
103:	Praise, My Soul, the King of Heaven 530
	Praise to the Lord, the Almighty 547
104:	All Things Bright and Beautiful 505
	Fire of God, Titanic Spirit 478
	God Sends Us His Spirit 724
	Joyful, Joyful, We Adore You 525
	O That I Had a Thousand Voices 546
	Over the Chaos of the Empty Waters 483
	Praise and Thanksgiving 682
	The Works of the Lord Are Created in Wisdom 504
105:	All Creatures of Our God and King 520
	For the Beauty of the Earth 557
	Thanks Be to God 526
105:40-41	Shepherd of Souls 728
106:4	Love Divine, All Loves Excelling 588
109:	The Works of the Lord Are Created in Wisdom 504
113:1-2	From All That Dwell below the Skies 521
113:1-6	The Day You Gave Us, Lord, Is Ended 678
116:13	By Gracious Powers 577
117:	From All That Dwell below the Skies 521
	Laudate Dominum 519
	Sing Praise to the Lord 539
118:	Christus Resurrexit 465
118:14	Christians, Lift Up Your Hearts 538
118:24	Christ Is Made the Sure Foundation 617
	This Is the Day When Light Was First Created 663
118:25-27	All Glory, Laud, and Honor 428, 805
118:26	Benedictus Qui Venit 429
118:19-20	Only Begotten, Word of God Eternal 666
127:	O Father, All Creating 744
137:	Alleluia, Song of Gladness 413
	By the Babylonian Rivers 426
	Confitemini Domino 561
142:5	Amazing Grace 583
145:	Let All Things Now Living 559

Scripture Passages Related to Hymns/*continued*

	The God of Abraham Praise 537
	To Jesus Christ, Our Sovereign King 497
	Sing to the Lord a Joyful Song 532
145:10	Joyful, Joyful, We Adore You 525
148:	All Creatures of Our God and King 520
	All People That On Earth Do Dwell 669, 670
	Earth and All Stars 517
	For the Beauty of the Earth 557
	Praise Him 545
	Praise the Lord of Heaven 551
	Praise the Lord! You Heavens, Adore Him 529
150:	All People That On Earth Do Dwell 669, 670
	Praise to the Lord, the Almighty 547
	Sing Alleluia, Praise the Lord 554
	Sing Praise to the Lord 539
	When in Our Music God Is Glorified 549
PROVERBS	
8:22	O Come, O Come, Emmanuel 357
8:24	Savior of the Nations, Come 372
WISDOM	
18:14-15	Creator of the Stars of Night 368
SIRACH (ECCLESIASTICUS)	
1:	Who Can Measure Heaven and Earth 509
3:2-6	Our Father, by Whose Name 570
3:12-14	Our Father, by Whose Name 570
42-43	The Works of the Lord Are Created in Wisdom 504
50:22	Now Thank We All Our God 560
ISAIAH	
2:2-3	Holy, Holy, Holy! Lord God Almighty 485
6:2-3	All Hail the Power of Jesus' Name 494, 495
	Holy God, We Praise Thy Name 524
	Holy, Holy, Holy! Lord God Almighty 485
	Immortal, Invisible, God Only Wise 512
	Let All Mortal Flesh Keep Silence 523
6:3	God, We Praise You 535
	The God of Abraham Praise 537
7:14	O Come, O Come, Emmanuel 357
	The King of Glory 501
9:6	The God of Abraham Praise 537
9:7	Hark! The Herald Angels Sing 387
11:1	All Hail the Power of Jesus' Name 494, 495
11:1	Lo, How a Rose E'er Blooming 374
	O Come, O Come, Emmanuel 357
11:1-10	O Day of Peace 654
11:9	God Is Working His Purpose Out 507
12:1-6	Surely It Is God Who Saves Me 584
22:22	O Come, O Come, Emmanuel 357
24:33	The God of Abraham Praise 537
28:16	The Voice of God Goes Out through All the World 358
35:1	Lo, How a Rose E'er Blooming 374
35:1-6,10	Awake! Awake, and Greet the New Morn 360
	When the King Shall Come Again 355
40:1-8	Comfort, Comfort, O My People 370
40:1-11	Take Comfort, God's People 361
40:3-5	On Jordan's Bank 356
40:4	People, Look East 359
40:25-26	God of Our Fathers 764

Scripture Passages Related to Hymns/*continued*

40:28 Sing to the Lord a Joyful Song 532
40:10 How Firm a Foundation 585
42:1-4 The Church of Christ in Every Age 626
42:1-9 The Voice of God Goes Out through All the World 358
43:1-2 How Firm a Foundation 585
49: In Christ There Is No East or West 659
49:14-15 Christian, Do You Hear the Lord 594
51:1-3 The Voice of God Goes Out through All the World 358
52:7 Come, O Long Expected Jesus 364
55:1-2 Come and Let Us Drink of That New River 723
55:6 We Walk by Faith 572
55:10-11 Word of God, Come Down on Earth 513
61:1-2 Come, O Long Expected Jesus 364
The Voice of God Goes Out through All the World 358
61:3 The God of Abraham Praise 537
62:3 All Hail the Power of Jesus' Name 494, 495
63:3 Mine Eyes Have Seen the Glory 686
66:1 Mine Eyes Have Seen the Glory 686

JEREMIAH
8:22 There Is a Balm in Gilead 608
23:5-6 The God of Abraham Praise 537
24:23 The God of Abraham Praise 537
31:33 O for a Heart to Praise My God 591
51:8 Sing Praise to God Who Reigns Above 528

LAMENTATIONS
1:12 All You Who Pass This Way 440
2:21 By Gracious Powers 577
3:19 All Hail the Power of Jesus' Name 494, 495

BARUCH
4-5 City of God, Jerusalem 362

EZECHIEL
21:14-15 Mine Eyes Have Seen the Glory 686
36:26 O for a Heart to Praise My God 591
48:35 All Who Love and Serve Your City 621

DANIEL
6-7 The Glory of These Forty Days 422
7:9 Immortal, Invisible, God Only Wise 512
7:9,22 Come, Now Almighty King 487
The God of Abraham Praise 537

HOSEA
6:3 Mine Eyes Have Seen the Glory 686

JOEL
2:12-18 Again We Keep This Solemn Fast 420
2:17 Parce Domine 416
3:1-5 God Sends Us His Spirit 724
Praise the Spirit in Creation 477

AMOS
6:1-7 O Christ, the Healer 747

MICAH
5:2 O Little Town of Bethlehem 386
6:6-8 What Does the Lord Require 624
When Jesus Came Preaching the Kingdom of God 614

Scripture Passages Related to Hymns/*continued*

7:18	Love Divine, All Loves Excelling 588
HABAKKUK	
2:14	God Is Working His Purpose Out 507
2:20	Let All Mortal Flesh Keep Silence 523
HAGGAI	
2:7	Angels, from the Realms of Glory 377
	O Come, O Come, Emmanuel 357
	Come, O Long Expected Jesus 364
MALACHI	
3:1	Love Divine, All Loves Excelling 588
3:1	On Jordan's Bank 356
	The God Whom Earth and Sea and Sky 405
3:2	How Firm a Foundation 585
4:2	Hark! The Herald Angels Sing 387
MATTHEW	
1:12-13	The Glory of These Forty Days 422
1:23	Praise We the Lord This Day 696
2:1-2	O Little Town of Bethlehem 386
2:1-11	Good Christian Friends, Rejoice 391
2:1-12	A Child Is Born in Bethlehem 384
	Angels, from the Realms of Glory 377
	As with Gladness Men of Old 409
	Songs of Thankfulness and Praise 410
	The First Nowell 408
	We Three Kings of Orient Are 406
2:2,9,10	What Star Is This 407
2:9-11	Angel Voices Richly Blending 395
	'Twas in the Moon of Wintertime 380
2:10-11	O Come, All Ye Faithful/Adeste Fideles 392
2:11	What Child Is This 411
2:16-18	By All Your Saints Still Striving 706
	Unto Us a Boy Is Born 381
3:	When John Baptized by Jordan's River 412
3:4	The Glory of These Forty Days 422
3:13-17	Songs of Thankfulness and Praise 410
4:	When Jesus Came Preaching the Kingdom of God 614
4:1-2	Forty Days and Forty Nights 419
4:1-11	Lord, Who throughout These Forty Days 417
4:4	Shepherd of Souls 728
4:12-23	Two Fishermen 633
4:16	Comfort, Comfort, O My People 370
4:18-20	Those Who Love and Those Who Labor 632
4:24	The King of Glory 501
	Your Hands, O Lord, in Days of Old 750
5:3-12	O Blessed Are the Poor in Spirit 620
5:3	O Breathe on Me, O Breath of God 725
5:13	Gather Us In 665
5:21-24	Forgive Our Sins 754
5:38-48	Lord of All Nations, Grant Me Grace 602
6:1-6,16-18	Again We Keep This Solemn Fast 420
6:9-10	Let There Be Light 653
6:9-15	Forgive Our Sins 754
6:12-15	O God, Empower Us 642
6:17-18	It Shocked Them That the Master Did Not Fast 637
6:24-34	This World, My God, Is Held within Your Hand 582
6:25-34	Lord of All Hopefulness 568
	Praise and Thanksgiving 682

Scripture Passages Related to Hymns/*continued*

6:33	Seek Ye First the Kingdom of God 580
7:7	Seek Ye First the Kingdom of God 580
9:9	By All Your Saints Still Striving 706
9:9-13	Come, You Sinners, Poor and Needy 756
9:11-13	The Master Came to Bring Good News 752
9:14-17	It Shocked Them That the Master Did Not Fast 637
9:35	Forth in the Peace of Christ 627
10:14	Forth in the Peace of Christ 627
10:26-33	By Gracious Powers 577
10:38	Weary of All Trumpeting 635
10:42	There's a Spirit in the Air 531
11:11	By All Your Saints Still Striving 706
11:25-30	All You Who Seek a Comfort Sure 490
	How Blessed Is This Place 710
	I Heard the Voice of Jesus Say 607
	O Jesus, Joy of Loving Hearts 605
12:21	Hope of the World 565
13:	Christ's Church Shall Glory in His Power 616
13:1-23	Word of God, Come Down on Earth 513
13:21-43	Come, Ye Thankful People, Come 759
13:44-52	O the Beautiful Treasures 689
	When Jesus Came Preaching the Kingdom of God 614
14:14	Love Divine, All Loves Excelling 588
14:22-33	How Firm a Foundation 585
	I Sought the Lord 593
14:36	By Gracious Powers 577
16:21-27	Take Up Your Cross 634
17:1-9	Christ upon the Mountain Peak 701
	The Glory of These Forty Days 422
	'Tis Good, Lord, to Be Here 700
17:21	It Shocked Them That the Master Did Not Fast 637
18:10-14	My Shepherd Will Supply My Need 606
	The King of Love My Shepherd Is 609
	The Living God My Shepherd Is 612
18:20	Draw Us in the Spirit's Tether 731
20:1-16	For the Fruits of This Creation 562
20:22	By Gracious Powers 577
21:1-17	All Glory, Laud, and Honor 428, 805
21:9	Benedictus Qui Venit 429
	Hosanna in Excelsis 430
21:33-43	Christ Is Made the Sure Foundation 617
	O Christ the Great Foundation 618
22:1-10	The Kingdom of God 615
22:1-14	City of God, Jerusalem 362
22:15-21	Reap Me the Earth 544
23:1-12	We Are Your People 623
23:37	O Jesus Christ, May Grateful Hymns Be Rising 646
23:39	Benedictus Qui Venit 429
24 & 25	Hills of the North, Rejoice 365
	The King Shall Come When Morning Dawns 373
25:1-13	How Brightly Beams the Morning Star 389, 390
	Wake, O Wake, and Sleep No Longer 371
25:14-30	God, Whose Giving Knows No Ending 631
25:31-46	There's a Spirit in the Air 531
25:37-45	For the Fruits of This Creation 562
26:30	When in Our Music God Is Glorified 549
26:52	Weary of All Trumpeting 635
27:45	A Stable Lamp Is Lighted 385
28:6-9	Christ the Lord Is Risen Today 452, 461, 462, 463
	Jesus Christ Is Risen Today 442
28:16-20	Hail the Day That Sees Him Rise 471

Scripture Passages Related to Hymns/*continued*

28:18 Alleluia! Sing to Jesus 737
Lord, You Give the Great Commission 470
28:19-20 Forth in the Peace of Christ 627
Go Make of All Disciples 628
The Church of Christ in Every Age 626
28:46 All You Who Pass This Way 440

MARK

1: When John Baptized by Jordan's River 412
1:1-4 The Glory of These Forty Days 422
1:1-8 Comfort, Comfort, O My People 370
1:12-15 Lord, Who throughout These Forty Days 417
1:14-20 I Danced in the Morning 636
Two Fishermen 633
1:16-18 By All Your Saints Still Striving 706
1:23-28 Silence! Frenzied, Unclean Spirit 751
1:29-39 Your Hands, O Lord, in Days of Old 750
1:30-34 Great God of Mercy 746
God, Whose Almighty Word 486
O Christ, the Healer 747
1:40-45 Your Hands, O Lord, in Days of Old 750
2:1-12 Come, You Sinners, Poor and Needy 756
Great God of Mercy 746
I Danced in the Morning 636
Songs of Thankfulness and Praise 410
2:18-20 It Shocked Them That the Master Did Not Fast 637
3:1-6 I Danced in the Morning 636
4: Christ's Church Shall Glory in His Power 616
4:21-25 Forth in the Peace of Christ 627
4:26-29 For the Fruits of This Creation 562
4:26-34 The Kingdom of God 615
4:35-41 How Firm a Foundation 585
5:15 God, Whose Almighty Word 486
O Christ, the Healer 747
5:21-43 Draw Us in the Spirit's Tether 731
O Jesus Christ, May Grateful Hymns Be Rising 646
6:1-6 By Gracious Powers 577
God Has Spoken by His Prophets 516
6:7-13 Forth in the Peace of Christ 627
6:30-34 I Heard the Voice of Jesus Say 607
There's a Wideness in God's Mercy 595, 596
6:30-44 The Church of Christ in Every Age 626
7:31-37 O Son of God, in Galilee 748
8:22-26 O Son of God, in Galilee 748
8:34 Take Up Your Cross 634
Weary of All Trumpeting 635
9:2-7 Christ upon the Mountain Peak 701
9:2-10 The Glory of These Forty Days 422
'Tis Good, Lord, to Be Here 700
9:30-37 The Church of Christ in Every Age 626
10:27 Christ's Church Shall Glory in His Power 616
10:32 Jesus, Lead the Way 611
10:35-45 The Church of Christ in Every Age 626
10:38 By Gracious Powers 577
11:1-11 All Glory, Laud, and Honor 428, 805
11:9 Benedictus Qui Venit 429
11:10 Hosanna in Excelsis 430
12:28-34 God Be in My Head 567
We Are Your People 623
12:41-44 Where Temple Offerings Are Made 622
13:2 Lord Christ, When First You Came to Earth 438

Scripture Passages Related to Hymns/*continued*

13:5-13	Go Make of All Disciples 628
13:24	Hills of the North, Rejoice 365
	The King Shall Come When Morning Dawns 373
14:22-25	Hail Our Savior's Glorious Body/Pange Lingua 813
14:26	When in Our Music God Is Glorified 549
15:17-18	O Sacred Head Surrounded 434
16:15-20	Go Make of All Disciples 628

LUKE

1:26-31	Hail Our Savior's Glorious Body/Pange Lingua 813
1:26-37	Ave Maria 713
1:26-38	Immaculate Mary 708
	Sing We of the Blessed Mother 714
1:26-45	Savior of the Nations, Come 372
1:28	Mary, How Lovely the Light of Your Glory 711
1:40-42	Hail, Queen of Heaven/Salve Regina 703
1:46	Magnificat 553
1:46-55	My Soul Gives Glory to the Lord 15
	Tell Out, My Soul, the Greatness of the Lord 534
1:68-79	Blessed Be the God of Israel 6
1:78-79	O Come, Divine Messiah 367
	O Come, O Come, Emmanuel 357
2:1-10	The First Nowell 408
2:1-18	From Heaven Above 388
2:1-20	A Child Is Born in Bethlehem 384
2:6-7	Savior of the Nations, Come 372
2:6-14	Silent Night, Holy Night 379
2:6-18	Angels, from the Realms of Glory 377
	God Rest You Merry, Gentlemen 383
	Go Tell It on the Mountain 397
	Infant Holy, Infant Lowly 393
	What Child Is This 411
2:7	A Child Is Born in Bethlehem 384
	A Stable Lamp Is Lighted 385
	Away in a Manger 378
	Christ Was Born on Christmas Day 396
	Good Christian Friends, Rejoice 391
	Lo, How a Rose E'er Blooming 374
	Now Every Child That Dwells on Earth 394
	Once in Royal David's City 402
	Sing of Mary, Pure and Lowly 404
	Unto Us a Boy Is Born 381
2:7-18	Angel Voices Richly Blending 395
	'Twas in the Moon of Wintertime 380
2:8-14	See amid the Winter's Snow 375
	While Shepherds Watched 382
2:10-11	God Rest You Merry, Gentlemen 383
	Good Christian Friends, Rejoice 391
	Go Tell It on the Mountain 397
	It Came upon the Midnight Clear 400
	O Come, All Ye Faithful/Adeste Fideles 392
2:10-11,14	From Heaven Above 388
2:10-14	Immaculate Mary 708
2:13-14	All Glory Be to God on High 527
2:13-15	O Come, All Ye Faithful/Adeste Fideles 392
2:13-18	Angels We Have Heard on High 376
2:14	From Heaven Above 388
	Gloria, Gloria 401
	Glory Be to God in Heaven 518
	Glory to God in the Highest 542
2:15	O Come, All Ye Faithful/Adeste Fideles 392

Scripture Passages Related to Hymns/*continued*

2:22 - 3:40 Our Father, by Whose Name 570
2:29-32,34-35 Hail to the Lord Who Comes 692
Nunc Dimittis 676
Lord, Bid Your Servant Go in Peace 691
We Praise You, Father 680
2:34-35 At the Cross Her Station Keeping 421
2:40 Sing of Mary, Pure and Lowly 404
2:41-52 Our Father, by Whose Name 570
3: When John Baptized by Jordan's River 412
3:4,6 On Jordan's Bank 356
Prepare the Way of the Lord 369
3:21-22 Songs of Thankfulness and Praise 410
4:1-2 Lord, Who throughout These Forty Days 417
4:1-13 Forty Days and Forty Nights 419
4:14-21 The Voice of God Goes Out through All the World 358
5:1-11 Two Fishermen 633
5:27 Two Fishermen 633
6:17,20-26 O Blessed Are the Poor in Spirit 620
6:27-38 Lord of All Nations, Grant Me Grace 602
7:11-17 Your Hands, O Lord, in Days of Old 750
8: Christ's Church Shall Glory in His Power 616
8:1 When Jesus Came Preaching the Kingdom of God 614
8:22-25 How Firm a Foundation 585
9:1-6 Forth in the Peace of Christ 627
9:18-24 Take Up Your Cross 634
9:23 Weary of All Trumpeting 635
9:28-36 Christ upon the Mountain Peak 701
The Glory of These Forty Days 422
'Tis Good, Lord, to Be Here 700
10:38-42 When Jesus Came Preaching the Kingdom of God 614
11:1-13 Seek Ye First the Kingdom of God 580
11:27 Virgin-born, We Bow before You 403
12:32-48 This World, My God, Is Held within Your Hand 582
12:49-53 God, Whose Purpose Is to Kindle 640
13:29 In Christ There Is No East or West 659
13:35 Benedictus Qui Venit 429
14:25-33 Take Up Your Cross 634
15:1-3 Our Father, We Have Wandered 755
15:3-7 The King of Love My Shepherd Is 609
15:11-31 Our Father, We Have Wandered 755
15:31-32 For the Fruits of This Creation 562
18:9-14 Gather Us In 665
18:22 Two Fishermen 633
19:35-40 A Stable Lamp Is Lighted 385
19:37-38 All Glory, Laud, and Honor 428, 805
19:41 All Who Love and Serve Your City 621
21:25-28,34-36 Now the Day of the Lord Is at Hand 687
21:28 The King Shall Come When Morning Dawns 373
23:28,34,43,46 All You Who Pass This Way 440
23:33,44,50-53 Were You There 436
23:39-43 God with Hidden Majesty/Adoro Te Devote 489
23:42 Jesus, Remember Me 423
24: Over the Chaos of the Empty Waters 483
24:1-2 Were You There 436
24:1-8 On This Day, the First of Days 662
24:1-12 O Sons and Daughters 447
24:28-35 Daylight Fades 448
Shepherd of Souls 728
24:34 Christ the Lord Is Risen Today 452,461,462,463
24:27 He Comes to Us as One Unknown 573

Scripture Passages Related to Hymns/*continued*

24:46-48 Go Make of All Disciples 628
24:46-53 Hail the Day That Sees Him Rise 471
24:50-53 Alleluia! Sing to Jesus 737
24:51-53 Love Divine, All Loves Excelling 588

JOHN

1:1 At the Name of Jesus 499
1:1-5 O Come, All Ye Faithful/Adeste Fideles 392
1:1-18 Christ Is the World's Light 543
1:9 I Heard the Voice of Jesus Say 607
O Gladsome Light 679
Thy Strong Word Didst Cleave the Darkness 511
1:14 O Come, All Ye Faithful/Adeste Fideles 392
Of the Father's Love Begotten 398
1:15-28 On Jordan's Bank 356
1:35-42 Those Who Love and Those Who Labor 632
1:45-50 By All Your Saints Still Striving 706
2:1-11 Jesus, Come! For We Invite You 564
Songs of Thankfulness and Praise 410
2:1-12 O Father, All Creating 744
2:13-25 Christ Is Made the Sure Foundation 617
3: O Christ the Great Foundation 618
3:4-8 This Is the Spirit's Entry Now 722
3:5 Hark! The Herald Angels Sing 387
3:14-21 A Spendthrift Lover Is the Lord 597
My Song Is Love Unknown 439
3:16 Christ Is Made the Sure Foundation 617
Morning Glory, Starlit Sky 587
What Wondrous Love Is This 600
4:5-42 I Heard the Voice of Jesus Say 607
4:14 I Heard the Voice of Jesus Say 607
4:20 Christ Is the World's Light 543
6: Eat This Bread 734
Father, We Thank Thee, Who Hast Planted 558
I Am the Bread of Life 738
O Jesus, Joy of Loving Hearts 605
6:32,54-56,68-69 Draw Near and Take the Body of Your Lord 732
6:35,51 Let All Mortal Flesh Keep Silence 523
6:41-51 I Received the Living God 735
O Food of Exiles Lowly 729
6:41-59 Alleluia! Sing to Jesus 737
6:48 Hope of the World 565
6:51 O Jesus, Joy of Loving Hearts 605
Shepherd of Souls 728
7:37-39 Come and Let Us Drink of That New River 723
8:12 Christ Is the World's Light 543
I Heard the Voice of Jesus Say 607
8:31 Faith of Our Fathers 571
8:32 How Shall They Hear the Word of God 629
I Received the Living God 735
God, Omnipotent, Eternal 563
Spirit of God within Me 480
9:1-41 Amazing Grace 583
He Healed the Darkness of My Mind 749
9:4 All Who Love and Serve Your City 621
10: Jesus, Shepherd of Our Souls 649
My Shepherd Will Supply My Need 606
The King of Love My Shepherd Is 609
10:1-6 You Satisfy the Hungry Heart 736
11:25-27 I Am the Bread of Life 738
12:1-7 Said Judas to Mary 644

Scripture Passages Related to Hymns/*continued*

12:12-16	All Glory, Laud, and Honor 428, 805
12:13	Hosanna in Excelsis 430
12:20-33	Before the Fruit Is Ripened by the Sun 418
	Now the Green Blade Rises 453
12:20-33	O God beyond All Praising 541
12:46	I Want to Walk as a Child of the Light 510
13:1-5,12,15,34,35	Mandatum Novum 812
13:1-15	Jesus Took a Towel 432
13:3-15	Jesu, Jesu, Fill Us with Your Love 431
13:34-35	Love Is His Word 599
14:1-3	Father, We Praise You 4
14:1-12	I Know That My Redeemer Lives 445
14:6	Come, My Way, My Truth, My Life 569
14:6	I Received the Living God 735
14:8-10	Christ Is the World's Light 543
14:15-21	Come Down, O Love Divine 472
14:18	Alleluia! Sing to Jesus 737
14:24-26	Come, Holy Ghost 482
	Veni Creator Spiritus 479
15:	Lord of All Nations, Grant Me Grace 602
15:1-8	How Brightly Beams the Morning Star 389,390
15:9-17	Within Your House, O God, Today 743
	The Master Came to Bring Good News 752
15:12	Help Us Accept Each Other 656
15:12-17	This Is My Commandment 603
	This Is My Will 590
15:26-27	God, Whose Almighty Word 486
16:13	Come, Now Almighty King 487
17:	At That First Eucharist 733
17:1-8	Your Love, O God, Has All the World Created 638
17:20-23	Lord Christ, the Father's Mighty Son 658
17:20-26	At That First Eucharist 733
	Within Your House, O God, Today 743
17:24	The God of Abraham Praise 537
18:11	By Gracious Powers 577
18:16-17,25-27	By All Your Saints Still Striving 706
19:	O Sacred Head Surrounded 434
	What Wondrous Love Is This 600
19:2	When I Survey the Wondrous Cross 433
19:16-37	Sing, My Tongue, the Song of Triumph 437
19:25	At the Cross Her Station Keeping 421
	Immaculate Mary 708
	Sing We of the Blessed Mother 714
19:28	All You Who Pass This Way 440
19:34	Ave Verum 730
	Come and Let Us Drink of That New River 723
	O Food of Exiles Lowly 729
	Were You There 436
19:33-34	All You Who Seek a Comfort Sure 490
19:34-35	To Christ, the Prince of Peace 491
19:34-37	The Royal Banners Forward Go 435
19:35,37	A Stable Lamp Is Lighted 385
19:36-42	I Danced in the Morning 636
20:	That Easter Day with Joy Was Bright 457
	O Sons and Daughters 447
20:1-9	This Is the Day When Light Was First Created 663
20:11-18	Christ the Lord Is Risen Today 452, 461, 462, 463
20:19-31	O Sons and Daughters 447
	Shout for Joy, Loud and Long 540
	We Walk by Faith 572
20:22-23	Let All on Earth Their Voices Raise 716

Scripture Passages Related to Hymns/*continued*

20:24-29	God with Hidden Majesty/Adoro Te Devote 489
	By All Your Saints Still Striving 706
21:1-19	Christian, Do You Hear the Lord 594
21:15-17	By All Your Saints Still Striving 706
21:18-19	Two Noble Saints 699
ACTS	
1:1-11	A Hymn of Glory Let Us Sing 469
1:8	Come Down, O Love Divine 472
	Come, Holy Ghost 482
	Fire of God, Titanic Spirit 478
	O Holy Spirit, by Whose Breath 475
	Spirit Divine, Accept Our Prayers 476
	Veni Creator Spiritus 479
	When God the Spirit Came 481
1:9	Alleluia! Sing to Jesus 737
1:9-11	Hail the Day That Sees Him Rise 471
2:	Christians, Lift Up Your Hearts 538
	When God the Spirit Came 481
2:1-4	On This Day, the First of Days 662
2:1-11	Fire of God, Titanic Spirit 478
	Spirit of God within Me 480
	This Is the Day When Light Was First Created 663
	Veni Sancte Spiritus (Taize) 473
2:12	How Good the Name of Jesus Sounds 610
2:43-47	Praise the Spirit in Creation 477
3:14-15	My Song Is Love Unknown 439
3:16	How Good the Name of Jesus Sounds 610
4:5-12	A Single Unmatched Stone 574
4:12	At the Name of Jesus 499
4:21	How Good the Name of Jesus Sounds 610
7:54-60	By All Your Saints Still Striving 706
8:14-17	Forth in the Peace of Christ 627
9:1-19	By All Your Saints Still Striving 706
9:15-20	Two Noble Saints 699
10:37	On Jordan's Bank 356
13:1-5	Forth in the Peace of Christ 627
15:36-41	Forth in the Peace of Christ 627
ROMANS	
1:28-32	O Christ, the Healer 747
4:20-21	The God of Abraham Praise 537
5:1-5	Blessed Feasts of Blessed Martyrs 718
6:1-4	Baptized in Water 720
6:3-11	I Know That My Redeemer Lives 445
6:4-5	Christians, Lift Up Your Hearts 538
6:4,9	We Know That Christ Is Raised 721
6:5-11	Christ Is Alive! 466
8:14-17	In Christ There Is No East or West 659
8:15-16	At the Name of Jesus 499
	Our Father, by Whose Name 570
8:17	Blessed Feasts of Blessed Martyrs 718
8:18-39	There's a Wideness in God's Mercy 595, 596
10:15	How Shall They Hear the Word of God 629
11:33-35	There's a Wideness in God's Mercy 595, 596
14:17	The Kingdom of God 615
1 CORINTHIANS	
1:15-20	We Know That Christ Is Raised 721
1:18	Sing, My Tongue, the Song of Triumph 437
	Lift High the Cross 704

Scripture Passages Related to Hymns/*continued*

3:11	Christ Is Made the Sure Foundation 617
	O Christ the Great Foundation 618
3:13-15	Come, Ye Thankful People, Come 759
5:18-20	God Is Working His Purpose Out 507
9:1-18	Forth in the Peace of Christ 627
10:16-17	You Satisfy the Hungry Heart 736
10:17	Lord Christ, the Father's Mighty Son 658
11:23-26	God with Hidden Majesty/Adoro Te Devote 489
	I Come with Joy to Meet My Lord 726
11:23-29	Let Us Break Bread Together 727
	Draw Us in the Spirit's Tether 731
12:	In Christ There Is No East or West 659
	There Is One Lord 657
	When Love Is Found 745
12:4-11	Come, Holy Ghost 482
	Fire of God, Undying Flame 474
	Fire of God, Titanic Spirit 478
	Veni Creator Spiritus 479
12:27-31	God Is Here! As We His People 667
13:	Not for Tongues of Heaven's Angels 589
13:2-8	Ubi Caritas 604, 598
13:12	Love Divine, All Loves Excelling 588
15:10	Amazing Grace 583
15:14-19	This Joyful Eastertide 449
15:20	Sing with All the Saints in Glory 467
15:20-28	Come, Ye Faithful, Raise the Strain 456
15:22-23	Spirit of God within Me 480
15:25	Christ Is the World's Light 543
15:51-54	The Strife Is O'er 451
15:55	Before the Fruit Is Ripened by the Sun 418
	Christ the Lord Is Risen Today 452, 461, 462, 463
16:	When in Our Music God Is Glorified 549
16:22	Maranatha! Alleluia! 454
2 CORINTHIANS	
3:18	Love Divine, All Loves Excelling 588
4:	Thy Strong Word Didst Cleave the Darkness 511
4:5	God Is Here! As We His People 667
5:17	Love Divine, All Loves Excelling 588
	O Christ the Great Foundation 618
6:2	O Sun of Justice 424
9:10-14	Come, Ye Thankful People, Come 759
	Now Join We to Praise the Creator 647
13:11	The God of Abraham Praise 537
13:13	May the Grace of Christ Our Savior 742
GALATIANS	
2:19	Alleluia, Alleluia, Give Thanks 441
2:20	I Heard the Voice of Jesus Say 607
3:28	In Christ There Is No East or West 659
4:4	Hark! The Herald Angels Sing 387
5:22	For the Fruits of This Creation 562
	When God the Spirit Came 481
6:14	When I Survey the Wondrous Cross 433
EPHESIANS	
1:9-11	God Is Working His Purpose Out 507
1:18-19	The Church of Christ in Every Age 626
1:19-23	Holy God, We Praise Thy Name 524
2:8	Amazing Grace 583
2:11-18	Christ Is the World's Light 543

Scripture Passages Related to Hymns/*continued*

2:19-22 What Is This Place 709
2:19-23 O Christ the Great Foundation 618
2:20-22 Christ Is Made the Sure Foundation 617
3:5 Awake, O Sleeper, Rise from Death 586
3:15 Our Father, by Whose Name 570
4: There Is One Lord 657
O Christ, the Healer 747
4:1-6 In Christ There Is No East or West 659
4:5-7 O Christ the Great Foundation 618
4:8 The God of Abraham Praise 537
5:8-10 I Want to Walk as a Child of the Light 510
5:14 Awake, O Sleeper, Rise from Death 586
Christus Resurrexit 465
Wake, O Wake, and Sleep No Longer 371
5:25-27 O Christ the Great Foundation 618
5:27 Love Divine, All Loves Excelling 588
6:9 For the Fruits of This Creation 562
6:10-12 Christ's Church Shall Glory in His Power 616

PHILIPPIANS
2:1-18 Lord of All Nations, Grant Me Grace 602
2:8 Hark! The Herald Angels Sing 387
2:9-10 All Hail the Power of Jesus' Name 494, 495
The God of Abraham Praise 537
2:10-11 Creator of the Stars of Night 368
Look, O Look, the Sight Is Glorious 468
2:11-12 At the Name of Jesus 499
3:7-11 When I Survey the Wondrous Cross 433
4:4-5 Rejoice, the Lord Is King 493

COLOSSIANS
1:16 Ye Watchers and Ye Holy Ones 707
1:18 Christ the Lord Is Risen Today 452, 461, 462, 463
3:11 In Christ There Is No East or West 659
3:12-21 Our Father, by Whose Name 570
3:13-14 Forgive Our Sins 754
3:16 Come, Rejoice before Your Maker 664
When in Our Music God Is Glorified 549

2 THESSALONIANS
2:15 God Is Here! As We His People 667

1 TIMOTHY
1:5 O for a Heart to Praise My God 591
1:17 Immortal, Invisible, God Only Wise 512
6:12 Faith of Our Fathers 571
6:15-16 Immortal, Invisible, God Only Wise 512

2 TIMOTHY
2:12 The Head That Once Was Crowned with Thorns 464
2:19 How Firm a Foundation 585
2:22 O for a Heart to Praise My God 591
4:3-7 Faith of Our Fathers 571

TITUS
2:14 God Is Here! As We His People 667

PHILEMON
1:20 O for a Heart to Praise My God 591

Scripture Passages Related to Hymns/*continued*

HEBREWS

1:3	Rejoice, the Lord Is King 493
2:9-10	The Head That Once Was Crowned with Thorns 464
4:16	Draw Near and Take the Body of Your Lord 732
7:1-2	The God of Abraham Praise 537
9:11-14	Alleluia! Sing to Jesus 737
9 & 10	The King of Glory 501
10:20	Alleluia! Sing to Jesus 737
11:	Faith of Our Fathers 571
11:8-12	God Spoke to Our Father Abraham 578
11:32-40	Faith of Our Fathers 571
12:1	For All the Saints 705
	By All Your Saints Still Striving 706
	I Want to Walk as a Child of the Light 510
12:1-3	Holy God, We Praise Thy Name 524
	Take Up Your Cross 634
12:18-19	How Blessed Is This Place 710
13:5	How Firm a Foundation 585
13:6	My Shepherd Will Supply My Need 606
13:8	I Know That My Redeemer Lives 445

JAMES

1:10-17	Immortal, Invisible, God Only Wise 512
1:17	For the Beauty of the Earth 557
	From All That Dwell below the Skies 521
	I Sing the Mighty Power of God 502
	America the Beautiful 763
2:1	In Christ There Is No East or West 659
5:13-16	Great God of Mercy 746
	O Christ, the Healer 747
	O Son of God, in Galilee 748
	Your Hands, O Lord, in Days of Old 750

1 PETER

2:4-6	Christ Is Made the Sure Foundation 617
	Christ's Church Shall Glory in His Power 616
	O Christ the Great Foundation 618
2:9-10	God Is Here! As We His People 667

2 PETER

1:4	How Firm a Foundation 585

1 JOHN

1:5	I Want to Walk as a Child of the Light 510
2:9	Christ Is the World's Light 543
2:27	Come, Holy Ghost 482
	Veni Creator Spiritus 479
3:18	Faith of Our Fathers 571
4:7	Beloved, Let Us Love 601
4:7-17	Love Divine, All Loves Excelling 588
4:9-10	What Wondrous Love Is This 600
	O God of Every Nation 650
4:10-16	Where True Love and Charity Are Found/Ubi Caritas 598
4:12,16	Ubi Caritas 604
	Where True Love and Charity Are Found/Ubi Caritas 598
4:20-21	Now Join We to Praise the Creator 647
5:6-8	Come and Let Us Drink of That New River 723
5:16	Within Your House, O God, Today 743

Scripture Passages Related to Hymns/*continued*

REVELATION

1:6	Forth in the Peace of Christ 627
1:8	Of the Father's Love Begotten 398
1:9	By All Your Saints Still Striving 706
1:12-18	He Walks among the Golden Lamps 684
1:15	He Comes to Us as One Unknown 573
1:18	Rejoice, the Lord Is King 493
	The Strife Is O'er 451
2:10	For All the Saints 705
	By All Your Saints Still Striving 706
3:20	Somebody's Knockin' at Your Door 415
4:	God, We Praise You 535
	Holy, Holy, Holy! Lord God Almighty 485
4-5	Heavenly Hosts in Ceaseless Worship 522
	Holy God, We Praise Thy Name 524
4:6	Alleluia! Sing to Jesus 737
4:8	Come, Now Almighty King 487
	Of the Father's Love Begotten 398
	The God of Abraham Praise 537
4:8-11	Holy, Holy, Holy! Lord God Almighty 485
4:10	Love Divine, All Loves Excelling 588
5:	Come, We That Love the Lord 552
	This Is the Feast of Victory 458
5:9	Alleluia! Sing to Jesus 737
	At the Lamb's High Feast We Sing 459, 460
	Crown Him with Many Crowns 496
	To Jesus Christ, Our Sovereign King 497
5:11-14	All Hail the Power of Jesus' Name 494, 495
5:12	Around the Throne a Glorious Band 719
5:13	All Glory, Laud, and Honor 428, 805
	The God of Abraham Praise 537
6:9-11	All Hail the Power of Jesus' Name 494, 495
	Holy God, We Praise Thy Name 524
7:2-4,9-14	For All the Saints 705
	By All Your Saints Still Striving 706
7:9-12	From All That Dwell below the Skies 521
7:9-15	Look, O Look, the Sight Is Glorious 468
7:9,14-17	A Multitude Comes from the East and the West 688
7:9-17	Blessed Feasts of Blessed Martyrs 718
7:12-17	Around the Throne a Glorious Band 719
8:3-4	How Blessed Is This Place 710
11:15	Look, O Look, the Sight Is Glorious 468
14:17-20	Mine Eyes Have Seen the Glory 686
15:1-8	Come, We That Love the Lord 552
15:4	Holy, Holy, Holy! Lord God Almighty 485
19:1,3,4	Alleluia, Song of Gladness 413
19:6-9	Wake, O Wake, and Sleep No Longer 371
19:11-16	Come, Now Almighty King 487
	Let All Mortal Flesh Keep Silence 523
19:12	Crown Him with Many Crowns 496
19:16	Look, O Look, the Sight Is Glorious 468
21:1-4	Jerusalem, My Happy Home 690
	O Holy City, Seen of John 685
21:1-5	What Is This Place 709
21:6	Unto Us a Boy Is Born 381
21:9	O Lord, You Died That All Might Live 740
21:9-13	Wake, O Wake, and Sleep No Longer 371
21:23	I Want to Walk as a Child of the Light 510
22:	Come, We That Love the Lord 552
	Jerusalem, My Happy Home 690
	O Holy City, Seen of John 685

Scripture Passages Related to Hymns/*continued*

22:1	Come and Let Us Drink of That New River 723
22:5	Christ's Church Shall Glory in His Power 616
22:17	Come, Lord, and Tarry Not 366
	I Heard the Voice of Jesus Say 607
	We Know That Christ Is Raised 721
22:20	Maranatha! Alleluia! 454

Hymns for the Church Year 1205

The following hymns are suggested for the Sundays of the three-year lectionary cycle. Those with an asterisk (*) are directly related to the scriptures of the day, while the others are suggested because of their relationship to the predominant focus of the day's readings.

ADVENT I
A - Wake, O Wake, and Sleep No Longer 371
B - Wake, O Wake, and Sleep No Longer 371
C - Now the Day of the Lord Is at Hand* 687

ADVENT II
A - On Jordan's Bank* 356
Lo, How a Rose E'er Blooming* 374
B - Comfort, Comfort, O My People* 370
Take Comfort, God's People* 361
On Jordan's Bank* 356
C - City of God, Jerusalem* 362
On Jordan's Bank* 356

ADVENT III
A - When the King Shall Come Again* 355
B - On Jordan's Bank* 356
The Voice of God Goes Out through All the World* 358
C - On Jordan's Bank* 356

ADVENT IV
A - O Come, O Come, Emmanuel* 357
Lift Up Your Heads, O Mighty Gates* 363
B - The Angel Gabriel from Heaven Came* 695
C - Savior of the Nations, Come 372

CHRISTMAS
see nos. 374-401

HOLY FAMILY
Once in Royal David's City 402

MARY MOTHER OF GOD
see nos. 403-405

EPIPHANY
see nos. 406-411

BAPTISM OF THE LORD
When John Baptized by Jordan's River 412

LENT I
A - Forty Days and Forty Nights* 419
B - Lord, Who throughout These Forty Days* 417
C - Forty Days and Forty Nights* 419

LENT II
A - 'Tis Good, Lord, to Be Here* 700
B - God Spoke to Our Father Abraham* 578
'Tis Good, Lord, to Be Here* 700
C - 'Tis Good, Lord, to Be Here* 700

LENT III
A - I Heard the Voice of Jesus Say* 607
B - Christ Is Made the Sure Foundation 617
The Stars Declare His Glory 506
C - The God of Abraham Praise 537

LENT IV
A - He Healed the Darkness of My Mind* 749
B - A Spendthrift Lover Is the Lord* 597
By the Babylonian Rivers* 426
C - Our Father, We Have Wandered* 755

LENT V
A - I Am the Bread of Life* 738
B - Before the Fruit Is Ripened by the Sun* 418
Lift High the Cross* 704
O God beyond All Praising 541
C - Forgive Our Sins* 754

PASSION SUNDAY
see nos. 428-430

HOLY THURSDAY
see nos. 431-432

GOOD FRIDAY
see nos. 433-440

EASTER VIGIL
see nos. 441-467

EASTER
see nos. 441-467

EASTER II
A - O Sons and Daughters* 447
We Walk by Faith* 572
B - O Sons and Daughters* 447
We Walk by Faith* 572
C - O Sons and Daughters* 447
We Walk by Faith* 572

EASTER III
A - Daylight Fades* 448
B - Daylight Fades 448
C - Christian, Do You Hear the Lord* 594

EASTER IV
A - Jesus, Shepherd of Our Souls* 649
B - A Single Unmatched Stone* 574
Jesus, Shepherd of Our Souls 649
C - A Multitude Comes from the East and the West 688
Jesus, Shepherd of Our Souls 649

EASTER V
A - Come, My Way, My Truth, My Life* 569
I Know That My Redeemer Lives* 445
B - This Is My Will 590
C - Lord of All Nations, Grant Me Grace* 602
Love Is His Word* 599

Hymns for the Church Year/*continued*

O Holy City, Seen of John* 685

EASTER VI
A - Come Down, O Love Divine 472
B - This Is My Will* 590
This Is My Commandment* 603
C - O Day of Peace 654

ASCENSION
see nos. 468-471

EASTER VII
A - Alleluia! Sing to Jesus 737
B - Alleluia! Sing to Jesus 737
C - Alleluia! Sing to Jesus 737

PENTECOST
see nos. 472-483

TRINITY SUNDAY
see nos. 484-487

BODY AND BLOOD OF CHRIST
see nos. 488-489

SACRED HEART
see nos. 490-491

ORDINARY TIME

SECOND SUNDAY
A - When Jesus Came to Jordan* 697
B - Those Who Love and Those Who Labor* 632
C - Jesus, Come! For We Invite You* 564

THIRD SUNDAY
A - Two Fishermen* 633
B - Two Fishermen* 633
C - The Voice of God Goes Out through All the World* 358

FOURTH SUNDAY
A - O Blessed Are the Poor in Spirit* 620
B - Silence! Frenzied, Unclean Spirit* 751
C - Not for Tongues of Heaven's Angels* 589

FIFTH SUNDAY
A - I Want to Walk as a Child of the Light 510
Let There Be Light 653
B - Your Hands, O Lord, in Days of Old 750
C - Two Fishermen* 633
Glorious in Majesty* 619

SIXTH SUNDAY
A - What Does the Lord Require 624
The Stars Declare His Glory 506
B - Your Hands, O Lord, in Days of Old* 750
C - O Blessed Are the Poor in Spirit* 620

SEVENTH SUNDAY
A - Lord of All Nations, Grant Me Grace* 602
B - Your Hands, O Lord, in Days of Old 750
C - Lord of All Nations, Grant Me Grace* 602

EIGHTH SUNDAY
A - Seek Ye First the Kingdom of God* 580
B - It Shocked Them That the Master Did Not Fast* 637
C - O for a Heart to Praise My God 591

NINTH SUNDAY
A - Christ Is Made the Sure Foundation 617
B - This Is the Day When Light Was First Created 663
C - Surely It Is God Who Saves Me 584

TENTH SUNDAY
A - Come, You Sinners, Poor and Needy 756
B - Silence! Frenzied, Unclean Spirit 751
C - Your Hands, O Lord, in Days of Old 750

ELEVENTH SUNDAY
A - When Jesus Came Preaching the Kingdom of God 614
B - The Kingdom of God 615
C - There's a Wideness in God's Mercy 595, 596

TWELFTH SUNDAY
A - By Gracious Powers 577
B - How Firm a Foundation* 585
C - Take Up Your Cross* 634

THIRTEENTH SUNDAY
A - Take Up Your Cross* 634
B - O Jesus Christ, May Grateful Hymns Be Rising 646
C - Weary of All Trumpeting* 635
Glorious in Majesty* 619

FOURTEENTH SUNDAY
A - All You Who Seek a Comfort Sure* 490
B - God Has Spoken by His Prophets 516
C - Lord, You Give the Great Commission 470

FIFTEENTH SUNDAY
A - Word of God, Come Down on Earth* 513
B - Lord, You Give the Great Commission 470
C - Lord of All Nations, Grant Me Grace* 602

SIXTEENTH SUNDAY
A - Come, Ye Thankful People, Come* 759
B - There's a Wideness in God's Mercy* 595, 596
C - We Are Your People 623
What Does the Lord Require 624

SEVENTEENTH SUNDAY
A - O the Beautiful Treasures 689
B - Praise and Thanksgiving 682
C - Seek Ye First the Kingdom of God* 580

Hymns for the Church Year/*continued*

EIGHTEENTH SUNDAY
A - You Satisfy the Hungry Heart 736
B - Shepherd of Souls* 728
C - O the Beautiful Treasures 689

NINETEENTH SUNDAY
A - How Firm a Foundation* 585
I Sought the Lord* 593
B - I Am the Bread of Life* 738
C - This World, My God, Is Held within Your Hand* 582
What Does the Lord Require 624

TWENTIETH SUNDAY
A - O God, Empower Us 642
B - I Am the Bread of Life* 738
C - God, Whose Purpose Is to Kindle* 640

TWENTY-FIRST SUNDAY
A - Christ's Church Shall Glory in His Power 616
B - I Am the Bread of Life* 738
The Church of Christ in Every Age 626
The Kingdom of God 615
C - A Multitude Comes from the East and the West* 688

TWENTY-SECOND SUNDAY
A - Take Up Your Cross* 634
B - O for a Heart to Praise My God 591
C - Gather Us In 665

TWENTY-THIRD SUNDAY
A - Draw Us in the Spirit's Tether* 731
B - O Son of God, in Galilee* 748
C - Take Up Your Cross* 634

TWENTY-FOURTH SUNDAY
A - Forgive Our Sins* 754
B - Take Up Your Cross* 634
C - Our Father, We Have Wandered* 755

TWENTY-FIFTH SUNDAY
A - There's a Wideness in God's Mercy 595, 596
B - The Church of Christ in Every Age 626
C - God, Whose Giving Knows No Ending 631

TWENTY-SIXTH SUNDAY
A - At the Name of Jesus* 499
Our Father, We Have Wandered 755
B - How Good the Name of Jesus Sounds 610
C - God, Whose Purpose Is to Kindle 640

TWENTY-SEVENTH SUNDAY
A - A Single Unmatched Stone* 574
Christ Is Made the Sure Foundation 617
B - A Spendthrift Lover Is the Lord 597
Our Father, by Whose Name 570
C - The Church of Christ in Every Age 626

TWENTY-EIGHTH SUNDAY
A - City of God, Jerusalem* 362
Gather Us In* 665
B - Weary of All Trumpeting 635
C - Surely It Is God Who Saves Me 584

TWENTY-NINTH SUNDAY
A - Reap Me the Earth 544
B - The Church of Christ in Every Age 626
C - God Is My Great Desire 581

THIRTIETH SUNDAY
A - Lord of All Nations, Grant Me Grace* 602
B - Your Hands, O Lord, in Days of Old 750
C - What Does the Lord Require 624

THIRTY-FIRST SUNDAY
A - What Does the Lord Require 624
B - God Be in My Head 567
C - I Heard the Voice of Jesus Say 607

THIRTY-SECOND SUNDAY
A - Wake, O Wake, and Sleep No Longer* 371
Who Can Measure Heaven and Earth 509
B - Where Temple Offerings Are Made* 622
C - God Is My Great Desire 581
The God of Abraham Praise 537

THIRTY-THIRD SUNDAY
A - God, Whose Giving Knows No Ending* 631
O the Beautiful Treasures 689
B - Now the Day of the Lord Is at Hand 687
C - Now the Day of the Lord Is at Hand 687

CHRIST THE KING
see nos. 492-501

1206 Liturgical Index

SEASONS AND FEASTS

ADVENT

360 Awake! Awake, and Greet the New Morn
429 Benedictus Qui Venit
362 City of God, Jerusalem
366 Come, Lord, and Tarry Not
569 Come, My Way, My Truth, My Life
364 Come, O Long Expected Jesus
370 Comfort, Comfort, O My People
368 Creator of the Stars of Night
619 Glorious in Majesty
684 He Walks among the Golden Lamps
365 Hills of the North, Rejoice
510 I Want to Walk as a Child of the Light
523 Let All Mortal Flesh Keep Silence
363 Lift Up Your Heads, O Mighty Gates
374 Lo, How a Rose E'er Blooming
588 Love Divine, All Loves Excelling
553 Magnificat
687 Now the Day of the Lord Is at Hand
367 O Come, Divine Messiah
357 O Come, O Come, Emmanuel
654 O Day of Peace
356 On Jordan's Bank
359 People, Look East
696 Praise We the Lord This Day
369 Prepare the Way of the Lord
493 Rejoice, the Lord Is King
372 Savior of the Nations, Come
550 Sing a New Song to the Lord
584 Surely It Is God Who Saves Me
361 Take Comfort, God's People
695 The Angel Gabriel from Heaven Came
405 The God Whom Earth and Sea and Sky
501 The King of Glory
373 The King Shall Come When Morning Dawns
358 The Voice of God Goes Out through All the World
371 Wake, O Wake, and Sleep No Longer
697 When Jesus Came to Jordan
355 When the King Shall Come Again
(also Topical Index: Second Coming, Trust)

CHRISTMAS SEASON

384 A Child Is Born in Bethlehem
385 A Stable Lamp Is Lighted
395 Angel Voices Richly Blending
377 Angels, from the Realms of Glory
376 Angels We Have Heard on High
360 Awake! Awake, and Greet the New Morn
378 Away in a Manger
396 Christ Was Born on Christmas Day
388 From Heaven Above
401 Gloria, Gloria
397 Go Tell It on the Mountain
383 God Rest You Merry, Gentlemen
391 Good Christian Friends, Rejoice
387 Hark! The Herald Angels Sing
389 How Brightly Beams the Morning Star
390 How Brightly Beams the Morning Star
393 Infant Holy, Infant Lowly
400 It Came upon the Midnight Clear
399 Joy to the World
523 Let All Mortal Flesh Keep Silence
363 Lift Up Your Heads, O Mighty Gates
374 Lo, How a Rose E'er Blooming
394 Now Every Child That Dwells on Earth
392 O Come, All Ye Faithful/Adeste Fideles
386 O Little Town of Bethlehem
398 Of the Father's Love Begotten
402 Once in Royal David's City
372 Savior of the Nations, Come
375 See amid the Winter's Snow
379 Silent Night, Holy Night
361 Take Comfort, God's People
695 The Angel Gabriel from Heaven Came
408 The First Nowell
405 The God Whom Earth and Sea and Sky
380 'Twas in the Moon of Wintertime
381 Unto Us a Boy Is Born
403 Virgin-born, We Bow before You
371 Wake, O Wake, and Sleep No Longer
411 What Child Is This
407 What Star Is This
382 While Shepherds Watched

HOLY FAMILY

742 May the Grace of Christ Our Savior
402 Once in Royal David's City
404 Sing of Mary, Pure and Lowly
403 Virgin-born, We Bow before You
411 What Child Is This
(also Christmas season)

MARY, MOTHER OF GOD

713 Ave Maria
374 Lo, How a Rose E'er Blooming
711 Mary, How Lovely the Light of Your Glory
398 Of the Father's Love Begotten
404 Sing of Mary, Pure and Lowly
405 The God Whom Earth and Sea and Sky
403 Virgin-born, We Bow before You

EPIPHANY

395 Angel Voices Richly Blending
377 Angels, from the Realms of Glory
409 As with Gladness Men of Old
401 Gloria, Gloria
389 How Brightly Beams the Morning Star
390 How Brightly Beams the Morning Star
510 I Want to Walk as a Child of the Light
668 Now the Silence
386 O Little Town of Bethlehem
410 Songs of Thankfulness and Praise
408 The First Nowell
511 Thy Strong Word Didst Cleave the Darkness
380 'Twas in the Moon of Wintertime
406 We Three Kings of Orient Are
411 What Child Is This
407 What Star Is This
(also Christmas season)

BAPTISM OF THE LORD

356 On Jordan's Bank
410 Songs of Thankfulness and Praise
412 When John Baptized by Jordan's River

SUNDAY BEFORE LENT

413 Alleluia, Song of Gladness

ASH WEDNESDAY

419 Forty Days and Forty Nights
414 Hear Us, Almighty Lord/Attende Domine
417 Lord, Who throughout These Forty Days
416 Parce Domine
422 The Glory of These Forty Days

LENTEN SEASON

597 A Spendthrift Lover Is the Lord
420 Again We Keep This Solemn Fast
421 At the Cross Her Station Keeping
418 Before the Fruit Is Ripened by the Sun
426 By the Babylonian Rivers
617 Christ Is Made the Sure Foundation
754 Forgive Our Sins
419 Forty Days and Forty Nights
578 God Spoke to Our Father Abraham
753 Have Mercy, Lord, on Us
749 He Healed the Darkness of My Mind
414 Hear Us, Almighty Lord/Attende Domine
738 I Am the Bread of Life
636 I Danced in the Morning
607 I Heard the Voice of Jesus Say
637 It Shocked Them That the Master Did Not Fast
423 Jesus, Remember Me
649 Jesus, Shepherd of Our Souls
427 Jesus Walked This Lonesome Valley
704 Lift High the Cross
417 Lord, Who throughout These Forty Days
439 My Song Is Love Unknown
591 O for a Heart to Praise My God
424 O Sun of Justice
755 Our Father, We Have Wandered
416 Parce Domine
644 Said Judas to Mary
425 Salvator Mundi
415 Somebody's Knockin' at Your Door
634 Take Up Your Cross
422 The Glory of These Forty Days
537 The God of Abraham Praise
506 The Stars Declare His Glory
595 There's a Wideness in God's Mercy
596 There's a Wideness in God's Mercy
700 'Tis Good, Lord, to Be Here
635 Weary of All Trumpeting
624 What Does the Lord Require
600 What Wondrous Love Is This
549 When in Our Music God Is Glorified
508 When Israel Was in Egypt's Land
638 Your Love, O God, Has All the World Created
(also Cross, Mercy, Sin, Social Concern)

PASSION SUNDAY (PALM SUNDAY)

428 All Glory, Laud, and Honor
805 All Glory, Laud, and Honor
499 At the Name of Jesus
429 Benedictus Qui Venit
496 Crown Him with Many Crowns
430 Hosanna in Excelsis
704 Lift High the Cross
363 Lift Up Your Heads, O Mighty Gates
434 O Sacred Head Surrounded
634 Take Up Your Cross

Liturgical Index/*continued*

436 Were You There
(also Lenten Season, Christ the King, Easter triduum)

HOLY THURSDAY (CHRISM MASS)
470 Lord, You Give the Great Commission
603 This Is My Commandment
590 This Is My Will
(also Ministry, Service)

EASTER TRIDUUM

HOLY THURSDAY (EVENING MASS OF THE LORD'S SUPPER
733 At That First Eucharist
730 Ave Verum
601 Beloved, Let Us Love
731 Draw Us in the Spirit's Tether
813 Hail Our Savior's Glorious Body/Pange Lingua
431 Jesu, Jesu, Fill Us with Your Love
432 Jesus Took a Towel
704 Lift High the Cross
599 Love Is His Word
812 Mandatum Novum
437 Sing, My Tongue, the Song of Triumph
435 The Royal Banners Forward Go
590 This Is My Will
604 Ubi Caritas (Taizé)
598 Where True Love and Charity Are Found/Ubi Caritas
(also Good Friday, Eucharist)

GOOD FRIDAY
548 Adoramus Te Domine
440 All You Who Pass This Way
421 At the Cross Her Station Keeping
730 Ave Verum
418 Before the Fruit Is Ripened by the Sun
427 Jesus Walked This Lonesome Valley
704 Lift High the Cross
438 Lord Christ, When First You Came to Earth
439 My Song Is Love Unknown
434 O Sacred Head Surrounded
416 Parce Domine
435 The Royal Banners Forward Go
425 Salvator Mundi
437 Sing, My Tongue, the Song of Triumph
436 Were You There
600 What Wondrous Love Is This
433 When I Survey the Wondrous Cross

EASTER VIGIL
578 God Spoke to Our Father Abraham
618 O Christ the Great Foundation
455 Rejoice, Angelic Choirs
508 When Israel Was in Egypt's Land
(also Easter season)

EASTER SEASON
441 Alleluia, Alleluia, Give Thanks
459 At the Lamb's High Feast We Sing
460 At the Lamb's High Feast We Sing
450 Be Joyful, Mary
466 Christ Is Alive!
543 Christ Is the World's Light
681 Christ, Mighty Savior
452 Christ the Lord Is Risen Today
461 Christ the Lord Is Risen Today
462 Christ the Lord Is Risen Today
463 Christ the Lord Is Risen Today
465 Christus Resurrexit
496 Crown Him with Many Crowns
723 Come and Let Us Drink of That New River
552 Come, We That Love the Lord
456 Come, Ye Faithful, Raise the Strain
448 Daylight Fades
518 Glory Be to God in Heaven
471 Hail the Day That Sees Him Rise
444 Hail Thee, Festival Day
389 How Brightly Beams the Morning Star
390 How Brightly Beams the Morning Star
738 I Am the Bread of Life
636 I Danced in the Morning
445 I Know That My Redeemer Lives
661 Is This a Day of New Beginnings
442 Jesus Christ Is Risen Today
492 Jesus Shall Reign
523 Let All Mortal Flesh Keep Silence
704 Lift High the Cross
454 Maranatha! Alleluia!
446 Morning of Splendor
453 Now the Green Blade Rises
443 O Queen of Heaven/Regina Caeli
447 O Sons and Daughters
662 On This Day, the First of Days
455 Rejoice, Angelic Choirs
425 Salvator Mundi
540 Shout for Joy, Loud and Long
467 Sing with All the Saints in Glory
457 That Easter Day with Joy Was Bright
464 The Head That Once Was Crowned with Thorns
451 The Strife Is O'er
663 This Is the Day When Light Was First Created
458 This Is the Feast of Victory
449 This Joyful Eastertide
511 Thy Strong Word Didst Cleave the Darkness
721 We Know That Christ Is Raised
707 Ye Watchers and Ye Holy Ones

ASCENSION
469 A Hymn of Glory Let Us Sing
494 All Hail the Power of Jesus' Name
495 All Hail the Power of Jesus' Name
737 Alleluia! Sing to Jesus
466 Christ Is Alive!
462 Christ the Lord Is Risen Today
463 Christ the Lord Is Risen Today
723 Come and Let Us Drink of That New River
496 Crown Him with Many Crowns
518 Glory Be to God in Heaven
471 Hail the Day That Sees Him Rise
444 Hail Thee, Festival Day
492 Jesus Shall Reign
468 Look, O Look, the Sight Is Glorious
470 Lord, You Give the Great Commission
493 Rejoice, the Lord Is King
464 The Head That Once Was Crowned with Thorns
497 To Jesus Christ, Our Sovereign King
707 Ye Watchers and Ye Holy Ones
(also Easter season)

PENTECOST
586 Awake, O Sleeper, Rise from Death
538 Christians, Lift Up Your Hearts
472 Come Down, O Love Divine
482 Come, Holy Ghost
731 Draw Us in the Spirit's Tether
478 Fire of God, Titanic Spirit
474 Fire of God, Undying Flame
542 Glory to God in the Highest
724 God Sends Us His Spirit
640 God, Whose Purpose Is to Kindle
573 He Comes to Us as One Unknown
602 Lord of All Nations, Grant Me Grace
668 Now the Silence
725 O Breathe on Me, O Breath of God
618 O Christ the Great Foundation
475 O Holy Spirit, by Whose Breath
646 O Jesus Christ, May Grateful Hymns Be Rising
483 Over the Chaos of the Empty Waters
477 Praise the Spirit in Creation
476 Spirit Divine, Accept Our Prayers
480 Spirit of God within Me
531 There's a Spirit in the Air
663 This Is the Day When Light Was First Created
479 Veni Creator Spiritus
473 Veni Sancte Spiritus (Taizé)
481 When God the Spirit Came
412 When John Baptized by Jordan's River
(also Confirmation)

ORDINARY TIME *(see Hymn for the Church Year Index)*

SOLEMNITIES OF THE LORD IN ORDINARY TIME

TRINITY SUNDAY
487 Come, Now Almighty King
655 Father, Lord of All Creation
518 Glory Be to God in Heaven
542 Glory to God in the Highest
592 God Is Unique and One
535 God, We Praise You
486 God, Whose Almighty Word
485 Holy, Holy, Holy! Lord God Almighty
560 Now Thank We All Our God
679 O Gladsome Light
484 O God, Almighty Father
662 On This Day, the First of Days
570 Our Father, by Whose Name
673 This Day God Gives Me
680 We Praise You, Father

BODY AND BLOOD OF CHRIST
730 Ave Verum
758 Come Adore/Tantum Ergo
489 God with Hidden Majesty/Adoro Te Devote
813 Hail Our Savior's Glorious Body/Pange Lingua
488 Jesus, My Lord, My God, My All
599 Love Is His Word
757 O Saving Victim/O Salutaris
736 You Satisfy the Hungry Heart
(also Eucharist)

SACRED HEART
490 All You Who Seek a Comfort Sure
730 Ave Verum
723 Come and Let Us Drink of That New River
569 Come, My Way, My Truth, My Life
607 I Heard the Voice of Jesus Say
729 O Food of Exiles Lowly
591 O for a Heart to Praise My God
605 O Jesus, Joy of Loving Hearts
595 There's a Wideness in God's Mercy
596 There's a Wideness in God's Mercy

Liturgical Index/*continued*

491 To Christ, the Prince of Peace

CHRIST THE KING
469 A Hymn of Glory Let Us Sing
428 All Glory, Laud, and Honor
805 All Glory, Laud, and Honor
494 All Hail the Power of Jesus' Name
495 All Hail the Power of Jesus' Name
737 Alleluia! Sing to Jesus
459 At the Lamb's High Feast We Sing
460 At the Lamb's High Feast We Sing
499 At the Name of Jesus
429 Benedictus Qui Venit
466 Christ Is Alive!
500 Christ Is the King
462 Christ the Lord Is Risen Today
463 Christ the Lord Is Risen Today
616 Christ's Church Shall Glory in His Power
366 Come, Lord, and Tarry Not
487 Come, Now Almighty King
552 Come, We That Love the Lord
496 Crown Him with Many Crowns
705 For All the Saints
627 Forth in the Peace of Christ
619 Glorious in Majesty
592 God Is Unique and One
535 God, We Praise You
498 He Is King of Kings
684 He Walks among the Golden Lamps
430 Hosanna in Excelsis
423 Jesus, Remember Me
492 Jesus Shall Reign
432 Jesus Took a Towel
536 Let All the World in Every Corner Sing
363 Lift Up Your Heads, O Mighty Gates
468 Look, O Look, the Sight Is Glorious
686 Mine Eyes Have Seen the Glory
530 Praise, My Soul, the King of Heaven
493 Rejoice, the Lord Is King
618 O Christ the Great Foundation
464 The Head That Once Was Crowned with Thorns
501 The King of Glory
373 The King Shall Come When Morning Dawns
458 This Is the Feast of Victory
497 To Jesus Christ, Our Sovereign King

SOLEMNITIES AND FEASTS

PRESENTATION OF THE LORD (February 2)
692 Hail to the Lord Who Comes
691 Lord, Bid Your Servant Go in Peace
676 Nunc Dimittis

JOSEPH, HUSBAND OF MARY (March 19)
694 Come Now, and Praise the Humble Saint
693 Joseph, Be Our Guide and Pattern

THE ANNUNCIATION OF THE LORD (March 25)
713 Ave Maria
708 Immaculate Mary
696 Praise We the Lord This Day
714 Sing We of the Blessed Mother
695 The Angel Gabriel from Heaven Came
405 The God Whom Earth and Sea and Sky

BIRTH OF JOHN THE BAPTIST (June 24 - Vigil and Day)
706 By All Your Saints Still Striving
698 The Great Forerunner of the Morn
697 When Jesus Came to Jordan
412 When John Baptized by Jordan's River

PETER AND PAUL (June 29 - Vigil and Day)
699 Two Noble Saints

TRANSFIGURATION (August 6)
701 Christ upon the Mountain Peak
422 The Glory of These Forty Days
700 'Tis Good, Lord, to Be Here

ASSUMPTION (August 15)
702 Hail, Holy Queen Enthroned Above
703 Hail, Queen of Heaven/Salve Regina
711 Mary, How Lovely the Light of Your Glory

TRIUMPH OF THE CROSS (September 14)
704 Lift High the Cross
437 Sing, My Tongue, the Song of Triumph
634 Take Up Your Cross
635 Weary of All Trumpeting
433 When I Survey the Wondrous Cross

ALL SAINTS (November 1)
706 By All Your Saints Still Striving
552 Come, We That Love the Lord
705 For All the Saints
535 God, We Praise You
620 O Blessed Are the Poor in Spirit
467 Sing with All the Saints in Glory
707 Ye Watchers and Ye Holy Ones

ALL SOULS (November 2)
741 Let Saints on Earth in Concert Sing
739 Lord of the Living

IMMACULATE CONCEPTION (December 8)
708 Immaculate Mary

DEDICATION OF A CHURCH
669 All People That On Earth Do Dwell
670 All People That On Earth Do Dwell
617 Christ Is Made the Sure Foundation
710 How Blessed Is This Place
618 O Christ the Great Foundation
666 Only Begotten, Word of God Eternal
709 What Is This Place

BLESSED VIRGIN MARY (also Mary, Mother of God
421 At the Cross Her Station Keeping
713 Ave Maria
450 Be Joyful, Mary
702 Hail, Holy Queen Enthroned Above
703 Hail, Queen of Heaven/Salve Regina
708 Immaculate Mary
553 Magnificat
711 Mary, How Lovely the Light of Your Glory
443 O Queen of Heaven/Regina Caeli
712 O Sanctissima
696 Praise We the Lord This Day
404 Sing of Mary, Pure and Lowly
714 Sing We of the Blessed Mother
534 Tell Out, My Soul, the Greatness of the Lord
695 The Angel Gabriel from Heaven Came

HOLY WOMEN
715 Let Us with Joy Our Voices Raise

APOSTLES
577 By Gracious Powers
535 God, We Praise You
716 Let All on Earth Their Voices Raise
653 Let There Be Light
717 This Is the Feast Day of the Lord's True Witness
707 Ye Watchers and Ye Holy Ones

HOLY MEN
717 This Is the Feast Day of the Lord's True Witness

MARTYRS
494 All Hail the Power of Jesus' Name
495 All Hail the Power of Jesus' Name
719 Around the Throne a Glorious Band
718 Blessed Feasts of Blessed Martyrs
706 By All Your Saints Still Striving
577 By Gracious Powers
705 For All the Saints
535 God, We Praise You
653 Let There Be Light
707 Ye Watchers and Ye Holy Ones

RITES OF THE CHURCH

BAPTISM OF CHILDREN
520 All Creatures of Our God and King
459 At the Lamb's High Feast We Sing
460 At the Lamb's High Feast We Sing
586 Awake, O Sleeper, Rise from Death
720 Baptized in Water
617 Christ Is Made the Sure Foundation
723 Come and Let Us Drink of That New River
569 Come, My Way, My Truth, My Life
456 Come, Ye Faithful, Raise the Strain
628 Go Make of All Disciples
588 Love Divine, All Loves Excelling
618 O Christ the Great Foundation
657 There Is One Lord
722 This Is the Spirit's Entry Now
491 To Christ, the Prince of Peace
633 Two Fishermen
721 We Know That Christ Is Raised
412 When John Baptized by Jordan's River
(also Topical Index: Praise, Church, Commitment, Discipleship, Trust, Light, Providence, Saints)

CHRISTIAN INITIATION OF ADULTS
520 All Creatures of Our God and King
459 At the Lamb's High Feast We Sing
460 At the Lamb's High Feast We Sing
586 Awake, O Sleeper, Rise from Death
720 Baptized in Water
617 Christ Is Made the Sure Foundation
723 Come and Let Us Drink of That New River
569 Come, My Way, My Truth, My Life
456 Come, Ye Faithful, Raise the Strain

Liturgical Index/*continued*

628 Go Make of All Disciples
640 God, Whose Purpose Is to Kindle
656 Help Us Accept Each Other
607 I Heard the Voice of Jesus Say
611 Jesus, Lead the Way
618 O Christ the Great Foundation
615 The Kingdom of God
657 There Is One Lord
722 This Is the Spirit's Entry Now
633 Two Fishermen
721 We Know That Christ Is Raised
412 When John Baptized by Jordan's River
(also Confirmation, Baptism of Children, Advent, Easter; Topical Index: Praise, Church, Commitment, Discipleship, Trust, Light, Saints, Thanksgiving)

CONFIRMATION
586 Awake, O Sleeper, Rise from Death
472 Come Down, O Love Divine
482 Come, Holy Ghost
731 Draw Us in the Spirit's Tether
627 Forth in the Peace of Christ
665 Gather Us In
542 Glory to God in the Highest
628 Go Make of All Disciples
724 God Sends Us His Spirit
640 God, Whose Purpose Is to Kindle
444 Hail Thee, Festival Day
611 Jesus, Lead the Way
602 Lord of All Nations, Grant Me Grace
725 O Breathe on Me, O Breath of God
618 O Christ the Great Foundation
591 O for a Heart to Praise My God
642 O God, Empower Us
475 O Holy Spirit, by Whose Breath
646 O Jesus Christ, May Grateful Hymns Be Rising
476 Spirit Divine, Accept Our Prayers
634 Take Up Your Cross
615 The Kingdom of God
531 There's a Spirit in the Air
633 Two Fishermen
479 Veni Creator Spiritus
473 Veni Sancte Spiritus (Taizé)
(also Baptism of Children, Pentecost, Christian Initiation of Adults; Topical Index: Brotherhood & Sisterhood, Commitment, Discipleship, Ministry, Mission)

EUCHARIST
737 Alleluia! Sing to Jesus
733 At That First Eucharist
459 At the Lamb's High Feast We Sing
460 At the Lamb's High Feast We Sing
730 Ave Verum
465 Christus Resurrexit
758 Come Adore/Tantum Ergo
723 Come and Let Us Drink of That New River
732 Draw Near and Take the Body of Your Lord
731 Draw Us in the Spirit's Tether
734 Eat This Bread
558 Father, We Thank Thee, Who Hast Planted
665 Gather Us In
578 God Spoke to Our Father Abraham
489 God with Hidden Majesty/Adoro Te Devote
813 Hail Our Savior's Glorious Body/Pange Lingua
656 Help Us Accept Each Other
738 I Am the Bread of Life
726 I Come with Joy to Meet My Lord
607 I Heard the Voice of Jesus Say
735 I Received the Living God
593 I Sought the Lord
510 I Want to Walk as a Child of the Light
431 Jesu, Jesu, Fill Us with Your Love
564 Jesus, Come! For We Invite You
523 Let All Mortal Flesh Keep Silence
727 Let Us Break Bread Together
658 Lord Christ, the Father's Mighty Son
599 Love Is His Word
454 Maranatha! Alleluia!
587 Morning Glory, Starlit Sky
589 Not for Tongues of Heaven's Angels
625 Now Let Us from This Table Rise
668 Now the Silence
729 O Food of Exiles Lowly
605 O Jesus, Joy of Loving Hearts
757 O Saving Victim/O Salutaris
447 O Sons and Daughters
728 Shepherd of Souls
609 The King of Love My Shepherd Is
612 The Living God My Shepherd Is
613 The Lord, the Lord, the Lord Is My Shepherd
657 There Is One Lord
603 This Is My Commandment
590 This Is My Will
604 Ubi Caritas
709 What Is This Place
598 Where True Love and Charity Are Found/Ubi Caritas
736 You Satisfy the Hungry Heart
(also Feasts of the Lord; Topical Index: Praise, Thanksgiving)

FUNERAL
688 A Multitude Comes from the East and the West
520 All Creatures of Our God and King
737 Alleluia! Sing to Jesus
583 Amazing Grace
459 At the Lamb's High Feast We Sing
460 At the Lamb's High Feast We Sing
586 Awake, O Sleeper, Rise from Death
418 Before the Fruit Is Ripened by the Sun
706 By All Your Saints Still Striving
452 Christ the Lord Is Risen Today
461 Christ the Lord Is Risen Today
462 Christ the Lord Is Risen Today
463 Christ the Lord Is Risen Today
594 Christian, Do You Hear the Lord
362 City of God, Jerusalem
723 Come and Let Us Drink of That New River
569 Come, My Way, My Truth, My Life
496 Crown Him with Many Crowns
677 Day Is Done
734 Eat This Bread
705 For All the Saints
567 God Be in My Head
573 He Comes to Us as One Unknown
585 How Firm a Foundation
738 I Am the Bread of Life
607 I Heard the Voice of Jesus Say
445 I Know That My Redeemer Lives
735 I Received the Living God
593 I Sought the Lord
510 I Want to Walk as a Child of the Light
690 Jerusalem, My Happy Home
442 Jesus Christ Is Risen Today
611 Jesus, Lead the Way
423 Jesus, Remember Me
525 Joyful, Joyful, We Adore You
741 Let Saints on Earth in Concert Sing
568 Lord of All Hopefulness
556 Lord of Our Growing Years
739 Lord of the Living
606 My Shepherd Will Supply My Need
453 Now the Green Blade Rises
668 Now the Silence
676 Nunc Dimittis
729 O Food of Exiles Lowly
579 O God, Our Help in Ages Past
740 O Lord, You Died That All Might Live
689 O the Beautiful Treasures
728 Shepherd of Souls
467 Sing with All the Saints in Glory
537 The God of Abraham Praise
609 The King of Love My Shepherd Is
612 The Living God My Shepherd Is
613 The Lord, the Lord, the Lord Is My Shepherd
451 The Strife Is O'er
608 There Is a Balm in Gilead
497 To Jesus Christ, Our Sovereign King
371 Wake, O Wake, and Sleep No Longer
680 We Praise You, Father
572 We Walk by Faith
600 What Wondrous Love Is This
707 Ye Watchers and Ye Holy Ones
(also Death, Easter, Eternal Life)

MARRIAGE
597 A Spendthrift Lover Is the Lord
601 Beloved, Let Us Love
569 Come, My Way, My Truth, My Life
564 Jesus, Come! For We Invite You
556 Lord of Our Growing Years
588 Love Divine, All Loves Excelling
742 May the Grace of Christ Our Savior
589 Not for Tongues of Heaven's Angels
744 O Father, All Creating
590 This Is My Will
604 Ubi Caritas
745 When Love Is Found
598 Where True Love and Charity Are Found/Ubi Caritas
743 Within Your House, O God, Today
(also Topical Index: Praise, Commitment, Love, Thanksgiving, Vocation)

PASTORAL CARE OF THE SICK
490 All You Who Seek a Comfort Sure
583 Amazing Grace
577 By Gracious Powers
594 Christian, Do You Hear the Lord
569 Come, My Way, My Truth, My Life
677 Day Is Done
746 Great God of Mercy
749 He Healed the Darkness of My Mind
585 How Firm a Foundation
610 How Good the Name of Jesus Sounds
607 I Heard the Voice of Jesus Say
593 I Sought the Lord
611 Jesus, Lead the Way
568 Lord of All Hopefulness
587 Morning Glory, Starlit Sky
606 My Shepherd Will Supply My Need
747 O Christ, the Healer
541 O God beyond All Praising
642 O God, Empower Us
748 O Son of God, in Galilee

Liturgical Index/*continued*

580 Seek Ye First the Kingdom of God
751 Silence! Frenzied, Unclean Spirit
634 Take Up Your Cross
612 The Living God My Shepherd Is
613 The Lord, the Lord, the Lord Is My Shepherd
752 The Master Came to Bring Good News
608 There Is a Balm in Gilead
595 There's a Wideness in God's Mercy
596 There's a Wideness in God's Mercy
600 What Wondrous Love Is This
750 Your Hands, O Lord, in Days of Old

PENANCE
583 Amazing Grace
586 Awake, O Sleeper, Rise from Death
426 By the Babylonian Rivers
594 Christian, Do You Hear the Lord
569 Come, My Way, My Truth, My Life
756 Come, You Sinners, Poor and Needy
368 Creator of the Stars of Night
754 Forgive Our Sins
746 Great God of Mercy
753 Have Mercy, Lord, on Us
414 Hear Us, Almighty Lord/Attende Domine
656 Help Us Accept Each Other
585 How Firm a Foundation
610 How Good the Name of Jesus Sounds
649 Jesus, Shepherd of Our Souls
525 Joyful, Joyful, We Adore You
636 I Danced in the Morning
607 I Heard the Voice of Jesus Say
593 I Sought the Lord
658 Lord Christ, the Father's Mighty Son
602 Lord of All Nations, Grant Me Grace
553 Magnificat
587 Morning Glory, Starlit Sky
606 My Shepherd Will Supply My Need
668 Now the Silence
591 O for a Heart to Praise My God
755 Our Father, We Have Wandered
416 Parce Domine
660 Peace with the Father
644 Said Judas to Mary
580 Seek Ye First the Kingdom of God
415 Somebody's Knockin' at Your Door
609 The King of Love My Shepherd Is
615 The Kingdom of God
612 The Living God My Shepherd Is
613 The Lord, the Lord, the Lord Is My Shepherd
752 The Master Came to Bring Good News
608 There Is a Balm in Gilead
657 There Is One Lord
595 There's a Wideness in God's Mercy
596 There's a Wideness in God's Mercy
624 What Does the Lord Require
600 What Wondrous Love Is This
638 Your Love, O God, Has All the World Created
(also Topical Index: Praise, Consolation, Love of God for Us, Trust, Mercy, Reconciliation, Repentance, Thanksgiving)

BENEDICTION
730 Ave Verum
758 Come Adore/Tantum Ergo
489 God with Hidden Majesty/Adoro Te Devote
813 Hail Our Savior's Glorious Body/Pange Lingua
488 Jesus, My Lord, My God, My All
757 O Saving Victim/O Salutaris
(also Body and Blood of Christ, Eucharist; Topical Index: Praise, Providence, Thanksgiving)

STATIONS OF THE CROSS
421 At the Cross Her Station Keeping

Topical Index 1207

ANGELS
548 Adoramus Te Domine
815 Ádoramus Te Domine
494 All Hail The Power of Jesus' Name
495 All Hail The Power of Jesus' Name
377 Angels from The Realms of Glory
376 Angels We Have Heard on High
419 Forty Days and Forty Nights
387 Hark, the Herald Angels Sing
522 Heavenly Hosts in Ceaseless Worship
524 Holy God We Praise Thy Name
485 Holy, Holy, Holy! Lord God Almighty
710 How Blessed is this Place, O Lord
400 It Came Upon the Midnight Clear
523 Let All Mortal Flesh Keep Silence
539 Sing Praise to the Lord
398 Of the Father's Love Begotten
530 Praise, My Soul, The King of Heaven
529 Praise The Lord! You Heav'ns Adore Him
707 Ye Watchers and Ye Holy Ones

ART
566 Come To Us, Creative Spirit
557 For the Beauty of the Earth
667 God Is Here! As We His People
549 When in Our Music God Is Glorified

BEAUTY
520 All Creatures of Our God and King
505 All Things Bright and Beautiful
557 For the Beauty of the Earth
716 Let All on Earth Their Voices Raise
541 O God beyond All Praising

BLESSING
617 Christ Is Made the Sure Foundation
569 Come, My Way, My Truth, My Life
677 Day Is Done
567 God Be in My Head
610 How Good the Name of Jesus Sounds
568 Lord of All Hopefulness
503 Many and Great, O God, Are Your Works
742 May the Grace of Christ Our Savior
668 Now the Silence
666 Only Begotten, Word of God Eternal

BROTHERHOOD AND SISTERHOOD
731 Draw Us in the Spirit's Tether
655 Father, Lord of All Creation
643 For the Healing of the Nations
619 Glorious in Majesty
592 God Is Unique and One
656 Help Us Accept Each Other
659 In Christ There Is No East or West
653 Let There Be Light
658 Lord Christ, the Father's Mighty Son
602 Lord of All Nations, Grant Me Grace
556 Lord of Our Growing Years
647 Now Join We to Praise the Creator
650 O God of Every Nation
685 O Holy City, Seen of John
644 Said Judas to Mary
604 Ubi Caritas
623 We Are Your People
635 Weary of All Trumpeting
508 When Israel Was in Egypt's Land
598 Where True Love and Charity Are Found/Ubi Caritas
(also City, Discipleship, Ministry, Mission, Nation, Social Concern, World)

CALL TO WORSHIP *(see Gathering)*

CELEBRATION
520 All Creatures of Our God and King
459 At the Lamb's High Feast We Sing
460 At the Lamb's High Feast We Sing
552 Come, We That Love the Lord
456 Come, Ye Faithful, Raise the Strain
521 From All That Dwell below the Skies
536 Let All the World in Every Corner Sing
533 New Songs of Celebration
668 Now the Silence
458 This Is the Feast of Victory
355 When the King Shall Come Again

CHALLENGE OF GOSPEL
667 God Is Here! As We His People
563 God, Omnipotent, Eternal
648 God, Who Stretched the Spangled Heavens
636 I Danced in the Morning
637 It Shocked Them That the Master Did Not Fast
615 The Kingdom of God
635 Weary of All Trumpeting
645 With Jesus for Hero
638 Your Love, O God, Has All the World Created

CHILDRENS HYMNS *(i.e., particularly suitable for children)*
520 All Creatures of Our God and King
428 All Glory, Laud, and Honor
805 All Glory, Laud, and Honor
505 All Things Bright and Beautiful
360 Awake! Awake, and Greet the New Morn
378 Away in a Manger
396 Christ Was Born on Christmas Day
723 Come and Let Us Drink of That New River
734 Eat This Bread
557 For the Beauty of the Earth
388 From Heaven Above
401 Gloria, Gloria
619 Glorious in Majesty
724 God Sends Us His Spirit
735 I Received the Living God
510 I Want to Walk as a Child of the Light
393 Infant Holy, Infant Lowly
555 Jubilate Deo
704 Lift High the Cross
568 Lord of All Hopefulness
394 Now Every Child That Dwells on Earth
367 O Come, Divine Messiah
357 O Come, O Come, Emmanuel
402 Once in Royal David's City
359 People, Look East
369 Prepare the Way of the Lord
544 Reap Me the Earth
580 Seek Ye First the Kingdom of God
540 Shout for Joy, Loud and Long
550 Sing a New Song to the Lord
415 Somebody's Knockin' at Your Door
361 Take Comfort, God's People
457 That Easter Day with Joy Was Bright
612 The Living God My Shepherd Is
380 'Twas in the Moon of Wintertime
604 Ubi Caritas (Taizé)
381 Unto Us a Boy Is Born
473 Veni Sancte Spiritus (Taizé)
707 Ye Watchers and Ye Holy Ones

CHRISTIAN LIFE
621 All Who Love and Serve Your City
500 Christ Is the King
594 Christian, Do You Hear the Lord
731 Draw Us in the Spirit's Tether
643 For the Healing of the Nations
627 Forth in the Peace of Christ
706 By All Your Saints Still Striving
619 Glorious in Majesty
628 Go Make of All Disciples
631 God, Whose Giving Knows No Ending
726 I Come with Joy to Meet My Lord
735 I Received the Living God
637 It Shocked Them That the Master Did Not Fast
630 Lord, Whose Love in Humble Service
625 Now Let Us from This Table Rise
620 O Blessed Are the Poor in Spirit
725 O Breathe on Me, O Breath of God
642 O God, Empower Us
480 Spirit of God within Me
634 Take Up Your Cross
626 The Church of Christ in Every Age
531 There's a Spirit in the Air
632 Those Who Love and Those Who Labor
633 Two Fishermen
623 We Are Your People
635 Weary of All Trumpeting
624 What Does the Lord Require
549 When in Our Music God Is Glorified
622 Where Temple Offerings Are Made

CHURCH
574 A Single Unmatched Stone
548 Adoramus Te Domine
815 Adoramus Te Domine
733 At That First Eucharist
362 City of God, Jerusalem
617 Christ Is Made the Sure Foundation
500 Christ Is the King
616 Christ's Church Shall Glory in His Power
538 Christians, Lift Up Your Hearts
571 Faith of Our Fathers
558 Father, We Thank Thee, Who Hast Planted
705 For All the Saints
557 For the Beauty of the Earth
627 Forth in the Peace of Christ
667 God Is Here! As We His People
710 How Blessed Is This Place
659 In Christ There Is No East or West
649 Jesus, Shepherd of Our Souls
536 Let All the World in Every Corner Sing
602 Lord of All Nations, Grant Me Grace
470 Lord, You Give the Great Commission
618 O Christ the Great Foundation
644 Said Judas to Mary
528 Sing Praise to God Who Reigns Above
626 The Church of Christ in Every Age
615 The Kingdom of God
371 Wake, O Wake, and Sleep No Longer
760 We Gather Together
481 When God the Spirit Came

Topical Index/*continued*

614 When Jesus Came Preaching the Kingdom of God
638 Your Love, O God, Has All the World Created
(also Discipleship, Ministry, Mission, Social Concern)

CITY *(see Nation, World, Social Concern)*

CITY OF GOD
409 As with Gladness Men of Old
362 City of God, Jerusalem
510 I Want to Walk as a Child of the Light
685 O Holy City, Seen of John
740 O Lord, You Died That All Might Live
(also Eternal Life, Lamb)

COMFORT
520 All Creatures of Our God and King
490 All You Who Seek a Comfort Sure
440 All You Who Pass This Way
583 Amazing Grace
360 Awake! Awake, and Greet the New Morn
737 Alleluia! Sing to Jesus
601 Beloved, Let Us Love
706 By All Your Saints Still Striving
577 By Gracious Powers
426 By the Babylonian Rivers
617 Christ Is Made the Sure Foundation
594 Christian, Do You Hear the Lord
362 City of God, Jerusalem
472 Come Down, O Love Divine
482 Come, Holy Ghost
569 Come, My Way, My Truth, My Life
364 Come, O Long Expected Jesus
370 Comfort, Comfort, O My People
677 Day Is Done
571 Faith of Our Fathers
705 For All the Saints
581 God Is My Great Desire
575 God Is Our Fortress and Our Rock
576 God Is Our Fortress and Our Rock
746 Great God of Mercy
414 Hear Us, Almighty Lord/Attende Domine
710 How Blessed Is This Place
585 How Firm a Foundation
610 How Good the Name of Jesus Sounds
607 I Heard the Voice of Jesus Say
445 I Know That My Redeemer Lives
593 I Sought the Lord
690 Jerusalem, My Happy Home
611 Jesus, Lead the Way
488 Jesus, My Lord, My God, My All
423 Jesus, Remember Me
427 Jesus Walked This Lonesome Valley
641 Lift Every Voice and Sing
739 Lord of the Living
606 My Shepherd Will Supply My Need
620 O Blessed Are the Poor in Spirit
642 O God, Empower Us
605 O Jesus, Joy of Loving Hearts
757 O Saving Victim/O Salutaris
689 O the Beautiful Treasures
416 Parce Domine
530 Praise, My Soul, the King of Heaven
361 Take Comfort, God's People
634 Take Up Your Cross
609 The King of Love My Shepherd Is
612 The Living God My Shepherd Is
613 The Lord, the Lord, the Lord Is My Shepherd
608 There Is a Balm in Gilead
595 There's a Wideness in God's Mercy
596 There's a Wideness in God's Mercy
635 Weary of All Trumpeting
600 What Wondrous Love Is This
614 When Jesus Came Preaching the Kingdom of God
(also Trust, Providence, Suffering, Shepherd)

COMMANDMENTS *(see Law)*

COMMISSIONING
500 Christ Is the King
594 Christian, Do You Hear the Lord
566 Come to Us, Creative Spirit
731 Draw Us in the Spirit's Tether
619 Glorious in Majesty
628 Go Make of All Disciples
567 God Be in My Head
515 His Voice Is in the Thunder, in the Storm
661 Is This a Day of New Beginnings
568 Lord of All Hopefulness
630 Lord, Whose Love in Humble Service
470 Lord, You Give the Great Commission
587 Morning Glory, Starlit Sky
580 Seek Ye First the Kingdom of God
618 O Christ the Great Foundation
629 How Shall They Hear the Word of God
526 Thanks Be to God
615 The Kingdom of God
590 This Is My Will
633 Two Fishermen
623 We Are Your People
481 When God the Spirit Came
549 When in Our Music God Is Glorified
614 When Jesus Came Preaching the Kingdom of God

COMMITMENT
499 At the Name of Jesus
569 Come, My Way, My Truth, My Life
571 Faith of Our Fathers
619 Glorious in Majesty
593 I Sought the Lord
630 Lord, Whose Love in Humble Service
662 On This Day, the First of Days
526 Thanks Be to God
700 'Tis Good, Lord, to Be Here
633 Two Fishermen
635 Weary of All Trumpeting
(also Discipleship, Mission)

COMMUNION *(see Liturgical Index: Eucharist)*

COMMUNION OF SAINTS
706 By All Your Saints Still Striving
557 For the Beauty of the Earth
535 God, We Praise You
741 Let Saints on Earth in Concert Sing
618 O Christ the Great Foundation
652 O God of Love, O King of Peace
707 Ye Watchers and Ye Holy Ones
(also Church, Saints)

COMMUNITY
665 Gather Us In
667 God Is Here! As We His People
726 I Come with Joy to Meet My Lord
556 Lord of Our Growing Years
747 O Christ, the Healer
623 We Are Your People
(also Unity)

COMPASSION
665 Gather Us In
619 Glorious in Majesty
631 God, Whose Giving Knows No Ending
640 God, Whose Purpose Is to Kindle
565 Hope of the World
610 How Good the Name of Jesus Sounds
630 Lord, Whose Love in Humble Service
588 Love Divine, All Loves Excelling
642 O God, Empower Us
584 Surely It Is God Who Saves Me
608 There Is a Balm in Gilead

COMPLACENCY
640 God, Whose Purpose Is to Kindle

CONFIDENCE *(see Trust)*

COUNTRY *(see Nation)*

COURAGE
583 Amazing Grace
706 By All Your Saints Still Striving
577 By Gracious Powers
538 Christians, Lift Up Your Hearts
571 Faith of Our Fathers
705 For All the Saints
665 Gather Us In
628 Go Make of All Disciples
575 God Is Our Fortress and Our Rock
576 God Is Our Fortress and Our Rock
724 God Sends Us His Spirit
640 God, Whose Purpose Is to Kindle
746 Great God of Mercy
565 Hope of the World
585 How Firm a Foundation
610 How Good the Name of Jesus Sounds
607 I Heard the Voice of Jesus Say
671 I Sing As I Arise Today
593 I Sought the Lord
661 Is This a Day of New Beginnings
690 Jerusalem, My Happy Home
611 Jesus, Lead the Way
423 Jesus, Remember Me
649 Jesus, Shepherd of Our Souls
427 Jesus Walked This Lonesome Valley
641 Lift Every Voice and Sing
568 Lord of All Hopefulness
602 Lord of All Nations, Grant Me Grace
556 Lord of Our Growing Years
606 My Shepherd Will Supply My Need
625 Now Let Us from This Table Rise
650 O God of Every Nation
685 O Holy City, Seen of John
646 O Jesus Christ, May Grateful Hymns Be Rising
634 Take Up Your Cross
526 Thanks Be to God
501 The King of Glory
609 The King of Love My Shepherd Is
608 There Is a Balm in Gilead
582 This World, My God, Is Held within Your Hand
635 Weary of All Trumpeting
508 When Israel Was in Egypt's Land
645 With Jesus for Hero
(also Comfort, Trust, Providence)

Topical Index/*continued*

COVENANT
526 Thanks Be to God
(also Faithfulness of God, Love of God for Us, Paschal Mystery)

CREATION
520 All Creatures of Our God and King
669 All People That On Earth Do Dwell
670 All People That On Earth Do Dwell
505 All Things Bright and Beautiful
681 Christ, Mighty Savior
639 Come, Let Us Love the Unborn Generations
664 Come, Rejoice before Your Maker
759 Come, Ye Thankful People, Come
517 Earth and All Stars
557 For the Beauty of the Earth
562 For the Fruits of This Creation
643 For the Healing of the Nations
563 God, Omnipotent, Eternal
535 God, We Praise You
683 God, Whose Farm Is All Creation
648 God, Who Stretched the Spangled Heavens
522 Heavenly Hosts in Ceaseless Worship
515 His Voice Is in the Thunder, in the Storm
636 I Danced in the Morning
512 Immortal, Invisible, God Only Wise
502 I Sing the Mighty Power of God
525 Joyful, Joyful, We Adore You
716 Let All on Earth Their Voices Raise
559 Let All Things Now Living
503 Many and Great, O God, Are Your Works
674 Morning Has Broken
533 New Songs of Celebration
398 Of the Father's Love Begotten
662 On This Day, the First of Days
682 Praise and Thanksgiving
545 Praise Him
551 Praise the Lord of Heaven
529 Praise the Lord! You Heavens, Adore Him
540 Shout for Joy, Loud and Long
506 The Stars Declare His Glory
504 The Works of the Lord Are Created in Wisdom
673 This Day God Gives Me
663 This Is the Day When Light Was First Created
511 Thy Strong Word Didst Cleave the Darkness
2 To God with Gladness Sing
549 When in Our Music God Is Glorified

CREATIVITY
566 Come to Us, Creative Spirit
549 When in Our Music God Is Glorified

CROSS
548 Adoramus Te Domine
418 Before the Fruit Is Ripened by the Sun
426 By the Babylonian Rivers
616 Christ's Church Shall Glory in His Power
754 Forgive Our Sins
578 God Spoke to Our Father Abraham
535 God, We Praise You
631 God, Whose Giving Knows No Ending
565 Hope of the World
636 I Danced in the Morning
704 Lift High the Cross
658 Lord Christ, the Father's Mighty Son
438 Lord Christ, When First You Came to Earth
630 Lord, Whose Love in Humble Service
541 O God beyond All Praising
425 Salvator Mundi
540 Shout for Joy, Loud and Long
437 Sing, My Tongue, the Song of Triumph
634 Take Up Your Cross
464 The Head That Once Was Crowned with Thorns
615 The Kingdom of God
609 The King of Love My Shepherd Is
511 Thy Strong Word Didst Cleave the Darkness
435 The Royal Banners Forward Go
635 Weary of All Trumpeting
436 Were You There
433 When I Survey the Wondrous Cross
697 When Jesus Came to Jordan

DEATH
520 All Creatures of Our God and King
459 At the Lamb's High Feast We Sing
460 At the Lamb's High Feast We Sing
586 Awake, O Sleeper, Rise from Death
418 Before the Fruit Is Ripened by the Sun
362 City of God, Jerusalem
575 God Is Our Fortress and Our Rock
576 God Is Our Fortress and Our Rock
573 He Comes to Us as One Unknown
585 How Firm a Foundation
510 I Want to Walk as a Child of the Light
690 Jerusalem, My Happy Home
741 Let Saints on Earth in Concert Sing
691 Lord, Bid Your Servant Go in Peace
568 Lord of All Hopefulness
556 Lord of Our Growing Years
739 Lord of the Living
606 My Shepherd Will Supply My Need
453 Now the Green Blade Rises
634 Take Up Your Cross
680 We Praise You, Father
600 What Wondrous Love Is This
(also Eternal Life; Liturgical Index: Funeral, Easter)

DEDICATION OF A CHURCH *(see Church; Liturgical Index: Dedication of a Church)*

DISCIPLESHIP
586 Awake, O Sleeper, Rise from Death
706 By All Your Saints Still Striving
577 By Gracious Powers
500 Christ Is the King
731 Draw Us in the Spirit's Tether
705 For All the Saints
627 Forth in the Peace of Christ
619 Glorious in Majesty
628 Go Make of All Disciples
507 God Is Working His Purpose Out
724 God Sends Us His Spirit
636 I Danced in the Morning
735 I Received the Living God
593 I Sought the Lord
510 I Want to Walk as a Child of the Light
637 It Shocked Them That the Master Did Not Fast
564 Jesus, Come! For We Invite You
611 Jesus, Lead the Way
432 Jesus Took a Towel
704 Lift High the Cross
599 Love Is His Word
587 Morning Glory, Starlit Sky
620 O Blessed Are the Poor in Spirit
618 O Christ the Great Foundation
541 O God beyond All Praising
634 Take Up Your Cross
626 The Church of Christ in Every Age
615 The Kingdom of God
612 The Living God My Shepherd Is
531 There's a Spirit in the Air
603 This Is My Commandment
590 This Is My Will
632 Those Who Love and Those Who Labor
700 'Tis Good, Lord, to Be Here
633 Two Fishermen
371 Wake, O Wake, and Sleep No Longer
635 Weary of All Trumpeting
614 When Jesus Came Preaching the Kingdom of God
(also Brotherhood & Sisterhood, Commitment, Ministry, Mission, Social Concern)

ECOLOGY
520 All Creatures of Our God and King
505 All Things Bright and Beautiful
639 Come, Let Us Love the Unborn Generations
557 For the Beauty of the Earth
562 For the Fruits of This Creation
502 I Sing the Mighty Power of God
525 Joyful, Joyful, We Adore You
559 Let All Things Now Living
647 Now Join We to Praise the Creator
(also Stewardship, Creation)

ECUMENISM *(see Unity)*

ESCHATOLOGY *(see Second Coming)*

EUCHARIST
569 Come, My Way, My Truth, My Life
567 God Be in My Head
578 God Spoke to Our Father Abraham
738 I Am the Bread of Life
726 I Come with Joy to Meet My Lord
736 You Satisfy the Hungry Heart

ETERNAL LIFE
688 A Multitude Comes from the East and the West
583 Amazing Grace
409 As with Gladness Men of Old
706 By All Your Saints Still Striving
594 Christian, Do You Hear the Lord
362 City of God, Jerusalem
759 Come, Ye Thankful People, Come
496 Crown Him with Many Crowns
734 Eat This Bread
4 Father, We Praise You
558 Father, We Thank Thee, Who Hast Planted
705 For All the Saints
692 Hail to the Lord Who Comes
485 Holy, Holy, Holy! Lord God Almighty
710 How Blessed Is This Place
585 How Firm a Foundation
690 Jerusalem, My Happy Home
741 Let Saints on Earth in Concert Sing
691 Lord, Bid Your Servant Go in Peace
606 My Shepherd Will Supply My Need
725 O Breathe on Me, O Breath of God
729 O Food of Exiles Lowly

Topical Index/*continued*

740 O Lord, You Died That All Might Live
757 O Saving Victim/O Salutaris
728 Shepherd of Souls
501 The King of Glory
609 The King of Love My Shepherd Is
612 The Living God My Shepherd Is
613 The Lord, the Lord, the Lord Is My Shepherd
497 To Jesus Christ, Our Sovereign King
572 We Walk by Faith
707 Ye Watchers and Ye Holy Ones
(also Heaven)

EVENING
520 All Creatures of Our God and King
681 Christ, Mighty Savior
368 Creator of the Stars of Night
677 Day Is Done
703 Hail, Queen of Heaven/Salve Regina
691 Lord, Bid Your Servant Go in Peace
568 Lord of All Hopefulness
676 Nunc Dimittis
679 O Gladsome Light
443 O Queen of Heaven/Regina Caeli
424 O Sun of Justice
678 The Day You Gave Us, Lord, Is Ended
511 Thy Strong Word Didst Cleave the Darkness
20 We Praise You, Father, for Your Gift
(also Light, Thanksgiving)

EXILE
413 Alleluia, Song of Gladness
426 By the Babylonian Rivers
362 City of God, Jerusalem
729 O Food of Exiles Lowly
755 Our Father, We Have Wandered
508 When Israel Was in Egypt's Land
355 When the King Shall Come Again
(also Pilgrimage)

FAITH
574 A Single Unmatched Stone
706 By All Your Saints Still Striving
500 Christ Is the King
448 Daylight Fades
571 Faith of Our Fathers
558 Father, We Thank Thee, Who Hast Planted
705 For All the Saints
665 Gather Us In
516 God Has Spoken by His Prophets
667 God Is Here! As We His People
575 God Is Our Fortress and Our Rock
576 God Is Our Fortress and Our Rock
573 He Comes to Us as One Unknown
749 He Healed the Darkness of My Mind
515 His Voice Is in the Thunder, in the Storm
502 I Sing the Mighty Power of God
593 I Sought the Lord
611 Jesus, Lead the Way
641 Lift Every Voice and Sing
658 Lord Christ, the Father's Mighty Son
553 Magnificat
606 My Shepherd Will Supply My Need
589 Not for Tongues of Heaven's Angels
676 Nunc Dimittis
618 O Christ the Great Foundation
605 O Jesus, Joy of Loving Hearts
447 O Sons and Daughters
372 Savior of the Nations, Come
467 Sing with All the Saints in Glory
612 The Living God My Shepherd Is
506 The Stars Declare His Glory
504 The Works of the Lord Are Created in Wisdom
657 There Is One Lord
604 Ubi Caritas (Taizé)
572 We Walk by Faith

FAITHFULNESS OF GOD
664 Come, Rejoice before Your Maker
516 God Has Spoken by His Prophets
672 How Beautiful the Morning and the Day
519 Laudate Dominum
568 Lord of All Hopefulness
530 Praise, My Soul, the King of Heaven
547 Praise to the Lord, the Almighty
526 Thanks Be to God
508 When Israel Was in Egypt's Land
(also Love of God for Us, Mercy, Providence)

FAMILY LIFE
601 Beloved, Let Us Love
557 For the Beauty of the Earth
556 Lord of Our Growing Years
742 May the Grace of Christ Our Savior
570 Our Father, by Whose Name
404 Sing of Mary, Pure and Lowly
603 This Is My Commandment
590 This Is My Will
403 Virgin-born, We Bow before You
745 When Love Is Found

FASTING
420 Again We Keep This Solemn Fast
419 Forty Days and Forty Nights
637 It Shocked Them That the Master Did Not Fast
417 Lord, Who throughout These Forty Days
422 The Glory of These Forty Days

FEAR
586 Awake, O Sleeper, Rise from Death
724 God Sends Us His Spirit
565 Hope of the World
614 When Jesus Came Preaching the Kingdom of God

FOOD
505 All Things Bright and Beautiful
569 Come, My Way, My Truth, My Life
558 Father, We Thank Thee, Who Hast Planted
683 God, Whose Farm Is All Creation
502 I Sing the Mighty Power of God
637 It Shocked Them That the Master Did Not Fast
727 Let Us Break Bread Together
606 My Shepherd Will Supply My Need
647 Now Join We to Praise the Creator
729 O Food of Exiles Lowly
605 O Jesus, Joy of Loving Hearts
682 Praise and Thanksgiving
728 Shepherd of Souls
612 The Living God My Shepherd Is
613 The Lord, the Lord, the Lord Is My Shepherd

FORGIVENESS *(see Love of God for Us, Mercy, Reconciliation, Repentance; Liturgical Index: Penance)*

FREEDOM
574 A Single Unmatched Stone
413 Alleluia, Song of Gladness
763 America the Beautiful
426 By the Babylonian Rivers
396 Christ Was Born on Christmas Day
616 Christ's Church Shall Glory in His Power
364 Come, O Long Expected Jesus
456 Come, Ye Faithful, Raise the Strain
643 For the Healing of the Nations
619 Glorious in Majesty
764 God of Our Fathers
724 God Sends Us His Spirit
640 God, Whose Purpose Is to Kindle
656 Help Us Accept Each Other
365 Hills of the North, Rejoice
735 I Received the Living God
653 Let There Be Light
641 Lift Every Voice and Sing
686 Mine Eyes Have Seen the Glory
762 My Country, 'Tis of Thee
356 On Jordan's Bank
662 On This Day, the First of Days
425 Salvator Mundi
358 The Voice of God Goes Out through All the World
595 There's a Wideness in God's Mercy
596 There's a Wideness in God's Mercy
760 We Gather Together
508 When Israel Was in Egypt's Land

FRIENDSHIP
731 Draw Us in the Spirit's Tether
726 I Come with Joy to Meet My Lord
740 O Lord, You Died That All Might Live
608 There Is a Balm in Gilead
603 This Is My Commandment
590 This Is My Will

GATHERING
520 All Creatures of Our God and King
669 All People That On Earth Do Dwell
670 All People That On Earth Do Dwell
441 Alleluia, Alleluia, Give Thanks
737 Alleluia! Sing to Jesus
617 Christ Is Made the Sure Foundation
538 Christians, Lift Up Your Hearts
487 Come, Now Almighty King
664 Come, Rejoice before Your Maker
566 Come to Us, Creative Spirit
552 Come, We That Love the Lord
456 Come, Ye Faithful, Raise the Strain
759 Come, Ye Thankful People, Come
732 Draw Near and Take the Body of Your Lord
665 Gather Us In
619 Glorious in Majesty
667 God Is Here! As We His People
522 Heavenly Hosts in Ceaseless Worship
710 How Blessed Is This Place
726 I Come with Joy to Meet My Lord
661 Is This a Day of New Beginnings
363 Lift Up Your Heads, O Mighty Gates
630 Lord, Whose Love in Humble Service
503 Many and Great, O God, Are Your Works
533 New Songs of Celebration
647 Now Join We to Praise the Creator
668 Now the Silence
546 O That I Had a Thousand Voices
662 On This Day, the First of Days

Topical Index/*continued*

666 Only Begotten, Word of God Eternal
483 Over the Chaos of the Empty Waters
537 The God of Abraham Praise
663 This Is the Day When Light Was First Created
547 Praise to the Lord, the Almighty
760 We Gather Together
709 What Is This Place
(also Praise, Thanksgiving)

GOD THE FATHER (Creator)
669 All People That On Earth Do Dwell
670 All People That On Earth Do Dwell
505 All Things Bright and Beautiful
664 Come, Rejoice before Your Maker
368 Creator of the Stars of Night
517 Earth and All Stars
4 Father, We Praise You
558 Father, We Thank Thee, Who Hast Planted
521 From All That Dwell below the Skies
542 Glory to God in the Highest
575 God Is Our Fortress and Our Rock
576 God Is Our Fortress and Our Rock
592 God Is Unique and One
648 God, Who Stretched the Spangled Heavens
651 Great God, Our Source and Lord of Space
522 Heavenly Hosts in Ceaseless Worship
671 I Sing As I Arise Today
502 I Sing the Mighty Power of God
512 Immortal, Invisible, God Only Wise
525 Joyful, Joyful, We Adore You
559 Let All Things Now Living
503 Many and Great, O God, Are Your Works
674 Morning Has Broken
679 O Gladsome Light
541 O God beyond All Praising
579 O God, Our Help in Ages Past
546 O That I Had a Thousand Voices
398 Of the Father's Love Begotten
662 On This Day, the First of Days
545 Praise Him
530 Praise, My Soul, the King of Heaven
551 Praise the Lord of Heaven
529 Praise the Lord! You Heavens, Adore Him
540 Shout for Joy, Loud and Long
528 Sing Praise to God Who Reigns Above
539 Sing Praise to the Lord
526 Thanks Be to God
506 The Stars Declare His Glory
504 The Works of the Lord Are Created in Wisdom
657 There Is One Lord
673 This Day God Gives Me
511 Thy Strong Word Didst Cleave the Darkness
20 We Praise You, Father, for Your Gift

GOING FORTH
586 Awake, O Sleeper, Rise from Death
500 Christ Is the King
538 Christians, Lift Up Your Hearts
627 Forth in the Peace of Christ
619 Glorious in Majesty
628 Go Make of All Disciples
567 God Be in My Head
507 God Is Working His Purpose Out
629 How Shall They Hear the Word of God
661 Is This a Day of New Beginnings
559 Let All Things Now Living
630 Lord, Whose Love in Humble Service
625 Now Let Us from This Table Rise
514 Thanks to God Whose Word Was Spoken
700 'Tis Good, Lord, to Be Here
614 When Jesus Came Preaching the Kingdom of God

GOSPEL *(see Word of God)*

GRACE
495 All Hail the Power of Jesus' Name
583 Amazing Grace
418 Before the Fruit Is Ripened by the Sun
594 Christian, Do You Hear the Lord
472 Come Down, O Love Divine
482 Come, Holy Ghost
368 Creator of the Stars of Night
655 Father, Lord of All Creation
557 For the Beauty of the Earth
518 Glory Be to God in Heaven
667 God Is Here! As We His People
672 How Beautiful the Morning and the Day
389 How Brightly Beams the Morning Star
390 How Brightly Beams the Morning Star
610 How Good the Name of Jesus Sounds
512 Immortal, Invisible, God Only Wise
611 Jesus, Lead the Way
716 Let All on Earth Their Voices Raise
653 Let There Be Light
363 Lift Up Your Heads, O Mighty Gates
556 Lord of Our Growing Years
742 May the Grace of Christ Our Savior
606 My Shepherd Will Supply My Need
533 New Songs of Celebration
560 Now Thank We All Our God
618 O Christ the Great Foundation
729 O Food of Exiles Lowly
679 O Gladsome Light
685 O Holy City, Seen of John
356 On Jordan's Bank
662 On This Day, the First of Days
530 Praise, My Soul, the King of Heaven
422 The Glory of These Forty Days
537 The God of Abraham Praise
615 The Kingdom of God
612 The Living God My Shepherd Is
595 There's a Wideness in God's Mercy
596 There's a Wideness in God's Mercy
407 What Star Is This

GRATITUDE *(see Thanksgiving)*

GROWTH
556 Lord of Our Growing Years
642 O God, Empower Us

GUIDANCE
469 A Hymn of Glory Let Us Sing
583 Amazing Grace
569 Come, My Way, My Truth, My Life
628 Go Make of All Disciples
764 God of Our Fathers
648 God, Who Stretched the Spangled Heavens
651 Great God, Our Source and Lord of Space
573 He Comes to Us as One Unknown
585 How Firm a Foundation
607 I Heard the Voice of Jesus Say
671 I Sing As I Arise Today
502 I Sing the Mighty Power of God
611 Jesus, Lead the Way
649 Jesus, Shepherd of Our Souls
559 Let All Things Now Living
606 My Shepherd Will Supply My Need
560 Now Thank We All Our God
654 O Day of Peace
650 O God of Every Nation
579 O God, Our Help in Ages Past
646 O Jesus Christ, May Grateful Hymns Be Rising
609 The King of Love My Shepherd Is
612 The Living God My Shepherd Is
613 The Lord, the Lord, the Lord Is My Shepherd
506 The Stars Declare His Glory
673 This Day God Gives Me
760 We Gather Together
407 What Star Is This

HARVEST
759 Come, Ye Thankful People, Come
562 For the Fruits of This Creation
507 God Is Working His Purpose Out
683 God, Whose Farm Is All Creation
647 Now Join We to Praise the Creator
682 Praise and Thanksgiving
(also Thanksgiving)

HEALING
574 A Single Unmatched Stone
583 Amazing Grace
414 Hear Us, Almighty Lord/Attende Domine
486 God, Whose Almighty Word
631 God, Whose Giving Knows No Ending
746 Great God of Mercy
749 He Healed the Darkness of My Mind
515 His Voice Is in the Thunder, in the Storm
565 Hope of the World
672 How Beautiful the Morning and the Day
610 How Good the Name of Jesus Sounds
593 I Sought the Lord
606 My Shepherd Will Supply My Need
747 O Christ, the Healer
541 O God beyond All Praising
650 O God of Every Nation
748 O Son of God, in Galilee
356 On Jordan's Bank
528 Sing Praise to God Who Reigns Above
410 Songs of Thankfulness and Praise
501 The King of Glory
612 The Living God My Shepherd Is
613 The Lord, the Lord, the Lord Is My Shepherd
358 The Voice of God Goes Out through All the World
608 There Is a Balm in Gilead
595 There's a Wideness in God's Mercy
596 There's a Wideness in God's Mercy

Topical Index/*continued*

750 Your Hands, O Lord, in Days of Old
(also Mercy, Love of God for Us; Liturgical Index: Pastoral Care of the Sick)

HEAVEN
688 A Multitude Comes from the East and the West
413 Alleluia, Song of Gladness
409 As with Gladness Men of Old
421 At the Cross Her Station Keeping
706 By All Your Saints Still Striving
452 Christ the Lord Is Risen Today
461 Christ the Lord Is Risen Today
462 Christ the Lord Is Risen Today
463 Christ the Lord Is Risen Today
552 Come, We That Love the Lord
759 Come, Ye Thankful People, Come
677 Day Is Done
4 Father, We Praise You
705 For All the Saints
522 Heavenly Hosts in Ceaseless Worship
710 How Blessed Is This Place
738 I Am the Bread of Life
510 I Want to Walk as a Child of the Light
690 Jerusalem, My Happy Home
611 Jesus, Lead the Way
525 Joyful, Joyful, We Adore You
741 Let Saints on Earth in Concert Sing
417 Lord, Who throughout These Forty Days
588 Love Divine, All Loves Excelling
503 Many and Great, O God, Are Your Works
606 My Shepherd Will Supply My Need
560 Now Thank We All Our God
618 O Christ the Great Foundation
685 O Holy City, Seen of John
740 O Lord, You Died That All Might Live
757 O Saving Victim/O Salutaris
546 O That I Had a Thousand Voices
689 O the Beautiful Treasures
402 Once in Royal David's City
493 Rejoice, the Lord Is King
467 Sing with All the Saints in Glory
537 The God of Abraham Praise
464 The Head That Once Was Crowned with Thorns
371 Wake, O Wake, and Sleep No Longer
(also Eternal Life; Liturgical Index: Easter, Funeral)

HOLINESS
368 Creator of the Stars of Night
478 Fire of God, Titanic Spirit
665 Gather Us In
485 Holy, Holy, Holy! Lord God Almighty
716 Let All on Earth Their Voices Raise

HOLY FAMILY *(see Liturgical Index)*

HOLY NAME
494 All Hail the Power of Jesus' Name
495 All Hail the Power of Jesus' Name
441 Alleluia, Alleluia, Give Thanks
499 At the Name of Jesus
558 Father, We Thank Thee, Who Hast Planted
705 For All the Saints
521 From All That Dwell below the Skies
573 He Comes to Us as One Unknown
524 Holy God, We Praise Thy Name
672 How Beautiful the Morning and the Day
512 Immortal, Invisible, God Only Wise
492 Jesus Shall Reign
716 Let All on Earth Their Voices Raise
545 Praise Him
529 Praise the Lord! You Heavens, Adore Him
526 Thanks Be to God
760 We Gather Together

HOLY SPIRIT *(see Liturgical Index: Pentecost, Confirmation)*

HOMECOMING
688 A Multitude Comes from the East and the West
606 My Shepherd Will Supply My Need
609 The King of Love My Shepherd Is
(also Exile)

HOPE *(see Trust)*

HORROR OF WAR
639 Come, Let Us Love the Unborn Generations
651 Great God, Our Source and Lord of Space
649 Jesus, Shepherd of Our Souls
653 Let There Be Light
642 O God, Empower Us
650 O God of Every Nation
638 Your Love, O God, Has All the World Created

HUMILITY
694 Come Now, and Praise the Humble Saint
370 Comfort, Comfort, O My People
643 For the Healing of the Nations
649 Jesus, Shepherd of Our Souls
523 Let All Mortal Flesh Keep Şilence
438 Lord Christ, When First You Came to Earth
553 Magnificat
647 Now Join We to Praise the Creator
591 O for a Heart to Praise My God
646 O Jesus Christ, May Grateful Hymns Be Rising
506 The Stars Declare His Glory
624 What Does the Lord Require
433 When I Survey the Wondrous Cross
614 When Jesus Came Preaching the Kingdom of God
638 Your Love, O God, Has All the World Created

HUNGER
734 Eat This Bread
562 For the Fruits of This Creation
656 Help Us Accept Each Other
653 Let There Be Light
647 Now Join We to Praise the Creator
682 Praise and Thanksgiving
626 The Church of Christ in Every Age
(also Food, Poverty, Social Concern)

IMMORTALITY *(see Death, Eternal Life, Heaven)*

INCARNATION
543 Christ Is the World's Light
410 Songs of Thankfulness and Praise
405 The God Whom Earth and Sea and Sky
(also Liturgical Index: Christmas Season, Annunciation)

JESUS CHRIST
548 Adoramus Te Domine
527 All Glory Be to God on High
428 All Glory, Laud, and Honor
805 All Glory, Laud, and Honor
494 All Hail the Power of Jesus' Name
495 All Hail the Power of Jesus' Name
440 All You Who Pass This Way
490 All You Who Seek a Comfort Sure
737 Alleluia! Sing to Jesus
421 At the Cross Her Station Keeping
459 At the Lamb's High Feast We Sing
460 At the Lamb's High Feast We Sing
499 At the Name of Jesus
730 Ave Verum
586 Awake, O Sleeper, Rise from Death
418 Before the Fruit Is Ripened by the Sun
706 By All Your Saints Still Striving
617 Christ Is Made the Sure Foundation
543 Christ Is the World's Light
681 Christ, Mighty Savior
452 Christ the Lord Is Risen Today
461 Christ the Lord Is Risen Today
462 Christ the Lord Is Risen Today
463 Christ the Lord Is Risen Today
701 Christ upon the Mountain Peak
616 Christ's Church Shall Glory in His Power
465 Christus Resurrexit
758 Come Adore/Tantum Ergo
723 Come and Let Us Drink of That New River
366 Come, Lord, and Tarry Not
569 Come, My Way, My Truth, My Life
364 Come, O Long Expected Jesus
456 Come, Ye Faithful, Raise the Strain
368 Creator of the Stars of Night
558 Father, We Thank Thee, Who Hast Planted
557 For the Beauty of the Earth
627 Forth in the Peace of Christ
419 Forty Days and Forty Nights
619 Glorious in Majesty
542 Glory to God in the Highest
575 God Is Our Fortress and Our Rock
576 God Is Our Fortress and Our Rock
592 God Is Unique and One
578 God Spoke to Our Father Abraham
535 God, We Praise You
489 God with Hidden Majesty/Adoro Te Devote
746 Great God of Mercy
471 Hail the Day That Sees Him Rise
444 Hail Thee, Festival Day
692 Hail to the Lord Who Comes
753 Have Mercy, Lord, on Us
573 He Comes to Us as One Unknown
749 He Healed the Darkness of My Mind
498 He Is King of Kings
684 He Walks among the Golden Lamps
414 Hear Us, Almighty Lord/Attende Domine
522 Heavenly Hosts in Ceaseless Worship

Topical Index/*continued*

365 Hills of the North, Rejoice
515 His Voice Is in the Thunder, in the Storm
565 Hope of the World
585 How Firm a Foundation
610 How Good the Name of Jesus Sounds
726 I Come with Joy to Meet My Lord
636 I Danced in the Morning
607 I Heard the Voice of Jesus Say
445 I Know That My Redeemer Lives
593 I Sought the Lord
510 I Want to Walk as a Child of the Light
659 In Christ There Is No East or West
661 Is This a Day of New Beginnings
637 It Shocked Them That the Master Did Not Fast
431 Jesu, Jesu, Fill Us with Your Love
442 Jesus Christ Is Risen Today
564 Jesus, Come! For We Invite You
611 Jesus, Lead the Way
488 Jesus, My Lord, My God, My All
423 Jesus, Remember Me
492 Jesus Shall Reign
649 Jesus, Shepherd of Our Souls
432 Jesus Took a Towel
427 Jesus Walked This Lonesome Valley
523 Let All Mortal Flesh Keep Silence
363 Lift Up Your Heads, O Mighty Gates
468 Look, O Look, the Sight Is Glorious
691 Lord, Bid Your Servant Go in Peace
658 Lord Christ, the Father's Mighty Son
438 Lord Christ, When First You Came to Earth
417 Lord, Who throughout These Forty Days
588 Love Divine, All Loves Excelling
599 Love Is His Word
812 Mandatum Novum
686 Mine Eyes Have Seen the Glory
587 Morning Glory, Starlit Sky
674 Morning Has Broken
446 Morning of Splendor
439 My Song Is Love Unknown
589 Not for Tongues of Heaven's Angels
625 Now Let Us from This Table Rise
687 Now the Day of the Lord Is at Hand
453 Now the Green Blade Rises
668 Now the Silence
618 O Christ the Great Foundation
747 O Christ, the Healer
367 O Come, Divine Messiah
654 O Day of Peace
591 O for a Heart to Praise My God
679 O Gladsome Light
541 O God beyond All Praising
646 O Jesus Christ, May Grateful Hymns Be Rising
605 O Jesus, Joy of Loving Hearts
740 O Lord, You Died That All Might Live
443 O Queen of Heaven/Regina Caeli
434 O Sacred Head Surrounded
757 O Saving Victim/O Salutaris
748 O Son of God, in Galilee
424 O Sun of Justice
398 Of the Father's Love Begotten
666 Only Begotten, Word of God Eternal
493 Rejoice, the Lord Is King
644 Said Judas to Mary
425 Salvator Mundi
372 Savior of the Nations, Come
437 Sing, My Tongue, the Song of Triumph
467 Sing with All the Saints in Glory
415 Somebody's Knockin' at Your Door
410 Songs of Thankfulness and Praise
634 Take Up Your Cross
457 That Easter Day with Joy Was Bright
626 The Church of Christ in Every Age
422 The Glory of These Forty Days
501 The King of Glory
373 The King Shall Come When Morning Dawns
615 The Kingdom of God
752 The Master Came to Bring Good News
358 The Voice of God Goes Out through All the World
608 There Is a Balm in Gilead
657 There Is One Lord
595 There's a Wideness in God's Mercy
596 There's a Wideness in God's Mercy
590 This Is My Will
632 Those Who Love and Those Who Labor
700 'Tis Good, Lord, to Be Here
497 To Jesus Christ, Our Sovereign King
633 Two Fishermen
371 Wake, O Wake, and Sleep No Longer
635 Weary of All Trumpeting
436 Were You There
433 When I Survey the Wondrous Cross
614 When Jesus Came Preaching the Kingdom of God
697 When Jesus Came to Jordan
412 When John Baptized by Jordan's River
675 When Morning Gilds the Sky
645 With Jesus for Hero
750 Your Hands, O Lord, in Days of Old
638 Your Love, O God, Has All the World Created

JOSEPH, ST. *(see Liturgical Index)*

JOY
469 A Hymn of Glory Let Us Sing
688 A Multitude Comes from the East and the West
669 All People That On Earth Do Dwell
670 All People That On Earth Do Dwell
505 All Things Bright and Beautiful
413 Alleluia, Song of Gladness
450 Be Joyful, Mary
577 By Gracious Powers
681 Christ, Mighty Savior
569 Come, My Way, My Truth, My Life
552 Come, We That Love the Lord
571 Faith of Our Fathers
557 For the Beauty of the Earth
521 From All That Dwell below the Skies
555 Jubilate Deo
726 I Come with Joy to Meet My Lord
607 I Heard the Voice of Jesus Say
735 I Received the Living God
502 I Sing the Mighty Power of God
510 I Want to Walk as a Child of the Light
661 Is This a Day of New Beginnings
690 Jerusalem, My Happy Home
525 Joyful, Joyful, We Adore You
559 Let All Things Now Living
588 Love Divine, All Loves Excelling
533 New Songs of Celebration
560 Now Thank We All Our God
591 O for a Heart to Praise My God
541 O God beyond All Praising
605 O Jesus, Joy of Loving Hearts
493 Rejoice, the Lord Is King
540 Shout for Joy, Loud and Long
550 Sing a New Song to the Lord
528 Sing Praise to God Who Reigns Above
532 Sing to the Lord a Joyful Song
615 The Kingdom of God
595 There's a Wideness in God's Mercy
596 There's a Wideness in God's Mercy
600 What Wondrous Love Is This
707 Ye Watchers and Ye Holy Ones

JUDGMENT
621 All Who Love and Serve Your City
759 Come, Ye Thankful People, Come
368 Creator of the Stars of Night
507 God Is Working His Purpose Out
684 He Walks among the Golden Lamps
738 I Am the Bread of Life
535 God, We Praise You
686 Mine Eyes Have Seen the Glory
687 Now the Day of the Lord Is at Hand
493 Rejoice, the Lord Is King
550 Sing a New Song to the Lord
526 Thanks Be to God
373 The King Shall Come When Morning Dawns
497 To Jesus Christ, Our Sovereign King
371 Wake, O Wake, and Sleep No Longer
(also Second Coming; Liturgical Index: Christ the King)

JUSTICE
639 Come, Let Us Love the Unborn Generations
562 For the Fruits of This Creation
643 For the Healing of the Nations
563 God, Omnipotent, Eternal
640 God, Whose Purpose Is to Kindle
512 Immortal, Invisible, God Only Wise
659 In Christ There Is No East or West
400 It Came upon the Midnight Clear
559 Let All Things Now Living
641 Lift Every Voice and Sing
602 Lord of All Nations, Grant Me Grace
686 Mine Eyes Have Seen the Glory
357 O Come, O Come, Emmanuel
654 O Day of Peace
650 O God of Every Nation
644 Said Judas to Mary
550 Sing a New Song to the Lord
626 The Church of Christ in Every Age
615 The Kingdom of God
595 There's a Wideness in God's Mercy
596 There's a Wideness in God's Mercy
358 The Voice of God Goes Out through All the World
381 Unto Us a Boy Is Born
624 What Does the Lord Require
709 What Is This Place
508 When Israel Was in Egypt's Land
614 When Jesus Came Preaching the Kingdom of God

Topical Index/*continued*

645 With Jesus for Hero
(also Brotherhood & Sisterhood, City, Discipleship, Nation, World, Peace, Social Concern)

KINGDOM
385 A Stable Lamp Is Lighted
362 City of God, Jerusalem
366 Come, Lord, and Tarry Not
575 God Is Our Fortress and Our Rock
576 God Is Our Fortress and Our Rock
563 God, Omnipotent, Eternal
558 Father, We Thank Thee, Who Hast Planted
665 Gather Us In
684 He Walks among the Golden Lamps
611 Jesus, Lead the Way
423 Jesus, Remember Me
492 Jesus Shall Reign
653 Let There Be Light
438 Lord Christ, When First You Came to Earth
689 O the Beautiful Treasures
580 Seek Ye First the Kingdom of God
532 Sing to the Lord a Joyful Song
678 The Day You Gave Us, Lord, Is Ended
537 The God of Abraham Praise
615 The Kingdom of God
700 'Tis Good, Lord, to Be Here
497 To Jesus Christ, Our Sovereign King
614 When Jesus Came Preaching the Kingdom of God
355 When the King Shall Come Again
645 With Jesus for Hero
(also Liturgical Index: Christ the King)

LABOR
621 All Who Love and Serve Your City
490 All You Who Seek a Comfort Sure
517 Earth and All Stars
562 For the Fruits of This Creation
667 God Is Here! As We His People
648 God, Who Stretched the Spangled Heavens
683 God, Whose Farm Is All Creation
631 God, Whose Giving Knows No Ending
498 He Is King of Kings
693 Joseph, Be Our Guide and Pattern
568 Lord of All Hopefulness
682 Praise and Thanksgiving
404 Sing of Mary, Pure and Lowly
504 The Works of the Lord Are Created in Wisdom
531 There's a Spirit in the Air
632 Those Who Love and Those Who Labor
624 What Does the Lord Require

LAMB
527 All Glory Be to God on High
459 At the Lamb's High Feast We Sing
460 At the Lamb's High Feast We Sing
496 Crown Him with Many Crowns
518 Glory Be to God in Heaven
542 Glory to God in the Highest
578 God Spoke to Our Father Abraham
522 Heavenly Hosts in Ceaseless Worship
510 I Want to Walk as a Child of the Light
685 O Holy City, Seen of John
740 O Lord, You Died That All Might Live
375 See amid the Winter's Snow
458 This Is the Feast of Victory
600 What Wondrous Love Is This
(also Eternal Life)

LAW
559 Let All Things Now Living
752 The Master Came to Bring Good News
506 The Stars Declare His Glory
624 What Does the Lord Require

LIBERTY *(see Freedom)*

LIFE
583 Amazing Grace
520 All Creatures of Our God and King
505 All Things Bright and Beautiful
543 Christ Is the World's Light
639 Come, Let Us Love the Unborn Generations
569 Come, My Way, My Truth, My Life
496 Crown Him with Many Crowns
557 For the Beauty of the Earth
648 God, Who Stretched the Spangled Heavens
640 God, Whose Purpose Is to Kindle
444 Hail Thee, Festival Day
389 How Brightly Beams the Morning Star
390 How Brightly Beams the Morning Star
636 I Danced in the Morning
607 I Heard the Voice of Jesus Say
445 I Know That My Redeemer Lives
502 I Sing the Mighty Power of God
512 Immortal, Invisible, God Only Wise
525 Joyful, Joyful, We Adore You
519 Laudate Dominum
559 Let All Things Now Living
630 Lord, Whose Love in Humble Service
503 Many and Great, O God, Are Your Works
446 Morning of Splendor
453 Now the Green Blade Rises
679 O Gladsome Light
685 O Holy City, Seen of John
605 O Jesus, Joy of Loving Hearts
424 O Sun of Justice
682 Praise and Thanksgiving
547 Praise to the Lord, the Almighty
540 Shout for Joy, Loud and Long
506 The Stars Declare His Glory
504 The Works of the Lord Are Created in Wisdom
381 Unto Us a Boy Is Born
750 Your Hands, O Lord, in Days of Old

LIGHT
583 Amazing Grace
409 As with Gladness Men of Old
360 Awake! Awake, and Greet the New Morn
586 Awake, O Sleeper, Rise from Death
601 Beloved, Let Us Love
500 Christ Is the King
543 Christ Is the World's Light
616 Christ's Church Shall Glory in His Power
368 Creator of the Stars of Night
677 Day Is Done
448 Daylight Fades
665 Gather Us In
563 God, Omnipotent, Eternal
486 God, Whose Almighty Word
692 Hail to the Lord Who Comes
565 Hope of the World
389 How Brightly Beams the Morning Star
390 How Brightly Beams the Morning Star
607 I Heard the Voice of Jesus Say
510 I Want to Walk as a Child of the Light
512 Immortal, Invisible, God Only Wise
525 Joyful, Joyful, We Adore You
559 Let All Things Now Living
653 Let There Be Light
691 Lord, Bid Your Servant Go in Peace
679 O Gladsome Light
475 O Holy Spirit, by Whose Breath
605 O Jesus, Joy of Loving Hearts
424 O Sun of Justice
356 On Jordan's Bank
662 On This Day, the First of Days
540 Shout for Joy, Loud and Long
678 The Day You Gave Us, Lord, Is Ended
506 The Stars Declare His Glory
663 This Is the Day When Light Was First Created
511 Thy Strong Word Did Cleave the Darkness
700 'Tis Good, Lord, to Be Here
473 Veni Sancte Spiritus (Taizé)
371 Wake, O Wake, and Sleep No Longer
406 We Three Kings of Orient Are
572 We Walk by Faith
407 What Star Is This

LORD'S DAY *(see Sunday)*

LOVE OF GOD FOR US
597 A Spendthrift Lover Is the Lord
505 All Things Bright and Beautiful
733 At That First Eucharist
459 At the Lamb's High Feast We Sing
460 At the Lamb's High Feast We Sing
360 Awake! Awake, and Greet the New Morn
586 Awake, O Sleeper, Rise from Death
601 Beloved, Let Us Love
466 Christ Is Alive!
617 Christ Is Made the Sure Foundation
594 Christian, Do You Hear the Lord
472 Come Down, O Love Divine
569 Come, My Way, My Truth, My Life
664 Come, Rejoice before Your Maker
561 Confitemini Domino
677 Day Is Done
558 Father, We Thank Thee, Who Hast Planted
474 Fire of God, Undying Flame
557 For the Beauty of the Earth
562 For the Fruits of This Creation
581 God Is My Great Desire
563 God, Omnipotent, Eternal
672 How Beautiful the Morning and the Day
607 I Heard the Voice of Jesus Say
593 I Sought the Lord
431 Jesu, Jesu, Fill Us with Your Love
649 Jesus, Shepherd of Our Souls
525 Joyful, Joyful, We Adore You
519 Laudate Dominum
658 Lord Christ, the Father's Mighty Son
438 Lord Christ, When First You Came to Earth
588 Love Divine, All Loves Excelling
599 Love Is His Word

Topical Index/*continued*

587 Morning Glory, Starlit Sky
446 Morning of Splendor
606 My Shepherd Will Supply My Need
439 My Song Is Love Unknown
560 Now Thank We All Our God
453 Now the Green Blade Rises
725 O Breathe on Me, O Breath of God
541 O God beyond All Praising
652 O God of Love, O King of Peace
546 O That I Had a Thousand Voices
689 O the Beautiful Treasures
660 Peace with the Father
359 People, Look East
682 Praise and Thanksgiving
550 Sing a New Song to the Lord
532 Sing to the Lord a Joyful Song
609 The King of Love My Shepherd Is
612 The Living God My Shepherd Is
613 The Lord, the Lord, the Lord Is My Shepherd
504 The Works of the Lord Are Created in Wisdom
595 There's a Wideness in God's Mercy
596 There's a Wideness in God's Mercy
603 This Is My Commandment
491 To Christ, the Prince of Peace
600 What Wondrous Love Is This
433 When I Survey the Wondrous Cross
508 When Israel Was in Egypt's Land
614 When Jesus Came Preaching the Kingdom of God
412 When John Baptized by Jordan's River
745 When Love Is Found
598 Where True Love and Charity Are Found/Ubi Caritas
638 Your Love, O God, Has All the World Created

LOVE FOR GOD
552 Come, We That Love the Lord
488 Jesus, My Lord, My God, My All
363 Lift Up Your Heads, O Mighty Gates
589 Not for Tongues of Heaven's Angels
591 O for a Heart to Praise My God
530 Praise, My Soul, the King of Heaven
550 Sing a New Song to the Lord
506 The Stars Declare His Glory
582 This World, My God, Is Held within Your Hand
604 Ubi Caritas (Taizé)

LOVE FOR OTHERS
733 At That First Eucharist
360 Awake! Awake, and Greet the New Morn
601 Beloved, Let Us Love
731 Draw Us in the Spirit's Tether
754 Forgive Our Sins
562 For the Fruits of This Creation
643 For the Healing of the Nations
592 God Is Unique and One
631 God, Whose Giving Knows No Ending
640 God, Whose Purpose Is to Kindle
656 Help Us Accept Each Other
431 Jesu, Jesu, Fill Us with Your Love
649 Jesus, Shepherd of Our Souls
432 Jesus Took a Towel
525 Joyful, Joyful, We Adore You
641 Lift Every Voice and Sing
658 Lord Christ, the Father's Mighty Son
602 Lord of All Nations, Grant Me Grace
812 Mandatum Novum
589 Not for Tongues of Heaven's Angels
725 O Breathe on Me, O Breath of God
654 O Day of Peace
591 O for a Heart to Praise My God
642 O God, Empower Us
652 O God of Love, O King of Peace
475 O Holy Spirit, by Whose Breath
570 Our Father, by Whose Name
660 Peace with the Father
682 Praise and Thanksgiving
644 Said Judas to Mary
752 The Master Came to Bring Good News
506 The Stars Declare His Glory
657 There Is One Lord
595 There's a Wideness in God's Mercy
596 There's a Wideness in God's Mercy
603 This Is My Commandment
590 This Is My Will
632 Those Who Love and Those Who Labor
604 Ubi Caritas
614 When Jesus Came Preaching the Kingdom of God
745 When Love Is Found
598 Where True Love and Charity Are Found/Ubi Caritas
(also Brotherhood and Sisterhood, Unity)

MAJESTY AND POWER
494 All Hail the Power of Jesus' Name
495 All Hail the Power of Jesus' Name
538 Christians, Lift Up Your Hearts
496 Crown Him with Many Crowns
655 Father, Lord of All Creation
581 God Is My Great Desire
575 God Is Our Fortress and Our Rock
576 God Is Our Fortress and Our Rock
592 God Is Unique and One
507 God Is Working His Purpose Out
651 Great God, Our Source and Lord of Space
684 He Walks among the Golden Lamps
522 Heavenly Hosts in Ceaseless Worship
672 How Beautiful the Morning and the Day
502 I Sing the Mighty Power of God
512 Immortal, Invisible, God Only Wise
716 Let All on Earth Their Voices Raise
553 Magnificat
503 Many and Great, O God, Are Your Works
686 Mine Eyes Have Seen the Glory
533 New Songs of Celebration
687 Now the Day of the Lord Is at Hand
666 Only Begotten, Word of God Eternal
529 Praise the Lord! You Heavens, Adore Him
550 Sing a New Song to the Lord
528 Sing Praise to God Who Reigns Above
361 Take Comfort, God's People
506 The Stars Declare His Glory
358 The Voice of God Goes Out through All the World
504 The Works of the Lord Are Created in Wisdom
673 This Day God Gives Me
508 When Israel Was in Egypt's Land

MARTYRS *(see Liturgical Index: Martyrs)*

MARY (BVM) *(see Liturgical Index)*

MERCY
527 All Glory Be to God on High
583 Amazing Grace
681 Christ, Mighty Savior
664 Come, Rejoice before Your Maker
756 Come, You Sinners, Poor and Needy
561 Confitemini Domino
558 Father, We Thank Thee, Who Hast Planted
754 Forgive Our Sins
518 Glory Be to God in Heaven
567 God Be in My Head
563 God, Omnipotent, Eternal
746 Great God of Mercy
753 Have Mercy, Lord, on Us
414 Hear Us, Almighty Lord/Attende Domine
565 Hope of the World
672 How Beautiful the Morning and the Day
389 How Brightly Beams the Morning Star
390 How Brightly Beams the Morning Star
585 How Firm a Foundation
636 I Danced in the Morning
525 Joyful, Joyful, We Adore You
519 Laudate Dominum
727 Let Us Break Bread Together
658 Lord Christ, the Father's Mighty Son
602 Lord of All Nations, Grant Me Grace
588 Love Divine, All Loves Excelling
553 Magnificat
606 My Shepherd Will Supply My Need
620 O Blessed Are the Poor in Spirit
740 O Lord, You Died That All Might Live
689 O the Beautiful Treasures
666 Only Begotten, Word of God Eternal
755 Our Father, We Have Wandered
416 Parce Domine
660 Peace with the Father
530 Praise, My Soul, the King of Heaven
547 Praise to the Lord, the Almighty
550 Sing a New Song to the Lord
528 Sing Praise to God Who Reigns Above
609 The King of Love My Shepherd Is
615 The Kingdom of God
612 The Living God My Shepherd Is
613 The Lord, the Lord, the Lord Is My Shepherd
752 The Master Came to Bring Good News
608 There Is a Balm in Gilead
595 There's a Wideness in God's Mercy
596 There's a Wideness in God's Mercy
511 Thy Strong Word Didst Cleave the Darkness
624 What Does the Lord Require
614 When Jesus Came Preaching the Kingdom of God
638 Your Love, O God, Has All the World Created
(also Love of God for Us, Reconciliation, Repentance; Liturgical Index: Penance)

Topical Index/*continued*

MINISTRY
594 Christian, Do You Hear the Lord
566 Come to Us, Creative Spirit
643 For the Healing of the Nations
627 Forth in the Peace of Christ
619 Glorious in Majesty
628 Go Make of All Disciples
567 God Be in My Head
648 God, Who Stretched the Spangled Heavens
631 God, Whose Giving Knows No Ending
640 God, Whose Purpose Is to Kindle
629 How Shall They Hear the Word of God
431 Jesu, Jesu, Fill Us with Your Love
432 Jesus Took a Towel
716 Let All on Earth Their Voices Raise
630 Lord, Whose Love in Humble Service
470 Lord, You Give the Great Commission
599 Love Is His Word
812 Mandatum Novum
587 Morning Glory, Starlit Sky
625 Now Let Us from This Table Rise
620 O Blessed Are the Poor in Spirit
618 O Christ the Great Foundation
642 O God Empower Us
646 O Jesus Christ, May Grateful Hymns Be Rising
477 Praise the Spirit in Creation
626 The Church of Christ in Every Age
531 There's a Spirit in the Air
603 This Is My Commandment
590 This Is My Will
633 Two Fishermen
623 We Are Your People
635 Weary of All Trumpeting
709 What Is This Place
481 When God the Spirit Came
614 When Jesus Came Preaching the Kingdom of God
(also Brotherhood & Sisterhood, Commitment, Discipleship, Mission, Service)

MISSION
586 Awake, O Sleeper, Rise from Death
478 Fire of God, Titanic Spirit
627 Forth in the Peace of Christ
628 Go Make of All Disciples
507 God Is Working His Purpose Out
563 God, Omnipotent, Eternal
629 How Shall They Hear the Word of God
611 Jesus, Lead the Way
593 I Sought the Lord
630 Lord, Whose Love in Humble Service
470 Lord, You Give the Great Commission
618 O Christ the Great Foundation
477 Praise the Spirit in Creation
526 Thanks Be to God
626 The Church of Christ in Every Age
615 The Kingdom of God
481 When God the Spirit Came
614 When Jesus Came Preaching the Kingdom of God

MORNING
520 All Creatures of Our God and King
669 All People That On Earth Do Dwell
670 All People That On Earth Do Dwell
360 Awake! Awake, and Greet the New Morn
577 By Gracious Powers
4 Father, We Praise You
557 For the Beauty of the Earth
567 God Be in My Head
656 Help Us Accept Each Other
485 Holy, Holy, Holy! Lord God Almighty
672 How Beautiful the Morning and the Day
389 How Brightly Beams the Morning Star
390 How Brightly Beams the Morning Star
636 I Danced in the Morning
607 I Heard the Voice of Jesus Say
671 I Sing As I Arise Today
611 Jesus, Lead the Way
492 Jesus Shall Reign
525 Joyful, Joyful, We Adore You
559 Let All Things Now Living
568 Lord of All Hopefulness
674 Morning Has Broken
446 Morning of Splendor
662 On This Day, the First of Days
528 Sing Praise to God Who Reigns Above
373 The King Shall Come When Morning Dawns
506 The Stars Declare His Glory
673 This Day God Gives Me
2 To God with Gladness Sing
675 When Morning Gilds the Sky
(also Praise)

MUSIC MINISTRY
566 Come to Us, Creative Spirit
667 God Is Here! As We His People
554 Sing Alleluia, Praise the Lord
539 Sing Praise to the Lord
549 When in Our Music God Is Glorified

MYSTERY OF GOD
516 God Has Spoken by His Prophets
507 God Is Working His Purpose Out
684 He Walks among the Golden Lamps
515 His Voice Is in the Thunder, in the Storm
524 Holy God, We Praise Thy Name
512 Immortal, Invisible, God Only Wise
523 Let All Mortal Flesh Keep Silence
514 Thanks to God Whose Word Was Spoken
504 The Works of the Lord Are Created in Wisdom

NATION
763 America the Beautiful
764 God of Our Fathers
686 Mine Eyes Have Seen the Glory
762 My Country, 'Tis of Thee
761 Star-Spangled Banner
760 We Gather Together
(also Brotherhood & Sisterhood, Social Concern, World, Universe)

NATURE *(see Life)*

NEW CREATION
527 All Glory Be to God on High
366 Come, Lord, and Tarry Not
592 God Is Unique and One
563 God, Omnipotent, Eternal
578 God Spoke to Our Father Abraham
486 God, Whose Almighty Word
564 Jesus, Come! For We Invite You
438 Lord Christ, When First You Came to Earth
618 O Christ the Great Foundation
483 Over the Chaos of the Empty Waters
477 Praise the Spirit in Creation
540 Shout for Joy, Loud and Long
358 The Voice of God Goes Out through All the World
721 We Know That Christ Is Raised
355 When the King Shall Come Again

NEW YEAR
567 God Be in My Head
507 God Is Working His Purpose Out
661 Is This a Day of New Beginnings
556 Lord of Our Growing Years
662 On This Day, the First of Days
663 This Is the Day When Light Was First Created

OBEDIENCE
578 God Spoke to Our Father Abraham
626 The Church of Christ in Every Age
614 When Jesus Came Preaching the Kingdom of God
645 With Jesus for Hero

OFFERING
566 Come to Us, Creative Spirit
4 Father, We Praise You
683 God, Whose Farm Is All Creation
631 God, Whose Giving Knows No Ending
565 Hope of the World
624 What Does the Lord Require
622 Where Temple Offerings Are Made

PARABLES
362 City of God, Jerusalem
759 Come, Ye Thankful People, Come
755 Our Father, We Have Wandered
615 The Kingdom of God
371 Wake, O Wake, and Sleep No Longer

PASCHAL MYSTERY
385 A Stable Lamp Is Lighted
459 At the Lamb's High Feast We Sing
460 At the Lamb's High Feast We Sing
499 At the Name of Jesus
730 Ave Verum
450 Be Joyful, Mary
418 Before the Fruit Is Ripened by the Sun
577 By Gracious Powers
452 Christ the Lord Is Risen Today
461 Christ the Lord Is Risen Today
462 Christ the Lord Is Risen Today
463 Christ the Lord Is Risen Today
723 Come and Let Us Drink of That New River
456 Come, Ye Faithful, Raise the Strain
448 Daylight Fades
732 Draw Near and Take the Body of Your Lord
619 Glorious in Majesty
542 Glory to God in the Highest
592 God Is Unique and One
563 God, Omnipotent, Eternal
578 God Spoke to Our Father Abraham
535 God, We Praise You
444 Hail Thee, Festival Day
692 Hail to the Lord Who Comes
565 Hope of the World
636 I Danced in the Morning
445 I Know That My Redeemer Lives
661 Is This a Day of New Beginnings
442 Jesus Christ Is Risen Today
427 Jesus Walked This Lonesome Valley

Topical Index/*continued*

704 Lift High the Cross
599 Love Is His Word
587 Morning Glory, Starlit Sky
625 Now Let Us from This Table Rise
453 Now the Green Blade Rises
740 O Lord, You Died That All Might Live
425 Salvator Mundi
372 Savior of the Nations, Come
540 Shout for Joy, Loud and Long
437 Sing, My Tongue, the Song of Triumph
404 Sing of Mary, Pure and Lowly
528 Sing Praise to God Who Reigns Above
634 Take Up Your Cross
514 Thanks to God Whose Word Was Spoken
464 The Head That Once Was Crowned with Thorns
501 The King of Glory
615 The Kingdom of God
435 The Royal Banners Forward Go
451 The Strife Is O'er
608 There Is a Balm in Gilead
722 This Is the Spirit's Entry Now
449 This Joyful Eastertide
721 We Know That Christ Is Raised
635 Weary of All Trumpeting
709 What Is This Place
433 When I Survey the Wondrous Cross
638 Your Love, O God, Has All the World Created

PASSION *(see Liturgical Index: Passion Sunday, Easter Triduum)*

PATIENCE
694 Come Now, and Praise the Humble Saint
611 Jesus, Lead the Way
589 Not for Tongues of Heaven's Angels
657 There Is One Lord
604 Ubi Caritas (Taizé)

PEACE
527 All Glory Be to God on High
621 All Who Love and Serve Your City
395 Angel Voices Richly Blending
763 America the Beautiful
360 Awake! Awake, and Greet the New Morn
586 Awake, O Sleeper, Rise from Death
639 Come, Let Us Love the Unborn Generations
366 Come, Lord, and Tarry Not
370 Comfort, Comfort, O My People
543 Christ Is the World's Light
496 Crown Him with Many Crowns
448 Daylight Fades
557 For the Beauty of the Earth
562 For the Fruits of This Creation
643 For the Healing of the Nations
627 Forth in the Peace of Christ
521 From All That Dwell below the Skies
518 Glory Be to God in Heaven
542 Glory to God in the Highest
516 God Has Spoken by His Prophets
764 God of Our Fathers
563 God, Omnipotent, Eternal
648 God, Who Stretched the Spangled Heavens
631 God, Whose Giving Knows No Ending
651 Great God, Our Source and Lord of Space
444 Hail Thee, Festival Day
565 Hope of the World
400 It Came upon the Midnight Clear
649 Jesus, Shepherd of Our Souls
559 Let All Things Now Living
653 Let There Be Light
658 Lord Christ, the Father's Mighty Son
438 Lord Christ, When First You Came to Earth
568 Lord of All Hopefulness
602 Lord of All Nations, Grant Me Grace
417 Lord, Who throughout These Forty Days
686 Mine Eyes Have Seen the Glory
762 My Country, 'Tis of Thee
533 New Songs of Celebration
560 Now Thank We All Our God
668 Now the Silence
620 O Blessed Are the Poor in Spirit
357 O Come, O Come, Emmanuel
654 O Day of Peace
591 O for a Heart to Praise My God
642 O God, Empower Us
650 O God of Every Nation
652 O God of Love, O King of Peace
475 O Holy Spirit, by Whose Breath
605 O Jesus, Joy of Loving Hearts
755 Our Father, We Have Wandered
660 Peace with the Father
491 To Christ, the Prince of Peace
2 To God with Gladness Sing
635 Weary of All Trumpeting
624 What Does the Lord Require
709 What Is This Place
508 When Israel Was in Egypt's Land
645 With Jesus for Hero
638 Your Love, O God, Has All the World Created

PETITION
574 A Single Unmatched Stone
420 Again We Keep This Solemn Fast
428 All Glory, Laud, and Honor
805 All Glory, Laud, and Honor
621 All Who Love and Serve Your City
421 At the Cross Her Station Keeping
617 Christ Is Made the Sure Foundation
681 Christ, Mighty Savior
594 Christian, Do You Hear the Lord
472 Come Down, O Love Divine
482 Come, Holy Ghost
366 Come, Lord, and Tarry Not
569 Come, My Way, My Truth, My Life
487 Come, Now Almighty King
364 Come, O Long Expected Jesus
566 Come to Us, Creative Spirit
759 Come, Ye Thankful People, Come
368 Creator of the Stars of Night
677 Day Is Done
655 Father, Lord of All Creation
558 Father, We Thank Thee, Who Hast Planted
474 Fire of God, Undying Flame
419 Forty Days and Forty Nights
665 Gather Us In
567 God Be in My Head
563 God, Omnipotent, Eternal
648 God, Who Stretched the Spangled Heavens
486 God, Whose Almighty Word
683 God, Whose Farm Is All Creation
640 God, Whose Purpose Is to Kindle
651 Great God, Our Source and Lord of Space
414 Hear Us, Almighty Lord/Attende Domine
656 Help Us Accept Each Other
565 Hope of the World
710 How Blessed Is This Place
610 How Good the Name of Jesus Sounds
512 Immortal, Invisible, God Only Wise
671 I Sing As I Arise Today
564 Jesus, Come! For We Invite You
611 Jesus, Lead the Way
488 Jesus, My Lord, My God, My All
423 Jesus, Remember Me
525 Joyful, Joyful, We Adore You
653 Let There Be Light
363 Lift Up Your Heads, O Mighty Gates
691 Lord, Bid Your Servant Go in Peace
658 Lord Christ, the Father's Mighty Son
568 Lord of All Hopefulness
602 Lord of All Nations, Grant Me Grace
739 Lord of the Living
588 Love Divine, All Loves Excelling
503 Many and Great, O God, Are Your Works
589 Not for Tongues of Heaven's Angels
367 O Come, Divine Messiah
591 O for a Heart to Praise My God
642 O God, Empower Us
650 O God of Every Nation
652 O God of Love, O King of Peace
685 O Holy City, Seen of John
475 O Holy Spirit, by Whose Breath
646 O Jesus Christ, May Grateful Hymns Be Rising
605 O Jesus, Joy of Loving Hearts
740 O Lord, You Died That All Might Live
443 O Queen of Heaven/Regina Caeli
434 O Sacred Head Surrounded
757 O Saving Victim/O Salutaris
748 O Son of God, in Galilee
424 O Sun of Justice
546 O That I Had a Thousand Voices
662 On This Day, the First of Days
666 Only Begotten, Word of God Eternal
570 Our Father, by Whose Name
416 Parce Domine
660 Peace with the Father
372 Savior of the Nations, Come
580 Seek Ye First the Kingdom of God
476 Spirit Divine, Accept Our Prayers
457 That Easter Day with Joy Was Bright
422 The Glory of These Forty Days
609 The King of Love My Shepherd Is
506 The Stars Declare His Glory
673 This Day God Gives Me
603 This Is My Commandment
590 This Is My Will
663 This Is the Day When Light Was First Created
582 This World, My God, Is Held within Your Hand
511 Thy Strong Word Didst Cleave the Darkness
700 'Tis Good, Lord, to Be Here
760 We Gather Together
680 We Praise You, Father
635 Weary of All Trumpeting
638 Your Love, O God, Has All the World Created
479 Veni Creator Spiritus

PILGRIMAGE
583 Amazing Grace
586 Awake, O Sleeper, Rise from Death

Topical Index/*continued*

552 Come, We That Love the Lord
585 How Firm a Foundation
607 I Heard the Voice of Jesus Say
593 I Sought the Lord
611 Jesus, Lead the Way
559 Let All Things Now Living
625 Now Let Us from This Table Rise
579 O God, Our Help in Ages Past
666 Only Begotten, Word of God Eternal
728 Shepherd of Souls
609 The King of Love My Shepherd Is
(also Shepherd, Exile)

POVERTY
621 All Who Love and Serve Your City
616 Christ's Church Shall Glory in His Power
647 Now Join We to Praise the Creator
620 O Blessed Are the Poor in Spirit
644 Said Judas to Mary
358 The Voice of God Goes Out through All the World
624 What Does the Lord Require
622 Where Temple Offerings Are Made

PRAISE
469 A Hymn of Glory Let Us Sing
548 Adoramus Te Domine
815 Adoramus Te Domine
520 All Creatures of Our God and King
527 All Glory Be to God on High
428 All Glory, Laud, and Honor
805 All Glory, Laud, and Honor
494 All Hail the Power of Jesus' Name
495 All Hail the Power of Jesus' Name
669 All People That On Earth Do Dwell
670 All People That On Earth Do Dwell
505 All Things Bright and Beautiful
441 Alleluia, Alleluia, Give Thanks
737 Alleluia! Sing to Jesus
583 Amazing Grace
459 At the Lamb's High Feast We Sing
460 At the Lamb's High Feast We Sing
499 At the Name of Jesus
730 Ave Verum
429 Benedictus Qui Venit
706 By All Your Saints Still Striving
466 Christ Is Alive!
617 Christ Is Made the Sure Foundation
500 Christ Is the King
543 Christ Is the World's Light
681 Christ, Mighty Savior
452 Christ the Lord Is Risen Today
461 Christ the Lord Is Risen Today
701 Christ upon the Mountain Peak
594 Christian, Do You Hear the Lord
538 Christians, Lift Up Your Hearts
758 Come Adore/Tantum Ergo
487 Come, Now Almighty King
664 Come, Rejoice before Your Maker
552 Come, We That Love the Lord
561 Confitemini Domino
496 Crown Him with Many Crowns
448 Daylight Fades
517 Earth and All Stars
4 Father, We Praise You
558 Father, We Thank Thee, Who Hast Planted
705 For All the Saints
557 For the Beauty of the Earth
521 From All That Dwell below the Skies
401 Gloria, Gloria
619 Glorious in Majesty
518 Glory Be to God in Heaven
542 Glory to God in the Highest
628 Go Make of All Disciples
667 God Is Here! As We His People
575 God Is Our Fortress and Our Rock
576 God Is Our Fortress and Our Rock
764 God of Our Fathers
535 God, We Praise You
683 God, Whose Farm Is All Creation
631 God, Whose Giving Knows No Ending
489 God with Hidden Majesty/Adoro Te Devote
813 Hail Our Savior's Glorious Body/Pange Lingua
471 Hail the Day That Sees Him Rise
444 Hail Thee, Festival Day
522 Heavenly Hosts in Ceaseless Worship
498 He Is King of Kings
684 He Walks among the Golden Lamps
365 Hills of the North, Rejoice
515 His Voice Is in the Thunder, in the Storm
524 Holy God, We Praise Thy Name
485 Holy, Holy, Holy! Lord God Almighty
430 Hosanna in Excelsis
672 How Beautiful the Morning and the Day
710 How Blessed Is This Place
389 How Brightly Beams the Morning Star
390 How Brightly Beams the Morning Star
610 How Good the Name of Jesus Sounds
502 I Sing the Mighty Power of God
512 Immortal, Invisible, God Only Wise
442 Jesus Christ Is Risen Today
492 Jesus Shall Reign
525 Joyful, Joyful, We Adore You
555 Jubilate Deo
519 Laudate Dominum
523 Let All Mortal Flesh Keep Silence
716 Let All on Earth Their Voices Raise
536 Let All the World in Every Corner Sing
559 Let All Things Now Living
727 Let Us Break Bread Together
704 Lift High the Cross
556 Lord of Our Growing Years
553 Magnificat
503 Many and Great, O God, Are Your Works
686 Mine Eyes Have Seen the Glory
674 Morning Has Broken
446 Morning of Splendor
606 My Shepherd Will Supply My Need
533 New Songs of Celebration
560 Now Thank We All Our God
729 O Food of Exiles Lowly
679 O Gladsome Light
484 O God, Almighty Father
541 O God beyond All Praising
579 O God, Our Help in Ages Past
646 O Jesus Christ, May Grateful Hymns Be Rising
757 O Saving Victim/O Salutaris
447 O Sons and Daughters
424 O Sun of Justice
546 O That I Had a Thousand Voices
398 Of the Father's Love Begotten
662 On This Day, the First of Days
682 Praise and Thanksgiving
545 Praise Him
530 Praise, My Soul, the King of Heaven
551 Praise the Lord of Heaven
529 Praise the Lord! You Heavens, Adore Him
547 Praise to the Lord, the Almighty
544 Reap Me the Earth
493 Rejoice, the Lord Is King
540 Shout for Joy, Loud and Long
550 Sing a New Song to the Lord
554 Sing Alleluia, Praise the Lord
528 Sing Praise to God Who Reigns Above
539 Sing Praise to the Lord
532 Sing to the Lord a Joyful Song
467 Sing with All the Saints in Glory
410 Songs of Thankfulness and Praise
584 Surely It Is God Who Saves Me
534 Tell Out, My Soul, the Greatness of the Lord
514 Thanks to God Whose Word Was Spoken
457 That Easter Day with Joy Was Bright
678 The Day You Gave Us, Lord, Is Ended
537 The God of Abraham Praise
501 The King of Glory
609 The King of Love My Shepherd Is
612 The Living God My Shepherd Is
506 The Stars Declare His Glory
451 The Strife Is O'er
504 The Works of the Lord Are Created in Wisdom
531 There's a Spirit in the Air
673 This Day God Gives Me
663 This Is the Day When Light Was First Created
511 Thy Strong Word Didst Cleave the Darkness
2 To God with Gladness Sing
497 To Jesus Christ, Our Sovereign King
371 Wake, O Wake, and Sleep No Longer
760 We Gather Together
680 We Praise You, Father
20 We Praise You, Father, for Your Gift
407 What Star Is This
549 When in Our Music God Is Glorified
675 When Morning Gilds the Sky
707 Ye Watchers and Ye Holy Ones

PRAYER *(see Praise, Mercy, Petition, Thanksgiving)*

PRESENCE OF GOD
389 How Brightly Beams the Morning Star
390 How Brightly Beams the Morning Star
502 I Sing the Mighty Power of God
512 Immortal, Invisible, God Only Wise
605 O Jesus, Joy of Loving Hearts
666 Only Begotten, Word of God Eternal
410 Songs of Thankfulness and Praise

PRIESTHOOD *(see Commitment, Discipleship, Mission; Liturgical Index: Christian Initiation of Adults, Baptism, Confirmation)*

PROPHECY *(see Word of God)*

PROVIDENCE
505 All Things Bright and Beautiful
669 All People That On Earth Do Dwell
670 All People That On Earth Do Dwell
440 All You Who Pass This Way
737 Alleluia! Sing to Jesus
421 At the Cross Her Station Keeping
677 Day Is Done

Topical Index/*continued*

558 Father, We Thank Thee, Who Hast Planted
562 For the Fruits of This Creation
516 God Has Spoken by His Prophets
581 God Is My Great Desire
575 God Is Our Fortress and Our Rock
576 God Is Our Fortress and Our Rock
592 God Is Unique and One
507 God Is Working His Purpose Out
648 God, Who Stretched the Spangled Heavens
683 God, Whose Farm Is All Creation
651 Great God, Our Source and Lord of Space
515 His Voice Is in the Thunder, in the Storm
565 Hope of the World
672 How Beautiful the Morning and the Day
389 How Brightly Beams the Morning Star
390 How Brightly Beams the Morning Star
445 I Know That My Redeemer Lives
671 I Sing As I Arise Today
502 I Sing the Mighty Power of God
593 I Sought the Lord
649 Jesus, Shepherd of Our Souls
536 Let All the World in Every Corner Sing
568 Lord of All Hopefulness
553 Magnificat
674 Morning Has Broken
606 My Shepherd Will Supply My Need
560 Now Thank We All Our God
676 Nunc Dimittis
579 O God, Our Help in Ages Past
424 O Sun of Justice
689 O the Beautiful Treasures
682 Praise and Thanksgiving
530 Praise, My Soul, the King of Heaven
547 Praise to the Lord, the Almighty
529 Praise the Lord! You Heavens, Adore Him
728 Shepherd of Souls
528 Sing Praise to God Who Reigns Above
532 Sing to the Lord a Joyful Song
584 Surely It Is God Who Saves Me
526 Thanks Be to God
678 The Day You Gave Us, Lord, Is Ended
612 The Living God My Shepherd Is
613 The Lord, the Lord, the Lord Is My Shepherd
506 The Stars Declare His Glory
504 The Works of the Lord Are Created in Wisdom
673 This Day God Gives Me
582 This World, My God, Is Held within Your Hand
632 Those Who Love and Those Who Labor
511 Thy Strong Word Didst Cleave the Darkness
508 When Israel Was in Egypt's Land
509 Who Can Measure Heaven and Earth
638 Your Love, O God, Has All the World Created

RECONCILIATION
385 A Stable Lamp Is Lighted
440 All You Who Pass This Way
733 At That First Eucharist
586 Awake, O Sleeper, Rise from Death
452 Christ the Lord Is Risen Today
461 Christ the Lord Is Risen Today
370 Comfort, Comfort, O My People
594 Christian, Do You Hear the Lord
538 Christians, Lift Up Your Hearts
754 Forgive Our Sins
753 Have Mercy, Lord, on Us
414 Hear Us, Almighty Lord/Attende Domine
636 I Danced in the Morning
649 Jesus, Shepherd of Our Souls
658 Lord Christ, the Father's Mighty Son
602 Lord of All Nations, Grant Me Grace
668 Now the Silence
591 O for a Heart to Praise My God
755 Our Father, We Have Wandered
660 Peace with the Father
752 The Master Came to Bring Good News
595 There's a Wideness in God's Mercy
596 There's a Wideness in God's Mercy
624 What Does the Lord Require
638 Your Love, O God, Has All the World Created
(also Repentance; Liturgical Index: Penance)

REDEMPTION
586 Awake, O Sleeper, Rise from Death
543 Christ Is the World's Light
452 Christ the Lord Is Risen Today
461 Christ the Lord Is Risen Today
462 Christ the Lord Is Risen Today
463 Christ the Lord Is Risen Today
542 Glory to God in the Highest
535 God, We Praise You
522 Heavenly Hosts in Ceaseless Worship
414 Hear Us, Almighty Lord/Attende Domine
593 I Sought the Lord
442 Jesus Christ Is Risen Today
523 Let All Mortal Flesh Keep Silence
417 Lord, Who throughout These Forty Days
446 Morning of Splendor
514 Thanks to God Whose Word Was Spoken
615 The Kingdom of God
501 The King of Glory
612 The Living God My Shepherd Is
613 The Lord, the Lord, the Lord Is My Shepherd
595 There's a Wideness in God's Mercy
596 There's a Wideness in God's Mercy
511 Thy Strong Word Didst Cleave the Darkness
497 To Jesus Christ, Our Sovereign King
600 What Wondrous Love Is This
412 When John Baptized by Jordan's River
355 When the King Shall Come Again
(also Salvation)

REIGN OF GOD *(see Kingdom of God)*

RENEWAL
656 Help Us Accept Each Other
661 Is This a Day of New Beginnings
674 Morning Has Broken

REPENTANCE
420 Again We Keep This Solemn Fast
413 Alleluia, Song of Gladness
586 Awake, O Sleeper, Rise from Death
694 Come Now, and Praise the Humble Saint
370 Comfort, Comfort, O My People
754 Forgive Our Sins
563 God, Omnipotent, Eternal
640 God, Whose Purpose Is to Kindle
414 Hear Us, Almighty Lord/Attende Domine
593 I Sought the Lord
525 Joyful, Joyful, We Adore You
417 Lord, Who throughout These Forty Days
591 O for a Heart to Praise My God
424 O Sun of Justice
356 On Jordan's Bank
415 Somebody's Knockin' at Your Door
609 The King of Love My Shepherd Is
697 When Jesus Came to Jordan
412 When John Baptized by Jordan's River
(also Reconciliation; Liturgical Index: Penance)

REST
601 Beloved, Let Us Love
706 By All Your Saints Still Striving
681 Christ, Mighty Savior
705 For All the Saints
710 How Blessed Is This Place
610 How Good the Name of Jesus Sounds
607 I Heard the Voice of Jesus Say
611 Jesus, Lead the Way
606 My Shepherd Will Supply My Need
740 O Lord, You Died That All Might Live
689 O the Beautiful Treasures
678 The Day You Gave Us, Lord, Is Ended
608 There Is a Balm in Gilead
673 This Day God Gives Me
663 This Is the Day When Light Was First Created
680 We Praise You, Father
20 We Praise You, Father, for Your Gift
645 With Jesus for Hero

RESURRECTION *(see Liturgical Index: Easter season)*

SACRIFICE
732 Draw Near and Take the Body of Your Lord
578 God Spoke to Our Father Abraham
642 O God, Empower Us
646 O Jesus Christ, May Grateful Hymns Be Rising
662 On This Day, the First of Days
626 The Church of Christ in Every Age
624 What Does the Lord Require

SAINTS
548 Adoramus Te Domine
815 Adoramus Te Domine
719 Around the Throne a Glorious Band
706 By All Your Saints Still Striving
500 Christ Is the King
694 Come Now, and Praise the Humble Saint
571 Faith of Our Fathers
705 For All the Saints
522 Heavenly Hosts in Ceaseless Worship
485 Holy, Holy, Holy! Lord God Almighty
585 How Firm a Foundation

Topical Index/*continued*

715 Let Us with Joy Our Voices Raise
620 O Blessed Are the Poor in Spirit
529 Praise the Lord! You Heavens, Adore Him
467 Sing with All the Saints in Glory
537 The God of Abraham Praise
698 The Great Forerunner of the Morn
717 This Is the Feast Day of the Lord's True Witness
699 Two Noble Saints
707 Ye Watchers and Ye Holy Ones
(also Church; Liturgical Index)

SALVATION
583 Amazing Grace
459 At the Lamb's High Feast We Sing
460 At the Lamb's High Feast We Sing
499 At the Name of Jesus
577 By Gracious Powers
732 Draw Near and Take the Body of Your Lord
4 Father, We Praise You
521 From All That Dwell below the Skies
716 Let All on Earth Their Voices Raise
438 Lord Christ, When First You Came to Earth
588 Love Divine, All Loves Excelling
439 My Song Is Love Unknown
533 New Songs of Celebration
618 O Christ the Great Foundation
425 Salvator Mundi
540 Shout for Joy, Loud and Long
550 Sing a New Song to the Lord
528 Sing Praise to God Who Reigns Above
539 Sing Praise to the Lord
410 Songs of Thankfulness and Praise
501 The King of Glory
615 The Kingdom of God
511 Thy Strong Word Didst Cleave the Darkness
508 When Israel Was in Egypt's Land
697 When Jesus Came to Jordan
(also Redemption; Liturgical Index: Penance)

SCIENCE AND SPACE
655 Father, Lord of All Creation
592 God Is Unique and One
648 God, Who Stretched the Spangled Heavens
651 Great God, Our Source and Lord of Space
559 Let All Things Now Living
504 The Works of the Lord Are Created in Wisdom

SEASONS
557 For the Beauty of the Earth
556 Lord of Our Growing Years
359 People, Look East
551 Praise the Lord of Heaven
375 See amid the Winter's Snow
582 This World, My God, Is Held within Your Hand

SECOND COMING
621 All Who Love and Serve Your City
499 At the Name of Jesus
466 Christ Is Alive!
362 City of God, Jerusalem
366 Come, Lord, and Tarry Not
759 Come, Ye Thankful People, Come
368 Creator of the Stars of Night
496 Crown Him with Many Crowns
705 For All the Saints
619 Glorious in Majesty
507 God Is Working His Purpose Out
684 He Walks among the Golden Lamps
365 Hills of the North, Rejoice
389 How Brightly Beams the Morning Star
390 How Brightly Beams the Morning Star
510 I Want to Walk as a Child of the Light
363 Lift Up Your Heads, O Mighty Gates
588 Love Divine, All Loves Excelling
454 Maranatha! Alleluia!
686 Mine Eyes Have Seen the Glory
687 Now the Day of the Lord Is at Hand
618 O Christ the Great Foundation
685 O Holy City, Seen of John
398 Of the Father's Love Begotten
402 Once in Royal David's City
359 People, Look East
369 Prepare the Way of the Lord
493 Rejoice, the Lord Is King
550 Sing a New Song to the Lord
584 Surely It Is God Who Saves Me
501 The King of Glory
373 The King Shall Come When Morning Dawns
458 This Is the Feast of Victory
371 Wake, O Wake, and Sleep No Longer
600 What Wondrous Love Is This
355 When the King Shall Come Again
(also Judgment)

SENDING FORTH *(see Going Forth, Mission)*

SERVICE
669 All People That On Earth Do Dwell
670 All People That On Earth Do Dwell
621 All Who Love and Serve Your City
706 By All Your Saints Still Striving
500 Christ Is the King
616 Christ's Church Shall Glory in His Power
538 Christians, Lift Up Your Hearts
664 Come, Rejoice before Your Maker
731 Draw Us in the Spirit's Tether
643 For the Healing of the Nations
619 Glorious in Majesty
628 Go Make of All Disciples
648 God, Who Stretched the Spangled Heavens
631 God, Whose Giving Knows No Ending
659 In Christ There Is No East or West
649 Jesus, Shepherd of Our Souls
555 Jubilate Deo
559 Let All Things Now Living
630 Lord, Whose Love in Humble Service
599 Love Is His Word
644 Said Judas to Mary
626 The Church of Christ in Every Age
590 This Is My Will
663 This Is the Day When Light Was First Created
623 We Are Your People
614 When Jesus Came Preaching the Kingdom of God
(also Ministry)

SHARING
643 For the Healing of the Nations
649 Jesus, Shepherd of Our Souls
647 Now Join We to Praise the Creator
682 Praise and Thanksgiving
644 Said Judas to Mary
624 What Does the Lord Require

SHEPHERD
669 All People That On Earth Do Dwell
670 All People That On Earth Do Dwell
649 Jesus, Shepherd of Our Souls
606 My Shepherd Will Supply My Need
434 O Sacred Head Surrounded
728 Shepherd of Souls
361 Take Comfort, God's People
609 The King of Love My Shepherd Is
612 The Living God My Shepherd Is
613 The Lord, the Lord, the Lord Is My Shepherd
2 To God with Gladness Sing

SICKNESS *(see Comfort, Healing, Suffering; Liturgical Index: Pastoral Care of the Sick)*

SIN
586 Awake, O Sleeper, Rise from Death
754 Forgive Our Sins
563 God, Omnipotent, Eternal
753 Have Mercy, Lord, on Us
749 He Healed the Darkness of My Mind
752 The Master Came to Bring Good News
595 There's a Wideness in God's Mercy
596 There's a Wideness in God's Mercy
412 When John Baptized by Jordan's River
(also Reconciliation, Victory over Sin and Death; Liturgical Index: Penance)

SOCIAL CONCERN
621 All Who Love and Serve Your City
426 By the Babylonian Rivers
616 Christ's Church Shall Glory in His Power
639 Come, Let Us Love the Unborn Generations
562 For the Fruits of This Creation
643 For the Healing of the Nations
619 Glorious in Majesty
764 God of Our Fathers
563 God, Omnipotent, Eternal
648 God, Who Stretched the Spangled Heavens
631 God, Whose Giving Knows No Ending
640 God, Whose Purpose Is to Kindle
651 Great God, Our Source and Lord of Space
656 Help Us Accept Each Other
565 Hope of the World
659 In Christ There Is No East or West
649 Jesus, Shepherd of Our Souls
641 Lift Every Voice and Sing
438 Lord Christ, When First You Came to Earth
602 Lord of All Nations, Grant Me Grace
470 Lord, You Give the Great Commission
686 Mine Eyes Have Seen the Glory
647 Now Join We to Praise the Creator
625 Now Let Us from This Table Rise
620 O Blessed Are the Poor in Spirit
618 O Christ the Great Foundation
747 O Christ, the Healer
654 O Day of Peace
642 O God, Empower Us
650 O God of Every Nation
685 O Holy City, Seen of John
646 O Jesus Christ, May Grateful Hymns Be Rising

Topical Index/*continued*

682 Praise and Thanksgiving
644 Said Judas to Mary
626 The Church of Christ in Every Age
752 The Master Came to Bring Good News
358 The Voice of God Goes Out through All the World
657 There Is One Lord
531 There's a Spirit in the Air
381 Unto Us a Boy Is Born
623 We Are Your People
624 What Does the Lord Require
508 When Israel Was in Egypt's Land
614 When Jesus Came Preaching the Kingdom of God
645 With Jesus for Hero
638 Your Love, O God, Has All the World Created
(also Brotherhood and Sisterhood, Discipleship, Justice, Peace, Stewardship, Ministry, Service)

SONG
469 A Hymn of Glory Let Us Sing
520 All Creatures of Our God and King
494 All Hail the Power of Jesus' Name
495 All Hail the Power of Jesus' Name
669 All People That On Earth Do Dwell
670 All People That On Earth Do Dwell
737 Alleluia! Sing to Jesus
413 Alleluia, Song of Gladness
459 At the Lamb's High Feast We Sing
460 At the Lamb's High Feast We Sing
360 Awake! Awake, and Greet the New Morn
706 By All Your Saints Still Striving
426 By the Babylonian Rivers
466 Christ Is Alive!
500 Christ Is the King
681 Christ, Mighty Savior
616 Christ's Church Shall Glory in His Power
538 Christians, Lift Up Your Hearts
362 City of God, Jerusalem
664 Come, Rejoice before Your Maker
552 Come, We That Love the Lord
496 Crown Him with Many Crowns
517 Earth and All Stars
4 Father, We Praise You
705 For All the Saints
521 From All That Dwell below the Skies
619 Glorious in Majesty
365 Hills of the North, Rejoice
485 Holy, Holy, Holy! Lord God Almighty
672 How Beautiful the Morning and the Day
502 I Sing the Mighty Power of God
442 Jesus Christ Is Risen Today
492 Jesus Shall Reign
525 Joyful, Joyful, We Adore You
716 Let All on Earth Their Voices Raise
536 Let All the World in Every Corner Sing
559 Let All Things Now Living
641 Lift Every Voice and Sing
674 Morning Has Broken
439 My Song Is Love Unknown
533 New Songs of Celebration
647 Now Join We to Praise the Creator
668 Now the Silence
679 O Gladsome Light
541 O God beyond All Praising
646 O Jesus Christ, May Grateful Hymns Be Rising
447 O Sons and Daughters
546 O That I Had a Thousand Voices
359 People, Look East
547 Praise to the Lord, the Almighty
550 Sing a New Song to the Lord
554 Sing Alleluia, Praise the Lord
528 Sing Praise to God Who Reigns Above
539 Sing Praise to the Lord
532 Sing to the Lord a Joyful Song
467 Sing with All the Saints in Glory
504 The Works of the Lord Are Created in Wisdom
458 This Is the Feast of Victory
511 Thy Strong Word Didst Cleave the Darkness
491 To Christ, the Prince of Peace
2 To God with Gladness Sing
635 Weary of All Trumpeting
600 What Wondrous Love Is This
549 When in Our Music God Is Glorified

SORROW *(see Comfort, Mercy, Sin, Trust, Providence)*

SPACE *(see Science and Space)*

STEWARDSHIP
639 Come, Let Us Love the Unborn Generations
643 For the Healing of the Nations
648 God, Who Stretched the Spangled Heavens
683 God, Whose Farm Is All Creation
647 Now Join We to Praise the Creator
644 Said Judas to Mary
624 What Does the Lord Require
(also Brotherhood and Sisterhood, Ministry, Discipleship)

STRENGTH
706 By All Your Saints Still Striving
681 Christ, Mighty Savior
677 Day Is Done
705 For All the Saints
581 God Is My Great Desire
585 How Firm a Foundation
417 Lord, Who throughout These Forty Days
650 O God of Every Nation
685 O Holy City, Seen of John
646 O Jesus Christ, May Grateful Hymns Be Rising
634 Take Up Your Cross
673 This Day God Gives Me
680 We Praise You, Father

SUFFERING
583 Amazing Grace
577 By Gracious Powers
426 By the Babylonian Rivers
571 Faith of Our Fathers
419 Forty Days and Forty Nights
578 God Spoke to Our Father Abraham
573 He Comes to Us as One Unknown
585 How Firm a Foundation
636 I Danced in the Morning
637 It Shocked Them That the Master Did Not Fast
427 Jesus Walked This Lonesome Valley
641 Lift Every Voice and Sing
453 Now the Green Blade Rises
620 O Blessed Are the Poor in Spirit
541 O God beyond All Praising
434 O Sacred Head Surrounded
748 O Son of God, in Galilee
634 Take Up Your Cross
464 The Head That Once Was Crowned with Thorns
436 Were You There
433 When I Survey the Wondrous Cross
(also Comfort, Hope; Liturgical Index: Lenten Season)

SUNDAY
459 At the Lamb's High Feast We Sing
460 At the Lamb's High Feast We Sing
444 Hail Thee, Festival Day
661 Is This a Day of New Beginnings
446 Morning of Splendor
662 On This Day, the First of Days
673 This Day God Gives Me
663 This Is the Day When Light Was First Created
458 This Is the Feast of Victory

TEACHING
566 Come to Us, Creative Spirit
517 Earth and All Stars
573 He Comes to Us as One Unknown
506 The Stars Declare His Glory
(also Mission, Guidance)

TEMPTATION
499 At the Name of Jesus
419 Forty Days and Forty Nights
581 God Is My Great Desire
611 Jesus, Lead the Way
427 Jesus Walked This Lonesome Valley
417 Lord, Who throughout These Forty Days
697 When Jesus Came to Jordan

THANKSGIVING
527 All Glory Be to God on High
505 All Things Bright and Beautiful
441 Alleluia, Alleluia, Give Thanks
639 Come, Let Us Love the Unborn Generations
664 Come, Rejoice before Your Maker
759 Come, Ye Thankful People, Come
561 Confitemini Domino
558 Father, We Thank Thee, Who Hast Planted
557 For the Beauty of the Earth
562 For the Fruits of This Creation
521 From All That Dwell below the Skies
518 Glory Be to God in Heaven
542 Glory to God in the Highest
683 God, Whose Farm Is All Creation
631 God, Whose Giving Knows No Ending
559 Let All Things Now Living
647 Now Join We to Praise the Creator
560 Now Thank We All Our God
646 O Jesus Christ, May Grateful Hymns Be Rising
546 O That I Had a Thousand Voices
682 Praise and Thanksgiving
493 Rejoice, the Lord Is King
528 Sing Praise to God Who Reigns Above
539 Sing Praise to the Lord
532 Sing to the Lord a Joyful Song
410 Songs of Thankfulness and Praise
584 Surely It Is God Who Saves Me
526 Thanks Be to God
514 Thanks to God Whose Word Was Spoken
678 The Day You Gave Us, Lord, Is Ended
673 This Day God Gives Me
511 Thy Strong Word Didst Cleave the Darkness
2 To God with Gladness Sing
497 To Jesus Christ, Our Sovereign King
760 We Gather Together

Topical Index/*continued*

680 We Praise You, Father
407 What Star Is This

TIME
496 Crown Him with Many Crowns
655 Father, Lord of All Creation
557 For the Beauty of the Earth
592 God Is Unique and One
507 God Is Working His Purpose Out
568 Lord of All Hopefulness
556 Lord of Our Growing Years
668 Now the Silence
506 The Stars Declare His Glory
504 The Works of the Lord Are Created in Wisdom
582 This World, My God, Is Held within Your Hand

TRANSFIGURATION *(see Liturgical Index)*

TRUST
505 All Things Bright and Beautiful
490 All You Who Seek a Comfort Sure
583 Amazing Grace
577 By Gracious Powers
426 By the Babylonian Rivers
617 Christ Is Made the Sure Foundation
594 Christian, Do You Hear the Lord
362 City of God, Jerusalem
366 Come, Lord, and Tarry Not
364 Come, O Long Expected Jesus
370 Comfort, Comfort, O My People
677 Day Is Done
734 Eat This Bread
516 God Has Spoken by His Prophets
581 God Is My Great Desire
575 God Is Our Fortress and Our Rock
576 God Is Our Fortress and Our Rock
592 God Is Unique and One
507 God Is Working His Purpose Out
578 God Spoke to Our Father Abraham
571 Faith of Our Fathers
419 Forty Days and Forty Nights
665 Gather Us In
565 Hope of the World
389 How Brightly Beams the Morning Star
390 How Brightly Beams the Morning Star
585 How Firm a Foundation
610 How Good the Name of Jesus Sounds
607 I Heard the Voice of Jesus Say
445 I Know That My Redeemer Lives
593 I Sought the Lord
690 Jerusalem, My Happy Home
564 Jesus, Come! For We Invite You
611 Jesus, Lead the Way
423 Jesus, Remember Me
649 Jesus, Shepherd of Our Souls
427 Jesus Walked This Lonesome Valley
525 Joyful, Joyful, We Adore You
568 Lord of All Hopefulness
606 My Shepherd Will Supply My Need
453 Now the Green Blade Rises
676 Nunc Dimittis
367 O Come, Divine Messiah
654 O Day of Peace
541 O God beyond All Praising
650 O God of Every Nation
652 O God of Love, O King of Peace
579 O God, Our Help in Ages Past
580 Seek Ye First the Kingdom of God
532 Sing to the Lord a Joyful Song
415 Somebody's Knockin' at Your Door
584 Surely It Is God Who Saves Me
634 Take Up Your Cross
678 The Day You Gave Us, Lord, Is Ended
537 The God of Abraham Praise
609 The King of Love My Shepherd Is
615 The Kingdom of God
612 The Living God My Shepherd Is
613 The Lord, the Lord, the Lord Is My Shepherd
506 The Stars Declare His Glory
504 The Works of the Lord Are Created in Wisdom
608 There Is a Balm in Gilead
657 There Is One Lord
582 This World, My God, Is Held within Your Hand
511 Thy Strong Word Didst Cleave the Darkness
604 Ubi Caritas
760 We Gather Together
680 We Praise You, Father
572 We Walk by Faith
508 When Israel Was in Egypt's Land

TRUTH
499 At the Name of Jesus
569 Come, My Way, My Truth, My Life
517 Earth and All Stars
474 Fire of God, Undying Flame
562 For the Fruits of This Creation
627 Forth in the Peace of Christ
521 From All That Dwell below the Skies
563 God, Omnipotent, Eternal
573 He Comes to Us as One Unknown
656 Help Us Accept Each Other
686 Mine Eyes Have Seen the Glory
654 O Day of Peace
550 Sing a New Song to the Lord
480 Spirit of God within Me
645 With Jesus for Hero
638 Your Love, O God, Has All the World Created

UNDERSTANDING
653 Let There Be Light
642 O God, Empower Us

UNITY
733 At That First Eucharist
360 Awake! Awake, and Greet the New Morn
586 Awake, O Sleeper, Rise from Death
601 Beloved, Let Us Love
617 Christ Is Made the Sure Foundation
500 Christ Is the King
543 Christ Is the World's Light
616 Christ's Church Shall Glory in His Power
362 City of God, Jerusalem
731 Draw Us in the Spirit's Tether
571 Faith of Our Fathers
655 Father, Lord of All Creation
558 Father, We Thank Thee, Who Hast Planted
643 For the Healing of the Nations
627 Forth in the Peace of Christ
521 From All That Dwell below the Skies
665 Gather Us In
631 God, Whose Giving Knows No Ending
656 Help Us Accept Each Other
365 Hills of the North, Rejoice
565 Hope of the World
726 I Come with Joy to Meet My Lord
659 In Christ There Is No East or West
536 Let All the World in Every Corner Sing
653 Let There Be Light
727 Let Us Break Bread Together
658 Lord Christ, the Father's Mighty Son
602 Lord of All Nations, Grant Me Grace
556 Lord of Our Growing Years
588 Love Divine, All Loves Excelling
742 May the Grace of Christ Our Savior
618 O Christ the Great Foundation
747 O Christ, the Healer
357 O Come, O Come, Emmanuel
642 O God, Empower Us
475 O Holy Spirit, by Whose Breath
570 Our Father, by Whose Name
660 Peace with the Father
526 Thanks Be to God
657 There Is One Lord
663 This Is the Day When Light Was First Created
2 To God with Gladness Sing
623 We Are Your People
598 Where True Love and Charity Are Found/Ubi Caritas
(also Church, Love, Peace)

UNIVERSE
648 God, Who Stretched the Spangled Heavens
365 Hills of the North, Rejoice
555 Jubilate Deo
519 Laudate Dominum
536 Let All the World in Every Corner Sing
504 The Works of the Lord Are Created in Wisdom

VICTORY OVER SIN AND DEATH
441 Alleluia, Alleluia, Give Thanks
737 Alleluia! Sing to Jesus
583 Amazing Grace
459 At the Lamb's High Feast We Sing
460 At the Lamb's High Feast We Sing
450 Be Joyful, Mary
577 By Gracious Powers
452 Christ the Lord Is Risen Today
461 Christ the Lord Is Risen Today
462 Christ the Lord Is Risen Today
463 Christ the Lord Is Risen Today
465 Christus Resurrexit
552 Come, We That Love the Lord
456 Come, Ye Faithful, Raise the Strain
496 Crown Him with Many Crowns
448 Daylight Fades
732 Draw Near and Take the Body of Your Lord
575 God Is Our Fortress and Our Rock
576 God Is Our Fortress and Our Rock
471 Hail the Day That Sees Him Rise
444 Hail Thee, Festival Day
585 How Firm a Foundation
445 I Know That My Redeemer Lives
442 Jesus Christ Is Risen Today
446 Morning of Splendor
453 Now the Green Blade Rises
447 O Sons and Daughters
443 O Queen of Heaven/Regina Caeli
467 Sing with All the Saints in Glory
634 Take Up Your Cross
457 That Easter Day with Joy Was Bright
464 The Head That Once Was Crowned with Thorns
501 The King of Glory
451 The Strife Is O'er
663 This Is the Day When Light Was First Created
433 When I Survey the Wondrous Cross

Topical Index/*continued*

VISION
583 Amazing Grace
480 Spirit of God within Me
700 'Tis Good, Lord, to Be Here
508 When Israel Was in Egypt's Land

VOCATION
594 Christian, Do You Hear the Lord
628 Go Make of All Disciples
603 This Is My Commandment
(see Commitment, Discipleship, Ministry, Mission)

WATER
720 Baptized in Water
723 Come and Let Us Drink of That New River
607 I Heard the Voice of Jesus Say
722 This Is the Spirit's Entry Now
491 To Christ, the Prince of Peace
721 We Know That Christ Is Raised

WAY, TRUTH & LIFE (also Truth)
569 Come, My Way, My Truth, My Life
735 I Received the Living God
510 I Want to Walk as a Child of the Light

WELCOME
667 God Is Here! As We His People
606 My Shepherd Will Supply My Need
668 Now the Silence
609 The King of Love My Shepherd Is
623 We Are Your People
(also Gathering)

WISDOM
517 Earth and All Stars
573 He Comes to Us as One Unknown
515 His Voice Is in the Thunder, in the Storm
502 I Sing the Mighty Power of God
689 O the Beautiful Treasures
682 Praise and Thanksgiving
506 The Stars Declare His Glory
504 The Works of the Lord Are Created in Wisdom
511 Thy Strong Word Didst Cleave the Darkness
371 Wake, O Wake, and Sleep No Longer

WITNESS
548 Adoramus Te Domine
815 Adoramus Te Domine
719 Around the Throne a Glorious Band
718 Blessed Feasts of Blessed Martyrs
538 Christians, Lift Up Your Hearts
552 Come, We That Love the Lord
571 Faith of Our Fathers
478 Fire of God, Titanic Spirit
628 Go Make of All Disciples
592 God Is Unique and One
648 God, Who Stretched the Spangled Heavens
564 Jesus, Come! For We Invite You
649 Jesus, Shepherd of Our Souls
716 Let All on Earth Their Voices Raise
470 Lord, You Give the Great Commission
531 There's a Spirit in the Air
717 This Is the Feast Day of the Lord's True Witness
508 When Israel Was in Egypt's Land
481 When God the Spirit Came
(also Brotherhood and Sisterhood, Discipleship, Ministry)

WORD OF GOD
499 At the Name of Jesus
616 Christ's Church Shall Glory in His Power
487 Come, Now Almighty King
619 Glorious in Majesty
516 God Has Spoken by His Prophets
575 God Is Our Fortress and Our Rock
576 God Is Our Fortress and Our Rock
507 God Is Working His Purpose Out
640 God, Whose Purpose Is to Kindle
573 He Comes to Us as One Unknown
515 His Voice Is in the Thunder, in the Storm
585 How Firm a Foundation
629 How Shall They Hear the Word of God
503 Many and Great, O God, Are Your Works
674 Morning Has Broken
625 Now Let Us from This Table Rise
541 O God beyond All Praising
551 Praise the Lord of Heaven
540 Shout for Joy, Loud and Long
514 Thanks to God Whose Word Was Spoken
626 The Church of Christ in Every Age
511 Thy Strong Word Didst Cleave the Darkness
709 What Is This Place
513 Word of God, Come Down on Earth

WORK *(see Labor)*

WORLD
548 Adoramus Te Domine
815 Adoramus Te Domine
571 Faith of Our Fathers
558 Father, We Thank Thee, Who Hast Planted
557 For the Beauty of the Earth
643 For the Healing of the Nations
627 Forth in the Peace of Christ
521 From All That Dwell below the Skies
516 God Has Spoken by His Prophets
507 God Is Working His Purpose Out
651 Great God, Our Source and Lord of Space
365 Hills of the North, Rejoice
659 In Christ There Is No East or West
555 Jubilate Deo
519 Laudate Dominum
716 Let All on Earth Their Voices Raise
536 Let All the World in Every Corner Sing
653 Let There Be Light
438 Lord Christ, When First You Came to Earth
602 Lord of All Nations, Grant Me Grace
647 Now Join We to Praise the Creator
560 Now Thank We All Our God
654 O Day of Peace
650 O God of Every Nation
644 Said Judas to Mary
526 Thanks Be to God
626 The Church of Christ in Every Age
358 The Voice of God Goes Out through All the World
663 This Is the Day When Light Was First Created
497 To Jesus Christ, Our Sovereign King
623 We Are Your People
600 What Wondrous Love Is This
645 With Jesus for Hero
638 Your Love, O God, Has All the World Created
(also Universe)

WORSHIP *(see Praise)*

1208 Hymns Which May Be Sung in Canon

To be sung unaccompanied, at the distance of one measure, and usually at the interval of one octave.

177 May Saints and Angels Lead You On
358 The Voice of God
362 City of God
366 Come, Lord
369 Prepare the Way
381 Unto Us A Boy
401 Gloria, Gloria
407 What Star Is This
409 As with Gladness
425 Salvator Mundi
427 Jesus Walked
429 Benedictus Qui Venit
430 Hosanna in Excelsis
457 That Easter Day
501 The King of Glory
507 God Is Working
536 Let All the World
553 Magnificat
555 Jubilate Deo
580 Seek Ye First
583 Amazing Grace
585 How Firm a Foundation
606 My Shepherd Will
645 With Jesus for Hero
648 God, Who Stretched
652 O God of Love
685 O Holy City
690 Jerusalem, My Happy
691 Lord, Bid Your Servant
694 Come Now, and Praise
705 For All the Saints
716 Let All on Earth
723 Come and Let Us
726 I Come with Joy
756 Come, You Sinners

Index of Composers, Authors and Sources 1209

Adkins, Leon McKinley 628
Afro-American Spiritual 397 415 436 508 608 613
Ahle, Johann R. 513
Ainger, Arthur C. 507
Alexander, Cecil Frances 402 505
Alford, Henry 572 759
Ambrose, St. 372
American Folk Hymn 427 727
American Melody 640 690 694 726 756
American Shaker Melody 636 689
Anders, Charles 648
Andrews, Carroll T. 139 234 742
Anonymous 328 487 593 735 752 938
Antoniano, Silvio 715
Aquinas, St. Thomas 489 757 758 813
Arlott, John 683
Arnatt, Ronald 110 518
Arundel Hymnal 712
Bach, Johann Sebastian 371 390 405 410 419 420 422 434 459 575 616 715 729 747 755
Bain, J. L. Macbeth 612
Baker, Henry Williams 398 434 539 609 652 662
Baker, Owen D. 672
Baker, Theodore 374 760
Baldwin, Lee M. 642
Baring-Gould, Sabine 695
Barnard, John 583
Barnby, Joseph 675
Bash, Ewald 426
Basque Carol 695
Batastini, Robert J. 27 74 87 132 150 161 171 192 215 222 228 302 303 734 766 773 774 783 826 886 892 909 913 924 930 946 947 955 965 1050 1058
Bates, Katherine L. 763
Baughen, Michael A. 664
Bayly, Albert F. 474 624 630 638 682
Becker, Cornelius 526 554
Bede, The Venerable 469 698
Beebe, Hank 483
Beethoven, Ludwig van 467 525
Bell, George K. A. 500
Bell, Maurice F. 422
Bender, Jan O. 517
Benedictine Nuns of St. Mary's Abbey 20 680
Benson, Robert H. 743
Bernard of Clairvaux, St. 434 605
Berthier, Jacques 287 295 297 298 329 336 337 369 401 423 425 429 430 440 454 465 473 519 548 553 555 559 561 604 657 676 734 812 815
Bevenot, Laurence, OSB 28 34 43 60 66
Bianco da Sienna 472
Billings, William 748
Blacker, Maxwell J. 666
Bohemian Brethren's *Kirchengesange* 438 455 460 528
Bonar, Horatius 366 601 607
Bonhoeffer, Dietrich 577
Borthwick, Jane 611
Bourgeois, Louis 358 403 412 533 558 669
Bowers, John Edward 538
Bowie, W. Russell 438 685
Brady, Nicholas 753
Brébeuf, St. Jean de 380
Bridges, Matthew 496
Bridges, Robert S. 679
Briggs, George W. 516
Brokering, Herbert 517
Bromehead, Joseph 690
Brooks, Philips 386
Brooks, R. T. 514
Browne, Thomas B. 551
Brownlie, John 373
Brustle, Ingrid 34
Buchanan, Annabel M. 726
Buck, Percy C. 532
Bunjes, Paul R. 449
Burleigh, Harry T. 659
Busarow, Donald A. 748
Byzantine Chant 240
Byzantine/Slavonic Chant 620
Cameron, Catherine 648
Campbell, Robert 459 460
Cantate Domino 600
Carroll, J. Robert 187 190 201 205 770 776 780 788 799 819 822 847 861 884 897 899 909 1053 1060
Carter, Sydney 636 644
Caswall, Edward 375 482 490 491 675 757
Catholic Youth's Hymn Book 461
Chandler, John 356 407
Chant 12 20 21 22 150 178 232 233 237 246 248 270 274 280 290 291 302 303 322 330 340-354 357 368 384 398 414 416 424 435 443 447 452 475 479 489 598 703 713 719 730 802 813 826 837 857 1023 1024
Chávez-Melo, Skinner 584
Chepponis, James J. 97 637 936 1036
Choralmelodien zum heiligen Gesange 702
Christian Lyre 404
Christmas Box 377
Clarke, Jeremiah 464
Clausener Gesangbuch 634
Coffin, Charles 356 407
Colvin, Tom 431 724
Compleat Psalmodist, The 442
Connaughton, Luke 358 515 544 578 599
Connolly, Michael 49
Corbiel, Pierre de 594
Cothran, Jeff 619
Cowper, William 594
Cox, Frances E. 528
Craig, Patricia 787
Croft, William 579
Cross, Stewart 655
Crossman, Samuel 439
Crown of Jesus Music 376
Crüger, Johann 476 560 746
Crum, John M. C. 453
Cummings, Jeremiah 708
Currie, Randolph 35 58 71 75 76 81 86 207 480 870 890 907 917 941 943 963 1027 1033
Cutts, Peter 514 589 621 658

Index of Composers, Authors and Sources/*continued*

Dakota Indian Hymn 503
Dakota Odowan 503
Damon's *Psalmes* 753
Daniel ben Judah 537
Danish Amen 245
Darwall, John 493
David's *Psalmen* 449
Davis, Frances W. 653
Davis, Katherine K. 559
Daw, Carl P., Jr 584 654
Dawney, Michael 544
Day, George H. 655
Dearmer, Geoffrey 632
Dearmer, Percy 4 381 645 731
Decius, Nikolaus 527
Didache 558
Dirksen, Richard 481 552
Distler, Hugo 635
Dix, William C. 409 411 737
Doran, Carol 418 574 597 751
Douglas, C. Winfred 436 443 685
Dowland, John 669
Draper, William H. 520
Drese, Adam 611
Driscoll, J., SJ 612
Dudley-Smith, Timothy 412 480 481 506 522 534 542 550 573 581 589 684
Duggan, Sean, OSB 692
Duguet, Dieu Donné 757
Dykes, John B. 485 728 740
Edwards, John 570
Edwards, Robert L. 631
Ellerton, John 678 692 744
Elvey, George J. 496 759
Engels, Andriaan 709 857
Englert, Eugene 25 30 44 48 79 91 876 933
English Carol 383 408
English Melody 6 383 408 411 490 505 607 656 710 745
English Praise 508
Essay on the Church Plain Chant 413
Ett's *Cantica Sacra* 693
Evans, David 509 557 646
Everest, Charles W. 634
Faber, Frederick W. 488 571 595 596
Farjeon, Eleanor 359 394 674
Farrell, Gerard, OSB 152 173 246 248 274 340-354 368 703 813
Finn, Ralph 752
Fishel, Donald 441
Foley, Brian 708 711
Fortunatus, Venantius 405 435 437 444
Foster, Thomas 453
Foundling Hospital Collection 529
Francis of Assisi, St. 520
Franz, Ignaz 524
Franzmann, Martin H. 511 635
Frazier, Philip 503
French Carol 376
French Melody 359 367 376 380 437 453 523 551
Freylinghausen's *Gesangbuch* 662
Friedell, Harold 731
Funk's *Compilation of Genuine Church Music* 585 606
Gaelic Melody 448 568 590 609 632 645 673 682 687 720 725
Gauntlett, Henry J. 402
Geistliche Kirchengesange 374 469 520 707
Gelineau, Joseph, SJ 24-56 58-63 65-71 73-82 84 87-90 106 115 121 127 132 141 156 161 163 305 327 577 766-785 787-800 806 811 814 819-825 836 838-856 860-966 1024 1027 1029 1033 1034 1035 1037 1040 1043 1045 1046 1048 1050 1053 1055 1057 1058 1060
Genevan Psalter 358 370 533 558 565 679
German 374 395 396
Gesangbuch der Herzogl 628
Geyer, John B. 721
Geystliche Gesank Buchleyn 372 474
Ghana Folk Song 431
Giardini, Felice de 486 487
Gibbons, Orlando 601 660
Glaser, Carl G. 586
Godwin, Jerry D. 706
Gonja Folk Song 724
Goss, John 375 530
Goudimel, Claude 370 403 565 679
Grail 416
Grant, John W. 475
Greatorex, Walter 534
Greek 679
Green, Fred Pratt 543 549 562 577 614 622 626 637 667 697 747 749
Gregory the Great, St. 4 420 422
Grenoble 708
Grenoble Antiphoner 625
Griffiths, Thomas V. 626 749
Gruber, Franz X. 379
Haas, David 188 198 795 954 1085 1105 1120 1123 1126 1135 1137 1143
Hallock, Peter 49
Hammond, William 552
Hampton, Calvin 105 536 596 650 670
Händel, George F. 399
Harkness, Georgia 565
Hart, Joseph 756
Harwood, Basil 625
Hassler, Hans Leo 388 434 576 755
Hatch, Edwin 725
Hatton, John 445 492 521
Haugen, Marty 183 191 314-316 360 665 853 1079 1081 1085 1089 1093 1095 1098 1105 1108 1112 1116 1130 1132 1141 1147 1150 1151
Havergal, William H. 491 700
Hawkes' *Collection of Tunes* 399
Heber, Reginald 403 485
Hellriegel, Martin B. 497
Helmore, Thomas 357
Hemy, Henry F. 571 743
Herbert, George 536 569
Herbranson, Thomas E. 722
Herbst, Martin 419

Index of Composers, Authors and Sources/*continued*

Herklots, Rosamund 754
Hernaman, Claudia F. 417
Hewlett, Michael 477
Hill, Rowland 719
Hillert, Richard 271 338 458 602
Hintze, Jakob 410 459
Hodges, Edward 467 525
Holden, Oliver 494
Holst, Gustavus 541
Hopkins, John H., Jr. 406
Hoppe, Anna 748
Horn, Johann 355 456
How, William W. 705
Howard, Samuel 366
Howe, Julia W. 686
Howell, Clifford, SJ 52 71
Hughes, Howard, SM 20 64 72 77 92 99 112 127 156 176 196 213 217 221 272 282 283 294 311-313 325 335 767 815 865 934 960 1037 1046
Hume, Ruth Fox 384
Hurd, David 40 264-269 275 277 290 291 385 435 446 477 608 653 671 681 727
Hutmacher, Robert M., OFM 89 94 300 599 848 879
Hymnal 1940, The 374 493
Hymnal 1982, The 368 483
Hymns for the Festivals and Saints' Days 696
Idle, Christopher 355 362 371 504 509 535 564 616
Innocent VI 730
International Commission on English in the Liturgy 178
Ireland, John 439
Irons, William J. 467
Isaak, Heinrich 729
Isele, David Clark 42 96 339 1078 1084 1088 1092 1097 1101 1107 1111 1115 1119 1122 1129 1134 1140 1146 1148 1149
Israeli Folk Song 501
Jabusch, Willard F. 501
Jackisch, Frederick F. 380
Jackson, Francis 562
Jacob, Gordon P. 612
Jacopone da Todi 421
Jewish Melody 619
John Day's Psalter 417
John of Damascus, St. 456 723
Johnson, J. Rosamund 641
Johnson, James W. 641
Joncas, Michael 15 180 839 849 878 903 940
Jones, Joseph D. 462
Jones, William 373
Kaan, Fred 592 625 643 647 649 656 663 739
Katholisches Gesangbuch 524 675
Kelly, Columba, OSB 852 860 914
Kelly, Thomas 464 468
Ken, Thomas 669
Kennedy, Robert K. 24
Kentucky Harmony 685 754
Kethe, William 669 670
Key, Francis S. 761
Kingsley, Charles 687
Kirbye, George 382
Kirkpatrick, William J. 378
Kitchin, George W. 704
Klig's *Geistliche Lieder* 391 420 422 747
Knapp, William 605
Knight, Gerald H. 559 754
Koch's *Gesangbuch* 629
Kocher, Conrad 409
König, Johann B. 546
Kremer, Marie 844 850 889
Kremser, Edward 504 760
Kreutz, Robert E. 76 361 736
Krisman, Ronald F. 208 299 564
Lafferty, Karen 580
Lambillotte, Louis, SJ 482
Landis, Keith 567
Landstad, Magnus B., 688
Lang, C. S. 547
Latin 357 368 381 384 413 414 424 442 443 450 451 455 457 459 460 490 598 617 666 703 713 716 717 718 719 732 837
Latin and German Carol 391
Latvian Folk Melody 426
Laycock, Geoffrey 426 647
LeBlanc, Robert 5 14 83 93 224 416 443 684 688 713 730 772 821 840 881
LeCroy, Anne K. 681 699
Le Mans Breviary 662
Leaf, Robert 639
Lee, John 244 278 324
Lee, M. Owen, CSB 702 729
Leeson, Jane E. 452 461
Leisentritt's *Catholicum Hymnologium* 491
Leisentritt's *Gesangbuch* 450
Lew, Timothy T'ingfang 618
Limburg Gesangbuch 484
Littledale, Richard F. 472 740
Liturgy of St. James 523
Lovelace, Austin C. 613 614
Lundeen, Joel W. 455
Luther, Martin 388 575 576 616
Lutheran Book of Worship 388 389 390 469
Lutheran Hymnal, The 546
Lutheran Worship 26 87
Lyon, Meyer 537 580
Lyra Davidica 442
Lyte, Henry F. 530
Mainz Gesangbuch 421 497 729 752
Mallory, Charles 441
Mann, Arthur H. 402
Mant, Richard 716
Marriott, John 486
Marshall, Jane M. 431
Mary of St. Philip 367
Mason, Lowell 586
Maurus, Rabanus 475 479 482
Mawby, Colin 711
McDougall, Alan G. 681
McFarland, John T. 378
McFarland, Samuel 572
McKeon, M. de La Salle, CSJ 814
Means, Alexander 600

Index of Composers, Authors and Sources/*continued*

Mediator Dei Hymnal 488
Medley, Samuel 445
Mehrtens, Frits 697 699
Mendelssohn, Felix 387
Mentzer, Johann 546
Methode du Plain-Chant 4
Mews, Douglas 37
Middleton, Jesse E. 380
Miller, Edward 433
Mims, George 441 756
Mohr, Joseph 379
Monastic Breviary, A 483
Monk, William H. 285 409 451 733
Monsell, John S. B. 532
Montgomery, James 377 728
Moore, William 648
Moultrie, Gerard 523
Mowbray, David 540 556 566
Moyer, J. Harold 593
Mozarabic Rite 681
Mozart, Wolfgang A. 502 750
Mueller, John T. 15
Murray, A. Gregory, OSB 25 27 32 33 35 38-41 45 49-51 53 56 63 66-68 70 73 85 90 279 560 609 673 682 720 725 797 859 863 881 898 944
Musikalisches Handbuch 356 698
Nachtwey, Roger 715
Neale, John M. 357 391 398 405 413 428 435 447 456 457 617 698 718 723 732
Neander, Joachim 547
Nelson, Horatio 706
Naumann, Johann G. 326
Newboldt, Michael R. 704
Newton, John 583 610 742
Newton-White, Muriel 693
Nichols, Kevin 755
Nicholson, Sydney H. 704
Nicolai, Philipp 371 389 390
Noel, Caroline M. 499
Oakeley, Frederick 392
Oakley, Charles E. 365
Olearius, Johann 370
Olivers, Thomas 537
Oosterhuis, Huub 709
Osler, Edward 529
Oude en Nieuwe Hollanste Boerenlities 595 630 718
Owen, William 468
Oxenham, John 659
Palestrina, Giovanni P. da 451
Palmer, George H. 513
Palmer, Ray 605
Palmer, Roland F., SJJE 404
Paris Antiphoner 4 543 739
Paris Breviary 491
Parry, Charles H. H. 516 539 573 615 631 654
Patrick, St. 671 673
Peacock, Peter 24
Pearsall, Robert L. 391
Pellegrin, Simon-Joseph 367
Peloquin, C. Alexander 206 214 223 226 257-263 331 334 649 789 811 891 898 939 1077 1083 1091 1096 1100 1104 1106 1110 1114 1118 1121 1125 1128 1131 1133 1136 1139 1142 1145
Perronet, Edward 494 495
Perry, Michael A. 518 541 545 575 629
Petti, Anthony G. 421 489 723
Pettman, Charles E. 695
Piae Cantiones 381 540
Pierpoint, Folliot S. 557
Plumptre, Edward H. 750
Polish Carol 393
Pott, Francis 451
Praetorius, Michael 374 407 457 527
Prebble, Sherrell 672
Prichard, Rowland H. 588 737
Primitive Baptist Hymn and Tune Book 495
Proulx, R. 2 12 21 22 26 28 29 32 36 39 42 49 51 54 55 57 59-62 69 80 90 95 136-138 147 148 168 169 175 178 192 202 210 212 218 231-233 237 243 244 251-256 270 273 281 284 293 304- 310 317-322 330 332 333 357 384 398 404 414 415 421 424 427 437 447 448 452 479 482 489 495 497 501 503 506 540 542 566 572 585 598 606 620 632 635 645 654 687 689 690 691 694 719 728 735 752 759 771 775 779 781 784 785 788 790-794 796 798 799 802 805 806 819 820 823 825 828 836 837 843 851 852 854 868 872 874 877 880 888 900 912 924 925 932 949 952 1023 1024 1034 1040 1048 1055 1057
Prudentis, Aurelius 398
Pruner, Marcia 309
Psallite 450
Pulkingham, Betty 288 441
Purcell, Henry 617 643
Quinn, James, SJ 2 6 395 513 590 627 660 673 677 691 746 758 805
Reagan, Donald J. 186 846
Redner, Lewis H. 386
Reed, Andrew 476
Reed, Edith M. G. 393
Rees, Bryn A. 615
Rees, John 583
Reid, William W. 650
Reinagle, Alexander R. 610
Reuning, Daniel G. 526 554
Revised Standard Version 603
Reynolds, William 372
Rickard, Jeffery 567
Riddle, Donald R. 640
Riley, John A. 707
Rinkart, Martin 560
Rippon's *A Selection of Hymns* 585
Rippon, John 494 495
Roberts' *Canaidau Y Cyssegr* 512 627
Roberts, Daniel C. 764
Robinson, Joseph A. 700
Roff, Joseph 230 1076 1082 1086 1090 1099 1103 1109 1113 1117 1124 1127 1138 1144
Roman Hymnal 702
Romischkatholisches Gesangbuchlein 488
Rothensteiner, John E. 484
Rouen Church Melody 666 717
Routley, Erik 533 563 568 603 621 624

Index of Composers, Authors and Sources/*continued*

Rowthorn, Jeffery 470
Rusbridge, A. E. 393
Rutter, John 276 323
Ryden, Ernest E. 710
Sarum Primer 567
Savoy, Thomas F. 78 79
Saward, Michael 478 720
Scagnelli, Peter J. 420 424 448 717 837 857
Schalk, Carl 515 666 668 717
Schein, Johann H. 389 405 715
Schiavone, John 46 77 225 578 651 769 864 951 937 1045
Schoen, Frank 237 797 800 806
Schola Antiqua 435 805
Scholefield, Clement C. 678
Schubert, Franz Peter 273 304
Schumann's *Geistliche Lieder* 388
Schutz, Heinrich 526 554
Schutz, Johann J. 528
Scottish Psalter 741
Sears, Edmund H. 400
Selner, John C., SS 703
Seltz, Martin Louis 372
Shaw, Geoffrey 381
Shaw, Martin 359 362 365 505 507 556 592
Sheets, Dorothy 587
Sjolund, Paul 397
Slovak Melody 602
Smart, Henry T. 377 563
Smith, Alfred M. 582
Smith, David 709
Smith, John S. 761
Smith, Joseph B. 69
Smith, Kenneth D. 364 683 723 742
Smith, Mark V. 15
Smith, Samuel F. 762
Smith, Walter C. 512
Smyttan, George H. 419
Snow, Robert 7 16 150 171 246
Southern Harmony 600 614
Sowerby, Leo 394 722
Spannaus, Olive W. 602
Speier Gebetbuch 374
Speiss, Johann Martin 696 700
Stainer, John 383 411
Stanford, Charles V. 549 721
Steefe, William 686
Stimmen der Volker in Liedern 712
Storey, William G. 12
Straslund Gesangbuch 547
Ströme, Peer O. 688
Struther, Jan 568
Sullivan, Arthur S. 732
Swanston, Hamish 582
Taizé Community 369 401 423 425 429 430 440 454 465 473 519 548 553 555 559 561 604 657 676 734 812 815
Tallis, Thomas 177 652 716
Tate, Nahum 382 753
Tattersall's *Improved Psalmody* 712
Taylor, Cyril V. 470 667 701
Teschner, Melchior 428 706
Thatcher, Reginald S. 638 663
Theodulph of Orleans, St. 428 805
Thesaurus Musicus 762
Thomerson, Kathleen 510
Thompson, Robert 768 882
Three Days, The 437
Thring, Godfrey 496
Timms, George B. 714
Tisserand, Jean 447
Toolan, Suzanne, SM 43 47 185 633 738 905
Traditional 396
Tredinnick, Noel H. 522 529 664
Trier Gesangbuch 714
Troeger, Thomas H. 418 574 597 751
Trueblood, David E. 640
Tucker, F. Bland 527 558 570 586
Turner, Jet E. 731
Turton, William H. 733
Tye, Christopher 382
Udulutsch, Irvin, OFM Cap 484
Utech, George 651
Vajda, Jaroslav 668
Valerius' *Neder-Landtsche Gedenck-Klanck* 504 709 760
Van Dyke, Henry 525
Vanstone, W. H. 587
Vaughan Williams, Ralph 6 396 444 469 472 490 499 520 538 569 607 656 669 705 707
Verdi, Ralph C., C PP S 289 915
Virginia Harmony 583
Vulpius, Melchior 286 372 474 500
Waddell, Chrysogonus, OCSO 29 65 98 432 838 862 873 910
Wade, John Francis 392 758
Walton, James G. 571 743
Walworth, Clarence 524
Ward, Samuel A. 763
Warren, George W. 764
Warren, Norman L. 545 661
Watts, Isaac 399 433 492 502 521 552 579 606
Weaving, T. H. 590
Webster, Bradford G. 646
Weissel, Georg 363
Weitz, Guy 90
Welsh Melody 559 627 642 677
Werner, Anthony 680
Wesley, Charles 364 387 442 462 463 471 493 588 591 741
Wesley, Samuel S. 618 744
West, Martin 710 745
Westendorf, Omer 361 736
Wilbur, Richard 385
Willan, Healey 367 484 702
Willcocks, David 378 387 392 408
Williams' *Psalmodia Evangelica* 363 466
Williams, G. W. 694
Williams, Robert 463 471
Williams, Thomas J. 511
Williamson, Malcolm 591 622
Willis, Richard S. 400

Index of Composers, Authors and Sources/*continued*

Wilson, David G. 478 550
Wilson, John W. 531 623
Winkworth, Catherine 363 370 547 560
Wipo of Burgundy 452 461 837
Witt, Christian F. 364 683 742
Wojcik, Richard J. 475
Woodward, George R. 449
Woolen, Russell 523
Wordsworth, Christopher 410
Work, John W., Jr. 397
Work, John W., III 498
Wren, Brian 466 531 623 639 658 661 701 726 745
Wright, Ralph, OSB 414
Wurth's *Katholisches Gesangbuch* 461
Wyeth's *Repository of Sacred Music* 535 691
Yigdal 537 580
Young, David M. 292
Young, John F. 379
Young, Michael E. 82
Zinzendorf, Nicolaus L. von 611

Metrical Index of Tunes 1210

SM (SHORT METER - 66 86)
491 NARENZA
366 ST. BRIDE
753 SOUTHWELL
696 700 SWABIA

SMD (SHORT METER DOUBLE)
496 DIADEMATA

CM (COMMON METER - 86 86)
399 ANTIOCH
586 AZMON
754 DETROIT
741 DUNDEE
572 DUNLAP'S CREEK
476 GRAEFENBERG
690 694 726 LAND OF REST
748 LEWIS-TOWN
659 MC KEE
691 MORNING SONG
583 NEW BRITAIN
591 622 O FOR A HEART
722 PERRY
728 ST. AGNES
579 ST. ANNE
725 ST. COLUMBA
417 ST. FLAVIAN
464 ST. MAGNUS
610 ST. PETER
373 ST. STEPHEN
382 WINCHESTER OLD

CM WITH REPEATS
494 CORONATION
495 DIADEM

CMD (COMMON METER DOUBLE)
400 CAROL
6 FOREST GREEN
490 607 KINGSFOLD
642 LLANGLOFFAN
763 MATERNA
502 750 MOZART
606 RESIGNATION
597 SPENDTHRIFT LOVER

LM (LONG METER - 88 88)
602 BEATUS VIR
368 CONDITOR ALME SIDERUM
670 DE TAR
625 DEUS TUORUM MILITUM
757 DUGUET
445 492 521 DUKE STREET
626 749 DUNEDIN
405 715 EISENACH
420 422 747 ERHALT UNS HERR
532 GONFALON ROYAL
12 424 719 JESU DULCIS MEMORIA
671 KING
627 LLEDROD
554 LOBT GOTT IN SEINEM HEILIGTUM
634 O JESU MI DULCISSIME
710 745 O WALY WALY
669 OLD 100TH
407 457 PUER NOBIS
433 ROCKINGHAM
590 SUANTRAI
177 652 716 TALLIS' CANON
20 TE LUCIS ANTE TERMINUM
363 466 TRURO
475 479 VENI CREATOR SPIRITUS
435 VEXILLA REGIS
388 VOM HIMMEL HOCH
605 WAREHAM
680 WERNER
356 698 WINCHESTER NEW

LM WITH ALLELUIAS
469 520 707 LASST UNS ERFREUEN

LM WITH REFRAIN
740 MELITA
571 ST. CATHERINE
488 SWEET SACRAMENT
357 VENI, VENI EMMANUEL

LM WITH REPEAT
482 LAMBILOTTE

LMD (LONG METER DOUBLE)
654 JERUSALEM
15 MAGNIFICAT

65 65 D
499 KING'S WESTON
551 UNE VAINE CRAINTE

6 6 6 6 4 44 4 or 6 6 6 6 88
2 CAMANO
493 DARWALL'S 148TH
365 556 592 LITTLE CORNARD
439 LOVE UNKNOWN
574 UNMATCHED STONE

66 4 666 4
762 AMERICA
486 487 ITALIAN HYMN

7 6 7 6 WITH REFRAIN
397 GO TELL IT ON THE MOUNTAIN
484 GOTT VATER SEI GEPRIESEN
505 ROYAL OAK

7 6 7 6 D
618 744 AURELIA
635 DISTLER
628 ELLACOMBE
355 456 GAUDEAMUS PARITER
813 GLORIA LAUS ET HONOR
656 KING'S LYNN

Metrical Index of Tunes/*continued*

434 755 PASSION CHORALE
650 PIKE
428 706 ST. THEODULPH

77 77
587 BINGHAM
419 HEINLEIN
531 LAUDS
662 LUBECK
372 474 NUN KOMM DER HEIDEN HEILAND
594 ORIENTIS PARTIBUS
381 PUER NOBIS NASCITUR
569 THE CALL

77 77 WITH ALLELUIAS
442 EASTER HYMN
462 GWALCHMAI
463 471 LLANFAIR
460 SONNE DER GERECHTIGKEIT
452 SURGIT IN HAEC DIES

77 77 WITH REFRAIN
376 GLORIA
375 HUMILITY
735 LIVING GOD

77 77 77
409 DIX
509 557 LUCERNA LAUDONIAE

77 77 D
759 ST. GEORGE'S WINDSOR
410 459 SALZBURG
461 VICTIMAE PASCHALI

8 4 8 4 888 4
677 AR HYD Y NOS
562 EAST ACKLAM

8 6 8 6 8 6
612 BROTHER JAMES' AIR
685 MORNING SONG

8 7 8 7
621 BIRABUS
664 JUBILATE DEO
426 KAS DZIEDAJA
640 LIBERTY
609 ST. COLUMBA
364 683 742 STUTTGART

8 7 8 7 WITH REFRAIN
411 GREENSLEEVES
497 752 ICH GLAUB AN GOTT
756 RESTORATION

8 7 8 7 8 7
564 BEST GIFT
413 DULCE CARMEN
477 JULION
530 LAUDA ANIMA
693 ORIEL
813 PANGE LINGUA GLORIOSI
437 523 PICARDY
377 563 REGENT SQUARE
758 ST. THOMAS
617 643 WESTMINSTER ABBEY

8 7 8 7 88 7
527 ALLEIN GOTT IN DER HOH'
438 455 528 MIT FREUDEN ZART

8 7 8 7 D
470 667 ABBOT'S LEIGH
751 AUTHORITY
448 632 DOMHNACH TRIONOIDE
511 EBENEZER
478 FIRE OF GOD
655 GENEVA
522 529 HEAVENLY HOSTS
648 HOLY MANNA
588 737 HYFRYDOL
467 525 HYMN TO JOY
595 630 718 IN BABILONE
518 LADUE CHAPEL
535 NETTLETON
714 OMNE DIE
404 PLEADING SAVIOR
584 RAQUEL
516 631 RUSTINGTON
596 ST. HELENA

8 8 8 8 8 8
542 RUSSWIN
743 ST. CATHERINE
651 SALVA NOS

888 WITH ALLELUIAS
447 O FILII ET FILIAE
451 VICTORY
500 GELOBT SEI GOTT

9 8 9 8
647 HARVEST
678 ST. CLEMENT
661 STEEPLE BELLS

10 10
732 COENA DOMINI
601 660 SONG 46

10 10 10 WITH ALLELUIAS
549 721 ENGELBERG
705 SINE NOMINE

10 10 10 10
515 FLENTGE
764 NATIONAL HYMN
418 RENEWING DEATH
582 SURSUM CORDA
358 TOULON

Metrical Index of Tunes/*continued*

534 WOODLANDS

10 10 11 11
539 615 LAUDATE DOMINUM
446 MORNING OF SPLENDOR

10 11 11 6 cf. 11 11 11 5

11 10 11 10
711 CHANCE
646 CHARTERHOUSE
565 DONNE SECOURS
577 LE CENACLE
639 LIFE ON EARTH
453 NOEL NOUVELET
638 663 NORTHBROOK

11 11 11 5
483 BICKFORD
4 543 739 CHRISTE SANCTORUM
746 HERZLIEBSTER JESU
666 717 ISTE CONFESSOR
681 MIGHTY SAVIOR

11 11 11 11
489 ADORO TE
378 CRADLE SONG
585 FOUNDATION
512 ST. DENIO
645 SIOBÁN NI LAOGHAIRE

IRREGULAR
713 AVE MARIA
730 AVE VERUM
394 BERKELEY
550 CANTATE DOMINO
431 CHEREPONI
567 FIELD
644 JUDAS AND MARY
620 KONTAKION
503 LACQUIPARLE
416 PARCE DOMINE
507 PURPOSE
443 REGINA CAELI
687 REMEMBER THE POOR
703 SALVE REGINA
761 STAR-SPANGLED BANNER
613 THE LORD IS MY SHEPHERD

IRREGULAR WITH REFRAIN
392 ADESTE FIDELES
608 BALM IN GILEAD
738 BREAD OF LIFE
458 FESTIVAL CANTICLE
508 GO DOWN MOSES
498 HE IS KING
432 JESUS TOOK A TOWEL
603 OF LOVE DIVINE
444 538 SALVE FESTA DIES
580 SEEK YE FIRST
636 SHAKER SONG
415 SOMEBODY'S KNOCKIN'
408 THE FIRST NOWELL

ONE OF A KIND
736 CM with ref. BICENTENNIAL
633 CMD with ref. LEAVE ALL THINGS
668 4 3 8 4 3 8 D with ref. NOW
393 44 7 44 7 4444 7 W ŻŁOBIE LEŻY
599 4 4 8 5 4 7 JULINORMA
517 4 5 7 D with ref. EARTH AND ALL STARS
653 4 7 7 6 SPRAGUE
545 4 8 7 6 6 6 10 PRAISE HIM
623 5 4 5 5 7 WHITFIELD
673 674 682 5 5 5 4 D BUNESSAN
712 55 7 55 7 O DU FRÖHLICHE
720 5 5 8 D BUNESSAN
611 55 88 55 ROCHELLE
675 66 6 D LAUDES DOMINI
624 6 6 6 6 33 6 SHARPTHORNE
540 666 66 with ref. PERSONET HODIE
692 6 6 6 6 6 6 PRESENTATION
570 6 6 6 6 888 RHOSYMEDRE
679 66 7 66 7 NUNC DIMITTIS
391 66 77 77 55 IN DULCI JUBILO
537 581 6 6 8 4 D LEONI
481 552 6 6 8 6 6 6 VINEYARD HAVEN
379 66 89 66 STILLE NACHT
641 66 10 66 10 14 14 66 10 ANTHEM
472 66 11 D DOWN AMPNEY
559 66 11 66 11 D ASHGROVE
449 6 7 6 7 D VRUECHTEN
560 6 7 6 7 6 6 6 6 NUN DANKET
697 699 7 6 7 6 DE EERSTEN ZIJN DE LAATSTEN
385 7 6 7 66 6 7 6 ANDUJAR
374 7 6 7 6 6 7 6 ES IST EIN' ROS' ENTSPRUNGEN
649 7 6 7 6 77 GOOD SHEPHERD
619 7 6 8 D with ref. SHIBBOLET BASADEH
506 7 6 8 6 8 6 ALDINE
480 7 6 8 6 8 6 8 6 ESCAMBIA
729 77 6 77 8 INNSBRUCK
387 77 77 D with ref. MENDELSSOHN
396 777 11 RESONET IN LAUDIBUS
367 7 8 7 6 with ref. VENEZ, DIVIN MESSIE
701 7 8 7 8 4 MOWSLEY
524 7 8 7 8 77 GROSSER GOTT
513 7 8 7 8 88 LIEBSTER JESU
702 8 4 8 4 777 4 5 SALVE REGINA COELITUM
450 8 5 8 4 7 REGINA CAELI
566 8 5 8 5 84 3 CASTLEWOOD
386 8 6 8 6 7 6 8 6 ST. LOUIS
383 8 6 8 6 8 6 with ref. GOD REST YOU MERRY
629 8 6 8 6 88 AUCH JETZT MACHT GOTT

Metrical Index of Tunes/*continued*

380 8 6 8 6 88 with ref. UNE JEUNE PUCELLE
362 8 6 8 7 8 6 12 8 PURPOSE
573 8 6 88 6 with repeat REPTON
684 8 6 888 6 REVELATION
514 8 7 8 7 4 7 WYLDE GREEN
731 8 7 8 7 44 7 UNION SEMINARY
468 8 7 8 7 444 77 BRYN CALFARIA
589 8 7 8 7 6 BRIDEGROOM
575 576 616 8 7 8 7 66 66 7 EIN' FESTE BURG
402 .8 7 8 7 77 IRBY
370 8 7 8 7 77 88 GENEVA 42
398 8 7 8 7 8 7 7 DIVINUM MYSTERIUM
526 8 7 8 7 8 8 7 DANKET DEM HERREN
359 87 98 87 BESANCON
384 8 8 with alleluias and ref. PUER NATUS
441 8 8 with ref. ALLELUIA NO. 1
406 88 44 6 with ref. KINGS OF ORIENT
658 88 5 8 6 HAMPTON POYLE
421 88 7 STABAT MATER
403 88 77 D MON DIEU PRETE-MOI L'OREILLE
389 390 88 7 88 7 22 44 48 WIE SCHÖN LEUCHTET
395 888 7 QUEM PASTORES
427 8 8 10 8 LONESOME VALLEY
371 89 8 89 8 66 4 44 8 WACHET AUF
412 533 558 9 8 9 8 D RENDEZ À DIEU
360 9 8 9 8 8 7 8 9 REJOICE, REJOICE
546 9 8 9 8 88 O DASS ICH TAUSEND ZUNGEN HÄTTE
709 9 8 9 8 9 66 KOMT NU MET ZANG
578 9 10 9 9 with ref. SACRIFICE
536 10 4 10 4 66 66 10 4 MAC DOUGALL
672 10 7 6 10 ST. OWEN
361 10 7 8 7 with ref. FIDDLER'S GREEN
544 10 7 10 7 with ref. BAY HALL
510 10 7 10 8 9 9 10 7 HOUSTON
637 10 8 8 10 MINTWOOD
723 10 9 10 9 NEW RIVER
665 10 9 10 10 D GATHER US IN
704 10 10 with ref. CRUCIFER
436 10 10 with ref. WERE YOU THERE
727 10 10 6 8 7 LET US BREAK BREAD
593 10 10 10 6 FAITH
733 10 10 10 10 with ref. UNDE ET MEMORES
695 10 10 12 10 GABRIEL'S MESSAGE
568 10 11 11 12 SLANE
614 11 8 11 8 D SAMANTHRA
688 11 9 11 9 CONSUMMATION
708 11 11 with ref. LOURDES HYMN
414 11 11 11 with ref. ATTENDE DOMINE
485 11 12 12 10 NICAEA
724 12 9 12 9 with ref. NATOMAH
600 12 9 12 12 9 WONDROUS LOVE
689 12 11 10 10 12 BEAUTIFUL TREASURES
504 760 12 11 12 11 KREMSER
501 12 12 with ref. KING OF GLORY
598 12 12 12 12 with ref. UBI CARITAS
541 13 13 13 13 13 13 THAXTED
547 14 14 47 8 LOBE DEN HERREN
686 15 15 15 6 with ref. BATTLE HYMN OF THE REPUBLIC

Index of Tunes 1211

ABBOT'S LEIGH 470, 667
ADESTE FIDELIS 392
ADORO TE DEVOTE 489
ALDINE 506
ALLEIN GOTT DER HOH' 527
ALLELUIA NO. 1 441
AMERICA 762
ANDUJAR 385
ANTHEM 641
ANTIOCH 399
AR HYD Y NOS 677
ASHGROVE 599
ATTENDE DOMINE 414
AUCH JETZT MACHT GOTT 629
AURELIA 618, 744
AUTHORITY 751
AVE MARIA 713
AVE VERUM 730
AZMON 586
BALM IN GILEAD 608
BATTLE HYMN OF THE REPUBLIC 686
BAY HALL 544
BEATUS VIR 602
BEAUTIFUL TREASURES 689
BERKELEY 394
BESANCON 359
BEST GIFT 564
BICENTENNIAL 736
BICKFORD 483
BINGHAM 587
BIRABUS 621
BREAD OF LIFE 738
BRIDEGROOM 589
BROTHER JAMES' AIR 612
BRYN CALFARIA 468
BUNESSAN 673, 674, 682, 720
CAMANO 2
CANTATE DOMINO 550
CAROL 400
CASTLEWOOD 566
CHANCE 711
CHARTERHOUSE 646
CHEREPONI 431
CHRISTE SANCTORUM 4, 543, 739
COENA DOMINI 732
CONDITOR ALME SIDERUM 368
CONSUMMATION 688
CORONATION 494
CRADLE SONG 378
CRUCIFER 704
DANKET DEM HERREN 526
DARWALL'S 148TH 493
DE EERSTEN ZIJN DE LAATSTEN 697, 699
DE TAR 670
DETROIT 754
DEUS TUORUM MILITUM 625
DIADEM 495
DIADEMATA 496
DISTLER 635
DIVINUM MYSTERIUM 398
DIX 409
DOHMNACH TRIONIDE 448, 632
DONNE SECOURS 565
DOWN AMPNEY 472
DUGUET 757
DUKE STREET 445, 492, 521
DULCE CARMEN 413
DUNDEE 741
DUNEDIN 626, 749
DUNLAP'S CREEK 572
EARTH AND ALL STARS 517
EAST ACKLAM 562
EASTER HYMN 442
EBEZNEZER 511
EIN' FESTE BURG 575, 616
EIN' FESTE BURG (ORIG.) 576
EISENACH 405, 715
ELLACOMBE 628
ENGELBERG 549, 721
ERHALT UNS HERR 420, 422, 747
ES IST EIN' ROS' ENTSPRUNGEN 374
ESCAMBIA 480
FAITH 593
FESTIVAL CANTICLE 458
FIDDLER'S GREEN 361
FIELD 567
FIRE OF GOD 478
FLENTGE 515
FOREST GREEN 6
FOUNDATION 585
GABRIEL'S MESSAGE 695
GATHER US IN 665
GAUDEAMUS PARITER 355, 456
GELOBT SEI GOTT 500
GENEVA 655
GENEVA 42 370
GLORIA 376
GLORIA LAUS ET HONOR 813
GO DOWN MOSES 508
GO TELL IT ON THE MOUNTAIN 397
GOD REST YOU MERRY 383
GONFALON ROYAL 532
GOOD SHEPHERD 649
GOTT VATER SEI GEPRIESEN 484
GRAEFENBERG 476
GREENSLEEVES 411
GROSSER GOTT 524
GWALCHMAI 462
HAMPTON POYLE 658
HARVEST 647
HE IS KING 498
HEAVENLY HOSTS 522, 529
HEINLEIN 419
HERZLIEBSTER JESU 746
HOLY MANNA 648
HOUSTON 510
HUMILITY 375
HYFRYDOL 588, 737
HYMN TO JOY 467, 525
ICH GLAUB AN GOTT 497, 752
IN BABILONE 595, 630, 718
IN DULCI JUBILO 391

Index of Tunes/*continued*

INNSBRUCK 729
IRBY 402
ISTE CONFESSOR 666, 717
ITALIAN HYMN 486, 487
JERUSALEM 654
JESU DULCIS MEMORIA 12, 424, 719
JESUS TOOK A TOWEL 432
JUBILATE DEO 664
JUDAS AND MARY 644
JULINORMA 599
JULION 477
KAS DZIEDAJA 426
KING 671
KING OF GLORY 501
KING'S LYNN 656
KING'S WESTON 499
KINGS OF ORIENT 406
KINGSFOLD 490, 607
KOMT NU MET ZANG 709
KONTAKION 620
KREMSER 504, 760
LACQUIPARLE 503
LADUE CHAPEL 518
LAMBILLOTTE 482
LAND OF REST 690, 694, 726
LASST UNS ERFREUEN 469, 520, 707
LAUDA ANIMA 530
LAUDATE DOMINUM 539, 615
LAUDES DOMINI 675
LAUDS 531
LE CÉNACLE 577
LEAVE ALL THINGS 633
LEONI 537, 581
LET US BREAK BREAD 727
LEWIS-TOWN 748
LIBERTY 640
LIEBSTER JESU 513
LIFE ON EARTH 639
LITTLE CORNARD 365, 556, 592
LIVING GOD 735
LLANFAIR 463, 471
LLANGLOFFAN 642
LLEDROD 627
LOBE DEN HERREN 547
LOBT GOTT IN SEINEM HEILIGTUM 554
LONESOME VALLEY 427
LOURDES HYMN 708
LOVE UNKNOWN 439
LUBECK 662
LUCERNA LAUDONIA 509, 557
MAC DOUGALL 536
MAGNIFICAT 15
MATERNA 763
MCKEE 659
MENDELSSOHN 387
MIGHTY SAVIOR 681
MINTWOOD 637
MIT FREUDEN ZART 438, 455, 528
MON DIEU PRETE-MOI L'OREILLE 403
MORNING OF SPLENDOR 446
MORNING SONG 685, 691
MOWSLEY 701
MOZART 502, 750
NARZENA 491
NATIONAL HYMN 764
NATOMAH 724
NETTLETON 535
NEW BRITAIN 583
NEW RIVER 723
NICAEA 485
NOEL NOUVELET 453
NORTHBROOK 638, 663
NOW 668
NUN DANKET 560
NUN KOMM DER HEIDEN HEILAND 372, 474
NUNC DIMITTIS 679
O DASS ICH TAUSEND ZUNGEN HÄTTE 546
O DU FRÖHLICHE 712
O FILII ET FILIAE 447
O FOR A HEART 591, 622
O JESU MI DULCISSIME 634
O WALY WALY 710
OF LOVE DIVINE 603
OLD HUNDREDTH 669
OMNE DIE 714
ORIEL 693
ORIENTIS PARTIBUS 594
PANGE LINGUA GLORIOSI 813
PARCE DOMINE 416
PASSION CHORALE 434, 755
PERRY 722
PERSONET HODIE 540
PICARDY 437, 523
PIKE 650
PLEADING SAVIOR 404
PRAISE HIM 545
PRESENTATION 692
PUER NATUS 384
PUER NOBIS 407, 457
PUER NOBIS NASCITUR 381
PURPOSE 362, 507
QUEM PASTORES 395
RAQUEL 584
REGENT SQUARE 377, 563
REGINA CAELI (CHANT) 443
REGINA CAELI (METERED) 450
REMEMBER THE POOR 687
RENDEZ À DIEU 412, 533, 558
RENEWING DEATH 418
REPTON 573
RESIGNATION 606
RESONET IN LAUDIBUS 396
RESTORATION 756
REVELATION 684
RHOSYMEDRE 570
ROCHELLE 611
ROCKINGHAM 433
ROYAL OAK 505
RUSSWIN 542
RUSTINGTON 516, 631
SACRIFICE 578
ST. AGNES 728

Index of Tunes/*continued*

ST. ANNE 579
ST. BRIDE 366
ST. CATHERINE 571, 743
ST. CLEMENT 678
ST. COLUMBA 609, 725
ST. DENIO 512
ST. FLAVIAN 417
ST. GEORGE'S WINDSOR 759
ST. HELENA 596
ST. LOUIS 386
ST. MAGNUS 464
ST. OWEN 672
ST. PETER 610
ST. STEPHEN 373
ST. THEODULPH 428, 706
ST. THOMAS 758
SALVA NOS 651
SALVE FESTE DIES 444, 538
SALVE REGINA 703
SALVE REGINA COELITUM 702
SALZBURG 410, 459
SAMANTHRA 614
SEEK YE FIRST 580
SHAKER SONG 636
SHARPTHORNE 624
SHIBBOLET BASADEH 619
SINE NOMINE 705
SIOBAN NI LAOGHAIRE 645
SLANE 568
SOMEBODY'S KNOCKIN' 415
SONG 46 601, 660
SONNE DER GERECHTIGKEIT 460
SOUTHWELL 753
SPENDTHRIFT LOVER 597
SPRAGUE 653
STABAT MATER 421
STAR-SPANGLED BANNER 761
STEEPLE BELLS 661
STILLE NACHT 379
STUTTGART 364, 683, 742
SUANTRAI 590
SURGIT IN HAEC DIES 452
SURSUM CORDA 582
SWABIA 696, 700
SWEET SACRAMENT 488
TALLIS' CANON 177, 652, 716
TE LUCIS ANTE TERMINUM 20
THAXTED 541
THE CALL 569
THE FIRST NOWELL 408
THE LORD IS MY SHEPHERD 613
TOULON 358
TRURO 363, 466
UBI CARITAS 598
UNDE ET MEMORES 733
UNE JEUNE PUCELLE 380
UNE VAINE CRAINTE 551
UNION SEMINARY 731
UNMATCHED STONE 574
VENEZ, DIVIN MESSIE 367
VENI CREATOR SPIRITUS 475
VENI CREATOR SPIRITUS 479
VENI SANCTE SPIRITUS 857
VENI VENI EMMANUEL 357
VEXILLA REGIS 435
VICTIMAE PASCHALI 461
VICTORY 451
VINEYARD HAVEN 481, 552
VOM HIMMEL HOCH 388
VRUECHTEN 449
W ŻŁOBIE LEŻY 393
WACHET AUF 371
WAREHAM 605
WERE YOU THERE 436
WERNER 680
WESTMINSTER ABBEY 617, 643
WHITFIELD 623
WIE SCHÖN LEUCHTET 390
WIE SCHÖN LEUCHTET (ORIG.) 389
WINCHESTER NEW 356, 698
WINCHESTER OLD 382
WONDROUS LOVE 600
WOODLANDS 534
WYLDE GREEN 514

1212 Psalm Refrains Set to Music

A light will shine on us this day: the Lord is born for us. 780
All my hope, O Lord, is in your loving kindness. 206
All power is yours, Lord God, our Mighty King, alleluia! 99
All the ends of the earth have seen the saving power of God. 781, 1082, 1083, 1084, 1085
Alleluia. 826
Alleluia, alleluia, alleluia. 50, 53, 1108
Arise, come to your God, sing him your songs of rejoicing. 53

Be merciful, O Lord, for we have sinned. 787, 1070, 1090, 1091, 1092, 1093
Be with me Lord, when I am in trouble. 789, 1094, 1095
Blessed are they who delight in the law of the Lord. 24
Blessed be God who chose us in Christ. 91
Blessed be the Lord, the God of Israel. 89
Bring an offering and enter his courts: in his temple worship the Lord. 52
By your wounds, O Christ, we have been healed. 95

Call upon the Lord and he will hear you. 49
Come, let us go rejoicing to the house of the Lord. 1147
Come to him and receive his light! 181
Create a clean heart in me, O God. 800, 825
Cry out with joy and gladness: for among you is the great and Holy One of Israel. 774

Day and night I cry to you, my God. 47
Do not forget the works of the Lord! 1050
Do not hide your face from me: In you I put my trust. 75

Father, I put my life in your hands. 814, 1156
Fill us with your love, O Lord, and we will sing for joy! 209, 947
For ever I will sing the goodness of the Lord. 776, 778, 901
For the sake of your name, O Lord, save my life. 228
From the voices of children, Lord, comes the sound of your praise. 27

Give back to me the joy of your salvation. 127
Give him/her eternal rest, O Lord, and may your light shine on him/her for ever. 161
Give thanks to the Lord for he is good, his love is everlasting. 65, 838
Give thanks to the Lord, his love is everlasting. 899
Give the Lord glory and honor. 949
Go out to all the world, and tell the Good News. 891
God has freed us and redeemed us with his mighty arm. 60
God, in your goodness, you have made a home for the poor. 930
God mounts his throne to shouts of joy. 851, 1113, 1114, 1115, 1116
God, my Lord, is my strength. 86
God, you are merciful and kind; turn to me and have mercy. 222
Great is the Lord, worthy of praise; tell all the nations "God is King"; spread the news of his love. 52
Guard us, O Lord, while we sleep, and keep us in peace. 90

Happy are they who follow the law of the Lord! 880
Happy are they who hope in the Lord. 882
Happy are those who do what the Lord commands. 190
Happy the people the Lord has chosen to be his own. 860, 921
Happy the poor in spirit; the kingdom of heaven is theirs! 874
Have mercy, Lord, and hear my prayer. 25
Have mercy, Lord, cleanse me from all my sins. 41
Have mercy on me, Lord; my strength is gone. 215
He who does justice will live in the presence of the Lord. 29, 912, 929
Here am I, Lord; I come to do your will. 868, 1029
His goodness shall follow me always to the end of my days. 32
His love is everlasting. 1103, 1104, 1105
Holy is God, holy and strong, holy and living for ever! 64
How can I repay the Lord for his goodness to me? 63
How great is your name, O Lord our God, through all the earth! 27
How lovely is your dwelling place, O Lord of hosts. 45

I believe that I shall see the good things of the Lord in the land of the living. 195, 852
I hope in the Lord, I trust in his word. 201
I love you, Lord, my strength. 952
I place all my trust in you, my God; all my hope is in your saving word. 71
I praise you, O Lord, for I am worderfully made. 1034
I rejoiced when I heard them say: let us go to the house of the Lord. 200, 766, 966
I shall live in the house of the Lord all the days of my life. 946, 1148
I thank you, Lord, for your faithfulness and love. 58
I trust in your merciful love. 28
I turn to you, O Lord, in time of trouble, and you fill me with the joy of salvation. 881
I will bless the Lord at all times. 187, 1127
I will give thanks to your name, because of your kindness and your truth. 1058
I will go the altar of God: praise the God of my joy. 38

Psalm Refrains Set to Music/*continued*

I will praise my God all the days of my life. 77
I will praise you, Lord, for you have rescued me. 822
I will praise you, Lord, in the assembly of your people. 846
I will praise your name for ever, Lord. 186
I will praise your name for ever, my king and my God. 847, 904, 957, 1075, 1142, 1143
I will rise and go to my father. 936
I will sing and make music for the Lord. 34
I will sing of your salvation. 44, 876
I will sing to the Lord all the days of my life. 82
I will take the cup of salvation, and call on the name of the Lord. 863
I will walk in the presence of the Lord, in the land of the living. 62, 199, 791, 935
If today you hear his voice, O harden not your hearts. 793, 918, 1133, 1134, 1135
If you, O Lord, should mark our sins, Lord, who would survive? 71
In every age, O Lord, you have been our refuge. 48, 223, 933
In the morning I will sing glad songs of praise to you. 42
In the sight of the angels I will sing your praises, Lord. 879
In the silent hours of night, bless the Lord. 72
In you, Lord, I have found my peace. 955
In you, my God, my body will rest in hope. 30

Jesus Christ is Lord! 92
Jesus is the image of the unseen God; the firstborn of all creation. 93
Justice shall flourish in his time, and fullness of peace for ever. 769

Keep me safe, O God; you are my hope. 820

Let all creation praise the Lord. 79
Let all praise the name of the Lord. 192, 204
Let all the earth cry out to God with joy. 848, 906, 1109, 1110, 1111, 1112
Let everything that lives give praise to the Lord. 81
Let my tongue be silenced, if I ever forget you! 797
Let the Lord enter; he is king of glory. 775
Let us bow down before the Lord, the God who made us. 51
Let us go rejoicing to the house of the Lord. 1144, 1145, 1146
Let us sing to the Lord; he has covered himself in glory. 821
Like a deer that longs for running streams, so my soul longs for you, my God. 219, 825
Listen, Lord, and answer me. 221
Lord, be my rock of safety. 889
Lord, come to my aid! 924
Lord, every nation on earth will adore you. 784, 1086, 1087, 1088, 1089
Lord, forgive the wrong I have done. 897
Lord, go up to the place of your rest, you and the ark of your holiness. 1045
Lord, give success to the work of our hands. 1048
Lord, God, be my refuge and my strength. 35
Lord, heal my soul, for I have sinned against you. 884
Lord, I love your commands. 913
Lord, if you will, you can make me clean. 41
Lord, in your great love, answer me. 898
Lord, it is good to give thanks to you. 888
Lord, let us see your kindness, and grant us your salvation. 770, 908, 1080, 1081
Lord, let your face shine on us. 840
Lord, let your mercy be on us, as we place our trust in you. 790, 845
Lord, make us turn to you, let us see your face and we shall be saved. 767
Lord, on the day I called for help you answered me. 915
Lord, send out your Spirit, and renew the face of the earth. 115, 819, 855, 856, 1117, 1118, 1119, 1120
Lord, this is the people that longs to see your face. 1053
Lord, when your glory appears, my joy will be full. 960
Lord, you are good and forgiving. 910
Lord, you have the words of everlasting life. 794, 1072, 1121, 1122, 1123
Lord, you will show us the path of life. 839
Lord, your love is eternal; do not forsake the work of your hands. 925

May God bless us in his mercy. 783
May the Lord bless and protect us all the days of our life. 944
May the Lord watch over this house, and keep us in peace. 70
My God, come quickly to help me. 156
My God, my God, why have you abandoned me? 31, 806, 1099, 1100, 1101, 1102
My prayers rise like incense, my hands like the evening offering. 74
My refuge, my stronghold, my God in whom I trust! 49
My shepherd is the Lord, nothing indeed shall I want. 32
My soul, give thanks to the Lord, and bless his Holy Name. 55
My soul is thirsting for the living God. 196
My soul is thirsting for the Lord: when shall I see him face to face? 37
My soul is thirsting for you, O Lord, my God. 42, 197, 220, 900, 958, 1073, 1131
My soul rejoices in my God. 87, 773

Night holds no terrors for me sleeping under God's wings. 49
No one who waits for you, O Lord, will ever be put to shame. 205

O blessed are those who fear the Lord and walk in his ways. 961

Psalm Refrains Set to Music/*continued*

O come, let us worship the Lord. 51
O God, let all the nations praise you! 850
O happy are those who fear the Lord and walk in his ways. 782
O Lord, come and save us. 772
O Lord, hear my prayer. 202
O Lord, hear my prayer; let my cry come to you. 54, 224
O Lord, our God, how wonderful your name in all the earth! 861
O Lord, our God, unwearied is your love for us. 46
O praise the Lord, Jerusalem! Zion, praise your God! 78
Oh, bless the Lord, my soul. 225
Oh God, I seek you, my soul thirsts for you, your love is finer than life. 1132
Our blessing-cup is a communion with the blood of Christ. 811, 1151
Our eyes are fixed on the Lord. 210
Our eyes are fixed on the Lord, pleading for his mercy. 227, 905
Our help is from the Lord who made heaven and earth. 951
Out of the depths I cry to you, O Lord. 71

Praise the Lord, all nations. 94
Praise the Lord and call upon his name. 132
Praise the Lord, my soul! 932
Praise the Lord, Jerusalem. 862
Praise the Lord who heals the brokenhearted. 878
Praise the Lord who lifts up the poor. 939
Precious in the eyes of the Lord is the death of his friends. 63
Proclaim his marvelous deeds to all the nations. 184, 870
Put your hope in the Lord; take courage and be strong. 217

Remember your mercies, O Lord. 940
Rest in God alone, my soul. 886
Return, O Lord, and rescue my soul. 26

Send forth your light and your truth: let these be my guide. 38
Since my mother's womb, you have been my strength. 1033
Sing a new song to the God of salvation. 80
Sing praise to our king, sing praise: for God is king of all the earth. 40
Sing to the Lord a new song, for he has done marvelous deeds. 1060
Sing with joy to God our help! 890

Taste and see the goodness of the Lord. 36, 121, 182, 798, 920, 923, 926, 1128, 1129, 1130
Teach me to do your will, my God. 213
Teach me your ways, O Lord. 872
The angel of the Lord will rescue those who fear him. 1037
The earth has yielded its fruits; God, our God has blessed us. 1057
The earth is full of the goodness of the Lord. 141, 819
The earth is full of your riches, O Lord, in wisdom you made them all. 56
The hand of the Lord feeds us; he answers all our needs. 914, 916
The just man is a light in darkness to the upright. 59, 877
The just will rejoice in the Lord; their hearts will be filled with glory. 43
The Lord comes to rule the earth with justice. 963
The Lord gave them bread from heaven. 917
The Lord has done great things for us; we are filled with joy. 69, 771
The Lord has revealed to the nations his saving power. 849
The Lord has set his throne in heaven. 853
The Lord hears the cry of the poor. 954
The Lord is compassionate to all his creatures. 191
The Lord is kind and merciful. 188, 198, 795, 883, 1138, 1139, 1140, 1141
The Lord is kind and merciful; slow to anger, and rich in compassion. 226, 934
The Lord is King for evermore. 50
The Lord is king; he is robed in majesty. 965
The Lord is king, the most high over all the earth. 854, 1043
The Lord is my light and my salvation. 106, 194, 792, 871, 1124, 1125, 1126
The Lord is my shepherd, nothing shall I want: he leads me by safe paths, nothing shall I fear. 32
The Lord is my shepherd; there is nothing I shall want. 163, 179, 796, 964, 1149
The Lord is near to all who call on him. 937
The Lord is near to broken hearts. 218
The Lord of hosts is with us; the God of Jacob is our stronghold. 39
The Lord said to my Lord: "Sit at my right hand." 57
The Lord speaks of peace to his people. 1040
The Lord will bless his people with peace. 785
The Lord will bless those who fear him, the little no less the great. 61
The Lord will guide me and guard me for ever. 66
The Lord upholds my life. 938
The Lord's kindness is everlasting to those who fear him. 189, 865
The precepts of the Lord give joy to the heart. 941
The queen stands at your right hand, arrayed in gold. 1046
The seed that falls on good ground will yield a fruitful harvest. 907
The Son of David will live for ever. 1027
The stone rejected by the builders has become the cornerstone. 843
The vineyard of the Lord is the house of Israel. 943
Their message goes out through all the earth. 1036
This is the day the Lord has made; let us rejoice and be glad. 836, 1071, 1106, 1107, 1108
To him be highest glory and praise for ever. 85

Psalm Refrains Set to Music/*continued*

To the upright I will show the saving power of God. 892
To you, glory and praise for evermore. 84, 859
To you I lift up my soul, O Lord my God. 33
To you, O Lord, I lift my soul. 193, 203, 216, 768, 1069, 1076, 1077, 1078, 1079
Today is born our Savior, Christ the Lord. 779
Truly we know our offenses, Lord, for we have sinned against you. 83
Turn to me, Lord, and have mercy. 207
Turn to the Lord in your need, and you will live. 909

Wake up and rise from death; Christ will shine upon you. 180
We are his people: the sheep of his flock. 844, 1074, 1136, 1137
We lift our eyes to the Lord till he show us his mercy. 68
We praise you, O Lord, who is and who was. 97
We praise your glorious name, O might God. 1055
We shall go up with joy to the house of our God. 67
When the Holy Spirit comes to you, you will be my witness! 183
With the Lord there is mercy, and fullness of redemption. 211, 799, 1096, 1097, 1098
Who is this king of glory? It is the Lord. 1024
Worthy is the Lamb that was slain. 96

You are a priest for ever in the line of Melchizedek. 864
You are my inheritance, O Lord. 903
You have redeemed us, Lord, God of truth. 208
You have searched me, and you know me, Lord. 212
You saved my life, O Lord; I shall not die. 214
You will be my witnesses to all the world. 185
You will draw water joyfully from the springs of salvation. 823
Your hand is ever upon me; you lead me and hold me fast. 73
Your kingdom is everlasting; you shall reign for ever! 76
Your ways, O Lord, are love and truth, to those who keep your covenant. 788
Your words, Lord, are spirit and life. 873
Your works, O Lord, are mighty and wonderful. 98

1213 Index of First Lines and Common Titles

Indented listings represent alternate titles by which some hymns are commonly known.

384 A Child Is Born in Bethlehem
469 A Hymn of Glory Let Us Sing
1024 A Light of Revelation to the Gentiles
575, 576 A Mighty Fortress Is Our God
688 A Multitude Comes from the East and the West
574 A Single Unmatched Stone
597 A Spendthrift Lover Is the Lord
385 A Stable Lamp Is Lighted
392 Adeste Fideles
815 Adoramus Te Domine (O Crucified Jesus)
548 Adoramus Te Domine (With the Angels)
489 Adoro Te Devote
420 Again We Keep This Solemn Fast
527 All Glory Be to God on High
520 All Creatures of Our God and King
428, 805 All Glory, Laud, and Honor
494, 495 All Hail the Power of Jesus' Name
669, 670 All People That On Earth Do Dwell
528 All Praise to God Who Reigns Above
505 All Things Bright and Beautiful
621 All Who Love and Serve Your City
440 All You Who Pass This Way
490 All You Who Seek a Comfort Sure
441 Alleluia, Alleluia, Give Thanks
737 Alleluia! Sing to Jesus
413 Alleluia, Song of Gladness
413 Alleluia, Song of Sweetness
583 Amazing Grace
763 America the Beautiful
395 Angel Voices Richly Blending
377 Angels, from the Realms of Glory
376 Angels We Have Heard on High
719 Around the Throne a Glorious Band
409 As with Gladness Men of Old
733 At That First Eucharist
421 At the Cross Her Station Keeping
459, 460 At the Lamb's High Feast We Sing
499 At the Name of Jesus
414 Attende Domine
713 Ave Maria
730 Ave Verum
360 Awake! Awake, and Greet the New Morn
586 Awake, O Sleeper, Rise from Death
378 Away in a Manger

720 Baptized in Water
450 Be Joyful, Mary
620 Beatitudes
418 Before the Fruit Is Ripened by the Sun
601 Beloved, Let Us Love
429 Benedictus Qui Venit
6 Blessed Be the God of Israel
718 Blessed Feasts of Blessed Martyrs
725 Breathe on Me, Breath of God
706 By All Your Saints Still Striving
577 By Gracious Powers
426 By the Babylonian Rivers

466 Christ Is Alive!
617 Christ Is Made the Sure Foundation
500 Christ Is the King
543 Christ Is the World's Light
681 Christ, Mighty Savior
462, 463 Christ the Lord Is Risen Today, All on Earth
452, 461 Christ the Lord Is Risen Today, Christians
701 Christ Upon the Mountain Peak
396 Christ Was Born on Christmas Day
616 Christ's Church Shall Glory in His Power
594 Christian, Do You Hear the Lord
538 Christians Lift Up Your Hearts
837 Christians, Praise the Paschal Victim
465 Christus Resurrexit
362 City of God, Jerusalem
758 Come Adore This Wondrous Presence
723 Come and Let Us Drink of That New River
472 Come Down, O Love Divine
482 Come, Holy Ghost
639 Come, Let Us Love the Unborn Generations
366 Come, Lord, and Tarry Not
569 Come, My Way, My Truth, My Life
487 Come, Now Almighty King
694 Come Now, and Praise the Humble Saint
664 Come, Rejoice before Your Maker
364 Come, O Long Expected Jesus
487 Come, Thou Almighty King
857 Come, Thou Holy Spirit, Come
364 Come, Thou Long Expected Jesus
372 Come, Thou Savior of Our Race
566 Come to Us, Creative Spirit
552 Come, We That Love the Lord
456 Come, Ye Faithful, Raise the Strain
759 Come, Ye Thankful People, Come
756 Come, You Sinners, Poor and Needy
370 Comfort, Comfort, O My People
561 Confitemini Domino
368 Creator of the Stars of Night
496 Crown Him with Many Crowns

677 Day Is Done
448 Daylight Fades
732 Draw Near and Take the Body of Your Lord
731 Draw Us in the Spirit's Tether

517 Earth and All Stars
734 Eat this Bread

571 Faith of Our Fathers
655 Father, Lord of All Creation
746 Father of Mercy
4 Father, We Praise You

Index of First Lines and Common Titles/*continued*

558 Father, We Thank Thee Who Hast Planted
743 Father, Within Thy House Today
478 Fire of God, Titanic Spirit
474 Fire of God, Undying Flame
705 For All the Saints
557 For the Beauty of the Earth
562 For the Fruits of This Creation
643 For the Healing of the Nations
754 Forgive Our Sins
627 Forth in the Peace of Christ
419 Forty Days and Forty Nights
521 From All That Dwell below the Skies
388 From Heaven Above

665 Gather Us In
736 Gift of Finest Wheat
401 Gloria, Gloria
619 Glorious in Majesty
518 Glory Be to God in Heaven
542 Glory to God in the Highest
628 Go Make of All Disciples
397 Go Tell It on the Mountain
567 God Be in My Head
484 God Father, Praise and Glory
516 God Has Spoken by His Prophets
667 God Is Here! As We His People
581 God Is My Great Desire
575, 576 God Is Our Fortress and Our Rock
592 God Is Unique and One
507 God Is Working His Purpose Out
764 God of Our Fathers
563 God, Omnipotent, Eternal
383 God Rest You, Merry Gentlemen
724 God Sends Us His Spirit
578 God Spoke to Our Father Abraham
535 God, We Praise You
648 God, Who Stretched the Spangled Heavens
486 God, Whose Almighty Word
683 God, Whose Farm Is All Creation
631 God, Whose Giving Knows No Ending
640 God, Whose Purpose Is to Kindle
489 God with Hidden Majesty
391 Good Christian Friends, Rejoice
391 Good Christian Men, Rejoice
746 Great God of Mercy
651 Great God, Our Source and Lord of Space

702 Hail, Holy Queen Enthroned Above
813 Hail Our Savior's Glorious Body
703 Hail, Queen of Heaven
471 Hail the Day That Sees Him Rise
444 Hail Thee, Festival Day
364 Hail, Thou Long Expected Jesus
692 Hail to the Lord Who Comes
387 Hark! The Herald Angels Sing
753 Have Mercy, Lord, on Us
573 He Comes to Us as One Unknown
749 He Healed the Darkness of My Mind
498 He Is King of Kings
684 He Walks among the Golden Lamps
414 Hear Us, Almighty Lord
522 Heavenly Hosts in Ceaseless Worship
656 Help Us Help Each Other
665 Here in This Place
365 Hills of the North, Rejoice
515 His Voice Is in the Thunder, in the Storm
524 Holy God, We Praise Thy Name
485 Holy, Holy, Holy! Lord God Almighty
565 Hope of the World
430 Hosanna in Excelsis
803 Hosanna to the Son of David
672 How Beautiful the Morning and the Day
710 How Blessed Is This Place
389, 390 How Brightly Beams the Morning Star
633 How Brightly Deep, How Glory Sprung
585 How Firm a Foundation
610 How Good the Name of Jesus Sounds
629 How Shall They Hear the Word of God
610 How Sweet the Name of Jesus Sounds

738 I Am the Bread of Life
726 I Come with Joy to Meet My Lord
636 I Danced in the Morning
607 I Heard the Voice of Jesus Say
176 I Know That My Redeemer Lives, and on
445 I Know That My Redeemer Lives, What Joy
735 I Received the Living God
671 I Sing As I Arise Today
502 I Sing the Mighty Power of God
593 I Sought the Lord
510 I Want to Walk as a Child of the Light
708 Immaculate Mary
512 Immortal, Invisible, God Only Wise
659 In Christ There Is No East or West
177 In Paradisum
393 Infant Holy, Infant Lowly
661 Is This a Day of New Beginnings
400 It Came upon the Midnight Clear
637 It Shocked Them That the Master Did Not Fast

690 Jerusalem, My Happy Home
431 Jesu, Jesu, Fill Us with Your Love
442 Jesus Christ Is Risen Today
564 Jesus, Come! For We Invite You
611 Jesus, Lead the Way
488 Jesus, My Lord, My God, My All
423 Jesus, Remember Me
492 Jesus Shall Reign
649 Jesus, Shepherd of Our Souls
432 Jesus Took a Towel
427 Jesus Walked This Lonesome Valley
693 Joseph, Be Our Guide and Pattern
399 Joy to the World
525 Joyful, Joyful, We Adore You
555 Jubilate Deo

519 Laudate Dominum
633 Leave All Things You Have

Index of First Lines and Common Titles/*continued*

523 Let All Mortal Flesh Keep Silence
716 Let All on Earth Their Voices Raise
536 Let All the World in Every Corner Sing
559 Let All Things Now Living
508 Let My People Go
741 Let Saints on Earth in Concert Sing
653 Let There Be Light
727 Let Us Break Bread Together
715 Let Us with Joy Our Voices Raise
641 Lift Every Voice and Sing
704 Lift High the Cross
363 Lift Up Your Heads, O Mighty Gates
374 Lo, How a Rose E'er Blooming
468 Look, O Look, the Sight Is Glorious
468 Look, Ye Saints, the Sight Is Glorious
691 Lord, Bid Your Servant Go in Peace
658 Lord Christ, the Father's Mighty Son
438 Lord Christ, When First You Came to Earth
568 Lord of All Hopefulness
602 Lord of All Nations, Grant Me Grace
556 Lord of Our Growing Years
739 Lord of the Living
733 Lord, Who at That First Eucharist Didst Pray
630 Lord, Whose Love in Humble
417 Lord, Who throughout These Forty Days
470 Lord, You Give the Great Commission
588 Love Divine, All Loves Excelling
599 Love Is His Word

553 Magnificat
812 Mandatum Novum
503 Many and Great, O God, Are Your Works
454 Maranatha! Alleluia!
711 Mary, How Lovely the Light of Your Glory
178 May Choirs of Angels
177 May Saints and Angels Lead You On
742 May the Grace of Christ Our Savior
686 Mine Eyes Have Seen the Glory
587 Morning Glory, Starlit Sky
674 Morning Has Broken
446 Morning of Splendor
762 My Country, 'Tis of Thee
606 My Shepherd Will Supply My Need
439 My Song Is Love Unknown
15 My Soul Gives Glory to the Lord

533 New Songs of Celebration
589 Not for Tongues of Heaven's Angels
394 Now Every Child That Dwells on Earth
647 Now Join We to Praise the Creator
625 Now Let Us from This Table Rise
560 Now Thank We All Our God
687 Now the Day of the Lord Is at Hand
453 Now the Green Blade Rises
668 Now the Silence
22 Nunc Dimittis (Sarum Tone)
676 Nunc Dimittis (Taizé)

763 O Beautiful, for Spacious Skies
620 O Blessed Are the Poor in Spirit
725 O Breathe on Me, O Breath of God
618 O Christ the Great Foundation
747 O Christ the Healer
392 O Come, All Ye Faithful
367 O Come, Divine Messiah
357 O Come, O Come, Emmanuel
654 O Day of Peace
744 O Father, All Creating
729 O Food of Exiles Lowly
591 O for a Heart to Praise My God
679 O Gladsome Light
484 O God, Almighty Father
541 O God beyond All Praising
642 O God, Empower Us
650 O God of Every Nation
652 O God of Love, O King of Peace
579 O God, Our Help in Ages Past
685 O Holy City, Seen of John
475 O Holy Spirit, by Whose Breath
646 O Jesus Christ, May Grateful Hymns Be Rising
605 O Jesus, Joy of Loving Hearts
386 O Little Town of Bethlehem
740 O Lord, You Died That All Might Live
539 O Praise Ye the Lord
443 O Queen of Heaven
12 O Radiant Light
434 O Sacred Head Surrounded
757 O Salutaris Hostia
712 O Sanctissima
757 O Saving Victim
761 O Say Can You See
748 O Son of God, in Galilee
447 O Sons and Daughters
424 O Sun of Justice
546 O That I Had a Thousand Voices
689 O the Beautiful Treasures
398 Of the Father's Love Begotten
356 On Jordan's Bank
662 On This Day, the First of Days
402 Once in Royal David's City
666 Only Begotten, Word of God Eternal
570 Our Father, by Whose Name
755 Our Father, We Have Wandered
579 Our God, Our Help in Ages Past
483 Over the Chaos of the Empty Waters

813 Pange Lingua Gloriosi
416 Parce Domine
660 Peace with the Father
359 People, Look East
682 Praise and Thanksgiving
545 Praise Him
530 Praise, My Soul, the King of Heaven
551 Praise the Lord of Heaven
529 Praise the Lord! You Heavens, Adore Him

Index of First Lines and Common Titles/*continued*

477 Praise the Spirit in Creation
537 Praise to the Living God
547 Praise to the Lord, the Almighty
696 Praise We the Lord This Day
369 Prepare the Way of the Lord

544 Reap Me the Earth
443 Regina Caeli
455 Rejoice, Angelic Choirs
493 Rejoice, the Lord Is King

644 Said Judas to Mary
175 Saints of God
425 Salvator Mundi
703 Salve Regina
372 Savior of the Nations, Come
375 See amid the Winter's Snow
580 Seek Ye First the Kingdom of God
728 Shepherd of Souls
395 Shepherds Left Their Flocks Astraying
540 Shout for Joy, Loud and Long
751 Silence! Frenzied, Unclean Spirit
379 Silent Night, Holy Night
550 Sing a New Song to the Lord
554 Sing Alleluia, Praise the Lord
437 Sing, My Tongue, the Song of Triumph
404 Sing of Mary, Pure and Lowly
528 Sing Praise to God Who Reigns Above
539 Sing Praise to the Lord
532 Sing to the Lord a Joyful Song
714 Sing We of the Blessed Mother
467 Sing with All the Saints in Glory
467 Sing with All the Sons of Glory
415 Somebody's Knockin' at Your Door
410 Songs of Thankfulness and Praise
595, 596 Souls of Men! Why Will You Scatter
476 Spirit Divine, Accept Our Prayers
476 Spirit Divine, Attend Our Prayers
480 Spirit of God within Me
828 Springs of Water, Bless the Lord
761 Star-Spangled Banner
584 Surely It Is God Who Saves Me

361 Take Comfort, God's People
634 Take Up Your Cross
758 Tantum Ergo
534 Tell Out, My Soul, the Greatness of the Lord
526 Thanks Be to God
514 Thanks to God Whose Word Was Spoken
457 That Easter Day With Joy Was Bright
695 The Angel Gabriel from Heaven Came
626 The Church of Christ in Every Age
618 The Church's One Foundation
678 The Day You Gave Us, Lord, Is Ended
408 The First Nowell
422 The Glory of These Forty Days
537 The God of Abraham Praise
405 The God Whom Earth and Sea and Sky
698 The Great Forerunner of the Morn
464 The Head That Once Was Crowned With Thorns
501 The King of Glory
609 The King of Love My Shepherd Is
373 The King Shall Come When Morning Dawns
615 The Kingdom of God
612 The Living God My Shepherd Is
613 The Lord, the Lord, the Lord Is My Shepherd
1023 The Lord Will Come to Us
752 The Master Came to Bring Good News
435 The Royal Banners Forward Go
506 The Stars Declare His Glory
451 The Strife Is O'er
358 The Voice of God Goes Out through All the World
504 The Works of the Lord Are Created in Wisdom
608 There Is a Balm in Gilead
105 There Is One God
657 There Is One Lord
531 There's a Spirit in the Air
595, 596 There's a Wideness in God's Mercy
750 Thine Arm, O Lord, in Days of Old
673 This Day God Gives Me Strength
603 This Is My Commandment
590 This Is My Will
663 This Is the Day When Light Was First Created
717 This Is the Feast Day of the Lord's True Witness
458 This Is the Feast of Victory
722 This Is the Spirit's Entry Now
582 This World, My God, Is Held within Your Hand
632 Those Who Love and Those Who Labor
486 Thou, Whose Almighty Word
638 Thy Love, O God, Has All Mankind Created
511 Thy Strong Word Didst Cleave the Darkness
700 'Tis Good, Lord, to Be Here
491 To Christ, the Prince of Peace
2 To God With Gladness Sing
497 To Jesus Christ, Our Sovereign King
380 'Twas in the Moon of Wintertime
633 Two Fishermen
699 Two Noble Saints
699 Two Noble Trees

598 Ubi Caritas et Amor (Chant)
604 Ubi Caritas et Amor (Taizé)
381 Unto Us a Boy Is Born

479 Veni Creator Spiritus
857 Veni Sancte Spiritus
473 Veni Sancte Spiritus (Taizé)
837 Victimae Paschali Laudes
403 Virgin-born, We Bow before You

Index of First Lines and Common Titles/*continued*

371 Wake, O Wake, and Sleep No Longer
623 We Are Your People
110 We Come to You, Lord Jesus
760 We Gather Together
721 We Know That Christ Is Raised
20, 680 We Praise You, Father, for Your Gift
406 We Three Kings of Orient Are
572 We Walk by Faith
635 Weary of All Trumpeting
436 Were You There
411 What Child Is This
624 What Does the Lord Require
709 What Is This Place
407 What Star Is This
600 What Wondrous Love Is This
481 When God the Spirit Came
433 When I Survey the Wondrous Cross
549 When in Our Music God Is Glorified
508 When Israel Was in Egypt's Land
614 When Jesus Came Preaching the Kingdom of God
697 When Jesus Came to Jordan
412 When John Baptized by Jordan's River
745 When Love Is Found
675 When Morning Gilds the Skies
355 When the King Shall Come Again
622 Where Temple Offerings Are Made
598 Where True Love and Charity Are Found
382 While Shepherds Watched
509 Who Can Measure Heaven and Earth
645 With Jesus for Hero
743 Within Your House, O God, Today
513 Word of God, Come Down on Earth

707 Ye Watchers and Ye Holy Ones
112 You Have Put on Christ
736 You Satisfy the Hungry Heart
750 Your Hands, O Lord in Days of Old
638 Your Love, O God, Has All the World Created